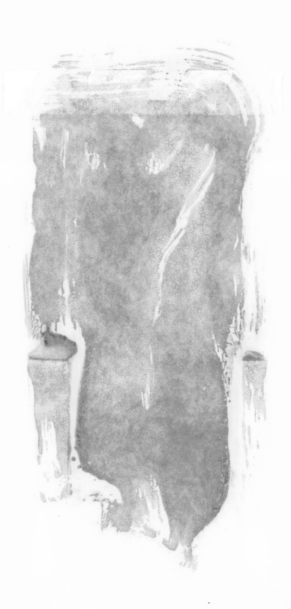

# THE INVERTEBRATES:

## *Echinodermata*

## McGraw-Hill Publications in the Zoological Sciences

### *E. J. Boell*, CONSULTING EDITOR

*Baitsell* · HUMAN BIOLOGY
*Breland* · MANUAL OF COMPARATIVE ANATOMY
*Hyman* · THE INVERTEBRATES: PROTOZOA THROUGH CTENOPHORA (Vol. I)
      THE INVERTEBRATES: PLATYHELMINTHES AND RHYNCHOCOELA (Vol. II)
      THE INVERTEBRATES: ACANTHOCEPHALA, ASCHELMINTHES, AND ENTOPROCTA
          (Vol. III)
      THE INVERTEBRATES: ECHINODERMATA (Vol. IV)
      THE INVERTEBRATES: SMALLER COELOMATE GROUPS (Vol. V)
*Leach* · FUNCTIONAL ANATOMY OF THE MAMMAL
*Mayr, Linsley, and Usinger* · METHODS AND PRINCIPLES OF SYSTEMATIC ZOOLOGY
*Mitchell* · A TEXTBOOK OF GENERAL PHYSIOLOGY
*Patten* · FOUNDATIONS OF EMBRYOLOGY
*Senning* · LABORATORY STUDIES IN COMPARATIVE ANATOMY
*Shull* · EVOLUTION
*Shull* · HEREDITY
*Snodgrass* · PRINCIPLES OF INSECT MORPHOLOGY
*Storer and Usinger* · ELEMENTS OF ZOOLOGY
*Storer and Usinger* · GENERAL ZOOLOGY
*Storer and Usinger* · LABORATORY MANUAL FOR ZOOLOGY
*Storer and Usinger* · LABORATORY WORKBOOK FOR ZOOLOGY
*Weichert* · ANATOMY OF THE CHORDATES
*Weichert* · ELEMENTS OF CHORDATE ANATOMY
*Weichert* · REPRESENTATIVE CHORDATES
*Welch* · LIMNOLOGY

*There are also the related series of McGraw-Hill Publications in the Botanical Sciences, of which Edmund W. Sinnott is Consulting Editor, and in the Agricultural Sciences, of which R. A. Brink is Consulting Editor.*

# THE INVERTEBRATES:
## *Echinodermata*
### *The coelomate Bilateria*

#### VOLUME IV

LIBBIE HENRIETTA HYMAN

*American Museum of Natural History*
*New York*

New York      Toronto      London

McGRAW-HILL BOOK COMPANY

1955

THE INVERTEBRATES: ECHINODERMATA

*Library of Congress Catalog Card Number 40-5368*

9 10 11 12 – MAMM – 7 5 4 3 2 1 0

31663

# PREFACE

It was intended that this volume should contain the phyla Chaetognatha, Echinodermata, and Hemichordata. However, the material on Echinodermata proved so voluminous that the necessity of devoting an entire volume to this phylum became apparent as the text neared completion. Although devoting a whole volume to echinoderms somewhat upsets my plan for the coelomate phyla, the inclusion of two smaller groups with echinoderms would have raised difficulties, for the remaining small coelomate phyla (Sipunculoida, Ectoprocta, Phoronida, Brachiopoda) would presumably not have sufficed to fill the next volume; but inclusion with them of one of the remaining phyla, all very large, would again have made too large a volume. Splitting one of these large phyla between two volumes would certainly have been unacceptable. Therefore it is anticipated that Volume V will dispose of all the small coelomate phyla (Chaetognatha, Hemichordata, Sipunculoida, Ectoprocta, Brachiopoda, and Phoronida), leaving the three remaining invertebrate phyla—Mollusca, Annelida (including Echiuroidea), Arthropoda (in the broad sense)—for future volumes. It is expected that Volume VI will deal with Mollusca. What disposal will be made of tardigrades, onychophores, and linguatulids has not been decided.

Geographical distribution has been much more extensively treated in the present than in the preceding volumes which no doubt were somewhat deficient in regard to this topic. The conspicuous place occupied by echinoderms in the littoral marine fauna has seemed to justify devoting considerable space to their distribution. However, the collection and collation of this material has been very laborious and time-consuming and I now wonder whether the discussion of geographical distribution will be worth to readers the labor it cost and the space it occupies in the volume.

I may say that I have found echinoderms a tough proposition but I have dealt with them to the best of my ability. Believing that the subject of palaeontology is best left to palaeontologists I have treated the extinct groups of echinoderms as briefly as possible. It did not seem proper to omit them altogether. Dr. Otto Haas of the department of invertebrate palaeontology of this museum has been very obliging in giving me access to fossil echinoderms in the collections in his department.

I have made all of the original drawings in this book. Those of live echinoderms were executed during a stay in the summer of 1952 at the museum's Lerner Marine Laboratory on the island of North Bimini in the

Bahamas. I am grateful to the director, Dr. C. M. Breder, for the facilities of the laboratory. Other original drawings were made from dry material in the museum's collections. Illustrations taken from the literature have been reproduced by photography when the originals are in black and white, but other types of illustration give a dull effect when reproduced by photography, and therefore I have copied these as faithfully as possible in line and stipple. To the comment that enlargement is not indicated in my illustrations I reply that this seems to me of no consequence; the point is to make the drawing large enough to show the required details clearly.

Dr. Elisabeth Deichmann of the Museum of Comparative Zoology, Harvard, and Dr. A. H. Clark of the United States National Museum have been most kind about answering inquiries concerning holothuroids and crinoids, respectively. I wish here to pay tribute to the memory of H. L. Clark, Th. Mortensen, W. K. Fisher, and A. H. Clark, whose lifelong devotion to the study of echinoderms has added greatly to our knowledge of these animals.

I also here salute the echinoderms as a noble group especially designed to puzzle the zoologist.

Libbie Henrietta Hyman

# CONTENTS

# CHAPTER XV

# THE ENTEROCOELOUS COELOMATES—PHYLUM ECHINODERMATA

## I. HISTORICAL

The echinoderms, being common and conspicuous marine animals, have been known since ancient times. The name Echinodermata appears to have originated with Jacob Klein (1734), who, however, applied it only to echinoids. Linnaeus in the 10th edition (1758) of his *Systema naturae* relegated all invertebrates except insects to one class, Vermes. This was subdivided into the orders Intestina, Mollusca, Testacea, Lithophyta, and Zoophyta. Linnaeus did not employ the term echinoderm; he placed the genera that he knew—*Asterias, Echinus,* and *Holothuria*—under the group Mollusca, which included a variety of naked, warty, or spiny animals, such as naked mollusks, some polychaetes, a few coelenterates and ctenophores, and *Priapulus.* Possibly Linnaeus surmised some relationship between *Asterias* and *Echinus,* as the latter follows the former in the text, but *Holothuria* is somewhat removed from them. The name Echinodermata was revived by Bruguière (1791), who divided the Vermes into six orders: Infusoria, Intestina, Mollusca, Echinodermata, Testacea, and Zoophyta. Echinodermata was thus recognized as a distinct group of invertebrates. Bruguière presented excellent figures of a number of echinoderms belonging to the asteroid, ophiuroid, and echinoid groups but apparently failed to realize the echinoderm nature of the holothuroids. Lamarck greatly improved the classificatory arrangement of the invertebrates, recognizing in 1801 seven classes: Mollusca, Crustacea, Arachnida, Insecta, Vermes, Radiata, and Polypi; but was less fortunate with regard to echinoderms, which he placed in the class Radiata. Radiata was divided into two orders, Echinodermes and Mollasses. In the former, asteroids, echinoids, and holothuroids were included, so that Lamarck may be credited with having realized the relationship of the holothuroids to the spiny types of echinoderms and thus having advanced the concept of the phylum; but Mollasses were medusoid coelenterates, and thereby Lamarck initiated the unfortunate association of the two main radiate groups of invertebrates that was to persist for nearly fifty years. Later (1816–1822) Lamarck added other classes of invertebrates (Infusoria, Annelida, Cirripedia, Tunicata) but continued to retain the association of echinoderms with coelenterates under the name Radiata. Cuvier, in his *Le règne animal,* first appearing in 1817, took a backward step in animal classification, recognizing four classes: Vertebrata, Mollusca, Articulata, and Radiata. Radiata or Zoophyta consisted of echinodermes, intestinaux, acalephes, polypes, and infusoires. While here the higher organization of the echinoderms is perhaps recognized by Cuvier's placing them at the top of the Radiata and removing them from the close proximity to the coelenterates in which Lamarck mistakenly placed them, Cuvier's arrangement shows little understanding of invertebrate anatomy. However, he retained his leadership in matters of animal classification for many years, and prominent zoologists continued to ally the echinoderms with the coelenterates under the name Radiata or Zoophyta until 1847, when Frey and Leuckart in their textbook of invertebrate anatomy separated Echino-

1

dermata as a group coordinate with the other main invertebrate groups. In 1854 Leuckart reiterated firmly his position that the prevailing Radiata concept was false and that the Echinodermata must be regarded as a separate main division of the animal kingdom, since their grade of structure is obviously higher than that of the coelenterates with which they had long been united. The correctness of Leuckart's position has been unanimously recognized since the middle of the nineteenth century. Since that time the Echinodermata have generally been regarded as a distinct phylum of invertebrates.

Attempts, however, have not been wanting to include the echinoderms in a larger assemblage based on embryological considerations. This was a natural outcome of the rise of investigations into invertebrate embryology during the last half of the nineteenth century. Huxley in 1875 proposed a group Deuterostomata for all the coelomate Bilateria, basing the name on the lack of relationship of the mouth to the blastopore. Deuterostomata was divided into three categories: Enterocoela for echinoderms, chaetognaths, and enteropneusts; Schizocoela for mollusks, polychaetes, and arthropods; and Epicoela for tunicates and Amphioxus. Huxley displayed remarkable perspicacity in thus anticipating much later views on the classificatory arrangement of coelomates. A little later Metschnikoff (1881) pointed out the striking resemblance between the larvae of echinoderms and enteropneusts and proposed to unite both groups under the name Ambulacraria.[1] Although this concept was accepted by Hatschek (1888), it gained little further support, for its lack of sufficient breadth soon became evident. Apparently Goette (1902) was the first to broaden the conception to include Chaetognatha, Enteropneusta, Echinodermata, and Chordata in one category that he named Pleurogastrica. At the same time K. C. Schneider (1902) presented the same assemblage of the four enterocoelous phyla under the name Enterocoelia and was perhaps the first to place this assemblage at the top of the animal series. It remained for Grobben (1908) to clarify and further promulgate the grouping of the four enterocoelous phyla under one classificatory division that he called Deuterostomia. Later Grobben carried the concept to the extremity of making a phylum of Deuterostomia and reducing the enterocoelous phyla to the rank of subphyla and classes. It is improbable that this extreme view will find any acceptance, but an increasing tendency is evident in larger zoological works to place the invertebrate enterocoelous phyla in proximity, and to lead from them directly to the chordates. This arrangement, for instance, appears in the new *Traité de zoologie* in which the enterocoelous phyla (except Chaetognatha) are treated in the last of the volumes on invertebrates. As previously explained, this procedure has not been adopted in the present treatise simply because the chordates are altogether omitted and cannot serve as a climax to which the Deuterostomia lead; hence it appears better to dispose of the Deuterostomia at a level of the treatise commensurate with their grade of structure. The terms Deuterostomia and Enterocoela or enterocoelous coelomates are here regarded as synonymous. They include the four phyla Chaetognatha, Echinodermata, Hemichordata, and Chordata. Whereas, as discussed in Chap. XV, the inclusion of the Chaetognatha in this assemblage is dubious, there appears little doubt at the present time of a relationship between Echinodermata, Hemichordata, and Chordata. This relationship, however, is too remote to justify the inclusion of these groups in a single phylum or even a superphylum. The terms Deuterostomia or Enterocoela are convenient expressions to indicate certain similarities of embryological development but should not, in the author's opinion, be employed as taxonomic categories.

The outstanding modern treatment of the echinoderms is that of Cuénot (1948)

---

[1] Persistently spelled Ambulacralia by all later authors, whether by mistake or intention the author was unable to discover.

in Volume XI of the *Traité de zoologie* (edited by P. Grassé).  This account is almost totally wanting in information on the physiology and ecology of echinoderms but includes the extinct groups.  The section on echinoderms by Bather (1900) in Lankester's *A treatise on zoology* is still useful because of the extensive consideration given to the fossil forms.  The five volumes on echinoderms by Ludwig in Bronn's *Klassen und Ordnungen des Tierreichs* present the most exhaustive available account of the phylum and therefore remain of value despite their age (1889–1907), but naturally must be supplemented by more recent literature.  An interesting though brief account, emphasizing natural-history aspects, is given by Mortensen and Lieberkind (1928) in the series *Die Tierwelt der Nord- und Ostsee*.  Tremendous monographs are in progress on the Echinoidea by Mortensen and on the recent Crinoidea by A. H. Clark, and large volumes on the Asteroidea have been published by W. K. Fisher.  As conspicuous marine animals, the echinoderms have always been of great interest to zoologists and lovers of natural history and therefore have evoked a large literature.

## II. CHARACTERS OF THE PHYLUM

**1. Definition.**—The Echinodermata or echinoderms are enterocoelous coelomates, having a pentaradiate construction derived from an original bilaterality, without definite head or brain, with a calcareous endoskeleton of separate plates or pieces, often bearing external spines or protuberances, and with a water-vascular system of coelomic nature that sends numerous small projections (podia) to the exterior and communicates with the external medium by a pore or cluster of pores, at least in juvenile stages.

**2. General Characters.**—The phylum Echinodermata as remarked by Bather (1900) is "one of the best characterized and most distinct phyla of the animal kingdom."  It is recognized at once by the pronounced radial symmetry, nearly always pentamerous and involving the absence of a definite anterior end or head, and by the general spiny or warty appearance.  The echinoderms are readily differentiated from the other radiate phyla (Cnidaria and Ctenophora) by their hollow interior and their general higher grade of organization.  The echinoderms are animals of modest to considerable size; none are microscopic.  They are for the most part free-moving although derived from sessile ancestors, and sessile stalked forms still survive in the class Crinoidea.  The body is either of simple contour, rounded to cylindrical, or star-like, with simple arms (nearly always five or some multiple of five in number) radiating from a central disk, or else branched feathery arms arise from the central body, which may or may not be attached by a stalk.  The body surface is rarely smooth; typically it is covered with hard calcareous projections (whence the name Echinodermata from the Greek *echino*, spiny, and *derma*, skin) that vary from small bumps or bosses to long spines.  Calcareous projections are, however, wanting in the class Holothuroidea, whose members, instead, are often warty.  As in other radiate animals the body is differentiated into oral and aboral surfaces;

holothurians, however, are orally-aborally elongated and lie upon one side that is often somewhat flattened. Asteroids and echinoids move with the oral surface against the substrate, but crinoids, whether attached or free, keep the aboral surface against the substrate and direct the oral surface upward. This was also the orientation of most extinct classes of echinoderms. On the surface of an echinoderm are found five (or sometimes more) symmetrically spaced radiating simple or branched grooves or bands termed *ambulacra*, at which the *podia* of the water-vascular system project to the exterior. The areas of the surface between the ambulacra are termed *interradii* or *interambulacra* (Fig. 1*B*).

The body wall consists of an outer epidermis, a middle dermis or cutis of connective tissue, and a lining coelomic epithelium or *peritoneum*. The dermis contains and produces the skeleton, which is thus an endoskeleton. This endoskeleton is one of the most characteristic features of the phylum and is rarely wanting. It may consist of closely fitted plates forming a shell, usually called *theca* or *test*, or may be composed of small separated pieces called *ossicles*. In the holothurians these ossicles take the form of microscopic bits strewn in the dermis. The externally projecting spines and tubercles are also parts of the endoskeleton and are clothed with epidermis. Beneath the dermis occurs such musculature as is present in the body wall; this is well developed in forms like the holothurians with very little endoskeleton but is scarcely evident in forms like echinoids that possess an elaborate test.

The *water-vascular system*, peculiar to echinoderms, is a system of tubes filled with a watery fluid that courses along the inner surface of the ambulacra from the mouth region to their tips. A *ring* canal encircles the esophagus and gives off a *radial* canal along each ambulacrum; from the radial canals branches extend into the *podia*, which are hollow external projections serving as food-gathering, locomotory, or sensory mechanisms. Food gathering was undoubtedly their original function. From the ring canal in one of the interradii, a canal extends to the aboral surface in asteroids and echinoids, opening by a *hydropore*. When the hydropore splits up into numerous channels through a plate of the endoskeleton, the latter is called *madreporite*. The canal itself is usually called *stone canal*, because in most cases it is hardened by calcareous impregnation. In ophiuroids the hydropore is situated on the oral surface, and in most holothuroids and present crinoids one or more stone canals open freely into the coelom, without reaching the surface; but a hydropore is always present during development.

The nervous system is somewhat primitive, consisting of networks concentrated into ganglionated nerve cords that follow the radiate pattern. There are generally three such networks present at different levels of the echinoderm. The *oral* or *ectoneural* system is located at the base of or shortly beneath the oral epidermis and is constituted mainly of a ring or pentagon around the esophagus and a ganglionated strand from this along each ambulacrum to its tip. This oral system is the main part of the nervous system in all the living echinoderm classes except Crinoidea, where it is diminished in importance in the adult. The deeper-lying *hyponeural* and the *aboral* or *entoneural* systems are patterned similarly to the oral system, but more weakly developed, except in crinoids where the aboral system dominates. There is a poor development of sense organs in the phylum.

The interior of the echinoderm forms a spacious coelom occupied mainly by the digestive and reproductive systems; except in crinoids where the interior is filled secondarily by webs and strands of connective tissue. The echinoderms are true coelomate animals of the enterocoelous category (II, page 22). The nature of a true coelom was explained in Volume II, (pages 21–24). A true coelom is a space in the entomesoderm separating the body wall, typically composed of epidermal, connective tissue, and muscular layers, from the digestive tube, also typically composed of epithelial, connective tissue, and muscular layers. The coelom is lined by an epithelium of mesodermal origin, called by the general term *peritoneum*, that lines the inner surface of the body wall as the parietal peritoneum and clothes the outer surface of the digestive tube and other viscera as the visceral peritoneum. Any organ that projects into the coelom is supported by a mesentery composed of two peritoneal layers (II, page 24, Fig. 7*C*). There is typically a dorsal and a ventral mesentery for the digestive tube, but in echinoderms these mesenteries, although present in embryos, are more or less wanting in the adult, especially the ventral mesentery; and because of the torsion that takes place during development, the dorsal mesentery becomes more or less horizontal in orientation.

Definite excretory and respiratory systems are wanting in most echinoderms, although some holothuroids possess what may be considered a respiratory system and in other echinoderms some sort of provision for respiration is often present. A circulatory system termed the *haemal* or *blood lacunar* system is typically present and reaches a considerable development in holothuroids and echinoids. Its channels are not definite vessels as they lack definite walls and have the peculiarity of being enclosed inside coelomic channels. The digestive tract is usually a more or less coiled tube extending from the mouth located on the oral surface to the anus (wanting in ophiuroids and some asteroids), situated centrally or excentrically on the aboral or oral surface. In crinoids both mouth and anus open on the oral surface (and this was also the case with primitive extinct echinoderms), and either may be central or excentric. The anus is on the oral surface in many irregular echinoids. In asteroids and ophiuroids the digestive tract lacks the usual coil and is short and straight with a pronounced stomachic enlargement. Voluminous digestive glands occupying the arm coeloms are peculiar to the class Asteroidea.

The reproductive system is of the simplest sort, consisting primitively of a single gonad definitely located with regard to the body radii and opening by a gonopore located in the same interradius with the hydropore and the anus. This condition is retained in Holothuroidea, but in most existing echinoderms radially symmetrical gonads corresponding to the body symmetry are present. Echinoderms are dioecious with few exceptions (there are a number of hermaphroditic holothurians and ophiuroids), and the sexes are usually not distinguishable externally. Although some echinoderms brood their young, the sex cells as a rule are discharged directly into the sea where fertilization occurs, and development of the indeterminate type proceeds to the formation of characteristic larvae of great phylogenetic importance. These larvae are bilaterally symmetrical, but if fed, undergo a remarkable metamorphosis with suppression of the anterior part of the right side into the radially symmetrical adult.

The foregoing remarks are to be understood as applying primarily to the existing echinoderms. The characteristics of the fossil groups are treated in the accounts of those groups.

The echinoderms are exclusively marine and are among the most common and widely spread of marine animals. They occur in all seas and at all latitudes and at all depths from the intertidal zone to the ocean deeps.

As in the case of other animal groups with a skeleton, the echinoderms preserve well as fossils, and there is a vast and bewildering array of fossil echinoderms, including at least five wholly extinct classes that are regarded as phylogenetically important. Only a brief and sketchy account of the fossil echinoderms will be given here as details are available in works on invertebrate palaeontology (listed in the bibliography).

## III. CLASSIFICATION OF THE PHYLUM

*Subphylum I. Pelmatozoa*

Mostly extinct echinoderms attached throughout life or in youth by the aboral surface, either directly or more often by a stalk supported by successive calcareous pieces; hence with the oral surface directed upward and bearing both oral and anal apertures; viscera enclosed in a calcareous test, the theca; ambulacra acting as food grooves, usually extended distally onto projecting arms; podia primarily food-catching; main nervous system aboral. For doubtful groups here omitted see Regnéll (1945).

**Class I. Heterostelea.** Extinct Pelmatozoa with mostly laterally flattened theca, fastened by a stalk apparently in a horizontal position; stalk at least in part of a double row of pieces; theca nonporous, without radial symmetry, often with differentiated marginal plates; mostly without arm extensions; Cambrian to Lower Silurian.

**Class II. Cystidea.** Extinct Pelmatozoa of oval or spheroidal form attached directly or by a stalk in an upright position; theca of rigid polygonal plates, usually not pentamerous; all or some of the plates porous, permeated with canals; ambulacra two to five, extended into brachioles without pinnules; brachioles bordering both edges of the ambulacra; Middle Ordovician to Middle Devonian, reaching their height in the Silurian.

Order 1. Rhombifera. Canals of the theca form pore rhombs in some or all of the thecal plates.

Order 2. Diploporita. Canals in the form of diplopores in some or all of the thecal plates.

**Class III. Blastoidea.** Extinct Pelmatozoa of bud-like shape, attached directly or by a short stalk in an upright position; with highly radial pentamerous theca of 13 plates in three cycles; with five petaloid ambulacra more or less bordered with brachioles, sometimes pinnulated; characteristic respiratory organs, the hydrospires, situated beneath the ambulacra; Ordovician to the Permian, mainly in the Mississippian.

**Class IV. Crinoidea.** Extinct and living Pelmatozoa usually attached by a stalk, but most living members stalkless and free-moving; oral surface directed upward; entire structure strongly pentamerous; theca differentiated into an aboral cup, the calyx, composed of nonporous plates arranged in pentamerous cycles, and an oral cover or roof, the tegmen, which is membranous or encloses supporting plates; with pentamerously arranged movable arms, originally simple but mostly branched, springing from the margin between calyx and tegmen by way of a basal ossicle, the radial, incorporated into the calyx; arms with or without pinnules; ambulacra extend along arms and pinnules to their tips; mouth usually central or nearly so; anus usually excentric but sometimes central, on the oral surface, often mounted on a tube; Ordovician to the present, reaching their climax in the Mississippian.

Order 1. Inadunata. Extinct crinoids in which the lower arm ossicles spring free from the calyx; calyx rigid; mouth covered over by tegminal plates but ambulacra mostly exposed; with or without pinnules; Silurian to Permian.

Order 2. Flexibilia. Extinct crinoids in which the lower arm ossicles are incorporated into the calyx but calyx and tegmen are flexible; mouth and ambulacra not covered; arms without pinnules; Ordovician to Permian.

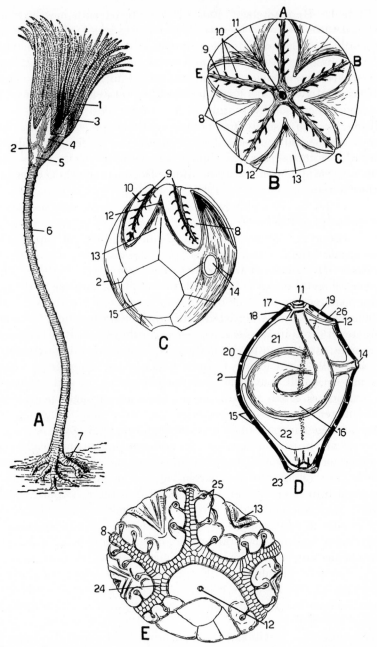

Fig. 1.—General features of echinoderms.  *A*, pelmatozoan echinoderm (blastoid, extinct), showing general appearance of early echinoderms (*after Bather*, 1899).  *B*, oral view of an early echinoderm (*Cystoblastus*, cystid, extinct).  *C*, side view of same.  (*B, C, after Volborth*, 1870; brachioles omitted.)  *D*, presumed internal structure of forms like *C*,

Order 3. Camerata. Extinct crinoids in which the lower arm ossicles are incorporated into the rigid calyx; tegmen plated, covering over mouth and ambulacra; arms pinnulate; Ordovician to Mississippian.

Order 4. Articulata. Extinct and living crinoids in which the lower arm ossicles are incorporated into the calyx; calyx flexible; tegmen leathery, containing calcareous particles or small plates; mouth and ambulacra exposed; Triassic to present.

**Class V. Edrioasteroidea.** Extinct Pelmatozoa of discoid shape without stalk or arms, lying free or attached directly by the aboral surface; theca flexible, of many small plates; five open straight or sinuous ambulacra, usually provided with cover plates; ambulacra pierced with pores for the podia; Lower Cambrian to the Carboniferous.

*Subphylum II. Eleutherozoa*

Stemless echinoderms, living free, moving with the oral surface downward or lying on one side; structure usually highly pentamerous; ambulacral system generally not food-gathering, typically employed in locomotion; anus when present usually on the aboral surface; main nervous system oral.

**Class VI. Holothuroidea.** Eleutherozoa elongated in the oral-aboral axis with secondary bilateral symmetry; usually lying on one side which may be differentiated; mouth surrounded by a set of tentacles attached to the water-vascular system; body surface coriaceous; endo-skeleton reduced to microscopic spicules or plates embedded in the body wall, sometimes absent; podia in the form of locomotory tube feet, sometimes wanting, usually occupying five ambulacral areas but may spread over the entire surface; gonad of a single or paired tuft of tubules.

Order 1. Aspidochirota. Holothurians with numerous podia; oral tentacles peltate; oral retractors wanting; respiratory trees present.

Order 2. Elasipoda. Holothurians with numerous podia; oral tentacles peltate; oral retractors and respiratory trees absent; deep-sea forms.

Order 3. Dendrochirota. Holothurians with numerous podia; oral tentacles dendroid; oral retractors and respiratory trees present.

Order 4. Molpadonia. Holothurians without podia except as

---

based on crinoid embryology. *E*, extinct echinoderm (*Glyptocystites*, cystid) (*after Jaekel*, 1899), showing manner of formation of five rays from an original three. 1, brachioles; 2, theca; 3, deltoid plates; 4, radial plates; 5, basal plates; 6, stalk; 7, roots; 8, ambulacra; 9, central groove of ambulacra; 10, branches of groove to brachioles (missing); 11, mouth; 12, hydropore; 13, interradii or interambulacra; 14, anus; 15, plates of theca; 16, intestine; 17, ring canal of water-vascular system; 18, ectoneural system accompanying same; 19, gonopore; 20, gonad; 21, left or oral coelom; 22, right or aboral coelom; 23, aboral nervous system; 24, covering plates of ambulacral grooves; 25, facets for brachioles, 26, stone canal. Letters A–E on figure *B* indicate the standard method of naming the five ambulacra or rays; the ray A is that opposite the hydropore.

anal papillae; oral tentacles digitate; posterior region generally tapering into a caudal portion; respiratory trees present.

Order 5. Apoda. Vermiform holothurians with smooth or warty surface totally devoid of podia; oral tentacles present; water-vascular system greatly reduced; respiratory trees absent.

**Class VII. Echinoidea.** Spheroidal, disciform, oval, or cordiform Eleutherozoa covered with movable spines; endoskeleton in the form of a continuous test of closely fitted calcareous plates, composed of alternating columns of ambulacral and interambulacral areas; ambulacral plates pierced with pores for the passage of the podia; podia mostly locomotory; ambulacra extend from the mouth region almost to the aboral pole; mouth central or displaced anteriorly, surrounded by a membranous peristome; anus surrounded by a membranous periproct, located at the aboral pole or displaced posteriorly or to the oral side along one of the interambulacral areas; gonads pentamerous; Ordovician to the present.

Subclass I. Bothriocidaroida. Extinct Ordovician echinoids of the single genus *Bothriocidaris;* with rigid globular test having two rows of plates in each ambulacrum and one row in each interambulacrum; without typical lantern; madreporite radial.

Subclass II. Regularia or Endocyclica. Echinoids of globular form and mostly circular, sometimes oval, outline; pentamerously symmetrical with two rows of interambulacral plates in all existing forms; peristome and periproct central, at the oral and aboral poles, respectively; periproct encircled by the apical system of plates; lantern well developed in all existing species.

Order 1. Lepidocentroida. Extinct and living echinoids with flexible test of imbricated or separated plates; ambulacral plates continue on peristome to mouth lip; extinct forms with more than two rows of interambulacral plates.

Order 2. Melonechinoida. Extinct Carboniferous echinoids with spherical, rigid test, having four or more rows of interambulacral and two or more rows of ambulacral plates; latter continue to the mouth lip.

Order 3. Cidaroidea. Extinct and living echinoids with rigid, globular test with two rows of long, narrow ambulacral plates of the simple type and two rows of interambulacral plates, both continuing to the mouth edge; each interambulacral plate bears one large spine, encircled basally by small spines; attachments for lantern muscles interradial on the perignathic girdle; gills and sphaeridia wanting; Mississippian to the present, reaching its height in the Jurassic and Cretaceous.

Order 4. Aulodonta. Extinct and living echinoids with a symmetrical globular test composed of two rows each in ambulacra and

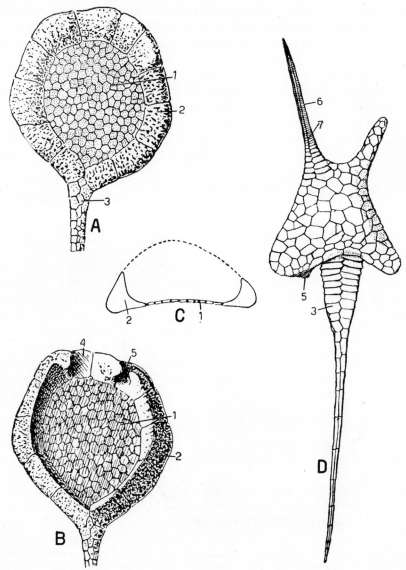

FIG. 2.—Class Heterostelea. *A*, *Trochocystites*, Cambrian, external view. *B*, same, longitudinal section. *C*, same, cross section. (*A–C*, *after Jaekel*, 1918.) *D*, *Dendrocystites*, Ordovician (*after Bather*, 1925). 1, interior plates; 2, marginal plates; 3, plates of stem; 4, mouth; 5, anus; 6, brachiole; 7, food groove on brachiole.

interambulacra; ambulacral plates compound, of two to ten elements; ambulacral and interambulacral rows cease at the edge of the peristome; lantern attachments radial on the perignathic girdle; gills and sphaeridia

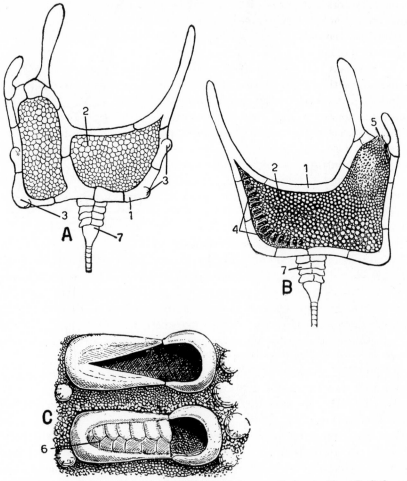

Fig. 3.—Class Heterostelea (concluded). *A, Cothurnocystis,* lower side. *B, Cothurnocystis,* upper side, with "gill slits." *C,* enlarged view of slits, upper one without, lower one with covering plates. (*All after Bather,* 1925.) 1, marginal plates; 2, interior plates; 3, knobs supporting theca on bottom; 4, slits; 5, anus; 6, covering plates of slits; 7, plates of stalk.

present; epiphyses of the lantern small and not meeting above the pyramids; teeth without a keel.

Order 5. Stirodonta. Mostly extinct echinoids with small lantern epiphyses, not meeting above the pyramids; teeth keeled; otherwise much as in Aulodonta.

Order 6. Camarodonta. Lantern epiphyses enlarged, meeting

above the pyramids to form a bar; teeth keeled; otherwise much as in Aulodonta, but test sometimes oval.

Following Mortensen, the three preceding groups are raised to the rank of orders but these differ primarily only in details of the lantern, and the author is in agreement with H. L. Clark and others that they should be reduced to suborders under the order Diadematoida (or Centrechinoida).

Subclass III.  Irregularia or Exocyclica.  Extinct and living echinoids with mostly flattened oval to circular test, altered along a bilateral axis; periproct displaced posteriorly along one interradius to a posterior aboral or oral position; lies outside the apical system of plates which remains at the aboral pole; aboral portions of the ambulacra often altered to a petaloid condition; peristome central or displaced anteriorly on the oral surface; podia generally not locomotory.

Order 1.  Holectypoida.  Mostly extinct echinoids with regular tests, simple ambulacra without petaloid differentiation, and centrally located peristome and apical system; periproct more or less removed from the apical system.

Order 2.  Cassiduloida.  Mostly extinct echinoids with round to oval test, more or less petaloid aboral ambulacra and floscelles around the peristome; lantern wanting in adults of existing species.

Order 3.  Clypeastroida.  Irregular echinoids with flattened test of oval or rounded outline; aboral ambulacral areas petaloid; lantern present; gills absent; phyllodes and bourrelets wanting.

Order 4.  Spatangoida.  Irregular echinoids with oval or cordiform test; four aboral ambulacra petaloid; fifth (anterior) ambulacrum not petaloid; peristome displaced anteriorly with phyllodes but no bourrelets; fascioles present; no lantern or gills.

**Class VIII.  Asteroidea.**  Flattened, mostly pentagonal Eleutherozoa of star-like form with five (sometimes more) long or short rays or arms radiating symmetrically from a central disk; oral surface held downward; ambulacra form pronounced grooves provided with locomotory podia; ambulacra limited to the oral surface, extending from the peristome to the tips of the rays; ambulacral pores between the ambulacral plates; endoskeleton flexible, of separated ossicles; gonads radially arranged; arms occupied by digestive glands; Cambrian to the present.

Order 1.  Platyasterida.  Extinct asteroids, of Ordovician and Devonian age, with widely open ambulacral grooves, almost flush with the surface; with inframarginal plates edging the arms; mouth frame not differentiated.

Order 2.  Hemizonida.  Extinct asteroids with definite ambulacral grooves; mouth frame not differentiated; Ordovician to middle Carboniferous.

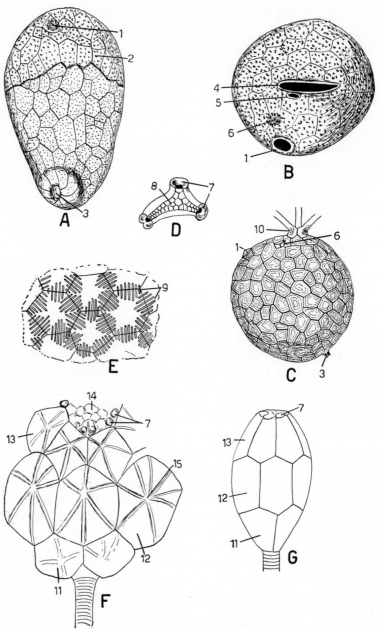

Fig. 4.—Cystidea. *A*, *Aristocystites*, side view; theca above heavy line is more worn away than below it, exposing the diplopores. *B*, *Aristocystites*, oral view, showing the openings. (*A, B, after Barrande*, 1887–1889). *C*, *Echinosphaerites*, with surface sculpturing intact (*after Jaekel*, 1899). *D*, *Echinosphaerites*, oral view of the three ambulacra with facets for the brachioles (*after Jaekel*, 1899). *E*, *Echinosphaerites*, with surface worn away, exposing the rhombs (*after Zittel*, 1915). *F*, *Caryocrinites*, with surface sculpturing (from a specimen). *G*, scheme of the plate arrangement in *Caryocrinites* (*after Bather*, 1906). 1, anus; 2, diplopores; 3, place of attachment; 4, mouth; 5, hydropore; 6, gonopore; 7, facets for brachioles; 8, covering plates of ambulacra; 9, rhomb canals; 10, brachioles; 11, basals; 12, infralaterals; 13, laterals; 14, radials; 15, umbo.

Order 3. Phanerozonia. Arms edged with conspicuous marginal plates in two rows, an aboral supramarginal and an oral inframarginal row; pedicellariae when present of the sessile or alveolar type; papulae limited to aboral surface; mouth frame of the adambulacral type.

Suborder 1. Pustulosa. Extinct Phanerozonia with small, slender spines mounted on hemispherical tubercles; Ordovician into Permian.

Suborder 2. Cribellosa. Phanerozonia with typical cribriform organs; podia without suckers; ampullae single; anus and intestine wanting.

Suborder 3. Paxillosa. Aboral surface formed of paxillae; podia without suckers; ampullae bifurcated.

Suborder 4. Notomyota. Aboral surface formed of reduced paxillae or flat plates; marginal plates spiny; podia with suckers; each arm with a pair of strong dorsolateral muscle bands, not found in any other asteroids; papulae in papularia.

Suborder 5. Valvata. Aboral surface formed of plates varying from paxillae to a flattened mosaic arrangement; podia with suckers.

Order 4. Spinulosa. Arms generally without conspicuous marginal plates; pedicellariae rarely present; aboral skeleton imbricated or reticulated with single spines or groups of spines, not infrequently paxilliform; mouth frame of the adambulacral type; podia with suckers; ampullae single or bifurcated.

Order 5. Forcipulata. No conspicuous marginal plates, aboral skeleton mostly reticulate; spines not in groups; papulae on both surfaces; pedicellariae all of the pedunculate type with a basal piece; podia mostly in four rows, with suckers; mouth frame of the ambulacral type.

**Class IX. Ophiuroidea.** Flattened pentamerous Eleutherozoa with long slender flexible arms, sometimes branched, sharply set off from the central disk; ambulacral grooves wanting; ambulacral canals relegated to the interior of the arms by the closure of endoskeletal plates below them; anus and intestine wanting; digestive system rarely extending into the arms; madreporite on the oral surface; gonads pentamerous, discharging through invaginated sacs of the body wall, the bursae, 10 in number, sometimes reduced or wanting; Mississippian to the present.

Order 1. Ophiurae. Arms simple, moving horizontally; main arm ossicles articulated by pits and projections; scalation of arms and disk mostly well developed; arms cannot twine around objects.

Order 2. Euryalae. Arms simple or branched; main arm ossicles articulated by hourglass projections at right angles on adjacent surfaces; disk and arm scalation often poorly developed and concealed by a thick skin; arms move vertically and may be entwined around objects.

**Class X. Ophiocistioidea.** Paleozoic Eleutherozoa of discoidal shape, moving on the oral surface; completely enclosed in a theca of plates except for the peristome; theca pentamerous on the oral surface only where five ambulacra of three plate rows alternate with five interambulacra of one plate row each; arms wanting; oral surface with a few, up to six, pairs of giant podia in each ambulacrum; podia covered with small imbricated scales.

## IV. THE NONCRINOID PELMATOZOA

**1. General Characters of the Noncrinoid Pelmatozoa.**—The noncrinoid Pelmatozoa are wholly extinct, having flourished in the Palaeozoic era, and hence are known only by the endoskeleton, surviving in the rocks in fossil form. These fossils begin in the early Cambrian, the geological period in which most metazoan groups make their first appearance, and already possess typical echinoderm characteristics so that the fossil record furnishes no clue to the origin of echinoderms from preceding forms. It is to be understood that these fossils were clothed in life by a living epidermis and that the interior contained viscera of which almost nothing is known except by inference from still-existing Pelmatozoa (Fig. 1D).

The noncrinoid Pelmatozoa (Fig. 1A) lived attached by the aboral surface, either directly or by way of a *stalk* or *stem* composed of a succession of calcareous pieces. The fossil endoskeleton typically consists of this stalk, a rounded, oval, disciform, or laterally flattened case of closely fitted polygonal plates, the *theca*, that enclosed the viscera, and one or more arm-like extensions from the aboral surface of the theca, termed *brachioles*. It is characteristic of the theca of the noncrinoid Pelmatozoa that it is completely closed up to the mouth. Its plates were originally without definite arrangement and often very numerous, but gradually they take on a pentamerous disposition.

The oral surface of the theca faces upward or at least away from the surface of attachment and bears both mouth and anus. The mouth is found at or near the center of the oral surface, often surrounded by or covered over by special plates; the anus is located to one side in one of the interradii (Fig. 1C, D) and also may have a covering of plates, forming the *anal pyramid*. Between the mouth and the anus in the same interradius is generally to be found the *hydropore* or entrance into the water-vascular system. There may be present in or near the same interradius another pore believed to be the *gonopore*, apparently combined with the anus in some cases. Apparently there was originally a single gonad.

From the mouth radiate the ambulacra, which seem to have varied from one to five in number (Fig. 1B, C, E). There is evidence that the eventual pentamerous condition arose from a trimerous condition by the forking of two of the three ambulacra (Fig. 1*E*). The ambulacra in their simplest form are grooves lined by a ciliated epithelium and serve to convey food particles to the mouth by means of ciliary currents; hence they are called *food grooves* throughout the literature on the Pelmatozoa. Here the term food groove or ambulacral groove will be employed to refer primarily to the food-catching groove itself, while the term ambulacrum will indicate the entire radius that bears the groove along its center. At first the ambulacra extend scarcely at all away from the mouth but mount at once onto simple erect arms called *brachioles*, which are supported by endoskeletal pieces. These brachioles are a characteristic feature of the noncrinoid Pelmatozoa (Fig. 1*A*), and even when they are missing from the fossil remains, their presence in the intact animal is indicated by facets on the theca (Fig. 4*D*) to which they were articulated. Ambulacra that mount at once on brachioles are spoken of as *exothecal*. Such brachioles are equal in number to the ambulacra and carry the food groove on their inner surface, being in fact devices for increasing the food-gathering area. In later stages of their evolution, the ambulacra continue away from the mouth for shorter or longer distances over the oral surface of the theca, either as grooves between the thecal plates (*endothecal* condition) or as grooves in the plates (*epithecal* condition), or finally the ambulacral grooves become lined with little plates of their own. In these cases, also, the food grooves finally mount on brachioles which may spring from the theca at the distal ends of the ambulacra or more often line both sides of the ambulacra. In the latter condition the brachioles are very numerous and give the pelmatozoan something of the appearance of a long-handled brush (Fig. 1*A*). As each of the many brachioles carries a food groove on its inner surface, the food-gathering area is enormously increased. Ambulacra may be protected by a covering of little plates (Fig. 1*E*) that can be erected to expose the food groove, or by extensions over them of the thecal plates (*hypothecal* condition), also probably erectile. It is presumed that beneath (aboral to) the ambulacra ran in life the radial canals of the water-vascular system, radial nerves, branches of the coelom, and so on. Also presumably the ambulacra were accompanied in life by small finger-like podia, but only in the Edriosteroidea were pores present for their emission. In all other Pelmatozoa the ambulacral system lies wholly to the oral side of the thecal plates and the ossicles of the brachioles.

**2. Class Heterostelea.**—This class corresponds roughly or in part to the pelmatozoan class Carpoidea of Jaekel (1918) and the cystoid order Amphoridea as emended by Bather (1900). It includes a group of early echinoderm fossils altogether lacking in radial symmetry. These forms were fastened by a stalk composed of two or more rows of skeletal

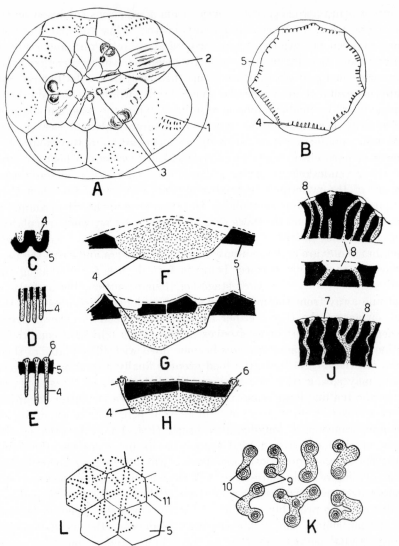

Fig. 5.—Cystidea (continued).  *A*, oral view of *Caryocrinites*, showing eight lateral plates, radials, and three pairs of brachiole facets (*after Bather*, 1906).  *B*, section through the theca of *Caryocrinites*, showing rhomb folds projecting into interior.  *C–E*, cross sections of different types of rhomb canals.  *F–H*, lengthwise views of the same.  *F*, simple fold, shown in cross section in *C*.  *G*, rhomb canal with vertical ends that show on the surface as pores; cross section in *D*.  *H*, rhomb canals with vertical ends concealed under surface knobs; cross section in *E*.  (*B–H, after Jaekel*, 1899.)  *J*, haplopores and diplopores seen in sections through the theca.  *K*, surface view of diplopores.  (*J, K, after Jaekel*, 1918.)  *L*, scheme of pore rhombs produced by slight weathering of rhomb canals of the types of *G* and *H*.  (Thecal plates in black in *C–K*.)  1, lateral plates with surface sculpturing partly worn away; 2, radial plates; 3, facets for brachioles; 4, rhomb canals; 5, thecal plates; 6, surface knobs; 7, haplopore; 8, various kinds of diplopore canals; 9, diplopores in surface view; 10, peripores; 11, pore rhomb.

elements, diminishing in some genera to a single row toward the attached end. The theca is generally laterally flattened, usually markedly so, and composed of irregularly arranged polygonal plates typically differentiated into a marginal row of large plates bounding a few large or numerous small interior plates (Fig. 2*A, B*). Not infrequently the plate arrangement differs on the two sides of the theca, and this fact, together with the flattened shape, is interpreted to mean that the Heterostelea lived in a horizontal orientation, swinging about on their stalks, and with one side always directed upward. Often, also, one surface, presumably that held next the substratum, is flattened or concave, and the other surface convex (Fig. 2*C*). In *Placocystis* and *Cothurnocystis* a skeletal element similar to a spine projects forward on each side from the anterior end of the theca (Fig. 3*A, B*). In some genera, as *Trochocystites* (Fig. 2*A, B*), an oral and an anal opening are evident in the free end; in others the anal opening appears posteriorly located, near the insertion of the stalk (Fig. 2*D*), and still others seem devoid of external openings, possibly because these were covered with protective erectile plates. The state of the ambulacral system in the Heterostelea is uncertain; it is never pentamerous and is not evident in most of the fossil material. In *Trochocystites* a groove, possibly a food groove, leads away from the oral opening to either side. *Dendrocystites* (Fig. 2*D*) is provided with two anterior projections, one of which seems to be a brachiole bearing a food groove covered with little protective plates; near the base of the brachiole occur a gonopore and a hydropore, whereas the anal opening is found near the insertion of the stalk. *Rhipidocystis* seems to have been provided with a number of brachioles having food grooves covered with protective plates. *Cothurnocystis* (Fig. 3) and some related genera have a row of slits, numbering 8 to 42, on one surface along the side or base of the theca; they are generally more or less covered by movable plates. The function of these slits is obscure; Bather (1925) regards them as serving for the intake of water into the digestive tract, in which case they would constitute the first appearance of gill slits in the enterocoelous line. An alternative idea that they were multiple mouths appears unreasonable.

**3. Class Cystidea.**—The cystids or cystoids are a well-known group of extinct pelmatozoans, mostly from the Ordovician and Silurian eras. Following Regnéll (1945), the forms often put in the orders Amphoridea and Aporita are here excluded from the Cystidea, and these orders are dropped altogether. The cystids present a more typical pelmatozoan appearance than do the Heterostelea, for they have an erect orientation with the oral surface facing upward, and a general vase-like form. The theca is usually sessile, fastened directly to the substratum, but sometimes a long or short stem is present, composed of a succession of hollow pieces and usually tapering to the attached end which may be fastened by root-like extensions.

The theca is usually of oval or spheroidal form composed of closely fitting, immovable, polygonal plates that range from numerous small ones without definite arrangement to a few large ones disposed in cycles. Among genera with numerous, irregularly arranged thecal plates may be mentioned *Aristocystites* (Fig. 4*A*), *Holocystites*, *Echinosphaerites* (Fig. 4*C*), and *Caryocystites*. Regnéll (1945) estimated 800 to 850 plates in a species of *Echinosphaerites*, and Bather (1906) found 150 to 200 in *Aristocystites*, but lesser numbers usually obtain. With reduction to a relatively few (around 20 to 30) large plates, these tend to arrange in cycles, typically five, named from the aboral end oralward: *basals*, *infralaterals*, *laterals*, *radials*, and *orals* or *deltoids*. The last two cycles occur on the oral surface and are related to the mouth and ambulacra. The similarity of names does not necessarily imply any homology with the plate cycles of crinoids. Schematically there are four basal plates and five each in the other four cycles, but other numbers are often encountered. Thus in *Caryocrinites*, a common North American cystid, there are typically four basals, six infralaterals, eight laterals, and a variable number of radials, probably six originally, as the radials may subdivide to accommodate the ambulacra (Fig. 4*F*, *G*). The thecal plates are often sculptured, sometimes with concentric ridges as in *Echinosphaerites* (Fig. 4*C*), more often with ridges radiating from a central knob (*umbo*) as in *Caryocrinites* (Fig. 4*F*). These ridges may be bordered by a row of knobs that are hollow, containing the blind outer ends of the canals of the thecal canal system.

An outstanding feature of the theca of cystids is that it is "porous," by which is meant that some or all of the thecal plates are permeated with canals. In their simplest form these canals run inward more or less at right angles to the surface (Fig. 5*J*). More commonly, however, they take the form of elongated folds that open on the surface as long slits (Fig. 4*E*), if the original skeletal surface is worn away. Next, the main part of the fold drops down to project into the interior of the theca, leaving the two ends to open on the surface as pores (Fig. 5*F*, *H*). These ends may open into depressions of the surface or begin as blind ends inside projecting knobs (Fig. 5*E*). It appears that in life the outer ends of the canals did not open through the surface but were covered not only by the epidermis and underlying tissue, but possibly also by a thin skeletal layer surfacing the theca and usually missing in fossils. The simple canals apparently opened onto the internal surface of the thecal plates (Fig. 5*J*), and the greater part of the folds projected into the interior (Fig. 5*B*). These flattened canals or folds occur in parallel groups that have the shape of a diamond, lozenge, or rhomboid and

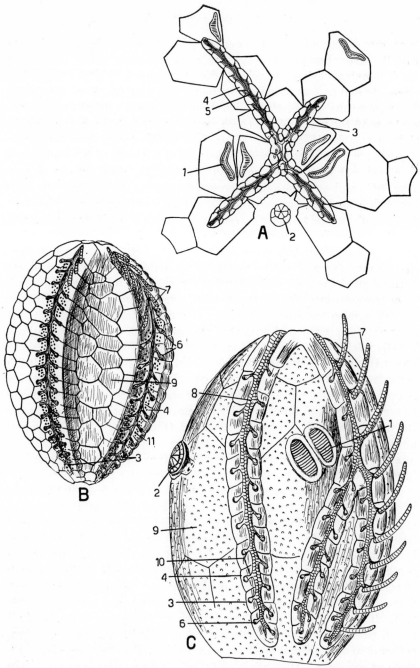

Fig. 6.—Cystidea (continued). *A*, *Lovenicystis*, oral region, showing ambulacral grooves paved with little plates (*after Regnéll*, 1945). *B*, *Proteroblastus*, diploporite, with ambulacra reaching the aboral pole. *C*, *Callocystites*, rhombifer, also with long ambulacra; brachioles retained on one side. 1, pectinirhombs; 2, anal pyramid; 3, ambulacra; 4, side plates of ambulacra; 5, flooring plates; 6, facets for brachioles; 7, brachioles; 8, covering plates of ambulacra; 9, thecal plates; 10, branches of ambulacral grooves to brachioles; 11, diplopores.

hence are called *rhombs*. The central folds of the rhomb are the longest, and the folds diminish in length to the sides of the rhomb (Fig. 4*E*). Each rhomb always occupies two adjacent plates; half of the rhomb is on one plate and half on an adjoining plate (Fig. 4*E*), which means that the folds pass through the suture between the plates. Primitively rhombs occur in all the plates of the theca, so that each plate bears the halves of several rhombs (Fig. 4*E*). When the thecal surface is slightly worn away, as is usually the case in these fossils, the ends of the folds, which form vertical canals (as shown in Fig. 5*D*, *E*) then appear as pores (Fig. 5*L*), and as these pores necessarily outline the rhombs, the latter are usually spoken of as *pore rhombs*, although obviously canal rhombs or fold rhombs would be more correct appellations. A still further wearing exposes the horizontal parts of the folds, which then appear on the thecal plates as parallel striations or slits (Fig. 4*E*). Rhombs evolve to more complicated types of folding in the thecal plates, and these complicated rhombs are known as *pectinate* rhombs, or more briefly *pectinirhombs*, from their resemblance to combs when exposed by surface weathering. Pectinirhombs are often encircled by a raised margin (Fig. 6*C*). By disappearance of the middle part of the pectinirhomb, the two ends, each usually enclosed in a raised rim, are left facing each other across the suture like a pair of combs (Fig. 6*C*). The two combs of such a pair may come to differ from each other, or one of the two may eventually disappear. Rhombs may occur on all the thecal plates or may be limited to certain ones, and this is usually the case with pectinirhombs, of which frequently only a few occur on the theca (Fig. 6*A*, *C*). The disappearance of rhombs is attributed by Bather (1900) to the proximity of internal organs to the inner surface of the theca, thus interfering with the functions of the rhombs.

The various types of rhombs are limited to the order Rhombifera; in the other cystid order, the Diploporita, a different type of canal system obtains. Here the canals are associated in groups of two (sometimes more); the two canals of each group begin in a blind chamber just beneath the external surface (Fig. 5*J*) and run in the thecal plate perpendicular to its surfaces. When the outer surface of the thecal plates is worn away, the chamber is exposed as an oval, polygonal, or crescentic depression, in the bottom of which the two canals appear as pores (Fig. 5*K*). These pairs of pores are known as *diplopores*, and weathered thecal plates of the Diploporita are peppered with these pairs of pores enclosed in variously shaped depressed areas (Fig. 5*K*), referred to by some as *peripores*. Here again the term diplopore appears unfortunate, and diplocanal would give a more correct idea of the actual condition. Single thecal canals appear on the surface as single pores, termed *haplopores*.

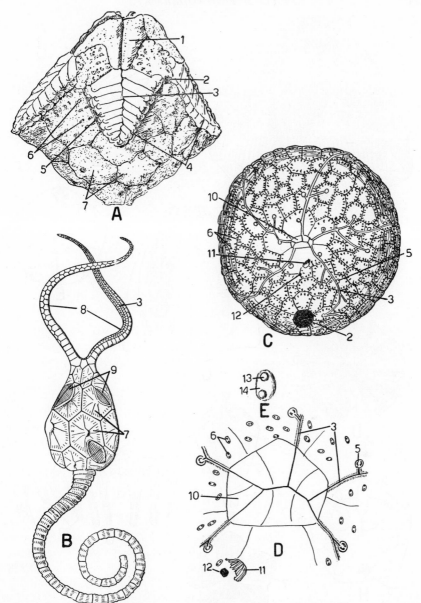

Fig. 7.—Cystidea (concluded). A, *Asteroblastus* (after *Jaekel*, 1918). B, *Pleurocystites* (after *Bather*, 1900). C, *Glyptosphaerites*. D, oral region of *Glyptosphaerites*, enlarged. E, a diplopore of C. (C–E, after *Jaekel*, 1899.) 1, deltoid plates; 2, anus; 3, ambulacral groove; 4, ambulacra; 5, facets for brachioles; 6, diplopores; 7, plates of theca; 8, brachiole; 9, pectinirhomb; 10, covering plates of mouth; 11, hydropore; 12, gonopore; 13, pore; 14, peripore.

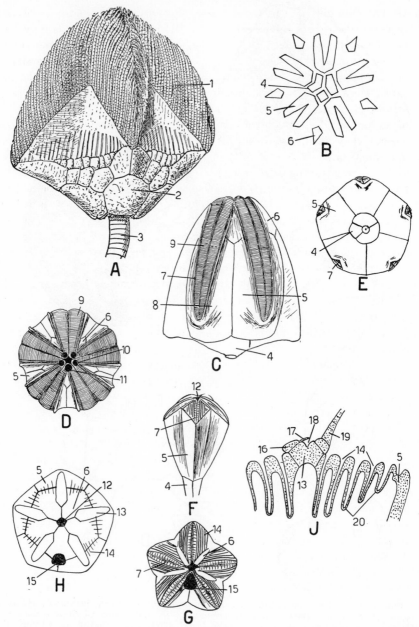

FIG. 8.—Blastoidea.   A, *Blastoidocrinus* with complete set of brachioles (*after Jaekel*, 1918).   B, scheme of the thecal plates of a blastoid (*after Zittel*, 1915).   C, a typical blastoid, *Pentremites*, from the side.   D, *Pentremites*, oral view.   E, *Pentremites*, aboral view of theca.   F, *Codaster*, side view.   G, *Codaster*, oral view.   (*C–G*, from specimens.) H, *Codaster*, oral surface removed to show plates.   J, *Codaster*, schematic section through a radial to show the hydrospire folds.   (*H, J, after Bather*, 1900.)   1, brachioles; 2, theca;

The function of the thecal canal system of the cystids is obscure (general discussion in Chauvel, 1941). Originally the canals may have been simply spaces occupied by the endoskeletal mesenchyme (called *stroma* by palaeontologists). A respiratory function is usually assigned, but acceptance of this depends on whether or not one supposes that the canals were cut off from the exterior by a calcareous layer as well as by soft surface tissues. Possibly these canals led into papulae, like those of asteroids. If in fact the simple canals opened internally into the coelom, they must have been clothed with peritoneum, and the coelomic fluid must have circulated in them; the system then appears as a device for supplying the thecal plates with food and oxygen. As the horizontal parts of the folds in the rhomb systems projected into the coelom, the same purpose would be achieved by diffusion through their thin walls.

In or near the center of the oral surface of the theca is found the mouth, which, together with a surrounding area (*peristome*), may be covered by a variable number of oral plates. The anus is located excentrically in one of the interradii and generally is covered by a little cone termed the *anal* or *valvular pyramid*, formed of small triangular plates (Fig. 6*C*) that presumably opened out for the emission of feces. Between the mouth and anus in the same interradius is found the gonopore, and between it and the mouth a hydropore may be evident. Some or all of these four openings may not be detectable in some specimens.

There appear to have been originally three ambulacra (Fig. 4*D*), with one in the radius opposite that containing the anus (so-called *anterior* radius) and the other two symmetrically disposed lateral to this. The number five results from the forking of the two lateral ambulacra (Fig. 1*E*), and the numbers two or four presumably from loss. Often the ambulacra branch at their outer ends, sometimes in palmate fashion, or may give off side branches. In their most primitive state the ambulacra, immediately outside the mouth, mount on brachioles, as in *Echinosphaerites* (Fig. 4*C*); later, they ran farther and farther out on the theca, eventually almost to the aboral pole (Fig. 6*B, C*). Their grooves occur between the thecal plates, or as furrows in the plates, or eventually come to be lined by little plates, as in *Lovenicystis* (Fig. 6*A*). The fully developed ambulacral grooves were often provided with covering plates that could close over them for protection (Fig. 6*A*). Eventually the ambulacra or their branches mounted on brachioles that seem to have been seldom preserved but whose existence and number are indicated by the facets preserved at the ends or along the sides of the ambu-

3, stalk; 4, basal; 5, radial; 6, deltoid; 7, ambulacra; 8, interradii; 9, side plates with grooves to brachioles; 10, spiracles; 11, spiracle plus anus; 12, mouth; 13, lancet plate; 14, slits of hydrospires; 15, anus; 16, side plate; 17, covering plate; 18. ambulacral groove; 19, base of brachiole; 20, folds of hydrospire.

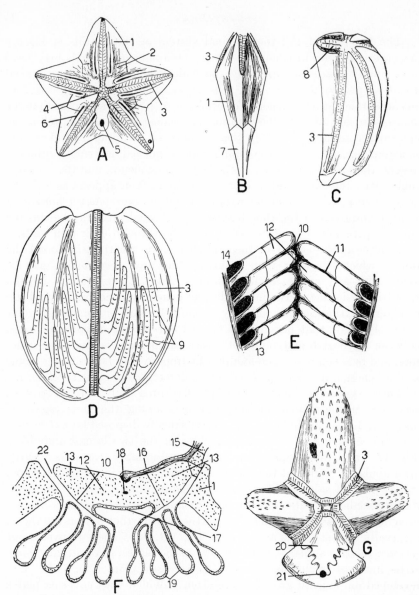

Fig. 9.—Blastoidea (concluded). *A, Orophocrinus,* oral view, with only outermost slit exposed on the surface *(after Meek and Worthen,* 1873). *B, Troostocrinus,* with shor'. ambulacra. *C, Eleutherocrinus,* side view, asymmetrical type with one short petaloid ambulacrum. *D, Orbitremites,* with long narrow ambulacra; brachioles retained in part. *(B–D,* from specimens.) *E,* enlarged view of a piece of an ambulacrum of *Pentremites,* showing side plates and hydrospire pores. *F,* schematic section through an ambulacrum of *Pentremites,* showing two hydrospires *(after Bather,* 1900). *G, Zygocrinus. (E, G. after Etheridge and Carpenter,* 1886.)   1, radial plate; 2, deltoid; 3, ambulacrum; 4, covering plates of mouth; 5, anus; 6, exposed last slit of hydrospire; 7, basal plates; 8, short ambulacrum; 9, brachioles; 10, ambulacral groove; 11, side branches of groove; 12, lancet plate; 13, side plates; 14, hydrospire pores; 15, base of brachiole; 16, cover plates of ambulacral groove; 17, sublancet plate; 18, canal for nerve; 19, hydrospire folds; 20, abnormal ambulacrum; 21, hole of uncertain nature; 22, canal to hydrospire pore.

lacra. Brachioles may occur in a row along each side of the ambulacra (Fig. 6*B*, *C*).

The Cystidea are divided into two orders, Rhombifera and Diploporita. The Rhombifera are provided with rhombs of one kind or another, although the earliest types seem to have had simple canals (haplopores). The theca evolves from a condition of numerous, irregularly arranged plates, all provided with pore rhombs, as *Echinosphaerites* (Fig. 4*C, E*), to a type with few plates arranged in somewhat pentamerous cycles and with a limited number of definitely located rhombs, as in *Pleurocystites* (Fig. 7*B*). Similarly, the ambulacral system evolves from an original number of three grooves of the exothecal type (Fig. 4*C, D*), that is, erected at once on brachioles, to a final number of five that run for various distances over the theca, even to the aboral pole, and become lined with their own little plates (Fig. 6*A, C*). Among the genera of the Rhombifera may be mentioned *Echinosphaerites* (Fig. 4*C–E*), *Echinoencrinites, Caryocystites, Glyptocystites* (Fig. 1*E*), *Cheirocrinus, Lepadocrinites, Callocystites* (Fig. 6*C*), *Caryocrinites* (Figs. 4*F, G*, 5*A, B*), *Cystoblastus, Pleurocystites* (Fig. 7*B*), and *Lovenicystis* (Fig. 6*A*).

The Diploporita are characterized by diplopores, although some seem to have had haplopores. They were usually stalkless, and the theca throughout consists of many small plates. The diplopores may occur on all the thecal plates or only on some of them and eventually are limited to the plates bordering the ambulacra (Fig. 6*B*). The ambulacral system follows the same evolutionary sequence as in the Rhombifera, progressing toward an eventual condition of five grooves extending far over the theca, often to the aboral pole as in *Proteroblastus* (Fig. 6*B*), lined by their own little plates and bordered laterally by brachioles, often missing. Representative diploporitic genera are *Aristocystites* (Fig. 4*A*), *Sphaeronites, Gomphocystites, Glyptosphaerites* (Fig. 7*C, D*), *Proteroblastus* (Fig. 6*B*), *Mesocystis*, and *Asteroblastus* (Fig. 7*A*).

**4. Class Blastoidea.**—The blastoids are a well-defined group of extinct Palaeozoic Pelmatozoa that lived from the Middle Ordovician to the Lower Permian, reaching their height in the Mississippian era, especially in North America, where the seas at that time abounded with them. It is maintained, no doubt correctly, by Jaekel (1918) and Regnéll (1945) that the blastoids are not separable from the cystids and should be reduced to a subclass of the latter. This, however, leads to a certain confusion and inconvenience since one must constantly explain whether the term Cystidea is being used in a broad sense to include Blastoidea or in the usual restricted sense (being then equivalent to the subclass Hydrophoridea). Consequently the long-established usage is retained here, with Blastoidea limited to what is termed Eublastoidea by some authors.

The blastoids as thus conceived were short-stemmed or stemless Pelmatozoa with a rigid compact theca of mostly oval, five-angled shape, bearing a considerable resemblance to the flower bud of a dicotyledonous plant or even to a hickory nut. The theca completes the process begun in the rhombiferous cystids and now consists of a definite limited number (13) of pentamerously arranged plates, namely, three basals, five radials, and five orals or deltoids (Fig. 8). The three basals derive from an original five as shown by the larger size of two of them, each formed by the fusion of two originally separate plates (Fig. 8*E*). The radials, which are the largest of the plates and form the greater part of the theca, are more or less deeply notched or forked for the reception of the ambulacra (Fig. 8*B*).

The ambulacra are now definitely five in number, forming linear to petaloid symmetrically spaced areas that radiate from the central pentagonal mouth over the theca, often nearly to the aboral pole (Fig. 8*C*). Near the mouth the oral or deltoid plates lie between the ambulacra; farther out the ambulacra fit into the notches of the radials (Fig. 8*C*). The center of the skeletal part of each ambulacrum consists of a long narrow plate, called from its shape the *lancet plate*, that extends to the tip of the ambulacrum; and in some blastoids a second plate, the *under lancet* plate or *sublancet*, underlies the lancet plate. The five lancet plates are situated in the notches of the radial plates, but as they are too narrow to fill these spaces altogether, a vacancy is left to either side of each lancet plate, and this is filled in by a row of small, laterally elongated *side* plates (Fig. 8*J*). External to the side plates is found in some blastoids still another row of quite small plates, the *outer side* plates, said by Bather (1900) to be formed of side plates that have been pushed out of the row. The lancets may be more or less concealed from surface view by the side plates that may somewhat overlap them. The lancet plate contains a median tube, presumed to have housed a radial nerve.

A narrow ambulacral groove runs along the center of the lancets and gives off at regular intervals numerous side branches alternating on the two sides. These run laterally between the side plates, which they equal in number, and then ascend brachioles. The ambulacra are thus bordered on each side by a row of brachioles, one brachiole to each side plate (Fig. 8*A*). The brachioles are usually missing in the fossils, but their occurrence is revealed by the row of facets along the outer edges of the side plates. From well-preserved specimens it is learned that the ambulacral grooves and their side branches were protected by a double row of little cover plates, and as the mouth and adjacent area (peristome) were also roofed over by a number of small plates, it appears that the main parts of the ambulacral system operated under cover.

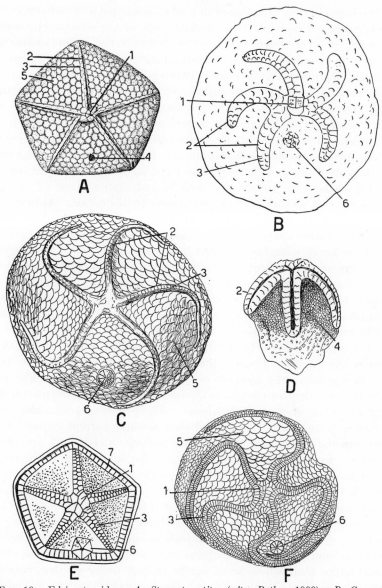

Fig. 10.—Edrioasteroidea. *A, Stromatocystites (after Bather, 1900). B, Carneyella. C, Cooperidiscus (after Clarke, 1901). D, Cystaster. E, Cyathocystis (after Jaekel, 1899). F, Lepidodiscus. (B, D, F, after Bassler, 1936.)* 1, covering plates of mouth; 2, ambulacra; 3, covering plates of ambulacra; 4, anus; 5, thecal plates; 6, anal pyramid.

The blastoids are provided with a set of remarkable structures known as *hydrospires*, whose presence is diagnostic of the class. The hydrospires appear to represent a further evolution of the rhomb system and are usually supposed to be of respiratory nature. Each hydrospire consists of parallel folds or pleats (varying in number from one to ten) of the skeletal material of the radial and deltoid plates or of the radials only. These folds run parallel to the margins of the ambulacra (Fig. 8*J*) so that there are two hydrospires to each ambulacrum, except that in the early stages of evolution of the hydrospire system, the hydrospires are lacking in the interradius that bears the anus, and therefore the early blastoids, as *Codaster* (Fig. 8*G*), had eight hydrospires. Later, by the shoving of the anus toward the mouth, hydrospires occur in the anal interradius also, so that they are eventually 10 in number. At first, as in *Codaster* (Fig. 8*F–J*), each hydrospire opens on the surface by parallel slits, one for each space between adjacent folds, but later the folds get pushed under or overgrown by the lancet and side plates, so that only the outermost slit is left exposed along each margin of each ambulacrum. By a still further process of the pushing of each group of folds into the interior, this slit becomes reduced to a large pore, or *spiracle*, to which the spaces between the folds communicate by a canal (Fig. 9*F*). There may be ten such spiracles or by fusion five, and the anus may unite with one of them that hence is larger than the others (Fig. 8*D*). The spiracles encircle the mouth between the ambulacra. Finally, in the most developed state of the hydrospire system, as in *Pentremites* (Fig. 9*E*), a row of pores develops between the outer edges of the side plates, thus along each side of each ambulacrum. These pores communicate with the hydrospires, and it is believed that a water current entered these pores, circulated between the hydrospire folds, and passed out of the spiracles. In the more advanced types the hydrospire folds dipped deeply into the interior of the theca so that each hydrospire appears suspended from the radial plate (Fig. 9*F*). The folds were thus bathed in coelomic fluid which no doubt circulated between them.

Among early forms may be mentioned *Codaster* (Fig. 8*F–J*), in which the spaces of the hydrospire folds opened directly on the surface as slits and spiracles and intake pores were wanting; and *Phaenoschisma*, in which the hydrospires were partly pushed under so that only the outer slits are visible on the surface. *Orophocrinus* (Fig. 9*A*) was similar to the latter but with sublancets formed by the fusion of the innermost folds of the two hydrospires of each ambulacrum. In the remaining genera to be mentioned, the hydrospires have been completely shoved under, and intake pores and spiracles are present. *Troostocrinus* (Fig. 9*B*) has narrow ambulacra, and *Pentremites* (Fig. 8*B–E*) broad and petal-like ones; in both genera the anus is fused with one of the spiracles.

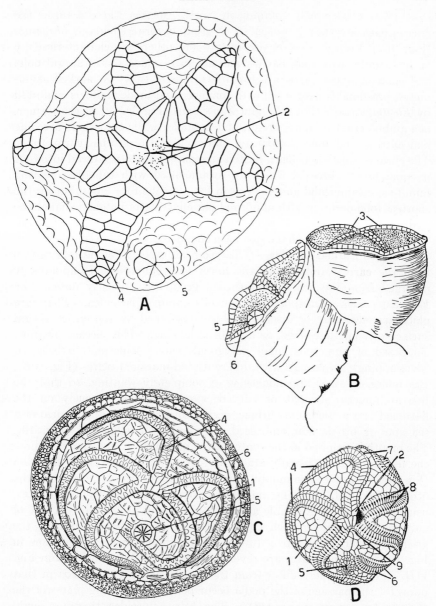

FIG. 11.—Edrioasteroidea (concluded). *A, Hemicystites. B, Cyathocystis,* side view.
(*A, B, after Jaekel,* 1899.) *C, Agelacrinites (after Clarke,* 1901). *D, Edrioaster (after
Bather,* 1900). 1, thecal plates; 2, covering plates of mouth; 3, ambulacra; 4, covering
plates of ambulacra; 5, anal pyramid; 6, marginal plates; 7, flooring plates revealed by
removal of covering plates; 8, pores for podia between flooring plates; 9, hydropore.

*Pentremites* is extremely common in North America where it forms the greater part of certain limestones. A group of forms such as *Orbitremites* (Fig. 9D), *Nucleocrinus*, *Schizoblastus*, and others are characterized by an oval theca, with long narrow ambulacra reaching to the aboral pole, and pendent hydrospires of a few folds, mostly two. A marked asymmetry, presumably associated with some peculiar mode of life, is exhibited by *Eleutherocrinus* (Fig. 9C) and *Zygocrinus* (Fig. 9G). In the former, one ambulacrum is short, broad, and petaloid, while the others are long and narrow; the anus is separate, and each hydrospire has seven folds. The curious *Zygocrinus* has a flattened, stemless theca produced into four unequal lobes, three of which are ornamented with tubercles bearing minute spines; normal ambulacra run between the four lobes, but on the shortest lobe occurs a fifth abnormal ambulacrum of petaloid shape; the hydrospires consist of a single fold to each side of each ambulacrum. The anus and spiracles have not been found.

**5. Class Edrioasteroidea.**—This group of extinct Pelmatozoa ranges from the early Cambrian to the lower Carboniferous. It apparently diverged from the other pelmatozoan groups at an early date. The Edrioasteroidea correspond to Jaekel's group Thecoidea. They are globular, sacciform, or disciform objects fastened by the entire aboral surface or sometimes free, as a stalk is lacking. The theca is flexible, composed of numerous small polygonal plates, sometimes imbricated (overlapping), sometimes with differentiated marginal plates (Fig. 10E). Brachioles or other appendages were completely wanting, so that the five ambulacra, straight or curved, stand out conspicuously on the flattened or rounded oral surface, giving somewhat the appearance of a sea star or brittle star embossed on a mosaic background (Fig. 10). The mouth is situated in the center of the oral surface and from it radiate the five ambulacra, usually gracefully curved, all in the same direction (Fig. 10C) or, more commonly, one or two in a direction opposite to the others (Fig. 10B, F). The ambulacra are grooves lined by little plates, usually arranged in a double alternating row and protected by a row of covering plates along each edge. The latter can be closed over the groove, converting it into a tunnel. Only the covering plates show in Fig. 10; the lining plates are revealed in three of the ambulacra in Fig. 11D. The ambulacra differ from those of all other Pelmatozoa in that pores for the passage of the podia occur between the lining plates of the ambulacral grooves (Fig. 11D). The Edrioasteroidea therefore could have led to the Eleutherozoa, and it is often supposed that they lie along the ancestral line of the latter. The anus is situated in the usual interradius and is protected by a pyramid of little triangular plates. A hydropore was probably present between mouth and anus.

The Edrioasteroidea have been arranged in families and genera by

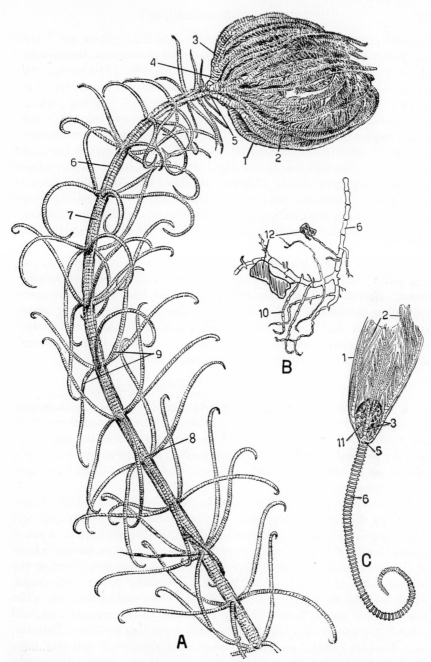

Fig. 12.—General crinoid structure, root forms. *A*, an existing stalked crinoid, *Cenocrinus asteria*, from the West Indies. *B*, root attachments of *Rhizocrinus*. (*A*, *B*, after *P. H. Carpenter*, 1884.) *C*, extinct crinoid, *Ctenocrinus*, Devonian, with flexible stem end (*after Goldring*, 1923). 1, crown; 2, pinnules; 3, arms; 4, lower brachials; 5, calyx; 6, columnals of stalk; 7, internode; 8, node; 9, whorl of cirri; 10, roots; 11, tegmen; 12, stones.

Bassler (1935, 1936). In *Stromatocystites* (Fig. 10A), there are several oral plates, straight ambulacra, and a flattened pentagonal theca covered aborally as well as orally by small polygonal plates. The similar *Walcottidiscus* differs in the curved ambulacra, one curved oppositely to the other four. In another family there are three oral covering plates, a large one adjacent to the anus and two small ones; here belong *Cystaster* (Fig. 10D) and *Carneyella* (Fig. 10B), with elongate theca fastened aborally; *Cystaster* has straight ambulacra, *Carneyella* curved ones, four in the same direction, one oppositely. In the related *Hemicystites* there is a thin flat theca widely attached aborally, with straight ambulacra (Fig. 11A). Numerous small oral plates, a single row of flooring plates in the ambulacra, long narrow curved ambulacra, and flattened disciform thecae characterize a group of genera including *Cooperidiscus* (Fig. 10C), with all five ambulacra curved in one direction; *Isorophus* and *Lepidodiscus* (Fig. 10F), with four ambulacra curved in one direction, one oppositely; and *Agelacrinites* (Fig. 11C) with a three and two arrangement. *Edrioaster* (Fig. 11D), characterized by long curved ambulacra extending onto the aboral surface and a double row of flooring plates, represents its family. *Cyathocystis* (Figs. 10E, 11B) and other members of its family are cylindroid, with a flat oral surface bearing straight ambulacra and bounded by a circlet of marginal plates.

## V. CLASS CRINOIDEA

**1. Definition.**—The Crinoidea are stalked or stalkless pentamerous Pelmatozoa with the theca reduced to an aboral cup covered orally by the tegmen, and with branched or unbranched pinnulated arms continuous skeletally with the radial plates of the theca and containing extensions of the food grooves, coelom, and nervous, water-vascular, and reproductive systems.

**2. General Remarks.**—The crinoids, like other groups of Pelmatozoa, flourished during the Palaeozoic era, beginning in the Cambrian and increasing in abundance to a climax in the Mississippian when in many places thick beds of limestone were laid down composed almost wholly of the remains of crinoids. Some of the best-known beds occur in the central states of the Mississippi Valley. Thereafter the crinoids diminished, and the Palaeozoic genera died out by the end of that era. The crinoids as a group, however, have continued to the present time, and some living genera begin in the Triassic. According to Moore, Lalicker, and Fischer (1952), something like 5000 species of crinoids have lived and died out in past geologic ages. At the present time there are about 630 living crinoids, of which only about 80, known as sea lilies, retain the typical stalked pelmatozoan form, now evidently in process of extinction. The others, called comatulids, or feather stars, have lost

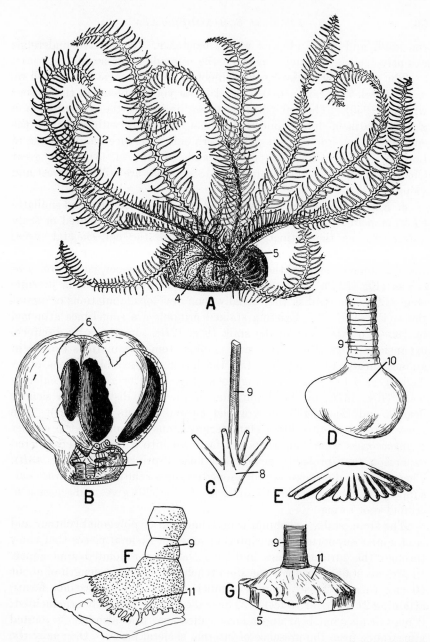

FIG. 13.—Crinoid structure, root forms (concluded). *A*, a living comatulid, *Antedon bifida* (*after W. B. Carpenter*, 1866). *B*, float of extinct *Scyphocrinites* (*after Springer*, 1917). *C*, anchor of *Ancyrocrinus*, extinct (*after Hall*, 1862). *D*, bulbous end of an extinct crinoid. *E*, lobulated disk attachment of extinct *Aspidocrinus*. (*D, E, after Goldring*, 1923.) *F*, attachment of existing articulate crinoid, *Phrynocrinus* (*after A. H. Clark*, 1915a). *G*, attachment disk of *Anomalocrinus*, extinct (*after Meek*, 1873). 1, arm; 2, pinnules; 3, ambulacral groove; 4, cirri; 5, stone; 6, chambers of float; 7, stem end with roots attached inside float; 8, anchor; 9, stem; 10, basal bulb; 11, attachment disk.

the stalk and have adopted a free existence. They have undergone extensive speciation and appear on the upgrade at present.

The existing crinoids are the subject of an exhaustive monograph by A. H. Clark that began in 1915 and is not yet completed at the present writing (1955). The published parts are limited to the comatulids and give a wealth of detail concerning them, especially with regard to the endoskeleton. For the soft parts of crinoids, reference may be made to Ludwig (1907), Chadwick (1907), and Cuénot (1948). The great Challenger reports (P. H. Carpenter, 1884, 1888) are still of interest and value.

**3. External Features.**—The stalked crinoids are constructed similarly to other pelmatozoans; living species present the same jointed or scaly appearance as the extinct members because the endoskeletal pieces show through the thin surface tissue. Their main structural parts are the attachment devices, the stalk, and the body proper, called *crown* or *corona* (Fig. 12A). The attachment consists primitively or in juvenile stages of a circular disk that usually soon develops lobulations or digitations (Fig. 13E–G). Existing stalked crinoids are sometimes attached by root-like extensions of the stalk (Fig. 12B), sometimes by disciform expansions (Figs. 13F, 14D), and similar stem terminations existed in extinct forms (Fig. 13D, G); but the latter also exhibit various other devices, as a terminal grappling hook (Fig. 13C), or a bulbous enlargement (Fig. 13D), or the diminution of the stem distally to a slender flexible end that could be wrapped around objects (Fig. 12C). The most curious of all crinoid stem terminations is found in the extinct *Scyphocrinites* where the roots are fastened into a terminal chambered expansion that probably acted as a float (Springer, 1917, Fig. 13B). These floats had been known for a long time under the name *Camarocrinus*, supposed to be a cystid. Ehrenberg (1922, 1929) gives a discussion of crinoid root forms.

The stem, stalk, or column is of cylindrical or polygonal contour and is of course supported by an internal series of skeletal pieces that show through the surface tissues and give the stem a jointed appearance. In present stalked crinoids the stem reaches a maximum length of about 50 cm. (nearly 2 feet), but was much longer in some extinct forms, attaining 21 m. (over 70 feet). The stalk is often variously ornamented; it may or may not bear appendages called *cirri* that also have a jointed appearance from the presence of internal skeletal pieces. Originally the cirri were limited to the stem base where as *radicular* cirri they supplemented the hold of the roots. Later they progressed along the entire stem where they occur in regularly spaced whorls (Fig. 12A), usually composed of five cirri, but sometimes of only two or three. The stem is lost during ontogeny in comatulids, but usually the cirri persist,

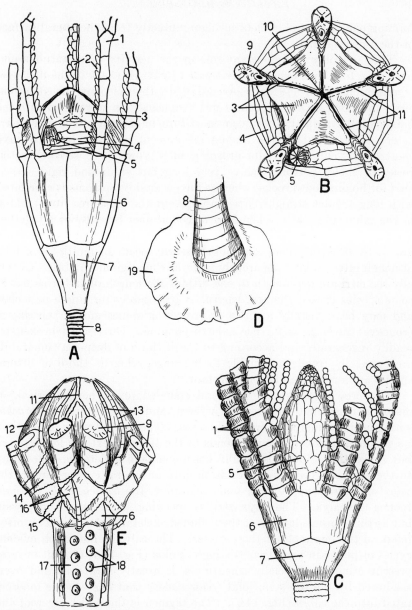

Fig. 14.—Structure of calyx and tegmen.  *A, Hyocrinus*, a primitive existing crinoid with high calyx and deltoid plates.  *B*, oral view of tegmen of *Hyocrinus*, showing deltoid plates.  (*A, B, after Carpenter*, 1884.)  *C, Calamocrinus diomedae*, another primitive existing crinoid with tall calyx and long anal tube.  *D*, attachment disk of *Calamocrinus*. (*C, D, after A. Agassiz*, 1892.)  *E*, comatulid *Zenometra* (*after Clark*, 1915a), showing short calyx with large attached top stem joint.  1, arms; 2, covering plates of ambulacral grooves; 3, deltoid plates; 4, small peripheral plates of tegmen; 5, anal cone; 6, radial plates of calyx; 7, basal plates of calyx; 8, stalk; 9, cut arm bases; 10, mouth; 11, ambulacral grooves; 12, tegmen; 13, oral pinnules; 14, secundibrachs; 15, first primibrach; 16, axillary or second primibrach; 17, top stem joint (centrodorsal); 18, facets for cirri of which two are shown; 19, attachment disk.

37

forming one to several circlets springing directly from the aboral surface
of the crown (Fig. 13A).

The cirri play an important role in the activity of comatulids and
have therefore been exhaustively treated by A. H. Clark in the first part
of his monograph (1915a).  According to this account the comatulid
cirri show great diversity in form and size, usually in correlation with the
habits of the animal; they also constitute important taxonomic characters.  Comatulids living among arborescent growths tend to have
short, stout, curved cirri for grasping such growths; those dwelling on
rocky or shelly bottoms evolve very long but stout and rigid curved
cirri for holding onto rocks; whereas life on muddy bottoms is correlated
with long slender straight cirri that prevent the creatures from sinking
in the mud (Fig. 44C).  The cirri of comatulids (sometimes altogether
wanting) vary in number from one or a few to over 80, but usually there
are 15 to 35 cirri.  They do not necessarily occur in multiples of five,
although often so, and apparently five was the original number.  Generally the cirri are one-fourth to one-fifth of the length of the arms but in
some species exceed the arm length.  Cirri usually terminate in a claw
and may have distally a series of projecting spines along their aboral
(concave) surface, as further aids to clinging.  Cirri when broken off
readily regenerate, and according to Clark those of deep-sea comatulids
are especially fragile and liable to breakage, whereas those of littoral
species are stronger and more resistant.

The crown consists of a central rounded, oval, hemispherical, or
discoidal mass that includes the viscera, and a set of arms or *brachia*
springing pentamerously from this mass.  The central mass, or at least
its supporting skeleton, corresponds to the theca of extinct Pelmatozoa,
but in existing crinoids is usually not a complete skeletal case closed up
to the mouth.  Rather it is divisible into an aboral cup or saucer, the
*calyx*[1] or *dorsal cup*, and an oral membrane, the *tegmen, disk,* or *vault,*
roofing the calyx.  The calyx, strictly speaking, is the aboral body wall,
but as this consists largely of the included skeletal plates, the term often
refers to the ensemble of these plates.  The calyx is high with evident
cycles of plates in primitive existing crinoids (Fig. 14A, C), but in most
present crinoids, especially comatulids, is greatly shortened and over-
shadowed by the top stem joint (*centrodorsal*) that has become incorporated into the calyx (Fig. 14E).  The tegmen is the oral body wall and
varies from a thin delicate membrane to a thick leathery one.  In
primitive existing forms it contains five deltoid plates encircled by
small plates (Fig. 14A, B) but lacks these in the great majority of present
crinoids and instead contains small plates that form a continuous sheet

---

[1] Often regarded as synonymous with theca but used here in place of dorsal cup
to avoid the objectionable application to echinoderms of the terms dorsal and ventral.

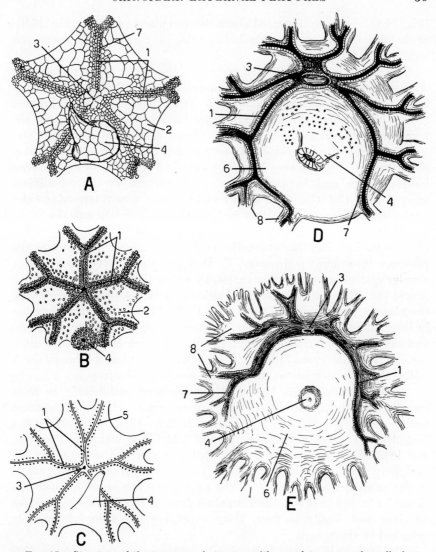

FIG. 15.—Structure of the tegmen. *A*, tegmen with complete armor of small plates. *B*, tegmen with incomplete armor, small plates mostly along ambulacral groove. *C*, apparently naked tegmen, has microscopic imbedded calcareous formations. (*A–C, after Clark*, 1915a.) *D*, tegmen of a comasterid, with central anus and displaced mouth, but all arms supplied with grooves. *E*, more advanced type of comasterid tegmen; some arms do not receive grooves. (*D, E, after Carpenter*, 1888.) 1, ambulacral grooves; 2, tegminal plates; 3, mouth; 4, anal tube; 5, saccules; 6, tegmen; 7, covering plates of grooves; 8, arm bases.

(Fig. 15*A*) or are concentrated along the ambulacral grooves (Fig. 15*B*); or the tegmen may appear naked containing only microscopic calcareous formations (Fig. 15*C*).

The mouth is usually located at or near the center of the tegmen but is displaced peripherally in the comatulid family Comasteridae (Fig. 15*D*, *E*). From the mouth, when central, five ambulacral grooves course in a nearly symmetrical pentamerous arrangement along the tegmen to the arm bases (Fig. 15*A–C*). The anus is situated excentrically (except in the Comasteridae) at the tip of a projecting cone, the *anal tube* or *cone*, sometimes very long (Fig. 14*C*). Consequently a plane that bisects mouth and anus also passes through one of the ambulacral grooves (Fig. 15*A–C*). This groove and adjacent area is termed in older works the *anterior ray;* the other rays are then called right anterior, right posterior, left anterior, and left posterior, as viewed by an observer facing the oral surface, and the interradius that bears the anus is known as the posterior interradius. However, P. H. Carpenter (1884) introduced a simpler system, now generally in use, by which the anterior ray is called A and the other rays, proceeding clockwise with the oral surface facing the observer, are named B, C, D, and E (Fig. 1*B*). The anus then lies in interradius CD. This system is generally applicable to echinoderms and expresses the fundamental bilaterality on which has been imposed a secondary pentamerous radiality. If the anus is centrally located, the A radius is that which passes through the mouth and hydropore.

As already indicated, the mouth is displaced peripherally in most members of the comatulid family Comasteridae. This displacement occurs along radius A or interradius AB (Fig. 15*D*, *E*), shortens the ambulacral grooves on the side toward which the mouth has moved, and lengthens the opposite grooves that now run in a curve along the periphery of the tegmen (Fig. 15*D*). The eventual result of this process is the gradual disappearance of the grooves to the arms opposite the mouth (Fig. 15*E*). From the normal number of ten the grooves diminish to eight and finally to four, those supplying the arms immediately adjacent to the mouth.

The tegmen is pierced interradially by numerous minute pores (500 to 1500) that are the external entrances to water canals (*ciliated funnels* of Chadwick, 1907) leading into internal coelomic spaces. These canals evidently serve for the ingress of water into the interior of the crinoid, presumably to maintain tension.

The arms or *brachia* spring from the boundary between calyx and tegmen and extend freely into the water; they, too, present a jointed or scaly appearance. There are primitively five arms, and this condition is retained in a few crinoid species (Figs. 14*A*, *C*, 16*A*), but usually the arms fork at once to 10, a common number among comatulids (Fig. 13*A*).

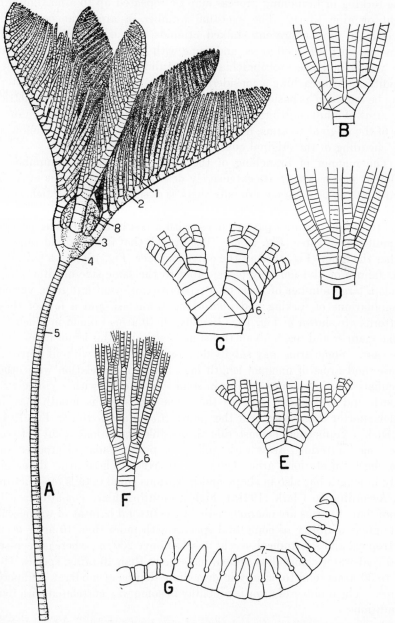

FIG. 16.—Arms and pinnules. *A, Ptilocrinus pinnatus*, stalked crinoid with five heavily pinnulated arms. *B–D*, branching types of various comatulids. *E, F*, branching types of two stalked crinoids. *E, Endoxocrinus parrae*. F, *Metacrinus acutus*. (*B–F, after Clark*, 1921a.) *G*, oral pinnule of *Comaster*, showing terminal combs. (*A, G, after Clark*, 1915a.) 1, pinnules; 2, brachials; 3, radial cycle of calyx; 4, basal cycle of calyx; 5, stalk; 6, axillaries; 7, combs; 8, tegmen.

The forking or branching process may be repeated up to a maximum of eight or nine times. The eventual number of arm branches hardly exceeds 40 among present stalked crinoids, but many comatulids are provided with 40 to 60 arms, and some with 80 up to 200 (Fig. 17); but the young of these multibrachiate comatulids remain in the 10-armed condition until reaching a considerable size, so that the 10-armed pattern may be regarded as basic for crinoids. According to A. H. Clark (1921a), the arms of adult multibrachiate crinoids have arisen, not by the branching of the original 10 arms, but by the proliferation of new arms following the shedding of the original ones.

The manner of branching of the adult arms follows a number of different patterns that are extensively described with diagrams in A. H. Clark (1921a). In some crinoids there is a simple repeated dichotomy (Fig. 16F), but often one of the two branches resulting from a dichotomy fails to divide when its partner does, with a resulting branching pattern in multiples of three (Fig. 18A). The branch that fails to divide may be either the inner (Fig. 16B) or the outer member (Fig. 16D) of a pair, and this failure of division may be repeated to the same side or alternately. Thus a large number of branching patterns can eventuate from various combinations of forking and nonforking branches, and a few of these patterns are shown in Fig. 16. Usually all 10 arms branch in much the same manner and reach about the same length, but this is not necessarily the case. Some arms may subdivide more than others without apparent cause, and arms of unequal length may occur in correlation with other peculiarities of structure. Thus in some comasterids with asymmetrical mouth and ambulacral grooves the arms opposite the mouth may be much shorter than those near the mouth (*Comatula pectinata*, Fig. 19A). In such asymmetrical comasterids all possible transitions occur between the long "anterior" arms with well-developed ambulacral grooves and the short "posterior" arms devoid of grooves. These arms differ not only in length but also in shape and in various small details of structure.

According to Clark (1921a), highly multibrachiate comatulids with more than 40 arms are characteristic of the littoral habitat of warm seas. The great majority of comatulid species with more than 10 arms occur in tropical and subtropical seas at depths above 200 m., whereas deep-sea and cold-water comatulids seldom have more than 10 arms; species with 25 to 30 arms tend to occupy intermediate depths of moderate temperatures. The number of arms is probably in some way correlated with food conditions.

Arms vary in shape from long and slender to short and broad ones, and the shape in some cases at least also appears correlated with temperature. Warm temperatures favor the evolution of long arms, cold temperatures short ones. The crinoid arm varies in length from 10 mm.

or less to nearly 300 mm. but is usually below 100, often below 50 mm. long. The crown is therefore usually of small to moderate size.

All the arms are typically bordered along each side by a row of short tapering side branches known as *pinnules;* the pinnules of the two rows of each arm alternate (Fig. 18*B*). Like the rest of the crinoid the

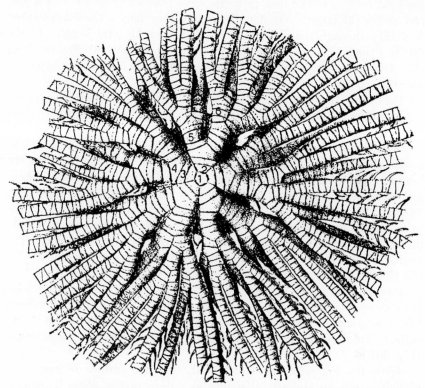

FIG. 17.—A multibrachiate comatulid, *Comanthina schlegelii,* from the Philippines, viewed from the aboral surface (*after Carpenter,* 1888). This species usually has 160 to 190 arms and lacks cirri. 1, centrodorsal; 2, radial cycle; 3, first primibrach; 4, second primibrach (axillary); 5, secundibrachs; 6, tertibrachs; 7, postpalmars.

pinnules present a jointed appearance owing to the visibility of the supporting endoskeletal pieces through the thin surface tissue. It is generally believed that neither arms nor pinnules are homologous with the brachioles of extinct Pelmatozoa. The pinnules have the same structure as the arms and may in fact be regarded as miniature arms. They are differentiated along the arms into three types: the proximal or *oral* pinnules, the middle or *genital* pinnules, and the distal pinnules (Fig. 19*B*). The oral pinnules are better differentiated in comatulids than in stalked crinoids. They comprise one to four or five pinnules to each side of the proximal parts of the arms. They differ, often markedly, from the remaining pinnules in both structure and function, being devoid of ambulacral grooves and podia and acting rather as tactile and protective devices. They are usually longer, often conspicuously so, than the other pinnules and often more rigid and spinelike, so that their power of movement is somewhat limited. Often they are held bent over the disk in a crisscross manner (Fig. 19*C*) as a protection for the latter. On the other hand, they may acquire augmented flexibility through the shortening of their basal skeletal joints. In the family Comasteridae the distal 3 to 30 joints of the oral pinnules bear thin triangular projections forming the *terminal combs* (Fig. 16*G*) of uncertain purpose.

Following the oral pinnules come the genital pinnules, so called because they contain the gonads whose presence at sexual maturity gives them a swollen appearance (Fig. 20*A*); at other times they are not particularly different in appearance from the distal pinnules. The proximal genital pinnules are usually short, thus contrasting with the long oral pinnules adjacent to them; distally the genital pinnules gradually increase in length and pass insensibly into the distal pinnules (Fig. 19*B*). The latter are mostly long and slender and remain of about the same length until near the arm end where the pinnule length rapidly diminishes to the very short terminal, newly forming members. The genital pinnules may or may not bear ambulacral grooves and podia, but these are always present on the distal pinnules.

Pinnules are generally more or less spiny distally in correlation with the degree of spinosity of the rest of the crinoid. The two to four distal joints of pinnules are always armed with recurved hooks on the aboral surface, and these reach their maximum development in the Comasteridae (Fig. 20*B*).

With the exceptions already noted, the oral surface of arms and pinnules bears an ambulacral groove as a deep furrow along its center. These grooves converge to the arm bases to form five main ambulacral grooves that course in the tegmen in a nearly pentamerous pattern (Fig. 15*A–C*) and enter a pentagonal depression around the more or less central mouth. The symmetry of the tegminal grooves is imperfect because the anal interradius is slightly arger than the other interradii. (Strong asymmetries of mouth and tegminal grooves in the Comasteridae were already noted.) The ambulacral grooves have raised edges that are usually scalloped into regularly repeated *lappets*, alternating on the two sides (Fig. 20*C*). The grooves are also accompanied throughout by the podia ("tentacles"), small delicate fingers fused basally into groups of three (Fig. 20*D*). Each such group occurs at the base of a lappet at its inner side so that the groups of podia like the lappets alternate on the two sides of the groove. Along the tegminal grooves the lappets often

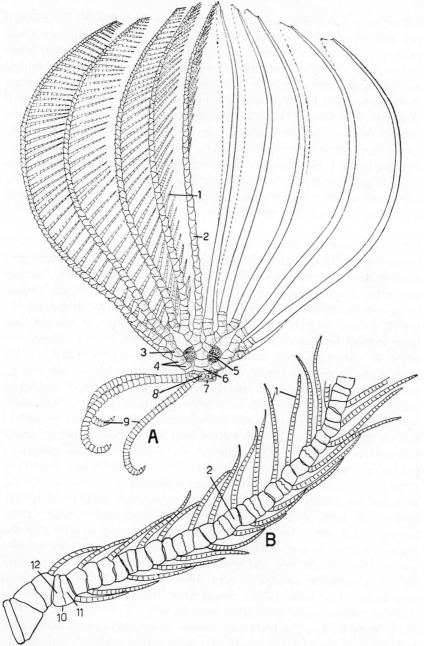

Fig. 18.—Arms and pinnules. *A*, a 30-armed comatulid, *Neometra acanthaster*, from the Philippines, showing branching pattern (*after Clark, 1915a*). *B*, a comatulid arm with pinnules, to show arrangement of the latter (*after Carpenter, 1888*). 1, pinnules; 2, arm joints (brachials); 3, secundibrachs; 4, primibrachs; 5, tegmen; 6, radial cycle of calyx; 7, centrodorsal; 8, cirrus facets; 9, cirri; 10, syzygy; 11, epizygal; 12, hypozygal.

45

reduce to a wavy line, and here also the podia reduce in height and gradually lose the trifid arrangement, becoming single projections. These single podia around the mouth, usually about 20 to 25 in number, borne on the outer rim of the pentagonal ambulacral depression that surrounds the mouth, are termed *oral* or *labial* podia. The ambulacral grooves are also accompanied by small spherical bodies known as *saccules*, imbedded in the surface tissues (Fig. 15*C*). On arms and pinnules they form a single row on either side, alternating with the lappets and podia, but may occur in double or triple rows along the tegminal grooves. They are wanting in the Comasteridae. Although colorless in life, the saccules are often highly colored in preserved specimens because the pigments dissolved out of the rest of the crinoid by preservatives (especially alcohol) tend to aggregate in the saccules.

It is said by A. H. Clark (1915a) that no marine animals exceed the littoral crinoids in beauty of coloration; coloration diminishes with increasing depth of habitat. As the colors are soluble in water and alcohol, they are unfortunately lost in preserved specimens. Almost any color may be found among comatulids, as white, cream, yellow, orange, green, olive, bright red, wine red, maroon, purplish red, purple, violet, brown, and black. Some species are uniformly colored, but most exhibit combinations of two or more colors. Some species also occur in numerous color variants. Thus the common *Antedon bifida* may be purple, reddish purple, brown, red, crimson, carmine, rose, orange, or yellow; or mottled and spotted with rose, orange, and yellow; or orange variegated with crimson, white, or light yellow. The most varied coloration is found in the Indo-Pacific region, whereas crinoids of eastern and northern Pacific waters lack bright colors, being mostly yellowish or brownish. The pigments of crinoids were investigated in a preliminary way by Krukenberg (1882), Moseley (1887), and MacMunn (1889). Krukenberg found a red pigment without absorption bands that he called comatulin and that he thought responsible for the red, brown, and yellow hues of the species studied. Abeloos and Teissier (1926) isolated what seems to be the same red pigment and showed that the yellow pigment is a chemical derivative of the red. Moseley isolated pentacrinin, pink in acid and green in alkaline solutions, with a characteristic absorption spectrum; also another pigment that he named antedonin. Lönnberg (1932) found that the brownish red color of *Antedon petasus* contains a yellow carotenoid.

**4. Body Wall.**—The body wall consists primarily of the endoskeleton, and this is of such importance in systematics that works on crinoids are usually devoted to it almost to the exclusion of the soft parts. The best accounts of the histology of the body wall are to be found in the older articles such as those of Ludwig (1877), Hamann (1889), and Reichensperger (1905).

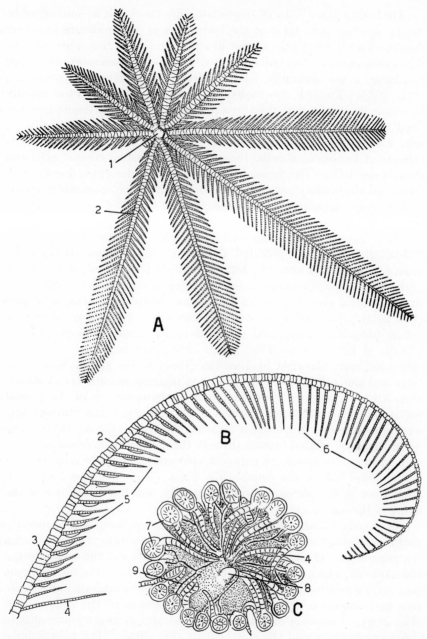

FIG. 19.—Arms and pinnules (continued). *A, Comatula pectinata*, Singapore, with unequal arms, associated with an exocyclic disk (*after Clark*, 1915b). *B*, arm of *Antedon*, to show differentiation of pinnules along the arm (*after Clark*, 1921a). *C*, comatulid disk, showing oral pinnules (*after Carpenter*, 1888). 1, centrodorsal; 2, brachials; 3, syzygy; 4, oral pinnule; 5, genital pinnules; 6, distal pinnules; 7, cut arm bases; 8, anal tube; 9, ambulacral groove.

The body surface is stated to possess a delicate cuticle in some crinoids, not in others. Over most of the body surface, the epidermis is poorly developed and apparently almost absent in some species; when present it is a thin, mostly syncytial, epithelium that lacks a basement membrane and hence is not definitely delimited from the underlying mesenchyme (Fig. 20*E*). Toward the ambulacral grooves the epidermis rapidly increases in height and definiteness, and the grooves themselves are lined throughout by a very tall epidermis of long attenuated ciliated cells with nuclei in several ranks (Fig. 20*F*). This groove epidermis consists of two sorts of cells, the ordinary supporting ciliated cells and the sensory cells. The former are very long slender ciliated cells (Fig. 20*G*), and the sensory cells are even more attenuated, resembling a hair with a bulge containing the nucleus (Fig. 21*A*). The epidermis of the ambulacral grooves is underlain by a thick nervous layer from which its cells are not definitely delimited (Fig. 20*F*). Schneider (1902) and Reichensperger (1908) reported numerous mucous gland cells in the groove epidermis of crinoids, but no published figures show them. A fairly thick epidermis is continued on the surface of the podia that faces the ambulacral groove (Fig. 21*F*) but thins rapidly on their outer surface (Fig. 24*D*). The podia are studded with papillae probably of sensory nature (described later), and these are also provided with gland cells. Clumps of five or more cells, presumably glandular, insunk from the epidermis, were observed by Hamann (1889) in the aboral wall of the calyx and along the sides of the arms and pinnules in various comatulids (Fig. 21*C*). There are also gland cells in the epidermis of the genital pinnules of female *Antedon*, located where the eggs break through and serving to secrete a cement that attaches the eggs to the pinnules. The water canals or ciliated funnels through the disk and arm bases are lined with inturned columnar to cuboidal epidermis that is heavily ciliated in the distal half of the canals (Fig. 21*B*). The epidermis lacks cilia other than in the places mentioned, namely, the water canals and the lining of the ambulacral grooves.

As already noted, the epidermis of the general body wall is directly continuous with the underlying dermis or mesenchyme that constitutes the greater part of the wall and contains and secretes the pieces of the endoskeleton, whose interstices it continues to occupy. The mesenchyme consists of a gelatinous ground substance in which lie fusiform and stellate cells and numerous fibers that represent processes of the stellate cells (Fig. 21*E*). Crowding of the fibers in a parallel arrangement results in a denser consistency of the mesenchyme (Fig. 20*E*). The mesenchyme also contains free cells, including amoeboid cells and lymph cells filled with gross inclusions. The latter appear related to the saccules already mentioned. These are sacs imbedded in the mesenchyme beneath the

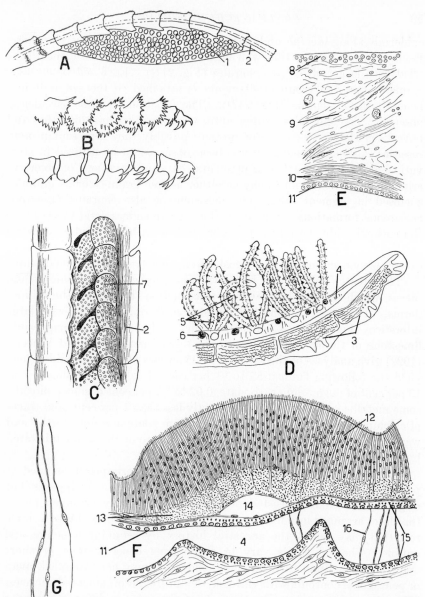

FIG. 20.—Pinnules (concluded); body wall. *A*, a genital pinnule, end broken off, original.
*B*, comasterid pinnule ends, showing spination (*after Clark*, 1921a). *C*, piece of pinnule
showing lappets containing skeletal elements (*after Carpenter*, 1884). *D*, pinnule end,
showing podia and saccules (*after Chadwick*, 1907). *E*, section of the general body wall of a
comatulid. *F*, transverse section of the ambulacral groove of a comatulid. *G*, ciliated
cells of the ambulacral groove epithelium. (*E–G*, *after Hamann*, 1889.) 1, ovary; 2,
pinnulars; 3, spiny terminal pinnulars; 4, canal of water-vascular system; 5, trifid group of
podia; 6, saccule; 7, lappets; 8, epidermis; 9, connective tissue; 10, denser connective
tissue; 11, coelomic endothelium; 12, ciliated epidermis of ambulacral groove; 13, layer
of oral nervous system; 14, coelomic canal; 15, longitudinal muscle fibers of wall of water
vessel; 16, muscle cells crossing lumen of water vessel.

epidermis alongside the ambulacral grooves, also sometimes elsewhere. Each sac consists of a thin wall that encloses a number of conical cells filled with large refringent spherules (Fig. 21*D*). Each cell tapers to a filament, and the group of filaments is attached to the sac wall just beneath the epidermis (Fig. 21*D*). The function of these saccules is obscure. The spherules readily absorb various dyes and pigments and have been shown to consist of protein; possibly they represent protein reserves, although they have not been observed to be utilized in starvation or regeneration. The pigments that lend a variety of colors to crinoids occur in the mesenchyme either as free granules or as granules enclosed in pigment cells. The mesenchyme also contains numerous calcareous formations, apart from the regular endoskeletal pieces. On the coelomic side the mesenchyme is clothed with a cuboidal syncytial epithelium (Fig. 20*E*). There are no muscle fibers in the body wall except in connection with the endoskeleton, and those are described below.

The greater part of the body wall is occupied by the endoskeletal pieces, which have a characteristic construction throughout the echinoderms. They are not solid but fenestrated, forming a mesh with large interstices (Fig. 33*B*). Chemically the crinoid skeleton is a magnesium limestone of the calcite type. Clark (1921a) and Clarke and Wheeler (1922) give analyses of the skeleton of 25 species of living crinoids which yield the following figures: 83 to 91 per cent of calcium carbonate, 7 to 13 per cent of magnesium carbonate, 0.02 to 5.7 per cent of silicon dioxide, some metallic oxides in quantities mostly less than 1 per cent, and traces of calcium phosphate. The high magnesium content is noteworthy and was found to vary directly with the temperature of the water inhabited by the crinoid concerned.

The stalk is supported by a single row of superimposed rounded or pentagonal skeletal pieces termed *columnals* (Fig. 12*A*). It appears that originally the stalk consisted of numerous irregularly arranged pieces that later arranged into five rows, and these eventually fused into a single row that may reflect the ancestral history by retaining a pentagonal outline. The columnals vary in shape from disks to long or short cylinders, sometimes with expanded ends, and may have rounded, oval, or pentagonal contours with variously sculptured or ornamented surfaces. The columnals may be alike throughout the stem or differ in shape or length at various levels. In the more primitive existing stalked crinoids, the stem lacks cirri and the columnals tend to similarity throughout the stem, being short and disciform in some articulates (Fig. 14*A, D*), long and slender with swollen ends in such articulates as *Bathycrinus* and *Rhizocrinus* (Fig. 22*D*). Where the stalk bears whorls of cirri, however, as in the pentacrinids, the columnals to which the cirri attach, known as *nodes*, are typically longer than the others, which form the *internodes*

(Fig. 22*A*). Even when not differing from the other columnals in shape or size, the nodes are distinguishable through carrying the facets to which the cirri articulate (Fig. 22*B*). The internodes consist of one or two up to 45 columnals, and the number may vary at different levels of the stem. The stem grows in length by the formation of new columnals at its top just below the calyx, also by the interpolation of columnals into the internodes. This process seems to continue until the number of internodal columnals reaches a figure typical of the species.

The end surfaces of the columnals are usually sculptured so as to fit in a lock-and-key manner the end surfaces of the adjacent columnals. This sculpturing shows a variety of patterns, copiously figured by Carpenter (1884) in the *Challenger* report on stalked crinoids. In the Pentacrinidae the markings are usually pentamerously petaloid (Fig. 22*C*) or suggestive of a five-pointed star, but in other families may take the form of radiating flutings or various ridges. The crinoid stem lacks muscles, but the columnals are held together by bundles of elastic fibrils that lend a certain amount of flexibility. In the pentacrinids there are five such bundles that course the length of the internodes in positions corresponding to the petals of the pattern on the end surfaces. In other stalked crinoids two such bundles (Fig. 22*E*) or a circle of short fibrils may bind adjacent columnals. In the Pentacrinidae each nodal columnal is closely and rather rigidly jointed to the internodal columnal just below it by very short elastic fibers. Such close unions are common among crinoids and are termed *syzygies;* as the stem lacks flexibility at the syzygies it is apt to break there.

All the columnals are pierced by a small central hole so that the stem contains a central tubular cavity in which run extensions of the coelom and nervous system.

The cirri are borne upon the nodes of the stem, fitting movably into the facets or sockets of the latter. Typically, in Pentacrinidae there are five cirri spaced symmetrically around each node (Fig. 12*A*), but sometimes only two or three. The cirri, like the stem, are supported by a row of skeletal pieces called *cirrals* (Fig. 22*F*, *G*), of which there are mostly 20 to 50 in each cirrus in stalked crinoids, 15 to 20 in comatulids. The cirrals, like the columnals, are pierced by a central tubular cavity that branches from the stem cavity and continues the same structures. In comatulids the cirri are concentrated around the aboral surface of the calyx to which they articulate by conspicuous facets (Fig. 14*E*).

The cirrals are not necessarily of the same shape or length along the cirrus; commonly in comatulids the basal cirrals, mostly two, are short and stout, the next ones gradually increase in length, and then distally the cirrals decline in length to the tip which forms a claw (Fig. 22*F*). The cirrals may show spiny projections (Fig. 22*H*), especially the distal

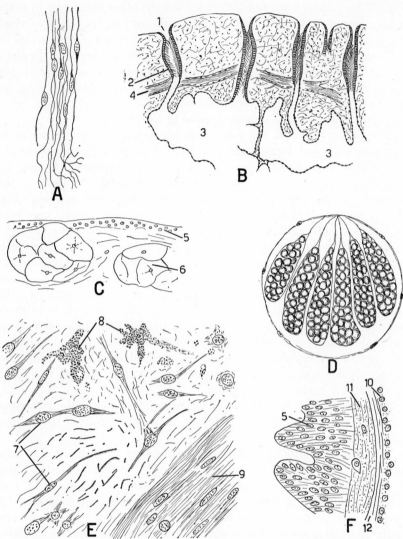

Fig. 21.—Body wall (concluded). *A*, sensory cells of the ambulacral groove epithelium. *B*, section through the tegmen, showing the ciliated water canals. *C*, glands of aboral wall of comatulids. *D*, saccule (*after Bury*, 1888). *E*, connective tissue of a comatulid. *F*, section of inner side of a podium. (*A–C, F, G, after Hamann*, 1889.) 1, external water pore; 2, ciliated canal; 3, coelomic spaces; 4, nerve fiber; 5, epidermis; 6, gland; 7, spindle cells of connective tissue; 8, pigment cells; 9, denser connective tissue; 10, coelomic endothelium; 11, nervous layer of oral nervous system; 12, longitudinal muscle fibers.

members, and the penultimate one may bear a long spine opposed to the terminal claw (Fig. 22*J*). The cirrals are held together by elastic ligaments (Fig. 22*G*).

The plates of the calyx, as seen in representative fossil crinoids or the more primitive existing stalked crinoids, continue the trend noticed among cystids, being arranged in two or three alternating pentamerous cycles. In the simpler condition, known as *monocyclic*, there are two cycles, an aboral cycle of five *basal* plates and oral to this a cycle of five *radial* plates (Fig. 14*A*, *C*). In the alternative condition, termed *dicyclic*, a circlet of five *infrabasal* plates is present to the aboral side of the basal series (Fig. 36*D*). Additional plates called *interradials* and *interambulacrals* may be present between the radials and arm bases, and a *radianal* and other extra plates may occur in the anal interradius in connection with the anal tube. All these extra plates are in fact tegminal armature and fall under the general category of *perisomatic* plates. A large number of these interpolated plates is especially characteristic of the extinct order Camerata (Fig. 37*A*). The infrabasal plates are often more or less fused to form one to four plates instead of the original five, and fusions may occur also among the basal and radial cycles (Fig. 14*A*, basals fused).

Existing crinoids depart to a greater or less extent from the foregoing picture. They are practically all monocyclic or at least appear so, for in many cases the infrabasals have been lost or reduced to minute elements or incorporated into the top columnal. In such cases the terms *pseudomonocyclic* or *cryptodicyclic* are applied by some authors. The previous presence of the infrabasal circlet can be detected in stalked crinoids by the relation of the angles of the stem to the radial symmetry of the calyx; for in a true monocyclic crinoid the stem angles are necessarily radial, whereas in a dicyclic crinoid or one derived from a previous dicyclic condition, the stem angles are interradial (this is known as the law of Wachsmuth and Springer). The reduction or loss of the infrabasals is the beginning of a general reduction of the plates of the calyx in present crinoids. Only in the more primitive existing stalked crinoids, such as *Hyocrinus* (Fig. 14*A*) and *Calamocrinus* (Fig. 14*C*), is there found a high calyx with conspicuous basal and radial cycles. In the pentacrinites the calyx is reduced in height, but basals are still evident and fairly well developed (Fig. 22*K*, *L*), whereas in comatulids the basals are greatly reduced and visible at the surface in only a very few species as *Atelecrinus* (Fig. 23*A*). The reduction in importance of the basals in the calyx is accompanied by an alteration in their orientation from an erect to a transverse position. Either they lean outward, thus presenting to the exterior only a thin ledge for the support of the radials, or they lean inward and gradually come to be pushed entirely into the interior, as in most present comatulids.

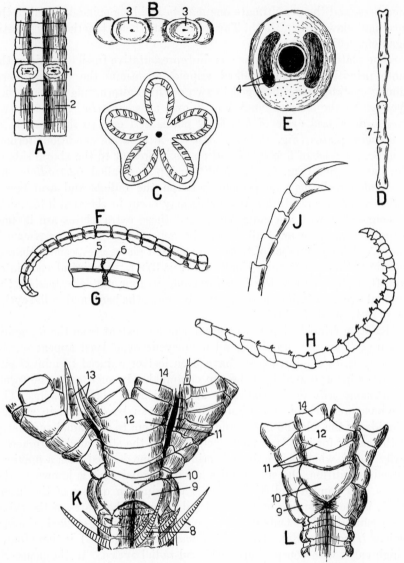

FIG. 22.—Skeleton of stalk and calyx. *A*, part of the stem of a pentacrinid, to show node and internodes. *B*, node enlarged. *C*, end surface of a node. *D*, portion of the stem of *Bathycrinus*, without cirri. *E*, end surface of a columnal of *D*. (*D*, *E*, *after Danielsson*, 1892.) *F*, an ordinary cirrus, original. *G*, two cirrals of same, enlarged. *H*, a spiny cirrus. *J*, cirrus end, with spine opposed to terminal claw. *K*, calyx and arm bases of *Metacrinus;* note four primibrachs before the first branching. *L*, calyx and arm bases of *Neocrinus;* note two primibrachs before the first branching. (*A–C, K, L, after Carpenter*, 1884; *H, J, after Clark*, 1915a.) 1, node; 2, internode; 3, facets for cirri; 4, muscle fossae; 5, canal of cirrals; 6, connecting elastic fibers; 7, columnals; 8, cirri; 9, basals; 10, radials; 11, primibrachs; 12, axillary; 13, pinnules; 14, secundibrachs.

The comatulid calyx thus comes to differ markedly from the ancestral plan. The top columnal of the juvenile stem enlarges greatly, fuses to the aboral surface of the calyx, and usually incorporates the infrabasal pieces. The syzygy that unites the top columnal with the underlying columnal breaks at some time during ontogeny, and the comatulid is then stemless and free-moving for the rest of its life. The top columnal, now called *centrodorsal*, forms the major part of the adult comatulid calyx in most species. In some that lack cirri or have only a few cirri, it is a thin pentagonal plate more or less insunk into the radial cycle; but in most comatulids it is a large saucer, bowl, or five-angled cylinder (Figs. 14*E*, 23*B–D*) covered externally with conspicuous facets for the articulation of the cirri. From its bearing many cirri one might suppose that the centrodorsal represents a number of fused columnals, but ontogenetic studies have shown that only the top columnal is involved in its formation. The greatly reduced basals are fused to form a little decagonal disk, the *rosette*, with a central hole (Fig. 23*F*). The rosette has been pushed into the interior where it sits like a cover over the interior cavity of the centrodorsal (Fig. 23*F*). The radials are thus in direct contact with the inner or oral face of the centrodorsal, and this face is usually marked off by five radiating ridges or grooves into five areas into which the radials fit (Fig. 23*E*). In many comatulids five rod-like pieces known as the *basal rays* extend from the rosette along the oral surface of the centrodorsal in the interradial position, that is, along the just-mentioned grooves or ridges (Fig. 23*G*). The outer ends of these basal rays may show at the surface between the centrodorsal and the radials (Fig. 23*D*) and have been mistaken for basals.

In the absence of developed infrabasals and basals, the radials thus form the major part of the true calyx of comatulids, since the centrodorsal is a columnal. The radials are rather large wedge-shaped pieces that together form the *radial pentagon*, lying upon the oral surface of the centrodorsal or on the basal rays when present. This aboral surface of the radials is mostly smooth (Fig. 23*F*), but its oral surface is very complicated for articulation with the arm bases and for the attachment of muscles and ligaments. This surface usually bears five depressions or fossae: a large hemispherical aboral fossa that lodges the attachment of the *extensor* ("dorsal") ligament of the arms; separated from this by a transverse ridge and oral to it a pair of fossae for the *interarticular* ligaments; and on the oral side of the radials a pair of fossae that lodge the proximal ends of the *flexor* muscles of the arms (Fig. 23*D*). There are a number of apertures in the radial plates for the passage of nerves. As the brachial faces of the radials are covered in life by the arm bases that fit into them, it follows that only a small part of the radials is visible on the external surface and sometimes they are completely

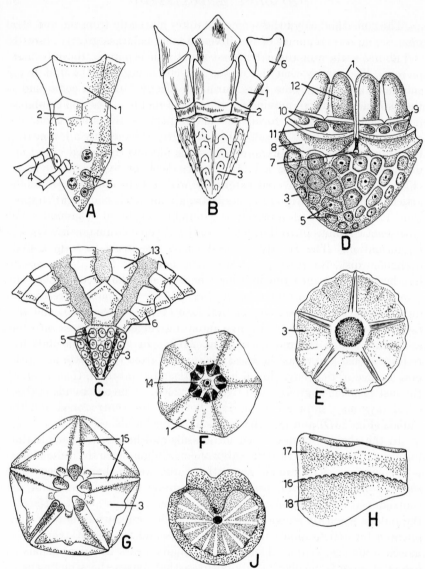

Fig. 23.—Skeleton of calyx and arms. *A*, species of *Atelecrinus* with large basals. *B*, another *Atelecrinus* species with small basals. *C*, comatulid calyx and arm bases in which the radials do not show at the surface. (*A*, *C*, after *Clark*, 1915*a*.) *D*, calyx of *Antedon* with arm bases removed to show articulating surface of radials. *E*, inner or oral surface of the centrodorsal of *Antedon* with five grooves. *F*, aboral surface of the radial pentagon of *Antedon*, with rosette in place. *G*, oral surface of the centrodorsal of *Antedon* with four of the five basal rays in place. (*B*, *D–G*, after P. H. *Carpenter*, 1888.) *H*, a syzygial pair seen from the outer (aboral) arm surface. *J*, the syzygial surface of one of a syzygial pair, showing the radiating ridges. (*H*, *J*, after W. B. *Carpenter*, 1866.) 1, radials; 2, basals; 3, centrodorsal; 4, cirri; 5, cirrus facets; 6, primibrachs; 7, end of basal ray; 8, fossa for extensor ligament; 9, transverse ridge; 10, fossae for interarticular ligaments; 11, hole for passage of nerve; 12, fossae for flexor muscles; 13, secundibrachs; 14, rosette; 15, basal rays; 16, syzygy; 17, epizygal; 18, hypozygal.

concealed by the primibrachs (Fig. 23*C*). The central cavity of the radial pentagon is separated from that of the centrodorsal by the rosette.

The arms are supported by a series of pieces called *brachials* that are in direct continuity with the radial plates (Fig. 22*K, L*); in fact, the radials probably belong to the arm skeleton and are not calyx plates phylogenetically. This is evidenced by the fact that the radial plates do not appear in the pentacrinoid larva until the arms are about to push out, whereas the infrabasal, basal, and deltoid plates may be present even in the doliolaria stage. Brachials that precede an arm fork are known as *axillaries*. The brachials of the unbranched arm, usually two in number, are called *primibrachs*, and the second primibrach is usually an axillary (Fig. 23*B*), occurring at the forking of the arms into 10. The brachials beyond this axillary, including the next axillary, are called *secundibrachs*, those beyond the next fork, if it occurs, are *tertibrachs* or *palmars*, and those of succeeding branches, if any, are *postpalmars*. Originally the arms were free beyond the radials, but in most present crinoids a variable number of brachials, called *fixed* brachials, are embraced by the tegmen but are not thereby necessarily rendered immovable as the tegmen is flexible. In comatulids usually the two primibrachs and the first three secundibrachs are imbedded in the tegmen. The brachials are rounded on their aboral surfaces, deeply grooved on their oral surfaces for the reception of the ambulacral grooves and associated parts. The axillaries have a pair of sloping shoulders for articulation with the branches that they support (Fig. 23*B*). The other brachials may have the form of disks or short cylinders but in comatulids usually present a wedge-shaped profile, being wider on one side than on the other, and as successive wedges are alternately oriented, the sutures between them give a zigzag effect (Fig. 18*B*). The eventual result of this process can be the pushing of alternate brachials to opposite sides of the arm so that the arm skeleton comes to consist of two rows of interdigitated brachials. This condition is termed *biserial* (Fig. 37*A*), while the original condition of a single row of brachials is called *uniserial* and is the rule in existing crinoids (Fig. 18*A*). The biserial condition, however, permits a greater number of pinnules and hence increases the efficiency of food gathering.

The articulations between brachials have been discussed by A. H. Clark (1909d) and Gislén (1924). They classify as movable and immovable articulations. The movable or muscular articulations between brachials are the same as those already described between the radials and the first primibrachs; that is, the articulating faces bear five fossae, an aboral hemispherical fossa for the extensor ligament, two medial fossae for the interarticular ligaments, and two fossae on the oral side for the flexor muscles. These muscular articulations may be straight

(Fig. 24*A*) or oblique (Fig. 24*B*). The immovable or ligamentary articulations are of two sorts, *synarthries* and *syzygies*. Synarthries are somewhat flexible, as the opposed surfaces are united by two large bundles of elastic fibers fitted into hemispherical depressions (Fig. 24*C*), and the suture between the two brachials of the synarthry is as obvious externally as that between ordinary brachials. The syzygy is a very close union between adjacent brachials by means of many very short elastic fibers distributed over the opposing surfaces. These surfaces are sculptured into radiating ridges (Fig. 23*J*), so that externally the syzygy appears as a wavy line (Fig. 23*H*) or a row of dots. The distal member of a syzygial pair is called the *epizygal*, the proximal member the *hypozygal*. In the 10-armed condition in comatulids, the syzygial pairs are very definitely distributed among the secundibrachs, being separated by one to four ordinary brachials, according to species and according to position along the arm. Commonly, the syzygial pairs are the 3d and 4th, 9th and 10th, and 14th and 15th (Fig. 24*E*) in the proximal part of the arm; distally the syzygial pairs are regularly separated by one to four brachials depending on the size of the species. In the case of multibrachiate species, the syzygies are greatly reduced in number among the tertibrachs and postpalmar series.

Pinnules are regularly borne on alternate sides on successive brachials except that they are wanting on the first brachial following an axillary and on the hypozygal of a syzygial pair (Fig. 18*B*). Therefore following a fork the first pinnule occurs on the second brachial after the axillary and on the outer side of the arm. The synarthroses are without effect on the distribution of the pinnules. The differentiation of pinnules along the arm into oral, genital, and distal types was already noted. Pinnules are supported by a series of skeletal pieces called *pinnulars* that are similar to brachials and are held together by muscles and elastic fibers. Brachials and pinnulars are pierced by a canal for the passage of nerve trunks.

The tegmen or disk varies from a flat membrane to a high dome, embracing in the latter case the arm bases to the height of several brachials. This condition is often accompanied by the presence of extra plates, interbrachials and interambulacrals, in the peripheral parts of the tegmen. The tegmen may or may not be supported by endoskeletal plates. Primitively it contained five deltoid plates around the mouth between the ambulacral grooves, and this condition recurs as an ancestral reminiscence in the larvae of present crinoids (Fig. 33*B*) but is retained in very few adults (Fig. 14*A*–*C*). Usually the tegmen is filled with small plates, closely fitted (Fig. 15*A*) or loosely imbedded (Fig. 15*B*); even when it appears naked (Fig. 15*C*) it is found to contain calcareous formations of microscopic size.

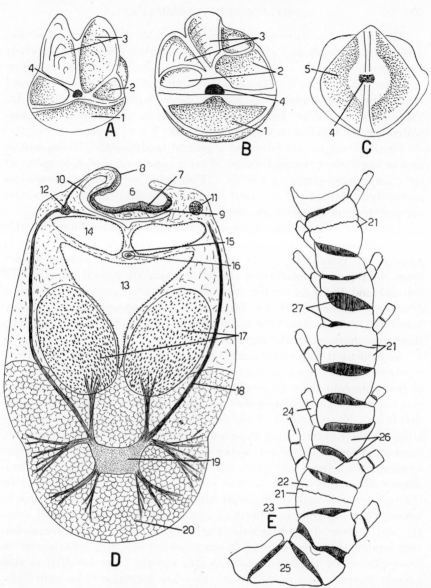

Fig. 24.—Arms (concluded). *A*, end surface of a brachial with straight muscular articulation. *B*, end surface of a brachial with oblique muscular articulation. *C*, end surface of a synarthrosis. (*A–C, after Gislen*, 1924). *D*, section through an arm (*slightly altered, after Hamann*, 1889.) *E*, proximal part of arm of *Antedon*, with three syzygial pairs (*after W. B. Carpenter*, 1866). 1, fossa for extensor ligament; 2, fossae for interarticular ligaments; 3, fossae for flexor muscles; 4, hole for nerve; 5, ligament fossae; 6, ambulacral groove; 7, groove epidermis; 8, podium; 9, band of ectoneural system; 10, water canal; 11, saccule; 12, lateral brachial nerve; 13, aboral coelomic canal; 14, subtentacular coelomic canals; 15, genital canal; 16, genital cord; 17, flexor muscle masses; 18, commissure from main brachial nerve to lateral brachial nerve; 19, main brachial nerve; 20, brachial; 21, syzygial pair; 22, epizygal; 23, hypozygal; 24, pinnule bases; 25, second primibrach (axillary); 26, secundibrachs; 27, ligaments.

The ambulacral grooves are lodged in a deep depression in the oral surface of brachials and pinnulars. The lappets, podia, and adjacent parts usually contain minute calcareous formations, such as simple or branched spicules and fenestrated plates, but in some families the lappets contain two rows of plates, the *side* and *covering* plates (Figs. 20*C*, 25*A*). These may close over the grooves and podia for protection. The side plates may be notched to lodge the saccules.

Finally there should be noted a general tendency for the deposition almost anywhere in crinoid tissues of calcareous bodies, such as spicules, rods, fenestrated plates, and so on. These tend to appear wherever the connective tissue is not occupied by regular skeletal pieces. The connective tissue of the body interior is also full of such formations.

According to an older terminology still sometimes encountered, the skeletal elements developed around the right coelom are termed *abactinal*, namely, the columnals, cirrals, calyx plates, brachials, and pinnulars; those developed in relation to the left coelom are *actinal*, that is, the deltoids and those associated with the ambulacral grooves; and those developed secondarily in the tegmen are *perisomatic*, including plates associated with the anal tube and occurring between the arm bases when these are embraced by the tegmen.

As evident from the foregoing account, crinoids lack regular muscle layers in the body wall, no doubt because the wall is stiffened and more or less immobilized by the endoskeletal pieces that occupy it. All the skeletal pieces are held together by what are called ligaments in the literature. These consist of parallel fibers usually regarded as elastic, although their nature is not clear and is subject to dispute. They must have some contractile power, as the cirri are capable of some movement although the cirrals are provided with elastic fibers only. Typical muscle fibers are limited to the arms and pinnules. The brachials (except syzygies and synarthries) are connected by a pair of muscle masses that run from one brachial to the next in fossae situated near the oral surface of the brachials (Fig. 24*D*). These are flexor muscles that enable the arms to bend inward toward the disk. Extension is accomplished by the ligaments that also run from one brachial to the next in fossae. As already noted, there are regularly three such ligaments between successive brachials, a large hemispherical one, the extensor ligament, occupying a fossa on the aboral side of the brachial, and a pair of smaller ligaments called interarticular ligaments, found at about the middle of the brachial (Fig. 24*A*). A similar arrangement of muscles and ligaments occurs between the pinnulars, at least between the more proximal ones. The muscles are described as a mixture of smooth, longitudinally striated, and diagonally striated fibers.

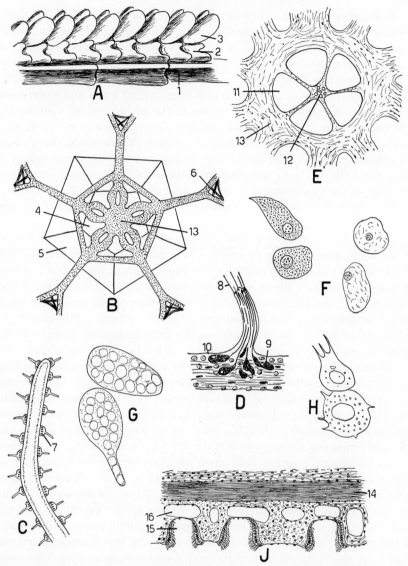

Fig. 25.—Groove skeleton, nervous system, coelom. *A*, portion of a pinnule showing groove plates (*after P. H. Carpenter*, 1884). *B*, aboral nervous center of *Antedon*. *C*, a podium of *Antedon*, enlarged. *D*, sensory papilla of podium, enlarged (*after Reichensperger*, 1908). *E*, section through the chambered organ of *Antedon*. *F*, coelomocytes of *Antedon*. (*B, E, F, after Hamann*, 1889.) *G, H*, coelomocytes of *Antedon* (*after Cuénot*, 1891.) *J*, longitudinal section of a pinnule, showing coelomic pits. (*C, J, after Chadwick*, 1907.) 1, pinnulars; 2, side plates; 3, covering plates; 4, centrodorsal; 5, radial plates; 6, decussating fibers; 7, sensory papilla; 8, sensory hairs; 9, gland cells; 10, epidermis; 11, chambered organ; 12, central stand with aboral end of axial gland; 13, aboral nervous center; 14, nerve strand; 15, coelomic pits; 16, coelomic spaces.

**5. Nervous System.**—The nervous system is subdivided into three systems occupying different body levels and communicating with each other. The *oral* or *superficial* or *ectoneural* system runs as a band in the ambulacral grooves of arms and pinnules immediately internal to the ciliated epidermis from which it is not definitely separable (Fig. 20*F*). These bands consist of nerve cells and longitudinal fibers and supply the ambulacral epidermis, the inner surface of the podia, and adjacent parts. The bands from all the grooves converge to five that cross in the tegmen to the mouth where they continue as a nerve sheath along the wall of the digestive tract. The *deeper oral* or *hyponeural* system consists of a pentagon (Fig. 27*A*) in the connective tissue of the tegmen lateral to the ring of the water-vascular system and of a number of nerves proceeding from this pentagon. Some of these nerves innervate the podia of the tegmen, the anal tube, and various internal structures but the main ones, 10 in number, proceed to the arms (Fig. 27*A*). These fork at the arm bases, sending two nerves into each arm, where they course along the sides of the arm not far below the surface as the lateral brachial nerves (Fig. 24*D*). These supply the musculature of the walls of the water vessels, the pinnules, and the outer surface of the podia and have strong connections with the aboral nervous system. The *aboral* or *entoneural* system is the main part of the nervous system in crinoids, in contrast to the other living echinoderm classes in which the oral system dominates. The aboral system centers in a cup-shaped mass occupying the apex of the cavity inside the calyx; from this nerves go directly into the cirrals in comatulids, or in stalked crinoids nervous tissue descends into the canal of the columnals ensheathing the structures that occupy this canal, and a similar sheath is given off into each cirrus at the nodes. The main nervous mass gives off laterally five stout trunks that immediately subdivide into ten, but these are soon united by a pentagonal commissure concentric with the main mass (Fig. 25*B*). This pentagon is lodged in the radial plates of the calyx. From its angles five main brachial nerves proceed to the five primary arms (Fig. 25*B*). They continue along the canal in the brachials; this canal was originally part of the groove lodging the ambulacral system but has become separated from it by the ingrowth of skeleton and closed over as a canal. At each axillary the brachial nerve forks, and the two nerves so formed are connected immediately by direct and decussating (crossed) commissures (Fig. 25*B*). In each brachial the brachial nerve presents a swelling from which is given off a pair of nerves into the flexor muscles and adjoining epidermis, nerves into the aboral part of the arm, and a pair of lateral commissures that join the lateral brachial nerves (Fig. 24*D*). Each pinnule is provided with a pair of nerves, one on each side. As in invertebrates in general, the so-called nerves are in reality ganglionated trunks, being accompanied by bipolar and multipolar nerve cells. The foregoing account is based primarily on Hamann's study of *Antedon mediterranea* (1889); slight differences in the pattern of the aboral pentagon and main trunks associated with it are given for some other species by Ludwig (1877).

**6. Sense Organs.**—Definite sense organs are poorly in evidence in crinoids, being represented only by the papillae with which the podia are liberally strewn. These are slender epidermal projections with a few sensory bristles and provided with basal gland cells whose long necks traverse the papilla and open at its tip (Fig. 25*D*). These papillae therefore combine sensory (probably tactile) and secretory functions; the secretion seems to be of an adhesive nature. Probably sensory functions in crinoids are served mainly by free nerve endings, as many of the nerves break up into branches that terminate in fine twigs to the surface.

**7. Coelom.**—As the crinoids are coelomate animals, an extensive cavity would be expected between the calyx and tegminal walls and the intestine. This, however, is not the case. In the mature crinoid the interior is so filled with strands, webs, and membranes of connective tissue often impregnated with calcareous formations that the expected coelom is broken up into many small spaces and in some species almost obliterated. The coelomic spaces are all lined by a cuboidal epithelium, also called endothelium, and communicate with one another. In the center of the body enclosed by the coils of the intestine is a vertical coelomic space called the *axial sinus* that orally surrounds the esophagus. The axial sinus and the other coelomic spaces of the body interior continue into the arms which enclose four coelomic canals, an aboral one between and below the two masses of the flexor muscle, a pair of *subtentacular* canals oral to the foregoing and separated from it by a horizontal septum and from each other by a vertical septum, and a small *genital* canal situated in the horizontal septum and housing a *genital cord* (Fig. 24*D*). There is also a minute coelomic canal between the water canal and the ectoneural nerve band. The main coelomic arm canals continue into the pinnules. They intercommunicate frequently. In the aboral wall of the aboral coelomic canals, especially in the pinnules, less often in the arms, there occur in groups of two to six little depressions known as *ciliated pits* (Fig. 25*J*). The sides of these are lined by a columnar, heavily ciliated epithelium, representing altered coelomic lining (that elsewhere lacks cilia), while the bottom of the pit consists of flattened nonciliated cells. The function of these pits is obscure, apart from causing some degree of circulation of the coelomic fluid through the action of their cilia. The partition between the subtentacular coelomic canals of the arms is lost proximally, and the five canals thus

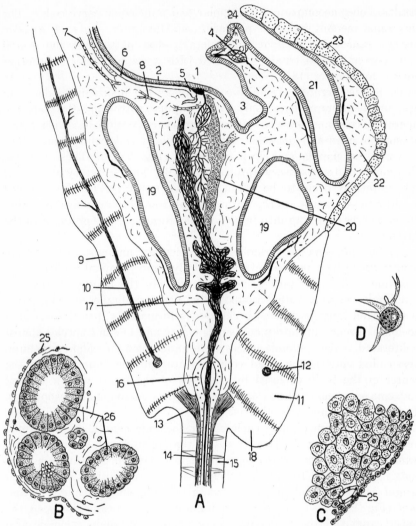

FIG. 26.—Internal structure.    A, longitudinal section of the body of the stalked crinoid
*Neocrinus decorus.*   B, histological structure of the axial gland (*after Hamann*, 1889).
C, histological structure of the spongy organ.   D, coelomocyte found inside a blood lacuna.
(*A, C, D, after Reichensperger*, 1905.)   1, mouth; 2, tegminal epidermis; 3, esophagus;
4, periesophageal plexus of haemal system; 5, ring canal of water-vascular system; 6, radial
canal of water-vascular system; 7, genital tube with inclosed ova; 8, subtegminal plexus of
haemal system; 9, brachials; 10, main brachial nerve; 11, radial; 12, nerve pentagon;
13, main aboral nerve center; 14, nerve from same down stalk; 15, columnals; 16, chambered organ; 17, axial gland; 18, basal; 19, sections of intestine; 20, spongy organ; 21,
rectum; 22, anal tube; 23, skeletal plates of anal tube; 24, anus; 25, coelomic endothelium;
26, gland tubules.

resulting become continuous with the oral end of the axial sinus; aborally this sinus merges with the coelomic spaces between the viscera (perivisceral spaces). However, aboral to the axial sinus the coelom of the body center is represented by a curious structure termed the *chambered organ*. This in comatulids is housed in the cavity between the rosette and the inner surface of the centrodorsal plate and in stalked crinoids occupies a similar position. It consists of five coelomic cavities arranged more or less symmetrically around a central axis (Fig. 25E), composed mainly of connective tissue, extensions of which form the partitions between the chambers. The chambered organ is encased in the cuplike cavity of the main mass of the aboral nervous system, so that it is surrounded by nervous tissue. The chambers are situated in the radii in dicyclic crinoids, interradially in monocyclic forms. In the oral direction the five cavities diminish and soon end blindly; aborally they continue as the canals of the cirri. These canals are subdivided by a horizontal partition of connective tissue continuous with that of the partitions of the chambered organ. The cirral canals are therefore of coelomic nature; they are embraced by the fibers of the cirral nerves. In comatulids the cirral canals arise from the chambered organ in five groups; in stalked crinoids the five chambers continue along the center of the stalk as five more or less evident canals grouped around a central cord of connective tissue continuous with the central axis of the chambered organ (Fig. 26A). At each node, each of the five canals gives off a canal into one of the five cirri usually present. These canals in columnals and cirri are sheathed by nervous tissue that forms the nerves of the stalk and cirri already mentioned.

The coelomocytes of crinoids have been described by Cuénot (1891, 1900), Hamann (1889), and Reichensperger (1912); they seem to differ somewhat in different crinoids. Cuénot first observed two sorts of cells, a small finely granular type with short pseudopods (Fig. 25H) and a larger pyriform or oblong, very slowly moving cell filled with coarse spherules (Fig. 25G); later he added a third type filled with safranophil rods, rounded when free in the coelomic fluid, pyriform when migrating through the tissues. Hamann noticed an abundance of wandering amoeboid cells in various crinoids and also figured two types (Fig. 25F), neither of which much resembles Cuénot's forms. In *Antedon* Reichensperger reported two kinds of coelomocytes, an amoeboid form with short pseudopods (Fig. 43A), clearly identical with Fig. 25H, and proved by him to have phagocytic functions (Fig. 43B), and a type similar to one of Hamann's, an elongate cell filled with rods and granules (Fig. 43C). All observers indicate that the coelomocytes wander about freely and in fact are more abundant in the tissues than in the coelomic fluid, being found in numbers, especially the granular type, in the connective tissues,

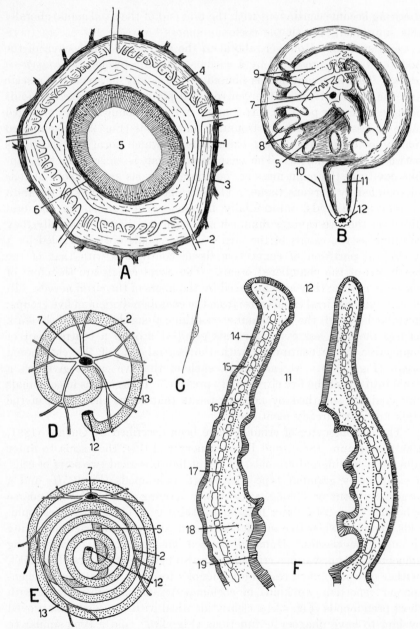

Fig. 27.—Water-vascular system, digestive system. *A*, transverse section through the esophagus of *Antedon*. *B*, digestive tract of *Antedon* with many diverticula (*after Chadwick*, 1907). *C*, epitheliomuscular cell of the wall of a radial water vessel. *D*, scheme of an endocyclic digestive system. *E*, scheme of an exocyclic digestive system. (*D*, *E*, *after Clark*, 1915a.) *F*, longitudinal section of the anal tube. (*A*, *C*, *F*, *after Hamann*, 1889.) 1, water-vascular ring; 2, radial water canals; 3, nerve pentagon of deeper oral system; 4,

beneath the intestinal epithelium, near the epidermis of pinnules, tegmen, and ambulacral grooves, and along the nerve cords.

**8. Axial Gland.**—Inside the axial sinus there is found an elongated glandular body, the *axial gland* (variously called in the past heart, dorsal organ, axial organ, genital stolon, ovoid gland, and other names). The axial gland consists of tubules of cuboidal glandular epithelium imbedded in connective tissue and covered externally by coelomic epithelium (Fig. 26*B*). It continues aborally through the central hole of the rosette into the central strand or cord of the chambered organ, but the glandular tubules soon diminish and disappear, leaving only connective tissue. In the oral direction the axial gland ceases in the vicinity of the mouth, where it is closely related to a plexus of the haemal system. An endocrine function of the gland is suggested by its histology, lack of a duct of discharge, and proximity to haemal plexi. The statement often seen that the axial gland gives rise ontogenetically to the genital stolons is erroneous.

**9. Water-vascular System.**—This system in crinoids follows the same general plan as in other echinoderms but differs in the lack of a direct connection with the exterior. The ambulacral grooves, accompanied by podia and saccules, begin at the tips of the pinnules, run along the oral surface of the pinnules and arms, and converge to five grooves that cross the tegmen and terminate in a pentagonal depression around the mouth. The absence of ambulacral grooves on certain pinnules and the asymmetries of the tegminal grooves in the Comasteridae were already noted. The ambulacral grooves are everywhere accompanied by an underlying canal of the water-vascular system. This canal lies beneath (aboral to) the epidermal nervous layer of the groove except that a small coelomic canal intervenes between the nervous band and the water canal (Fig. 24*D*). In each arm the water canal branches alternately to each side into the pinnules (including pinnules that lack ambulacral grooves) and similarly in arms and pinnules alternately into the groups of podia when present. Each group of three podia receives one water canal (Fig. 20*D*) that branches to become the hollow interior of each podium of the group. The water canals from the arms converge to five main *radial* canals lying beneath the ambulacral grooves of the tegmen, and these enter the main *ring* canal, a flattened pentagonal vessel (Fig. 27*A*) encircling the mouth internal to the pentagonal ambulacral depression around the mouth. The ring canal sends a branch into each of the labial podia (which as already noted occur as single fingers)

water tubes (omitted on one side); 5, esophagus; 6, nervous layer of esophageal wall, continuation of oral system; 7, mouth; 8, diverticula; 9, long branched diverticula; 10, anal tube; 11, rectum; 12, anus; 13, intestine; 14, body-wall epidermis; 15, body-wall connective tissue; 16, spaces in connective tissue; 17, circular muscles of rectum; 18, connective tissue of rectum; 19, lining epithelium of rectum.

and to its outer side gives off a large number (about 30 in each interradius in common comatulids) of small short tubes, the *stone canals*, that open into the coelom at their free ends (Fig. 27*A*). The ciliated funnels through the tegmen were already noticed.

The water vessels, being of coelomic nature, are lined by a cuboidal endothelium, outside of which lies a layer of longitudinal muscle fibrils; these, according to Hamann (1889), are processes of the endothelial cells, hence the latter are epitheliomuscular cells (Fig. 20*F*). The lumina of the larger water vessels are frequently crossed by strands of muscle fibers that presumably act to diminish the diameter of the water vessels, whereas the longitudinal fibers of the wall would shorten and broaden the vessels on contraction. The podia are clothed with epidermis taller on their inner than on their outer sides and frequently elevated into the sensory papillae already described. Beneath the epidermis of the inner side of the podia lies a nervous stratum continuous with the ectoneural band of the ambulacral grooves, while the outer side of the podia is supplied from the lateral brachial nerves (Fig. 24*D*). The podia are therefore exceedingly well innervated and are in communication with all three nervous systems. Internal to the nervous stratum is found a layer of longitudinal muscle fibers, and the cavity of the podia is lined by coelomic endothelium (Fig. 21*F*). The walls of the water vessels and podia also contain some connective tissue; circular muscles are entirely wanting.

**10. Digestive System.**—In the majority of crinoids, the mouth is more or less central on the disk, a condition spoken of as *endocyclic* (Fig. 15*A–C*), but in some comasterids the mouth is greatly displaced to the periphery of the disk (Fig. 15*D, E*), and such crinoids are termed *exocyclic*. The mouth leads into a short esophagus from which in endocyclic crinoids the intestine or mid-gut proceeds aborally and laterally, approaching the inner surface of the calyx and making a complete turn in a clockwise direction (Fig. 27*D*) as viewed from the oral surface, finally proceeding orally as the rectum in the anal tube and opening by the anus, sometimes edged with small papillae. The intestine may be enlarged as compared with the esophagus and often bears lateral outpouchings, two of which in common species of *Antedon* are very long and branched distally (Fig. 27*B*). In exocyclic crinoids the intestine makes four coils that are not wider than the esophagus and that lack diverticula (Fig. 27*E*).

The ambulacral epithelium of very tall attenuated ciliated cells continues down the esophagus, where it is liberally provided with mucous goblets (Fig. 28*A*). The epithelium is underlain by a nervous layer of the ectoneural system continuous with the nervous bands of the ambulacral grooves. This nervous layer forms a sheath in the base of the

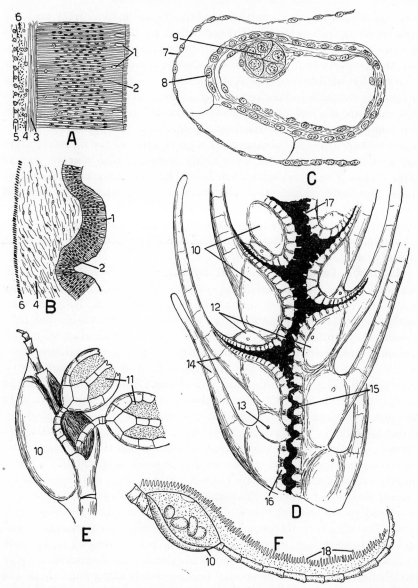

Fig. 28.—Digestive system (continued), reproductive system. *A*, section through the esophagus. *B*, section through the rectum. *C*, section through the genital canal. (*A–C, after Hamann*, 1889.) *D*, arm of male *Notocrinus virile* with testes at the pinnule bases. *E*, pinnule of *Phrixometra nutrix* with pentacrinoid young in the marsupium. *F*, pinnule of *Isometra vivipara* with marsupium opened to show contained eggs. (*D–F, after Mortensen*, 1920c.) 1, goblets; 2, epithelium; 3, nervous layer; 4, connective tissue; 5, coelomic endothelium; 6, circular muscle fibers; 7, genital canal (coelomic); 8, genital tube (haemal); 9, genital cord with sex cells; 10, marsupium; 11, pentacrinoid larvae; 12, testes; 13, pore of sperm discharge; 14, pinnules; 15, ambulacral groove; 16, lappets; 17, covering plates; 18, podia.

esophageal and intestinal epithelium but gradually diminishes and disappears along the intestine. The epithelium of the entire digestive tract except the terminal part of the rectum is ciliated. In the esophagus outside the nervous layer is found a slight amount of connective tissue followed by well-developed circular muscle fibers forming a sphincter several layers thick. This reduces to a single layer along the intestine. The anal tube is a body-wall projection that encloses the rectum to which it is bound by connective-tissue septa (Fig. 27F). The rectal epithelium is diminished in height as compared with the rest of the digestive tract and gradually loses its cilia but is richly furnished with mucous goblets (Fig. 28B). The rectal epithelium is heavily underlain with connective tissue, here much thicker than elsewhere in the digestive tube, followed by a layer of circular muscle fibers. The anal tube is capable of considerable movement and is reported to engage in rhythmical contractions, taking in and ejecting water, possibly as an aid in the elimination of feces, possibly as a kind of respiration.

**11. Blood Lacunar or Haemal System.**—This consists of a well-developed but somewhat indefinite system of intercommunicating spaces in the strands and webs of connective tissue that fill the body interior. As these spaces lack a definite lining, they are better termed lacunae than vessels; they are outlined by connective tissue covered externally with coelomic endothelium. They are distinguishable from ordinary connective-tissue spaces by the fact that the contained blood coagulates on fixation and takes a definite stain in sections. The morphology of the lacunar system is not too clear, as the system can be followed only in sections. Original findings on the system have been published by Hamann (1889), Reichensperger (1905), and Chadwick (1907). It appears that there is a plexus of large lacunae around the esophagus close to the main ring of the water-vascular system (Fig. 26A). This is termed *periesophageal plexus* by Cuénot (1948). It is connected with a general plexus just beneath the tegmen (*subtegminal plexus*) that in turn is related to the genital tubes of the arms. From the periesophageal plexus branches with thickened walls pass aborally into a cellular reticulum called the *spongy organ*, which is best or only developed on one side and is intimately related to the axial gland. In *Neocrinus decorus* (Reichensperger, 1905), the spongy organ extends along one side of the axial gland (Fig. 26A) for the entire length of the latter, but in the comatulids investigated, accompanies only the oral half of the gland. In either case the spongy organ sends a mesh of lacunae toward the axial gland, but most observers deny the presence of blood lacunae between the tubules of the gland. The spongy organ consists largely of rounded cells (Fig. 26C) forming a mesh with very small lacunae in the interstices. It was noticed by early workers under the name of *labial* *plexus* but does not seem to be an ordinary haemal plexus. Cuénot regards it as a lymphoid organ that produces the coelomocytes. The axial gland may also be supplied directly from the periesophageal ring. In the more aboral parts of the body there are large lacunae arranged in a circular fashion between the axial sinus and the intestinal coil and sending branches into the latter by way of the connective-tissue layer of its wall. The genital tube conveying the sex cells represents the only blood lacuna in the arms, as all other spaces of the latter are coelomic.

The blood filling the lacunar system is a highly proteinaceous colorless fluid that coagulates on fixation and hence becomes visible. It seldom contains any cells; any that do occur are identical with the coelomocytes, which as already indicated tend to wander everywhere in the crinoid body. Reichensperger (1905) figures a blood lacuna containing an amoeboid coelomocyte of the type with short pointed pseudopods (Fig. 26*D*).

**12. Reproductive System.**—The gonads are located either in the arms or in the genital pinnules, usually the latter, and are evident at sexual maturity as swollen areas. Crinoids are dioecious, but the sexes are indistinguishable externally except for the brood chambers of the females of some species. The gonads are not definite bodies but simply masses of sex cells filling the genital cavity of arms or pinnules. The primordial sex cells reach their definitive location by way of the *genital cords,* which are strands of cells located in a *genital canal* traversing the arms. The genital canal is a coelomic extension lined by endothelium located in the partition between the aboral and subtentacular coelomic canals of the arms (Fig. 24*D*). Typically, the genital canal contains another tube, the *genital tube,* suspended in it by strands of connective tissue, and inside this is found the genital cord or rachis, a solid strand of cells attached to one wall of the tube (Fig. 28*C*). In some crinoids, however, as *Antedon bifida,* described by Chadwick (1907), the genital tube appears wanting, and the genital cord, at first solid, later developing a cavity, occupies the genital canal directly. The genital canal gives off a branch into each genital pinnule, and this expands therein into a cavity that becomes filled with sex cells. The genital tube is usually stated to be a blood lacuna connected with the subtegminal plexus. The genital cords along which the primordial sex cells reach the gonads cannot be satisfactorily traced centrally in adult crinoids; they are gradually lost in the meshes of the subtegminal lacunar plexus.

Crinoids probably breed at a definite season of the year over a period of 1 or 2 months, but different species, even in the same locality, may breed at different times. A. H. Clark (1921a) has listed the data available to that time on the breeding season of comatulids; for most of the species the time of breeding lies between January and October. The

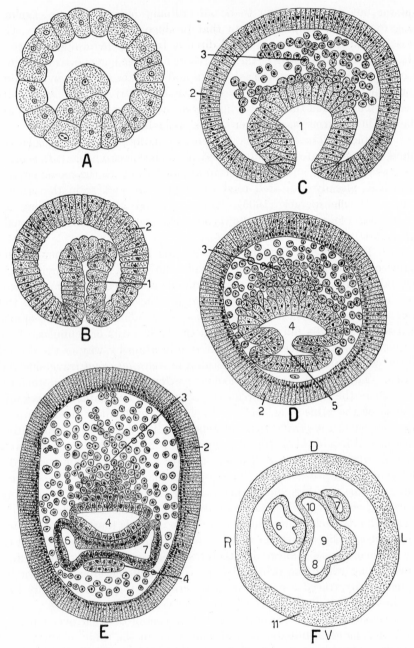

Fig. 29.—Embryology.  *A*, beginning gastrulation by unipolar ingression.  *B*, continuance of gastrulation by emboly.  *C*, invaginating archenteron giving off entomesoderm. *D*, blastopore closed, archenteron constricting transversely.  *E*, longitudinal horizontal section, showing beginning formation of the coelomic sacs.  (*A–E*, *after Seeliger*, 1892.)

common littoral comatulid of western Europe, *Antedon bifida*, spawns from the end of May into July; the Mediterranean species, *A. mediterranea*, mostly in April and May, but apparently also throughout the year; and the Adriatic species, *A. adriatica* (= *rosacea*), from April to the end of June. Mortensen (1937), working at Ghardaqa on the Red Sea, found *Tropiometra andouini* shedding eggs at the end of April and *Lamprometra kleinzingeri* at the beginning of May; the latter regularly spawned at 7 P.M. In the same region, *Heterometra savignyi* spawns in late August, at about 3 P.M. (Mortensen, 1938). The same author (1920b) observed the spawning of *Tropiometra carinata* in March and April at night in the British West Indies and found specimens of *Florometra serratissima* with attached young in June and July at British Columbia. The most exact observations on crinoid spawning are those of Dan and Dan (1941) on *Comanthus japonicus*, a littoral Japanese comatulid. Observations continued over 4 years showed that this species spawns once annually, during the first half of October, when the moon is in the first or last quarter. Practically all individuals spawn on the same afternoon, around 3 to 5 P.M. Individuals placed in laboratory aquaria 2 weeks before the spawning was due, and thus removed from any action of the tides, nevertheless spawned simultaneously with those in nature, and the same was true of isolated arms and pinnules.

The sex cells escape by rupture of the pinnule wall, and the eggs either fall to the bottom or are stuck to the pinnules by the secretion of the cement glands already mentioned. Attachment of the eggs to the pinnules is characteristic of the genus *Antedon*. In *Comanthus japonicus*, rupture occurs through preformed thin spots on elevated areas of the pinnules (Dan and Dan, 1941), and the same is probably true of other crinoids. Typically, males spawn first, and this stimulates the discharge of eggs, which are thus fertilized immediately upon extrusion. Dan and Dan report that all arms of the multibrachiate *Comanthus japonicus* spawn simultaneously or nearly so.

The fertilized eggs are enclosed in a definite membrane, probably a fertilization membrane, smooth or covered with spines or otherwise ornamented. Dan and Dan (1941) noted the appearance of spines on the fertilization membrane during its elevation after fertilization of the eggs of *Comanthus japonicus*. In most crinoids development occurs inside the membrane to a ciliated stage that escapes through holes in the membrane, probably the result of enzyme action, and swims about as a characteristic larva (Fig. 30) for a varying period before attachment. However, the eggs develop in brood chambers in a number of antarctic

---

*F*, cross section of a stage similar to *E*, showing subdivisions of the coelom (*after Bury*, 1888). 1, archenteron; 2, ectoderm; 3, entomesodermal mesenchyme; 4, enterohydrocoel; 5, somatocoel; 6, right somatocoel; 7, left somatocoel; 8, axocoel; 9, hydrocoel; 10, enteron; 11, beginning stomodaeal thickening. D, V, R, L, dorsal, ventral, right, left.

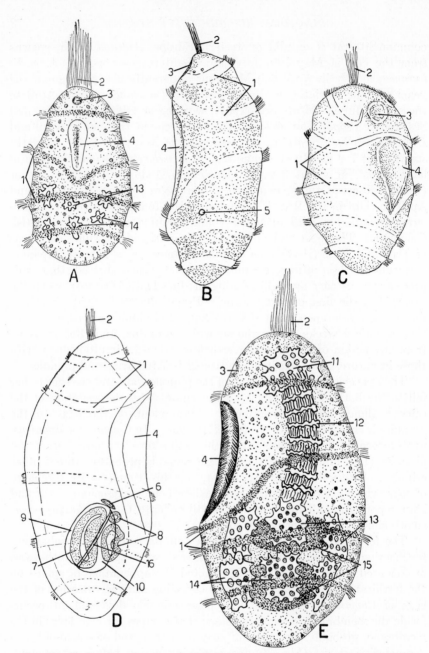

Fig. 30.—Embryology (continued); doliolaria larva. *A*, doliolaria of *Antedon bifida*, with four ciliary rings. *B*, doliolaria of *Antedon mediterranea*, with five ciliary rings, seen from the left side. *C*, same as *B*, seen from the right side. (*B, C, after B·vry*, 1888.) *D*, doliolaria of *Antedon adriatica*, seen from the right, showing primordia inside (*after Seeliger*, 1892). *E*, late doliolaria of *A, bifida*, seen from the left, with beginning skeleton. (*A, E, after Thomson*, 1865.) 1, ciliary rings; 2, apical sensory tuft; 3, adhesive pit; 4, vestibule; 5, hydropore; 6, axocoel; 7, enteric sac; 8, hydrocoel; 9, right coelom; 10, left coelom; 11, attachment plate; 12, columnals; 13, basals; 14, deltoids; 15, viscera; 16, primary mesentery. Vestibule marks the ventral side of the larva.

comatulids, mostly of the genera *Isometra, Notocrinus*, and *Phrixometra* (Mortensen, 1920b; John, 1938). Gonads and brood chambers are located in the arms at the pinnule bases in *Notocrinus* (Fig. 28D), in the pinnules in the others. The brood chamber or *marsupium* is formed of a body-wall invagination adjacent to the gonad, and this expands into a sac retaining an external aperture. Apparently the eggs get into the marsupium by rupture through the wall intervening between ovary and marsupium. In these brooding species, the ciliated free-swimming stage is more or less suppressed, and in *Phrixometra nutrix*, probably also in *Kempometra grisea*, development in the marsupium continues to the stage of the stalked larva, which is found projecting from the marsupium (Fig. 28E). The egg production of viviparous species is generally reduced as compared with that of other comatulids, and usually only a few eggs are found in each marsupium (Fig. 28F). In *Isometra vivipara* it was discovered by Andersson (1908) and verified by Mortensen (1920b) that sperm are present in the genital tube of the ovary, so that the eggs are apparently fertilized before extrusion. How the sperm are able to get into the interior of the ovary remains unexplained.

**13. Development.**—Knowledge of crinoid embryology derives chiefly from old studies, those of Thomson (1865), W. B. Carpenter (1866, 1876), Metschnikoff (1871), Perrier (1886), Barrois (1888), Bury (1888), and Seeliger (1892). These workers used species of *Antedon*. Considerable information on the development of species of other genera has been furnished by Mortensen (1920b, 1931, 1937, 1938), but the most complete account is still that of Seeliger (1892) for *Antedon adriatica* (which he called *rosacea*), and his description is here followed. The *Antedon* egg undergoes indeterminate, holoblastic, nearly equal cleavage of the radial type (I, page 257), that is, the tiers of blastomeres lie in line with each other. There results a typical coeloblastula. Gastrulation begins as unipolar ingression (Fig. 29A) but gradually alters to the embolic type (Fig. 29B). The advancing entodermal invagination proliferates to a stratified condition and begins to give off numerous cells into the blasto-coel (Fig. 29C); these represent the first part of the entomesoderm and take on the appearance and functions of mesenchyme (Fig. 29E). After the completion of gastrulation the blastopore closes and the archenteron is cut off as a closed sac lying in the blastocoel surrounded on three sides by mesenchyme (Fig. 29D). In *A. adriatica* this stage is reached after about 36 hours of development.

The axis of the embryo passing through the site of the blastopore may be regarded as the anteroposterior axis. The archenteron lies in the posterior part of the embryo, which otherwise is filled with the entomeso-dermal mesenchyme. There now forms around the middle of the archenteral sac a circular constriction in the transverse plane, dividing this sac into two vesicles, an anterior one, the *enterohydrocoel*, and a posterior one, the *somatocoel* (Fig. 29*D*). The formation of mesenchyme has continued up to about this time. The somatocoel elongates laterally, becoming a dumbbell-like figure with expanded right and left ends and constricted middle (Fig. 29*E*). These two ends are the *right* and *left somatocoels* (called posterior coeloms in older works). The enterohydrocoel curves around the constricted middle part of the somatocoel in a plane at right angles to the elongation of the latter and takes on a crescentic shape, with one horn of the crescent dorsal to the middle of the somatocoel, the other ventral to it, and its main part directed anteriorly. The embryo thus now presents a distinct bilateral morphology with right and left sides, dorsal and ventral surfaces, and anterior and posterior ends defined. The somatocoel continues to constrict medially and finally ruptures into two sacs, the right and left somatocoels (Fig. 29*F*). The enterohydrocoel gives off a considerable ventral process that separates as a coelomic sac, the *hydrocoel* (corresponding to the left hydrocoel of other echinoderms); there also comes from it a narrow dorsal evagination, the *axocoel* (Fig. 29*F*). What remains of the central part of the original enterohydrocoel sac together with the two horns sent out from this sac fuse to become the *enteric sac*, which represents the future intestine. This stage is reached after about 3 days in *A. adriatica*.

Meantime the embryo has been elongating in the anteroposterior axis and now presents an oval shape. At its anterior end, the end opposite the original blastopore, there appears a typical apical sensory plate provided with a tuft of cilia (Fig. 30). This is underlain by nervous tissue of ectodermal origin from which nervous strands proceed under the ectoderm along the sides of the embryo. There have also been forming around the embryo by ectodermal differentiation four or five ciliated bands, about equally spaced along the axis. In *Antedon bifida*, figured by Wyville Thomson (1865), there are four bands (Fig. 30*A*), whereas in *A. mediterranea* (Bury, 1888) and *A. adriatica* (Seeliger, 1892), there are five (Fig. 30*B*). In the mid-ventral line near the apical tuft the larva bears a glandular ectodermal depression, the *adhesive pit*, that interrupts the first ciliary band when five are present (Fig. 30*C*) but lies above it when there are four (Fig. 30*A*). An elongated mid-ventral depression, the *stomodaeum* or *vestibule*, occurs between the first and second bands (Fig. 30*A*) or second and third (Fig. 30*C*), distorting the band below it. The coelomic and enteric sacs lie concentrated in a small area in the posterior part of the larva (Fig. 30*D*), and the remainder and larger part of the interior is filled with mesenchyme. During the fifth day the *Antedon* larva ruptures the egg membrane, probably with the aid of enzymatic secretion, and swims about for a variable period, usually a few hours to a few days. Haeckel's term

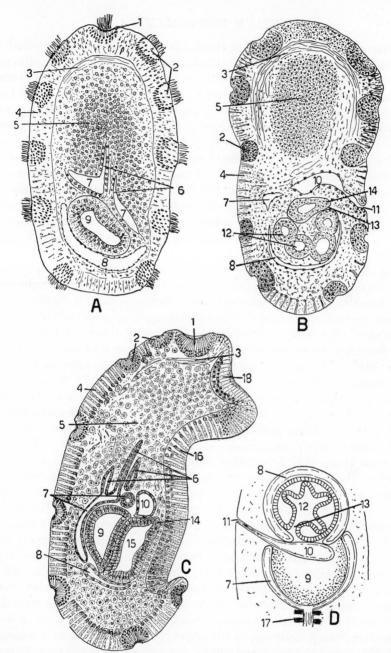

Fig. 31.—Embryology, doliolaria larva (continued). *A*, horizontal section of doliolaria of *Antedon*, 7 days old, taken near the dorsal surface. *B*, similar section, near the ventral surface. (*A, B, after Bury*, 1888.) *C*, vertical longitudinal section of similar larva (*after Seeliger*, 1892). *D*, viscera seen from ventral side before rotation (*after Barrois*, 1888). 1, apical sensory pit; 2, ciliary rings; 3, nervous tissue associated with sensory tuft; 4, ectoderm; 5, mesenchyme; 6, outgrowths to form chambered organ; 7, right coelom; 8, left coelom; 9, enteric sac; 10, axocoel; 11, hydropore; 12, hydrocoel evaginations; 13, gap in hydrocoel horseshoe; 14, evagination for stone canal; 15, hydrocoel; 16, vestibule; 17, columnals; 18, adhesive pit.

*doliolaria*, revived by Dawydoff (1928, 1948), is a convenient appellation for the larva. Sooner or later the doliolaria attaches by the adhesive pit, and the original anterior end thus becomes the attached or aboral surface, while the original posterior or blastoporal end becomes the free or oral surface. The ciliated bands and apical tuft and accompanying nervous tissue degenerate, and the ectoderm of these areas reverts to an ordinary epithelium.

By this time the endoskeletal ossicles have begun to appear and various changes occur in the coelomic and enteric sacs and in the stomodaeum. The latter, composed of tall ciliated cells, deepens and lengthens, and its edges begin to fuse, from its posterior end anteriorly. There is left for some time an anterior (aboral) opening (Fig. 32*A*), but this also eventually closes, and the stomodaeum, which has now lost its cilia, remains as a flattened sac, usually called *vestibule*, lying in the interior along the ventral surface. In the posterior, now oral, end of the larva lies the enteric sac surrounded by the four coelomic sacs; the right and left somatocoels, the hydrocoel, and the axocoel (Fig. 31*C*). The axocoel early makes a connection with the surface, opening there by the hydropore (Fig. 31*B*), located on the left side of the ventral surface of the doliolaria, immediately anterior to the third or fourth ciliated band (Fig. 30*B*). The axocoel and hydrocoel are the first and second coelomic compartments of the left side; the corresponding right members are missing in crinoids. The two somatocoels are the right and left components of the third coelomic compartment. The hydrocoel, lodged between the vestibule and the enteric sac, elongates to a crescentic form and puts out five evaginations that butt against the inner wall of the vestibule (Figs. 31*B*, 32*A*); these are the primary podia, later the radial canals of the water-vascular system. From the left end of the crescentic hydrocoel there is sent out a small projection (Fig. 31*B*), which later meets the axocoel to form the stone canal or canal connecting the water-vascular ring with the hydropore. The two somatocoels, which at their origin were symmetrically disposed, shift to asymmetrical positions. The right one expands and shifts dorsally and posteriorly, coming to occupy temporarily an almost completely dorsal position (Fig. 30*D*). The left somatocoel similarly expands and shifts ventrally, also anteriorly, coming in contact with the hydrocoel (Fig. 30*D*). Wherever the inner walls of the two somatocoels meet, there is formed a longitudinal mesentery, which, however, as a result of the shifts mentioned, is oblique (Fig. 30*D*), rather than longitudinal, and curved, with the concavity of the curvature directed anteriorly.

At about this stage of differentiation, shortly after attachment, there occurs a rotation of the internal organs of about 90 degrees from the ventral to the posterior (oral) position. The vestibule, previously

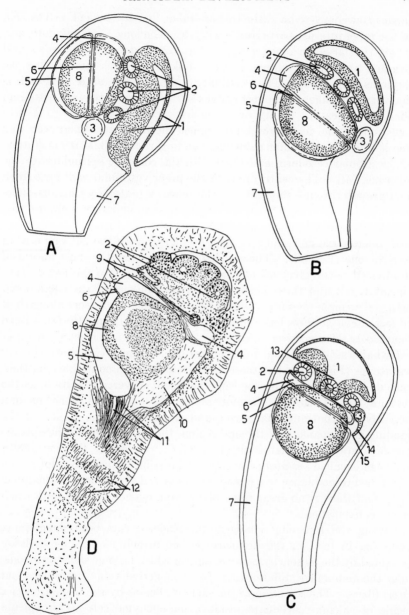

FIG. 32.—Embryology (continued), rotation of viscera. *A–C*, successive stages of rotation (*after Barrois*, 1888). *D*, vertical longitudinal section of larva after rotation (*after Bury*, 1888), larva 7 days old. All figures are now oriented with the original anterior end down. 1, vestibule; 2, hydrocoel evaginations; 3, axocoel; 4, left or oral coelom; 5, right or aboral coelom; 6, horizontal mesentery; 7, larval stalk; 8, enteric sac; 9, hydrocoel ring; 10, aboral vertical mesentery; 11, outgrowths for chambered organ; 12, columnals; 13, evagination to form mouth and pharynx; 14, canal from axocoel to hydropore; 15, hydropore.

ventral, now comes to lie in the free or oral end of the larva (Fig. 32*A*, *B*), and the other internal parts rotate with it.   The long, originally anterior, part of the larva becomes a stalk (Fig. 32) and rapidly narrows and elongates, already containing a series of skeletal pieces representing the columnals (Fig. 33*B*).   The vestibule, occupying the whole oral end, is somewhat bowl-like, with outer convex surface close to the oral ectoderm and inner concavity fitting over the hydrocoel (Fig. 32*B*).   The five projections of the hydrocoel butt against the inner vestibular wall and force it into the vestibular cavity as five fingers (Fig. 32*D*) thus clothed with vestibular ectoderm and lined with the coelomic epithelium of the hydrocoel wall.   The central part of the inner vestibular wall puts forth an outgrowth through the center of the space embraced by the horseshoe-shaped hydrocoel; this outgrowth fuses with the underlying enteric sac, and mouth and esophagus are thus established (Figs. 32*C*, 33*B*, *C*).  Both somatocoels now embrace the enteric sac, with the left one oral to the right one (Fig. 32).   The right somatocoel, now the most aboral of the internal parts, gives off five tubular extensions into the larval stalk (Fig. 31*A*, *C*), and these become the five chambers of the chambered organ.   The main mesentery where the two somatocoels meet along their surfaces of contact now has a horizontal orientation (Fig. 32*B–D*).   Both somatocoels are somewhat crescentic; their blind ends meet each other near what was the original mid-ventral line, forming two short vertical mesenteries (Fig. 32*D*), but these are not exactly in line with each other, hence do not both show on the same longitudinal vertical section, as the more oral one is to the left, the more aboral one to the right, of the median line.   By the continued narrowing and elongation of the stalk and the rounding and expansion of the oral region, the larva takes on the appearance of a stalked pelmatozoan (Fig. 33*D*).   Following Perrier (1886), this stage is called *cystidean* by some authors, including Dawydoff, from a presumed resemblance to a cystid.   Others find the name objectionable, and in fact there is no great resemblance to a cystid; but the term has a certain convenience.

During the foregoing changes, the skeleton has been developing, beginning, in fact, in the doliolaria before attachment.   The skeleton is secreted by the mesenchyme cells, part of which become skeletogeneous, while the remainder differentiate into connective tissue, muscles, and elastic fibers.   The secretion of the skeleton begins by the formation of a spicule of calcium carbonate inside a mesenchyme cell.   This spicule begins to branch, and other mesenchyme cells gather around to assist in the formation of more branches.   These branches fuse to form a fenestrated plate (Fig. 33*A*), and such fenestrated plates constitute the juvenile endoskeleton (Fig. 33*B*, *D*).   They increase in size peripherally by the production and fusion of more branches, and by the same process eventually become three-dimensional. In the larval stalk a row of columnals appears at an early cystidean stage (Fig. 32D); these gradually curve into a horseshoe shape and eventually close around the five extensions of the chambered organ, thus becoming hollow cylinders. The attached end of the cystidean larva expands into a simple or lobulated disk inside which a skeletal plate is secreted (Fig. 33D). In the crown region there appears a series of plates in cycles encircling the viscera. At this time there are two main cycles, both interradial in position, an aboral cycle of five basal plates and an oral cycle of five oral or deltoid plates; and usually there is also present aboral to the basal cycle a cycle of three to five small infrabasals (Fig. 33B) that soon fuse with the top columnal to become the centrodorsal piece. The skeleton of the *Antedon* larva thus recapitulates that of an ancestral stalked pelmatozoan of the dicyclic type.

Throughout this period the larva remains closed orally and hence is unable to nourish itself. However, nutrition is obtained from cells that come to fill the cavity of the enteric sac and are there histolyzed and digested. According to Seeliger (1892), these cells are entodermal, being freed from the wall of the enteric sac, but Mortensen (1920b) inclines to regard them as inwandered mesenchyme cells. One suspects that they are amoeboid mesenchyme cells that have acquired food stores by phagocytizing degenerating tissues elsewhere in the larva.

After a few days of attached life, the oral surface of the larva opens. Up to this time the oral surface has formed the roof of the vestibule and contains the five deltoid plates. Five grooves form, alternating with these plates (Fig. 33D), and the oral surface splits along these grooves into five lobes or valves, each containing a deltoid plate. These lobes stand erect, and the definitive oral surface, which was the vestibular floor, is now exposed to the exterior (Fig. 34). The podia, which meantime have each put out two lateral podia, so that there are five radial groups of three each, extend freely into the water (Fig. 34). They are much elongated and already provided with conspicuous sensory papillae. Soon two additional podia appear in each interradius between the primary groups, so that there are finally 25 podia. The first saccules have already appeared as five conspicuous bodies, one in each radius between adjacent deltoid plates (Fig. 33D). They are formed by the aggregation of 8 to 12 mesenchyme cells that rearrange around a cavity and become enclosed by a thin membrane. At the time of breakthrough of the oral surface, the *Antedon* larva is slightly more than 1 mm. in length. It is capable of considerable movement and feeds and grows while internal changes continue.

The enteric sac, which now is provided with a mouth and esophagus, elongates into a curved stomach from which a slender outgrowth con-

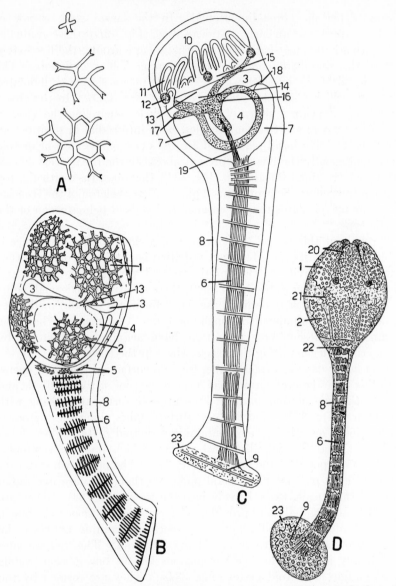

Fig. 33.—Embryology (continued), formation of skeleton. *A*, stages in the formation of a skeletal plate. *B*, young cystidean stage, showing skeletal plates. *C*, late cystidean stage, showing viscera. (*A–C, after Seeliger, 1892.*) *D*, end of cystidean stage (*after Thomson, 1865*), showing oral valves. 1, deltoid plates; 2, basal plates; 3, oral coelom; 4, enteric sac; 5, infrabasal plates; 6, columnals; 7, aboral coelom; 8, larval stalk; 9, skeletal plate of attachment disk; 10, cavity of vestibule; 11, podia; 12, saccules; 13, mouth; 14 esophagus; 15, hydrocoel ring; 16, intestinal outgrowth; 17, site of future anus; 18, horizontal mesentery; 19, axial sinus; 20, oral valves containing deltoids; 21, radial plates; 22, centrodorsal; 23, attachment disk.

tinues the curve (Fig. 33C) and becomes the intestine. This grows in a curve to the left in the horizontal plane but remains blind for a long time, finally, however, piercing the surface as the anus in the same interradius that contains the hydropore. The anus is formed without any proctodaeal invagination. The hydrocoel has remained in a horseshoe shape for a long time during which a tubular projection has arisen from one end, as already noted. This finally unites with the axocoel so that a water tube, corresponding to the stone canal of other echinoderms, now connects the hydrocoel with the surface by way of the hydropore situated in the anal interradius. The two ends of the hydrocoel finally fuse to form the definitive water ring around the esophagus. The podia alter at their bases so that each opens separately into the water ring. The left somatocoel, now oral in position, works its way between the stomach and the hydrocoel but remains of crescentic form with its blind ends meeting to form the more oral or superior vertical mesentery. The similar but larger right or aboral somatocoel forms with its two blind ends the aboral or inferior vertical mesentery (Fig. 32D) and loses its connection with the five chambers of the chambered organ that previously arose from it. The axial gland is said to arise in the aboral vertical mesentery.

Knowledge of the development of the gonad is in an unsatisfactory state. According to Russo (1902) and Mortensen (1920b), a primary gonad appears as a compact cord of cells in the main horizontal mesentery (thus of peritoneal origin) in the same interradius that contains the anus and the primary hydropore. This fact is considered of great phylogenetic importance as indicating that the crinoids originally had a single gonad contained inside the calyx in a definite interradius. However, his primary gonad vanishes, and no statement about the origin of the definitive gonad has been found except that of Dawydoff (1948), who says that it appears as an elongated strand of compact cells located in the aboral vertical mesentery. This strand is closely applied to the axial gland (whence the usual statement that the definitive gonad originates from the axial gland) and extends with the latter into the stalk in the center of the chambered organ. From it germ cells later migrate into the arms and it then disappears.

The oral or ectoneural nervous system originates as a thickening of the ectoderm along the course of the hydrocoel and podia and is well developed in the later larva where in fact it forms the only nervous system. No satisfactory information was found in the literature as to the origin of the two other nervous systems of the adult crinoid. Seeliger (1892) reported that he could find no traces of them in the most advanced larvae available to him, so that evidently they arise rather late in ontogeny.

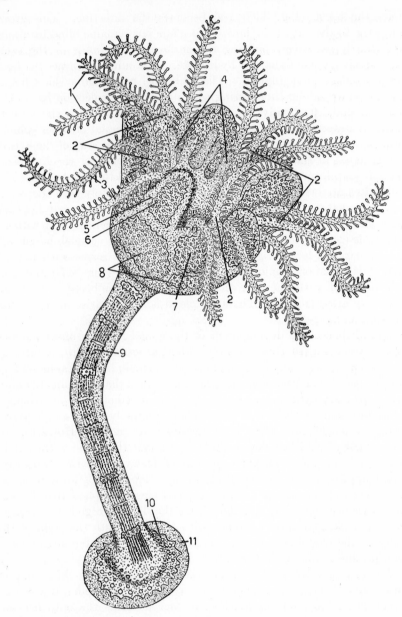

Fig. 34.—Embryology (continued), pentacrinoid larva of *Antedon* (*after Thomson*, 1865). 1, sensory papillae of podia; 2, five primary podia; 3, secondary podia, making five groups of three each; 4, tertiary podia; 5, oral lobes; 6, deltoid plates; 7, radial plates; 8, basal plates; 9, columnals; 10, plate inside attachment disk; 11, attachment disk.

After about 6 weeks of attached life the *Antedon* larva, now about 3.3 mm. in length, begins to put out arms and is now called a *pentacrinoid* larva, from a presumed resemblance to the extinct crinoid genus *Pentacrinites*. Some authors, however, apply the term pentacrinoid from the time the larva takes on a distinct pelmatozoan appearance, before the opening of the oral surface. Prior to the outgrowth of the arms five radial plates appear in the radii between the bases of the deltoids (Fig. 33D). The late appearance of the radials and their intimate relation to the formation of the arms indicate that they are not true thecal or calycinal plates but the first plates of the brachial series. The arms grow out as projections from the periphery of the oral surface of the pentacrinoid larva in the radial positions (Fig. 35), and as they grow, additional brachial plates appear in them in linear succession. The primary podia disappear, except the original five which form the central podia of the five podial groups. These become incorporated into the outgrowing arms, lengthening with them and becoming the radial canals of the water-vascular system. The terminal part of the original podium remains for some time at the tip of the radial canal, thus corresponding to the terminal tentacle of the ambulacra of other echinoderms, but eventually disappears. The definitive podia grow out as evaginations from the radial water canal. Extensions of the oral and aboral coeloms grow out into the arms, the former as the subtentacular coelomic canals, the latter as the aboral canal of the arms. Eventually the mesenteries in the interior of the calyx atrophy, the two coeloms fuse and also unite with the axocoel so that the stone canal comes to open directly into the coelom. Eventually the original coelomic cavities lose their individuality, being broken up into numerous spaces through the growth of the connective tissue. To the original stone canal are added four others, one in each interradius. These are compounded of an ingrowing canal from the surface and an outgrowing canal from the hydrocoel ring. The two outgrowths meet and form complete canals for a time, leading from the tegmen to the ring canal, but eventually the connection is broken. Later many more such canal growths form but do not meet to become complete water canals; in this manner the adult condition arises with numerous water pores or canals through the tegmen into coelomic spaces and numerous stone canals hanging from the ring canal into the coelom. The original hydropore and anus have moved up onto the oral surface of the larva, and at a late stage the anus comes to be mounted on the anal cone, supported by a skeletal plate.

Following the outgrowth of the arms, the oral lobes disappear and the deltoid plates atrophy in most crinoids, being replaced by small plates or spicules strewn throughout the tegmen. The basal plates in *Antedon* fuse to form the rosette that becomes concealed in the interior of the

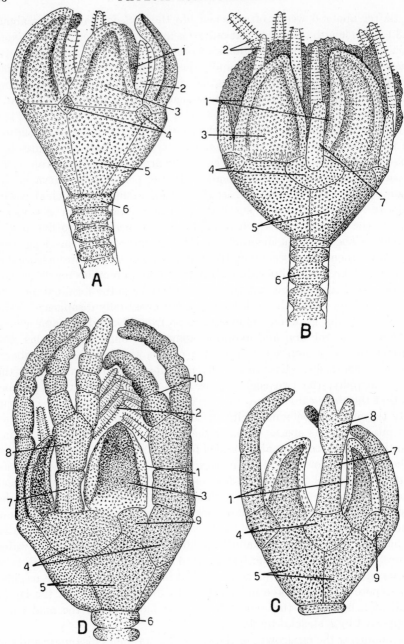

Fig. 35.—Embryology (concluded), four stages in the development of the arms in *Isometra vivipara* (*after Mortensen*, 1920). *A*, radial plates appearing. *B*, arms beginning to grow out. *C*, arms starting to fork. *D*, arms well established. 1, oral valves; 2, podia; 3, deltoid plates; 4, radial plates; 5, basal plates; 6, columnals; 7, first brachial; 8, second primibrach, with fork; 9, anal plate; 10, definitive arms.

calyx. After several months of existence as a pentacrinoid larva, the young comatulid breaks from the stalk at the junction of the centrodorsal with the top columnal and thereafter leads a free existence. Cirri have already been formed prior to detachment from the stalk.

The pentacrinoid larvae of a number of different comatulids are described and figured by A. H. Clark in the second part (1921a) of his monograph of the existing crinoids.

The foregoing account is based on *Antedon*, the only crinoid genus of which the development is fully known. In 1920b Mortensen furnished interesting but fragmentary accounts of the development of other comatulid species belonging to six different genera. Although the development of these species may differ in small details from that of *Antedon*, its general course is similar, especially in the later stages. The doliolaria of *Tropiometra carinata* has but four ciliated bands, and the anterior band is scarcely evident in that of *Compsometra serrata*. The greatest variation from *Antedon* is naturally found in the embryology of the viviparous species, *Isometra vivipara* and *Notocrinus virilis*, where early processes are altered by the yolkiness of the egg. The egg of *Isometra* does not cleave, but through nuclear multiplication nuclei become spread throughout the yolky interior. Cell walls then appear and ectoderm and archenteron separate by delamination without any gastrulation process or formation of a blastopore. The *Isometra* doliolaria is provided with the usual ciliated bands, although its swimming period is probably of very short duration, whereas the *Notocrinus* doliolaria completely lacks the bands.

**14. Order Inadunata.**—The classification of the wealth of fossil crinoids has proved difficult, but at the present time it is usual to recognize four orders (raised to the rank of subclasses by Moore and Laudon, 1943). In the order Inadunata the monocyclic or dicyclic calyx is composed of firmly fitted plates with conspicuous basals (Fig. 36*A*–*D*). The arms are typically free beyond the radials and may be three, five, or more in number, branched or unbranched, and with or without pinnules. Among the monocyclic inadunates an asymmetry is often evidenced at the base of ray C by the division, fusion, or displacement of the radial, primibrachs, and plates associated with the anal tube. The mouth is usually subtegminal, that is, covered with small plates, and the ambulacral grooves are generally provided with covering plates. The tegmen frequently is supported by five deltoid plates, a primitive condition, but may contain small plates instead. The anal tube is often of enormous length provided with numerous supporting plates (Fig. 36*C*). The Inadunata flourished from the Ordovician to the Permian, and from the Palaeozoic era Moore and Laudon (1943) list 53 families and over 300 genera.

**15. Order Flexibilia.**—This is a totally extinct group that ranged irom the Ordovician to the Permian (monograph by Springer, 1920).

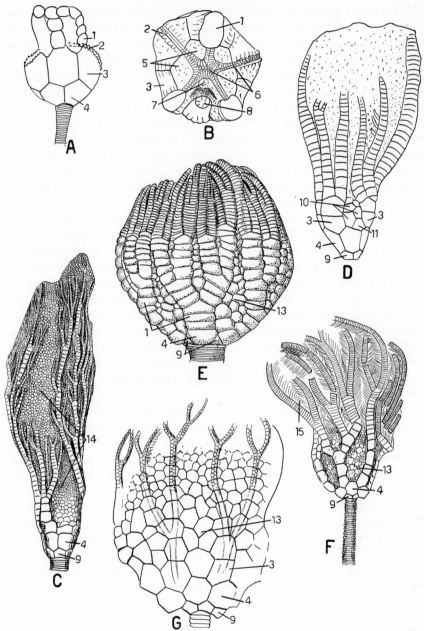

Fig. 36.—Orders Inadunata, Flexibilia, and Camerata. *A*, monocyclic primitive inadunate with three arms, *Hybocystites*. *B*, view of tegmen of *Hybocystites*. *C*, dicyclic inadunate *Ottawacrinus* with enormous anal tube. (*A–C, after Springer*, 1911.) *D*, dicyclic inadunate *Anartiocrinus* (*after Springer*, 1926) showing interpolated plates in anal region. *E*, an example of the Flexibilia, *Forbesiocrinus* (*after Springer*, 1920). *F*, primi-

The Flexibilia are dicyclic crinoids in which the lower brachials (usually three) are flexibly incorporated into the calyx. The stalk consists of short disciform columnals of circular contour and is usually devoid of cirri, although sometimes provided with radicular cirri. There are three infrabasals, one small and two large, with the small one invariably situated in ray C. The infrabasals are typically exposed on the surface but in the later evolution of the group diminish in size and may be concealed by the top of the stem. The basals and radials, five each, are unusually thick and massive but are nevertheless loosely articulated. The arms are always branched but devoid of pinnules and typically curved inward; and the naked, curved, uniserial arms forming a globular crown lend a characteristic appearance to the Flexibilia, as in Fig. 36E. The tegmen, also flexible, is covered with numerous small plates. The open mouth is surrounded by larger plates, possibly deltoids, one of which, in the anal interradius, larger than the others, is perforated with water pores and appears to have become a madreporite. The open ambulacra are lined with little plates. The mostly short anal tube is supported by many very small plates plus a row of larger plates along its outer surface. Springer in 1920 recorded 176 known species, arranged in 4 families and 31 genera. In their 1943 article Moore and Laudon acknowledge 10 families and 47 genera but unfortunately do not state the number of species described to that date.

**16. Order Camerata.**—This is another wholly extinct group, limited to the Palaeozoic era, ranging from the Ordovician to the Permian. The order as understood at present includes the Adunata of Bather (1899, 1900). The camerate or box crinoids are characterized by the rigid calyx of thick sutured plates into which is incorporated a variable number of the lower brachials as well as a number of small interradial and interbrachial plates. In consequence the typical camerate calyx appears composed of many small polygonal plates; it may be monocyclic or dicyclic. The arms are branched and pinnulated. The tegmen is armored with many small plates, into which are incorporated the plates that roof over the mouth and ambulacral grooves. An anal tube is usually present. The arm brachials may have a uniserial or biserial arrangement. Moore and Laudon (1943) take as the most primitive camerates the monocyclic genus *Xenocrinus* and the dicyclic genus *Reteocrinus*. In both genera the five radials are separated from each other by numerous very small interradial plates that are continuous in the oral direction with similar numerous small interbrachial plates.

tive dicyclic camerate, *Reteocrinus*, with prominent arm bases. *G*, dicyclic camerate, *Archeocrinus*, with inconspicuous arm bases. (*F*, *G*, *after Wachsmuth and Springer*, 1897.) 1, arm bases; 2, ambulacral grooves; 3, radial plates; 4, basal plates; 5, deltoid plates; 6, covering plates of mouth and grooves; 7, gonopore; 8, anal pyramid; 9, infrabasals; 10, anal plates; 11, radianal; 12, primibrach; 13, interbrachial plates; 14, anal tube; 15, pinnules.

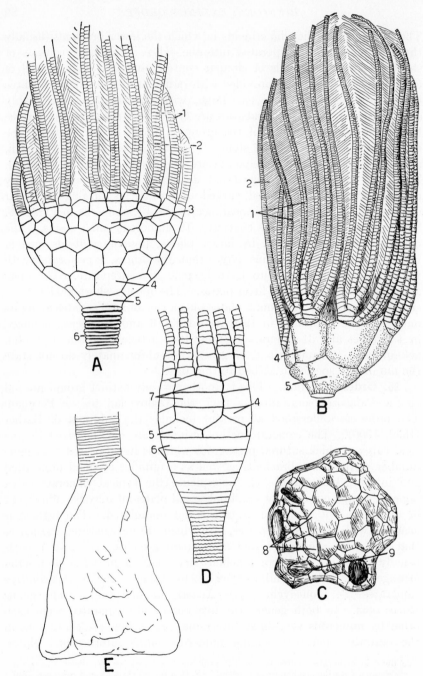

FIG. 37.—Camerata (concluded), Articulata. *A*, monocyclic camerate *Technocrinus*, without distinct arm bases. *B*, *Platycrinites*, with radials in contact. *C*, tegmen of *Platycrinites*. (*A–C*, after Wachsmuth and Springer, 1897.) *D. Apiocrinus*. *E*, attachment of *Apiocrinus*. (*D, E, after Loriol*, 1882.) 1, biserial arms; 2, pinnules; 3, region of intermingled arm bases and interbrachial plates; 4, radials; 5, basals; 6, columnals; 7, primibrachs; 8, tegminal plates; 9, holes where arms have broken off.

These interradial areas of many small plates constitute depressed regions lying between the arm bases that stand out like ridges and are also incorporated into the calyx (Fig. 36*F*). A ridge of larger pieces also occurs in the anal interradius. From this condition there is an evolutionary trend toward increase in size and decrease in number in the plates of the interradial areas and flattening out of the arm ridges which still remain slightly indicated in such genera as *Archaeocrinus* (Fig. 36*G*). The eventual disappearance of the arm ridges results in the typical camerate theca composed of a number of polygonal plates in which the basal brachials are not readily distinguishable; hence the arm branches seem to spring directly from the calyx cup (Fig. 37*A*). There follows a process of displacement of the plates of the interradial regions in the oral direction, and hence the radials again make contact to form a circle, and the arm bases, being no longer incorporated into the tegmen, spring free, as in *Platycrinites* (Fig. 37*B, C*). By this roundabout process the camerates attain the calyx condition typical of the inadunates but differ in the structure of the tegmen. The Camerata were treated by Wachsmuth and Springer in a classical monograph (1897), but their familial arrangement has been considerably altered by Moore and Laudon (1943), who list 29 families and 129 genera.

**17. Order Articulata.**—The members of this order are relatively recent compared to other crinoid orders, having begun in the Triassic and continued into the present time. All existing crinoids are now placed in the Articulata, which of course also includes many extinct species. The Articulata have a pentamerous calyx without asymmetries caused by the inclusion of pieces originally perisomatic. The columnals when present are rounded, elliptical, or pentagonal, and the top columnal is fused to the aboral pole of the calyx. The calyx is fundamentally dicyclic but usually appears monocyclic from the invisibility of the infrabasals on the surface or their actual disappearance. The basals may also disappear from surface view. The lower brachials are incorporated into the calyx, but the first primibrachs have a muscular articulation with the radials, hence the arm bases remain movable. The radials and brachials are perforated by a canal for the passage of nerves from the aboral nerve center. The arms are uniserial, pinnulated, and generally branched. The coriaceous tegmen is usually studded with small plates or minute ossicles; deltoids are generally wanting in the adult although forming conspicuous parts of the skeleton in larval stages. The mouth and ambulacral grooves are held open and exposed, although the grooves may be partially closed by the plates in the lappets.

The classification within the Articulata is apparently very difficult because of the small degree of morphological difference between its members. A division into three groups was proposed by H. L. Clark

(1946) and one into six groups by Ubaghs (1953).    If the Articulata are
regarded as an order, these groups become suborders.    According to the
Ubaghs classification, the existing stalked crinoids with stem cirri fall
into the suborder Isocrinida and are placed in the family Isocrinidae.
The existing members of this family, usually referred to as pentacrinites,
have a relatively long stalk of mostly pentagonal contour, encircled at
frequent intervals by whorls of five cirri borne on nodes (Fig. 12A), and
a flower-like crown of uniserial, much branched, pinnulated arms.    Not
too much is known of the basal attachment, as most specimens are
obtained by dredging and get broken from the base in the process; but
complete individuals have been found growing on telegraph cables, and
these are fastened by a slight basal expansion of the stalk.    It appears,
however, that pentacrinites often break naturally at a syzygy and lead
a more or less mobile existence, attaching temporarily by the cirri;
evidence for this consists in the frequent taking of specimens with worn
stem ends and with the adjacent cirrus whorl curved into a grasping
attitude.    The ends of the columnals of pentacrinites show the well-
known petaloid areas (Fig. 22C) caused by the five bundles of elastic
fibers that course through the length of the stalk.    The calyx is usually
monocyclic or appears so, and the flexible tegmen containing scattered
or closely set small round plates embraces the arm bases and bears a
relatively short anal tube.    The generic allocation of the existing pentacrinites is in the same state of confusion that characterizes crinoid
taxonomy generally.    A. H. Clark (1923) recognized nine genera, one
of which, however, has been rejected by other specialists.    Inspection
of Clark's key to these genera shows that they are distinguished almost
entirely by the number of brachials between branch forks ("division
series").    The most common existing pentacrinite genus is *Metacrinus*,
distinguished from all other living genera of the family by the occurrence
of at least four brachials between the radials and the first branching; or,
in other words, the first axillary is at least the fourth primibrach.    In
all the other existing genera, the first axillary is the second primibrach.
In *Metacrinus*, also, all the forks are separated by a considerable number
of brachials, so that the long stretches of arm between branches give this
genus a characteristic appearance (Fig. 16F).    The species of *Metacrinus*
are distributed mostly in the Japan-Malay-Australian region.    *Cenocrinus asteria* (Fig. 12A), one of the most frequently reproduced figures
from the *Challenger* report on stalked crinoids, inhabits the West Indies
at rather moderate depths, and *Neocrinus decorus*, object of a valuable
histological study by Reichensperger (1905), also dwells in the Florida–
West Indies area.

Of extinct genera belonging to the Isocrinida may be mentioned
*Pentacrinites* (the spelling *Pentacrinus* appears invalid).    As now under-

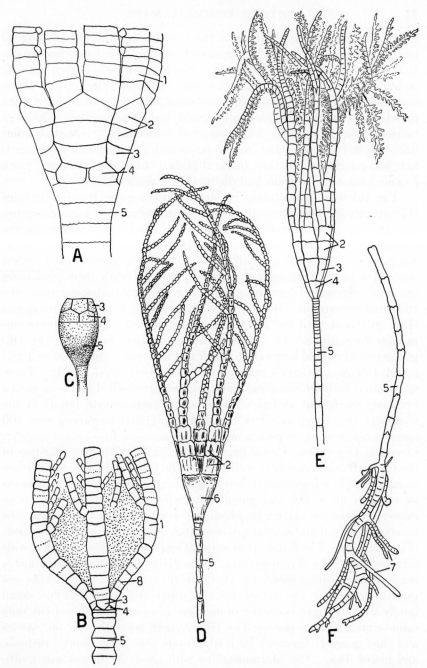

Fig. 38.—Articulata (continued).  A, *Millericrinus* (*after Loriol*, 1883).  B, *Phrynocrinus* (*after A. H. Clark*, 1915a).  C, *Bourgueticrinus* (*after Valette*, 1916).  D, *Rhizocrinus lofotensis* (*after P. H. Carpenter*, 1884; for attachment see Fig. 12B).  E, crown of *Bathycrinus carpenteri*.  F, root attachment of *B. carpenteri*.  (*E, F, after Danielsson*, 1892.)  1, brachials; 2, primibrachs; 3, radials; 4, basals; 5, columnals; 6, calyx; 7, roots; 8, syzgy.

stood, this genus became extinct in the Jurassic, and the species assigned to it in the *Challenger* report have since been transferred to other genera. It is characterized by the numerous, closely set whorls of cirri and the large bushy arms pinnulated along one side only (Fig. 39A). Many complete, beautifully preserved specimens of *Pentacrinites* have been found in the Lower Jurassic in England and Würtemberg. The pentacrinoid stage in crinoid development is named after *Pentacrinites* but does not in fact bear much resemblance to it. The genus *Isocrinus* is now also restricted to extinct forms that died out in the Miocene. Both *Pentacrinites* and *Isocrinus* had distinct infrabasals.

The suborder Comatulida or comatulids includes those articulates that in early life break from the stem and thereafter lead a free existence. The living comatulids are divided by A. H. Clark into two groups, the *oligophreate* and *macrophreate* forms. In the former, the cavity in the centrodorsal (Fig. 40A) is small and shallow, the tegmen is more or less studded with small plates or completely covered with them, and there are generally more than 10 arms. The macrophreates comprise the 10-armed comatulids with a large and deep cavity in the centrodorsal (Fig. 40B) and with the tegmen naked or containing only minute calcareous formations. The majority of comatulids belong to the Oligophreata, the consideration of which has now been completed in Parts 3 and 4 of A. H. Clark's monograph (1931, 1941, 1947, 1950). There are around a dozen families, distinguished by small differences in the brachials, cirri, and pinnules. The largest oligophreate family is the Comasteridae, which in Clark's monograph (1931) comprises over 100 species, assigned to 19 genera with such names as *Comatula, Comaster, Comissia, Comanthus, Comatella*, and *Capillaster*. The peculiarities of the Comasteridae have been indicated in the foregoing pages. They are usually multibrachiate comatulids without saccules, with terminal combs on some or all of the oral pinnules, usually without cirri, and with an exocyclic digestive system in which the mouth is near the margin, the anus central, and ambulacral grooves often wanting on some of the arms (Fig. 15D, E). The family is mostly littoral and sublittoral with a wide distribution. The Zygometridae, with main genus *Zygometra*, are a small family distinguished by the fact that the two primibrachs are united by syzygy instead of by the usual synarthrosis. The small family Eudiocrinidae is worthy of mention as comprising almost the only comatulids with five arms. The Himerometridae with over 50 species and chief genus *Heterometra* have 10 or more arms, very short brachials, and naked disk. The Mariametridae with about 30 species are multibrachiate comatulids with two secundibrachs. The Colobometridae comprise 17 genera and about 50 species; they are distinguished by the armature of the cirri in the form of one or two serrate transverse ridges or paired or tricuspid spines (Fig. 22H) on the aboral (concave) surface. In the three preceding families the pinnules, at least the distal ones, are slender and cylindrical, composed of elongated pinnulars, and the side and covering plates of the ambulacral grooves of the pinnules are poorly developed or wanting. In the next oligophreate families the pinnules are stout and prismatic (triangular in cross section), mostly with short pinnulars. Among these families, the Tropiometridae, with the single genus *Tropiometra*, are distinguished by the absence of side and covering plates for the ambulacral grooves of the pinnules; *Tropiometra* is a 10-armed form with stout cirri. In the remaining oligophreate families the pinnules are provided with well-developed side and covering plates. In this category the main families are the Thalassometridae and Charitometridae, discussed by Clark in 1950. The Thalassometridae are listed as having 14 genera and about 60 species; they are characterized by the long slender cirri of more than 25 cirrals with prominent spination on the concave surface, also by the longer first than second pinnule joint. In some genera of this family the arms are laterally compressed and ornamented with a keel. The main genus, *Thalassometra*, however, has rounded arms, mostly 10 in number, thickly beset basally with small spines or tubercles. In the Charitometridae, with 8 genera and over 30 species, the cirri are short, stout, and strongly curved, without conspicuous spination, and the pinnule joints are all of about the same length.

The macrophreate comatulids comprise five families, of which the large and widely distributed Antedonidae is the most important. Of the other four families, two are very small: the Notocrinidae for the viviparous *Notocrinus* (page 75), with two species, and the Apocrinidae for *Apocrinus*, with three species. Both genera were formerly placed under the Antedonidae. The two other families, Atelecrinidae and Pentametrocrinidae, are also small but show some points of interest. The former are deep-water forms in which the basals reach the external surface of the calyx, especially in the genera *Atelecrinus* (Fig. 23A, B) and *Atopocrinus;* the latter is among the few comatulids with only five arms. Five-armed species also occur in the Pentametrocrinidae, namely in *Pentametrocrinus* and *Thaumatocrinus*.

The family Antedonidae is the largest family of existing crinoids, comprising 46 genera and over 130 species. It consists mostly of 10-armed species, characterized by very slender and delicate outer pinnules, wedge-shaped brachials, and regularly spaced syzygies. The Antedonidae occur everywhere, on all shores, from the tidal zone to a depth of 6000 m., and are the most common comatulids outside of tropical areas. The best-known genus, *Antedon*, now reduced to seven species, is represented in the littoral zone of western Europe and the Mediterranean by the species *bifida* (Fig. 13A), *mediterranea*, and *adriatica;*

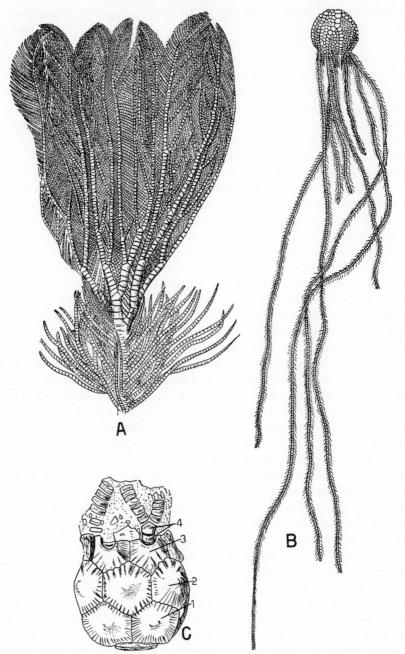

FIG. 39.—Articulata (continued). *A, Pentacrinites,* Jurassic of England (*after Miller,* 1821). *B, Uintacrinus* (*combined after Stringer,* 1901). *C, Marsupites* (*after Dixon,* 1850). 1, infrabasals; 2, basals; 3, radials, 4, primibrachs.

these three species have been much utilized in embryological studies, for which they are especially suitable as the embryos develop while attached to the pinnules.  Some other genera are *Leptometra*, common in the deeper waters of the Mediterranean, *Heliometra*, characteristic of the arctic and other northern waters, and *Florometra*, along the shores of the eastern Pacific, northward to the Aleutian Islands and Japan.  These and other antedonid genera are distinguished by small details of the pinnules and cirri.

Ubaghs's third suborder, called Millericrinida, includes existing stalked crinoids with no or rudimentary cirri or with radicular cirri, limited to the attached end of the stem.  In the families Apiocrinidae and Phrynocrinidae the stem is attached by a heavy basal expansion (Fig. 37*E*).  The Apiocrinidae include some well-known extinct crinoid genera such as *Apiocrinus*, in which the top columnals are expanded to equal the calyx (Fig. 37*D*), and *Millericrinus* (Fig. 38*A*), with scarcely enlarged top columnals; some species of *Millericrinus* break from their attachment in later life, and the crown floats about after having absorbed the stalk.  Here are included also two living species, *Proisocrinus ruberrimus*, of a striking scarlet color, dredged by the *Albatross* in the Philippines at about 1700 m. (A. H. Clark, 1910d), and *Carpenterocrinus mollis*, known only from the imperfect crown taken by the *Challenger* off Japan at about 1000 m. (Carpenter, 1884; A. H. Clark, 1908d).  The family Phrynocrinidae contains the existing species *Phrynocrinus nudus* (Fig. 38*B*), dredged off southern Japan at about 1200 m.  (A. H. Clark, 1907a), and *Naumachocrinus hawaiiensis*, taken in the Hawaiian Islands at about 1000 m., the first stalked crinoid to be found in that locality (A. H. Clark, 1912b).  In the Bourgueticrinidae and Bathycrinidae the stem is attached by basal roots.  The former family is distinguished by the expansion of the top columnal (then called *proximal*) to participate in the calyx; this top columnal is jointed to the next columnal by a synarthrosis, and hence no new columnals can be formed between the stem and the calyx.  The family as thus limited includes the extinct *Bourgueticrinus* (Fig. 38*C*) and *Mesocrinus* from the Cretaceous.  In the Bathycrinidae (reviewed by Gislén, 1938a), the top columnal does not participate in the calyx, and hence new columnals are continuously formed beneath the calyx.  This family includes a number of existing stalked crinoids in the genera *Rhizocrinus, Bathycrinus, Monachocrinus,* and *Democrinus*.  *Rhizocrinus* is best represented by *R. lofotensis*, which was discovered off the coast of Norway in 1864 and fully described and discussed by Sars in 1868.  A number were also taken by the *Challenger*, and the best illustrations of the species appear in the *Challenger* report on stalked crinoids (Carpenter, 1884).  The species has been found in a number of localities in the North Atlantic, and a specimen was dredged by Verrill in 1883 off the Massachusetts coast at about 1100 m. (A. H. Clark, 1908b). Although Clark made a separate species of the Verrill specimen, it appears to be only a geographic variant of the original Norwegian form. Sars recognized the archaic nature of *R. lofotensis*, and the finding of a living representative of a supposedly long extinct family aroused great zoological interest at the time. *Rhizocrinus lofotensis* (Fig. 38*D*) is a small creature, only 80 mm. long, with abundant root attachments, a naked stem of somewhat elongated columnals, a funnel-like calyx of more or less fused radials and basals, and five pinnulated arms. As to the other existing bathycrinids, Gislén (1938a) ascribed nine species to *Bathycrinus*, seven to *Monachocrinus*, and ten to *Democrinus;* but as these species have been shifted about by crinoid specialists from one genus to another, the generic distinctions cannot be very definite. Good figures and descriptions of bathycrinids appear in the *Challenger* report (Carpenter, 1884), in the report on stalked crinoids collected by the *Siboga* in Indonesia (Döderlein, 1907), and on those taken by the *Valdivia* on the German Deep Sea Expedition (Döderlein, 1911); and an excellent study of *Bathycrinus carpenteri* (Fig. 38*E, F*), taken on the Norwegian North Atlantic Expedition between Norway, Spitsbergen, and Iceland, was made by Danielsson (1892). A species of *Bathycrinus* was dredged by Verrill in 1884 off Chesapeake Bay at 3700 m. (A. H. Clark, 1908b). The existing Millericrinida are for the most part inhabitants of ocean abysses and hence are known only from dredging explorations. They have been taken in widely separated localities, although most of the specimens come from the North Atlantic.

Two interesting fossils, believed to have become adapted for floating, comprise the fourth articulate suborder, Uinticrinida. Both have globular calyces without cirri, in which the true calyx plates are continuous with the lower brachials and interbrachials, so that the whole forms a rounded but flexible test of polygonal pieces from which the arms spring. *Uinticrinus*, so called from its discovery in the Uinta Mountains of Utah, had 10 simple pinnulated arms that reached a length of a meter, with a total arm spread of 2½ m. (Fig. 39*B*). The single species, *U. socialis* (monographed by Springer, 1901), appears to have lived in floating swarms, in which the long arms were inextricably intermingled. *Uinticrinus* is further interesting in having the same marginal displacement of the mouth and ambulacral grooves as in the Comasteridae. *Marsupites*, of which the best specimens come from the English chalk, differs in the few and large plates of the test (Fig. 39*C*), short arms, and symmetrical ambulacral system.

The fifth suborder may be passed as including only fossils, and we turn to the sixth suborder, Cyrtocrinida, which contains the remaining existing stalked articulates as well as the curious genus *Holopus*, first described in 1837 by D'Orbigny and since dredged in several localities in the Caribbean at moderate depths. *Holopus* was adequately described by A. Agassiz in 1878a and in the *Challenger* report on stalked crinoids (Carpenter, 1884). It is a short stout creature (Fig. 40C) up

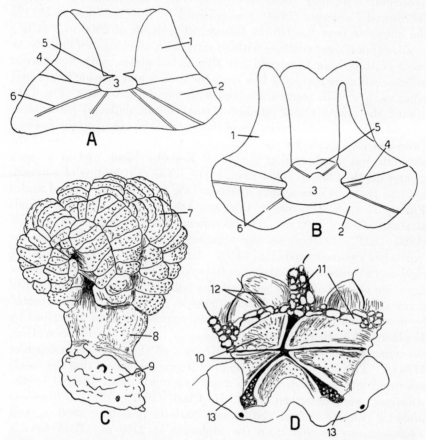

Fig. 40.—Articulata (concluded). *A*, scheme of the oligophreate calyx. *B*, scheme of the macrophreate calyx. (*A, B, simplified after Clark*, 1915a.) *C, Holopus*, side view of entire animal. *D*, disk of *Holopus*. (*C, D, after P. H. Carpenter*, 1884.) 1, radials; 2, centrodorsal; 3, cavity of centrodorsal; 4, boundary between radials and centrodorsal; 5, rosette; 6, cirral nerves; 7, arms; 8, stalk; 9, object to which attached; 10, deltoid plates; 11, small plates of tegmen; 12, arm bases; 13, cut surface of arm bases.

to 80 mm. in height, with basals and radials fused into a short thick tubular calyx attached basally by an irregular expansion. There are 10 stout pinnulated arms that are strongly curved inward in the available preserved specimens. Cirri and saccules are wanting. The tegmen is provided with five deltoid plates surrounded by some small plates (Fig. 40D). Persistence of the deltoid plates also characterizes the family Hyocrinidae, which appears to fit into this sixth suborder, according to the analysis of Gislén (1938b), although formerly the Hyocrinidae were considered to belong to the Inadunata and hence to constitute living representatives of an otherwise wholly extinct group. The first hyocrinid, *Hyocrinus bethellianus* (Fig. 14*A*), described by Thomson (1876) and Carpenter (1884), was collected by the *Challenger* in 1873 in the antarctic near the Crozet Islands, at a depth of 2900 m. It is a small, slender, rigid creature without cirri, with an elongated monocyclic calyx of three thin basal and five thin radial plates, with five narrow unbranched arms springing free from the radials and provided with long pinnules, and with tegmen armored with five deltoid plates (Fig. 14*B*) around the mouth and a number of small interambulacral plates more peripherally. Another specimen of this species was taken on the German Deep Sea Expedition by the *Valdivia* in the same general region of the antarctic but much farther south, off Enderby Land, and at a much greater depth, 4936 m. (Döderlein, 1911). The next finding of a hyocrinid was that of *Calamocrinus diomedae* (Fig. 14*C*) by the United States Fishery steamer *Albatross* in 1890 and 1891 off the Galapagos Islands at about 700 and 1400 m. The specimens were described by A. Agassiz (1890, 1892). In this case the attachment in the form of a disk-like expansion was recovered (Fig. 14*D*). Again the stem lacks cirri and the rigid calyx consists of basal and radial cycles, five plates in each, but the arms are somewhat branched, and the tegminal armor is composed of many small plates without definite deltoids. A tall anal cone supported by many small plates is present. *Gephyrocrinus grimaldii* (described by Koehler and Bather, 1902) was dredged in 1901 by the *Princess Alice*, belonging to the marine station at Monaco, off the Azores at a depth of 1786 m. This species closely resembles *Hyocrinus*, except that the basals are fused into a cylinder. Two more hyocrinids, both dredged by the *Albatross*, were described by A. H. Clark (1907b, 1911), *Ptilocrinus pinnatus* (Fig. 16*A*) from the Queen Charlotte Islands at 2860 m., and *Thalassocrinus pontifer* from the Moluccas at 2270 m. Both have a long stalk devoid of cirri, a flaring monocyclic calyx with conspicuous basal and radial cycles, and five unbranched slender pinnulated arms articulated to the middle of the upper edge of the radials. In *Ptilocrinus* the dome-like tegmen lacks deltoids, but in *Thalassocrinus* (figured later by A. H. Clark, 1915a), the tegmen is armed with five deltoids encircled by small plates. Two other *Ptilocrinus* species (*antarcticus, brucei*) have been found in the antarctic (Bather, 1908; John, 1937).

**18. Ecology: Habits and Behavior.**—*Antedon* (and other littoral comatulids so far as observed) normally remain attached by the cirri to a stone or some other object with the arms spread out more or less horizontally and their tips somewhat flexed (Marshall, 1884; Moore,

1924; Fig. 41*A*). In British waters *Antedon bifida* is often found clinging to the wicker baskets let down for the capture of crabs and lobsters (Chadwick, 1907), and the same species is reported to occur in numbers at Roscoff, on the channel coast of France, attached to the roots and stems of seaweeds. Similar habits obtain for tropical comatulids. At Torres Strait (between Australia and New Guinea) a large comatulid population occurs in shallow water attached to the lower surface of rock fragments or among branches of coral (H. L. Clark, 1915), and at Tobago in the West Indies *Tropiometra carinata* is found sitting upright on coral fragments on the bottom in shallow water, mostly in the open but sometimes partly shaded by seaweeds, or less often hanging upside down from the under surface of larger rock or coral masses (H. L. Clark, 1917). The attached position bears no reference to gravity. If satisfactory conditions continue the animal may remain attached to the same object for many weeks without change of attitude or location. The cirri have but feeble powers of movement and are used primarily for clinging, which they accomplish with great tenacity.

When detached from their hold, all comatulids except the Comasteridae swim gracefully by raising and lowering some of the arms, alternately with the remaining arms. The arms are raised with the pinnules folded against the arm axis, then lashed downward with the pinnules fully extended. Ten-armed species usually swim by alternately flexing and extending the two arms of a pair, that is, while arms 1, 3, 5, 7, and 9 are being raised, arms 2, 4, 6, 8, and 10 are being struck downward. Multibrachiate species seem to operate in the same fashion, by successive use of the arms of each set; thus in a 40-armed species, arms 1, 9, 17, 25, and 33 would strike simultaneously, followed by arms 2, 10, 18, 26, and 34, next by arms 3, 11, 19, 27, and 35, and so on until all the arms had come into action, whereupon the sequence begins again (H. L. Clark, 1915). The stroke is strong and rapid at first, occurring about 100 times per minute, and propelling the animal a distance about equal to the length of its own arms, at a speed of about 5 m. per minute, but the comatulid soon tires, and H. L. Clark (1915) saw no individual that swam continuously for a distance of more than 3 m. However, intermittent swimming continues until a suitable place for attachment is found and appears to be the normal method of locomotion of comatulids except comasterids.

The Comasteridae have rarely been observed to swim and in general are of a sluggish disposition. Their habits have been observed by H. L. Clark (1915, 1917) at Torres Strait and at Tobago. When detached, the comasterids creep in a slow and laborious fashion by extending some arms and catching hold of a suitable object by the pinnule tips aided by adhesive secretion, then pulling themselves up by contracting these arms while at the same time pushing with the opposite arms.    This creeping may be continued for hours, at a rate of about 40 m. per hour, if a suitable attachment site is not available.    In the case of comasterids with arms of unequal length (Fig. 19*A*), as *Comatula purpurea*, common in Torres Strait, the long arms are regularly used in reaching out, grasping an

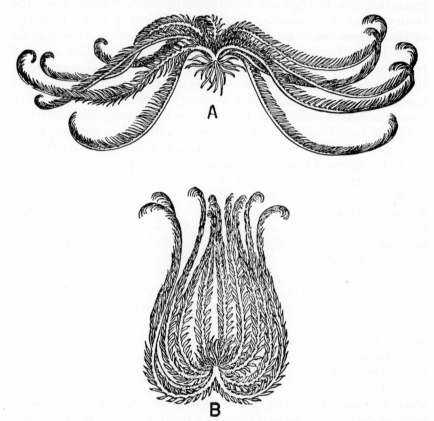

FIG. 41.—Behavior of *Antedon*.  *A*, resting position of *Antedon*.  *B*, aboral flinging of arms on stimulation of cirri.  (*Both after A. R. Moore*, 1924.)

object, and pulling the animal along, while the short arms are employed in pushing from behind.    Such comasterids therefore show a more or less definite anteroposterior orientation.

All comatulids swim or creep with the oral surface upward.    If turned over with the oral surface against the substratum, they promptly right themselves.    This is done by pushing with some arms against the substratum so as to raise one side of the disk, then reaching backward over the aboral surface with some arms of the raised side, securing an anchorage with the tips of these arms, and then pulling the disk over;

or after raising one side of the disk well above the substratum, the animal may turn over by a combination of violent flexion of adjacent arms combined with swimming.

The best account of response to mechanical stimuli is that of Marshall (1884) for *Antedon mediterranea*. The aboral surface of the calyx is insensitive to mechanical and chemical stimuli. Mechanical stimulation of the aboral or lateral surfaces of the arms evokes arm flexion and extension of adjacent pinnules. Stronger or more prolonged stimulation of these areas induces more pronounced movements of the arms concerned, bending of adjacent arms toward the irritated spot, and eventually detachment and flight of the animal. Stimulation of pinnules results successively, according to strength and duration, in movements of the pinnules, of the whole arm, of adjacent arms, and finally of escape of the animal. Slight stimulation of the oral pinnules causes them to fold over the disk, and stronger irritation causes the arms to close over the disk or the animal to detach and swim away. The epithelium of the ambulacral grooves is the most sensitive part of the crinoid. The slightest touch on this epithelium evokes instantaneous movements of the adjacent four or five pairs of pinnules, which fold toward the groove and attempt to grasp the stimulating agent. Stronger or continued stimulation of the ambulacral epithelium brings about flexion of the arm concerned, also of adjacent arms, toward the irritated spot. Stimulation of the tegmen between the grooves evokes a moderate amount of arm movement. The reactions of detached arms are similar to those of arms in place; when dead, detached arms remain strongly extended, as there are no live muscles to oppose the action of the extensor ligaments.

Marshall also experimented on the role of the nervous system in response to mechanical stimuli. In comatulids the whole of the visceral mass is easily removed from the calyx; this destroys the connections of the ectoneural and hyponeural nervous systems while leaving the aboral system intact. Such eviscerated specimens behave normally and swim and attach themselves in a normal manner. Arms and pinnules respond to contact stimulation as in the intact animal, and the righting reaction is carried out normally although perhaps somewhat slowly. Direct stimulation of the aboral nerve center evokes violent arm movements, especially flexion. Following destruction of the aboral nerve center, the animal falls to the bottom with arms strongly extended and is incapable of movement, although individual arms will respond to direct stimulation. Destruction of a short stretch of the subepithelial nervous band of the ambulacral groove does not prevent transmission in the proximal direction of a stimulus applied distal to the destroyed area. The same result follows removal of a band of all the soft tissues of an arm.

Such experiments prove that transmission along the arms is mediated chiefly by the main brachial nerve, as could be deduced from anatomical considerations.   It will be recalled that this nerve runs in a canal inside the brachials, hence is not affected by destruction of the soft external tissues.   Attempts by Marshall to cut this nerve in an arm usually resulted in the animal's throwing off the arm at the injured site.   When successful, section of the main brachial nerve in one arm destroys all communication of this arm with other arms; stimulation of the proximal cut end of a brachial nerve evokes violent movements of all the arms. Destruction of the aboral nerve center does not destroy communication between the arms as this can still be mediated by the pentagonal commissure encircling the main mass.   Following destruction of this pentagon, which it will be recalled is located inside the radial plates of the calyx (Fig. 25*B*), communication of one pair of arms with the other pairs is lost, but transmission is still possible between the two arms of a pair by way of the decussating fibers at the forking of the brachial nerve inside the second primibrach.   If a pair of arms is amputated proximal to this decussation, stimulation of one arm of the pair evokes movements of the other.

Later experiments of A. R. Moore (1924) and Langeloh (1937) have not added greatly to our knowledge of *Antedon* behavior and neuro-muscular mechanism.   Moore found that an isolated ray composed of two arms will remain active for hours and that stimulation of one arm of such a preparation evokes the swimming movement in both, that is, the stimulated arm executes the downward stroke, while the other flexes in an upward curve.   Contact stimulation of the cirri inhibits swimming and righting reactions.   Thus if the animal is turned oral side down while the cirri are still clutching a stone, no righting movement occurs; but in such a situation the cirri soon release their grasp, whereupon the animal rights itself.   Contact stimulation of the oral surface thus releases the grasp of the cirri.   Stimulation of the freed cirri or picking up an inverted *Antedon* by the cirri results in marked aboral bending of the arms (Fig. 41*B*).

Langeloh comments on the great acrobatic ability of *Antedon*.   Thus it can hang to rock ledges or projections by one or two arms, then pull itself up, and can free itself from complicated fetters even when suspended, so that it cannot assist itself by grasping something solid.   It will also remove a piece of rubber tubing pulled over an arm.   Langeloh observed that *Antedon* may sometimes be made to creep after the manner of a comasterid by properly regulating the stimulation and will also run on the arm tips preliminary to swimming.   If a resting animal is suddenly stimulated by a pinch, it may raise itself on the arms tips while releasing the cirri and run on the tips before taking to swimming.   The cirri have limited powers of response and movement. When the animal is fastened, a light touch on the cirri evokes general commotion, but in detached animals, stimulation of the slackly hanging cirri produces no response. Sufficient stimulation of the cirri causes them to loosen their hold, preceded by a strong curvature of the arms toward the aboral side, as also seen by Moore (Fig. 41B). Langeloh found that isolated pinnules do not react, but isolated pieces of arms show normal responses, including responses of their pinnules, and even right themselves by means of their pinnules. Although Langeloh admits that the coordination of arm movements is accomplished mainly by way of the pentagonal commissure, he found that cutting through this pentagon does not altogether abolish communication between the arms adjacent to the cut. Such communication could be accomplished by way of the aboral nerve center, but according to this author there is still some conduction possible after destruction of this center in addition to section of the pentagon. Apparently a roundabout route is available through the other nervous systems. Langeloh regards the aboral nerve center as functioning, not so much in coordination, as in exciting the remainder of the nervous system and augmenting incoming stimuli. Conduction in the pentagonal commissure suffers a strong decrement with distance and hence requires to be continuously strengthened. Destruction of the aboral nerve center (with retention of the pentagon) is not quite as disastrous as thought by the earlier workers. Ability to escape from fetters is practically abolished, but the righting reflex may be slowly executed after a long delay, and momentary swimming can be evoked by repeated stimulation. But in general such an animal lies slackly on the bottom and is extremely insensitive to stimulation. A normal animal adjusts its remaining arms to fill spaces left by removal of arms, and this behavior is also wanting after destruction of the aboral center.

As regards light response, H. L. Clark (1915) noticed general avoidance of direct sunlight and retreat into shaded situations in the comatulids of Torres Strait. If a rock bearing comatulids on its underside was turned over, the animals would promptly move, usually to the new undersurface of the same rock or, less often, into available crevices and shaded sites. *Antedon bifida* on the channel coast of France also shows strong aversion to direct sunlight while accommodating itself well to general daylight (Perrier, 1873). On the other hand, *Tropiometra carinata* at Tobago proved indifferent to light, neither seeking dark or shaded spots nor avoiding direct exposure to sunlight in shallow water.

The temperature relations of crinoids also vary with locality. Gislén (1924) found that laboratory cultures of *Antedon petasus* from the Norwegian coast must be maintained at 10 to 12°C., and that temperatures above 14°C. are detrimental or fatal to the animals. *Antedon bifida* also requires rather cool temperatures. On the other hand, littoral tropical comatulids show a tolerance of or preference for warmer temperatures. The comatulids of Torres Strait were found to move from colder to warmer water with an optimum of 26 to 27°C. and an avoidance of 29 to 31°C., thus exhibiting a slight range of temperature tolerance. Here, also, *Tropiometra carinata*, at Tobago, proved more adaptable with a temperature range of at least 15°C. This species could recover from short exposures to 33 or 34°C. but not from 35° or above.

Indifference to considerable changes of salinity was shown by tropical comatulids in H. L. Clark's tests (1915, 1917), either in the direction of decreased salinity (down to 75 per cent sea water) or of increased salt content (10 per cent above normal).

The anatomy of crinoids sufficiently indicates that they are ciliary-mucus feeders and therefore can capture only small organisms. The food of crinoids has been frequently determined through investigation of the intestinal contents (review in Gislén, 1924). The food varies with locality but in general consists of diatoms, unicellular and filamentous green algae, radiolarians, foraminiferans, dinoflagellates, other Protozoa, small crustaceans, crustacean and other larvae, and other small planktonic animals. Radiolarians and foraminiferans were found to have constituted the main food of some of the stalked crinoids dredged by the *Challenger* (P. H. Carpenter, 1884). Material sucked from the mouth of live *Antedon petasus* with a pipette contained detritus, diatoms, copepods, ostracods, a veliger larva, nauplius larvae, crustacean appendages, a peridinean, and sponge spicules (Gislén, 1924). After examining the excrement and intestinal contents of a number of preserved crinoids, Gislén (1924) concluded that their food consists of a mixture of detritus, plankton, and benthonic organisms.

Gislén (1924) also observed the feeding behavior of *Antedon petasus* in laboratory aquaria. When hungry, *Antedon* sits with outstretched arms, spread pinnules, and stiffly erected podia. When plankton or carmine grains infused with crab liver is added, arms and pinnules spring into activity, and the podia bend rapidly in toward the ambulacral groove. The latter, ordinarily somewhat closed, opens as soon as food falls on it, and the mouth, also usually more or less closed to a slit, expands to a rounded shape. The podia, whenever food falls on them, whip toward the groove, into which they cast the food particles. As already noted, podia and ambulacral groove are supplied with glands secreting a mucous or adhesive material. Food particles and organisms become entangled in this material, and the whole is swept into the mouth by the action of the cilia lining the ambulacral groove. It is believed by some observers (e.g., Reichensperger, 1908) that the secretion of the glands associated with the sensory papillae of the podia is toxic to small animals, but this has not been definitely established. Nothing is known of the digestive process.

In addition to the ciliary currents in the ambulacral grooves, which beat strongly toward the mouth, Gislén (1924) observed ciliary currents, also beating toward the mouth, in the interambulacral areas; these, however, are checked in the mouth region by the ridges bordering the

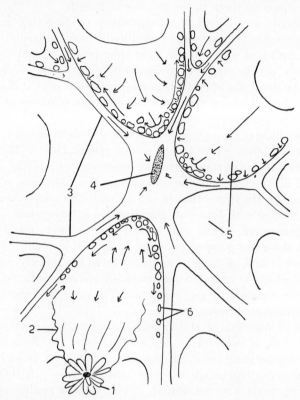

Fig. 42.—Ciliary currents of the disk of *Antedon* (*after Gislén*, 1924). 1, papillae around anus; 2, anal tube; 3, ambulacral grooves; 4, mouth; 5, interradial areas of disk; 6, particles being carried off disk.

grooves and then turn back alongside the grooves, thus carrying particles to the edge of the disk where they fall off. In this way the disk is cleansed of small particles, although apparently some food would be lost by this mechanism. A weak ciliation at the base of the anal cone beating upward was noticed, but it is too feeble to carry feces away. The latter are formed into large yellow balls held together by mucus; these balls usually fall upon the disk, where they gradually slide off through the movements of the animal.

It has been noticed in the foregoing pages that in the family Comasteridae the ambulacral system is reduced, often markedly so, while at the same time the intestine is several times longer than in other comatulids. These facts have suggested to Gislén (1924) that the comasterids must have some supplementary method of feeding (although the type of food is about the same), and he considers that the terminal combs peculiar to this family may be employed in pinching off edible bits in the vicinity and passing them to the grooves or mouth.

The crinoids are devoid of a respiratory or excretory mechanism. While some respiratory exchange undoubtedly occurs through the podia, and the pumping of water by the anal tube (page 70) and through the water canals of the tegmen presumably contributes to respiratory exchange, the small size of crinoids in relation to the large surface expanse secured by the branching arms and innumerable pinnules obviates the necessity of a special respiratory system. Nothing is known of the excretory products of crinoids or the manner of their elimination. Cuénot (1948) surmises that excretory products accumulate in the coelomic lining, whence they are transported by amoebocytes into the connective tissues that fill the body interior and occupy the interstices in the endoskeletal pieces. He states that in old animals the connective tissue of these sites is filled with brownish granules and little crystals.

**19. Regeneration.**—It is well known that crinoids readily cast off arms when these are grasped or under unfavorable conditions, as high temperatures or lack of oxygen, and that these are quickly regenerated. Partially or wholly eviscerated specimens are sometimes found, and such losses are also repaired by regeneration. The powers of regeneration of the Mediterranean *Antedon* were tested at Naples by Przibram (1901). Extirpation of one-fifth of the animal, including a pair of arms, disk, calyx, and cirri, is followed by replacement, and the removed fifth is capable of regenerating arms. If the animal is halved, most halves die, but the survivors regenerate the five missing arms (whether also the other missing parts was not stated). The tegmen readily regenerates when removed or cast off (this happens when arm bases are severed) and also can be replaced by a tegmen transplanted from another individual, as proved by using tegmina of contrasting colors. Removal of four pairs of arms at their bases in the calyx is followed by their regeneration (Fig. 43*M*), but if all ten arms are so extirpated, so that only the calyx cup and cirri remain, the animal dies. If all the cirri are removed simultaneously, none regenerate. Regeneration fails if the aboral nervous center is destroyed.

The natural autotomy of the arms appears to be related to the syzygies. Minckert (1901) reported that 75 to 90 per cent of preserved comatulids with regenerating arms that he examined had lost their arms at the syzygies; and of 30 preserved regenerating specimens of *Neocrinus decorus* available to Reichensperger (1912), 17 had broken off at the syzygies, 10 between the first and second primibrachs, 7 between the radials and the first primibrachs, and only 2 at muscular unions. Evidently non-muscular or poorly muscular unions, especially syzygies, are particularly liable to breakage, no doubt because of their lack of flexibility.

The details of arm and pinnule regeneration have been studied by Perrier (1873) and with more modern methods by Reichensperger (1912). After cutting, some fluid exudes from the severed radial water and coelomic canals, but this contains few if any cells and consequently no coagulum forms. Instead the wound is partially covered by cellular debris from degenerating ambulacral epidermis and associated connective tissue, but skeletal elements and muscle bundles remain exposed. Regeneration begins promptly with the important assistance of two types of coelomocytes. One of these, the type of amoebocyte shown in Fig. 25*H*, with short pointed pseudopods, reveals itself as phagocytic, accumulating at the wound site, ingesting injured and degenerating tissues (Fig. 43*B*), and transporting the food supplies so acquired to regenerating structures. The other type of amoebocyte, filled with rods and granules and corresponding to one of those in Fig. 25*F*, was previously noticed by Reichensperger as particularly abundant along nerve cords. These cells, immediately after the operation, spring into activity, take on an elongated shape (Fig. 43*C*), and stream in numbers to the injured site, where they appear to assist in the regenerative processes while not themselves transforming into tissues.

Regeneration of an arm begins by the outpushing of the radial water canal accompanied by mesenchyme, the whole forming a slight bud-like projection (Fig. 43*K*). The canal in this bud soon reveals itself as a generalized coelomic canal, for it divides to form the definitive water canal and the other coelomic canals of the regenerating arm (Fig. 43*D–G*). The surface cells of the bud differentiate into epidermis. The cut end of the main brachial nerve soon proliferates into the bud, but according to Reichensperger, many of the ganglion cells of this proliferation arise by differentiation of cells of the adjacent coelomic canals, being thus of peritoneal origin. In general, however, the structures of the regenerated arm arise by proliferation from the same structures in the arm stump (Fig. 43*H*). As the regeneration bud continues to grow out, brachials arise in it by secretion from mesenchyme cells as in embryonic development. As the regenerating arm continues to elongate, pinnules arise from it in the same manner as did the arm itself, initiated by the extension of the water canal into a bud of mesenchyme. Similarly, podia arise from the pinnules as outpushings of the pinnular water canal. Each group of three podia begins as a single podium that after attaining a certain length divides longitudinally into two podia, one of which lags

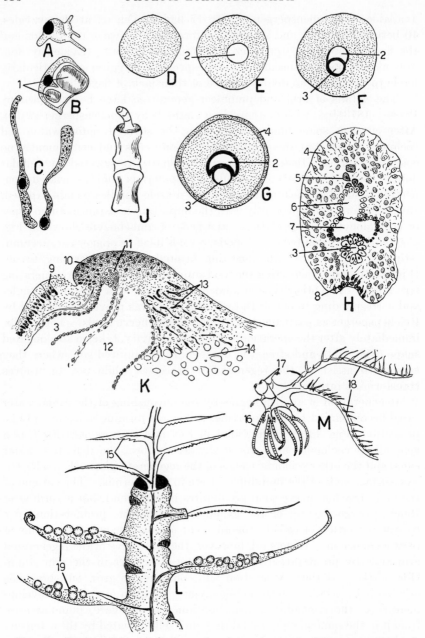

Fig. 43.—Regeneration.  *A–C*, types of coelomocytes involved in regeneration.  *A*, amoebocyte with short pseudopodia.  *B*, same, phagocytizing two bits of degenerating muscle.  *C*, wandering type of coelomocyte with heavy inclusions.  *D–G*, scheme of regenerating arm.  *D*, regeneration bud composed of mesenchyme.  *E*, coelomic canal pushing into bud.  *F*, coelomic canal divides in two.  *G*, later stage of two canals.  *H*,

behind the other in growth; and this shorter one then produces the third podium of the group by a similar longitudinal division. A regenerated arm is easily recognizable for some time by its smaller dimensions and pale color (Fig. 43L).

The cirri are also easily broken off and regenerate readily, either from a stump (Fig. 43J) or from the cirrus socket, but details of the process are not available. The statement of Prizibram that the cirri will not regenerate if all are removed at the sockets requires verification.

The visceral mass is easily removed from *Antedon* or is sometimes found missing in dredged specimens, probably through injury by the dredge. Such specimens retain the aboral nervous system intact. The bottom of the calyx cup is revealed lined by connective tissue, and a torn edge is left around the periphery by the rupture of the tegmen. The regeneration of the visceral mass has been followed incompletely by Dendy (1886). Regeneration begins by proliferation of the connective tissue in the bottom of the cup and of the cut tegminal edges to close over the surface. In a few days the mouth and alimentary canal are indicated, apparently by downgrowth from the restored tegmen. The ambulacral grooves are left as depressed areas during the ingrowth of the tegmen from the torn edges. The anal cone appears as a small elevation that slowly elongates. Complete restoration of the removed parts is accomplished in about 3 weeks.

**20. Ecology: Geographic Distribution.**—The comatulids reach their greatest abundance as shallow-water inhabitants in the Indo-Pacific region, extending from southeastern Africa, Madagascar, and Mauritius eastward through southern Asia, the Malay Archipelago, and the Netherland East Indies to southern Japan (A. H. Clark, 1912a). This area includes the majority of known species of comatulids, especially oligophreate forms, and a number of oligophreate families are limited to this region. The comatulid population is centered at maximum density in a triangular area bounded by Luzon, Borneo, and New Guinea, and from this center the comatulid fauna declines in all directions. It reduces toward Australia, which has about 80 species, mostly limited to the coral reefs of the northern and eastern coasts, whereas very few comatulids occur on the other coasts of the Australian continent (H. L. Clark, 1946). To the east of the main center of occurrence, the comatulid

section of regenerating arms, showing differentiation of definitive structures. *J*, cirrus regenerating. *K*, longitudinal section through regenerating area of an arm. *L*, regenerating arm. (*A–L*, after *Reichensperger*, 1912.) *M*, *Antedon*, regenerating four arm pairs (*after Przibram*, 1901). 1, bits of ingested muscle; 2, coelomic canal; 3, water canal; 4, differentiating epidermis; 5, regenerating main brachial nerve; 6, aboral coelomic canal; 7, subtentacular canals; 8, differentiating ectoneural nerve band; 9, cut epidermis of ambulacral groove; 10, regeneration bud; 11, advancing end of water vessel; 12, coelomic canal; 13, coelomocytes migrating to wound; 14, endoskeletal piece (decalcified); 15, regenerated pinnules; 16, cirri; 17, regenerating arms; 18, old arms: 19, genital pinnules.

fauna rapidly attenuates among the numerous Pacific Islands; none are found on the New Zealand coast. There is less reduction in the comatulid fauna to the north, as they exist in good numbers in the Red Sea, southern Asia, and the southern part of Japan. The abundance of crinoids around southern Japan was also noted by Gislén (1927), who listed a total of 91 species, including some stalked forms. All families of crinoids are represented in the Indo-Pacific area except the Holopidae. In general, *Tropiometra* is the most common littoral tropical comatulid.

In striking contrast to the richness of littoral comatulids in the Indo-Pacific region is their paucity in the Atlantic and eastern Pacific. There are some littoral comatulids, mostly macrophreates of the family Antedonidae, in the eastern part of the North Atlantic, from Scandinavia and Iceland to the British Isles, into the Mediterranean, and along the west coast of Africa to the equator; but they are very scarce in the rest of the Atlantic except the arctic, antarctic, and Caribbean–West Indian region, and none at all are known from the eastern Pacific, that is, the western shores of the Americas, except near the poles. No reasons are evident for the want of littoral comatulids in these areas. The cooler temperatures cannot be responsible, as crinoids are not uncommon in both arctic and antarctic areas. There is an outburst of littoral comatulids in the Caribbean–West Indian region, extending southward along the Brazilian coast. Here again, *Tropiometra* is the principal shallow-water crinoid encountered. A. H. Clark (1923b) stated that there were known at that time 85 species of crinoids from the entire Atlantic basin, including 31 species of Antedonidae, 13 species of Comasteridae, and 21 species of stalked crinoids; and 40 of these Atlantic species are restricted to the Caribbean–West Indian region. The genus *Antedon* ranges from Norway and Iceland south into the Mediterranean basin, then southward along the west coast of Africa to the equator, then west to tropical America. In some localities off Scandinavia, the bottom is completely covered with *Antedon* (Gislén, 1927).

The deeper-water crinoids, including the stalked forms, show a less restricted distribution since conditions of life are more uniform in deeper parts of the oceans. Comatulids descend into rather deep waters with a lower limit of 1500 m., according to the findings of the *Challenger*. Stalked crinoids occur mostly from 200 to 5000 m. but in a few restricted places may ascend into shallow water around 50 m. in depth (A. H. Clark, 1908f), and many are found above 1000 m. Whereas the Hyocrinidae and Millericrinida are generally limited to ocean deeps, the pentacrinites proper are more commonly found at more moderate depths. They further seem most common in the Indo-Pacific area, whereas the other types of stalked crinoids have a haphazard distribution, although a number occur in the North Atlantic. Most of the pentacrinites, chiefly members of the genus *Metacrinus*, taken by the *Challenger*, were dredged in the Indo-Pacific region, principally near the Kei Islands (west of New Guinea), the Kermadec Islands (north of New Zealand), and the Meangis Islands (near the Philippines), and also off Japan. In his report on the crinoids of southern Japan, Gislén (1927) noted the taking of three stalked crinoids, one bathycrinid and two species of *Metacrinus*. A number of different pentacrinites, also species of *Bathycrinus* and *Rhizocrinus*, were collected by the *Siboga* in the Netherland East Indies (Döderlein, 1907), and two pentacrinites were dredged near Sumatra by the German Deep Sea Expedition (Döderlein, 1911). The Caribbean–West Indian region constitutes another area in which pentacrinites are often found by dredging, but pentacrinites are mostly wanting elsewhere in the Atlantic.

Crinoids are surprisingly common in cold waters. The Danish *Ingolf* Expedition (A. H. Clark, 1923b), which collected between Denmark and Iceland, took 11 species of crinoids at depths between 15 and 150 m.; the most common comatulids found were *Poliometra prolixa*, *Hathrometra sarsii*, and *Trichometra cubensis*, and three species of stalked crinoids were taken in some abundance (*Bathycrinus carpenteri, Rhizocrinus lofotensis*, and *Monachocrinus sexradiatus*). *Heliometra glacialis*, an unusually large comatulid, is very common in northern and arctic waters, ranging from Nova Scotia and Greenland to the Kara Sea, Sea of Okhotsk, and northern part of the Sea of Japan. Crinoids have been collected from the antarctic on several expeditions (A. H. Clark, 1915b; John, 1937, 1938, 1939), chiefly from the antarctic adjacent to South America. All the antarctic comatulids are macrophreates. The most common species is *Promachocrinus kerguelensis;* others repeatedly taken include *Anthometra adriani, Isometra vivipara, Notocrinus virilis, Notocrinus mortenseni, Florometra mawsoni*. Many of the antarctic comatulids have viviparous habits, as previously noted. The occurrence of hyocrinids (*Hyocrinus, Ptilocrinus*) in the antarctic was noted in the discussion of that family (page 100). The antarctic crinoids tend to spread up the South American coast and into the Strait of Magellan.

Comatulids in general inhabit rough and rocky bottoms, most frequently coral reefs, and very few occur on sandy or muddy substrata. The relation of cirrus form to type of bottom was discussed on page 38 and is illustrated in Fig. 44. Stalked crinoids are often brought up from areas of mud bottom, but as the basal part is usually missing, the manner of attachment to such a substratum is unknown.

Some comatulids exhibit the phenomenon of geographic variation. Thus the common *Antedon bifida* of western European coasts increases in size with depth, having a spread of 120 mm. in shallow water, 220 mm. or more at greater depths. The characteristic arctic comatulid, *Helio-*

*metra glacialis*, is relatively small in northern European waters, reaches an expanse of 500 mm. toward Greenland, and grows even larger in the opposite direction, in the Seas of Okhotsk and Japan, where at freezing temperatures it reaches a spread of 700 mm. (A. H. Clark, 1908f). These size variations are probably related to temperature, not to food supply, as supposed by Clark. However, according to this author, in tropical waters comatulids tend to decrease in size with increasing depth. But tropical comatulids are mainly oligophreates, which, as already indicated, are more or less restricted to warm tropical and subtropical waters and shallow depths and apparently are unsuited to the cooler

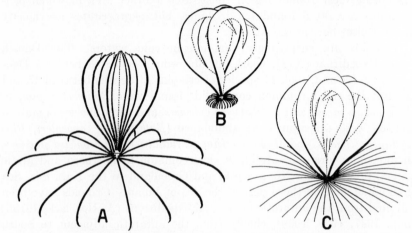

Fig. 44.—Comatulids, showing types of cirri. *A, Asterometra macropoda* with long strong cirri related to rough bottom. *B, Pentametrocrinus tuberculatus*, with short strong cirri for holding to objects. *C, Pentametrocrinus varians*, fine straight cirri adapted to a muddy bottom. (*All after A. H. Clark*, 1921b.)

temperatures of deeper waters. The macrophreates, on the other hand, are adapted to colder waters and are in fact the only comatulids to be found in polar regions and ocean depths.

It has been noticed by all collectors of crinoids that they tend to occur in aggregations, often very dense. Thus Verrill (1882), in one haul of the dredge at 240 m. off Martha's Vineyard, brought up around 10,000 specimens of the antedonid *Hathrometra tenella*. The steamer *Blake* in its dredging operations in the Florida–West Indies region brought up large numbers of crinoids (Agassiz, 1878b, 1879). Off Sand Key, at the edge of the Florida reef, at 550 to 700 m., so many *Rhizocrinus* came up that Agassiz remarked that the dredge must have passed through a forest of them, judging by the number of stems and heads of all sizes. Throughout the Lesser Antilles, numerous pentacrinites were taken, on one occasion 124 (presumably *Neocrinus decorus*) in a single haul of the tangles. In a similar haul the *Porcupine* obtained 20 specimens of *Annacrinus wyville-thomsoni* off Portugal at 2000 m. (Thomson, 1872). The occurrence of large aggregations of *Antedon bifida* on seaweeds at Roscoff and of *Antedon petasus* on the sea bottom off Scandinavia was already mentioned, and similarly in the Mediterranean the common antedonids (*Antedon mediterranea, A. adriatica, Leptometra phalangium*) are found in large numbers in certain localities. It further appears that in the tropics certain dominant species of comatulids may occur in great numbers in favorable localities. This tendency of crinoids to occur in aggregations is probably to be attributed to the slight amount of dispersal afforded by the feeble swimming powers of the larvae. They settle close to the parents and if conditions are suitable grow to maturity near the latter, and a large population soon results, especially as the adults are not much inclined to leave a favorable situation.

**21. Ecology: Biological Relations.**—The crinoids, as more or less sedentary animals, are subject to extensive infestation by other organisms, ranging from accidental visitors to harmful parasites and including a wide variety of animal groups. A. H. Clark (1921a) has given an exhaustive review of the available information on association of other animals with crinoids. A few protozoan inhabitants of crinoids have been reported. Large numbers of a dinoflagellate, *Prorocentrum micans*, were observed by Cuénot (1891c) inhabiting as temporary parasites some of the intestinal diverticula of *Antedon bifida*. A holotrichous ciliate is said by Chadwick (1907) to occur abundantly in the digestive tract of channel specimens of *A. bifida*, and a peritrichous ciliate, *Hemispeiropsis antedonis*, related to *Trichodina*, is found gliding about on the aboral surface of the calyx of *Antedon* species, among the cirri (Perrier, 1886; Cuénot, 1891c; Chadwick, 1907). As may be expected, hydroids are frequently found growing on the stems and cirri of crinoids, presumably using them simply as available substrata. Ophiuroids often shelter on crinoids as on other arborescent objects, but apparently those of the genus *Ophiomaza* have a genuine associative relationship with crinoids. These live on the disk of the crinoid with their arms wrapped around the aboral surface and have been noticed by Suhm (1876) and Potts (1915) to correspond in color pattern with the host colors. Small polychaete annelids of the genus *Polynoe* associate with crinoids and also present coloration harmonizing with that of the host. The chief annelid guests of crinoids, however, are the curious, highly altered polychaetes known as myzostomes, which live exclusively as ectoparasites on echinoderms, chiefly crinoids. They are small or minute creatures of bizarre appearance (Fig. 45A–C), typically disciform (although elongated shapes also occur) with sensory projections around the margin and suckers and aborted parapodia armed with hooks on the ventral surface. The

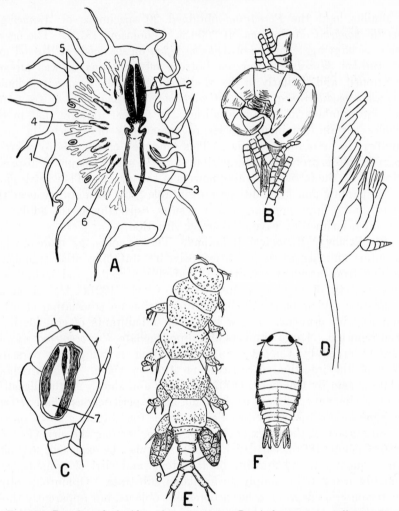

FIG. 45.—Parasites of crinoids.   A, a myzostome.  B, spiral myzostome gall on a pinnule
that contained two myzostomes.   C, myzostome gall of the crinoid arm, opened to show
partition.   (A–C, after Graff, 1884.)   D, parasitic snail, *Melanella ptilocrinicola*, feeding
on a dredged stalked crinoid (*after Bartsch*, 1907).   E, parasitic copepod, *Enterognathus
comatulae* (*after Giesbrecht*, 1900).   F, parasitic isopod, *Cirolana lineata* (*after Potts*, 1915).
1, sensory cirri; 2, pharynx; 3, intestine; 4, parapodia; 5, suckers; 6, intestinal branches;
7, partition; 8, egg sacs.

habits of the numerous species of myzostomes vary: some run around
freely over the surface of the crinoid host; others are sluggish, remaining
attached to one spot; a number inhabit swellings, galls, or other deformi-
ties that they evoke in the pinnules, arms, or disk of crinoids (Fig. 45B, C);
and finally a few become true entoparasites, lodging in the host's interior.
*Myzostomum cirriferum* is an example of a myzostome that moves about

freely on the disk and arms of species of *Antedon*, whereas *M. glabrum* remains attached around the mouth, or even within the mouth (Beard, 1884). Various swellings, galls, cysts, and other excrescences evoked by myzostomes on crinoids were described and figured by von Graff (1877, 1884), who had received for study the myzostomes from the crinoids collected on the *Porcupine*, *Triton*, and *Challenger* expeditions. Cysts may contain a pair of myzostomes but this is not necessarily the case; males, in case of dioecious species, are usually much smaller than the females. The species *M. pulvinar* inhabits the esophagus of the common Mediterranean antedonid *Leptometra phalangium*, with head pointed away from the mouth, ventral surface against the esophageal epithelium, and concave dorsal surface forming a groove for the food stream (Prouho, 1892). The infestation of crinoids with myzostomes is prodigious; in many localities practically every specimen bears them, often in numbers. In the Mediterranean, there is an average of 10 *M. cirriferum* per crinoid, but off the west coast of Sweden, *Antedon* individuals may harbor 100 up to 300 or 400 specimens of *M. cirriferum* (Jägersten, 1940). Beard (1884) remarked of *M. glabrum* that so many of them were clustered around the mouth of Mediterranean *Antedon*, he wondered how the crinoid retained any food. The myzostomes are true parasites, since they rob the host of food, by inserting their pharynx into the food streams and appropriating their fill. Suhm (1876) and Potts (1915) noted protective-color resemblance between myzostomes and their crinoid hosts, but apparently such resemblance is often wanting, and the color of the parasites may contrast markedly with that of the disk or arms on which they occur.

Among the worst enemies of crinoids are small delicate carnivorous snails of the family Melanellidae, belonging to the genera *Stilifer*, *Stylina*, *Sabinella*, and *Melanella* (Fig. 45D). They move about on the host and with their proboscis bore through hard skeletal parts, as the calyx, brachials, pinnulars, or cirrals, into the soft tissue which they then devour. An account of one of the most common of these snails, *Stylina comatulicola*, found attached to the anal tube or cirri of Mediterranean antedonids, was published by von Graff (1875).

Crinoids are also infested with a variety of small crustaceans, to which they furnish food and shelter gratis. Among the commoner of these are alpheid prawns of the genus *Synalpheus* that generally live in pairs on the disk and if disturbed dig their claws into the disk or seek refuge among the pinnules; pontoniid prawns of the genera *Periclimenes* and *Pontoniopsis;* little crabs of the genus *Galathea;* an isopoda *Anilocra* that dwells inside the anal tube (P. H. Carpenter, 1884); another isopod *Cirolana lineata*, common on the tropical *Comanthus annulatus*, where it spends most of its time inside the digestive tract (Potts, 1915); an amphipod, *Cyclotelson purpureum*, also found by Potts (1915) on the surface of *Comanthus annulatus;* another amphipod of more parasitic habits, *Laphystiopsis iridometrae*, that burrows into the disk of *Iridiometra* (A. H. Clark, 1921a); and two copepods, *Collocheres gracilicauda* and *Enterognathus comatulae*, found on Mediterranean comatulids. The former of the two copepods is of normal appearance, moving about on the disk of the *Antedon* (Rosoll, 1888), but *Enterognathus comatulae* shows parasitic alteration (Fig. 45E); females and young live in the intestine of the crinoid, whereas the males lead a free existence (Giesbrecht, 1900). *Synagoga metacrinicola*, a parasitic barnacle of the ascothoracic group, lives attached to the surface of *Metacrinus rotundus;* the body enclosed in a bivalve shell retains typical barnacle structure (Okada, 1926).

In a study of the inhabitants of crinoids, especially *Comanthus annulatus*, in the Torres Strait region, Potts (1915) emphasized a striking color correspondence between the comasterid and its crustacean associates. The comasterid occurs in a wide range of colors, from light specimens composed of a combination of white, light green, and yellow, to dark green and almost black individuals. The accompanying crustaceans, including the alpheid and pontoniid prawns, the galatheid crabs, and the isopods and amphipods are mostly dark-colored with light longitudinal bands (Fig. 46). The width of the light stripes varies with the color of the individual *Comanthus* occupied; on light-colored specimens, the prawns and crabs tend also toward a light coloration, achieved by a broadening of the light bands and a narrowing of the dark-colored areas. This color adaptation, presumably of protective value, was most conspicuous in the alpheid prawns, which were almost white on light-green *Comanthus* individuals, striped on *Comanthus* showing a barred pattern, and dark dorsally on dark-green or blackish hosts. *Hippolyte hunti*, striped carmine and yellow, also shows color adapation to its host *Antedon bifida* (Nouvel, 1953).

It has been remarked by A. H. Clark (1921b) and others that the infestation of crinoids with other animals is most pronounced among the tropical littoral crinoids of the Indo-Pacific region, except as regards myzostomes and snails, which attack crinoids everywhere. These Indo-Pacific littoral crinoids are mostly comasterids, a group more open to parasite attack than are other crinoids, because they are somewhat larger, have sluggish habits, long and numerous arms, and open ambulacral grooves that cannot be closed. Members of many other comatulid families are able to prevent the stealing of food from the grooves and mouth by closing down the side and covering plates. Deeper-water and stalked crinoids have fewer pestiferous associates but are also afflicted with myzostomes, especially the types that inhabit galls and

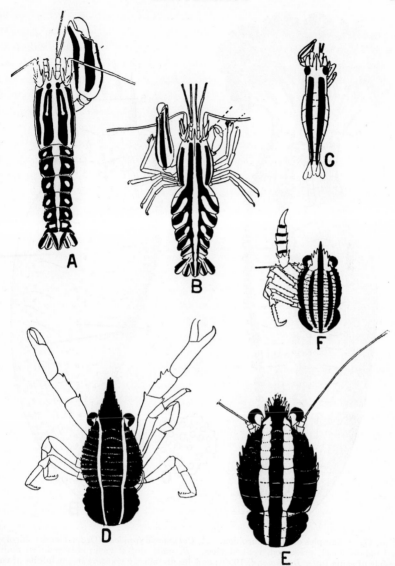

FIG. 46.—Crustacean commensals of crinoids, showing protective coloration. *A, B,* two kinds of *Synalphaeus* shrimps. *C,* a pontoniid prawn of the genus *Pontoniopsis.* *D–F,* three kinds of crabs of the genus *Galathea.* (*All after Potts, 1915.*)

cysts. Cysts attributable to myzostomes are also known on crinoid fossils.

## VI. SUBPHYLUM ELEUTHEROZOA

This subphylum comprises the remaining four classes of echinoderms and includes the great majority of the living members of the phylum.

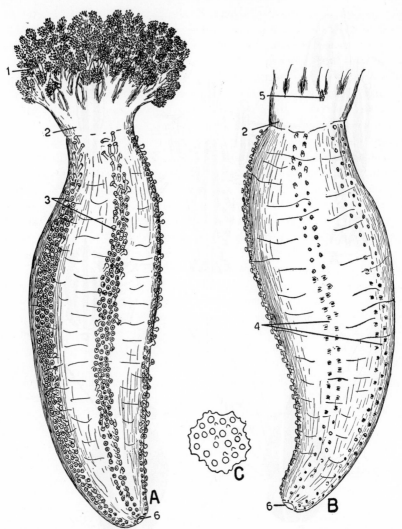

Fig. 47.—Examples of Holothuroidea.  *A, Cucumaria frondosa* (Order Dendrochirota),
New England coast, preserved, ventral view.  *B,* same, dorsal view; note reduced podia.
*C,* ossicle of same (*after Deichmann,* 1930); ossicles are mostly wanting in the adults of this
species.  1, crown of 10 dendritic tentacles; 2, introvert; 3, ventral ambulacra with locomotory podia; 4, dorsal ambulacra with aborted podia; 5, genital papilla; 6, anus.

The Eleutherozoa are seldom attached by a stalk at any period of their
life history, but lead a free existence in which the oral surface is carried
downward against the substratum; except in the Holothuroidea which
commonly lie and crawl upon one side.  The orientation of the body is
thus opposite to that of the Pelmatozoa and furnishes perhaps the most
striking point of contrast between the two subphyla.  A marked pen-

tamerous symmetry prevails throughout the Eleutherozoa; it is practically perfect in the asteroids and ophiuroids, whose body form in general is that of a five-pointed star, but inclines to secondary asymmetry among the echinoids with globose to discoid body and among the holothuroids that are more or less vermiform. The ambulacral system retains the same plan of structure as in the Pelmatozoa, but the ambulacral grooves usually do not serve for food conveyance, and the podia are chiefly locomotory although not infrequently losing this function secondarily. The ambulacral system differs from that of the Pelmatozoa, except Edrioasteroidea, in that the podia pass from the interior to the exterior between or through the ambulacral plates and are typically provided with ampullae. The endoskeleton forms a continuous theca or test only in the echinoids, consisting of separate ossicles in the other classes, and these are of microscopic size among the holothuroids. The aboral nervous system is greatly reduced or wanting, and the oral system takes over the dominant role. The digestive tract has the typical elongated recurved form in echinoids and holothuroids but is reduced to a short straight form with stomachic enlargement in asteroids and ophiuroids. The anus, wanting in ophiuroids and some asteroids, is typically located aborally at the opposite end of the body axis from the mouth; but in irregular echinoids tends to wander to an oral position. The gonad remains primitively single in the holothuroids but is pentamerous in the three other classes.

The Eleutherozoa divide sharply into two groups, one consisting of the class Holothuroidea, and the other comprising the three classes Asteroidea, Echinoidea, and Ophiuroidea. These classes will now be treated in the order named.

### VII. CLASS HOLOTHUROIDEA

**1. Definition.**—The Holothuroidea[1] are echinoderms with orally-aborally elongated cylindroid bodies having the mouth at or near one end and the anus at or near the other, usually dorsoventrally differentiated, hence lying upon a ventral surface formed of rays B, A, and E, with a circle of tentacles representing altered podia encircling the mouth, with an endoskeleton in the form of microscopic ossicles imbedded in the body wall, and with a nonradial gonad opening anteriorly by a gonopore located in interradius CD. There are about 500 described species.

**2. General Remarks.**—The holothurians or sea cucumbers have been known from ancient times, as they are conspicuous animals of the ocean littoral and common in the Mediterranean region. It is improbable that the animal called *holothurium* by Aristotle actually was a sea cucumber but his name has remained attached to this group of

[1] The original spelling Holothurioidea is also often employed.

animals. The common name of sea cucumber apparently derives from Pliny's term *cucumis marinus* that he applied to a true holothurian. Scientific study of holothurians did not begin, however, until the latter half of the sixteenth century and from that time was pursued with increasing vigor until the present era when interest in this group appears relegated to taxonomic specialists. An exhaustive historical account is furnished by Ludwig (1889–1892) in the volume on the Holothuroidea in Bronn's *Klassen und Ordnungen des Tierreichs*. Many new and curious forms were described by Théel (1882, 1886a) in the *Challenger* reports, and later advances in knowledge of holothurians have come chiefly from other collecting expeditions, such as those of the *Albatross*, *Blake*, *Siboga*, and *Valdivia*, several sponsored by the marine station at Monaco, and a number of antarctic voyages. The holothurians of the Atlantic coast of the Americas, from Cape Cod to Brazil, have been monographed by Deichmann (1930), and Pacific Coast forms have been treated by Ludwig (1894), Edwards (1907b), and Deichmann (1937, 1938a, 1941). In addition to the Ludwig volume in Bronn just mentioned, still useful despite its age, a modernized account by L. Cuénot (1948) appears in Volume XI of the *Traité de zoologie*.

**3. External Characters.**—The body form is typically that of a short to long cylinder, with the mouth, encircled by variously shaped tentacles, at or near one end, and the anus, often edged with more or less evident papillae, at or near the other. Pentaradiate symmetry is sometimes externally evidenced by the presence of five equally spaced meridional ambulacra bearing podia, as in *Cucumaria* (Fig. 47*A*, *B*); but most holothurians habitually lie upon one side that differentiates as a flattened ventral creeping surface or *sole*, bearing all the locomotory podia and contrasting with the opposite arched dorsal surface on which the podia are represented by warts and papillae, as in *Holothuria*, *Stichopus*, and *Actinopyga* (Figs. 48*A*, *B*, 52*A*). Such holothurians display a more or less pronounced bilateral symmetry. Typically, the body proportions are those of a cucumber, but in the order Apoda a vermiform shape obtains (Fig. 49*D*); in the Molpadonia the body is usually narrowed posteriorly into a tail-like region bearing the anus at its tip (*Molpadia*, Fig. 49*B*); and various aberrant shapes occur in the curious members of the order Elasipoda, including a postanal tail-like projection (Fig. 49*C*), rounded or flattened. A thin rim formed of fused papillae frames the body proper in a number of elasipod genera, as *Bathyzona*, *Perizona*, *Pelopatides*, *Allopatides*, and *Euphronides* (Fig. 50*B*), possibly as a floating device for these deep-water creatures. A plump, almost spherical, shape is seen in *Sphaerothuria* (Fig. 50*A*), in which the dorsal surface is shortened so that the body ends face more or less upward. A similar but more pronounced dorsal displacement of the body ends with reference

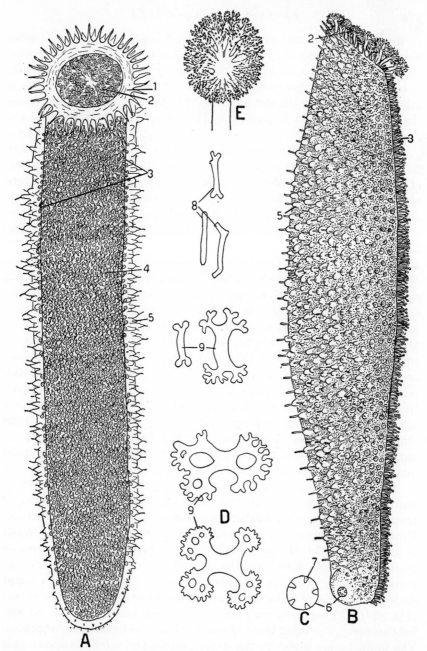

Fig. 48.—Examples of Holothuroidea (continued). *A*, *Actinopyga agassizi* (Order Aspidochirota), ventral view, showing creeping sole (*from life, Bahamas*). *B*, same, side view. *C*, anus, showing teeth. *D*, body-wall ossicles of same (*partly after Deichmann,* 1930). *E*, tentacle of *Actinopyga*, illustrating peltate type. 1, tentacular collar; 2, peltate tentacles; 3, creeping sole; 4, locomotory podia; 5, papillae; 6, anus; 7, anal teeth; 8, rod ossicles; 9, rods with branched end forks.

to the main axis occurs in *Psolus* (Fig. 50*C*) and other psolids, where mouth end and anus are located on the dorsal surface and the ventral surface is altered into a highly differentiated adhesive sole (Fig. 50*D*). A contrary ventral displacement obtains in many Elasipoda as well as other holothurians with the anterior end shoved ventrally and facing the substratum, as in *Euphronides* (Fig. 49*C*), *Elpidia* (Fig. 53*A*), and *Deima* (Fig. 52*D, E*).

The mouth, which, as just indicated, may be terminal or displaced dorsally or ventrally, is of circular shape and surrounded by a thin area of body wall (*buccal membrane*), bordered by a circlet of tentacles invariably present in all Holothuroidea. The number of tentacles ranges from 10 to 30, being usually some multiple of five, but irregular numbers also occur. There are usually 10 tentacles in the Dendrochirota, 18 to 30 in the Aspidochirota (Fig. 49*A*), 12 to 15 in the Apoda (Fig. 49*D*), 15 in the Molpadonia (Fig. 51*G*), and 10 to 20 in the Elasipoda (Figs. 50*B*, 53*B*). The tentacles are actually labial or buccal podia, containing extensions of the water-vascular system as branches from the radial canals. They are usually all of the same size except in the Dendrochirota where typically some are much smaller than the others (Fig. 70*A*), although the common dendrochirote genus *Cucumaria* often has 10 equally developed tentacles (Fig. 47*A, B*). Usually when 10 tentacles are present in members of this order, the 2 belonging to the midventral radius (A) are almost invariably smaller than the others (Fig. 51*A*). In case of dendrochirotes with 15 or more tentacles, 5 or more of these are dwarfed and distributed regularly or irregularly between the larger tentacles. The tentacles are almost always disposed in a single circlet, but in a few of the dendrochirotes with several dwarf tentacles the latter may be displaced inward to form an inner circlet (Fig. 86*B*).

The form of the tentacles differs in the different orders of Holothuroidea and in fact constitutes a character of ordinal value. *Dendritic* tentacles, branching in an arborescent manner, are limited to the order Dendrochirota typified by such genera as *Cucumaria* (Fig. 47*A*), *Thyone* (Fig. 51*A, C*), and *Psolus* (Fig. 50*C*). When fully extended such tentacles reach considerable length relative to the size of the animal. *Pinnate* tentacles, characteristic of the Apoda, consist of a central axis bearing on each side a series of a few to many digitiform or leaf-like side branches (Fig. 49*D*). They, too, are rather conspicuous features of the external appearance. The other types of tentacles are short and less conspicuous. The tentacles are *peltate* in the Aspidochirota and most Elasipoda, that is, resembling a nasturtium leaf, with a central short stalk giving off short horizontal branches (Figs. 48*E*, 49*A*). The Molpadonia have *digitate* tentacles, short plump projections with or without small terminal fingers (Fig. 51*G*).

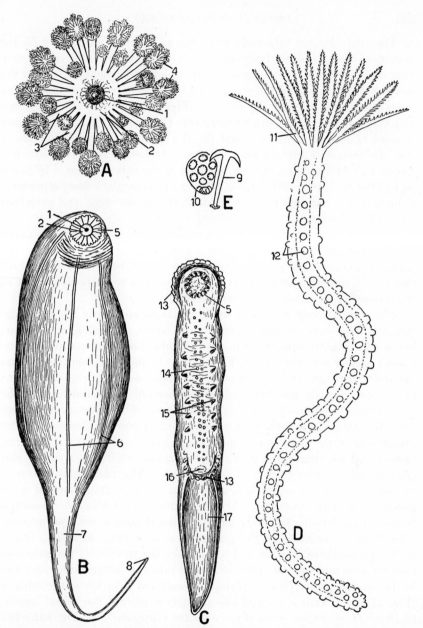

Fig. 49.—Examples of Holothuroidea (continued). *A*, tentacles of *Actinopyga*, expanded, showing peltate type (*from life, Bahamas*). *B, Molpadia musculus* (Order Molpadonia) with tail (*after H. L. Clark, 1907a*). *C, Psychropotes*, from deep water (Order Elasipoda, *after Ludwig, 1894*). *D, Euapta lappa* (Order Apoda), with pinnate tentacles (*from life, Bahamas*). *E*, anchor and anchor plate from body wall of *Euapta lappa*. 1, mouth; 2, buccal membrane; 3, stalks of peltate tentacles; 4, fronds of tentacles; 5, crown of digitate tentacles; 6, ambulacra; 7, tail; 8, location of anus; 9, anchor; 10, anchor plate; 11, crown of pinnate tentacles; 12, warts; 13, rim of fused papillae; 14, locomotory podia of mid-ventral ambulacrum; 15, papillate podia of ambulacra B and E; 16, anus; 17, postanal tail.

The tentacles are extremely retractile and can be withdrawn by the closure of the adjacent body wall over them when fully contracted. This capacity is best developed in the order Dendrochirota where the anterior end just behind the circle of tentacles is altered to a smooth thin collar-like region termed the *introvert* (Figs. 50*C*, 51*A*). This together with the tentacles can be drawn down into the interior by the contraction of a set of retractor muscles, and the rim of the body wall then closes over the retracted anterior end. Retractor muscles also occur in a few Apoda and Molpadonia but are wanting in the other orders. In many aspidochirotes a projecting rim of body wall (*tentacular collar*) often with a fimbriated margin (Fig. 48*A*) similarly closes over the retracted tentacular crown.

In the middorsal line, representing interradius CD, there is found between the adjacent tentacles or at a level more or less posterior to the crown of tentacles, the *genital papilla* as an evident projection (Fig. 47*B*). Close to it there occurs in some holothurians the hydropore or a set of small pores representing a madreporic plate.

The general body surface is thick, leathery, and slimy in most holothurians and more or less covered with warts, tubercles, or papillae, but is only slightly roughened in most Apoda and often so thin that the viscera may be seen through it (Fig. 68*A*). Podia appear on the external surface in three of the five orders of Holothuroidea, being wholly absent in the order Apoda and but slightly represented in altered form in the Molpadonia. Typically, they take the form of locomotory tube feet (called *pedicels* by holothurian specialists). These are hollow tubular projections of the body wall containing a branch of the water-vascular system and terminating in a concave expansion acting as a sucker and often supported internally by a skeletal disk. The podia may also take the form of papillae, which lack a terminal sucking expansion and serve primarily sensory functions. Arrangement of the podia in five ambulacral radii extending the body length occurs in only a few holothurians, notably most members of the genus *Cucumaria* (Fig. 47*A*, *B*). Even in this genus there is evidenced a tendency for the dorsal podia to lose their suckers and for the podia to spread into the interradial areas; and in the related genus *Thyone*, podia are scattered over the entire surface (Fig. 51*A*, *B*), with a gradual loss of suckers toward the dorsal region. In *Phyllophorus*, also, podia occur over the entire surface (Fig. 86*B*) but tend to be arranged in meridional rows in some species. As, however, the shape of holothurians compels them to lie upon one side (unless supported in burrows), it is not surprising that the locomotory podia are generally restricted to the functional ventral surface and are wanting dorsally or altered into nonlocomotory papillae. The ventral surface bearing the locomotory podia thus becomes a flattened creeping sole,

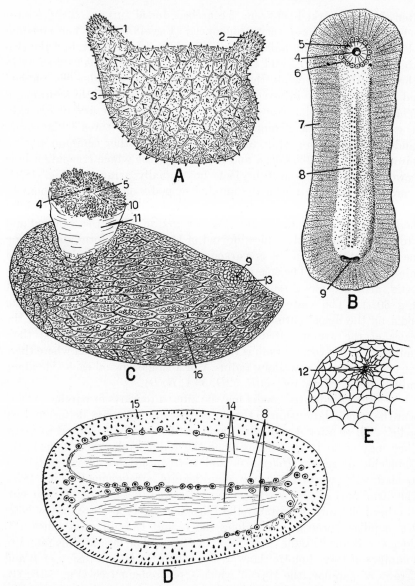

Fig. 50.—Examples of Holothuroidea (continued). *A, Sphaerothuria*, with scaly armor (Order Dendrochirota). *B, Euphronides*, with rim of fused papillae (Order Elasipoda). (*A, B, after Ludwig*, 1894.) *C, Psolus fabricii*, preserved, with dorsal mouth and anus and scaly armor (Order Dendrochirota). *D*, same, ventral view, showing sole. *E*, anterior end of *Psolus squamatus*, showing scales around the retracted introvert. 1, mouth end; 2, anal end; 3, spiny scales; 4, mouth; 5, buccal membrane; 6, ring of peltate tentacles; 7, rim of fused papillae; 8, row of locomotory podia; 9, anus; 10, crown of tentacles; 11, introvert; 12, site of withdrawn introvert; 13, scales around anus; 14, creeping sole; 15, rim of lateral body wall around creeping sole; 16, body scales.

often sharply marked off from the arched dorsal surface, as by a projecting rim, sometimes very pronounced (Fig. 48A, B). The creeping sole embraces three ambulacral radii, namely, E, A, and B, and the two interradii AB and AE, and thus constitutes what is called a *trivium* in other Eleutherozoa, while the dorsal body region includes the radii C and D and the three interradial strips BC, CD, and DE, thus forming a *bivium*. The fact that the creeping sole involves three ambulacra may be evidenced by the arrangement of the podia in three longitudinal bands, as in *Stichopus* (Fig. 52A). However, in other common aspidochirote genera, as *Holothuria* and *Actinopyga*, the whole creeping sole is crowded with numerous tube feet, not radially arranged (Fig. 48A). A pronounced reduction in the number of podia on the sole is common among holothurians, and among the Dendrochirota is exemplified by the much modified genus *Psolus* (Fig. 50C, D) in which the armored and strongly arched dorsal surface, devoid of podia in any form and bearing the introvert and the anus, is markedly set off from the creeping sole by a thin wide margin. The sole itself bears a limited number of locomotory podia, arranged along radii B and E and in some species also along A (Fig. 50D). The related genera *Psolidium* and *Theelia* differ in retaining podia on the dorsal surface, altered into papillae emerging through the scales of the armor. Reduction of the locomotory podia and their limitation to the ventral radii is the rule among the Elasipoda where there is usually a double row along radius A or a single row on each side along radii B and E (Figs. 49C, 50B, 52D, 53A, B, D).

As already indicated, podia may be altered to warts or papillae, which bear the same relationship to the water-vascular system as do locomotory podia. These altered podia are found on the dorsal and lateral surfaces. They may occur irregularly or along the ambulacral radii. Thus in the aspidochirote genera *Holothuria* and *Actinopyga* the dorsal surface is covered with warts that lack any definite arrangement (Fig. 48B). The distal part of such warts is often narrowed to a contractile filament. In other holothurians, notably the Elasipoda, there are often a few large stiff papillae borne in rows along the C and D radii, sometimes also along the B and E radii (Figs. 52D, E, 53C). The lateral rims found in a number of these holothurians arise through the lateral fusion of B and E rows of papillae, the tips of which often remain free (Fig. 53B, C). The tentacular collars in aspidochirote holothurians that close over the retracted tentacles are also formed by the fusion of papillate podia as shown by their fimbriated edge (Fig. 48A). The crescentic fold behind the anus in *Psychropotes* (Fig. 49C) has also obviously arisen by the union of papillate podia. Perhaps the most curious of all Elasipoda are those in which papillate podia are united to form a sort of sail or velum. In the genera *Peniagone* (Fig. 53D) and *Scotoanassa* (Fig. 88A)

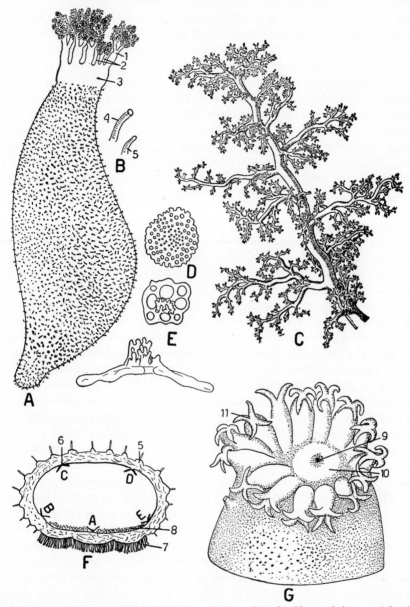

FIG. 51.—Examples of Holothuroidea (continued). *A*, *Thyone briareus*, Atlantic Coast, preserved, with podia over the entire surface (Order Dendrochirota). *B*, podia of same. *C*, expanded tentacle of same. *D*, end ossicle of locomotory podium of same. (*C*, *D*, *after Coe*, 1912.) *E*, table type of ossicles of same (*after Deichmann*, 1930); in mature specimens of this species ossicles are limited to the body ends. *F*, section through *Actinopyga* (Order Aspidochirota), to show axial relations. *G*, anterior end of *Caudina arenata* (Order Molpadonia), to show digitate tentacles (*after Gerould*, 1896). 1, normal tentacles; 2, dwarfed mid-ventral pair of tentacles; 3, introvert; 4, locomotory podium from ventral side; 5, dorsal papillate podium; 6, longitudinal muscle bands; 7, creeping sole; 8, ampullae of podia; 9, mouth; 10, buccal membrane; 11, digitate tentacles.

this is an erect transverse membrane composed of two or four papillate podia located dorsally near the anterior end.  In *Pelagothuria* (Fig. 87*A*) behind the conspicuous circlet of tentacles is another partial or complete circlet of long papillae united basally by a web.

The dendrochirote genera *Psolus*, *Psolidium*, and *Theelia* are notable among holothurians in having a protective armor of hard rounded or rhomboidal calcareous plates imbedded at the surface.  These are smooth and imbricated in the well-known species *Psolus squamatus* (Fig. 50*E*), warty and not overlapping in some other *Psolus* species (Fig. 50*C*).  A similar but less conspicuous hardening of the surface by imbedded calcareous plates occurs in *Deima* (Fig. 52*D, E*) and some other elasipods.

The anus is terminal in the Molpadonia and Apoda but in the other orders is often displaced dorsally or ventrally.  The formation of a creeping sole which usually conditions a more or less ventral displacement of the mouth seems to favor a dorsal displacement of the anus.  The anus is often encircled with small papillae, usually so in the Molpadonia, or by calcareous plates or teeth.  Five calcareous teeth around the anus or within its rim occur in a number of holothurians and are a conspicuous identifying feature of the aspidochirote genus *Actinopyga* (Fig. 48*C*).

The axial relations of holothurians in comparison with other echinoderms have probably already been sufficiently indicated.  The midventral ambulacrum is the radius A, flanked to the right by ambulacrum B and to the left by ambulacrum C (Fig. 51*F*).  The middorsal line lies along the center of interradius CD, and this interradius can be identified by the presence of the gonopore at or along its anterior end, further in some holothurians by the occurrence at the surface of a hydropore or madrepore.  The five radii are not necessarily equidistant.  As the anus is usually terminal or can be displaced either dorsally or ventrally, its location is useless for establishing axial relationships.

The Holothuroidea are mostly of moderate size but vary within wide limits, like most animal groups.  Very small forms, a few centimeters in length, occur among the Elasipoda and Dendrochirota and in the genus *Leptosynapta* among the Apoda.  Moderate size prevails among the Molpadonia.  The Aspidochirota are mostly of moderate to large size, and the largest holothurians that retain the cucumber shape occur in the aspidochirote genera *Holothuria*, *Actinopyga*, and *Stichopus*, often 30 to 50 cm. in length.  *Stichopus variegatus* from the Philippines was reported by Semper (1868) to reach a length of a meter with a diameter of 21 cm. The greatest lengths are seen among the Apoda, whose vermiform shape and thin body wall permit some of the larger species to stretch themselves out to lengths of 1 or even 2 m.

The Holothuroidea are mostly of dull coloration, occurring in shades

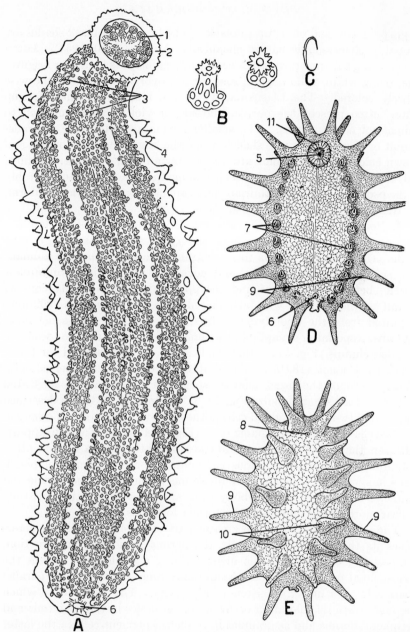

Fig. 52.—Examples of Holothuroidea (continued). *A, Stichopus badionotus* (Order Aspidochirota), with creeping sole of three rows of podia (*from life, Bahamas*). *B,* table ossicles of same. *C,* C ossicle of same. *D, Deima* (Order Elasipoda), deep-sea form, ventral view. *E, Deima,* dorsal view, showing large papillae along ambulacra. (*D, E, after Théel,* 1882.) 1, peltate tentacles; 2, tentacle collar; 3, locomotory podia along ambulacra E, A, and B; 4, papillate podia; 5, mouth; 6, anus; 7, locomotory podia along ambulacra E and B; 8, gonopore; 9, papillae of ambulacra E and B; 10, papillae of ambulacra C and D; 11, ring of digitate tentacles.

of gray, brown, and olive, up to black. The brown and black shades are probably of melanistic nature chemically (Millott, 1950, 1953). Often the creeping sole contrasts with the dorsal region by its lighter or brighter hue, being white, yellow, pink, rose, or terra cotta in animals otherwise soberly colored. The Elasipoda, which are mostly residents of deep water, often present the purple, maroon, or violet shades common to animals of ocean depths. The smaller Apoda are often pale or transparent or of pinkish or rose shades, while the larger ones run to gray and brown colors, although some are orange, terra cotta, or violet. Yellow, red, and orange hues are also seen among the dendrochirotes, notably in the psolids. While holothurian colors are usually more or less uniform, contrasting spots and stripes also occur.

4. **Body Wall.**—The body wall varies much in thickness in different holothurians, being relatively thin in the Apoda and Molpadonia, thicker in the other groups. It has the structure typical of coelomate animals. The surface is devoid of cilia and covered with a thin, structureless cuticle, beneath which is found the epidermis. This usually consists of tall epithelial cells with attenuated bases that are not definitely delimited from the underlying dermis (Fig. 54A, B). In some holothurians, especially synaptids, the epidermal cells tend to occur in rounded clumps (Fig. 54J); this condition was also described for *Cucumaria* by Cuénot (1891a). The epithelial cells are interspersed with sensory cells of the usual neurosensory type, with swollen nucleated middle and attenuated ends (Fig. 58C). Hamann (1884) has described and figured two types of gland cells in the body-wall epidermis of *Synapta*, goblet cells and ordinary gland cells (Fig. 58A, B). It would appear, however, that gland cells are more common in the Apoda than in other holothurians, as their secretions compensate for the absence of podia. Even in synaptids, they are more numerous in the buccal membrane and tentacles than in the general body wall, and in other holothurians they appear more or less limited to the former locations.

The dermis constitutes the greater part of the body wall and determines its thickness. Peripherally the dermis is of loose construction, composed of connective-tissue fibers forming a mesh that encloses the endoskeletal ossicles, while more internally more closely placed parallel fibers achieve a firmer consistency (Fig. 54A). The pigments to which the body owes its coloration occur as free granules in the epidermis and peripheral dermis and as granules in branched pigment cells in the latter situation. Pigment granules are often associated with nervous elements of the dermis. The dermis contains stellate connective-tissue cells, also often wandering coelomocytes which may, however, be concentrated in a lacuna to the inner side of the dermis (Fig. 54A). There is a general nerve plexus throughout the dermis which is especially noticeable in the

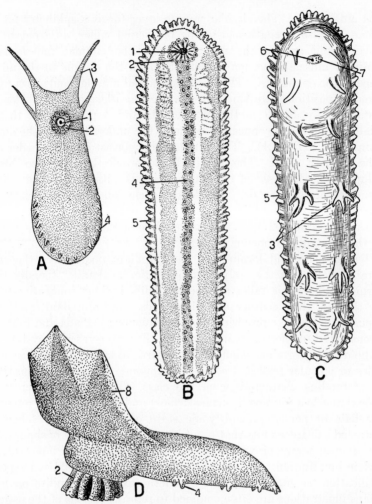

FIG. 53.—Examples of Holothuroidea (concluded). *A, Elpidia. B, Benthodytes,* with rim of fused papillae, ventral view. *C, Benthodytes,* dorsal view, with large papillae on dorsal ambulacra. (*B, C, after Sluiter,* 1901.) *D. Peniagone,* with sail. (*A, D, after Théel,* 1882.) All are Elasipoda. 1, mouth; 2, ring of peltate tentacles; 3, papillate podia; 4, locomotory podia (lack suckers); 5, rim of fused papillae; 6, gonopore; 7, madreporic pores; 8, sail.

vicinity of sense organs. Jourdan (1883) and Hamann (1884) have reported the presence of another plexus, the subepidermal plexus, situated immediately beneath the epidermis (Fig. 58*A*) in at least some holothurians.

The dermis is followed by a layer of circular muscle fibers that may form a complete cylinder but usually is interrupted at five points by the five longitudinal muscle bands that course along the inner surface of the ambulacra.   The circular muscle layer forms a sphincter for the anus and is also strengthened in the tentacular collar, adjacent to the introvert, and around the mouth.   From the circular muscle layer columns of muscle fibers may ascend through the dermis to the under-surface of the epidermis.   The five longitudinal muscle bands, occupying the radial positions, are single in the Apoda, Elasipoda, and Dendro-chirota, usually double in the Molpadonia and Aspidochirota, that is, medially attached by connective tissue to the undersurface of the ambu-lacrum (Figs. 57D, 64A).   The muscle fibers consist of long slender cells of the smooth type.   The longitudinal muscle bands when highly developed are composed of cylindrical strands with the muscle cells at the surface of the strands.   The long muscle cells of the retractors of *Cucumaria miniata* contain 2 to 20 fibrils imbedded in a connective-tissue mesh (Hall, 1927).   The inner surface of the body wall is clothed with the ciliated peritoneum.

The tentacles and locomotory and papillate podia have the same general structure as the body wall but differ in detail.   Usually their covering epidermis is taller and better defined, their connective-tissue layer thinner, their sensory and gland cells more abundant, and their nervous and muscular provision more conspicuous.   Podia and tentacles are considered further in connection with the water-vascular system.

The dermis contains, chiefly in its superficial layers, the endoskeletal ossicles or spicules (called *deposits* in taxonomic works) that constitute the outstanding characteristic of the class.   They are of microscopic size (except when forming a surface armor) and are believed to represent an archaic or persistent embryonic state of the skeleton.   They are fenestrated calcareous bits that occur in an endless variety of shapes, and these shapes, many of which have acquired distinctive but fantastic names in holothurian taxonomy, are of paramount importance in species identification, so much so that in modern taxonomic studies on holo-thurians illustrations are often confined to representations of the ossicles. Each species is characterized by the forms of its ossicles.   However, ossicles are lacking in a few holothurians and in others may be wanting from large areas of the body wall.   If the body wall is thin, the ossicles can be seen by mounting a bit for microscopic examination, but in thick-walled species the ossicles must be freed by dissolving a piece of body wall in caustic solutions.

The shapes of ossicles found in a given holothurian may bear some, but not much, relation to its ordinal or familial position, and surprisingly different ossicles may be found in related genera.   The simpler shapes include smooth or warty or spiny rods, with or without end knobs and branches, and various sorts of fenestrated plates.   Such rods and plates are seen in *Actinopyga* (Fig. 48D) and *Cucumaria* (Fig. 47C).   An oval

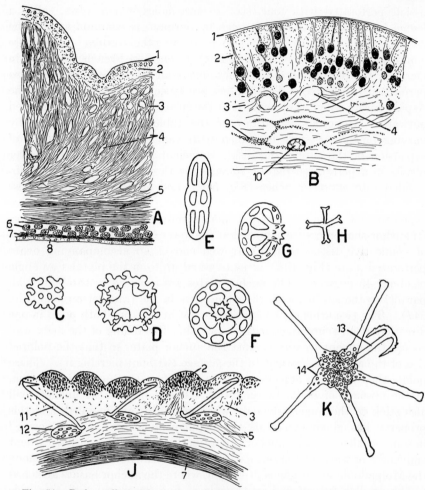

Fig. 54.—Body wall, ossicles. *A*, section through the body wall of a holothurian. *B*, enlarged view of the epidermis of a holothurian. (*A*, *B*, *after Jourdan*, 1883.) *C*, rosette. *D*, basket. (*C*, *D*, *after Deichmann*, 1930.) *E*, button. *F*, table, from above. *G*, table, from the side. *H*, young state of ossicle, typical four-rayed shape with forked ends. (*E–H*, *Holothuria*, from life.) *J*, section through the body wall of *Synapta*, with anchors in place (*after Woodland*, 1906). *K*, anchor type of *Molpadia* (*after Danielsson and Koren*, 1882). 1, cuticle; 2, epidermis; 3, outer loose connective tissue of dermis; 4, holes in same where ossicles were removed with acid; 5, inner dense layer of dermis; 6, lacuna filled with coelomocytes; 7, circular muscle layer; 8, coelomic lining epithelium; 9, pigment cell; 10, coelomocyte; 11, anchor in place; 12, anchor plate; 13, anchor; 14, supporting fenestrated rods.

ossicle perforated with four, six, or more holes in two rows, called a *button* in English, a *buckle* or *clasp* in German, is common among the Aspidochirota (Fig. 54*E*) but also found in other orders. In a more complicated type, termed *table* in English, *tower* in French, and *stool* in German, the perforated disk or plate bears an erect spire or tower, also perforated (Fig. 52*B*). These tables are especially characteristic of the Aspidochirota where they occur near the surface with the towers directed outward. Numerous variations of the table type are produced by varying heights of spire combined with varying shapes or degrees of expansion of the supporting disk. Sufficient suppression of the tower results in a perforated plate. *Rosettes* are short pump rods much subdivided into short branches (Fig. 54*C*), and *baskets* are more or less concave perforated plates with a toothed edge (Fig. 54*D*). A distinctive type of ossicle peculiar to the apodous family Synaptidae is the *anchor*, an anchor-shaped ossicle attached at the lower end of its shank by means of connective tissue to the narrowed end of an accompanying ovate perforated plate (Fig. 49*E*), so as to stand up from the plate at an angle of about 45 degrees. The anchor plates are oriented in the body wall parallel to the surface with their long axes in the transverse plane (Fig. 54*J*). The two arms of the anchor are not in line, but both point in one direction at an acute angle with the shank. Stretching of the body wall causes the anchor to sink against the anchor plate, so that the pointed tips of the arms are brought to the surface (without piercing it). These points then catch on objects and thus serve for attachment in crawling, in the absence of podia in synaptids. The points of the anchors will also stick to the fingers strongly when synaptids are handled, and this property has given synaptids the popular name of "anchor worms" in some localities. The anchors are often lodged in more or less evident eminences or warts of the surface (Fig. 49*D*). Anchors also occur among the Molpadonia in the genus *Molpadia*, where the anchor base is attached to the swollen fenestrated inner ends of five (or more) radiating rods (Fig. 54*K*). Another apodous family, the Chiridotidae, is characterized by *wheels*, a type of ossicle formed like a tiny wheel with 6 to 24 spokes (Fig. 55*E*, *F*). In *Chiridota*, the wheels are generally aggregated into warts or papillae called *wheel papillae* that may be distributed over the whole surface or may be limited to interradial areas, especially the dorsal interradii. Wheels are also found in the order Elasipoda (Fig. 55*A*), but a more characteristic ossicle of this order is some variant of a four-branched type, especially one consisting of four arched spiny legs bearing one or more spiny projections (Fig. 55*B*, *C*). Ossicles resembling a C also occur in the Elasipoda, as well as in the aspidochirote genus *Stichopus* (Fig. 52*C*). Various small solid ossicles are called *miliary granules*.

There are ossicles in the tentacles, papillate podia, and usually as end

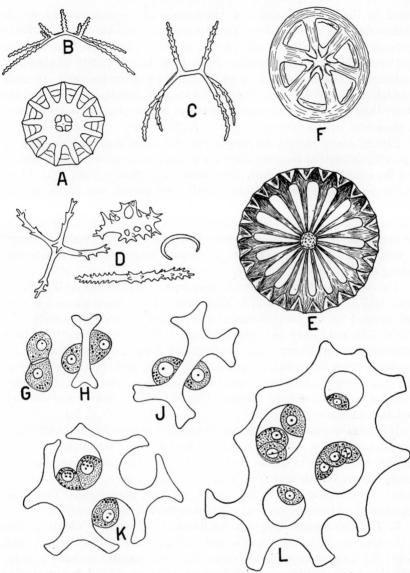

Fig. 55.—Ossicles (continued). *A–D*, ossicle types of Elasipoda (*after Théel*, 1882). *A*, wheel. *B*, *C*, types with four spiny legs. *D*, four-rayed type, spiny rods, C. *E*, wheel of chiridotid *Myriotrochus* (*after Danielsson and Koren*, 1882). *F*, six-spoked wheel of *Chiridota* (*after H. L. Clark*, 1907). *G–L*, stages in the development of ossicles of *Cucumaria* (*after Woodland*, 1906). *G*, rod beginning between two mesenchyme cells. *H*, rod forked at ends. *J*, forks enlarged. *K*, forks branching. *L*, branches fused to form perforated plate.

plates in the adhesive disks of the locomotory podia, further in the mesenteries and other internal structures; and all of these may differ in shape or size from the ossicles of the general body wall. Further, the developmental stages of ossicles differ from the definitive shapes and thus complicate taxonomic determinations based on the ossicles. Juvenile holothurians may be provided with types of ossicles wanting in the adult; thus wheels are present in synaptid larvae (Fig. 56C) but absent in the adults of this family.

Finally there should be mentioned the large surface scales of the family Psolidae that form a protective armor for the general body surface and the anus and close over the retracted introvert (Fig. 50C, E). These scales are rounded or rhomboidal perforated plates, smooth or with a warty surface (Fig. 50C, E), imbricated in the familiar species *Psolus squamatus* (Fig. 50E). In some species of *Psolus*, the protective scales for the introvert and anus are five in number, symmetrically arranged around the openings (Fig. 86A). A surface armor of scales also occurs among the Elasipoda.

The development of ossicles has been repeatedly described (Woodland, 1906, 1907; Domantay, 1933). Most types of ossicles begin as a minute rod secreted by the cooperation of two or more mesenchyme cells (Fig. 55G). This rod increases in size and soon forks at the ends into a shape somewhat resembling an X; by repeated forkings and union of the branches types of ossicles based on a fenestrated plate result (Fig. 55H–L). Wheels, however, begin as minute disks on which the spokes originate as scallops of the margin (Fig. 56A–C). Anchors start as rods that fork at one end only.

It is usually stated that the ossicles consist of pure calcium carbonate, but the author has failed to find any chemical analyses of them. They dissolve completely in acidic media. In many Molpadonia ossicles may become coated with layers of a yellow, brown, or wine-red substance shown by Mörner (1902) to consist of iron phosphate. This may completely replace the original calcium carbonate of the ossicles.

**5. The Calcareous Ring and the Retractor Muscles.**—The beginning of the pharynx of holothurians is encircled by a ring of calcareous plates, called the *calcareous ring*, and probably homologous, at least in part, with the Aristotle's lantern of echinoids. This ring is of importance as a support for the pharynx, nerve ring, and water vessels, and as a point of insertion of the longitudinal muscle bands. In size and shape the pieces forming the ring vary greatly in different holothurians. They are bound firmly together by means of connective tissue. Typically there are five radial and five interradial pieces; the latter are generally smaller than the former. In the Apoda there are often more than 10 plates in the ring, up to 18, through the interpolation of additional interradials in relation to the number of tentacles; such addition of interradial pieces may be limited to the dorsal side.  On the other hand, the calcareous ring may be greatly reduced, as generally in the Elasipoda, and this reduction may involve the disappearance of the interradial plates; but at least the radial pieces are always present.

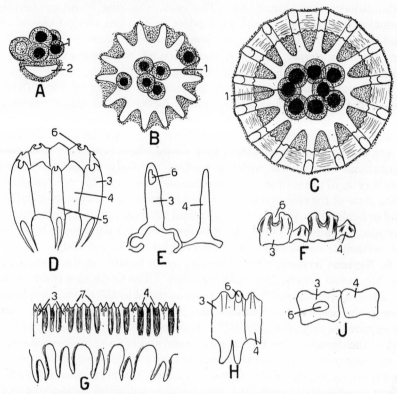

Fig. 56.—Ossicles (concluded), calcareous ring.   *A–C*, stages in the development of the wheel of the synaptid larva (*after Woodland*, 1907).   *D*, calcareous ring of *Thyone briareus*. *E*, two pieces of the calcareous ring of *Cucumaria frondosa* (*after H. L. Clark*, 1904).   *F*, four pieces of the calcareous ring of *Holothuria mexicana*.   *G*, calcareous ring of *Acaudina* (Molpadonia) opened and spread out (*after Sluiter*, 1901); note difference of middorsal interradial from the others.   *H*, two pieces of calcareous ring of *Chiridota* (Apoda).   *J*, two pieces of the calcareous ring of *Leptosynapta* (Apoda).   (*H, J, after H. L. Clark*, 1907.) 1, mesenchyme cells; 2, early disk stage of wheel; 3, radial piece; 4, interradial piece; 5, dwarfed mid-ventral piece; 6, notch or hole for passage of radial water vessel; 7, enlarged middorsal interradial piece.

The pieces forming the calcareous ring are in general squarish or rectangular plates whose anterior margins are often drawn out into pointed or blunt projections, while the posterior margins of the radial pieces often bear two tail-like projections that enclose the corresponding radial water canal between them (Figs. 56*D*, *G*, 62*A*).  These tails or the entire calcareous ring may be made up of numerous small pieces

(Fig. 62*A*).   The anterior end of the radial plates is notched or perforated with a hole (Fig. 56*D–J*) for the passage of the radial water canal, and the inner surface of these plates bears a groove into which the main stems of the radial canals fit.   The longitudinal muscle bands and pharynx retractors insert in depressions on the outer surface of the anterior part of the radial pieces (Fig. 61*A*).   The calcareous ring is not necessarily symmetrical; often, especially in dendrochirotes, the ventral pieces are smaller (Fig. 56*D*) than the corresponding dorsal pieces and may differ from them in shape.   Further, the shape of the pieces may exhibit bilaterality with right-left mirror imaging.

The longitudinal muscle bands terminate anteriorly on the anterior part of the outer surfaces of the radial pieces of the calcareous ring; consequently contraction of these bands would tend to pull the buccal membrane and surrounding tentacles inward.   However, in all Dendrochirota and in a few Molpadonia and Apoda, there is split off from each longitudinal band in the anterior part of the body a special retractor muscle (Fig. 67) that crosses the coelom and inserts on the corresponding radial plate of the calcareous ring, either in common with the longitudinal band or behind it.   When the longitudinal bands are paired, the retractors may also be paired.   These pharynx retractors act to pull the introvert and tentacular crown completely into the interior of the body.

**6. Nervous System.**—The nervous system consists of the main nerve ring, the radial nerves, and their branches.   The nerve ring is a circular or somewhat pentagonal flattened band situated in the buccal membrane close to the bases of the tentacles and just anterior to or slightly within the calcareous ring (Fig. 57*A–C*).   The nerve ring lies in the innermost part of the dermis of the buccal membrane and is more or less in contact on its inner side with a circular coelomic cavity in this membrane, termed the *peribuccal sinus*.   From its outer surface, the nerve ring gives off a strong ganglionated nerve into each tentacle and from its inner or both surfaces nerves arise that supply the buccal membrane and pharynx (Fig. 57*B, C*).   At each radius, a radial nerve issues from the nerve ring and passes outward through the notch or hole of the radial plate of the calcareous ring.   The five radial nerves course along the ambulacra in the innermost fibers of the dermis of the body wall, just external to the radial water vessel.   To the outer side of the radial nerve lies a cavity, the *epineural* canal or sinus, and to its inner side another cavity, the *hyponeural* canal or sinus, separated by a thin partition from the underlying radial water vessel (Fig. 57*D*).   The epineural sinuses are continuous anteriorly with a circular sinus lodged in a furrow on the anterior face of the nerve ring and giving off sinuses along the tentacular nerves. The hyponeural sinuses end blindly anteriorly.

The radial nerve is a somewhat flattened ganglionated cord divided

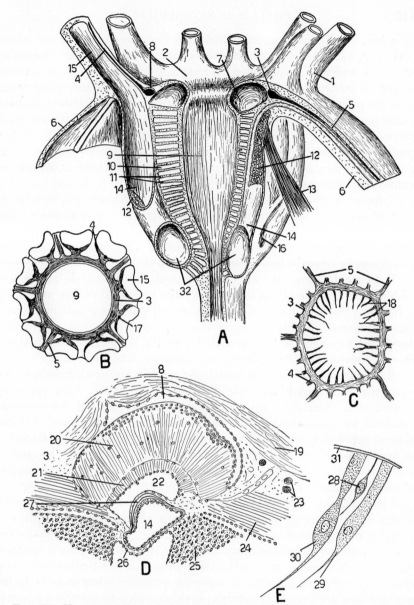

Fig. 57.—Nervous system. *A*, longitudinal section through the anterior end of *Cucumaria*, showing location of the nerve ring. *B*, transverse section through the tentacle bases, showing the nerve ring, *Cucumaria*. (*A, B, after Hérouard*, 1889.) *C*, nerve ring of *Kolga* (Elasipoda) (*after Danielsson and Koren*, 1882). *D*, section through an ambulacrum of *Caudina*, showing radial nerve. *E*, sensory nerve cell of *Caudina*, with accompanying cells. (*D, E, after Gerould*, 1896.) 1, tentacle base; 2, buccal membrane; 3, nerve ring; 4, tentacular nerve; 5, radial nerve; 6, cut body wall; 7, peribuccal sinus; 8, epineural sinus; 9, pharynx; 10, peripharyngeal sinus; 11, suspensors of pharynx; 12, pieces of calcareous ring; 13, retractor muscle; 14, radial canal of water-vascular system; 15, water-vascular canal of tentacle; 16, communication of peripharyngeal sinus with general coelom; 17, blood sinus of tentacle; 18, nerves to buccal membrane; 19, dermis of body wall; 20, ectoneural part of radial nerve; 21, hyponeural band of radial nerve; 22, hyponeural sinus; 23, muriform coelomocytes; 24, circular muscle layer of body wall; 25, longitudinal muscle bands; 26, coelomic lining; 27, small coelomic canal; 28, sensory nerve cell; 29, ordinary epidermal cell; 30, gland cell; 31, cuticle; 32, water ring.

by a thin longitudinal partition into a thicker outer and a thinner inner part (Fig. 57*D*).  The outer or ectoneural part together with the nerve ring with which it is continuous corresponds to the ectoneural nervous system of other echinoderms.  The ectoneural band of the radial nerve gives off ganglionated nerves (accompanied by a branch of the epineural sinus) into the locomotory and papillate podia and ramifies into a general plexus in the body wall that probably supplies the sense organs.  At the posterior end the ectoneural band terminates with the last podia.  The inner or hyponeural band of the radial nerve is regarded as mainly or exclusively motor; it supplies the muscle fibers of the body wall and also participates in the general body-wall plexus.  Anteriorly it dies away without reaching the main nerve ring and posteriorly it ceases before reaching the body end.  It no doubt corresponds to the deeper oral or hyponeural system of other echinoderms.  The aboral system, so prominent in crinoids, is completely wanting in holothurians.

**7. Sense Organs.**—As already indicated, the dermis is permeated with a general nerve plexus originating from the radial nerves, and there is further evidence of an additional subepidermal plexus running immediately beneath the inner ends of the epidermal cells (Fig. 58*A*), best developed according to Hamann (1884) at the body ends.  With these plexi are connected the ordinary neurosensory cells, presumably tango- or chemoreceptors, that are found throughout the epidermis but are especially numerous in the more sensitive body ends.  They are long slender cells (Fig. 58*C*) with an enlargement containing the nucleus, proximal to which the cell narrows to a filament continuous with the general nerve plexus.  More complicated sense organs are known chiefly in synaptids, where they appear to compensate for the lack of podia.  The surface of synaptids is roughened or warty, and these elevations are of glandulosensory nature, containing a sensory bud encircled by gland cells (Fig. 58*D*).  These sensory buds are composed of neurosensory cells whose basal filaments converge to form a nerve fiber that enters a ganglion of the dermal nerve plexus (Fig. 58*D*).  Such a ganglion underlies each of the glandulosensory elevations of the synaptid.  Another type of sense organ occurs on the inner surface of the tentacle stalks of synaptids and other Apoda.  A series of little elevations here (1 to 30 per tentacle) are found on microscopic examination to contain a sensory pit ciliated at the bottom (Fig. 58*E, F*).  Cuénot (1948) surmises that these pits serve to test the properties of the surrounding medium.

Statocysts, presumably serving to orient the animal with respect to gravity, occur in synaptids, elasipods, and molpadonians.  In synaptids, there is a pair of statocysts along each radial nerve shortly after exit of the latter from the calcareous ring.  Synaptid statocysts (Fig. 59*B, C*) are hollow spheres of flattened nonciliated epithelium,

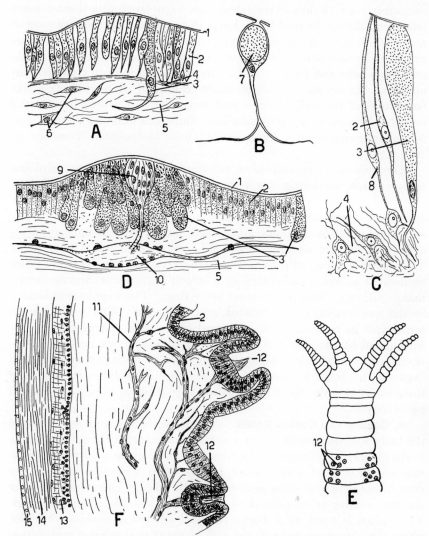

FIG. 58.—Nervous system, sense organs. *A*, section through the body wall near the anus of a synaptid, showing subepidermal plexus. *B*, goblet type of gland cell of a synaptid. *C*, neurosensory cell of a synaptid with accompanying cells. *D*, section through the body wall of a synaptid, showing sensory bud with accompanying glands. *E*, inner surface of a tentacle of *Leptosynapta*, showing tentacular pits. (*A–C, E, after Hamann,* 1884.) *F*, section through inner wall of a tentacle of a synaptid, showing tentacular pits, also nerve plexus. (*D, F, after Cuénot,* 1891a.) 1, cuticle; 2, ordinary epidermal cells; 3, gland cell; 4, subepidermal plexus; 5, dermis; 6, connective-tissue cells; 7, goblet; 8, neurosensory cell; 9, sensory bud; 10, ganglion of sensory bud; 11, general nerve plexus of dermis; 12, tentacular pits; 13, tentacular nerve; 14, longitudinal muscle layer of tentacle; 15, coelomic lining of tentacle lumen.

enclosing 1 to 20 lithocytes; these are vacuolated cells containing a refringent inorganic material. Each statocyst is supplied by a short nerve trunk from the adjacent radial nerve. The occurrence of statocysts in the elasipod family Elpidiidae was reported by Théel (1882) and Danielsson and Koren (1882). In the species investigated there are numerous statocysts (up to 100) disposed around the nerve ring at the beginnings of the radial nerves and along the two ventrolateral radial nerves. Five pairs of statocysts with numerous granules located close to the nerve ring occur in *Paracaudina* (Order Molpadonia, Yamanouchi, 1929a).

The general body surface of holothurians is sensitive to light, but the receptors mediating this *dermoptic* sense have not been definitely identified. Organized photoreceptors occur in a few synaptids (several species of *Synaptula*, *Euapta lappa*, and *Opheodesoma glabra*). The scanty information available about these photoreceptors appears in the articles of Ludwig and Barthels (1891) and H. L. Clark (1898, 1907). They occur as a pair of pigmented eye-like structures at the base of each tentacle (Fig. 59*D*), innervated by a strong branch from the tentacular nerve or directly from the adjacent nerve ring. These eyes are imbedded in the mesenchyme, not situated at the surface. The nerve branch terminates in a swollen end composed of a group of transparent cells surrounded by pigment and covered over by altered vacuolated mesenchyme also containing pigment (Fig. 59*E*). Pigment spots found between the tentacle bases of various other synaptids and originally thought to be eyes have been shown to consist of clumps of colored coelomocytes.

**8. Coelom and Coelomocytes.**—A spacious coelom is present between the body wall and the digestive tract, extending from the calcarous ring to the cloacal attachment. The coelom is but slightly subdivided by the mesenteries of the digestive tract, mostly three in number, as these are very incomplete and often permeated with holes. The arrangement of the mesenteries is considered in connection with the digestive tract. The coelom is lined by a flat to cuboidal ciliated epithelium that also forms the outermost layer of the wall of the digestive tract and clothes both surfaces of the mesenteries, which are double-walled, as typical of coelomate animals. The interior of the mesenteries consists of connective tissue and muscle fibers (Fig. 61*C*).

The hyponeural sinuses that accompany the nervous system and the water-vascular canals are also of coelomic nature and are lined by coelomic epithelium. A portion of the main coelom is more or less cut off around the pharynx. Anteriorly the pharynx passes through the calcareous ring to which it is attached by strands composed of connective tissue and muscle fibers, known as the *pharynx suspensors*. These may be irregularly or regularly arranged. Posteriorly the pharynx passes through the main ring of the water-vascular system, and the five radial canals ascend along the sides of the pharynx. Thus the coelom adjacent to the pharynx is somewhat enclosed by all these structures associated with the pharynx, although at first communicating widely with the main coelom. But in many holothurians these wide communications are diminished by the growth of tissue between the ascending radial canals. The pharynx thus comes to be surrounded by another wall, with a coelomic cavity, the *peripharyngeal sinus*, between the two walls (Fig. 57*A*); this sinus is crossed by the strands of the pharyngeal suspensors (Figs. 57*A*, 62*B*). The peribuccal sinus in the buccal membrane already mentioned lies just anterior to but completely closed off from the peripharyngeal sinus (Fig. 57*A*). The apertures of communication between the peripharyngeal sinus and the general coelom are of varying size and location (Figs. 61*A*, 62*A*, *B*). A coelomic sinus may also surround the esophagus and stomach. A coelomic ring, the *perianal sinus*, completely cut off from the general coelom, lies in the body wall around the anus; it is wanting in synaptids. The coelom opens to the exterior by a pore near the anus in *Labidoplax buski* (Order Apoda, Becher, 1912). Five such pores, one at the base of each of the anal papillae, were reported for *Paracaudina* (Order Molpadonia) by Kawamoto (1927), but later Kitao (1935) found that the pores are inconstant in number and present only in older animals as a result of rupture through thin places in the ambulacra.

The order Apoda is characterized by the possession of certain peculiar coelomic organs wanting in other holothurians. The best known of these are the *ciliated urns* or *funnels* that apparently are present in all members of the order. They vary much in number, size, and location in different species but are usually found on the mesenteries near the attachment of the latter to the body wall or on the wall near these attachments. In shape they resemble a minute cornucopia or calla lily rather than an urn or funnel (Fig. 60*B*). They are lined by a tall ciliated epithelium and are clothed externally with coelomic epithelium that also covers the attachment stalk. In some Apoda a number of urns may be mounted on mesenterial folds, forming what are called *trees of urns* (Fig. 60*A*). The cavity of the urns is filled with clumps of coelomocytes and amorphous material. Following injection of carbon or carmine particles into the coelom of Apoda, the color can be seen through the thin body wall gradually aggregating along the lines of location of the urns, and histological investigation of such injected specimens shows that the particles have accumulated in the urns (Fig. 60*C*), either directly or enclosed in coelomocytes (Schultz, 1895; H. L. Clark, 1899; Cuénot, 1902). The color later disappears as the loaded coelomocytes make their way into

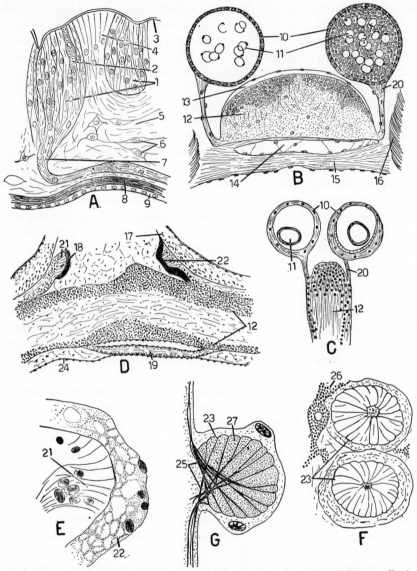

FIG. 59.—Sense organs (concluded), coelomic organs.  A, section of inner wall of a
tentacle of *Caudina*, showing sensory buds (*after Gerould*, 1896).   B, section through the
beginning of a radial nerve of Leptosynapta, showing the two statocysts (*after Cuénot*,
1891a); one statocyst is cut through the center, the other through the wall; note numerous
lithocytes.   C, statocysts of *Synaptula hydriformis*, with single lithocyte.   D, horizontal
section through nerve ring and tentacle base of *Synapta vivipara*, showing location of eyes
(*after H. L. Clark*, 1898).   E, section through an eye of *Synaptula hydriformis*.   (C, E,
*after H. L. Clark*, 1907.)   F, two contractile rosettes of *Rhabdomolgus*.   G, schematic section through a contractile rosette.   (F, G, *after Becher*, 1907.)   1, sensory bud; 2, gland
cell; 3, cuticle; 4, ordinary epidermal cells; 5, dermis; 6, connective-tissue cells; 7, branch of
tentacular nerve; 8, longitudinal muscle layer of tentacular wall; 9, coelomic lining of

the body wall. The masses gathered by the urns may also fall into the coelom, contributing to waste clumps known as *brown bodies*. These observations indicate an excretory or athrocytic function of the urns. Another type of coelomic organ known for only a very few synaptids and best described for *Rhabdomolgus ruber* by Becher (1907) is the *pulsatile rosette*. These are little rounded projections of the coelomic wall found near the calcareous ring. They are covered externally with peritoneum and are composed internally of radiating columns of connective tissue interspersed with muscle fibers (Fig. 59*F*, *G*). These rosettes pulsate a few times per minute. Finally Cuénot (1948) has reported in two synaptids *vibratile clubs*, minute clubs with ciliated ends projecting into the coelom along the longitudinal muscle bands. No function has been suggested for either the rosettes or the clubs.

The coelom is filled with a fluid, the chemical nature of which is considered under physiology. In this fluid float a variety of free cells that will be called by the general name of coelomocytes, despite the fact that they also occur abundantly in the tissues and in the water-vascular and haemal systems. These cells are mentioned in almost every article about the morphology of holothurians, but particular attention has been paid to them by Hérouard (1889), Becher (1907), Haanen (1914), Théel (1921), Kindred (1924), Kawamoto (1927), and Ohuye (1934, 1936). The types of cells present seem to vary in form and number in different holothurians, but several kinds appear to be common throughout the class (Fig. 60).

*a. Hemocytes.*—These are found throughout the class, especially in the haemal system, but also elsewhere, and are generally regarded as corresponding to the red blood corpuscles of vertebrates. They are circular or oval flattened, generally biconvex, nucleated disks that are straw yellow singly, red en masse, and so numerous in some species as to lend a red color to the haemal system, the coelomic contents, or the entire animal. They are capable of movement and may put out one or more long thin pseudopodia, especially when removed from the body. They have been proved to contain haemoglobin by Howell (1885, 1886) and Van der Hyde (1922a) for *Thyone*, Hogben and Van der Lingen (1928) for *Cucumaria*, and Kobayashi (1932) for *Paracaudina chilensis* and *Molpadia roretzii*. The haemoglobin is not identical with that of vertebrates and probably differs in different holothurians. There are 150,000 hemocytes per cubic millimeter in the coelomic fluid of *Paracaudina* (Okazaki and Koizumi, 1926).

---

tentacular lumen; 10, statocyst; 11, statoliths; 12, radial nerve; 13, epineural sinus; 14, radial water vessel; 15, circular muscle; 16, longitudinal muscle bands; 17, tentacle base; 18, eye; 19, buccal nerve; 20, nerve to statocyst; 21, sensory cells of eye; 22, mesenchymal cap of eye; 23, contractile rosette; 24, coelomic lining; 25, muscle fibers of rosette; 26, pigment cell; 27, connective-tissue columns of rosette.

*b. Phagocytes.*—These are active amoeboid cells of varying appearance that phagocytize degenerating tissues and cells. They are called various names in the literature, as cells with long pseudopods (Hérouard), hyaline amoeboid corpuscles (Ohuye), and bladder amoebocytes (Kindred). The name bladder amoebocyte refers to the petaloid pseudopods (Fig. 60*F*) often put out by these cells, especially after removal from the body.

*c. Amoebocytes with Colorless Spherules.*—This type of coelomocyte, a rounded or oval amoebocyte packed with colorless spherules, is widespread among holothurians and usually found in numbers wandering in the body wall. They are the cells designated by Hamann (1883, 1884) as plasma wandering cells. According to Cuénot (1891a), who calls them *muriform* (mulberry-like) cells, the spherules are of protein nature and hence represent food reserves.

*d. Amoebocytes with Colored Spherules.*—These resemble the preceding type in general appearance and behavior, but the spherules are colored yellow to brown and are generally believed to represent excretory material.

*e. Homogeneous Amoebocytes.*—Amoeboid cells without definite inclusions are reported by Hamann (1884) and Becher (1907). They may represent stages of some of the other types.

*f. Crystal Cells.*—Small cells nearly filled with a crystal, mostly of rhomboidal shape, have been noticed by several authors (Théel, Kawamoto, Ohuye).

*g. Vesicular Amoebocytes.*—Cells nearly filled with a large vesicle are listed by Théel and Ohuye.

*h. Other Types.*—Less common forms recorded are *spindle* amoebocytes of elongated spindle shape (Fig. 60*E*) and *minute* corpuscles (Fig. 60*D*), very small rounded cells; the latter may be free peritoneal cells.

Some examples may be cited of the combinations found in different holothurians. In the synaptid *Rhabdomolgus ruber* Becher (1907) reported hemocytes, phagocytes, homogeneous amoebocytes, amoebocytes with colored spherules, and giant wander cells containing large inclusions that he believed to represent phagocytes enlarged with ingested material. *Mesothuria* (Aspidochirota) is provided with hemocytes, amoebocytes with colorless spherules, homogeneous amoebocytes, and vesicular amoebocytes (Haanen, 1914). Very complete studies were made on the Molpadonia by Kawamoto (1927), who studied *Paracaudina*, and Ohuye (1936), who studied *Molpadia*. In the former were found hemocytes, amoebocytes with colorless spherules, those with colored spherules, and crystal and minute cells; in addition to these five kinds, *Molpadia* also possesses phagocytes, vesicular amoebocytes, and spindle

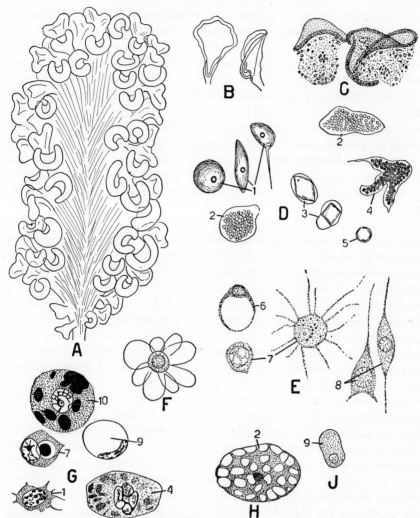

Fig. 60.—Coelomic organs (concluded), coelomocytes. *A*, tree of urns of *Chiridota*. *B*, urns of *Anapta*. (*A, B, after Semper*, 1868.) *C*, synaptid urns after injection of carbon (*after Cuénot*, 1902). *D*, coelomocytes of *Paracaudina* (*after Kawamoto*, 1927). *E*, additional types found in *Molpadia* (*after Ohuje*, 1936). *F*, petaloid stage of phagocyte of *Cucumaria* (*after Kindred*, 1924). *G*, coelomocytes of *Rhabdomolgus* (*after Becher*, 1907). *H*, amoebocyte with colorless spherules of *Holothuria*. *J*, homogeneous amoebocyte of *Cucumaria*. (*H, J, after Hamann*, 1884.) 1, hemocytes; 2, amoebocytes with colorless spherules; 3, crystal cells; 4, amoebocyte with colored spherules; 5, minute corpuscle; 6, vesicular amoebocyte; 7, phagocytes; 8, spindle amoebocytes; 9, homogeneous amoebocyte; 10, giant phagocyte.

amoebocytes.  It is, of course, always possible that some of the described types of coelomocytes represent phases or stages of others.

Coelomocytes appear to originate from mesenchyme cells in the main channels of the haemal system and not in the polian vesicles as supposed by Cuénot (1891b).

In the coelom of holothurians are often found small clumps known as *brown bodies*, free or attached by strands.  These may consist exclusively of amoebocytes with colored spherules (Becher, 1907); parasites, especially gregarines, and other ejecta are often included.

**9. Water-vascular System.**—This system is built on the same pentamerous radial plan as in other echinoderms.  The center of the system is the *water ring* or *ring canal*, a usually conspicuous tube that encircles the proximal part of the pharynx, more or less posterior to the calcareous ring (Fig. 63*A*).  The ring canal is lined by a ciliated epithelium, underlain by a layer of circular muscle fibers (Fig. 61*D*); this is followed by connective tissue, often containing coelomocytes and sometimes calcareous ossicles, and finally the ring is covered externally by peritoneum. The ring canal bears two kinds of appendages, the *polian vesicles* and the *stone canals*.  A polian vesicle is a rounded, ovoid, or elongated sac hanging from the ring canal into the coelom and opening into the ring canal by a narrowed neck (Figs. 61*A*, 62*A*, *B*).  It varies in size from a small appendage to a long tube that may reach half or more of the body length.  Ontogenetically the polian vesicle is single and dependent from the ventral or left-ventral side of the ring canal, and this condition persists throughout life in many species; but often the number augments during growth.  Two or three up to ten or twelve polian vesicles are common among the Dendrochirota and Aspidochirota, whereas the Molpadonia and Elasipoda usually retain the single condition.  The greatest tendency to multiplication of polian vesicles is seen among the Apoda, where most species have several vesicles and a few up to fifty or more.  When numerous, the vesicles may continue to be borne on the ventral or left side of the water ring or may spread around the ring. Sometimes several vesicles attach to the ring by a single neck, thus presenting a branched appearance.  The wall of the vesicle is histologically similar to the wall of the water ring but thinner (Fig. 61*G*); often the interior contains coelomocytes.  The vesicles appear to function as expansion chambers for the water-vascular system.

A *stone canal* is a tube with calcified wall that springs from the ring canal and terminates in a madreporic plate or swelling perforated with holes and canals.  In holothurians there is typically a single stone canal that arises from the dorsal surface of the water ring, pursues a more or less sinuous course supported by the dorsal mesentery, and terminates in a madreporic swelling of varied shape.  Ontogenetically the stone canal

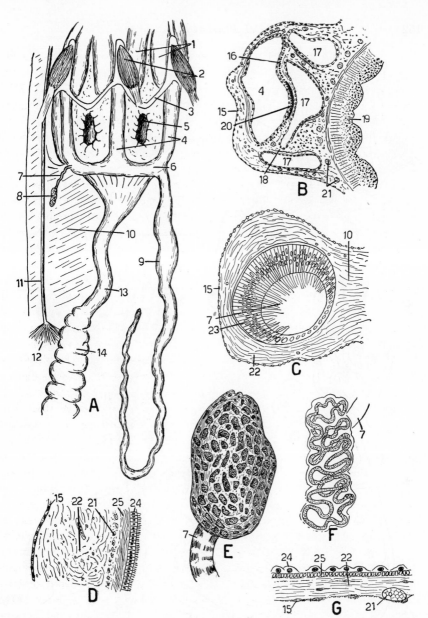

Fig. 61.—Water-vascular system. *A*, aquapharyngeal bulb of *Cucumaria*, from a dissection. *B*, part of a section through the aquapharyngeal bulb of *Cucumaria* (*after Hérouard*, 1889). *C*, section through the stone canal of *Caudina* (*after Gerould*, 1897). *D*, section through the ring-canal wall of *Stichopus* (*after Sivickis and Domantay*, 1928). *E*, madreporic body of *Mesothuria* (*after Haanen*, 1924). *F*, madreporic body of *Cucumaria* (original). *G*, section through the wall of a polian vesicle (*after Jourdan*, 1883). 1, tentacular ampullae; 2, retractor muscles of pharynx, cut across; 3, calcareous ring; 4, radial canals ascending aquapharyngeal bulb; 5, communication of peripharyngeal sinus with coelom; 6, ring canal; 7, stone canal; 8, madreporic body; 9, polian vesicle; 10, dorsal mesentery; 11, gonoduct; 12, gonad; 13, stomach; 14, intestine; 15, coelomic epithelium; 16, longitudinal muscle fibers of radial canal; 17, cavities of peripharyngeal sinus; 18, pharynx suspensors; 19, lining epithelium of pharynx; 20, blood sinus; 21, coelomocytes; 22, connective tissue; 23, epithelium of stone canal; 24, lining epithelium; 25, muscle layer.

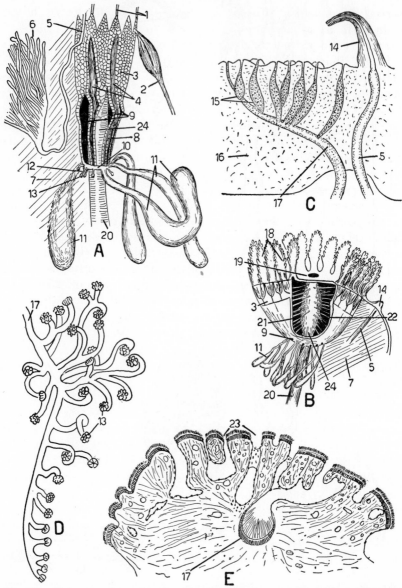

FIG. 62.—Water-vascular system (continued).  A, calcareous ring and aquapharyngeal bulb of *Thyone sacellus* (*after Selenka*, 1867); note four polian vesicles, five stone canals, long tails of calcareous ring, numerous small pieces composing ring.  B, aquapharyngeal bulb of a synaptid with numerous polian vesicles; single stone canal does not show.  (*A, B, after Selenka*, 1867.)  C, surface madrepore of an elasipod, with a number of pores (*after Théel*, 1882).  D, branching stone canal with many internal madreporic bodies, synaptid (*after J. Muller*, 1854).  E, section of internal madreporic body of *Mesothuria* (*after Haanen*, 1914).  1, radial canals exiting from calcareous ring; 2, retractor muscle (cut); 3, calcareous ring; 4, radial canals along aquapharyngeal bulb; 5, gonoduct; 6, gonad; 7, dorsal mesentery; 8, tails of radial pieces of calcareous ring; 9, communication of peri-

opens on the middorsal surface by a hydropore, but in the adult connection with the surface by one or several to many pores or canals is retained only in a few holothurians, chiefly Elasipoda (Fig. 62C). Usually in adult holothurians, connection with the surface is lost; the madreporic swelling may remain attached to the inner side of the body wall; more commonly, it loses contact with this wall; and often, especially in the Aspidochirota, support by the dorsal mesentery is also lost, so that stone canal and madrepore hang freely into the coelom. Like the polian vesicle the stone canal is subject to multiplication. A single canal is the rule among the Molpadonia and Elasipoda, but in the other orders there are usually several to many canals (Fig. 64B), especially among the Dendrochirota and Apoda. In some synaptids the single stone canal gives off a few to many branches, each with a madreporic termination (Fig. 62D). In case of several stone canals these tend to arise from the dorsal or right side of the water ring, thus opposite to the polian vesicles, but when sufficiently numerous may have any relation to the water ring. Of course, also, they are not related to the dorsal mesentery and hang into the coelom. Stone canals are usually short, but in some holothurians the single canal attains considerable length, up to 10 cm. or more. The canal is lined by a ciliated epithelium, very tall on the side away from the mesenterial attachment; this is followed by a connective-tissue layer packed with ossicles, and externally the canal is clothed with the coelomic epithelium continuous with that of the mesentery (Fig. 61C).

The madreporic termination of each stone canl consists of canals and pores through the surface near the gonopore in a few holothurians, as already noted, and in such cases the water-vascular system is in connection with the surrounding sea water. In most holothurians, however, the madreporic termination forms a definite body of rounded to elongated form that lies in the coelom, so that the water-vascular system no longer communicates with the exterior. The madreporic body (Fig. 61E, 62E) is permeated with ciliated pores and canals that open into the stone canal, either directly or by way of a central chamber. Not infrequently the madreporic surface shows a winding band, actually a ciliated groove with pores along its bottom (Fig. 61F). Like the stone canal, the madreporic body is stiffened by ossicles. It is entered laterally by the stone canal.

From the ring canal the five large conspicuous main stems of the radial canals ascend anteriorly along the pharynx complex (except in

---

pharyngeal sinus with general coelom; 10, water ring; 11, polian vesicles; 12, stone canals; 13, madreporic bodies; 14, genital papilla; 15, canals to external pores of madreporite; 16, cut body wall; 17, stone canal; 18, tentacles (contracted); 19, mouth; 20, stomach; 21, peripharyngeal sinus; 22, pharynx suspensors; 23, pores of internal madreporic body; 24, pharynx.

the Apoda).   As already noted, the pharynx is more or less enclosed
by an incomplete outer wall to which it is attached by suspensor strands
crossing the coelomic space between the two walls (Fig. 62*B*).   The
ascending radial canals form part of this outer wall (Fig. 61*A*) and
between them are seen the openings by which the enclosed coelomic space
communicates with the general coelom.   The calcareous ring is also
imbedded in the outer wall (Figs. 61*A*, 62*A*).   The whole complex is
called *aquapharyngeal bulb* in the older literature, and although the name
seems to have passed somewhat out of usage, it remains convenient.
The radial canals pass to the inner side of the radial pieces of the calcareous ring and there give off a branch into each tentacle (Fig. 63*A*).
The radial canals, now greatly diminished in diameter, then proceed
through the notch or hole in the corresponding radial pieces of the calcareous ring and run backward along the inner surface of the ambulacra.
In the Apoda the canals for the tentacles spring directly from the ring
canal, and there are no radial canals in the body wall.   In this order,
then, the entire water-vascular system consists of the ring canal with
its appendages and the tentacular canals; this condition, of course, is
correlated with the entire absence of podia (except the tentacles) in the
Apoda.   In histological construction the radial canals along the pharynx
are similar to the ring canal, except that the muscle fibers are longitudinal,
at least in part (Fig. 61*B*).

The tentacles, as already indicated, are actually podia of the water-
vascular system and as such are more properly termed buccal podia.
Their external features were already described.   They are hollow
extensions of the body wall and their lumina or tentacular canals are of
course water-vascular canals.   At the point of exit of each tentacular
canal from the radial canal there is found a valve that retards backflow
from the tentacles.   The tentacular canals are usually provided with
*ampullae*.   This is a short to long blind appendage arising from each
tentacular canal as the latter clears the anterior margin of the calcareous
ring and projecting backward.   When small, as in the Apoda, the
tentacular ampullae are more or less attached to the outer surface of the
calcareous ring.   In the Molpadonia and Aspidochirota, especially in
the latter, the tentacular ampullae are long and narrow and hang freely
into the coelom as a circle of long sacs around the aquapharyngeal bulb
(Fig. 63*A*, 64*B*).   Tentacular ampullae are lacking in the Elasipoda
and poorly developed, if at all present, in the Dendrochirota.

The tentacular wall, especially that of the stalk, resembles the body
wall histologically but differs in that the muscle fibers are always longitudinal (Fig. 63*D*); further, the tentacular nerve forms a broad band in
the inner tentacular wall (side facing the mouth) between the muscle
layer and the dermis.   In *Rhabdomolgus* there is a complete ring of

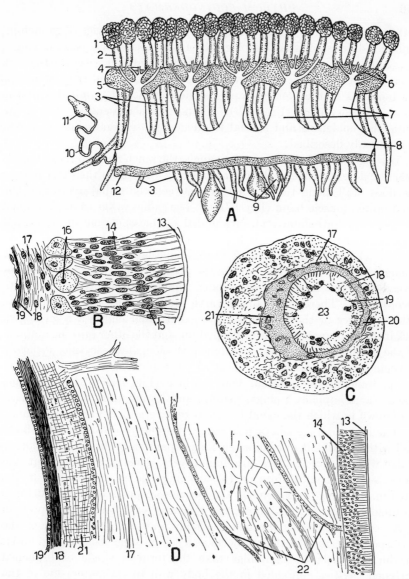

Fig. 63.—Water-vascular system (continued). *A*, main stems of the radial water canals of *Stichopus*, seen from the inner side, opened out, to show the tentacular branches (*after Sivickis and Domantay*, 1928). *B*, longitudinal section through a tentacle tip of *Holothuria* (*after Jourdan*, 1883). *C*, cross section of a tentacle of *Rhabdomolgus* with ring of nervous tissue (*after Becher*, 1907). *D*, longitudinal section through the stalk of a tentacle of *Leptosynapta* (*after Hamann*, 1884). 1, frond of tentacle; 2, stalk of tentacle; 3, tentacular ampullae; 4, radial canal emerging from calcareous ring; 5, calcareous ring; 6, tentacular branches from radial canals; 7, main stem of radial water canals; 8, ring water canal; 9, polian vesicles; 10, stone canal; 11, madreporic body; 12, cut edge; 13, cuticle; 14, epidermis; 15, neurosensory cells; 16, ganglion cells; 17, dermis; 18, longitudinal muscle layer; 19, coelomic lining; 20, nervous layer; 21, tentacular nerve; 22, nerve branches; 23, tentacular canal.

155

nervous tissue in the tentacle (Fig. 63*C*).  The finer twigs of branching tentacles differ somewhat histologically from the tentacle base, having a very tall epidermis and thin dermal and muscular layers (Fig. 63*B*).  A branch from the tentacular nerve proceeds into each end twig or lobe of the tentacles in the Dendro- and Aspidochirota and terminates at the tip in a sensory plate (Fig. 65*B*).  Gland and neurosensory cells of the tentacular epidermis and special tentacular sense organs in the Apoda were already described.

Having given off the tentacular canals, the much reduced radial canals clear the anterior edge of the calcareous ring and run in the inner part of the body wall along the ambulacra, between the radial nerve and the longitudinal muscle band (Fig. 57*D*).  The radial water canals are lined by coelomic epithelium and surrounded by mesenchyme in which are imbedded longitudinal muscle fibers on the side toward the radial nerve. The radial water canals give off to each side lateral branches or *podial canals* to supply the podia.  When the podia are irregularly arranged or spread into the interradii, the podial canals to them vary in length accordingly.  There is usually a valve present along the podial canal. After a longer or shorter course the podial canal makes a right-angled fork into one branch going into the podium and the other into the ampulla of the podium (Fig. 66*A*), a rounded or elongated sac that typically projects into the coelom in a position corresponding to the position of the podium on the external body surface (Fig. 64*A*).  Usually each podial canal supplies a single podium and its ampulla, but some cases are known in which the canal branches to several podia and ampullae.

The locomotory podia or pedicels are tubular projections of the body wall with or without a terminal sucking expansion or disk.  Locomotory podia with terminal disks are found very generally throughout the Dendro- and Aspidochirota on the creeping sole or on the radii of the trivium.  Among the Elasipoda the locomotory podia often lack definite terminal disks.  As just noted, the lumen of each locomotory podium is typically continuous through the body wall with the lumen of the corresponding ampulla that projects as a sac into the coelom (Fig. 66*A*). In the Elasipoda the ampullae take the form of single or branched flattened cavities concealed in the body wall to the outer side of the circular musculature.

The wall of the locomotory podia is similar histologically to the body wall except that the muscle layer, next to the coelomic lining of the lumen, is longitudinal in direction.  Each podium is supplied by a podial nerve that springs wholly from the ectoneural band of the radial nerve and is more or less accompanied by a branch of the epineural sinus. The podial nerve runs distally along one side of the podium, external to the muscle layer, and spreads out as a nervous layer beneath the tall

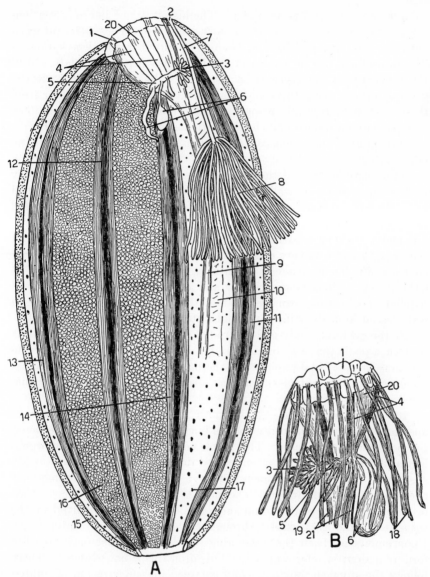

Fig. 64.—Water-vascular system (continued). *A*, interior ot *Holothuria mexicana* (*from life, Bahamas*), showing ampullae of creeping sole; tentacular ampullae omitted. *B*, aquapharyngeal bulb of same, showing long tentacular ampullae that surround it. 1, calcareous ring; 2, gonopore; 3, mass of stone canals; 4, radial water canals; 5, water ring; 6, polian vesicles; 7, gonoduct; 8, gonad; 9, intestine; 10, dorsal mesentery; 11, longitudinal muscle band of ambulacrum D; 12–14, longitudinal muscle bands of ambulacra A, B, and E respectively; 15, cut body wall; 16, ampullae of locomotory podia of sole; 17, ampullae of papillate podia (warts); 18, tentacular ampullae; 19, haemal ring; 20, aquapharyngeal bulb; 21, blood vessels.

epidermis of the tip (Fig. 66*A*, *D*).   The histology and nervous relations
are practically the same for locomotory podia with (Fig. 65*D*) and without (Fig. 66*C*) terminal disks.   There is usually, but not always, present
in the terminal disk an ossicle in the form of a perforated plate, called
the *end plate;* but end ossicles may also occur in locomotory podia without
disks.   In both types the wall usually contains ossicles that differ from
those of the body wall, being generally more or less rod-like.   The
ampullae are both lined and clothed with coelomic epithelium and have a
layer of muscle fibers, mostly longitudinal, next to the coelomic lining
(Fig. 66*A*).

As already stated, all the papillae, warts, and other nonlocomotory
protrusions of the body wall are homologous with podia, hence here called
*papillate podia*.   Each receives a water canal from the nearest radial
canal and is also provided with an inconspicuous ampulla.   In the large
aspidochirotes such as *Actinopyga* and *Holothuria*, the papillate podia of
the dorsal surface consist of slightly contractile warts bearing a highly
contractile filament that can be entirely withdrawn into the wart (Fig.
65*E*).   The various rims, fringes, and collars are composed of fused
papillate podia, as shown by the fact that each component receives a
water canal from the adjacent radial water canal (Fig. 66*B*).

At the posterior body end the radial canals terminate as the lumina
of the last podia that may or may not be altered to anal papillae encircling
the anus.   These anal papillae are the only podia present in the Molpadonia (except the tentacles) and here also contain the ends of the radial
canals as their lumina.

**10. Digestive System.**—The mouth is a circular or slightly oval
aperture situated in the center of the buccal membrane that is bordered
by the circlet of tentacles.   This whole complex represents the morphological anterior end but is often curved dorsally or ventrally as already
described.   The mouth is encircled by a sphincter muscle, sometimes
enclosed in a lip-like ridge.   The mouth leads into the pharynx that
occupies the center of the aquapharyngeal bulb (being supported by the
suspensors) and that passes through the calcareous and water rings.
Upon emergence from the water ring the digestive tract may take the
form of a short slender esophagus, but often this is not evident.   There
follows the stomach, obvious as an enlarged muscular region of limited
length in some forms as *Thyone* (Fig. 67) and synaptids (Fig. 68*A*) but
not definitely demarcated in many cases.   A slight constriction usually
marks the passage of the stomach into the intestine.   The intestine of
holothurians is typically very long, two or three to several times the
body length, and consequently is looped within the coelom (Figs. 67,
68*A*, 72*B*, 73, 74, 75).   The looping shows a definite arrangement,
corresponding to that of crinoids.   The intestine first descends toward

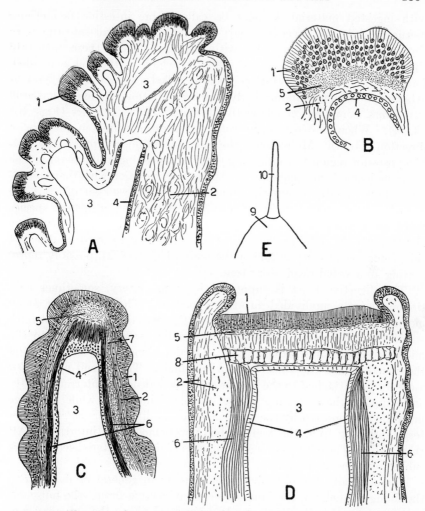

FIG. 65.—Water-vascular system (continued). *A*, section of a frond of a peltate tentacle of *Holothuria*. *B*, end of one of the tentacle branches of *A*. *C*, longitudinal section of a branch of a synaptid tentacle. *D*, longitudinal section of locomotory podium with terminal disk of *Holothuria*. (*A–D, after Hamann*, 1883.) *E*, papillate podium of *Actinopyga* with distal retractile filament (*from life*). 1, epidermis; 2, connective tissue; 3, tentacle lumen; 4, coelomic lining; 5, nervous end plate; 6, longitudinal muscle fibers; 7, branch of tentacular nerve; 8, spaces left by dissolution of skeletal end plate; 9, basal wart; 10, contractile filament.

the posterior end along the middorsal region, then bends and ascends anteriorly along the left side to nearly the level of the aquapharyngeal bulb. It then turns again and descends along the mid-ventral region directly backward to the anus. As this last descending part differs functionally from the rest of the intestine, being usually found distended with ingested material, it may be called large intestine (sometimes rectum), while the preceding part may be called small intestine. In those groups that are provided with respiratory trees, these open into the terminal part of the large intestine which is thereby expanded, forming a mostly short region usually called cloaca. The cloaca is attached to the surrounding body wall by radiating strands, the *cloacal suspensors*, composed of connective tissue and muscle fibers (Figs. 67, 73, 74). When viewed from in front, the intestine spirals in a clockwise direction. In the Molpadonia the cloaca continues through the tail-like posterior region to its tip (Fig. 49B), diminishing in diameter. The intestine is much shortened in the Apoda in correlation with their vermiform shape; in this group the stomach is usually well set off, but the intestine makes only a slight forward bend (Fig. 68A), or in some species takes an almost straight course to the anus. In some elasipods the cloaca gives off a blind sac or caecum extending forward on the left side, sometimes to the middle of the body (Théel, 1882), possibly representing an aborted respiratory tree.

The digestive tract is supported by a mesentery, sometimes continuous, mostly subdivided into three portions. The first part or *dorsal* mesentery attaches the anterior part of the digestive tract (esophagus, stomach, and a variable length of descending small intestine) to the middorsal interradius, namely, CD. The dorsal mesentery also supports the gonoduct and the stone canal when single. The second part or *left* mesentery is attached to the body wall in the left dorsal interradius, DE, and supports the ascending part of the small intestine; while the large intestine is supported by the third mesenterial division or *ventral* mesentery, springing from the ventral body wall mostly in interradius AB (Fig. 68B). The extents and attachments of the mesenterial sections are subject to some variation.

Histologically the digestive tract consists in general of five layers: the lining epithelium, the inner layer of connective tissue, the muscular layer, usually of both circular and longitudinal fibers, the outer layer of connective tissue, often very thin or even wanting, and the covering ciliated peritoneum. The inner wall of the pharynx and stomach is thrown into lengthwise folds. The pharynx is always lined by cuticle and the stomach usually so; and often cuticle extends into the intestine for a variable distance, even throughout its length. The lining epithelium of the digestive tract is sometimes ciliated, at least in part. It usually consists of tall epithelial cells that are generally interspersed with gland cells, often heavily so in the pharynx and stomach, although either may lack them. The lining epithelium of the digestive tract usually diminishes in height along the intestine and here is often devoid of gland cells, although these may be scantily present. The inner

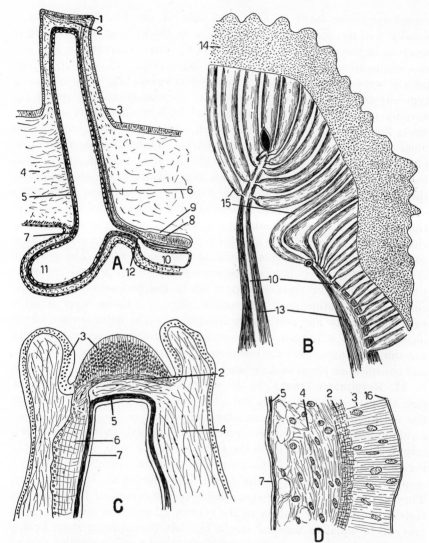

Fig. 66.—Water-vascular system (concluded). *A*, scheme of a locomotory podium with its ampulla. *B*, dissection of the lateral fringe of *Psychropotes*, showing water canal into each component of fringe (*after Théel*, 1882). *C*, longitudinal section through the end of a papillate podium (*after Hamann*, 1884). *D*, section of the tip of a locomotory podium (*after Hamann*, 1883). 1, terminal disk; 2, nervous layer; 3, epidermis; 4, dermis; 5, longitudinal muscle layer; 6, podial nerve; 7, coelomic lining; 8, radial nerve; 9, epineural sinus; 10, radial water canal; 11, ampulla; 12, valve; 13, longitudinal muscle band of body wall; 14, fringe; 15, water branches to fringe; 16, cuticle.

connective-tissue layer to the outer side of the lining epithelium is
usually well developed and sometimes very thick, (Fig. 69A, B) but is
wanting in the pharynx and stomach of *Cucumaria* where the very tall
epithelium rests directly on the muscle layer (Figs. 68C, D, 69C). The
muscle layer is usually well or strongly developed (Fig. 69A), consisting
typically of inner longitudinal and outer circular fibers. Generally the
anterior part of the pharynx is provided with circular fibers only (Fig.
68C), and the longitudinal fibers begin more posteriorly, lying to the
inner side of the circular fibers (Fig. 68D). These directional relations
of the muscle layers persist through the digestive tract in many cases,
but in most Aspidochirota and Apoda they reverse in the stomach or at
the beginning of the small intestine, with the circular fibers to the inner
side of the longitudinal fibers throughout the remainder of the digestive
tract (Fig. 70A, B). The normal arrangement may be resumed in the
cloaca (Fig. 70D) where the circular layer forms a sphincter at the anus
continuous with the circular layer of the body wall. The place of
reversal of the muscle layers is believed to constitute a weak region at
which the digestive tract constricts off in the process of evisceration
common in holothurians. The outer connective-tissue layer is often
extremely scanty and scarcely demonstrable. The outer surface of the
digestive tract is formed, as in coelomate animals in general, of peritoneum. Coelomocytes are common in the wall of the digestive tract,
and conspicuous blood lacunae may be present.

**11. Respiratory Trees.**—In the orders Dendrochirota, Aspidochirota,
and Molpadonia there spring from the anterior part of the cloaca near
the entrance of the large intestine, separately or by way of a short
common stem, two arborescent tubes, right and left, that ascend anteriorly in the coelom, often up to the aquapharyngeal bulb. These branching tubes are known as *respiratory trees* since they constitute the main
respiratory mechanism of the larger and thick-walled holothurians.
They occupy the available space between the intestinal loops and are
fastened to the body wall or to the viscera by irregular strands. They
may be of equal or unequal size. The left tree appears more or less
intermingled with the lacunar network attached to the ascending part of
the small intestine (Fig. 73). The numerous branches of the trees
terminate in small, rounded, thin-walled vesicles. The histology of the
respiratory trees is similar to that of the digestive tract, of which the
trees are in fact evaginations. The main stem and branches are lined
by a flat to columnar epithelium, followed by a connective-tissue layer,
a muscular stratum of two directions of fibers, an outer connective-
tissue layer, and a peritoneal covering (Fig. 71B). The wall of the
terminal vesicles is very thin and consists of scarcely more than two
flattened epithelia (Fig. 71C). The respiratory trees are permeated

with coelomocytes, especially the type with colored spherules, and with groups of granules of excretory nature.

**12. The Tubules of Cuvier.**—In some species of the aspidochirote genera *Holothuria* and *Actinopyga* (= *Mülleria*) there are found attached to the common stem of the respiratory trees or to the bases of the trees, especially the left one, a number of white, pink, or red tubules named after Cuvier, their discoverer.  In *Holothuria* the tubules spring separately from the tree (Fig. 71*D*, *E*) and may be few in number or so numerous as to give the impression of tufts; whereas in *Actinopyga* the tubules branch from one or more common stems (Fig. 71*F*).  The manner of employment of the tubules has been frequently observed in common Channel and Mediterranean species of *Holothuria* (*nigra*, *forskali*, *helleri*).  When irritated the animal curves its anal end toward the irritating object, undergoes a general contraction, and begins to emit the cuvierian tubules from the anus, blind ends first.  These blind ends, often swollen, dart about in all directions, and the tubules rapidly elongate into intensely sticky slender threads (Fig. 72*A*, Minchin, 1892; Russo, 1899; Mines, 1912).  The long sticky threads wrap around the offending object, which in nature would be an animal of some size as a lobster, and render it incapable of movement.  The threads break from their attachment and are left behind as the holothurian crawls away.  When numerous tubules are present, only part of them are emitted at one time, and the number may suffice for several responses.  The tubules are readily regenerated.  Reflection on the anatomy of the parts concerned will show that the tubules can emerge only through a rupture in the cloacal wall, and such rupture does in fact occur, probably at a preformed weak spot.  The mechanism of elongation of the tubules is uncertain, but the theory of Mines (1912) that water is forced into the lumina of the tubules by body contraction appears plausible.  Mines has shown that injection of the lumina with water by means of a hypodermic needle causes normal elongation and that isolated tubules do not exhibit the typical behavior.  Probably, however, the arrangement of the musculature of the tubule wall (see below) plays some role in the behavior, conferring great elasticity on the tubules.

The foregoing account of the behavior of the tubules is not, however, applicable to all species that possess cuvierian tubules.  In *Actinopyga agassizi*, observed by the author in the Bahamas, the entire tuft of pink tubules is emitted from the anus on proper stimulation but shows no movement, elongation, or stickiness.  In this species, however, the tubules are highly toxic to fish and other animals (Atz, 1952; Nigrelli, 1952) and thus accomplish the function of defense in another way.  The matter of toxicity of holothurians is discussed later under ecology.

The histological construction of the cuvierian tubules has been

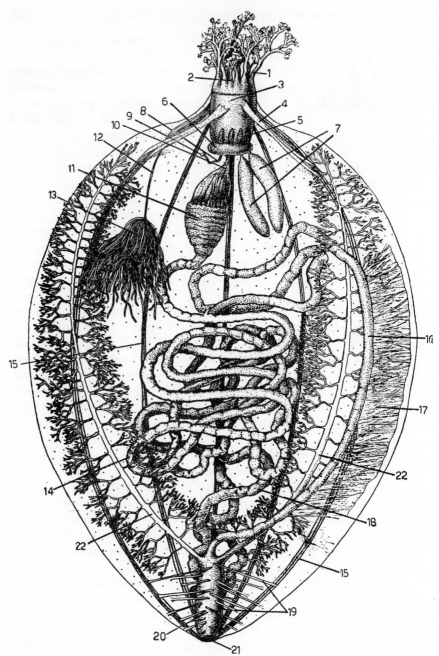

Fig. 67.—Anatomy of *Thyone briaereus* (*after Coe*, 1912). 1, tentacles; 2, short ventral tentacles; 3, aquapharyngeal bulb; 4, retractor muscles; 5, tails of pieces of calcareous ring; 6, water ring; 7, polian vesicles; 8, stone canal; 9, madreporic body; 10, esophagus; 11, stomach; 12, gonoduct; 13, gonad; 14, descending small intestine; 15, longitudinal muscle band; 16, large intestine; 17, mesentery; 18, ascending small intestine; 19, cloacal suspensors; 20, cloaca; 21, anus; 22, respiratory tree.

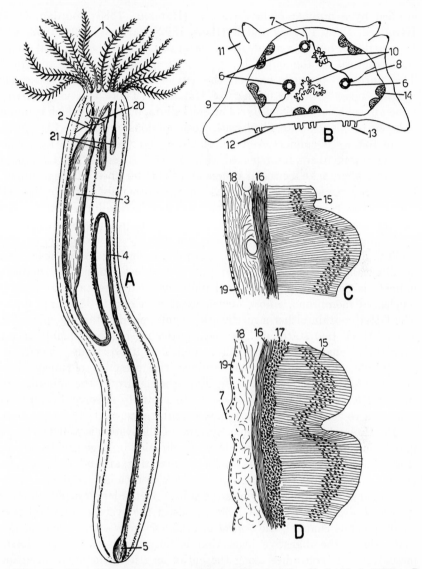

FIG. 68.—Digestive tract. *A, Synaptula hydriformis (after H. L. Clark,* 1898). *B,* schematic section of *Stichopus* to show arrangement of mesenteries *(after Selenka,* 1867). *C.* transverse section of the upper part of the pharynx of *Cucumaria. D,* transverse section of the lower part of same. *(C, D, after Hamann,* 1883.) 1, pinnate tentacles; 2, esophagus; 3, stomach; 4, intestine; 5, cloaca; 6, sections of intestine; 7, dorsal mesentery; 8, left mesentery; 9, ventral mesentery; 10, sections of respiratory trees; 11, warts (papillate podia); 12, creeping sole; 13, locomotory podia in three rows; 14, longitudinal muscle bands; 15, lining epithelium; 16, circular muscle layer; 17, longitudinal muscle layer; 18, outer layer of connective tissue; 19, coelomic lining; 20, gonad; 21, polian vesicles.

studied by a number of investigators (Hamann, 1883; Jourdan, 1883; Hérouard, 1889; Ludwig and Barthels, 1892; Barthels, 1896, 1902; and Russo, 1899), but no agreement has been reached on the essential point, the structure of the outer layer that furnishes the sticky secretion. The author's preparations of the cuvierian tubules of *Actinopyga agassizi* agree with the findings of Hamann. There is a very narrow lumen in each tubule lined by a low epithelium, outside of which is found a layer of gland cells filled with eosinophilous granules (Fig. 71*G*). There follows a connective-tissue stratum and then a wide area containing muscle fibers, interspersed with connective tissue. In *Actinopyga* the inner fibers take a circular course and the outer ones are longitudinal, but the reverse seems to be the case in some other species investigated. There is general agreement that the fibers interlace to form a lattice and further that the longitudinal fibers spiral, thus permitting elongation. The outermost layer of the tubules, presumably altered coelomic epithelium and more or less thrown into folds according to the species, is histologically difficult to interpret. The most consistent findings indicate large, sharply demarcated units, covered externally by a thin, mucleated membrane, whose nuclei possibly belong to the large units. The latter contain either a meshwork or pale, poorly staining spherules, and as these two states do not coexist, the meshes presumably result from the discharge of the spherules. Guislain (1953) studied the cuvierian tubules chemically and determined the presence of mucus and polysaccharides but could not elucidate the nature of the spherules of the surface layer. They were resistant to a variety of solvents and tests and seem to consist of some highly inert substance.

**13. Haemal or Blood Lacunar System.**—This system is well developed in holothurians, reaching its greatest complication in large aspidochirotes (Fig. 73*A*). The main parts are a haemal ring around the pharynx giving off branches that accompany the water canals, and two main lacunae or sinuses along the digestive tube. In the larger aspidochirotes such as *Holothuria* (Fig. 73*A*), the details of the system are as follows. A conspicuous channel, the *ventral* or *antimesenterial* sinus, accompanies that side of the digestive tract that is not suspended by the dorsal mesentery. It continues along the entire length of the small intestine and also extends along the large intestine to a greater or less extent, finally dying away; it also diminishes in the anterior direction, toward the pharynx. Throughout its course the ventral sinus is connected to the intestinal wall by numerous branches. At about the middle of its course along the descending intestine, the ventral sinus gives off a transverse connection to the part of itself that runs along the ascending intestine (Fig. 73*A*). A still more conspicuous *dorsal* or *mesenterial* sinus runs along the side of the intestine that is attached by the dorsal mesentery, and this also communicates with the intestinal wall by numerous branches. Before reaching the posterior end of the descending small intestine, the main part of the dorsal sinus crosses over and ascends along the ascending small intestine, leaving a smaller part or several branches to supply the rest of the descending intestine as well as the turn of the intestine and the beginning part of the ascending small intestine. The dorsal sinus is connected to the ascending small intestine by way of numerous tufts of lacunae, forming what is called a *rete mirabile* or wondrous blood network. Between these tufts of the lacunar network and the wall of the ascending intestine is found a *collecting* vessel that connects the lacunar tufts with the ascending intestine by numerous branches (Fig. 73*B*). This collecting vessel is continuous with the main dorsal sinus at both ends either directly or by way of small sinuses. The lacunar tufts of the rete mirabile are closely entangled with the terminal tufts of the left respiratory tree.

Anteriorly both dorsal and ventral sinuses diminish toward the pharynx and may or may not open into the haemal ring that encircles the rear end of the pharynx directly behind and closely applied to the water ring. The gonad is supplied by a branch from the dorsal sinus or directly from the haemal ring. From the haemal ring five radial sinuses ascend the aquapharyngeal bulb in company with the radial water canals and after giving off branches into the tentacles, accompany the latter along the inner side of the body wall, lying between the hyponeural sinus and the radial water canals. These radial haemal sinuses give off branches into the podia.

In *Stichopus* (Sivickis and Domantay, 1928), another large aspido-chirote, the arrangement of the haemal system is similar but differs in details (Fig. 74). The transverse connection of the ventral sinus is the largest part of this vessel. The dorsal sinus runs some distance away from the descending intestine to which it is connected by a complicated network of sinuses; lacunar tufts similar to those of *Holothuria* occur along the ascending intestine and are there intermingled with the left respiratory tree.

The haemal system of the larger Molpadonia has been described and figured for *Paracaudina* (Fig. 75) by Kawamoto (1927) and for *Molpadia* by Hatanaka (1939). Here the typical tufts of the rete mirabile are wanting, but as in *Stichopus*, the dorsal sinus runs at a considerable distance from the descending intestine and is connected with it by a complicated mesh of sinuses. The descending and ascending parts of the ventral sinus are connected by several transverse or diagonal sinuses.

In the smaller holothurians and in the orders Apoda and Elasipoda, the haemal system is less complicated than in the foregoing examples but retains the main parts, the dorsal and ventral sinuses accompanying

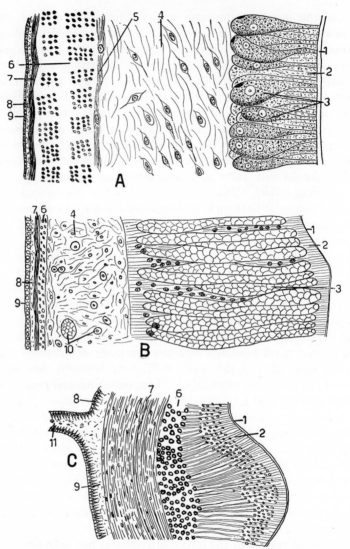

Fig. 69.—Histology of the stomach region.  *A*, transverse section of the stomach of *Leptosynapta* with heavy musculature.  *B*, transverse section of the poorly differentiated stomach of *Holothuria* with thin musculature.  (*A, B, after Hamann*, 1884.)  *C*, transverse section of the stomach wall of *Cucumaria* (*after Gerould*, 1896), without glands or inner connective-tissue layer.  1, cuticle; 2, lining epithelium; 3, gland cells; 4, inner connective-tissue layer; 5, nervous layer; 6, longitudinal muscle layer; 7, circular muscle layer; 8, outer connective-tissue layer; 9, coelomic lining; 10, coelomocytes; 11, dorsal mesentery.

the digestive tract and the haemal ring and its branches along the radial water canals. However, there are no complicated networks or lacunar tufts connecting with the intestine, although cross connections between ascending and descending parts of the intestinal sinuses are usually present, as in *Cucumaria* (Fig. 72*B*).

Despite the intertwining of the branches of the left respiratory tree with the lacunar tufts of the rete mirable, no histological continuity exists. It appears, however, that the blood spaces of the haemal ring are often continuous with the lumen of the water ring and even with the peripharyngeal sinus. Such communications allow an exchange of coelomocytes and fluid between the coelom and haemal and water-vascular systems.

The channels of the haemal system are not definite vessels, as they lack a lining, and hence are better referred to as sinuses or lacunae. The wall of the haemal channels is clothed externally with coelomic epithelium, inside of which is a layer of muscle fibers and then connective tissue (Fig. 76*A*). In the intestinal wall the blood channels consist simply of spaces in the inner connective-tissue layer. The author has sectioned the lacunar tufts of the rete mirabile attached to the ascending small intestine of *Actinopyga* and found that they consist mainly of a very tall coelomic epithelium containing eosinophilous inclusions and are lined by connective tissue without any muscular layer (Fig. 76*B*, *C*).

There appears little doubt that the coelomocytes are manufactured in the connective-tissue layer of the larger haemal channels (Prosser and Judson, 1952), and not in the polian vesicles as supposed by Cuénot.

**14. Axial Complex.**—The author has found very little information in the literature concerning the existence of the axial complex (axial sinus, axial gland) in holothurians. According to Cuénot (1891a) the part of the coelom that gives rise to the axial sinus disappears during the embryology of holothurians. However, a few authors have described what they considered to be an axial gland in various holothurians. The most authentic of these reports are those of Heding (1935) and Hatanaka (1939) for *Molpadia* and other Molpadonia. Here a network of connective tissue to the inner side of the water ring gives rise to a tubular outgrowth that extends backward along the dorsal wall of the esophagus in the dorsal mesentery and also accompanies the gonoduct to the base of the gonad. Hérouard (1889) considered the axial gland to be represented by some lacunar tissue full of amoebocytes located at the base of the stone canal. Cuénot (1891a) found spongy glandular tissue developed to different degrees in different species of *Cucumaria*, located immediately in front of the water ring, and also noted in *Holothuria* a spongy glandular ring around the pharynx and extending along the radial haemal lacunae. This author regarded such spongy tissue as a site of manufacture of

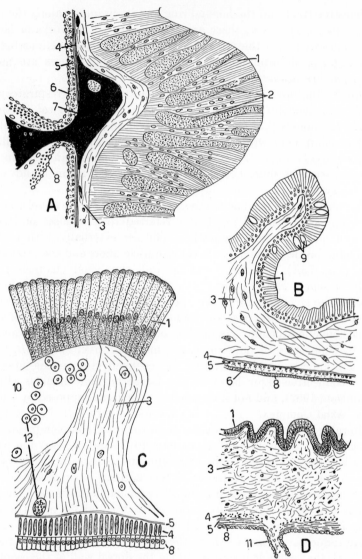

Fig. 70.—Histology of the intestine. *A*, transverse section of the small intestine of *Holothuria*. *B*, transverse section of the small intestine of *Leptosynapta*. (*A, B, after Hamann*, 1884.) *C*, longitudinal section of the small intestine of *Caudina* (*after Gerould*, 1896). Note reversal of the muscle layers in *A* and *B*, but not in *C*. *D*, transverse section of the cloaca of *Stichopus* (*after Sivickis and Domantay*, 1928). 1, lining epithelium; 2, gland cells; 3, inner connective-tissue layer; 4, circular muscle layer; 5, longitudinal muscle layer; 6, outer connective tissue; 7, dorsal blood lacuna; 8, coelomic lining; 9, goblets; 10, blood lacuna; 11, cloacal suspensor; 12, coelomocytes.

amoebocytes. Mortensen's account (1894) of an axial gland in still another species of *Cucumaria* differs somewhat from that of Cuénot and agrees more with the report for molpadonians; the gland is said by him to be an elongation from the haemal ring along the haemal sinus supplying the gonad. It seems probable that there is some confusion between the true axial gland and sites of amoebocyte formation in the walls of the haemal sinuses, especially the haemal ring. In any case, the axial complex is evidently poorly developed in holothurians.

**15. Reproductive System and Reproductive Habits.**—The majority of the Holothuroidea are dioecious; the sexes cannot be distinguished externally except in the case of females found brooding their young. There are, however, some hermaphroditic species, as *Cucumaria laevigata* and a few other cucumarids among the dendrochirotes, *Mesothuria intestinalis* among the aspidochirotes, and a number of synaptids. In lacking a pentamerous arrangement, the reproductive system of holothurians differs from that of all other existing echinoderms. The single gonad is located in the anterior part of the coelom in interradius CD and opens to the exterior along this interradius in company with the external madreporite, when present (Figs. 53*C*, 62*C*). Such an arrangement is found otherwise only in extinct Pelmatozoa and at once rates the Holothuroidea as offshoots of some very primitive echinoderm stock. The gonad usually consists of numerous tubules (Figs. 61*A*, 62*A*, 64*A*, 67, 73*A*) united basally into one tuft attached to the left side of the dorsal mesentery or into two tufts, one to either side of the mesentery. The tubules may be simple elongations (Figs. 64*A*, 67) or may be branched in various ways (Figs. 73*A*, 74, 75). Although usually long and numerous, the gonadial tubules may be short and few in number. In synaptids, the gonad usually consists of two branched tubules, one to either side of the mesentery (Fig. 68*A*) and in some elasipods it takes the form of a pair of sacs (Fig. 76*D*). Typically the gonad at sexual maturity is very voluminous, consisting of a multitude of long tubules. The prodigious increase of size of the gonad with the approach of sexual maturity is illustrated by the data of Mitsukuri (1903) on *Stichopus japonicus*, where the tubules grow from a length of 2 cm. in October to 25 to 35 cm. in July.

The tubules open into the hollow gonadial base attached to the mesentery, and from this common base the gonoduct proceeds in the mesentery to the gonopore, mounted or not on a genital papilla. The gonopore is located in the middorsal line, in interradius CD, and may be situated between the tentacles (Fig. 47*B*) or shortly behind them (Fig. 62*B*); in the Elasipoda the gonopore is characteristically found some distance behind the tentacles (Figs. 52*E*, 53*C*). Not infrequently the gonoduct subdivides before reaching the surface, so that there may be a

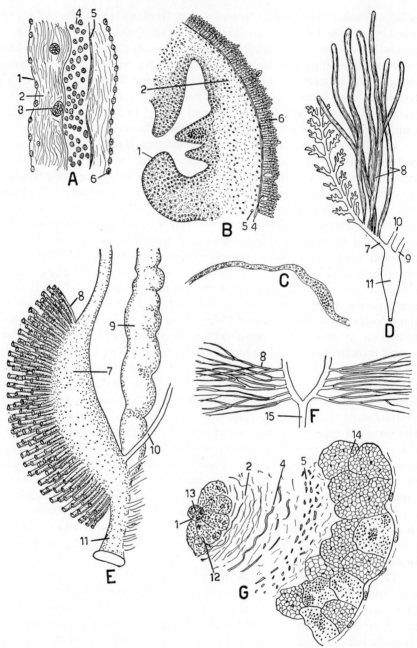

FIG. 71.—Respiratory tree, cuvierian tubules.  *A*, longitudinal section of the stem of the respiratory tree of *Caudina* (*after Gould*, 1896).  *B*, cross section of the stem of the respiratory tree of *Holothuria*.  *C*, wall of end vesicle of respiratory tree of *Holothuria*. (*B, C, after Bertolini*, 1933.)  *D*, base of left respiratory tree of *Holothuria impatiens*, with

cluster of a few to many gonopores. The length of the gonoduct or, in other words, the level of attachment of the gonad to the dorsal mesentery varies in different holothurians. In some, as most synaptids and molpadonians, the gonoduct is short (Fig. 68A), whereas it is generally long in aspidochirotes and dendrochirotes (Figs. 61A, 64A, 67, 72B). Except for this basal attachment, the gonad hangs free in the coelom.

The gonadial tubules are clothed externally with the coelomic epithelium, varying from a flat to a columnar form, followed by a thin musculature, usually having both circular and longitudinal fibers, then comes a connective-tissue layer, and finally the lumen is lined by the germinal epithelium, from which the sex cells originate (Fig. 77D). Among the hermaphroditic synaptids, each tubule produces both eggs and sperm, generally at the same time (H. L. Clark, 1907), although possibly at different times in some species, which may then be mistakenly regarded as dioecious species. Having noticed that in a lot of about 80 spawning specimens of *Leptosynapta inhaerens* only four shed eggs while the rest gave off sperm, S. Runnström (1927) suggested that perhaps this species is male when young and becomes female only when a few years of age. In *Cucumaria crocea*, also, eggs and sperm are produced in the same gonadial tubules (Ludwig, 1898a), but more complicated conditions obtain in some other hermaphroditic dendrochirotes. In *Cucumaria laevigata* (Ackermann, 1902), the developing tubules at the gonadial base are sexually indifferent at first but become female and release eggs as they lengthen; with still further elongation the female elements are destroyed by phagocytic coelomocytes and the same tubules then produce sperm. Thus the gonadial tuft consists of small basal indifferent tubules, larger female tubules, and some very long male tubules (Fig. 76G). Eventually the old male tubules are also phagocytized and resorbed and replaced by newly transformed female tubules. In *Mesothuria intestinalis* (Théel, 1901), the gonadial tubules branch distally, forming tufts, and some of these tufts are male, others female (Fig. 77C). As in the preceding species, old and discharged tufts are resorbed and destroyed by coelomocytes, and new ones grow out from the gonadial base. Probably a similar process of destruction of spent tubules and formation of new ones at a growing zone in the gonad base occurs in holothurians generally.

The gonoduct consists of a ciliated epithelium surrounded by con-

---

few cuvierian tubules (*after Russo*, 1889). *E*, base of left respiratory tree of *Holothuria catanensis* with numerous cuvierian tubules (*after Hérouard*, 1889). *F*, branched cuvierian tubules of *Actinopyga agassizi*. *G*, transverse section of a cuvierian tubule of *Actinopyga*. 1, lining; 2, connective tissue; 3, coelomocyte; 4, circular muscle layer; 5, longitudinal muscle layer; 6, coelomic epithelium; 7, base of left respiratory tree; 8, cuvierian tubules; 9, large intestine; 10, base of right respiratory tree; 11, cloaca; 12, gland cells; 13, lumen; 14, layer that furnishes the adhesive secretion; 15, common stem of respiratory trees.

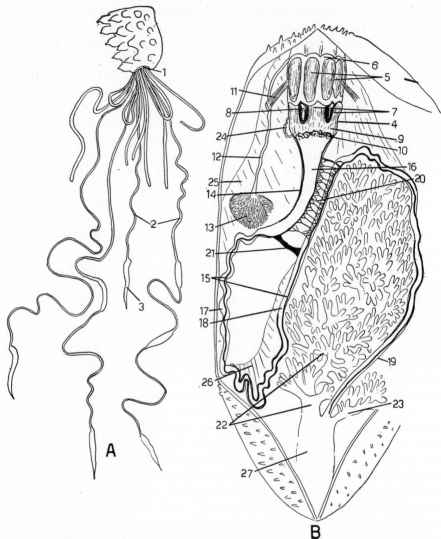

Fig. 72.—Cuvierian tubules (concluded), haemal system.   *A*, posterior end of *Holo-thuria forskali*, discharging its cuvierian tubules (*after Russo*, 1899).   *B*, dissection of *Cucumaria planci*, showing digestive and haemal systems (*after Hérouard*, 1899).   1, anus; 2, cuvierian tubules; 3, swollen head; 4, aquapharyngeal bulb; 5, tentacular ampullae; 6, calcareous ring; 7, radial water canals; 8, openings into peripharyngeal sinus; 9, water ring; 10, haemal ring; 11, retractor muscle; 12, gonoduct; 13, gonad; 14, dorsal haemal sinus; 15, ventral haemal sinus; 16, stomach; 17, descending small intestine; 18, ascending small intestine; 19, large intestine; 20, connections between descending and ascending parts of the ventral haemal sinus; 21, transverse connection of dorsal sinus; 22, left respiratory tree; 23, base of right respiratory tree; 24, stone canal; 25, dorsal mesentery; 26, left mesen-tery; 27, cloaca.

nective tissue continuous with that of the dorsal mesentery in which the duct is imbedded (Fig. 77*E*).

Available data on the spawning of holothurians indicate that each species breeds for one or more months at a definite time of the year, mostly spring and summer in temperate latitudes. The older data are tabulated by Ludwig (1889–1892), but the species identifications in this table are probably not reliable. On the New England coast *Leptosynapta inhaerens* and *roseola* spawn in spring and summer (H. L. Clark, 1899), and *Thyone briaereus* in June (Ohshima, 1925; Colwin, 1948). Gerould (1896) observed the spawning of male specimens of *Caudina arenata* on the Massachusetts coast from February to April. In the Bahamas *Actinopyga agassizi* spawns from July to the middle of August (Edwards, 1889). The viviparous species *Synaptula hydriformis* and *Chiridota rotifera* are found with developing young in the coelom in Jamaica and Bermuda from April through the summer or even later (H. L. Clark, 1898, 1910a), but it is not clear from these accounts just when the germ cells are ripe. Possibly such tropical viviparous forms breed throughout the year. *Parastichopus californicus* spawns in Puget Sound during July and August (Courtney, 1927), but other Puget Sound holothurians spawn in spring (the Johnsons, 1950). Spawning data are available for several Japanese species: *Stichopus japonicus* from May to early July (Mitsukuri, 1903), *Paracaudina chilensis* from May to June (Inaba, 1930), *Cucumaria echinata* from the middle of June into early August (Ohshima, 1918), and *Molpadia roretzii* probably in November or December (Hatanaka, 1939). During studies of echinoderm development on the Egyptian coast of the Red Sea, Mortensen (1937, 1938) reported the spawning of a number of holothurians. The following spawned between April 18 and June 27 in 1936: *Synaptula reciprocans* and *vittata*, *Stichopus variegatus*, *Actinopyga serratidens* and *mauritiana*, and *Holothuria marmorata*, *arenicola*, *scabra*, and *spinifera;* at a later stay, between July 1 and Sept. 12, 1937, spawning occurred in *Synaptula vittata*, *Opheodesoma grisea*, and *Holothuria impatiens*, *pardalis*, *papillifera*, *difficilis*, and *nobilis*. Many studies of holothurian development have been pursued along Mediterranean shores, especially at Naples. Here *Cucumaria kirchsbergii* breeds in summer (Kowalewsky, 1867), *Cucumaria planci* in March and April (Selenka, 1876), and *Labidoplax digitata* in March and April (Remiers, 1912); but *Holothuria tubulosa* seems sexually ripe throughout the year although at a maximum in August and September (Selenka, 1876). June breeding is reported for the viviparous *Phyllophorus urna* at Naples (Ludwig, 1898b). The northern species *Cucumaria frondosa* spawns in the North Sea and other parts of the North Atlantic in February and March (the Runnströms, 1921), but in June and July still farther north in arctic waters. *Psolus phantapus* breeds in the North Sea in March and April (the Runnströms, 1921), but *Stichopus tremulus* in August. Another northern form, *Labidoplax buski*, breeds from October to December off the Swedish coast (Nyholm, 1951). The viviparous antarctic species *Cucumaria crocea* and *Psolus ephippifer* were found with young in January and February (Thomson, 1878). Widely distributed species may spawn at different times in different parts of the world as the common *Leptosynapta inhaerens*, reported as spawning in spring and summer on the New England coast but in August and September off Norway; however, Deichmann (1930) and other holothurian specialists suggest that different species are confused under this name.

Most observers report that holothurians usually spawn in the late afternoon or evening or during the night, apparently in response to dim light. Probably temperature also plays a role, as Colwin (1948) noticed some stimulation of spawning in *Thyone briaereus* by exposure to water about 4°C higher than the previous temperature. No doubt the general tendency of holothurians of temperate zones to spawn in spring and summer is related to rise of temperature at these seasons in such zones. It has also been frequently noticed that holothurians brought in from nature and placed in laboratory aquaria tend to spawn in the late afternoon or evening of the same day. As a rule in a group of holothurians, the males spawn first, soon followed by the females; but isolated individuals may spawn, although eggs so shed are unfertilizable.

Oviparous species shed their sex cells directly into the sea water and fertilization at once ensues. In *Thyone briareus* (Colwin, 1948), the animal prior to shedding expands and elongates and starts waving its tentacles about. The sex cells issue from the gonopore in a slow stream and are well dispersed by tentacular movements. Spawning usually continued for about 30 minutes but ranged in different individuals from 15 minutes to over 4 hours. The northern synaptids *Leptosynapta inhaerens* (S. Runnström, 1927) and *Labidoplax buski* (Nyholm, 1951) when spawning erect themselves part way out of their burrows and swing about while emitting the sex cells. For the latter hermaphroditic species it is interesting to learn that eggs and sperm are ripe simultaneously in the gonadial tubules but are not shed simultaneously; the same individual sheds one kind of sex cell at one time and the other kind a day or two later, but is not self-sterile. *Holothuria marmorata* when spawning raises the anterior end vertically (Mortensen, 1937). A holothurian does not necessarily discharge its entire load of ripe sex cells during one spawning act but may spawn at intervals.

A number of dendrochirote and apodous holothurians brood their young in some manner or other. This habit is particularly developed in residents of polar waters; of the 30 brooding species known at present,

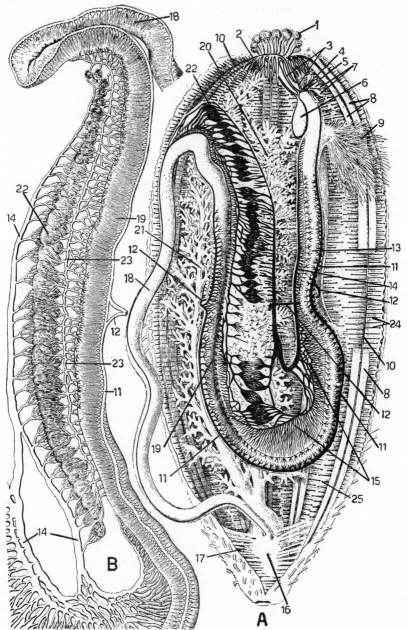

Fig. 73.—Digestive and haemal systems of *Holothuria*.  A, dissection of *Holothuria*. B, ascending intestine enlarged, to show the haemal plexus (rete mirabile).  (*A, B, after Ludwig*, 1889–1892.)  1, tentacles; 2, tentacular ampulla; 3, radial water canals; 4, water ring; 5, haemal ring; 6, polian vesicle; 7, cluster of stone canals; 8, longitudinal muscle band; 9, gonad; 10, radial water vessel; 11, ventral haemal sinus; 12, transverse connection of 11; 13, descending small intestine; 14, dorsal haemal sinus; 15, network from dorsal sinus into bend of intestine; 16, cloaca; 17, cloacal suspensors; 18, large intestine; 19, ascending small intestine; 20, right respiratory tree; 21, left respiratory tree; 22, haemal tufts (rete mirabile) of dorsal haemal sinus; 23, collecting vessel; 24, podial canals of locomotory podia; 25, ampullae of locomotory podia.

15 inhabit the antarctic and 1 the arctic, and 3 others live in far northern waters. The prevalence of brooding echinoderms in the antarctic has not been satisfactorily explained; presumably the avoidance of a free-swimming larval stage must be somehow advantageous in polar waters. It is characteristic of brooding holothurians that they produce large, yolky eggs, which in several species have a diameter of around 1 mm. The available facts about brooding holothurians to the date of publication have been well summarized by Vaney (1925).

In the simplest cases the eggs develop and the young are held on the external surface of the mother. In *Psolus antarcticus*, the young adhere to the smooth part of the creeping sole (Ludwig, 1897a, 1898a); a maximum of 22 young occurred on one mother (Fig. 78*A*). A similar location is seen in *Cucumaria curata*, California, although details have not been furnished (H. L. Clark, 1902). In *Cucumaria planci*, the eggs are retained briefly in the tentacular crown (Vaney, 1925) but are soon ejected into the sea water, and Ohshima (1915) reported a preserved male specimen of *Bathyplotes natans* with eggs stuck to the tentacles. As a next step, development occurs in depressions or pockets of the body surface, of the back in *Thyonepsolus nutriens* from California (H. L. Clark, 1901; Wootton, 1949), of the sole in five antarctic species: *Psolus granulosus* (Vaney, 1907, Fig. 77*A*), *Cucumaria parva* (Ludwig, 1898a), and *Psolidium incubans, Psolus figulus*, and *Psolus punctatus* (Ekman, 1925). Ekman found 40 eggs imbedded in the sole of *Psolus punctatus*, and as many as 70 young were seen by Ludwig attached to *Cucumaria parva;* the latter employs plant material stuck to the podia to help keep the young in place. *Psolus ephippifer*, antarctic, also carries its young on its back, but here the young are held in cavities beneath the large dorsal scales (Théel, 1886, Fig. 78*D*). The method of placing the eggs in surface depressions has been observed for *Thyonepsolus nutriens* (Wootton, 1949). Spawning females arch their expanded tentacles to form an interlocking mesh in which the extruded eggs are caught. The eggs are then transferred to the dorsal surface by the tentacles and by two unusually extensile podia located near the gonopore; other dorsal podia pass the eggs along the animal's back into the preformed pits of the surface. Escaped eggs are often picked up by the tentacles or podia. The eggs are very adhesive for about an hour after spawning.

A further stage in the brooding habit consists in the development of definite incubatory pockets, at first external. Thus in the antarctic *Psolus Koehleri*, there are five widely open pouches in the body wall around the anterior end (Vaney, 1914, Fig. 78*E*), and five similarly placed but deeper pockets with narrowed interradial apertures are found in *Cucumaria Joubini* (Vaney, 1914). The well-known antarctic species *Cucumaria crocea* was found on the *Challenger* expedition with numerous

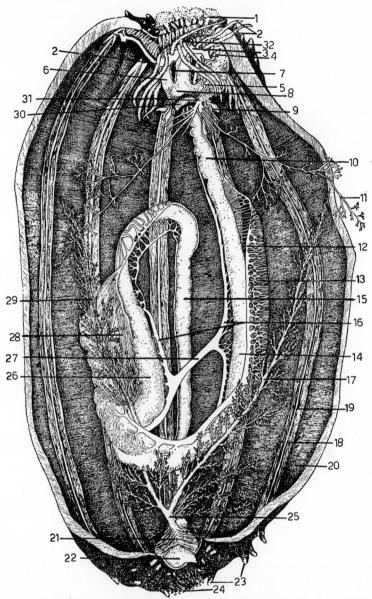

FIG. 74.—Digestive and haemal systems of *Stichopus* (*after Sivickis and Domantay*, 1928). 1, tentacles; 2, tentacular ampullae; 3, calcareous ring; 4, madreporic body; 5, stone canal; 6, aquapharyngeal bulb; 7, communications of peripharyngeal sinus with the coelom; 8, water ring; 9, polian vesicle; 10, stomach region; 11, gonad; 12, dorsal haemal sinus; 13, network from 12 into intestine; 14, descending small intestine; 15, large intestine; 16, ventral haemal sinus; 17, right respiratory tree; 18, longitudinal muscle band of body wall; 19, radial water canal; 20, transverse musculature of body wall; 21, cloaca; 22, anus; 23, papillate podia; 24, locomotory podia; 25, common stem of respiratory trees; 26, ascending small intestine; 27, transverse connection of ventral haemal sinus; 28, rete mirabile of dorsal sinus; 29, left respiratory tree; 30, haemal ring; 31, gonoduct; 32, location of nerve ring.

179

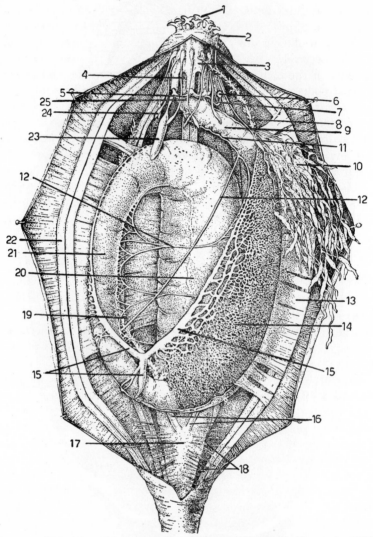

Fig. 75.—Digestive and haemal systems of *Paracaudina* (*after Kawamoto*, 1927). 1, tentacles; 2, gonopore; 3, aquapharyngeal bulb; 4, communication of peripharyngeal sinus with coelom; 5, water ring; 6, madreporic body; 7, stone canal; 8, upper end of right respiratory tree; 9, stomach; 10, gonad; 11, ventral haemal sinus; 12, communicating vessels of 11; 13, dorsal mesentery; 14, haemal plexus from dorsal sinus to descending small intestine; 15, dorsal haemal sinus; 16, bases of respiratory trees; 17, cloaca; 18, cloacal suspensors; 19, left respiratory tree; 20, large intestine; 21, ascending small intestine; 22, longitudinal muscle band of body wall; 23, polian vesicle; 24, tentacular ampullae; 25, haemal ring.

young attached to its dorsal ambulacra (Thomson, 1878); but later work (MacBride and Simpson, 1908) revealed two incubatory pockets in the ventral body wall (Fig. 78*B*, *C*), containing in one case 110 and 30 embryos, respectively. Apparently in this species the embryos develop considerably in the incubatory pockets and then emerge and attach to the reduced podia of the bivium. Two incubatory pockets in the body wall also occur in *Cucumaria coatsi* (Ekman, 1925). Further evolution along this line results in the formation of internal incubatory sacs, usually two in number and ventral in position, formed by deep integumentary invaginations into the coelom and opening separately near the tentacular crown (Fig. 76*H*). Mortensen (1894) has shown that these sacs consist of thinned inturned body wall in which the connective-tissue layer has suffered the greatest decrease. Such internal incubatory sacs occur in *Cucumaria glacialis*, from the arctic (Mortensen, 1894; Ludwig, 1900a); in three antarctic species, *Cucumaria lateralis* (Vaney, 1907), *laevigata* (Lampert, 1889), and *vaneyi* (Cherbonnier, 1949); in two species from the Aleutian Islands, *C. ijimai* and *lamperti* (Ohshima, 1915); and in *Thyone imbricata* from Sakhalin (Ohshima, 1915). In the last, the two sacs have a common orifice. The embryos in incubatory sacs may be of the same stage of development or of varied stages. It appears anatomically impossible that the eggs could get into the incubatory sacs directly, and presumably they are discharged to the exterior and assisted into the sacs by the mother.

A different type of incubatory habit is seen in a number of dendrochirote and apodous holothurians, none from polar regions. In these the eggs rupture from the gonads and develop to an advanced stage with tentacles inside the coelom. How fertilization occurs remains problematical, except in hermaphroditic species. However, in one such species with coelomic incubation, *Synaptula hydriformis*, it is stated that the sperm are discharged to the exterior and reach the coelom through the anus by way of openings through the wall of the large intestine (H. L. Clark, 1898). Coelomic incubation is known for *Leptosynapta minuta*, North Sea (Becher, 1906), *Synaptula hydriformis* and *Chiridota rotifera*, West Indies (H. L. Clark, 1898, 1910a), *Phyllophorus urna*, Mediterranean (Ludwig, 1898b), *Thyone rubra*, California (H. L. Clark, 1901), *Pseudocucumis africanus*, Japan (Ohshima, 1916), and *Trochodota dunedinensis*, New Zealand (John, 1939). A variant is seen in the antarctic *Taeniogyrus contortus*, in which the ovaries themselves act as incubatory sacs (Ludwig, 1897b, 1898a). The young in cases of coelomic incubation escape by rupture in the anal region.

**16. Development.**—The principal articles on oviparous development are those of Metschnikoff (1870), Selenka (1876, 1883), Semon (1888), Ludwig (1891), Edwards (1909), Newth (1916), Ohshima (1918, 1921,

1925), J. and S. Runnström (1921), S. Runnström (1927), Inaba (1930), Rustad (1938), and Nyholm (1951); those of H. L. Clark (1898, 1910a) and of Wootton (1949) concern development in brooding species. Eggs of species that develop in sea water are usually small and transparent and more or less floating, whereas those that are brooded tend to large size and yolky content. The course of development is much the same in both types of eggs, except that free larval stages are omitted when the eggs are brooded.

Cleavage is typically equal, holoblastic, and of the radial type with tiers of cells in line with each other, very perfectly so in some species (I, Fig. 73*E*), irregularly so in others. There results a typical coeloblastula (I, Fig. 73*L*) that undergoes typical embolic gastrulation (I, Fig. 73*M*). However, in the yolky eggs of incubating species, cleavage may be superficial, and the blastula may consist of a surface layer of cells enclosing the yolk (Wootton, 1949); gastrulation, however, occurs as usual. In typical development, the embryo soon becomes flagellated and escapes from the fertilization membrane. Mesenchyme is given off continuously from the tip of the archenteron as it advances (Fig. 78*G*) and in some species begins migrating inward from the vegetal pole even before the onset of the gastrular invagination (Fig. 78*F*). The blastocoel thus becomes filled with entomesoderm in the form of mesenchyme. The distal part of the archenteron is of coelomic nature, the proximal part, next the blastopore, is the primordium of the digestive tract, and the blastopore becomes the larval anus. In three species, *Stichopus tremulus* (Rustad, 1938), *Labidoplax digitata* (Selenka, 1883), and *Synaptula hydriformis* (Clark, 1898), the coelomic part of the archenteron, before separating from the enteric part, puts out a tubular projection toward the dorsal surface, establishing a hydropore there (Figs. 79*A*, 82*D*); this tube is then the hydroporic canal. In all other species studied, this event happens considerably later. The coelomic sac or hydroenterocoel comprises the larger part of the archenteron and typically separates from the enteric portion by first taking up a somewhat lateral relation to it (Fig. 79*C*). After the separation the hydroenterocoel forms an elongated sac to the left side of the enteric sac and sooner or later constricts into an anterior hydrocoel and a posterior somatocoel (Figs. 79*D*, 82*F*). Before or after this separation the somatocoel is seen dividing into two sacs, the right and left somatocoels (Figs. 80*B*, 81*A*). The hydrocoel bears a small protrusion that represents the axocoel and will give rise to the definitive stone canal (Figs. 80*A*, 81*B*). As in crinoids, only the left hydrocoel and axocoel are present and the right members are wanting. Meantime a stomodaeum has formed in the middle of the ventral surface (Figs. 80*B*, 82*E*), and this joins the enteric sac, which has elongated to become the larval digestive tract. This has a general L form and rapidly differentiates into a fore-gut, of which only a slight part is stomodaeal, an expanded sacciform mid-gut or stomach, and a narrowed intestine or end gut leading to the larval anus (blastopore, Fig. 80B).

At about this time, about the third day of development, the embryo in many holothurians becomes a free-swimming larva, of the type called *auricularia*. The ectoderm flattens, its flagella disappear except along certain sinuous ridges, and the larva then presents a characteristic appearance (Fig. 80C, D). It is a transparent creature of pelagic habits, mostly 0.5 to 1 mm. or slightly more in length, that swims by means of a continuous flagellated band definitely arranged. This band proceeds in sinuous curves along the sides of the larva, then dips ventrally on the anterior part of the larva to form the *preoral loop* passing above the mouth, and similarly curves forward in the posterior ventral region as the *anal loop* that encircles the anus (Fig. 81C). This locomotory band is customarily referred to in the literature as ciliated, but the sections of it published by Remiers (1912) show that it consists of elongated flagellated cells (Fig. 82C). In the interior of the larva is seen the curved digestive tract with its sacciform stomach and the three coelomic sacs (hydrocoel, right and left somatocoels), of which the hydrocoel is already lobulated to indicate the primary tentacles. The hydrocoel is connected by a tubular canal with the hydropore on the dorsal surface. In some larvae or at an earlier stage there is present an apical flagellated ectodermal thickening or sensory plate. Figures of the auricularias of a number of different holothurian species are given by Mortensen (1937, 1938). Relatively gigantic auricularias, up to 15 mm. in length, have been collected in the plankton off the Canary Islands, Japan, and Bermuda (Chun, 1896; Ohshima, 1911; Garstang, 1939). These are further characterized by an excessively frilly flagellated band (Fig. 83). The adults are unknown, but from the presence in these giant auricularias of wheel ossicles, one may assign them to the Apoda.

The auricularia soon transforms into a *doliolaria* larva (called *pupa* in the older literature), greatly resembling the doliolaria of crinoids (Fig. 82B). This change is accomplished by partial degeneration of the flagellated band, leaving short pieces that join to form flagellated rings (Fig. 81D), three to five in number, depending on species. The embryo may bypass the auricularia stage and develop directly into a doliolaria, as in *Cucumaria planci* (Ludwig, 1891), *C. quinquesemita* ( = *chrondjhelmi*, the Johnsons, 1950), *Leptosynapta inhaerens* (S. Runnström, 1927), *Labidoplax buski* (Nyholm, 1951), and *Paracaudina chilensis* (Inaba, 1930). It may omit both stages and swim about as a simple oval larva, completely flagellated or ciliated, as in *Cucumaria saxicola* (Newth, 1916), *Cucumaria frondosa* (the Runnströms, 1921), and *Psolus phantapus*

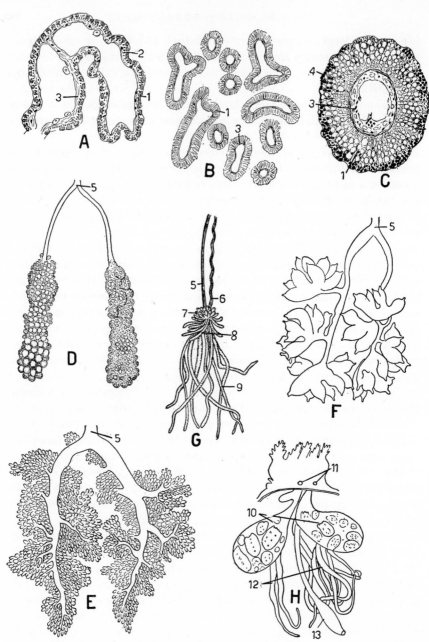

Fig. 76.—Haemal system (concluded), reproductive system. *A*, section of a blood lacuna of *Cucumaria* (*after Hamann*, 1883). *B*, section of the rete mirabile of *Actinopyga*. *C*, one of the lacunae of *B*. *D–F*, types of gonads of Elasipoda (*after Théel*, 1882). *G*, hermaphroditic gonad of *Cucumaria laevigata* (*after Ackermann*, 1902). *H*, *Cucumaria glacialis* opened to show brood sacs (*after Mortensen*, 1894). 1, coelomic lining; 2, muscle layer; 3, connective tissue; 4, eosinophilous spherules; 5, gonoduct; 6, genital blood sinus; 7, indifferent tubules; 8, female tubules; 9, male tubules; 10, brood sacs; 11, openings of brood sacs; 12, gonad tubules; 13, intestine.

(Thorson, 1946). According to Edwards (1909), a larval stage is altogether wanting in *Holothuria floridana*, which hatches as a juvenile with tentacles and podia. In those holothurians that brood their young, these develop to a similar advanced stage while in the maternal coelom or attached to the mother's surface, although for *Chiridota rotifera*, H. L. Clark (1910a) reported a doliolaria stage during the coelomic development.

Regardless of differing external appearances, the development of internal structures is much the same throughout the class. The hydrocoel takes on a curved form and begins to encircle the fore-gut, meantime developing lobulations. Either five hydrocoel lobes arise simultaneously or three that soon subdivide to five (Figs. 80*A*, 81*A*). These five lobes represent the five primary tentacles; there rapidly appears a sixth lobe, the polian vesicle (Fig. 81*A*, *B*). The hydrocoel base continues to curve around the fore-gut (Figs. 81*B*, 82*B*), and eventually its ends meet and fuse, establishing the water ring. Alternating with the five primary tentacles there grow out from the water ring five more processes that become the radial water canals; the fact that in holothurians the primary tentacles apparently do not become the radial water canals is difficult of interpretation. Apparently the mid-ventral radial canal always precedes the others in development. No radial canals form in the embryology of the Apoda, but the five radial nerves bud out between the tentacle bases. The proximal part of the embryonic hydroporic canal enlarges to become the definitive stone canal and madreporic body, and its distal part together with the hydropore disappear except presumably in species with surface madreporic openings. Mesenchyme cells gathering in front of the water ring secrete the calcareous ring.

Around the ventrally located mouth the ectoderm begins to thicken greatly (Fig. 81*B*) and sinks into the interior as a vestibule (Fig. 82*A*) that continues the stomodaeal invagination. As it sinks inward the vestibule also carries the mouth inward. The vestibular aperture closes to a narrow slit. The ectodermal floor of the vestibule proliferates to form the nerve ring, and from this the radial nerves grow out between the bases of the five primary tentacles (Fig. 84*D*). Cavities originating from the vestibule accompany the formation of the ring and radial nerves and become the epineural ring and radial sinuses, thus shown to be noncoelomic. The primary tentacles that have hitherto consisted only of hydrocoelic wall push out into the vestibule and thus acquire an ectodermal covering (Fig. 84*D*, *E*). They soon project into the vestibular cavity. A large embryonic area, the preoral lobe, occurs anterior to the ventrally located vestibule. As in crinoids, the vestibule, carrying all adjacent parts with it, rotates to the anterior end, thus eliminating the preoral lobe. The vestibule opens out, its floor becomes the buccal

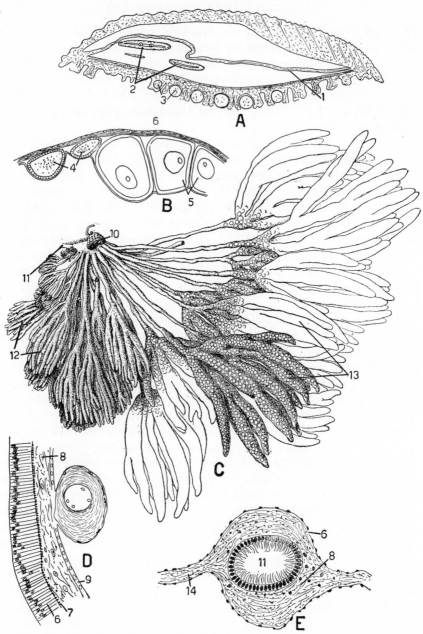

Fig. 77.—Reproduction (continued). *A, Psolus granulosus*, longitudinal section, show-·
ing embryos held in pockets of sole (*after Vaney*, 1925). *B*, section of the hermaphroditic
gonad of a synaptid (*after Semper*, 1868). *C*, hermaphroditic gonad of *Mesothuria intestinalis* (*after Théel*, 1901). *D*, section of ovary of *Cucumaria* (*after Hamann*, 1883). *E*, cross
section of the gonoduct in the dorsal mesentery (*after Ackermann*, 1902). 1, intestine;
2, ovarian tubules; 3, embryos in pockets; 4, sperm; 5, eggs; 6, coelomic epithelium; 7,
muscle fibers; 8, connective tissue; 9, germinal epithelium; 10, basal growing zone; 11,
gonoduct; 12, tufts of male tubules; 13, tufts of female tubules; 14, dorsal mesentery.

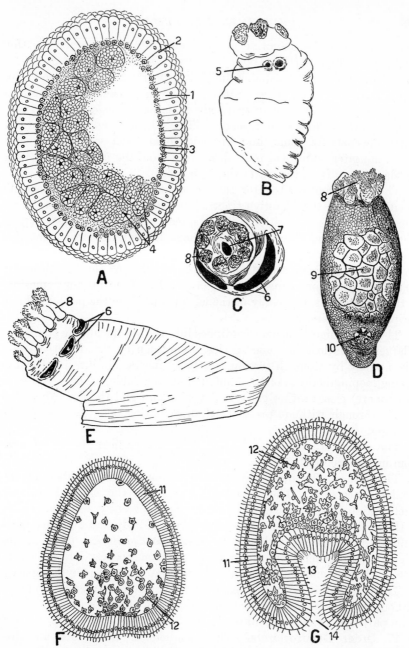

Fig. 78.—Reproduction (concluded). *A*, ventral view of *Psolus antarcticus* with 22 young on the sole (*after Ludwig, 1898a*). *B*, *Cucumaria crocea* with two ventral incubatory pockets in the body wall. *C*, same as *B* with pockets opened. (*B. C, after MacBride and Sampson, 1908.*) *D, Psolus ephippifer* with large scales covering the dorsal brood pockets (*after Théel, 1886*). *E, Psolus koehleri*, with five brood pockets around the neck (*after Vaney, 1914*). *F*, beginning gastrula giving off mesenchyme from vegetative pole. *G*, gastrula with archenteron giving off mesenchyme. (*F, G, after Selenka, 1876*.) 1, rim of sole; 2, scales of dorsal surface; 3, podia; 4, embryos; 5, entrance to pockets; 6, pockets; 7, mouth; 8, tentacles; 9, scales covering incubatory pockets; 10, anal eminence with scales; 11, ectoderm; 12, mesenchyme; 13, archenteron; 14, blastopore.

membrane, and the definitive anterior end with five tentacles is thus established (Fig. 84D). About this time podia grow out from the precocious mid-ventral canal, usually two near the posterior end (Fig. 85A), sometimes one (Fig. 85B). The young cucumber with five primary tentacles and one or two podia is termed a *pentactula* (Fig. 85A, B) and starts leading an independent life. The five-tentacled condition usually persists for some time, but additional podia soon appear (Fig. 85C), and later additional tentacles sprout from the primary ones or in Apoda directly from the water ring (Fig. 84D).

The two somatocoels after their separation from the hydrocoel lie to either side of the digestive tract as flattened sacs that undergo considerable changes of position. They spread around the digestive tract (Fig. 84C, E) and eventually throughout the interior space, meeting ventrally and dorsally to form mesenteries; but the ventral mesentery breaks through giving a continuous coelom here. As the dorsal mesentery forms, the stone canal becomes enclosed in it. Anterior extensions of the somatocoels, especially of the left one, produce the peribuccal and peripharyngeal sinuses.

The larval digestive tract continues into the adult, but the stomachic enlargement is lost in some species. The loop of the digestive tract arises partly by stomach torsion, partly by increase in intestinal length forcing looping because of the limited space available. The larval anus (blastopore) closes rather early in development, and the definitive anus breaks through without proctodaeal invagination near the site of the blastopore.

The gonad originates in the dorsal mesentery near the stone canal from mesenterial cells.

The fate of the mesenchyme is not thoroughly described in the available accounts. The mesenchyme secretes the skeletal ossicles, often initiated in the auricularia stage, and apparently also contributes to the muscular and connective-tissue layers of body and digestive-tract walls in some species, although in *Synaptula hydriformis* these tissues originate altogether from the wall of the somatocoels (H. L. Clark, 1898). The haemal system apparently originates as mesenchymal spaces.

The holothurian larva thus passes directly into the juvenile condition without undergoing any radical changes and with the retention of the main parts from the larval state.

**17. Order Dendrochirota.**—The members of this order are distinguished by the dendritic tentacles that are not provided with conspicuous ampullae. The tentacles are part of an introvert that can be pulled down into the pharynx by the contraction of the five retractor muscles attached to the radial pieces of the calcareous ring. Podia are conspicuously present over the whole body or limited to the ambulacra

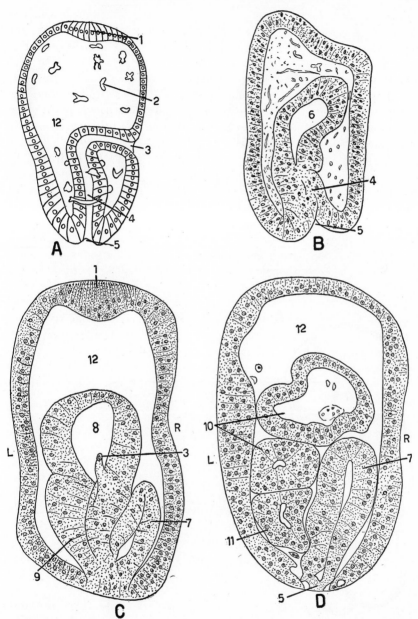

Fig. 79.—Embryology. *A*, precocious formation of the hydropore in *Labidoplax digitata* (*after Selenka, 1883*). *B*, coelomic sac beginning to separate from the enteric sac. *C*, continued separation of the coelomic sac. *D*, coelomic sac completely constricted from enteric sac. (*B–D*, *Leptosynapta inhaerens*, *after S. Runnström, 1927*.)  1, apical sensory plate; 2, mesenchyme; 3, hydropore; 4, archenteron; 5, blastopore; 6, coelomic sac; 7, enteric sac; 8, hydrocoel part of coelomic sac; 9, somatocoel part of coelomic sac; 10, hydrocoel; 11, somatocoel; 12, blastocoel; L, left; R, right.

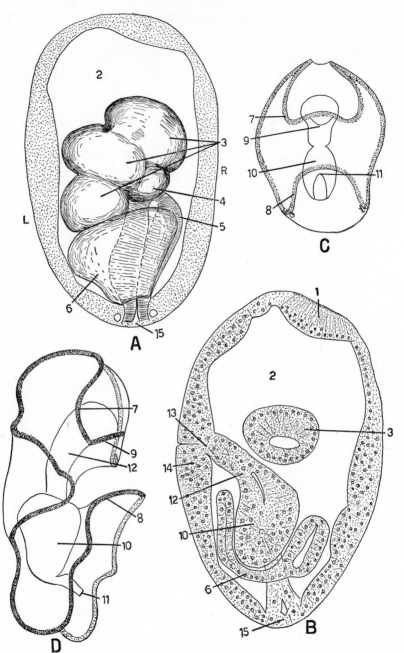

Fig. 80.—Embryology (continued). *A*, dorsal view of embryo with lobulated hydro-coel. *B*, median sagittal section of same stage as *A*. (*A*, *B*, *Leptosynapta inhaerens; after S. Runnström*, 1927.) *C*, young auricularia. *D*, mature auricularia, from the side. (*C*, *D*, *after Mortensen*, 1938.) 1, apical sensory plate; 2, blastocoel; 3, lobes of hydrocoel; 4, axocoel; 5, enteric sac; 6, somatocoel; 7, preoral loop of flagellated band; 8, anal loop; 9, location of mouth; 10, stomach; 11, anus; 12, pharynx; 13, future mouth; 14, vestibular thickening; 15, site of blastopore closure.

or to certain of these. The gonadial tubules are arranged in two tufts, one to either side of the dorsal mesentery. Respiratory trees are present but cuvierian tubules are wanting. The circulatory system is relatively simple without any extensive rete mirable (Fig. 72*B*). In the family Cucumariidae, *Cucumaria* and *Thyone* are common and familiar genera. In the former, the podia are arranged in five ambulacral bands with little scattering into the interambulacral areas (Fig. 47), whereas in *Thyone* they are distributed over the entire body surface without definite relation to the ambulacra (Fig. 51*A*). Both genera are provided with 10 tentacles, equal or with a smaller mid-ventral pair. Special articles are available about two common northern species of *Cucumaria*, *frondosa* (Edwards, 1910) and *glacialis* (Mortensen, 1894); the former is notable for the numerous (up to 50) outlets of the male gonoduct. *Sphaerothuria* (Fig. 50*A*) and *Echinocucumis* are characterized by the spheroidal body clothed with large rounded scales, each bearing a spine. In the genus *Pentacta* (= *Colochirus*), with 10 tentacles, two smaller than the others, the ventral surface is more or less flattened as a creeping sole bearing three bands of podia, and the dorsal surface is warty or papillate (Fig. 85*D*, *E*); the thickened ends of the ambulacra form valves for the introvert and also usually for the anus. The body wall of *Pentacta* is greatly stiffened by an abundance of ossicles.

The differentiation of a creeping sole reaches a climax in the family Psolidae, in which the ventral surface is developed as a thin-walled sole with scanty podia along its periphery and in some species also along the mid-ventral radius; whereas the arched dorsal surface is covered with calcareous scales that ascend the introvert and the anal elevation. There are usually 10 tentacles, of which the two mid-ventral ones may be reduced in size. The members of this family are often red, orange, or pink in color. The main genus *Psolus* with a number of species is devoid of podia dorsally (Fig. 50*C*, *D*); in some species there are five valve-like scales that serve to close over the introvert and the anus (Fig. 86*A*). Dorsal podia projecting through holes in the scales are present in the genera *Thyonepsolus* and *Psolidium* (Fig. 85*F*). As noted above, the Psolidae include a number of brooding species.

The third and last dendrochirote family, the Phyllophoridae, is distinguished by the more numerous tentacles, 15 to 30, of two sizes or of intergrading sizes, more or less arranged in two circlets. The podia may be limited to the ambulacra or also scattered in the interambulacral areas. The main genus *Phyllophorus* (Fig. 86*B*) has up to 20 tentacles of varying size and scattered podia; it is limited to tropical and subtropical waters.

**18. Order Aspidochirota.**—In this order the tentacles are of the peltate type and usually numerous (15 to 30, mostly 20). Pharyngeal retractors are wanting, and the radial longitudinal muscle bands are generally divided in two by a median connective-tissue attachment along the ambulacrum (Fig. 64*A*). The body bears numerous podia, including both locomotory and papillate types. There is a pair of well-developed respiratory trees, and the large intestine is attached to the right-ventral interradius AB. In the family Holothuriidae there is but one tuft of gonadial tubules, attached to the left side of the dorsal mesentery. It is in this family that the rete mirable of the dorsal vessel reaches its highest expression, forming lacunar tufts along the whole length of the ascending small intestine and involving the left respiratory tree (Fig. 73*A*). Cuvierian tubules occur in some members of this family (Fig. 71*D–F*). The Holothuriidae are mostly large, warty cucumbers (Fig. 48*A*, *B*), common in tropical and subtropical waters, especially in the Indo-Pacific region. Typically, there is a ventral creeping sole bearing suckered locomotory podia, arranged in three bands or without arrangement (Fig. 48*A*), whereas the dorsal surface is warty or papillate (Fig. 48*B*), although other arrangements may occur. On opening a holothuriid, one is struck at once by the very long, slender tentacular ampullae encircling the aquapharyngeal bulb (Fig. 64*B*). The main genus *Holothuria* was monographed by Panning (1931–1936), who listed over 100 species; they are mostly elongated forms, of dull coloration, varying from white, cream, and gray to brown and black. In *Actinopyga* (= *Mülleria*), the creeping sole with locomotory podia is very definitely delimited from the warty dorsal surface (Fig. 48*A*, *B*), and the anal opening is provided with five calcareous teeth (Fig. 48*C*).

The family Stichopodidae also has long tentacular ampullae (Fig. 63*A*) and an extensive rete mirabile involving the left respiratory tree (Fig. 74), but there are two gonadial tufts, one to each side of the dorsal mesentery. The main genus *Stichopus* was monographed by H. L. Clark (1922), who recognized nearly 20 species. The species of *Stichopus* are large, conspicuous, warty cucumbers, mostly of warmer waters, with a warty or papillate dorsal surface and a flattened creeping sole bearing three bands of locomotory podia (Fig. 52*A*). *Parastichopus* is cylindroid, not flattened ventrally, and smaller podia appear among the dorsal conical warts.

In the third aspidochirote family, Synallactidae, tentacular ampullae are wanting, and the stone canal opens on the dorsal surface, or at least the madreporic body remains permanently attached to the inside of the body wall. The haemal system is simple. The members of this family typically inhabit deep water and hence are known chiefly from dredging expeditions; many have been taken at depths of 1500 to 5000 m., but some inhabit moderate depths. Among the several genera of this family may be mentioned *Pseudostichopus*, *Bathyplotes*, *Pelopatides*, and *Syn-*

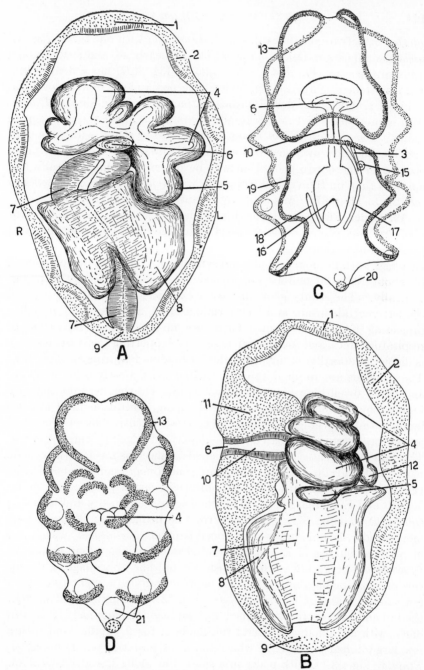

Fig. 81.—Embryology (continued). *A*, ventral view of embryo with lobulated hydrocoel. *B*, sagittal view of same stage as *A*. (*A, B, Leptosynapta inhaerens; after S. Runnström*, 1927.) *C*, mature auricularia, 14 days old, ventral view. *D*, transitional stage from
auricularia to doliolaria. (*C, D, after Mortensen*, 1938.) 1, apical sensory plate; 2, flagellated bands; 3, hydrocoel; 4, tentacular lobes of hydrocoel; 5, lobe representing polian
vesicle; 6, mouth; 7, digestive tract; 8, somatocoel; 9, site of closed blastopore; 10, pharynx;
11, vestibular thickening; 12, axocoel; 13, preoral loop; 14, stomach; 15, hydropore; 16,
anus; 17, left somatocoel; 18, right somatocoel; 19, anal loop; 20, ossicle; 21, spheres
probably for floating.

*allactes* with two gonadial tufts, and *Mesothuria* with one tuft.   *Pseudo-stichopus* appears to be devoid of ossicles or nearly so, and a deep notch leads to the anus (Fig. 86*C*).   *Bathyplotes* (Fig. 86*D*) has a floating rim and a flattened ventral sole provided with podia along the lateroventral radii (B and E); the dorsal surface is papillate.   The similar *Pelopa-tides* is more flattened and generally bears podia along the mid-ventral radius.   *Synallactes* has an elongated, cylindroid shape with numerous papillae dorsally, arranged in longitudinal rows.   In *Mesothuria* podia occur over the entire body and may be better developed dorsally and laterally than on the ventral surface.   An extensive study of *Mesothuria intestinalis* (Fig. 87*B*) was made by Haanen (1914).

**19. Order Elasipoda.**—The Elasipoda are a group of holothurians of bizarre appearance, being provided with large conical papillae, marginal rims, tail-like appendages, and so on.   They are often more or less flattened, with pronounced bilateral symmetry.   The mouth, surrounded by about 10 to 20 tentacles of the peltate type, is generally displaced ventrally.   The scanty podia are usually reduced to one or two rows on the flat ventral surface and lack terminal disks, also the usual ampullae projecting into the coelom.   There are no pharyngeal retractors or respiratory trees, and the ventral mesentery supporting the large intestine is displaced dorsally, occurring in the interradius BC, usually close to C. The elasipods are all inhabitants of ocean depths, mostly below 1000 m., and many dwell between 2000 and 5000 m.   On this account they are known only from the collections of dredging expeditions and are not familiar to the average zoologist.   The most extensive account of them is that of Théel (1882), based on the material dredged by the *Challenger*. Théel, in fact, created the name Elasipoda, as well as most of the generic names in the group.   Among the many genera may be mentioned *Deima* (Fig. 52*D*, *E*), with hard encrusted surface, a row of podia along ambu-lacra B and E, and large conical papillae arranged dorsally and laterally; *Oneirophanta* (Fig. 87*C*), with two rows of podia along B and E and more slender, flexible lateral and dorsal papillae; *Laetmogone*, with a row of podia along B and E and a row of slender papillae along C and D; *Psychropotes* (Fig. 49*C*), with a posterior tail-like appendage, a double row of small podia along A, lateral papillae forming a slight rim, and a few small dorsal papillae; *Benthodytes* (Fig. 53*B*, *C*), similar, but without the tail and with more numerous dorsal papillae; *Euphronides* (Figs. 50*B*, 86*E*), with a pronounced lateral rim made of fused papillae and with a few large dorsal papillae, of which the most posterior one is unpaired; *Elpidia* (Fig. 53*A*), with podia in a single row along B and E and a few paired dorsal papillae; *Peniagone* (Fig. 53*D*), with a sail on the anterior dorsal region; *Scotoanassa* (Fig. 88*A*), also with a sail but with the podia clustered at the posterior end, making a fringe there; and *Kolga*, with a

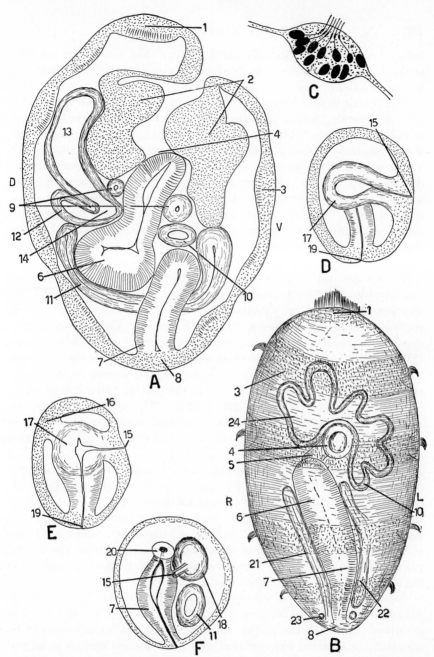

FIG. 82.—Embryology (continued). *A*, sagittal section of larva with ring canal closed. *B*, mature doliolaria, 3 days old. (*A*, *B*, *Leptosynapta inhaerens; after S. Runnström*, 1927.) *C*, section of the flagellated band (*after Reimers*, 1912). *D–F*, stages of the development of *Synaptula hydriformis* (*after H. L. Clark*, 1898). *D*, precocious formation of the hydropore. *E*, formation of the stomodaeum. *F*, hydrocoel separated from the somatocoel. 1, apical sense plate; 2, vestibular invagination; 3, flagellated bands; 4, definitive mouth; 5, pharynx; 6, stomach; 7, intestine; 8, site of closed blastopore; 9, anterior extensions of coelom; 10, polian vesicle; 11, somatocoel; 12, axocoel; 13, tentacular lobe of hydrocoel; 14, water ring; 15, hydropore; 16, stomodaeum; 17, hydroenterocoel; 18, hydrocoel; 19, blastopore; 20, larval mouth; 21, right somatocoel; 22, left somatocoel; 23, ossicles; 24, lobulated hydrocoel; D, dorsal; V, ventral.

reduced sail of a few, partially fused papillae (Fig. 86*F*). An extensive account of *Kolga hyalina*, dredged in subarctic waters off Norway at around 2000 m., was given by Daniellsen and Koren (1882). It is highly probable that some of these elasipods are bathypelagic, as the various appendages such as the sails, rims, and tails appear to be floating or natatory devices. There is, moreover, an elasipod genus, *Pelagothuria*, that is definitely pelagic and has been taken floating on the surface. Three species of *Pelagothuria* are known. The first, *P. natatrix*, was described by Ludwig (1894) on the basis of 18 specimens taken in the vicinity of the equator by the *Albatross* in its explorations off the west coast of South America. Some were collected swimming at the surface, others were caught at unknown levels on the net as it came up from the depths. On a later cruise of the *Albatross*, 33 more individuals were obtained off Peru and around the Galapagos Islands (H. L. Clark, 1920), so that the creature appears common in the eastern Pacific at low latitudes. Better knowledge of the appearance of the animal in life was presented by Chun (1900), who was present at the taking of 11 specimens of another species, *P. ludwigi*, by the *Valdivia* Expedition near the Seychelles Islands, and who gave sketches of the living animal (Fig. 87*A*). At least some of these were caught in a closing net at 800 to 1000 m. Still a third species, *P. bouvieri*, is known from a single specimen taken at the surface in 1905 in the central Atlantic west of the Cape Verde Islands (Hérouard, 1906a, 1923). The combined information shows that *Pelagothuria* has an oval gelatinous body devoid of ossicles. Around the large terminal mouth is a circlet of tentacles with bifurcated ends; there are 13 to 16 such tentacles in *P. natatrix*, 14 in *P. ludwigi*, and 20 in *P. bouvieri*. Shortly behind the tentacular circlet occurs the floating web or sail, supported by long, projecting papillae. This web, with 12 supporting papillae, is limited to the dorsal side in *P. bouvieri* but completely encircles the body in *P. natatrix* (papillae equal to the number of tentacles) and in *P. ludwigi* (12 papillae). There are traces of podia, and the stone canal opens on the surface near the genital papilla (Heding, 1940). *Pelagothuria* appears to float at a range from the surface to considerable depths.

Several specimens of another pelagic holothurian, *Planktothuria diaphana*, were netted in deep water off the Cape of Good Hope and described by Gilchrist (1920). According to the unsatisfactory description the creature was provided with tentacles and curious podia and enclosed in an oval mass of jelly, hence presumably is pelagic. Heding (1950), on the basis of material secured by the German Deep Sea Expedition, declares that *Pelagothuria ludwigi* is identical with *P. natatrix* and that *Planktothuria diaphana* is identical with *Pelagothuria bouvieri*, which in turn is identical with *Enypniastes ecalcarea*. There is therefore but one species of *Pelagothuria*, namely, *natatrix*. Heding proposes that the pelagic holothurians, comprising *P. natatrix*, *Enypniastes ecalcarea*, and one other species of the latter genus, be placed in a separate order of Holothuroidea, Pelagothurioidea. Heding's conclusions here must await evaluation by other holothurian specialists.

**20. Order Molpadonia.**—The Molpadonia are mostly stout, relatively smooth cucumbers of some size, with the posterior region usually narrowed to simulate a tail (Fig. 49*B*), containing the elongated cloaca and bearing the anus at its tip. The terminal anterior end forms a flat circular disk provided with 15 (10 in one genus) digitate tentacles, simple or with fingers (Fig. 51*G*). The tentacles usually have free tentacular ampullae. Radial water canals are present, but podia are lacking, except in *Gephyrothuria* (Fig. 88*F*), in which a few, widely spaced, very slender papillae occur on the middorsal interradius. The radial canals terminate posteriorly in small anal papillae. There are no pharyngeal retractors, and the longitudinal bands of the body wall are divided into two bands (Fig. 75). Respiratory trees are present and also a well-developed haemal system with

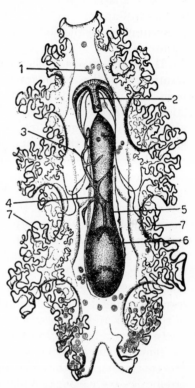

Fig. 83.—Embryology (continued). Giant frilled auricularia (*after Chun* 1896). 1, wheel ossicles; 2, pharynx; 3, hydropore; 4, hydrocoel; 5, fore-gut; 6, stomach; 7, frills of flagellated band.

an extensive network between the dorsal sinus and the small intestine (Fig. 75), at least in the larger species. The gonad occurs as two tufts of simple or branched tubules. Because of the lack of podia, the Molpadonia and the Apoda are known as *apodous* holothurians and have been given a valuable treatment by H. L. Clark (1907).

The main genus *Molpadia* (= *Ankyroderma*, *Trochostoma*) with well-developed caudate region (Fig. 49*B*) is characterized by the form of the tentacular digits; these occur as one to three side pairs and a large unpaired terminal finger (Fig. 88*B*). A good anatomical account of the Japanese *M. roretzii* has been furnished by Hatanaka (1939). *Caudina* has generally a long caudate region and four equal tentacular digitations (Fig. 51*G*). An outstanding account of the New England *Caudina* *arenata* was published by Gould (1896). *Paracaudina* differs only in the form of its ossicles. *Paracaudina chilensis* (Fig. 75) has served for excellent anatomical (Kawamoto, 1927) and physiological (see later) studies by Japanese workers. In *Acaudina* the caudate region is lacking, and tentacular ampullae are wanting in *Eupyrgus*, a genus of small arctic forms.

**21. Order Apoda.**—The Apoda, as the name implies, are totally wanting in podia, except for the tentacles. They are modified, vermiform holothurians with rough or warty surface. The tentacles, 10 to 20 or even more in number, are simple, digitate, or pinnate; shortened pinnate tentacles grade into the digitate type. Tentacular ampullae are wanting, and the tentacular canals spring directly from the water ring; there are no radial canals. Pharyngeal retractors are present in some Apoda. The longitudinal muscle bands are single strips, and unlike the state of affairs in other holothurians, do not interrupt the layer of circular muscles at the radii. In correlation with the vermiform shape, the loops of the digestive tract are much reduced and even almost wanting. There are no respiratory trees, and the haemal system is simple, with dorsal and ventral sinuses connecting to lacunae in the wall of the digestive tract; the haemal ring supplies the tentacles, but radial haemal vessels are wanting. The gonad consists of one pair of more or less branching tubules that are often hermaphroditic. Characteristic of this order are anchor and wheel ossicles.

In the family Synpatidae there are no wheel or sigmoid ossicles and the tentacles are always more or less pinnate; anchors with anchor plates are conspicuous in the thin body wall. Members of this family are often excessively elongated and, when fully extended, may reach lengths of 2 or 3 feet. In some genera (*Synapta, Synaptula*), there is found immediately behind the calcareous ring another supporting ring, called the cartilaginous ring, composed of dense connective tissue. Genera with well-developed pinnate tentacles, mostly about 15, as *Synapta*, *Euapta* (Fig. 49D), and *Opheodesoma*, are distinguished from each other chiefly by details of the anchors. In the mostly smaller genus *Synaptula*, there are 10 to 15 tentacles, often short with few side branches. *Synaptula hydriformis*, with brooding habits, was extensively treated by H. L. Clark (1898) (Fig. 68A). *Leptosynapta* contains a number of species of small to moderate size, with 10 to 13 pinnate tentacles, often somewhat short, and mostly one polian vesicle, whereas the preceding genera tend to numerous polian vesicles. This genus is further characterized by burrowing habits. In *Labidoplax* and *Protankyra* there are 10 to 12 digitate tentacles, with three or four digits in the former, two in the latter. *Anapta* with 12 short pinnate tentacles lacks all the typical synaptid ossicles, having only small calcareous bodies. *Rhabdomolgus*

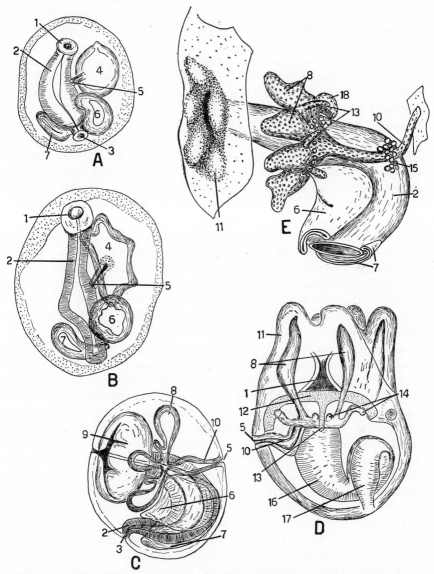

FIG. 84.—Embryology (concluded). *A–D*, further stages of *Synaptula hydriformis* (*after H. L. Clark*, 1898). *A*, hydrocoel separated from somatocoels. *B*, hydrocoel becoming lobulated. *C*, vestibule invaginated. *D*, tentacular lobes pushing out ectoderm to form five primary tentacles. *E*, late stage of *Labidoplax digitata* (*after Selenka*, 1883), radial canals growing from the water ring. 1, mouth; 2, digestive tract; 3, anus; 4, hydrocoel; 5, hydropore; 6, left somatocoel; 7, right somatocoel; 8, tentacular lobes of hydrocoel; 9, vestibular invagination; 10, larval stone canal; 11, ectodermal parts of primary tentacles; 12, nerve ring; 13, radial nerves; 14, buds of secondary tentacles; 15, ossicles; 16, stomach; 17, intestine; 18, polian vesicle.

is provided with 10 simple tentacles; the small, red *R. ruber* (Fig. 88*C*) has been well studied by Becher (1907), who regards it as a very primitive holothurian.

The Chiridotidae have short stout tentacles that tend toward the peltate type; they lack anchors but are typically provided with six-spoked wheels (Fig. 55*F*); in the absence of wheels, conspicuous sigmoid or C-shaped bodies are present. In the main genus *Chiridota* (Fig. 89*B*), there are 12 tentacles, and the wheels are aggregated into wheel papillae. The most familiar species, *C. rotifera*, is viviparous, and the development of the young inside the coelom has been studied by H. L. Clark (1910a). *Taeniogyrus*, with 10 or 12 tentacles, is also provided with wheel papillae but possesses large sigmoid ossicles in addition. In *Sigmodota* ( = *Scoliodota*, *Trochodota*), wheels and sigmoid ossicles are scattered throughout the body wall, not in papillae; there are 10 tentacles.

Anchors are also wanting in the Myriotrochidae, whose characteristic ossicle is a wheel with eight or more spokes, not aggregated into papillae. The members of this family are typically inhabitants of colder waters. They are small cucumbers with short tentacles approaching the digitate type. In *Myriotrochus* (Fig. 89*A*), the wheels have 10 to 25 spokes, and triangular teeth point inward from the rim (Fig. 55*E*). These teeth are lacking in *Trochoderma* where the wheels are provided with 10 to 16 spokes and ornamented with knobs along the rim; the wheels occur in several layers, making the body wall firm and hard.

**22. Fossil Holothuroidea.**—Because of the slight development of an endoskeleton in the Holothuroidea, little may be expected in the way of fossil members. The available knowledge together with an exhaustive bibliography was presented in 1932 by Croneis and McCormack. What are claimed to be impressions of holothurian bodies have been reported several times in the literature. The specimens concerned in these reports are probably actually impressions of holothurians in two cases: Giebel's description and figures (1857) of impressions from the famous lithographic limestones of Solenhofen, Bavaria, from the Jurassic, and Broili's (1926) finding of a fossil resembling a molpadonian from the Jurassic, also in Germany. In 1911, Walcott assigned to the Holothuroidea a number of fossil impressions of mid-Cambrian age, but H. L. Clark (1912) strongly opposed the holothurian nature of these remains. Ossicles of undoubted holothurian nature occur in the rocks as far back as the Carboniferous (Etheridge, 1881), and ossicles obviously belonging to the Apoda were figured by Schlumberger (1889, 1890) from the Eocene of France. As Croneis and McCormack remark, the work of Schlumberger showed that the recent families Synaptidae, Chiridotidae, and Myriotrochidae were well differentiated at least as long ago as the early Tertiary. A number of later reports on fossil holothurian ossicles

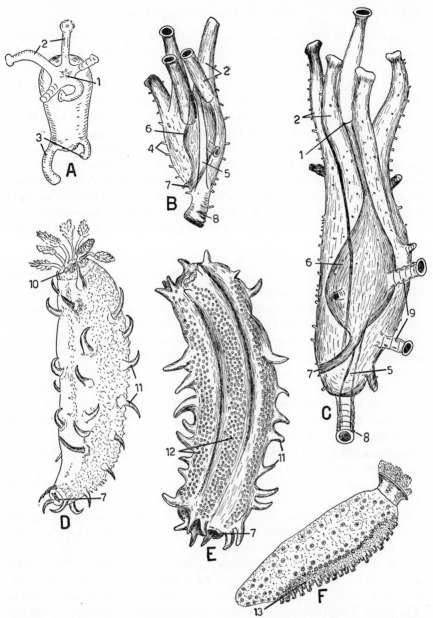

FIG. 85.—Juvenile cucumbers, dendrochirotes. *A*, young of *Cucumaria frondosa*, with five primary tentacles and two podia from the mid-ventral water canal (*after the Runnströms*, 1921). *B*, young of *Holothuria*, 9 days old, with one podium from the mid-ventral water canal. *C*, young *Holothuria*, 33 days old, with several podia. (*B, C, after Edwards*, 1909.) *D*, *Pentacta*, dorsal view (*after Sluiter*, 1901). *E*, *Pentacta*, ventral view, not same species as *D* (*after Théel*, 1886). *F*, *Psolidium convergens*, Antarctic, with dorsal podia (*after Perrier*, 1905). 1, mouth; 2, primary tentacles; 3, first-formed podia; 4, projecting ossicles (tables); 5, mid-ventral water canal; 6, stomach; 7, anus; 8, first podium; 9, later podia; 10, small tentacles; 11, papillae; 12, rows of podia; 13, creeping sole.

are available in the literature (e.g., Frentzen, 1944). In 1939, MacBride and Spencer described, under the name *Eothuria*, a test from the Ordovician of Scotland that they considered to represent a primitive holothurian. This test has five ambulacra of plates perforated for the passage of the podia, and the interambulacral areas are completely covered with small rounded plates. This fossil would seem to be an echinoid rather than a holothurian.

**23. Asexual Reproduction.**—Asexual reproduction by transverse constriction into halves that regenerate has been observed in several holothurians. Small individuals of *Cucumaria planci* brought into laboratory aquaria were observed to divide in two in three cases (Chadwick, 1891), and one posterior piece again subdivided. In the same species, also under laboratory conditions, Monticelli (1896) repeatedly saw division into two, sometimes three, pieces (Fig. 89*D*) by constriction, twisting, or pulling apart; the pieces so resulting regenerated perfectly, until through repeated subdivisions they were too reduced in size for survival. Crozier (1914) noted under laboratory conditions transverse division in very young individuals (6 mm. in length) of *Holothuria parvula* and in adult specimens of *Holothuria surinamensis* (Crozier, 1917a). Out of 446 specimens of the latter species collected in nature, 23 were found with regenerating oral ends and 27 with regenerating anal ends. As these regenerating individuals were about half normal size, it is reasonable to suppose that they represent cases of transverse division of this species under natural conditions. Crozier further found one individual in the field that had just undergone fission, as the halves were still connected by a length of intestine. In examining a collection of preserved holothurians from the West Indies, Deichmann (1922) noticed a high percentage of regenerating forms that had evidently resulted from fission; of 82 specimens of *Actinopyga difficilis*, 18 were regenerating orally and 24 anally, and of 123 specimens of *Holothuria parvula*, 43 were regenerating orally, 41 anally. In both species the fission appeared limited to partially grown individuals. Regenerating specimens of *H. parvula* were also found in nature by Kille (1936).

**24. Evisceration and Autotomy.**—It is well known that under unfavorable conditions, such as fouling of the water, rise of temperature, excessive irritation, many holothurians rupture and eject their viscera. The place of rupture and the organs expelled differ somewhat in different cucumbers. In the large aspidochirotes, as species of *Holothuria*, *Stichopus*, and *Actinopyga*, the usual course of events is rupture of the cloaca following contraction of the body wall, and the emission through the rupture out of the anus of the entire digestive tract (except the ends), one or both respiratory trees, and usually the gonad tubules (Domantay, 1931; Bertolini, 1933a; Dawbin, 1949). Evisceration may also occur

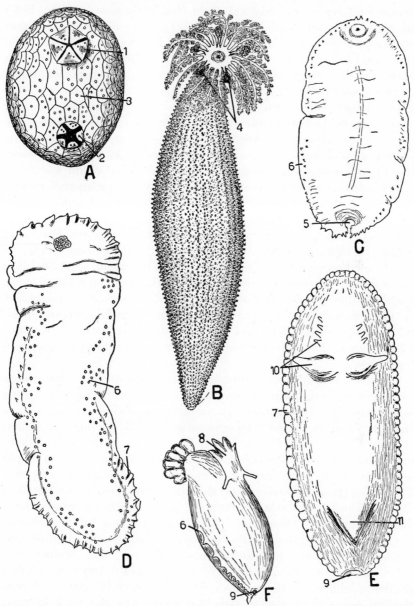

FIG. 86.—Dendrochirotes (continued), aspidochirotes, elasipods. *A*, species of *Psolus* with five oral and five anal scales (*after Ludwig*, 1894). *B*, *Phyllophorus urna*, Mediterranean, with 15 long and 5 short tentacles. *C*, *Pseudostichopus*, with anal notch (*after Fisher*, 1907). *D*, *Bathyplotes* with floating rim (*after Sluiter*, 1901). *E*, *Euphronides*, dorsal view, ventral view in Fig. 50*B*. *F*, *Kolga* with small sail. (*E*, *F*, *after Hérouard*, 1902.) 1, oral scales; 2, anal scales; 3, scales of armor; 4, small tentacles; 5, anal notch; 6, podia; 7, floating rim; 8, sail; 9, anus; 10, papillae; 11, tail-like unpaired papilla.

through ruptures in the body wall as in *Holothuria parvula* (Kille, 1937) and *Holothuria surinamensis* (Crozier, 1915). The process is somewhat different in *Thyone briareus* and the related *Phyllophorus* (Pearse, 1909; Scott, 1914; Domantay, 1931; Kille, 1935). Here body contraction distends the introvert which, being thin-walled, soon ruptures, and a variable amount of viscera escapes through the rupture; the retractor muscles break, and eventually the entire anterior end including the aquapharyngeal bulb and associated parts is cast off. There remains the body wall, the cloaca with attached respiratory trees, the gonad tufts, and the greater part of the dorsal mesentery. As discussed below, eviscerated holothurians regenerate if kept under good conditions.

The question arises whether evisceration occurs in a state of nature. The finding of specimens with regenerating digestive tracts indicates that this may happen especially during the warmer parts of the year. Kille (1936) found 4 regenerating specimens among 65 *Holothuria floridana* in summer in the Tortugas region, and Bertolini (1932) at Naples noted regenerating intestines in 110 of 119 individuals of *Stichopus regalis* during October but saw none in spring. On the other hand, Dawbin (1949a) considers evisceration a rare process in *Stichopus mollis*, Australia, as only 6 eviscerated specimens were found in 330 examined, and all of these had been cast up on shores after storms. Minchen (1892) remarks that ejected viscera are often brought up by fishermen on English coasts.

Suitable holothurians may usually be caused to eviscerate by crowding them in standing water in an aquarium, and some will eviscerate in time under even the best laboratory conditions. Various authors have sought rapid means of inducing evisceration, chiefly by injecting chemicals into the coelom. Pearse (1909) injected about 20 different substances into *Thyone briareus* but obtained only 19 eviscerations in 246 specimens, chiefly with strychnine and methylene blue. Kille (1931, 1935), using the same species, obtained rapid and dependable evisceration with dilute ammonia water. Strychnine and ammonia water have failed with other species. Domantay (1931) injected a long list of chemicals into large aspidochirotes, chiefly *Holothuria sanguinolenta* and *Stichopus chloronotus*, but complete evisceration with recovery was obtained only with distilled water, codeine, and turpentine; other substances when at all effective might evoke partial evisceration or powerful body-wall contractions followed by death. Distilled water was also used to good advantage on *Stichopus mollis* by Dawbin (1949a). Making a tear in the cloaca evoked evisceration in *Holothuria parvula* after the foregoing methods had failed (Kille, 1937). Subjecting the animal to an electrical current is apparently one of the best and most reliable methods (Kille, 1931, 1935, 1936; Bertolini, 1933a).

Evisceration is often called autotomy in the literature, but this term is better applied to the phenomenon of self-separation of body portions that include the body wall as well as the viscera. Autotomy occurs in synaptids by the constricting of the body into short pieces (Fig. 89E), either simultaneously or successively from the posterior end forward (H. L. Clark, 1899; Pearse, 1909; Domantay, 1931). As synaptids cannot regenerate the anterior end, all such pieces die except the most anterior one.

**25. Regeneration.**—Aspidochirotes and dendrochirotes have high powers of regeneration. Following evisceration, the course of regeneration in species of *Holothuria* has been studied by Bertolini (1933a) and Kille (1936). The cloaca and the esophagus each send out a hollow tubular outgrowth along the torn edge of the mesentery, and these meet to become the new digestive tract in as little as 25 days. These tubular outgrowths consist of the layers of the digestive tract in simplified form, and these later differentiate to the definitive condition. Thus in species of *Holothuria*, the layers of the digestive tract are proliferated by the same layers of the stumps. A somewhat different story obtains for species of *Stichopus* (Bertolini, 1930, 1931a, 1931b; Dawbin, 1949a) that further regenerate much more slowly. Here the digestive tract is regenerated in place along the torn edge of the mesentery, wholly from the cells of the mesentery. A thickening appears along this edge, a lumen develops in the thickening, and the walls of the thickening then differentiate into the layers of the digestive wall (Fig. 90A–D). The completion and differentiation of the digestive tract require some 4 months. In both genera the respiratory trees arise as buds from the cloaca, and the haemal system is replaced by arrangement of the cells of the mesentery into strands that hollow out.

Regeneration of a dendrochirote following evisceration, as exemplified by *Thyone briareus*, has been described by Scott (1914) and Kille (1935). In this species the anterior end is shed and the body wall then closes by muscular contraction and soon heals over by way of a connective-tissue plug that is continuous with the anterior edge of the mesentery. The digestive tract forms much as in *Stichopus*, by a thickening along the edge of the mesentery that soon hollows out and differentiates into the parts and tissues of the digestive tract; but there appear to be cellular invasions from the two ends, which furnish the lining epithelium. The torn ends of the radial water canals grow forward and inward, and after budding off the tentacles unite to form the water ring. The pharynx has meantime developed from the anteriormost part of the mesentery, where it has fused to the connective-tissue plug. The anterior ends of the longitudinal muscle bands split off branches that become the retractor muscles. In regard to the regeneration of the gonad, Kille (1939) has found for

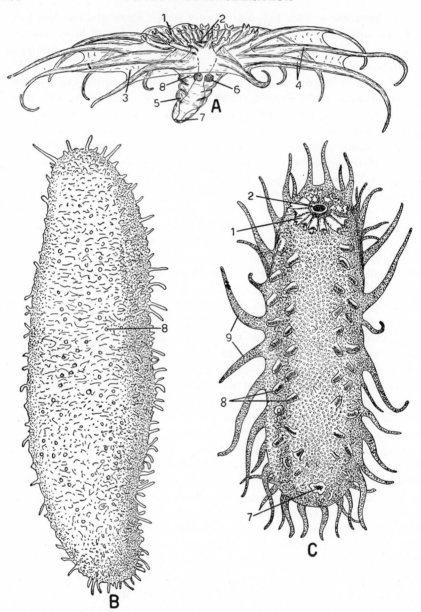

Fig. 87.—Aspidochirotes, elasipods (continued).  A, *Pelagothuria ludwigi* (*after Chun*, 1900).  B, *Mesothuria intestinalis* (*after Haanen*, 1914), dorsal view.  C, *Oneirophanta mutabilis* (*after Théel*, 1882).  1, tentacles; 2, mouth; 3, web; 4, supporting papillae of web; 5, body; 6, gonads; 7, anus; 8, podia; 9, papillae.

*Thyone* that the gonad grows from the gonad base in the mesentery and will regenerate as long as this base or center of proliferation remains intact, but not if it is removed. This center of proliferation contains nests of germ cells.

Body halves regenerate following natural transverse fission and also in the same species if the body is artificially transected (Crozier, 1915; Kille, 1937). Torelle (1909) performed transection experiments on six dendrochirote, three aspidochirote, and three synaptid species but never published a full report and gave only a brief account of results, chiefly concerning *Cucumaria grubei*. Both halves of this species regenerate completely, but a short anterior portion will not complete itself posteriorly, and if the body is transected into thirds, only the posterior third regenerates into a complete individual. Short posterior pieces, about one-sixth the body length, showed growth but had failed to complete regeneration within the time limits of the experiments. Longitudinal halves failed to survive. Various sorts of cuts through the body wall heal readily. Apparently the dendrochirotes in general, except for *Cucumaria planci* and *grubei*, are unable to regenerate the cloaca; anterior halves of *Thyone briareus* also failed to regenerate a cloaca in Kille's experiments (1935). Synaptids have poor regenerative ability, and body pieces without anterior ends die; presumably anterior pieces can regenerate posteriorly (H. L. Clark, 1899), but complete data are not available.

**26. Ecology: Habits and Behavior.**—Apart from *Pelagothuria* and relatives and the presumably bathypelagic elasipods that are provided with floating or swimming devices, the holothurians are in general benthonic animals. They have sluggish habits, often remaining in one place for long periods if conditions are suitable. Some are addicted to rocky bottom, living concealed under rocks or coral slabs or tucked into crevices and crannies. Some small species live among bunches of seaweeds, as *Synaptula hydriformis* (H. L. Clark, 1898), or among coral branches. In warm shallow waters of tropical and subtropical regions, large aspidochirotes of such genera as *Holothuria*, *Stichopus*, and *Actinopyga* lie around by the hundreds or even thousands on the sandy bottom, fully exposed or slightly concealed by bits of shell and plant material. A good many holothurians, including some dendrochirotes and aspidochirotes, but mostly molpadonians and other apodous types, live wholly or partly buried in muddy and sandy bottoms. Thus the common *Thyone briareus* of the New England coast is found buried in muddy bottom with the two ends protruding (Pearse, 1908). Molpadonians such as *Caudina arenata* (Gerould, 1896), *Molpadia roretzii* (Hatanaka, 1939), and *Paracaudina chilensis* (Yamanouchi, 1926) live buried in sandy or muddy bottoms with the body directed downward,

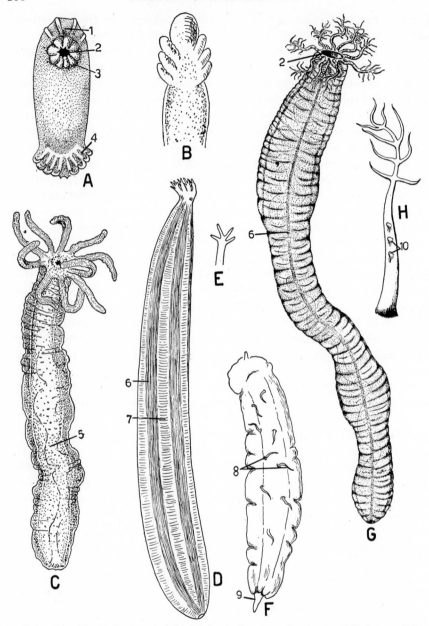

FIG. 88.—Elasipods (concluded), molpadonians, apodans. *A, Scotoanassa* (*after Théel*, 1882). *B*, tentacle of *Molpadia* (*after Daniellsen and Koren*, 1882). *C, Rhabdomolgus ruber* (*after Becher*, 1907). *D, Labidoplax thomsoni. E*, tentacle of *D. F, Gephyrothuria* (*after Hérouard*, 1923). *G, Leptosynapta inhaerens. H*, tentacle of *G.* (*G, H, after Coe*, 1912.)  1, sail; 2, mouth; 3, tentacles; 4, podia; 5, intestine; 6, longitudinal muscle bands; 7, circular muscles; 8, papillae; 9, protruded cloaca; 10, tentacular pits.

but dorsal side up at an angle to the surface, and the posterior tip at the surface for respiratory purposes. Synaptids such as species of *Leptosynapta* (H. L. Clark, 1899; S. Runnström, 1927) spend their entire lives completely buried in soft bottoms, moving around below the surface. These burrowing forms, when removed from their burrows and placed on top of mud or sand, dig in again. *Thyone* accomplishes this by ploughing into the substrate dorsal side up through alternate circular and longitudinal contractions until the middle region is buried; the process requires some 2 to 4 hours and is facilitated by attachment of the podia to some solid object. *Molpadia* and *Paracaudina* exhibit pronounced positive geotaxis; the head curves downward against the sand, the tentacles push the sand away, and the animal advances into the substrate by tentacular action plus circular contractions proceeding from the anal region anteriorly. Cooperation of the tentacles with the the muscular action is necessary, as animals deprived of their tentacles cannot burrow. The animal comes to rest with the trunk at an angle of 30 to 50 degrees with the surface, dorsal side up, and the tail or caudate region more or less vertical with the tip at the surface. Isolated caudate regions exhibit negative geotaxis when buried, orient themselves vertically, with the tail tip up, and proceed vertically until the tail tip reaches the surface. Species of *Leptosynapta* also combine tentacular and muscular action in burrowing. They first head vertically into the sand, loosening it with their tentacles, then burrow around below the surface in any direction, occasionally sticking the head end out. Clark has noticed that the anchors are larger and more numerous in the posterior part of the body and are propped against the burrow wall to prevent backward slipping when circular contractions force the anterior region onward. The apodous holothurians are more efficient burrowers than *Thyone*, as *Leptosynapta* advances through the sand at a rate of 2 or 3 cm. per minute and can completely bury itself in 5 or 6 minutes. The larger *Molpadia* is slightly slower, progressing downward at a rate of 1 cm. per minute and getting into position below the surface in 10 to 20 minutes.

It was remarked by Semper (1868) that many holothurians are somewhat nocturnal, fully expanding their tentacles only at night. Stier (1933) noticed that *Thyone briareus* is most active in winter from late afternoon until an hour or two after midnight and remains with tentacles partly contracted during morning and early afternoon; this daily periodicity is less marked in summer. An annual periodicity was reported for *Stichopus japonicus* by Mitsukuri (1903); this species at the end of the breeding season in early July retires to a dark sheltered place and remains contracted without feeding until cooler temperatures arrive in October.

Pedate holothurians (i.e., those provided with podia) are able to move about by attaching the terminal disks to objects, but even podia without disks can be employed in locomotion. As the locomotory function of the podia is best investigated in the Asteroidea, discussion of it will be deferred to the account of that class. The aspidochirotes, especially those with differentiated creeping sole, are able to progress with fair speed, and even large species can climb the glass walls of aquaria. Probably some muscular action of the body wall is also involved in their

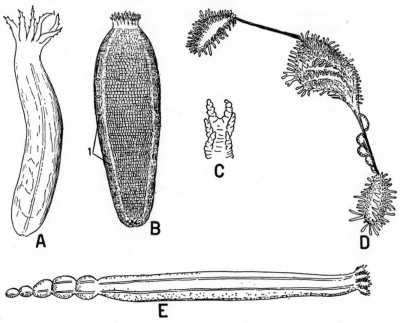

Fig. 89.—Apoda (concluded), autotomy. *A*, *Myriotrochus rinkii*, Arctic, natural size (*after Danielssen and Koren*, 1882). *B*, *Chiridota marenzelleri*, Strait of Magellan. *C*, tentacle of *B*. (*B*, *C*, *after Perrier*, 1904.) *D*, *Cucumaria planci* pulling into three pieces (*after Monticelli*, 1896). *E*, *Leptosynapta inhaerens* undergoing autotomy (*after Pearse*, 1907). 1, wheel papillae.

locomotion, but *Stichopus panimensis* observed by Parker (1921) appears unusual in that obvious muscular waves, passing from anal to oral end, participate in the creeping, so that the locomotion resembles that of a "gigantic caterpillar." At the beginning of a muscular wave, the rear end is lifted from the substrate and advanced through longitudinal contraction, then the middle region is similarly lifted and advanced, and when the wave reaches the anterior end, the whole animal has been advanced by about 1 cm. These locomotory waves pass over the animal's body about once a minute and enable the animal to cover a distance of a meter in about 15 minutes. No such locomotory waves were noticed by the author in several kinds of large aspidochirotes under observation in the Bahamas; they advanced smoothly, seemingly almost entirely through the activity of the podia. Dendrochirote holothurians appear disinclined to move about, and an aquarium specimen of *Cucumaria planci* remained in the same spot for at least 2 years (Noll, 1881). The thin rim of the creeping sole of Psolidae is used to clamp the animal to rocks. As already noted, the apodous holothurians mostly burrow and have poor powers of locomotion when removed from their burrows. They can, however, advance by using the tentacles as holdfasts and by constrictions passing from the anal to the oral end. *Synaptula hydriformis* does not burrow but clambers about on seaweeds, pulling itself along by attaching the tentacles to objects, aided by alternate contractions and elongations of the body musculature. Here, too, the anchors are extensively employed in clinging tenaciously to the seaweeds (Olmsted, 1917). Young specimens of *Leptosynapta inhaerens* were caught by Costello (1946) swimming at the surface at night in the Woods Hole region. The fully extended body is curved into a U shape, and the middle region advances, though somewhat aimlessly, by the sudden thrashing of the body ends together, after the manner of the scissors kick of swimmers. This swimming behavior appeared strictly nocturnal and could not be elicited in daylight hours even in individuals placed in darkness.

As regards feeding habits, the holothurians fall into two categories, although in both feeding is implemented by the tentacles. The dendrochirotes are plankton feeders. When undisturbed they stretch their tentacles to the fullest extent into the sea water or may sweep them over the surface of the substrate. Minute organisms and detritus adhere to the tentacles through mucous secretion. One by one, without definite order but mostly successively from more or less opposite sides, the loaded tentacles are bent over and thrust into the pharyngeal lumen, the mouth closes around the tentacular stalk, and as the tentacle is pulled out, the food material adhering to it is wiped off into the pharynx. The small ventral tentacles, when present, bend over the mouth and assist in wiping off the food and preventing its escape. The stomachs of seven freshly collected *Thyone briareus* were found to contain protozoans, diatoms, nematodes, filamentous and unicellular algae, copepods, ostracods, and bits of plant material (Pearse, 1908). Pieces of algae, small crustacean larvae, pieces of shells, ectoprocts, Foraminifera, Radiolaria, diatoms, and detritus constituted the contents of the stomach region of *Holothuria* (Oomen, 1926). Noll (1881) observed that crab larvae and small medusae adhered to the tentacles of a captive *Cucumaria* and were ingested. *Synaptula hydriformis* feeds entirely on algae (Olmsted, 1917).

Nondendrochirotes in general simply shovel the surrounding substrate into their mouths by means of the tentacles, and burrowing forms swallow the substrate as they advance through it.  Such organic nutrition as the substrate contains is then digested out, and the remainder, not appreciably diminished in bulk, is voided after a considerable sojourn in the large intestine.  When such holothurians are opened, shortly after collection, the small intestine appears relatively empty, whereas the large intestine is distended with a load of bottom material.  A marked functional difference between the two parts of the intestine is thus indicated.  In undisturbed conditions the ejected substrate may form a cone around the rear end of the cucumber, and some idea of the amount of substrate passed through a cucumber can be obtained by gathering and weighing these cones.  This was done for *Paracaudina* by Yamanouchi (1926) and Tao (1930), who reached figures of 6 to 8 g. per hour or 125 to 140 pounds annually.  Crozier (1918), studying the feeding of *Stichopus*, concluded that the animals filled and emptied themselves of substrate at least three times daily and that the aspidochirotes present in a sound (1.7 square miles of surface) in the Bermuda region would pass 500 to 1000 tons of sand through their bodies annually.  No diminution of particle size occurred during the passage of substrate through the animal, but the digestive fluid is sufficiently acid to dissolve calcareous fragments.

To general mechanical stimulation such as contact, jarring, prodding, or other disturbance, holothurians respond by contraction.  The tentacles contract, the body ends retract, and the animal in general shortens.  If the disturbance is of sufficient magnitude, the entire anterior end is drawn down into the interior by the retractor muscles when present, or the tentacular collar closes over the contracted tentacular crown, and so on.  Forms that live in burrows withdraw into the burrows; those that live partly buried with both ends protruding draw these ends beneath the substrate and disappear from view (Grave, 1905; Pearse, 1908).  A similar general contraction is given to handling by man.  These contractions are accompanied by the emission of water from the cloaca, so that the animal appears much reduced in size.

A more detailed study of response to touch was made by Crozier (1915) for *Holothuria surinamensis*, by Olmsted (1917) for *Synaptula hydriformis*, and by Yamanouchi (1929a) for *Paracaudina chilensis*.  All responses are negative except that in *Synaptula* a light touch on the outer surface of the tentacles evokes a positive reaction, a clinging to the stimulating object, whereas in *Holothuria* and *Paracaudina* a similar stimulation causes retraction of the tentacle touched.  In all three a stronger stimulus produces retraction of all the tentacles with or without the turning of anterior end away from the stimulated side.  Eventually the tentacles are drawn down into the mouth, or in *Holothuria* the tentacular collar closes over them.  Strong stimulation of the tentacles

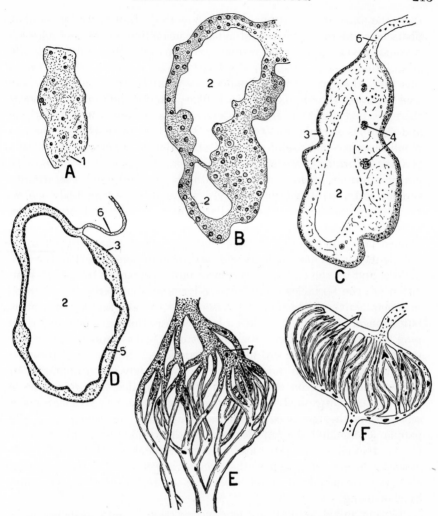

Fig. 90.—Regeneration, physiology. *A–D*, stages in the regeneration of the intestine of *Stichopus* (*after Bertolini*, 1930, 1931b). *A*, mesentery immediately after evisceration. *B*, tissue of mesentery proliferating, lumen formed. *C*, coelomic epithelium organized. *D*, intestine almost complete, lining epithelium organized. *E, F*, rete tufts of *Holothuria* with enzymatic granules moving through them (*after Enriques*, 1902). 1, torn edge of mesentery; 2, lumen; 3, coelomic epithelium; 4, coelomocytes; 5, lining epithelium of intestine; 6, mesentery; 7, enzymatic granules.

of *Synaptula* results in the animal's loosening its hold on the vegetation and dropping to the bottom. In *Holothuria*, locomotory and papillate podia were found about equally sensitive but less so than the tentacles. Tactile stimuli evoke contraction of the podia to a degree dependent on the intensity of the stimulus. In the case of papillate podia, the contractile filament is first drawn down into the basal wart (Fig. 65*E*) and then the wart itself flattens down. Vigorous stimulation of papillate podia close to the anterior end evokes contraction of the tentacles and tentacular collar prior to the response of the papillae themselves. Similar stimulation of a papilla near the body middle results in contraction of this and adjacent papillae, followed by local contraction of the body wall by way of the circular muscles. The posterior end is more responsive than the body middle, although less responsive than the anterior end, and vigorous stimulation of papillate podia here or, better, of the anal papillae, evokes closure of the anus, retraction of the posterior end, and perhaps a turning away of the posterior end. Locomotory podia when pinched retract, even completely into the interior, and the stimulus spreads anteriorly and posteriorly. Stimulation of the body surface between the podia produces similar effects, contraction of tentacles, collar, and nearby papillae, and turning away, when the stimulus is applied near the anterior end; but has little effect when applied to the middle region. Thus the body ends are far more sensitive than the body middle, and on the ends the structures most responsive to tactile stimulation are the tentacles, tentacular collar, and anal papillae. Similarly in *Synaptula* the body middle is insensitive to light tactile stimulation, but stronger stimulation evokes a local constriction with eventual dropping to the bottom. Here, too, the posterior end is more sensitive than the middle, responding by local constriction, bending away from the stimulus, and eventual shortening of the entire body and dropping to the bottom, depending on the strength of the stimulus. In *Paracaudina*, however, the entire body surface is responsive to touch although not as sensitive as the tentacles and tentacular region, including the genital papilla. Touching the anterior part of the trunk results in retraction of the tentacles and the anterior region; touching the body middle evokes a local contraction of the circular muscles and if strong enough also of the longitudinal muscles; and the tail region responds to contact by shortening.

Crozier failed to find any evidence of thigmotactic response in *H. surinamensis*, but in *Thyone* thigmotaxis plays an important role in the activities of the animal (Pearse, 1908). Here contact with a solid object immediately evokes an attachment response from the podia, and as already mentioned, such attachment greatly facilitates burrowing. In *Synaptula* the tentacles exhibit positive thigmotaxis, and this is understandable in view of the animal's habit of climbing about in algae by attaching the tentacles and pulling the body along. Although experiments are wanting, it would seem that the habit of many holothurians of hiding under rocks and cramming themselves in crevices must be mediated through a positive thigmotactic response. Possibly this thigmotaxis is confined to the podia, which attach to objects even when cut off from the animal (Crozier, 1915). It is obvious that pedate holothurians in nature are always so oriented that the locomotory podia remain in contact with objects. Burrowing apodous holothurians must possess a general thigmotactic sense over the entire body surface. This was shown for *Paracaudina* by Yamanouchi (1929a); the animal relaxes and extends through decreased muscle tonus when buried, but in a few seconds after removal from the sand hardens into a short rounded shape with definite demarcated tail region through increased muscle tonus.

Middle and posterior body regions of *Synaptula* react to water currents of varying intensity by body shortening; the tentacles and anterior end respond only to stronger currents, also by shortening or eventually by loosening hold.

As already noted, some burrowing holothurians exhibit a pronounced positive geotaxis, no doubt mediated by the statocysts. If placed on an inclined surface, *Leptosynapta* crawls downward and reverses if the inclination is reversed (H. L. Clark, 1899). A similar positive geotaxis was noted by Buddenbrock (1912) in the synaptid *Labidoplax digitata*. The geotactic response of these burrowing synaptids ceases as soon as they have completely buried themselves; in short, the stimulus to burrow downward consists in exposure of the body surface. Buddenbrock found that *L. digitata* would not burrow if completely enclosed in sand in a tube, regardless of the orientation of the tube, but if the rear part of its body was uncovered, would turn the anterior end downward and start burrowing whenever the orientation of the tube was altered. In *Paracaudina* the anterior part of the body is positively geotactic, but the tail region is negatively geotactic. Animals buried beneath the surface back to the surface until the tail tip is exposed. This behavior occurs equally well if the nerve ring is destroyed but is correspondingly slowed downed by removal of various lengths of the tail region. Negative geotropism is strongest in the tail tip and decreases along the tail region. *Synaptula hydriformis* is definitely negative to gravity, thus differing from other synaptids tested, no doubt in correlation with its climbing habits. It will ascend a glass plate if this is held at least 20 degrees from the horizontal and also turns if the plate is turned. Anterior ends cut off just behind the calcareous ring also ascend, whereas the headless body shows no response to gravity (Olmsted, 1917). Whereas statocysts are thus indicated as the effective georeceptors in synaptids, they cannot be involved in the tail reaction of *Paracaudina*. Further a pronounced positive geotaxis is recorded for a dendrochirote, *Cucumaria cucumis*, that lacks statocysts. This species will climb aquarium walls until it reaches the top, where it remains indefinitely, and will ascend a glass plate, turning upward whenever the plate is turned (Loeb, 1891). Other pedate holothurians tested on inclined surfaces fail to give a definite geotactic response (*Thyone*, Pearse, 1908; *Holothuria*, Crozier, 1915).

Holothurians in general right themselves when turned over. Their shape is such that, when placed on their backs, many tend to fall over to one side or the other, and the podia in pedate forms then take hold and pull the body into normal position; or else the anterior end will twist in such a way as to bring its podia in contact with the bottom, and this twist then travels along the animal's length. As righting is performed by species that do not react to gravity, it presumably results from the positive thigmotaxis of the locomotory podia; but it might be pointed out that apodous holothurians also right themselves, possibly through the action of the statocysts. Righting obtains in *Paracaudina* (Yamanouchi, 1926) and in various synaptids (Semon, 1887; Olmsted, 1917).

The reaction of *Paracaudina* to centrifugal force was tested by Yamanouchi (1929c). When buried in sand and rotated horizontally, 100 to 120 times per minute, the animal would be found with the head turned outward (centrifugally) and the tail inward and somewhat upward (centripetally). No alteration of position through rotation occurs in cucumbers killed by heat or in pieces of rubber tubing.

The general nocturnal habits of holothurians indicate a general negativity to light in this group, despite the fact that many species may remain exposed on the bottom during daylight. Pearse (1908) found that *Thyone* would gradually move away from the lighted side of a container without, however, orienting its body with respect to the direction of light, and when burrowing in glass containers, would stay away from the sides. It gave no reaction to increased illumination but would at once withdraw either exposed end when subjected to sudden decreased illumination, i.e., a shadow. *Paracaudina*, on the other hand, does not react to shadow or decreased illumination, but any part of the body exposed to sudden increased illumination responds by contraction (Yamanouchi, 1929a). Similarly, *Holothuria poli* responds to sudden illumination of the expanded anterior end by contracting this end, and a flash of light lasting only a fraction of a second is sufficient to evoke the response (Hess, 1914). Sensitivity decreases with repeated flashes and is greater in animals that have been kept in the dark. More detailed experiments with light were made by Crozier (1914, 1915) on *Holothuria parvula* and *surinamensis* and by Olmsted (1917) on *Synaptula hydriformis*. All three species give a definite phototactic response, turning and moving directly away from horizontal light. To spots of light shone upon various body regions, response similar to response to tactile stimuli is elicited, namely, local contraction. The entire body is sensitive to illumination, but as in the case of other stimuli the two ends are more responsive than the middle. *H. surinamensis* also gives a shadow reflex, showing no response to sudden increase of illumination but contracting the two ends to sudden decrease in the form of a shadow. Although the shadow reflex is best shown by the tentacles, for a single tentacle when shaded will retract, it can also be elicited from the whole body surface, although best from the two ends. Isolated fragments of the tentacular crown also give the shadow reflex.

Data on response to temperature change are given by the same authors for the same species. *Thyone* proved unresponsive to local applications of heat and cold and might recover from an exposure of nearly 3 hours to 37°C. and from freezing. *Paracaudina* responds by local contraction to local applications of sea water heated to 60 to 80°C. or the approach of a heated rod. Rise of temperature caused relaxation and softening of the body with 39°C. the upper limit for recovery, whereas cold resulted in body hardening with recovery from about 1°C. *H. surinamensis* gave no definite response to local application of heated sea water or heated rods or needles. Similar lack of thermal sensitivity was shown by *Synaptula*.

Much attention was paid by the foregoing authors to the response of cucumbers to a long list of chemicals, but such work must be regarded rather as an exercise in physical chemistry than as related to the life of the animal in nature. Only Pearse (1908) tested the reaction to food substances; he was unable to elicit any response from the tentacles of *Thyone* when crab or fish extract or the mud of their natural habitat was allowed to flow over them. H. L. Clark (1899) found that synaptids would retract the tentacles and turn the anterior end away from a decayed bit of starfish. In *H. surinamensis* (Crozier, 1915), the entire body surface is responsive to salts, acids, alkalies, alkaloids, essential oils, and a variety of organic substances, but no response was given to mere differences of osmotic pressure (pure water versus concentrated sugar solutions). Solutions were applied with a pipette held 5 mm. away from the animal's surface. To practically all chemicals of sufficient strength, a negative reaction was given; extended parts retract and local areas of body wall contract, forming a depression. The order of sensitivity is similar to that found for other stimuli, namely, tentacles, anterior end, posterior end, papillate podia, middle region. Acids were the most effective of the substances tried, and carbohydrates and other organic compounds the least effective. Of the usual series of chlorides of the alkaline earths, the order of effectiveness was potassium, sodium, lithium. Similarly *Synaptula* is sensitive to chemicals over the entire body surface, but as with other stimuli, response is greatest from the tentacles and anterior end, less from the posterior end, and least from the body middle. The usual response of the anterior end consists in retracting the tentacles and dropping to the bottom. Response was obtained to acids, alkalies, salts, alkaloids, anesthetics, and organic substances when applied in sufficient concentration. The decreasing order of effectiveness of the cations of the usual salts was potassium, calcium, ammonium, sodium, and magnesium. Contrary to the results with *Holothuria*, *Synaptula* reacts vigorously to alterations of osmotic pressure, that is, to diluted and concentrated sea water. *Paracaudina* is also responsive to chemicals over the entire surface, especially the anterior end. Local contraction, forming a depression, is the reaction given to local application of adequate concentrations of acids, alkalies, salts, alkaloids, and narcotics. Cations of effective salts gave the following series: potassium, ammonium, sodium, lithium. When applied at the same hydrogen ion concentration, weaker acids and alkalies are more effective than stronger ones. *Paracaudina* is unresponsive to diluted sea water but contracts on application of concentrated sea water.

The foregoing data on salinity relations are limited to local application of solutions of altered osmotic pressure. Pearse tested the survival of *Thyone* in sea water of altered concentration. In slowly evaporating sea water, *Thyone* lived normally for about 3 weeks, then began to degenerate. In sea water diluted one-half or more with fresh water, *Thyone* might remain in good condition and survive exposures up to 24 hours, but failed to exhibit normal behavior while immersed in such dilutions. There was no recovery from fresh water or greatly diluted sea water. *Thyone* may be found living in nature at the mouths of rivers in one-half normal salinity.

**27. Physiology.**—As regards the chemical constituents of holothurians, most interest has been shown in their pigments and lipoids. A water-and-alcohol soluble, fluorescent green pigment can be extracted from the body wall of *Holothuria nigra* and *grisea* (Cornil, Mosinger, and Calen, 1935; Bierry and Gouzon, 1937; Villela, 1951). It is usually mingled with a yellow carotenoid pigment that can be separated from it by ether. The green fluorescence is irreversibly diminished or lost in acid and alkaline solutions. According to Cornil, Mosinger, and Calen, the pigment occurs as dark-brown granules throughout the body wall held in a protoplasmic film adherent to the meshes of a network composed of connective tissue and muscle fibers. They report that the pigment constantly degenerates and is cast out through the intestine and is constantly renewed. The researches of Millott (1950, 1952, 1953) indicate that the black pigment of the body wall of *Holothuria forskali* and *Thyone briareus* is melanin, that it originates from the spherules of coelomocytes deposited in the body wall, and that these coelomocytes contain an enzyme of the phenolase type usually associated with the production of melanin.

In a series of researches, Lönnberg (1931, 1934b) has shown the presence of fatty yellow pigments belonging to the carotenoid group, including xanthophylls, in a number of holothurians and in the orange or yellow gonads of *Mesothuria intestinalis*. Manunta (1943, 1944, 1947) also extracted with fat solvents the respiratory trees, mesentery, digestive tract, and gonads of *Holothuria forskali, tubulosa,* and *polii* and found lipoid substances, including carotenoids, in all cases, in increasing amounts in the organs in the order named. Lipoid substances constitute 8 to 15 per cent of the dry weight of these cucumbers. Spectroscopic examination revealed the presence of beta carotene, xanthophyll, and astacine among the carotenoids present. An interesting finding was the general greater percentage of lipoid substances in females than in males, especially in the gonads. Small quantities of carotenoids were detected in *Cucumaria planci* and *cucumis* but none in *Phyllophorus urna* or *Stichopus regalis*, despite the red color of the latter. The carotenoids are presumably derived from the food and hence must pass through the wall of the digestive tract to reach the other organs in which they are found. Bergmann (1949) has concentrated his researches on the occurrence of sterols in marine invertebrates. Sterols are fatty substances of the type of cholesterol consisting of a higher alcohol united with a benzine ring complex and contained in the unsaponifiable fat portion of extracts. Echinoderms have nearly 20 times as much unsaponifiable fats as do vertebrates. Holothurians contain a definite sterol termed stellasterol; and a higher alcohol, batyl alcohol, was identified in abundance in the crystalline fraction of the unsaponifiable fat of *Cucumaria quinquesemita* by Matsumoto, Yajima, and Toyama (1943). The foregoing workers indicate the presence of ordinary (saponifiable) fats in cucumbers, but no definite data appear to have been published.

A few other scattered chemical data may be mentioned. Glycogen appears to be absent in cucumbers (Benazzi-Lentati, 1941). Arginine is present in holothurians, but not creatine (Bergmann, 1949). Typical cellular enzymes have been found. Norris and Rao (1935) note the presence in the tissues of *Parastichopus californicus* of a phosphatase active in alkaline solution (pH 9.2) and of both acid (pH 5.4) and alkaline phosphatase (pH 9.2) in the coelomic fluid. Phosphatase was also found in *Thyone* (Lipman, 1940). Carbonic anhydrase, an enzyme concerned in respiration, occurs in the respiratory trees of *Stichopus* (Sobotka and Kann, 1941).

The permeability of the body wall has been studied in *Paracaudina chilensis* by Koizumi (1932, 1935a, 1935b), by immersing the body in such a way as to exclude participation of mouth and anus. When immersed in diluted sea water the body gains weight, reaching an equilibrium in about 6 hours, and loses weight when replaced in normal sea water, but requires a longer time, about 10 hours, to reach an equilibrium. Pieces of body wall fastened over the end of a graduated tube filled with a medium made isotonic with sea water and immersed in a medium kept isotonic but containing varied concentrations of ions passed both anions and cations equally well in either direction and at the typical rates. Thus, of the anions, chloride penetrated much more rapidly than sulphate, and of the cations, the decreasing order of speed of entry was potassium, sodium, calcium, and magnesium. These experiments indicate full permeability of the body wall to water and salts. Similar results were obtained by Henri and Lalou (1903) with *Holothuria tubulosa* and *Stichopus regalis*. In diluted sea water the coelomic fluid also dilutes, reaching an equilibrium in about 4 hours, but no change occurs if the diluted external medium is brought up to the same osmotic pressure as normal sea water by means of organic substances. The body wall of cucumbers thus shows no resistance to alterations of osmotic pressure.

It is therefore to be expected that the coelomic fluid of holothurians is practically identical with sea water. This has been shown for a number of cucumbers (Henri and Lalou, 1903; Garrey, 1905; Botazzi, 1908; Okazaki and Koizumi, 1926; Bialaszewicz, 1932; Koizumi, 1935c; Parker and Cole, 1940; Cole, 1940), at least as regards the salt content. The coelomic fluid differs from sea water in some respects, for instance, in its pH value; it is almost invariably less alkaline than sea water. The pH of the coelomic fluid is given as 4.9 for male *Paracaudina*, 4.78 for females (Tadokoro and Watanabe, 1928), although Okazaki and Koizumi (1926) had previously reported 7.5 to 8.2 for the same species; 6.8 for *Holothuria grisea* (Villela, 1951); variously as 6.72 to 7.8 for *Cucumaria frondosa* (Sarch, 1931; Cole, 1940; Parker and Cole, 1940); and 7.00 for *Chiridota laevis* (Cole, 1940); whereas sea water generally has a pH of 8.1 or 8.2. Consequently the coelomic fluid has a buffering action greater than that of sea water (Gellhorn, 1927; Sarch, 1931), and the latter attributes the buffering action to the presence of carbonates and phosphates. The coelomic fluid further contains more nitrogenous material than sea water (Gellhorn, 1927; Sarch, 1931), but apparently the nitrogenous material is not of protein nature (Howell, 1885b; Botazzi, 1909). In *Paracaudina* the researches of Tadokoro and Watanabe (1928) indicate a sexual difference in the composition of the coelomic fluid; the content of nitrogenous and sulphur compounds is higher in the male, that of phosphorus compounds in the female. On standing exposed to air, the coelomic fluid throws down a coagulum that consists of aggregated coelomocytes without participation of hemocytes (Howell, 1885b; Millott, 1953).

As the coelomic epithelium is ciliated, a circulation of the coelomic fluid may be assumed. In *Paracaudina* the coelomic fluid circulates at a rate of about 10 to 15 mm. per second, depending on the internal pressure, which varies from 10 to 20 cu. mm. of water in the resting state of the animal, to 30 to 40 cu. mm. when the animal is digging, to a maximum of 45 to 50 mm. under extreme contraction. The coelomic fluid moves anteriorly along the middle part of the interior and posteriorly along the inner surface of the body wall; in the tentacles the current passes toward the tip along the oral side of the tentacles and basally along their outer walls.

The fluids of the water-vascular and haemal systems appear similar to the coelomic fluid so far as tested, although slight differences may obtain and they may show some lag in reaching equilibrium with the external medium.

Some attention has been paid to the properties of holothurian muscle, especially the longitudinal bands. In *Paracaudina* (Koizumi, 1935d), these contain slightly less water (77 per cent) than the general body wall (79 per cent), more potassium and sodium and less magnesium, chloride, and sulphate. Steinbach (1937) also noted a much higher potassium content of the retractor muscles of *Thyone* than that of sea water but a free passage of chloride between the muscle and its medium. The potassium appeared concentrated in the fibrils of the muscle cells. The longitudinal muscles of holothurians lengthen when weighted with a load, eventually developing a resistance to further lengthening, and shorten when the weight is removed (Jordan, 1914; Tao, 1927). In an elaborate analysis of holothurians as hollow animals whose shape and activities depend upon an inner turgor balanced by a resistant tension of the body wall, Jordan (1914) has concluded that the longitudinal muscles do not show the necessary resistance to tension, since they tend to lengthen when subjected to loading, and hence that the tension of the body wall is maintained by its nonmuscular tissues. The isolated longitudinal muscle is highly responsive to mechanical, chemical, thermal, and electrical stimuli (Henri, 1903a), giving a single contraction at the point stimulated; but the contraction is not propagated unless the nervous connections are intact. Transverse cuts through the body wall at an ambulacrum do not prevent transmission of the stimulus to the length of longitudinal muscle so isolated, an indication of the existence of a nerve net in the body wall through which transmission can occur if the radial nerve is transected. Nervous connections reach the longitudinal muscles through the connective tissue that binds them to the undersurface of the ambulacra, and if this attachment is locally severed, this part of the muscle will not contract on stimulation of the corresponding radial nerve, but the rest of the longitudinal muscle, before and behind the detached portion, will contract. In general, the body-wall musculature of holothurians will not exhibit spontaneous contractions when isolated from its nervous connections (also Budington, 1937, for *Thyone;* Tao, 1927, for *Paracaudina*). It merely relaxes and lengthens. But if excised with a piece of body wall and suspended in a suitable medium under some tension, the longitudinal muscle will begin to undergo spontaneous rhythmic contractions, after 2 hours or more in *Thyone*, sooner in *Paracaudina*. In the latter, the rhythmicity has a rate of 0.5 to 3.5 minutes. These and other experiments of Henri, Tao, and Budington show that the body-wall musculature is under nervous control of the radial nerves and nerve net. The longitudinal muscle bands are innervated from the radial nerves at all levels, for if a band is cut across at several levels and its radial nerve stimulated, all parts of the muscle contract. The radial nerve responds to drugs like the vertebrate nervous system. Strychnine augments its sensitivity so that the merest touch on the body surface evokes a contraction of the longitudinal muscle of that radius; atropine diminishes excitability and finally abolishes the contraction response; and nicotine evokes a strong contraction that lasts 5 to 10 minutes during which the muscle is refractory to stimulation (Henri, 1903b).

The longitudinal muscles and presumably also the circular muscles are thus operated by the nervous system, and as all the activities of holothurians are merely combinations of muscle contraction and extension, they also are evidently under nervous control. Although normally impulses are transmitted along the radial nerves from the nerve ring (for instance, stimulation of the nerve ring evokes contraction of the longitudinal bands), it is probable that most responses are not dependent on the presence of the nerve ring. Pearse (1908) found that the posterior half of *Thyone* would exhibit the usual reactions, righting, negative phototaxis, and shadow retraction. Similarly Crozier (1915) reported that *Holothuria*, deprived of its anterior end, would move about as usual and give a negative response to light; but response to tactile stimuli, although normal, was decreased in amplitude, and the righting reaction was greatly delayed. The cloacal part of holothurians carries on normal respiratory activities when isolated from the anterior part.

The orders Dendrochirota, Aspidochirota, and Molpadonia are provided with a respiratory system in the form of the pair of respiratory trees. As is well known, these are aerated by a rhythmic pumping action of the cloaca, and therefore it is necessary in cucumbers with respiratory trees that the anal end of the animal be kept freely exposed to the sea water. The most complete account of the physiology of the cloaca is that of Crozier (1916) for *Holothuria surinamensis;* studies have also been made on *Thyone briareus* by Pearse (1908) and Budington (1937) and on *Paracaudina chilensis* by Tao (1927, 1930). The normal sequence of events is as follows. The anal sphincter opens and a wave of expansion that draws water into the cloaca travels anteriorly along the cloaca through the contraction of the cloacal suspensors and relaxation of the circular muscle fibers of the cloacal wall; the anus then closes, the cloacal wall contracts, the entrance into the main stem of the respiratory trees opens (while the exit of the intestine into the cloaca remains closed), and water is forced into the respiratory trees. The water is then expelled by a reversal of these actions, assisted by the contraction of the trees themselves. The respiratory trees, including the terminal vesicles, carry on strong rhythmic contractions, so that water is forced out of even the terminal vesicles at each expiration. The respiratory trees respond to local stimulation by a strong local contraction, and isolated portions of trees, including the end vesicles, show movements for long periods (Henri, 1903d; Budington, 1937). In *Holothuria* the cloacal pumping is cyclic; in the undisturbed animal there is a succession of 6 to 10 inspirations at intervals of 1 or more minutes, then a pause with the anus held widely open, during which water is expelled, in a vigorous expiration. At some (one in every four to ten in *Paracaudina*) of the expirations, feces are expelled. Expirations may be accompanied by tentacle retraction and general body contraction. Similar conditions obtain in *Paracaudina*, but in *Thyone*, according to Pearse, water is expelled after each inspiration. Crozier has shown for several holothurians that the rate of cloacal pumping is more rapid per unit size or weight, the smaller the animal. If cloacal pumping is prevented for some time by prodding the posterior end into a state of contraction, the pumping when resumed is not more rapid and even slower, but shows an increased amplitude. Eviscerated animals that have lost most of their respiratory trees continue to pump at the usual rate; in such case the water goes directly into the coelom.

The mechanism of cloacal pumping resides in the posterior part of the body and operates independently of the nerve ring although subject to regulation from anterior levels, e.g., stimuli that cause tentacular retraction and general body contraction also result in anal closure and temporary cessation of pumping. Isolated posterior body ends cut off at the level of the anterior end of the cloaca begin to pump rhythmically after a time (often several hours) and continue for a long period, although with gradually decreasing rate and amplitude. The pumping of isolated ends is continuous, not interrupted by a pause for expiration as in the normal intact animal; consequently the expiratory pause must be controlled by more anterior levels of the animal. Continuous pulsation without periodicity was also observed in isolated cloacal regions of *Cucumaria frondosa* by Wyman and Lutz (1930) and in *Stichopus* by Lutz (1930) and may be assumed to be characteristic of cucumbers with trees in general. The impulse for cloacal pumping apparently originates in the anterior part of the cloaca, for pulsations are much weakened in pieces cut through more posterior levels of the cloaca.

The cloacal wall itself will not pulsate if isolated from the corresponding body wall or if the cloacal suspensors are cut away. Consequently cloacal pumping originates in and is controlled by the nervous system of the adjacent body wall, and the nervous impulses reach the cloacal wall by way of the suspensors. Areas of cloacal wall of *Thyone* attached to either interradial or radial pieces of body wall will contract, but more rapidly and in more orderly fashion when the radial nerve is present in the attached body wall. The extreme posterior end including the anal sphincter may pulsate when isolated.

Lutz (1930) experimented with the effect of oxygen supply on isolated longitudinal strips of the cloacal region of *Stichopus*. In running sea water such strips beat regularly for hours, at first with increasing tone and amplitude, later with gradually decreasing tone. In standing sea water or in water of decreased oxygen content, the amplitude increases for a time and the beat becomes intermittent, with periods of cessation of increasing length. If the oxygen content is too low or in the presence of sufficient concentration of cyanide, the tone and the amplitude fall at once and the pulsation soon ceases. Thus a certain degree of oxygen lack increases the amplitude of the contractions, i.e., leads to more vigorous pumping, and initiates an expirational pause, presumably associated with a stronger expiration.

The effect of various drugs on the excised cloacal region of *Cucumaria frondosa* was tried by Wyman and Lutz (1930). Under normal conditions such isolated regions of course pulsate rhythmically without periodic pauses. Adrenalin decreases tone, amplitude, and rate. Physostigmine, nicotine, and histamine cause a progressive rise in tone, but a gradual decline in rate and amplitude. Curare, strychnine, and atropine decrease the amplitude progressively and lead to cessation of pulsation, whereas pilocarpine is without any effect.

The respiratory trees are watertight. In an opened preparation retaining the digestive tract and respiratory trees, Henri (1930d) injected colored sea water into the main stem of the trees and found absolutely no passage of color through the walls of the trees, although the latter carry on strong pulsations for hours, thus putting the contained fluid under pressure. Henri and Lalou (1903) state that the respiratory trees are perfect semipermeable membranes and do not pass chlorides, sugar, sulphates, or urea.

That the respiratory trees constitute a respiratory mechanism would seem to be obvious, yet this has been doubted by many of the older observers. Bertolini (1933b) anesthetized *Holothuria tubulosa* by means of deoxygenated sea water and injected reduced methylene blue (white) into the coelom. When opened about 2 hours after such cucumbers had resumed pumping in aerated sea water, the coelomic surface of the respiratory trees was found colored deep blue, an indication of the passage of oxygen through their walls. The rete was also colored blue, so that apparently the haemal system takes up oxygen from the coelomic fluid. The close association of the rete with the adjacent respiratory tree is thus explained. Bertolini (1934) detected catalases but no peroxidases or indophenoloxidase in extracts of the respiratory trees. A better proof of the respiratory function of the respiratory trees had been furnished by Winterstein (1909), who found that the oxygen consumption of cucumbers is reduced by 50 to 60 per cent if the anus is covered with a rubber membrane and so prevented from taking in water. This procedure causes the animals to extend body and tentacles to their fullest extent. One might suppose that considerable passage of oxygen might take place through the expanded tentacles, yet Winterstein found no effect upon the oxygen consumption by covering the anterior end with a rubber membrane. Still, it may be recalled that eviscerated holothurians lacking respiratory trees live and regenerate if in good conditions. Apparently the oxygen requirement of cucumbers is very low, as Crozier found that individuals would live for a long time in sealed jars of boiled sea water and that isolated posterior ends under the same conditions would continue to pulsate for 12 hours. Very few actual measurements have been made of the oxygen consumption of cucumbers. The data of Hiestand (1940) give a figure of 0.013 or 0.014 cc. of oxygen consumed per gram per wet weight per hour for *Thyone*, and a similar figure, 0.01 to 0.037, was obtained by Tao (1930) for *Paracaudina*. As in the case of animals in general, the rate is higher the smaller the individual. According to Nomoura (1926), the oxygen consumption of *Paracaudina* is highly dependent on the oxygen content of the surrounding water, but no such relation exists in *Thyone* (Hiestand, 1940), which continues to consume oxygen at the same rate until the oxygen content of the medium has fallen to about one-seventh of the saturation value. *Thyone*, however, is markedly affected by the acidity of the medium, and its oxygen consumption steadily falls as the acidity of the medium is increased from pH 8.8 to pH 5.4.

In addition to their respiratory function, the respiratory trees undoubtedly regulate the body turgor, which in turn is a very important factor in all activities. They further are concerned in excretory processes (see below).

Not much information is available about the circulation of the blood in holothurians. It appears that only the dorsal sinus is contractile (Enriques, 1902; Henri, 1903d; Kawamoto, 1927; Prosser and Judson, 1952), that the center of contraction is the part of the dorsal sinus that accompanies the curve of the intestine, and that the blood goes forward in the dorsal sinus, primarily along the ascending intestine. The rate of beat is given as 10 to 12 per minute by Henri, once or twice per minute by Kawamoto; Prosser and Judson found that the excised vessel 5 cm. long, suspended in a moist chamber, would beat 4 to 5 times per minute. The beat, however, varies much with conditions and, according to Enriques, attains its maximum value when the vessels are moderately distended, and reduces to a minimum or is scarcely evident in a collapsed or greatly expanded condition of the vessels. This author associates changes in the degree of expansion of the vessels with the progress of digestion. The only account of the course of the circulation of the blood is that of Kawamoto (1927) for *Paracaudina*. In this form the blood runs from the intestine through the haemal network into the dorsal sinus (consult Fig. 75). The center of contraction is the main part of the dorsal sinus, where its main trunks form a Y arrangement. This beat drives the blood mainly along that part of the dorsal sinus that accompanies the ascending intestine. The blood then passes through the intestinal walls into the ventral sinus and through the communicating sinuses to the anterior part of the ventral sinus that accompanies the descending intestine. Here it passes through the intestinal walls into the haemal network again and also ascends to the haemal ring, from which the blood is distributed to the body wall by way of the radial haemal channels in the ambulacra.

The beat appears to be of myogenic nature. It is accelerated by adrenalin but slowed by atropin (Wyman and Lutz, 1930) and inhibited by physostigmine, nicotine, tetramethyl ammonium bromide, and by acetylcholine in very dilute solution. Electrical stimulation of the contractile region causes a local contraction but does not affect the pulsation of the rest of the vessel (Henri, 1903d), a further evidence of the myogenic nature of the beat.

The physiology of the digestive tract of holothurians has been studied by a number of investigators but is not yet well understood. Large aspidochirotes are usually employed, and as these will not feed in captivity, difficulties are at once introduced into the experiments. The feeding methods of cucumbers were described above, and it appears that these animals subsist on very small amounts of nutrition. The time required for the passage of food through the digestive tract was estimated at about 8 hours for *Stichopus* by Crozier (1918); by injecting carmine into the animal's mouth, Olmsted (1917) colored the food and found that about 20 hours elapsed before the colored feces were emitted by *Synaptula*. According to Yamanouchi (1929), the time is much shorter for *Paracaudina*, only 2 or 3 hours. The food is carried along the digestive tract by the usual peristaltic waves, and the isolated intestine suspended in sea water or balanced salt medium will continue to show peristalsis for some time (Olmsted, 1917; Schreiber, 1930) but thereafter rapidly deteriorates. In *Synaptula* (Olmsted, 1917) the peristaltic waves occur at intervals of 2 seconds in the intact animal, 3 seconds in the isolated digestive tract, and are much affected by the salt content of the medium.

The digestive tract of the feeding animal contains a yellowish digestive fluid that is acid in reaction and gives off a strong aromatic odor. In the captive animal that has ceased to feed, the fluid loses these properties in 2 or 3 days. The reaction of the fluid is given as pH 5.1 to 5.6 for *Holothuria* (Oomen, 1926b); 7.4 to 7.8 in the stomach and 7.0 to 7.6 at the beginning of the intestine to 7.7 to 8.2 near the end for *Thyone* (Van der Heyde, 1922b); 5.0 for *Holothuria* (Schreiber, 1930); 4.8 to 5.5 for *Stichopus* (Crozier, 1918) during digestion but 5.2 to 6.5 in empty animals; and 7.3 to 7.7 for *Paracaudina* (Sawano, 1928). Both the odor and the acidity are attributed by Schreiber (1932b) to the presence of unsaturated fatty acids. Various enzymes are found in the digestive tract and also in extracts of its wall. In *Thyone*, Van der Heyde (1922b) reported a protease acting on gelatin and egg white, and an invertase but no amylase or lipase. The digestive fluid and intestinal wall of *Holothuria* contain a protease that hydrolyzes peptone, gelatin, fibrin, and caseinate, and increases in activity with increased alkalinity of the medium (Oomen, 1926b); there were also present in the juice and extracts an amylase that would hydrolyze glycogen, saccharose, maltose, and starch, acting best in an acid medium at 6.6, and a weak lipase. In glycerin extracts of the digestive tract of *Holothuria*, Clerc (1904) identified amylase, invertase, and a weak lipase but scarcely any protease. Sawano (1928) tested the enzyme content of the digestive fluid and water and alcoholic extracts of the ground wall of the digestive tract of *Paracaudina* and found lipase, amylase, maltase, invertase, glycogenase, and a protease resembling trypsin. Apparently holothurians are well supplied with carbohydrate-digesting enzymes and usually contain a proteolytic enzyme similar to trypsin acting in alkaline medium, but are weak in lipases.

Several observers have tested the permeability of the isolated digestive tube by placing various solutions inside the tube ligated at both ends and testing the surrounding medium for the passage of these substances after a few hours. It has been generally found that the digestive wall is permeable to water in both directions but is absolutely impermeable to chlorides, glucose, sulphates, urea, dyes such as methylene blue and trypan blue, pentose, and saccharose (Henri and Lalou, 1903; Oomen, 1926a; Schreiber, 1930). This observation raises the question as to how the digested food reaches the body tissues; to this question a very strange and unexpected answer has been returned by several investigators.

It was noticed by Frenzel (1892) in histological preparations of the wall of the digestive tract of several holothurians that the anterior part of the tract is full of amoebocytes with spherules traversing the wall and passing through the lining epithelium into the lumen. This author even thought that the gland cells figured in the lining epithelium by Hamann and others (see Figs. 69*A*, *B*, 70*A*) are in fact amoebocytes with spherules caught moving through the epithelium, but this view seems a little extreme. It was suggested by Enriques (1902) and more or less verified by Oomen (1926) and Schreiber (1930, 1932a, b, c) that these amoebocytes both carry enzymes into the digestive tract and carry away the products of digestion (Fig. 90*E*, *F*). The work of these authors indicates that the digestive enzymes and the fatty acid of the digestive fluid are secreted by the coelomic epithelium of the lacunae of the rete. It has been noticed already that this epithelium is packed with spherules (Fig. 76*C*). It was shown by Enriques that extracts of the rete are acid and contain the same sorts of enzymes as the digestive fluid and wall and that the contents of rete extracts vary with the nutritional state of the animal. Schreiber has described the partial destruction and regeneration of the coelomic epithelium of the rete network in the removal of the secretion spherules from the rete into the haemal system by the amoebocytes. The work of these authors further indicates that the products of digestion are picked up by the amoebocytes and carried into the haemal system for general distribution. As the wall of the digestive tract is permeated with lacunar spaces directly continuous with the rete and the main channels of the haemal system, a direct route is available to such loaded amoebocytes.

If intact holothurians are placed in a container of sea water to which has been added a little milk or dye (congo red, methylene blue) or yeast, and opened later, colored particles or fat droplets and casein strands or clumps of amoebocytes with ingested yeast cells are found in or on the respiratory trees, on the rete, and in the coelom; but nothing in the digestive tract (Enriques, 1902; Oomen, 1926b; Schreiber, 1930). Evidently such material may enter in the respiratory current and pass through the walls of the respiratory trees into the coelom, but as the respiratory trees are impermeable, presumably such transport is accomplished by amoebocytes, although Schreiber thinks the particles are squeezed through the end vesicles of the trees when these contract strongly. Whether normally cucumbers obtain food from their surroundings in this manner remain problematical.

Reports concerning excretion and nitrogenous wastes in holothurians are scanty and often contradictory; a summary is given by Delaunay (1931). It is generally stated that the coelomocytes and the respiratory trees play an important role in excretion. In the Apoda, a group that lacks respiratory trees, india ink or carmine particles injected into the coelom are ingested by coelomocytes, which then proceed into the urns and through these into the body wall (Schultz, 1895; H. L. Clark, 1899).

In holothurians without urns but provided with respiratory trees, the coelomocytes that have ingested such particles migrate through the walls of the respiratory trees and are eliminated in the expiratory current (Schultz, 1895; Bartels, 1895; Bertolini, 1937). Bordas (1899) observed that the expiratory water contains numerous amoebocytes of the type with brown granules, and both he and Schultz (1895) noted crystals in the walls of the respiratory trees, identified by their shape as uric acid and urates. Bertolini (1937) found that soluble dyes injected into the coelom were eliminated directly through the respiratory trees, intestine, and gonadial tubules; but particulate dyes were ingested by coelomocytes that migrated into the lumina of the three organs mentioned and were thus eliminated to the exterior. Millott (1950) injected iron saccharate into the coelom of *Thyone* and observed that amoebocytes ingested the particles which were then eliminated by way of the cloaca. In confirmation of Bertolini, Millot found that methylene blue injected into the coelom was rapidly eliminated by the respiratory trees, intestine, and body wall. It thus appears that in holothurians, the body wall, respiratory trees, digestive tract, and gonads all participate in the elimination of unwanted materials and that coelomocytes convey the materials in many cases to these sites of elimination.

It appears definitely established that holothurians produce nitrogenous wastes, but the amounts are so small that contradictory results are often reported. Sea water in which holothurians have lived for 24 hours contains more nonprotein nitrogen than does sea water itself (Delaunay, 1926, 1934), and according to this author, the soluble excreted nitrogen is mainly in ammoniacal form, but some urea and purine nitrogen is present, whereas uric acid is absent. Sulima (1914) also failed to find any uric acid in extracts of *Holothuria* and *Stichopus;* Haurowitz and Waelsh (1926) reported the absence of urea, uric acid, creatine, and creatinine in holothurian extracts; Van der Heyde (1923) could not find any urea, ammonia, or creatinine in *Thyone;* and Bergmann (1949) regards creatine as generally absent in holothurians. On the other hand, Sanzo (1907) reported a trace of urea in the coelomic fluid of *Holothuria*, and Van der Heyde (1923) detected uric acid in the coelomic fluid of *Thyone.* The latter also noted considerable uric acid in the cloaca, and both Delaunay and Van der Heyde are of the opinion that much nitrogen excretion, especially of insoluble compounds, occurs by way of the intestine. The available data indicate that holothurians may dispose of nitrogenous wastes or other unwanted materials by depositing them in the body wall or by conveying them, mostly with the aid of amoebocytes, to any hollow organ that has an external opening.

From what is known of the physiology of holothurians, it would seem that these animals operate on a very primitive basis, that each organ system covers more than its usual function, and that amoebocytes play a remarkable role in the economy.

**28. Ecology: Geographical Distribution.**—The holothurians inhabit all seas and all depths from the intertidal zone to the greatest abysses. Apart from the floating or swimming elasipods already noted, they are primarily of benthonic habits, and although in shallow waters they may occur in rocky crevices or under rocks, the majority are found on sandy or mucky bottoms, lying upon the bottom or more or less buried or concealed. As in the case of crinoids, the Indo–West Pacific area appears to harbor the richest holothurian fauna. Large aspidochirotes of the genera *Holothuria*, *Stichopus*, and *Actinopyga* are conspicuous elements of the fauna there. In an account of the littoral holothurians of the Indian Ocean, Koehler and Vaney (1905) listed 51 species, of which 27 are aspidochirotes, including 21 species of *Holothuria*. In his record of a sojourn in the Philippines, Semper (1868) gave colored plates of some of the common species of *Holothuria* of the region. H. L. Clark (1921) in his study of the echinoderms of Torres Strait, located in the heart of the Indo–West Pacific area, noted a large number of species of *Holothuria;* among those common in the area may be mentioned *Holothuria arenicola*, *argus*, *atra*, *coluber*, *difficilis*, *edulis*, *impatiens*, *leucospilota* (= *vagabunda*), *marmorata*, *pardalis*, *pervicax*, and *scabra*. Other common aspidochirotes of the Indo-Pacific include *Stichopus chloronotus* and *variegatus*, *Thelenota* (= *Stichopus*) *ananas*, and *Actinopyga mauritiana* and *miliaris*. Dendrochirotes of the area include a number of species of *Cucumaria* and *Pentacta* (= *Colochirus*). Other species listed by Clark as common and widespread throughout the Indo-Pacific area are *Synapta maculata*, *Chiridota rigida*, *Pseudocucumis aciculus*, *Paracaudina chilensis*, and *Molpadia musculus*. A rich collection of shallow-- water holothurians taken by the *Siboga* in the Netherland East Indies (Sluiter, 1901) included 38 species of *Holothuria*, 5 of *Actinopyga*, 5 of *Stichopus*, 17 of *Cucumaria*, 7 of *Thyone*, 8 of *Pentacta*, 2 of *Chiridota*, 2 of *Pseudocucumis*, 6 of *Phyllophorus*, 4 of *Euapta*, and 11 of *Chondrocloea* (a synaptid). The most common *Holothuria* species were *atra*, *edulis*, *impatiens*, *scabra*, *leucospilota*, *pardalis*, *argus*, and *monocaria*. Other common species in the collection were *Actinopyga miliaris* and *maculata*, *Stichopus chloronotus* and *variegatus*, *Cucumaria imbricata*, *Thyone sacellus* and *castanea*, *Pentacta luteus*, *doliolum*, and *quadrangularis*, *Pseudocucumis africana*, *Molpadia scabrum* and *perforata*, *Euapta glabra* and *grisea*, *Chondrocloea lactea*, *beselii*, and *reticulata*, and *Chiridota rufescens*. The Indo-Pacific shallow-water holothurians have extended onto the Australian coasts where H. L. Clark (1946) lists 158 species; among the more common ones are met the same species of *Holothuria*, *Actinopyga*, and *Stichopus* named above, further *Thelenota ananas*,

*Paracaudina chilensis* and *australis, Synapta maculata, Leptosynapta dolabrifera, Chiridota rigida,* and *Sigmodota roebucki.*

A similar littoral holothurian fauna occurs throughout the world in tropical and subtropical waters, and some species, such as *Holothuria arenicola* and *impatiens* and *Molpadia musculus,* are circumtropical or nearly so. The most common species of the Hawaiian Islands (Fisher, 1907) are *Actinopyga mauritiana* and *Holothuria atra;* also abundant are *Holothuria pervicax, pardalis, impatiens,* and *parvula.* Of the 45 species reported from the Hawaiian Islands by Fisher, only 9 are confined to the islands and the rest are common tropical forms. A very large synaptid, *Opheodesoma spectabilis,* is one of the most characteristic Hawaiian species. The shallow waters of the West Indies and Bermuda are also dominated by large aspidochirotes, mostly not of same species as those of the Indo-Pacific. Among the more common forms (H. L. Clark, 1933, 1942) may be mentioned *Holothuria cubana, impatiens, arenicola, parvula, surinamensis, glaberrima, grisea, floridana,* and *mexicana, Actinopyga agassizi, Stichopus badionotus, Phyllophorus occidentalis, Thyone surinamensis, Euapta lappa, Synaptula hydriformis,* and *Chiridota rotifera.*

Reports of the littoral holothurians of the corresponding area of the eastern tropical Pacific, that is, from Peru and the Galapagos Islands northward to California and the Gulf of California, have been published by Deichmann (1937, 1938a, 1941). In addition to the circumtropical holothuriids already mentioned, a characteristic aspidochirote of this area is the large, reddish, warty *Parastichopus californicus,* found chiefly on rocky bottom. *Stichopus fuscus* is typical to the south. Cucumariids are common, notably *Cucumaria californica* and *dubiosa,* further *Pentamera chierchia,* and other species of *Pentamera,* a genus closely related to *Cucumaria.* There are a number of psolids, including the brooding species *Thyonepsolus nutriens. Paracaudina chilensis* is an example of a cucumber with a very wide distribution, ranging from the Strait of Magellan up the Pacific Coasts of the American continents to Japan, China, and northern Australia.

Moving northward up the Pacific Coast of North America (Edwards, 1907; Bush, 1918; Ricketts and Calvin, 1953), one finds *Parastichipus californicus* still the most conspicuous cucumber and about the only littoral aspidochirote north of California, although *Stichopus parvimensis* occurs in tide pools along southern California. Cucumariids are common, including the tiny black *Cucumaria curata,* the somewhat larger *C. lubrica,* both dwelling in coralline algae, the large reddish *C. japonica* (= *miniata*), the whitish *C. quinquesemita* (= *chronhjelmi*), and the small black *C. vegae* from Alaskan waters. The psolids are represented by the red *Psolus chitinoides,* and the synaptids by *Leptosynapta inhaerens,* or at least a closely similar species.

Proceeding further northward and around to Japan, one finds some of the foregoing species extending along Alaskan coasts and the Aleutian Islands into the northern parts of the Japanese empire. Characteristic species of this area (Mitsukuri, 1912; Ohshima, 1915) include *Cucumaria californica, lamperti, vegae, ijimai, glacialis, calcigera, japonica,* and *quinquesemita, Psolus squamatus* and *chitinoides, Chiridota albatrossi* and *discolor, Mytriotrochus rinkii,* and synallactids, especially in the deeper waters. The former Japanese Empire extended over a wide range of latitude, and its more southerly islands fall within the Indo-Pacific area already discussed, with their littoral holothurian fauna dominated by the same large aspidochirotes. Northward toward the main Japanese islands these disappear and are replaced by different species of sticho-podids, chiefly *Stichopus japonicus* and *nigripunctatus.* Other common holothurians of the main Japanese islands include *Cucumaria echinata, japonica, capensis, multipes,* and *nozawai, Pentacta doliolum* and *inornatus, Phyllophorus japonicus, Pseudocucumis japonicus, Paracaudina chilensis,* and *Molpadia roretzii* and *oolitica* (Augustin, 1908; Mitsukuri, 1912; Ohshima, 1912, 1915).

Turning now to the Atlantic Coast of North America (H. L. Clark, 1904; Coe, 1912; Deichmann, 1930), one finds no littoral aspidochirotes north of Florida. The littoral holothurians of Florida are more or less identical with those of the West Indian region, already considered, and described in Deichmann (1930). Dendrochirotes and synaptids con-stitute the main forms found on the Atlantic Coast north of Florida. The most common species here are *Cucumaria frondosa* and *pulcherrima, Thyone briareus, scabra,* and *unisemita,* and *Leptosynapta inhaerens* and *roseola. Cucumaria frondosa* (Fig. 47) is one of the most characteristic cucumbers of the North Atlantic, ranging from New England to northern Europe and Scandinavia. The molpadonians are represented on the New England coast by *Caudina arenata* (Fig. 51G), admirably described by Gerould (1896).

The Mediterranean holothurians have become well known as objects of research of European investigators. Among the common Mediter-ranean cucumbers may be mentioned *Holothuria impatiens, tubulosa, polii, forskali* (= *nigra*), *helleri, stellati,* and *mammata, Stichopus regalis, Cucumaria planci* and *grubei, Thyone inermis, Phyllophorus urna, Mol-padia musculus,* and *Labidoplax digitata.* Some of these species are limited to the Mediterranean, but others spread over a wide area of the adjacent North Atlantic, along the shores of western Europe, and around the British Isles. Species common here (Koehler, 1921, 1924, 1927; Mortensen, 1927; Nobre, 1938) include *Holothuria forskali, Stichopus tremulus* and *regalis, Cucumaria frondosa, montagui* (= *saxicola*), *planci, elongata, hyndmani, lactea,* and *lefevrei, Thyone fusus, inermis,* and *raphanus, Pseudocucumis mixta, Psolus phantapus, Leptosynapta inhaerens* and *gallienei*, and *Labidoplax digitata, thomsoni,* and *buski*. A familiar species of the English Channel, *Holothuria forskali*, is known as the cotton spinner, from its habit when disturbed of emitting its cuvierian tubules, which "spin out" into long, darting, sticky threads. Proceeding eastward along the North and Baltic Seas one notes a diminished littoral echinoderm fauna, as these animals avoid the brackish waters prevalent along much of this coast. The holothurians found in this area (Mortensen and Lieberkind, 1928) include *Stichopus tremulus, Cucumaria lactea* and *elongata, Thyone fusus, Thyonidium pellucidum, Psolus phantapus, Leptosynapta inhaerens* and *bergensis, Rhabdomolgus ruber, Labidoplax buski,* and *Myriotrochus vitreus.* One notices here, as also along American coasts and in the Japanese area, the gradual disappearance of littoral aspidochirotes with increasing coldness of the water. Only the genera of the Stichopodidae extend into northern latitudes.

North of the areas so far considered lie artic and subarctic waters from which a number of collections of holothurians have been made, chiefly in the regions from Siberia to Greenland (Daniellsen and Koren, 1882; Ludwig, 1900a; Kalischewskij, 1907; Deichmann, 1936, 1938b); comparative discussions of arctic holothurians have been given by Théel (1886a) and Ekman (1925). In these Far Northern waters there is found a characteristic assemblage of holothurians, consisting of a relatively few, but widely distributed, species, several practically circumpolar, and marked by a general absence of aspidochirotes and synaptids and a preponderance of dendrochirotes, molpadonians, and apodans other than synaptids. As typical arctic and subarctic species may be listed *Cucumaria glacialis, frondosa,* and *calcigera, Psolus fabricii, phantapus,* and *squamatus, Eupyrgus scaber, Molpadia arctica, borealis,* and *jeffreysii, Trochoderma elegans, Mytriotrochus rinkii,* and *Chiridota laevis.* Two aspidochirotes, *Stichopus tremulus* and *Bathyplotes natans,* ascend the west coast of Norway to a latitude of about 70°, and *Leptosynapta inhaerens* is found as far north as Lofoten. Characteristic artic forms from deeper waters are *Kolga hyalina*, taken near Spitsbergen at 2000 m., and *Elpidia glacialis,* of general occurrence to 2800 m.

Turning now to the Southern Hemisphere, not much information is available concerning the holothurian fauna of the coasts of Africa and of South America north of the Strait of Magellan. Deichmann (1948) reported that the littoral holothurians of South Africa are mostly endemic species, not found elsewhere, although the deeper-water forms bear some resemblance to those of the Indian Ocean. New Zealand holothurians, also, differ from those elsewhere and are not related to Australian forms (Perrier, 1905). A large amount of information has been accumulated about antarctic holothurians from various expeditions. Ludwig (1898a) reported on the Strait of Magellan, Perrier (1905) on Patagonia, Vaney (1906, 1914) on the collections of two French Antarctic Expeditions, Hérouard (1906b) on the holothurians of the Belgian Antarctic Expedition, Vaney (1908) on the material of the Scottish Antarctic Expedition, Ekman (1925) on the holothurians of the Swedish Antarctic Expedition and (1927) on those of the German South Polar Expedition. Most of the explorations concerned the southern end of South America, including the Strait of Magellan, Tierra del Fuego, and the Falkland Islands, and the holothurian fauna of these areas is well known as a result. The antarctic is richer in holothurian species than the arctic, but a general similarity prevails between the two regions in the absence of littoral aspidochirotes and synaptids and the prevalence of dendrochirotes, especially cucumariids and psolids, and of molpadonians and nonsynaptid apodans. There is no holothurian species in common between the antarctic and arctic, but *Psolus antarcticus* is very similar to *Psolus squamatus* and is regarded by some as a geographic variant of it.

The best analysis of the antarctic holothurian fauna is that of Ekman (1925), who divides the region into three areas. The Magellanic area, including the Strait of Magellan, Tierra del Fuego, and the Falkland Islands, best regarded as subantarctic, is inhabited by a well-known assemblage of littoral holothurians. Common members of this assemblage are *Cucumaria crocea, laevigata, parva, leonina, godfroyi, attenuata* (= *Joubini*), *steineni* (= *antarctica*), and *liouvillei, Psolus koehleri, antarcticus, charcoti, ephippifer*, and *turqueti, Thyone spectabilis* and *lechleri, Psolidium convergens, coatsi*, and *dorsipes, Molpadia antarctica* and *violaceum, Taeniogyrus contortus, Sigmodota purpurea*, and *Chiridota pisanii* and *marenzelleri*. Members of this fauna may spread up the Chilean and Patagonian coasts, and in the latter area it is interesting to note a species of *Stichopus, S. patagonicus*, so that here again a stichopodid is the only littoral aspidochirote to extend into cold waters. The west antarctic, including Graham Land and the South Shetlands and Orkneys, is regarded by Ekman (1925) as the true or high antarctic. The most typical cucumbers of this region are *Cucumaria turqueti, attenuata, secunda*, and *psolidiiformis, Thyone scotiae* and *turricata, Psolus koehleri, granulosus*, and *belgicae*, and *Psolidium gaini*. Many of the holothurians here are thus specifically different from those of the Magellanic region, although there are some species in common. The island of South Georgia to the east of the foregoing regions is considered in Ekman's analysis a third or eastern part of the South American antarctic. Here the holothurian fauna is intermediate between that of the high antarctic and the Magellanic area. Two species, *Psolidium incubans* and *Psolus figulus*, occur on South Georgia which are not found in the two other areas, but many of the species are the same as those of the Magellanic region. At Kerguelen, which lies in the southern part of the Indian Ocean, on about the same latitude as South Georgia, *Cucumaria laevigata* and *parva* were found (Ekman, 1927), and the holothurians of Kaiser Wilhelm II Land, still farther east and much farther south, are not much different from those of the South American antarctic. Recorded from here (Ekman, 1927) are *Cucumaria liouvillei, turqueti, steineni, denticulata, georgiana, parva* and *psolidiiformis, Psolidium navicula* and *gaini, Psolus koehleri*, and *Taeniogyrus contortus*. In this article Ekman removed *Cucumaria liouvillei* and *turqueti* to a new genus, *Staurocucumis*.

Although many holothurians are distributed through a considerable range of depth and some species that are littoral in polar waters may occur in deep waters in lower latitudes, in general the holothurians of ocean depths differ specifically from those of the littoral zone. The richness and distinctive character of the deep-sea holothurians was first revealed by the dredged collections of the *Challenger*, reported by Théel (1882, 1886). It was then discovered that an entire holothurian order, the Elasipoda, of bizarre appearance, inhabits deep water and is practically limited to such depths. The characteristic genera of the Elasipoda have been named and figured in the preceding pages. Prior to the Théel reports, two elasipods, *Kolga hyalina* and *Irpa abyssicola*, had been described by Danielssen and Koren (1882), from the dredgings of the Norwegian North Atlantic Expedition of 1876–1878, which found these species at over 2000 m. depth in the area between Norway, Spitsbergen, and Iceland. These authors were also familiar with *Elpidia glacialis*, described by Théel in 1877, and one of the most widely distributed elasipods, found at depths varying from 100 to nearly 6000 m. To these three known species the *Challenger* reports added 52 others, and the same species or others of the same genera are found wherever the deep waters are dredged. Some species are known to have a wide, probably cosmopolitan, distribution, as *Elpidia glacialis, Laetmogone violacea, Oneirophanta mutabilis*, and *Benthogone rosea*. *Deima blakei*, taken at 1000 m. in the West Indies on one of the *Blake* expeditions (Théel, 1886b), also appears to be widely distributed. Other species are probably more limited in distribution. From the collections of the *Albatross* in the eastern tropical Pacific from Mexico to the Galapagos Islands, Ludwig (1894) reported 17 species of elasipods, 13 new, from depths of 1200 to 3000 m. The *Investigator* dredgings in the Indian Ocean yielded 17 elasipod species, of which 11 were new (Koehler and Vaney, 1905). A few others were added from the dredgings conducted by the oceanographic station at Monaco from the Mediterranean to the Azores (Marenzeller, 1893; Hérouard, 1902, 1903). Scarcely any new elasipods have come to light in recent years; thus of the 13 species taken by the German Deep Sea Expedition on the *Valdivia*, only one was new (Heding, 1940).

The elasipods often live in aggregations of the same or of mixed species and occur in the greatest abundance on bottoms of clay or ooze (Théel, 1882).

The aspidochirote families Holothuriidae and Stichopodidae are mostly confined to littoral and sublittoral waters, but the family Synallactidae, including the genera *Pseudostichopus, Bathyplotes, Pelopatides, Synallactes*, and *Mesothuria*, typically inhabits deep waters, and members are regularly taken on dredging expeditions. This family seems best represented in the Indo-Pacific area, where a number of species appear in the Koehler and Vaney (1905) report. Many synallactids were also taken in deep waters on the Monaco dredgings in the North Atlantic, on the *Valdivia* expedition, and on the various expeditions to the antarctic. Some of the more widely distributed synallactids are *Mesothuria intestinalis, rugosa, verrilli*, and *maroccana, Zygothuria* ( = *Mesothuria*) *lactea, Bathyplotes natans* and *pourtalesi*, and *Pseudostichopus villosus*. The synallactids are typically found at depths of 1000 to 5000 m.

The dendrochirotes are also predominantly littoral forms, but some species occur in deep waters, notably *Cucumaria abyssorum*, found by Ludwig (1894) and H. L. Clark (1920) to be common in the eastern tropical Pacific at 2000 to 4000 m.; it was also taken by the *Valdivia* (Heding, 1940) in the Atlantic at 4600 m. *Sphaerothuria bitentaculata* (Fig. 50*A*) is limited to deep waters (1400 to 4000 m.), and the same is true of the related genus *Echinocucumis*.

Many of the apodous holothurians inhabit deeper waters, especially molpadonians, the species of which often occur over a considerable range of depth. *Molpadia violacea* and *danielsseni* are examples of molpadonians that are littoral in the antarctic but spread northward in deeper waters at 1000 to 3000 m. *Molpadia bathybia*, taken off Peru at 6000 m. (H. L. Clark, 1920), appears to be an abyssal species. Most of the species of *Molpadia* live at fair to considerable depths. *Caudina arenata* of the New England coast is reported to range to a depth of 1000 m., and *Caudina californica* was taken by Ludwig (1894) off California at over 3000 m. There are also a number of deep-sea forms among the Apoda, as *Protankyra abyssicola* found in the Atlantic at 2000 to 5000 m. It is interesting to note that of the nine species of animals brought up from the bottom of the Philippine Trench at the second greatest depth yet explored, 10,540 m., the most common was a holothurian of the genus *Myriotrochus* (Bruun, 1951).[1]

**29. Ecology: Biological Relations.**—Little information is available concerning growth and longevity of cucumbers. The older workers were

---

[1] The greatest ocean abysses so far known are the Mariana Trench, 10,863 m. (35,640 feet), the Philippine Trench, 10,540 m. (34,580 feet), and the Japanese Trench, 10,374 m. (34,035 feet) (Thompson, 1953). It is to be noted that these abysses are long and narrow.

of the opinion that the large aspidochirotes require several years to attain full size and probably live about 10 years at least. Mitsukuri (1903) found that *Stichopus japonicus*, which reaches a maximum length of 40 cm., attains sexual maturity in its third year and lives at least 5 years. The young grew steadily and regularly from a length of 4 mm. in the middle of July to 20 mm. by early August and had reached a length of 25 cm. by the end of their first year. Edwards (1908) reared the young of *Holothuria floridana* in the laboratory and found an increase from 0.33 mm. at 5 days of age to 4.00 mm. at 75 days, probably a slower rate than under natural conditions but an indication that a few years would be required for this large species to attain full size. Tao (1930) was of the opinion that 3 or 4 years are required for the much smaller *Paracaudina chilensis* to reach full size. A specimen of *Cucumaria planci* was still in healthy condition after 3 years and 4 months in an indoor aquarium (Noll, 1881).

Cucumbers appear on the whole to be helpless and defenseless animals, yet there are a number of reports of their toxicity. In an old book about coral islands (Cooper, 1880), it is stated that the cuvierian tubules of a cucumber there, apparently *Holothuria argus*, produce blisters and inflammation if they touch the skin and that the water squirted from the cloaca of this animal evokes dangerous inflammation, especially of the eyes. These statements have been copied into a succession of books and articles, yet H. L. Clark (1921) categorically denies any toxicity to man of the cucumbers or their cuvierian tubules of the Torres Strait region where *H. argus* is a common species. However, there is definite proof of the toxicity of holothuriids to nonhuman animals, although it is not clear whether the poison is associated with the cuvierian tubules. Smith (1947) reported that the natives of Majuro Atoll in the Marshall Islands use pounded or mashed black cucumbers to poison fish as an aid in catching them. On Guam, Frey (1951) saw natives cut a common black cucumber in two and squeeze the contents into rock pools to stupefy fish. The fish would come to the surface of the pools, behaving in a weakened fashion. Apparently in recent years cucumbers have been widely used by natives in the Indo-Pacific region to poison fish as aids in capturing them. The species employed seems to be *Holothuria atra*, which is not provided with cuvierian tubules. Recently there has been under investigation the toxic properties of *Actinopyga agassizi*, a common holothuriid of the West Indies (Atz, 1952; Nigrelli, 1952). It was known that this cucumber is toxic to fish and other animals, which will die in a short time if placed in aquaria that had been occupied by it. This species possesses cuvierian tubules, which, however, do not elongate, move, or become sticky on emission into the sea water. It has been found that these tubules contain the toxic substance, but this is also contained in other parts of the cucumber, especially the body wall. The nature of the toxin is under investigation by biochemists. The toxin will kill mice on injection, but the author experienced no symptoms whatever on handling the cuvierian tubules of *Actinopyga agassizi*. No toxic action is known for the "cotton-spinning" types of cuvierian tubules that act simply by entangling intruders. Apparently fish will not eat the viscera or body wall of cucumbers. But it might be pointed out that natives eat the fish that they have captured by means of holothurian poison—so that apparently man is not affected by such poison—and that species both with and without cuvierian tubules are employed in making trepang.

Holothurians appear very unappetizing to Western eyes, but in the Indo-Pacific region a large trade is carried on in dried cucumbers, which under the name of *trepang* or *bêche de mer* are sold, chiefly to the Chinese, for use as a delicacy in cookery. Trepang is made of large holothuriids that are called by various native names. It has been found that a number of different native names may be applied to the same species or the same name to different species. The species used for trepang have been identified by various zoologists, e.g., H. L. Clark (1921), the Sellas (1940), and Panning (1944). The most favored species is *Thelenota ananas*, called by a native name meaning prickly red fish. Some other species used are *Holothuria nobilis, mauritiana, scabra, lecanora, argus, edulis,* and *echinites,* and *Stichopus variegatus* and *japonicus*. The methods of preparation of holothurians to make trepang vary in different regions, but in general the cucumbers are first boiled to cause them to eviscerate and to shorten and thicken. The body wall is then dried in the sun or by smoking or dried by combinations of sun and smoking; drying must be thorough or spoilage will occur. Usually also some means is taken to rid the body wall of ossicles, although Panning (1944) examined samples of trepang that contained the full complement of ossicles. Trepang therefore consists of the cured body wall of certain large holothuriids. In using trepang the dried object is cut into small pieces which are added to soups and stews and are said to impart a delicate flavor. When so cooked the pieces of trepang swell into a gelatinous condition and are also so eaten as tidbits. Trepang appears to be highly nutritious. The Indo-Pacific product contains 15 to 30 per cent ash, 35 to 52 per cent protein, and 21 to 23 per cent water; carbohydrates are wanting but some fat is present (Greshoff and Sack, 1900; Greshoff and van Eck, 1901). The Mediterranean product is even more nutritious, containing 56 to 65 per cent protein, 13 to 24 per cent ash, about 0.7 per cent fats, and 10 to 11 per cent water (the Sellas, 1940). According to Fränkel and Jellinek (1927), the protein constituents of trepang are completely soluble in pepsin, so that the product appears highly digestible. In some localities in the Indo-Pacific, holothuriids are irritated until they eviscerate, and the cuvierian tubules and gonads are then eaten raw, and entire cucumbers may be eaten raw also.

As sluggish and almost defenseless benthonic animals, holothurians are subject to a long list of commensals and parasites. Two species of ciliate Protozoa inhabit the terminal parts of the respiratory trees as apparently harmless commensals which, however, obtain shelter, food, and oxygen without conferring any benefits in return. *Licnophora macfardlandi* (I, Fig. 63*E*) is common in the respiratory tree of the Pacific Coast aspidochirote, *Parastichopus californicus*, where it glides about on its basal disk or remains attached, swinging the anterior end about (Stevens, 1901, 1903; Balamuth, 1941). In the same situation occurs the smaller holotrichous ciliate *Boveria subcylindrica* (another species of *Boveria* is shown in I, Fig. 13*A*), temporarily attached by its basal cilia and extending its body out into the lumen of the tree. Both species feed on diatoms and other organisms in the respiratory current, further, on discarded host cells, and *Licnophora* is also apt to eat the smaller *Boveria* (Stevens, 1901). The same or similar species of *Licnophora* and *Boveria* were found by Beauchamp (1909) in

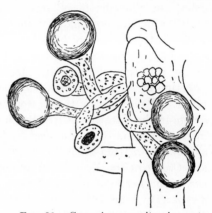

FIG. 91.—Gregarine parasites in cysts attached by stalks to haemal channels (*after Minchin*, 1893).

the respiratory trees of the European *Cucumaria planci* but not in other species of holothurians of the French coast. Peritrichous ciliates (I, page 199) are also common commensals of cucumbers, as *Trichodina synaptae* in the coelomic fluid of *Leptosynapta inhaerens*, where it runs about on the surface of the viscera (Cuénot, 1891b); *Urceolaria synaptae* in the intestine of synaptids (Cosmovici, 1913, 1914); and *Rhabdostyla* species on the surface of *Leptosynapta inhaerens* and on the buccal membrane of *Cucumaria cucumis* (Cuénot, 1891b). Gregarines appear to be of common occurrence in the interior of holothurians, either free in the coelom or enclosed in vesicles attached by stalks to the intestine or haemal channels (Fig. 91) or lying in the intestinal or haemal lumina (Cuénot, 1891c, 1912, Minchin, 1893). Later Goodrich (1925) gave more specific descriptions of *Urospira chiridotae*, found in great numbers in the haemal channels of *Chiridota laevis*, and of *Lithocystis brachycercus*, in the intestinal epithelium of the same species.

Numerous metazoans also live in association with holothurians.

Among the smaller forms one may recall the bdelloid rotifer *Zelinkiella synaptae*, living in pits in the skin of synaptids (II, page 112), and the entocommensal turbellarians, mostly of the rhabdocoel family Umagillidae (II, page 140), inhabiting the coelom or intestine of various cucumbers, mostly large aspidochirotes. The family Umagillidae has been recently reviewed by Stunkard and Corliss (1951) with a full bibliography. The list of umagillid associates of holothurians includes *Umagilla elegans, Anoplodiera voluta,* and *Wahlia macrostylifera* in the intestine of *Stichopus tremulus* off the Norwegian coast; *Anoplodium stichopi* in the coelom of the same animal; *Umagilla forskalensis* in the intestine and *Anoplodium gracile* in the coelom of *Holothuria forskalii* at Naples; *Anoplodium parasita* in the coelom of *Holothuria forskalii, polii,* and *tubulosa* at Naples; *Anoplodium evelinae* in the coelom of unidentified holothurians off Brazil; *A. chirodotae* in the coelom of *Chiridota laevis, A. myriotrochi* in the intestine of the arctic *Myriotrochus rinkii, A. schneideri* in the intestine of *Stichopus variegatus* and *Actinopyga lecanora* in the Philippines; *A. mediale* in the coelom of *Stichopus japonicus, Anoplodiera loutfia* in the intestine of Red Sea holothurians, *Cleistogamia holothuriana* in the intestine of *Actinopyga mauritiana* from the Andamans; *Macrogynium ovalis* from the intestine of an unidentified *Stichopus* at Bermuda; and *Ozametra* (= *Xenometra*) *arbora* in the intestine of *Stichopus japonicus.* Another type of turbellarian, *Meara stichopi,* related to *Nemertoderma* (II, page 132), lives in the intestine of *Stichopus tremulus* off Norway (Westblad, 1949).

Most common of the larger associates of holothurians are parasitic mollusks that often show a high degree of parasitic degradation. Most of these are gastropods, but a few bivalve parasites have been noticed. Semper (1868) observed a small bivalve creeping about on the surface of a synaptid in the Philippines. Voeltzkow (1890) found a very small bivalve, *Entovalva mirabilis,* living in the descending intestine of *Leptosynapta inhaerens* and robbing the host of food. A related species, *Entovalva Perrieri,* lives on the outside of this same cucumber, mostly near the anal end, firmly attached by the orifice of the byssal gland (Malard, 1903; Anthony, 1916). These bivalves are usually but slightly modified, except that the shell is generally covered by the reflexed mantle, whereas the parasitic snails of holothurians may be altered almost beyond recognition. A general account of these parasitic snails has been given by Rosen (1910) and Vaney (1913b). The less modified forms, of typical gastropod appearance, but generally lacking a radula and with a simplified digestive tract, belong to the families Melanellidae (= Eulimidae) and Stiliferidae and have long been known as parasites of echinoderms. Semper (1868) declared that snails of these families are common in and on Philippine holothurians. He found one of them moving about rapidly inside the digestive tract of a cucumber, and Voeltzkow (1890) made a similar observation. Habe (1952) reported three species of *Melanella* on the surface of common Indo-Pacific species of *Holothuria* and *Stichopus* off Japan and another *Melanella* in the coelom of *Stichopus chloronotus*. Species of *Melanella* also occur on the surface of and in the digestive tract of *Mesothuria intestinalis* (Rosen, 1910; Habe, 1952). *Megadenus holothuricola*, belonging to the Stiliferidae, inhabits the respiratory trees of *Holothuria mexicana*, Bahamas, piercing with its proboscis the wall of the trees into the coelom (Rosen, 1910). A species of *Stilifer* was reported by Gould (1848) in holothurians from the Fiji Islands.

The existence of highly altered snail parasites in holothurians was discovered by J. Müller (1852), who noticed in the interior of *Labidoplax digitata* long tubular objects resembling gonad tubules and attached by one end to a branch of the ventral haemal sinus. He named these objects *Entoconcha mirabilis* and observed that they contained young snails but considered them part of the anatomy of the cucumber. This mistake was corrected by Baur (1864), who gave a more detailed description of the creature. The parasite is attached to a haemal channel at its anterior end, and the long, spirally coiled body (up to 8 cm. in length) contains only a simplified digestive tract and the hermaphroditic reproductive system (Fig. 92*A*, *B*). The eggs develop inside the parent body into tiny snails of typical gastropod appearance, but their method of escape is uncertain. Other similar, highly degraded snail parasites of holothurians have since been described as *Entocolax Ludwigii*, fixed to the inside of the body wall of the arctic *Myriotrochus rinkii* (Voigt, 1888, Fig. 93*A*); *Entocolax schiemenzii*, similarly fastened in *Chiridota pisanii*, Chile (Voigt, 1901); *Enteroxenos östergreni* (Fig. 92*C*) in the coelom of *Stichopus tremulus*, Norway, lying free or attached to the outside of the intestine (Bonnevie, 1902); *Gasterosiphon deimatis* (Fig. 93*C*) attached to the inside of the body wall of *Deima blakei* with an opening to the exterior (Koehler and Vaney, 1903); and *Parenteroxenos dogieli*, found in the coelom of *Cucumaria japonica* (Ivanov, 1947), attached to the intestine or free in the coelom. This last form reaches a tremendous length, 130 cm., and is hollow, lacking all systems except the reproductive organs (Fig. 93*B*). It is generally accepted (Schiemenz, 1889; Vaney, 1913a) that these snails get into the interior of the holothurian by boring through the body wall with their proboscis. In this process a fold of the anterior part of the snail grows back over the visceral part of its body as a *pseudopallium*, which forms a chamber for the incubation of the young. As the penetration progresses, body systems except the reproductive gradually degenerate. A much less altered but shell-less snail, *Paedophorus dicoelobius*, of uncertain taxonomic position, occupies the polian vesicle of *Eupyrgus pacificus*, with its long proboscis

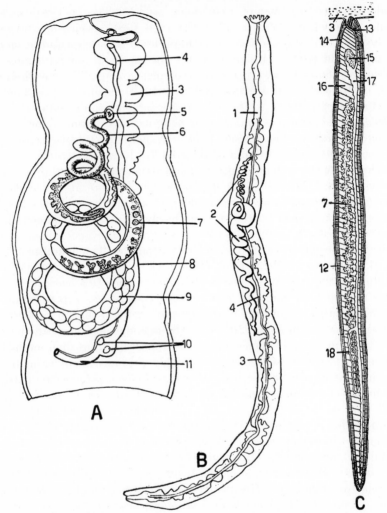

Fig. 92.—Parasitic snails in holothurians.  *A, Entoconcha mirabilis.  B, Entoconcha* shown in place in the interior of *Labidoplax digitata.  (A, B, after Baur*, 1864.)  *C, Entero-xenos (after Bonnevie*, 1902).  1, stomach of holothurian; 2, the parasite; 3, intestine of holothurian; 4, ventral sinus of holothurian; 5, mouth of snail; 6, intestine of snail; 7, snail ovary; 8, pseudopallium; 9, sacs of embryos in pseudopallium; 10, snail testes; 11, end of intestine; 12, body wall of snail; 13, ciliated canal; 14, coelomic membrane of host; 15, testis; 16, connective tissue; 17, central cavity of parasite; 18, oviduct.

inserted into the intestine (Ivanov, 1933); the young are brooded in a depression of the foot.

The flat elongated shape and slithering style of locomotion of poly-chaete annelids eminently qualify them for a commensal mode of life, and some occur in relation to holothurians.   The presence of a polynoid polychaete on the common Indo-Pacific aspidochirote *Stichopus chloronotus* was noted by Saville-Kent (1893), H. L. Clark (1921), and Sivickis and Domantay (1928).   The creature, colored like the cucumber, clings tightly to the dorsal surface between the warts.   Another polynoid, *Harmothoe lunulata*, is found constantly associated with synaptids in their burrows off the French coast (Cuénot, 1912).   Two kinds of polychaetes, a polynoid and a hesionid, were noted by Okuda (1936) living in the burrows of a Japanese apodous holothurian (*Protankyra bidentata*).   Still another polynoid, *Arctonoe pulchra*, inhabits the surface of *Parastichopus californicus* in Puget Sound.   Experiments have shown that this worm is attracted by water coming from an aquarium containing the cucumber (Davenport, 1950).   The MacGinities (1949) mention other polynoids associated with cucumbers: *Malmgrenia nigralba*, black, on the white *Chiridota* and *Harmothoe lunulata* in the burrows of *Leptosynapta albicans*.

Arthropods associated with holothurians include a copepod, *Synaptiphilus luteus*, living in the esophagus of synaptids (Cuénot, 1912); a crab, *Pinnixa timida*, found in the cloaca of *Paracaudina chilensis*, Japan (Tao, 1930); a related form, *Pinnixa barnharti*, in the cloaca of *Caudina arenicola*, California (the MacGinities, 1949); still another crab, *Ophisthopus transversus* in *Parastichopus californicus* (the MacGinities, 1949); and juvenile pycnogonids inhabiting the surface of a Japanese aspidochirote, *Holothuria lubrica* (Ohshima, 1927).

Undoubtedly the best-known associate of holothurians and indeed perhaps the most famous of all commensals is the pearl fish *Carapus* (old name *Fierasfer*).   This is a small, very slender fish reaching a length of around 15 cm., with a delicate, pale body, and long, slim tail.   The several species of *Carapus* live in association with various invertebrates, chiefly aspidochirote holothurians, in tropical and subtropical waters. Accounts of the habits of the fish in relation to cucumbers have been published by Emory (1889), Linton (1907), and Zänkert (1940, 1951). The fish occupies the main stem of one of the respiratory trees, with its head protruding from the anus.   If removed from the cucumber it seeks about restlessly but finds the cucumber only through chance contact with its snout, apparently not being aided by the respiratory current. It then shows excitement and moves about on the cucumber's surface, making repeated contact, until it reaches the anus, which it enters tail or head first; if the latter, it immediately whips around so that the tail lies in the cloaca and gradually works its body up the respiratory tree. The cucumber appears to resist the entry of the fish by closing the anal aperture, but as it must eventually open for respiratory purposes, it cannot prevent the fish from finally pushing its way in.   The fish apparently uses the cucumber only as a refuge and shelter and finds its own food, consisting chiefly of small crustaceans, during nocturnal wanderings from its host. The fish will also enter the mouth, if this is relaxed by narcosis, or dead cucumbers, or artificial openings in the body wall, or pieces of cucumbers so short that it sticks out at both ends; but will not

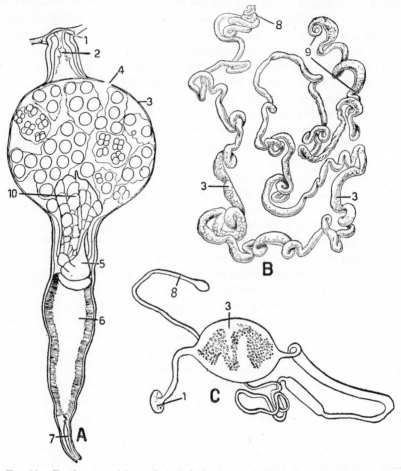

Fig. 93.—Further parasitic snails in holothurians. *A, Entocolax ludwigii (after Voigt,* 1888). *B, Parenteroxenos dogieli (after Ivanov,* 1947). *C, Gasterosiphon deimatis (after Koehler and Vaney,* 1903). 1, attachment to inside of cucumber wall; 2, ciliated canal; 3, pseudopallium containing embryos; 4, aperture of 3; 5, oviduct; 6, digestive tube; 7, esophagus; 8, end attached to host intestine; 9, visceral part of snail; 10, ovary.

enter other objects of cucumber shape. In any one area usually only a small per cent of the suitable cucumbers harbors the pearl fish. There is generally but one fish present in a cucumber but up to three have been found. Apparently the pearl fish can live indefinitely apart from its host.

## VIII. CLASS ASTEROIDEA

**1. Definition.**—The Asteroidea are free-living eleutherozoan echinoderms, moving on the oral surface, with a flattened, flexible body in the form of a pentagonal or stellate disk or more often a disk continuous with five to many, usually five, ray-like extensions called arms, each of which contains gonads and a pair of digestive glands, with open ambulacral grooves limited to the oral surface and provided with two or four rows of podia, with the radial water canals located to the outer side of the ambulacral ossicles, and with an endoskeleton of separate calcareous pieces bound together by connective tissue and usually bearing externally projecting knobs, tubercles, or spines.

**2. General Remarks.**—The Asteroidea comprise the marine animals commonly known as starfish or sea stars,[1] familiar to every visitor at the seashore. The sea stars have of course been known from the earliest times, and the Greeks applied to them the name *Aster*, meaning star. Linnaeus confused all the stellate echinoderms, i.e., sea stars, serpent stars, and comatulids, under the one name *Asterias*, and this confusion persisted for many years under names that were raised to familial or even ordinal rank, as Lamarck's Stelleridae, which included *Asterias, Ophiura, Comatula,* and *Euryale*. The name *Asterias* was used by these authors in a sense equivalent to the entire class Asteroidea. In the 1830's the comatulids were excluded from the assemblage, and in 1837 Burmeister applied the name Asteroidea to the combined sea stars and serpent stars. The union of ophiuroids with asteroids persisted for many years despite their separation into distinct orders by Forbes in 1841. Separation of ophiuroids under the name Ophiuroidea originated with Norman (1865), who retained the name Asteroidea for the sea stars. However, a tendency to reunite the two groups under the name Stelleroidea has persisted for years (e.g., in Gregory, 1900). Grounds for retaining the separation of the two groups will be stated in the discussion of phylogeny.

Valuable accounts are those of Sladen (1889), reporting on the asteroids collected by the *Challenger* and several preceding British collecting ships, Ludwig (1897) on the asteroids of the Mediterranean in the famous *Fauna und Flora des Golfes von Neapel* series, Ludwig and Hamann (1899) in Bronn's *Klassen und Ordnungen des Tierreichs*, Gregory (1900) in Lankester's *A Treatise on Zoology*, and Cuénot (1948) in the *Traité de zoologie*. Of purely taxonomic works, those of Fisher (1911, 1919, 1928, 1930, 1940), are outstanding; others present the asteroids taken on the numerous collecting and dredging expeditions of the last 50 years,

---

[1] It is suggested that zoologists drop the name starfish in favor of sea stars, as the former is apt to mislead the public.

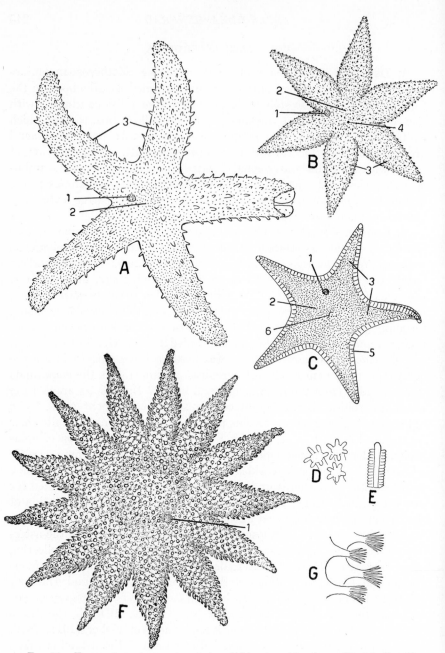

FIG. 94.—Types of sea stars. *A*, red star, *Echinaster echinophorus*, West Indies, illustrating typical shape. *B*, six-rayed star, *Leptasterias hexactis*, Puget Sound, regularly has six rays. *C*, mud star, *Ctenodiscus crispatus*, Maine coast, with short rays and conspicuous marginal plates (Order Phanerozonia). *D*, flower-like spines (paxillae) of aboral surface of *C*. *E*, marginal plate of *C*. *F*, *Crossaster papposus*, sun star, many-rayed, Puget Sound (*after Gregory*, 1900). *G*, marginal spines of *F*. 1, madreporite; 2, disk; 3, ray or arm; 4, anus; 5, supramarginal plates; 6, conical eminence.

already mentioned in connection with the previously considered echinoderm classes.

Although H. L. Clark (1946) estimated about 1200 described species of existing asteroids, other echinoderm specialists indicate a figure of around 2000; there are also many extinct species beginning in the Ordovician.

Apart from taxonomic reports, asteroids are most frequently met with in modern literature as sources of eggs for experimental embryology; however, studies on their behavior, physiology, and neuromotor mechanisms are not infrequent.

**3. External Characters.**—The general appearance of a sea star is quite different from that of the echinoderms hitherto considered. The body is strongly flattened in the oral-aboral axis and therefore presents very distinctly differentiated oral and aboral surfaces. The typical shape is that of a five-pointed star in which the central area or *disk* passes insensibly into five symmetrically spaced projections, the *arms* or *rays*, which taper gradually to blunt tips. However, ray numbers other than five are not infrequent. There appear to be no regularly four-rayed species, and specimens with four arms are either the result of injury or are incidental variants of five-rayed species. Some asteroids are constantly six-rayed, as a group of species of the genus *Leptasterias*, common on the Pacific Coast of North America (Fig. 94*B*). The sun stars, of the genus *Solaster*, may have 7 to 14 rays (Fig. 94*F*) and in the 20-rayed star of Puget Sound, *Pycnopodia helianthoides*, there are 15 to 24 arms. All members of the Brisingidae, a deep-water family with long, slender arms, have at least 7 rays (Fig. 95*A*); the genus *Labidiaster*, belonging to the Asteriidae, has 25 to 45 rays; and *Heliaster* (family Heliasteridae) is also many-rayed with 15 to 50 arms (Fig. 151). In general, the number of rays, if in excess of six or seven, is not constant, but varies with individuals. Many-rayed species usually already show an excess of hydrocoel lobes during development, but the number of rays may also increase during growth, mostly without rule or regularity. However, *Pycnopodia helianthoides* has five rays at first, soon produces a sixth ray between B and C, and then proceeds to form new arms bilaterally in pairs to either side of this sixth ray, between it and B and C (Ritter and Crocker, 1900), so that the new rays are all in one region of the body (Fig. 158*D*).

Contributing also to external appearance are the relative proportions of disk and arms. Typically, the length of the arms is two or three times the diameter of the disk, and the arms are of tapering cylindroid shape with fairly broad bases (Fig. 94*A*). From this norm, the shape may vary in the direction of long and slender, usually numerous, arms with narrow bases, as in the Brisingidae (Fig. 95*A*). In the other

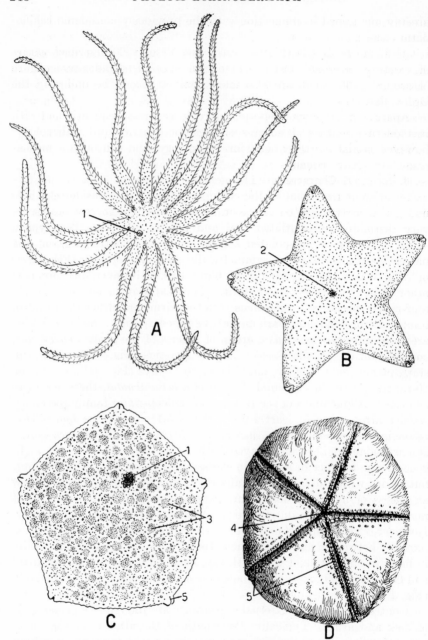

FIG. 95.—Types of sea stars (continued). *A, Freyella* (Family Brisingidae) with many slender rays. *B*, cushion star, *Pteraster tesselatus*, Puget Sound. *C, Culcita*, aboral view. Indo-Pacific, without rays. *D, Culcita*, oral view (*after Gregory*, 1900). 1, madreporite; 2, opening (osculum) of nidamental chamber; 3, papular areas; 4, mouth; 5, ambulacral grooves.

direction the arms become progressively shorter and more broadly based, so that the animal resembles a five-pointed star, a shape here termed *stellate*, as in *Ctenodiscus* (Fig. 94*C*), *Pteraster* (Fig. 95*B*), and many other phanerozonic genera. The climax of this type of shape is reached in *Culcita* (Fig. 95*C*, *D*), whose shape is that of a plump, slightly five-angled disk, and may be referred to as *pentagonal*. In taxonomic descriptions of asteroids it is customary to state the measurements $R$, from the disk center to the arm tip, and $r$, the diameter of the disk.

The external surface is generally more or less rough, warty, tuberculate, or spiny, because of protuberances borne by the underlying ossicles of the skeleton but usually not fused to them. The arms may be fringed with spines, as in *Pectinaster* (Fig. 98*C*). Often the ossicles are arranged in a reticulate pattern with fleshy areas between the meshes of the network and tubercles borne on the angles, as in *Oreaster* (Fig. 96*A*). On the other hand, in many asteroids the endoskeletal ossicles are plate-like, giving the surface a pavement-like or mosaic appearance (Fig. 98*D*) and a hard texture. In the order Phanerozonia, the arms are bordered laterally by two rows of conspicuous rectangular plates (Fig. 94*C*), an oral and an aboral row, so that the line of meeting of the two rows exactly defines the boundary of the two surfaces. In the two other orders, Spinulosa and Forcipulata, conspicuous marginal plates are usually wanting, and oral and aboral surfaces often grade insensibly into each other.

On the aboral surface of the disk, the madreporite is readily noticed as a circular, grooved plate (Fig. 94*A*), always situated in an interradius that thereby becomes interradius CD on Carpenter's system. The rays CD therefore constitute a *bivium*, the other three rays a *trivium*, as in holothuroids, but this concept has little significance in the biology of the animal. Although the great majority of asteroids have but one madreporite, multiplication of madreporites is not rare and occurs in the families Asteriidae, Echinasteridae, and Linckiidae. The presence of more than one madreporite is usually associated with irregularity or increase beyond five of arm number or the occurrence of asexual reproduction by fission. Species of Asteriidae with 6 to 12 arms may have up to 4 madreporites, and in the fissiparous genus *Allostichaster* with 6 to 8 rays there are 1 to 5 madreporites. The normally 5-rayed *Linckia* may, as a result of fission, show a range of 1 to 9 arms and 1 to 5 madreporites. Multiple madreporites, 5 to 16, are present in the normally multirayed genus *Acanthaster* (Fig. 97*A*). However, many regularly multirayed asteroids as *Solaster* and *Crossaster* (Fig. 94*F*), *Heliaster* (Fig. 151), *Pycnopodia*, and the Brisingidae have but 1 madreporite. The additional madreporites show no regularity of arrangement although always interradial; each leads into a stone canal.

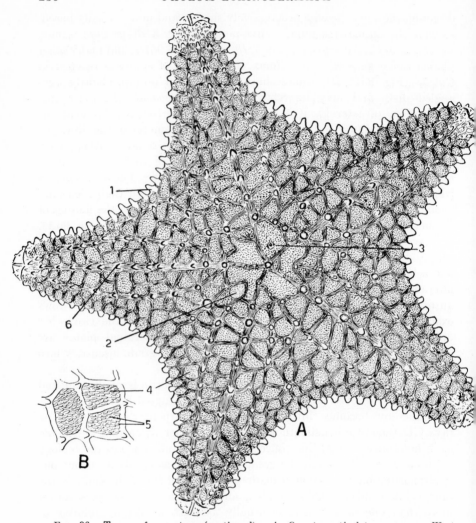

Fig. 96.—Types of sea stars (continued). *A, Oreaster reticulatus,* common West Indian star, with reticular skeleton outlining papular areas. *B,* three meshes of the skeleton, enlarged, showing papulae. 1, supramarginal plates; 2, madreporite; 3, anus; 4, papular area; 5, papulae; 6, carinal spines.

The mostly small and inconspicuous anus (wanting in the families Porcellanasteridae and Luidiidae and in some Astropectinidae) is located more or less excentrically on the aboral surface of the disk in interradius BC, thus definitely related positionally to the madreporite. In the Porcellanasteridae, the center of the aboral surface of the disk is raised into a conical eminence (Fig. 94*C*), called by some *epiproctal cone,* of unknown significance, not related to the digestive tract, as this family lacks anus and intestine.

In the center of the oral surface is seen the mouth, surrounded by a membranous peristome and guarded by spines. From the peristome an ambulacral groove radiates along the middle of the oral surface of each arm to its tip (Fig. 97B). Each ambulacral groove contains two or four rows of locomotory podia, usually provided with terminal disks (suckers); suckers are wanting in some phanerozonic families. At the arm tip, the podial rows end with an unpaired *terminal tentacle*, bearing on the oral side of its base a red spot that marks the position of a number of ocelli (Fig. 106E). The ambulacral grooves are guarded laterally by movable spines that can be crisscrossed over them.

The fleshy areas of the body wall between the ossicles are provided with small retractile projections, the gills or *papulae*, presumably respiratory. They are hollow evaginations of the body wall, and hence their lumen is continuous with the coelom and is lined with coelomic epithelium. They are usually of simple tubular or conical shape but are branched in *Luidia* (Fig. 98E), *Pycnopodia* (Fig. 104F), *Aphanasterias*, and the Pterasteridae. When the endoskeleton is reticulate, as in Fig. 96A, large numbers of papulae emerge in the areas enclosed by the meshes of the skeletal network (Fig. 96B). When the skeleton consists of closely set plates, as in most Phanerozonia, the papulae emerge singly between these plates (Fig. 98D). Papulae are typically present on both surfaces in the orders Spinulosa and Forcipulata, but in the Phanerozonia are generally limited to the aboral surface and are frequently absent from the center of disk and along the median region of the arms. They are sometimes limited to definite rounded areas known as papular areas or *papularia*, as in *Linckia*, where these areas are scattered irregularly on the aboral surface of the arms (Fig. 98A) but occur in a row on the sides of the arms between the supra- and inframarginal rows of plates. In the deep-water family Benthopectinidae (constituting the whole of the phanerozonic suborder Notomyota) there are only five papularia, one on the aboral surface of each arm base (Fig. 98C). Papulae are wanting in most genera of the phanerozonic family Porcellanasteridae (being there replaced functionally by the cribriform organs, see below) and in certain genera of the forcipulate family Brisingidae (*Brisinga, Freyella*).

The family Porcellanasteridae, constituting the whole of the phanerozonic suborder Cribellosa, is characterized by the presence of *cribriform organs*. In their typical form these are found on the sides of the arms in the interradii between the marginal plates and vary in number from 1 in each interradius in *Porcellanaster* to 14 in *Thoracaster*. When fully developed they consist of a vertical depression between adjacent marginal plates (extending the whole width of both series of marginal plates) lined with a series of thin vertical plates like the leaves of a book or with vertical rows of papillae (Fig. 99C, D), supported by calcareous deposits

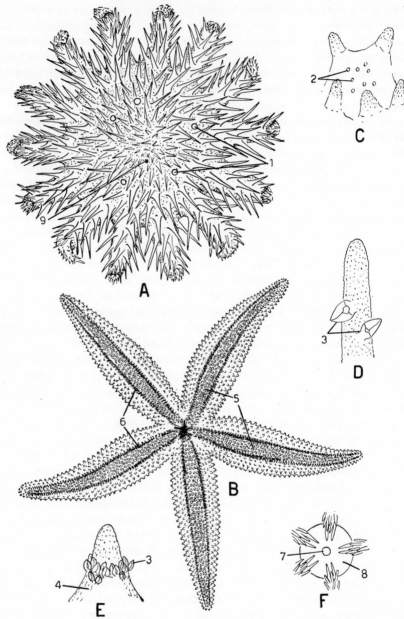

FIG. 97.—Types of sea stars (concluded).  A, spiny star, *Acanthaster*, Philippines, with many rays and several madreporites.  B, common star, *Asterias*, oral view to show ambulacral grooves.  C, papular area of *Asterias*, between surface tubercles.  D, adambulacral spine of *Asterias* with straight pedicellariae.  E, tubercle of general surface of *Asterias* encircled with pedicellariae on a fleshy sheath.  F, mouth armature of *Asterias*. 1, madreporites; 2, papulae; 3, pedicellariae; 4, sheath; 5, ambulacral groove; 6, adambulacral spines; 7, mouth; 8, peristome; 9, anus.

and clothed with a tall ciliated epithelium. In *Ctenodiscus* the cribriform organs are reduced to a groove between successive marginal plates forming a series along the sides of the whole length of the arms (Fig. 99*E*). These grooves contain a few lamellae guarded by scalloped calcareous edges (Fig. 99*F*); they continue ventrally onto the oral surface between the adambulacral plates to the ambulacral grooves (for function see page 372).

Pedicellariae are present in the orders Phanerozonia and Forcipulata, but are usually obvious to the naked eye only in the latter where they often occur in thick rosettes around spine bases (Fig. 97*E*); but very large bivalved pedicellariae occur in some Phanerozonia.

The orientation of asteroids is simple; with the oral surface held upward, the arm opposite the madreporite becomes A and the others follow in alphabetic order in a clockwise direction.

The size range of asteroids is considerable. There are little stars measuring only a centimeter or two from arm tip to arm tip. Most species are of moderate size from 10 to 30 cm. across, but there are some large ones, measuring 50 to 60 cm. from tip to tip. Among the largest species is the common 20-rayed star of Puget Sound, *Pycnopodia helianthoides*, that can easily fill the bottom of a large washtub. Among the largest forms are also many species of the deep-sea family Brisingidae with numerous long and slender arms for which *R* may equal 25 to 30 cm.

Whereas many common sea stars are of a dull yellowish hue, brilliant colors also obtain in the class. There are many red and orange species, also some blue, green, gray, and brown ones. Mottled and banded patterns in contrasting colors also occur. The color is ordinarily best developed on the aboral surface and pales on the oral side. Not uncommonly, the same species may occur in color variants or show a wide range of colors or color patterns.

**4. Body Wall and Endoskeleton.**—The body surface is clothed with a definite cuticle, consisting of two layers (J. E. Smith, 1937), an outer thicker homogeneous layer and an inner thinner layer that shows hexagonal impressions from the underlying epidermal cells. The latter vary in length and shape in different regions and in different species. They are tall flagellated cells that may be columnar throughout (Fig. 100*A*) or attenuated at both ends or basally (Fig. 100*B*). They often contain, especially over nervous areas, a long elastic filament that extends through the nervous layer (Fig. 100*C*). The epidermal cells are interspersed with neurosensory cells (Fig. 100*C*) and with two sorts of gland cells (Cuénot, 1887), varying in abundance with region and species: mucous gland cells or goblets, with finely granular contents (Fig. 100*D*), and muriform cells, filled with coarse spherules (Fig. 100*E*). Large glands extending like little sacs into the dermis (Fig. 100*F*) open onto the aboral surface in some Echinasteridae (Cuénot, 1887; Barthels, 1906; Hayashi, 1935) and pour out an abundant gelatinous secretion in response to irritation. The epidermis contains the pigment granules responsible for the external colors. In the base of the epidermis is found a nervous layer, varying in thickness in different areas and penetrated by the attenuated bases of the epidermal cells or their elastic filaments (Fig. 100C). A delicate basement membrane separates the epidermis from the underlying, thick dermis, of fibrillar connective tissue, which secretes and houses the endoskeletal ossicles and binds them together (Fig. 99G). Next comes a smooth muscle layer, of outer circular and inner longitudinal fibers. These muscle layers are on the whole weakly developed except in the aboral wall where stronger longitudinal bundles radiate from the center of the disk along the middorsal line of each arm, no doubt serving to bend the arms aborally. The inner surface of the body wall next to the coelom is clothed with coelomic epithelium (peritoneum), consisting of flagellated cuboidal cells. The dermis just to the outer side of the muscle layer is permeated with a system of canalicular spaces that form a ring space around the base of each papula (Fig. 106C).

The endoskeleton consists of calcareous ossicles that have the usual fenestrated structure with the fenestrations filled in life with connective tissue. It is divisible into the main supporting skeleton, imbedded in the dermis of the body wall, and the more superficial skeleton of more or less projecting spines, tubercles, warts, granules, and so on, that are always borne on the underlying deeper skeleton and are clothed in life with epidermis and a thin layer of dermis, although this covering may rub off the more prominently projecting parts. The main skeleton consists of discrete ossicles of various shapes bound together with connective tissue and often overlapping. They may take the form of more or less elongated rods, or of four-angled pieces, or of rounded, polygonal, or squarish plates. The shape of the ossicles may be such that when bound together they form a reticulate skeleton, leaving spaces for the emergence of groups of papulae (Fig. 96A), as generally in the Asteriidae; or plate-like ossicles may be closely set to produce a pavement-like surface (Fig. 101A), permitting the emergence of only single papulae; or provision may be made for special papular areas.

In the Phanerozonia, as already noted, the sides of the arms are formed of two rows of large, rounded, squarish, or rectangular plates, the supra- and inframarginal plates. The remainder of the body surface (apart from the ambulacral areas) in most Phanerozonia and especially in the suborder Paxillosa is supported by closely set plates that send up erect columns with expanded tops covered with little tubercles or spinelets. The entire skeletal piece, somewhat resembling a mushroom, is called a *paxilla* (Fig. 100J), and in asteroids with such paxilliform ossicles

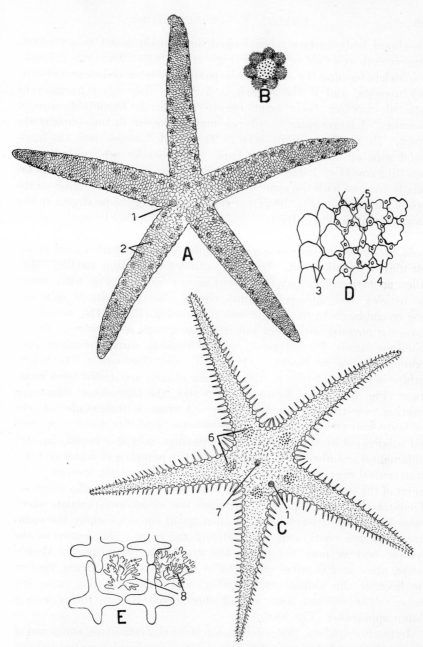

Fig. 98.—Papulae. A, Linckia laevigata, Philippines, with scattered papular areas. B, papular area of A, enlarged, with surrounding skeletal plates covered with granules. C, Pectinaster, Panamic region, with five papularia. D, plates of part of aboral side of ray of Astropecten, showing papulae emerging singly (after Fisher, 1911). E, four skeletal plates of Luidia and two arborescent papulae (after Fisher, 1919). 1, madreporite; 2, papular area; 3, median plates of ray; 4, lateral plates of ray; 5, papula; 6, papularium; 7, anus; 8, branching papula.

the aboral body surface when looked down upon under magnification often resembles a field of flowers (Figs. 100G, 135). The little tubercles or spinelets forming the crown of the paxilla are more or less movable by tiny muscles, and if the animal is irritated, they bend horizontally outward, meeting their neighbors to produce a formidable surface covering. A larger spine or tubercle may be present in the center of the crown. In another variant, seen in *Tosia* and *Pentagonaster*, the large, round tops of the paxillae are bare, and tubercles are limited to an encircling row (Fig. 103B). The marginal plates in the Phanerozonia are usually covered with the same little tubercles or spinelets as found on the tops of the paxillae (Fig. 100H); or these may enlarge to produce a row of marginal spines (Fig. 101D).

The Spinulosa, although not sharply demarcated from the Phanerozonia, lack conspicuously enlarged marginal plates and have a more or less reticulated endoskeleton. However, ossicles simulating paxillae, then called *pseudopaxillae*, may be present as in *Crossaster* (Fig. 94G), where the ossicles send up erect columns tipped with a bundle of spinelets. Less resemblance to paxillae is seen in *Henricia* (Fig. 101B), where the surface is covered with erect but irregular groups of spinelets. In the spinulose family Pterasteridae, or the cushion stars, including such common genera as *Pteraster* (Fig. 95B) and *Hymenaster*, the aboral surface is formed of true paxillae. Their crowns are united by a membrane (Fig. 101F) that forms an outer roof, the *supradorsal membrane*, covering over the true aboral surface. A space is thus made between the body wall and the supradorsal membrane, and this space, supported and subdivided by the columns of the paxillae, acts as a brood chamber (nidamental chamber) that is aerated by the pumping of water out of a large central aperture, the osculum, supported by spines, located in the center of the supradorsal membrane (Fig. 95B). There are also a number of contractile pores (spiracles) through the membrane through which water enters, as well as a series of openings at the sides where the membrane becomes continuous with sides of the rays. The crowns of the paxillae may or may not pierce the supradorsal membrane. Madreporite, anus, and papulae are found in the true aboral surface, that is, the floor of the nidamental chamber, and hence are not externally visible. The cushion stars are all short-rayed stellate forms with a plump appearance (Fig. 95B).

In the Forcipulata, the endoskeleton is usually reticulate, composed of elongated or angled or rounded pieces, often overlapping or imbricated, bound together by connective tissue so as to leave papular areas between. An example of a forcipulate endoskeleton is given in Fig. 101E, which shows part of a ray from the middorsal region to the ambulacral area. Often there is present a row of distinguishable ossicles, termed *carinals*,

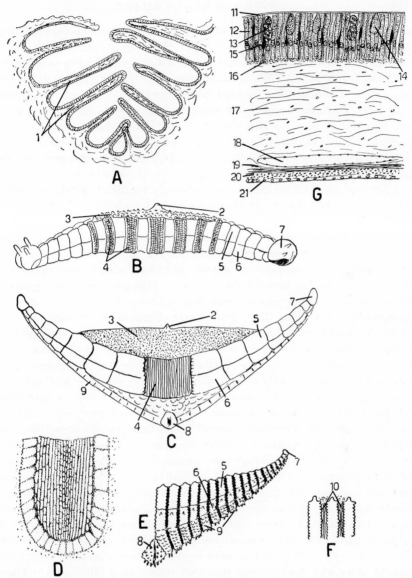

Fig. 99.—Cribriform organs, body wall. *A*, section through a cribriform organ (*after Lieberkind*, 1932). *B*, two arms of *Hyphalaster*, seen from the side, with seven cribriform organs. *C*, side view of *Porcellanaster*, showing the single cribriform organ in the interradius. *D*, cribriform organ of *Porcellanaster*, enlarged. (*B, D, after Sladen*, 1888.) *E*, side view of an arm of *Ctenodiscus* with reduced cribriform organs along the length of the arm. *F*, three supramarginal plates of *E* enlarged. *G*, schematized section through the asteroid body wall. 1, lamellae of cribriform organ; 2, conical eminence; 3, disk; 4, cribriform organ; 5, supramarginal ossicles; 6, inframarginal ossicles; 7, terminal ossicle; 8, adambulacral piece of peristomial ring; 9, adambulacral ossicles; 10, grooves containing reduced cribriform organs; 11, cuticle; 12, epidermis; 13, muriform gland; 14, mucous gland; 15, neurosensory cell; 16, nervous layer; 17, dermis; 18, dermal space; 19, circular muscle fibers; 20, longitudinal muscle fibers; 21, coelomic epithelium.

257

along the median aboral line of the ray, and the other ossicles extending laterally from this row may form more or less of a pattern with longer ossicles next the carinals and more rounded or four-lobed ones laterally. The two rows next to the adambulacrals are called supra- and infra-marginals, although they are no larger than the others. The ossicles may also be arranged somewhat in rows transverse to the ray, and these are referred to as skeletal arches. In the Forcipulata, externally projecting spines and tubercles are borne separately on the skeletal ossicles and are not grouped into clusters or bundles surmounting erect columns as in the preceding orders.

The endoskeletal ossicles are often poorly visible in the living animal and not infrequently are concealed by a thick or leathery membrane or "skin" that presumably represents the outer layers of the body wall. Often the ossicles are fairly evident in dried specimens, but for exact studies it is usually necessary to macerate the animal.

A definite arrangement of ossicles, obtaining throughout the Asteroidea, supports the ambulacral grooves. The grooves themselves are formed of two rows of opposite rod-shaped pieces, the *ambulacral ossicles*, that meet in a V (Fig. 102*C, D*). Their aboral ends, forming the apex of the V, project into the coelom and produce, as seen from the coelomic side, a conspicuous ridge, the *ambulacral ridge*, likened by older workers to a vertebral column. The podia pass to the exterior *between* the ambulacral ossicles, each of which bears a concavity or half pore for this purpose. These concavities usually form a single row on each side, so that there are two rows of podia in the ambulacral groove (Fig. 102*F*). In some asteroids, however, especially the family Asteriidae, the concavities alternate in position in successive ossicles, so as to form two rows of pores on each side in each groove, whence there appear to be four rows of podia per groove (Fig. 102*E*). Actually, however, only one podium emerges between any two successive ambulacral ossicles. The ambulacral ossicles never bear any spines, tubercles, or other external appendages. Lateral to the outer ends of the ambulacral ossicles, forming the edges of the grooves, is a row of ossicles, called the *adambulacral ossicles*, that meet the ambulacral ossicles oppositely or alternately on their medial sides and always bear movable spines (Fig. 102*C, D*). These spines are mounted on little tubercles of the adambulacral ossicles and are operated by two small muscles, one of which, the depressor muscle, lowers the spine across the ambulacral groove, and the other, the elevator, erects it again (Fig. 103*E*). In some phanerozonic asteroids there is present a row of small *supra-ambulacral* ossicles in the angle of the arms on the inside, not externally visible, lying in contact with the outer ends of the ambulacral ossicles (Fig. 102*C*).

In phanerozonic asteroids with slender arms, the adambulacrals are in

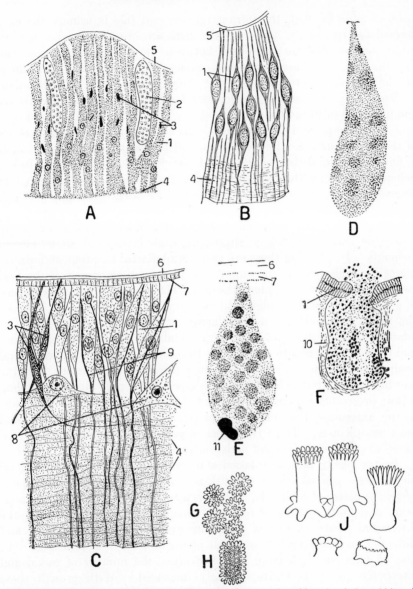

Fig. 100.—Histology of the body wall, endoskeleton. *A*, epidermis of the middorsal region of the arm of *Marthasterias*. *B*, aboral epidermis of *Asterias* (*after Hamann*, 1885). *C*, epidermis and radial nerve (*after Meyer*, 1906). *D*, mucous type of gland cell. *E*, muriform type of gland cell. (*A, D, E, after Smith*, 1937.) *F*, large gland of aboral wall of *Henricia* (*after Hayashi*, 1935). *G*, paxillae of *Mediaster*, seen from above. *H*, marginal plate of *Mediaster*. *J*, various shapes of paxillae. 1, epidermal cells; 2, muriform gland; 3, neurosensory cell; 4, nervous plexus; 5, cuticle; 6, outer layer of cuticle; 7, inner layer of cuticle; 8, ganglion cell; 9, elastic fiber of epidermal cells; 10, connective tissue; 11, nucleus.

contact laterally with the inframarginals, and this is usually the case toward the tips of the arms. If the arms are broadly based, however, additional ossicles are interposed between the adambulacrals and the inframarginals. These interposed ossicles are usually similar to those of the general aboral surface, but they may differ. In forcipulate asteroids, the two rows of ossicles next lateral to the adambulacrals are simply called infra- and supramarginals. They are mostly of rounded or four-lobed shape and do not differ especially from the general ossicles of the aboral surface. Between them and the carinals are usually found a number of lobulated or elongated ossicles, known as dorsolaterals. Schematic sections through an arm of a phanerozonic and a forcipulate asteroid to show the arrangement of the ossicles are given in Fig. 102*C*, *D*.

At their central ends, the rows of ambulacral and adambulacral ossicles join to form a peristomial skeletal ring or *mouth frame* edging the peristome and composed of alternating ambulacral and adambulacral elements. In this ring there are two adambulacral and four ambulacral pieces for each arm, as the ambulacral pieces are composed of the first two ambulacrals of each side of the ray. This is shown by the occurrence of a podial pore in the ambulacral piece, marking the boundary between the fused first and second ambulacrals of the row (Fig. 102*A*). The adambulacral components in the peristomial ring continue to bear spines, and these act as a mouth armature. In some asteroids the adambulacral components of the peristomial ring are the most conspicuous, and the pair in each interradius form a wedge-shaped, very spiny piece, resembling a jaw, projecting prominently inward (Fig. 102*B*). In other asteroids, as the Asteriidae, the ambulacral pieces in the ring are the larger and more conspicuous. These two types of peristomial skeleton are termed *adambulacral* and *ambulacral* peristomes, respectively.

In the newly metamorphosed star the arrangement of the skeletal pieces in the aboral side of the disk is strongly suggestive of the apical system of plates of echinoids. There is a central plate, to which the anus bears a definite positional relation, surrounded by five plates in the interradial positions, one of which incorporates the madreporite, and these are encircled by five terminal plates in the radial positions. (In case of asteroids with more than five arms, the number of radial and interradial plates is correspondingly increased.) With growth these juvenile plates are usually shifted apart by the interpolation between them of additional skeletal elements and in most asteroids are unrecognizable in the adult, although they do remain detectable by their larger size in a few species, as in *Tosia* (Fig. 103*A*) and *Pentagonaster*. As the arms grow out they carry the terminal plates at their tips, and the row of plates that arises behind the terminal plates in the radial position becomes the row of carinals in the middorsal line of the arms. The

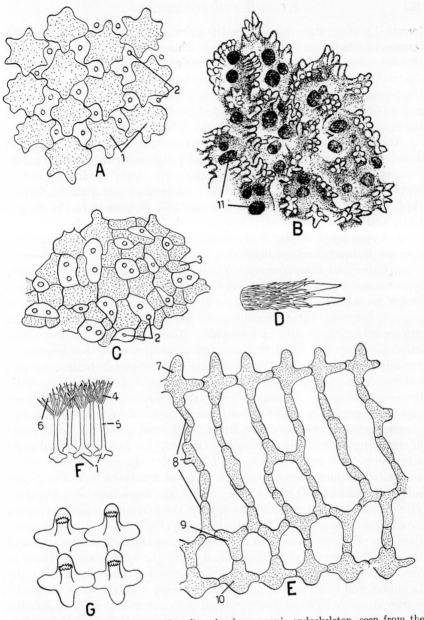

Fig. 101.—Endoskeleton (continued). A, phanerozonic endoskeleton, seen from the inside, showing basal plates of the paxillae. B, surface of *Henricia* (*after Hayashi*, 1935). C, endoskeletal ossicles of *Henricia*. (A, C, after Fisher, 1911.) D, inframarginal plate of *Astropecten*, bearing marginal spines. E, arrangement of endoskeletal ossicles of one of the Asteriidae from center of ray laterally (*after Fisher*, 1928). F, paxillae of one of the Pterasteridae, showing formation of supradorsal membrane. G, ossicles of *Solaster* with pseudopaxillae. 1, base of paxilla; 2, papula; 3, endoskeletal ossicle; 4, crown of paxilla; 5, column or shaft of paxilla; 6, supradorsal membrane; 7, carinals; 8, dorsolaterals; 9, supramarginals; 10, inframarginals.

terminal plates come to embrace the primary podia, which become the terminal tentacles of the podial rows. These terminal plates at the arm tips are quite conspicuous in many asteroids (Fig. 99B), inconspicuous in others. Asteroids grow by the interpolation of endoskeletal plates to the central side of the terminal plates, so that the youngest ambulacral and adambulacral ossicles are situated next to the terminal plates and the age of these ossicles increases in the central direction.

At the arm angles the body wall is continued inward for a varying distance, as the *interradial* or *interbrachial septum*, usually supported by ossicles but membranous in some cases (Fig. 109A). These internal septa demarcate the arms in asteroids that seem to lack arms, as *Culcita* (Fig. 95C, D). Calcareous deposits may also be present in the mesenteries and other internal parts but are usually wanting in the podia.

**5. Appendages of the Body Wall.**—These include the surface calcareous protuberances, pedicellariae, papulae, and podia.

*a. Calcareous Protuberances.*—These form a surface armature varying from spines of some length to very small deposits, called granules, and confer on asteroids a great diversity of appearance and texture; in general, however, these protuberances lack the variety of shapes and surface sculpturings seen in echinoids. They rest upon the underlying ossicles but are not fused to them and thus allow a certain amount of flexibility. Most sea stars have a merely warty or tuberculate surface, but really spiny stars occur, as in the genus *Acanthaster* (Fig. 97A), from tropical seas. In some Phanerozonia the spines of the marginal plates get gradually larger toward the margin, where they form a row of spines edging the arms (Figs. 101D, 102B), and bristly arms also occur in the forcipulate family Brisingidae (Fig. 95A). In *Pteraster* and some other pterasterid genera, but not in *Hymenaster*, the adambulacral spines are united by membranes to form a series of transverse fans along each side of the ambulacral grooves (Fig. 102G), and these fans are continuous with a lateral membrane laid flat against the oral surface and supported by a series of long parallel transverse spines (Fig. 102G). In *Hymenaster* these lateral membranes with their supporting spines form the oral wall between the ambulacral areas (Fig. 148B). In forcipulates a more or less evident row of tubercles may be borne on the carinals. In the Luidiidae and some astropectinid genera there are present between the marginal plates vertical grooves lined with minute, heavily flagellated spines, recalling the clavules of spatangoids. These "vibratile" spines (Fig. 103F) presumably function to produce respiratory currents in the margin. The surface protuberances are covered in life with epidermis rich in gland cells and nervous tissue, underlain by connective tissue in which the calcareous piece is imbedded (Fig. 106C) and in which the muscle fibers, when present, are found.

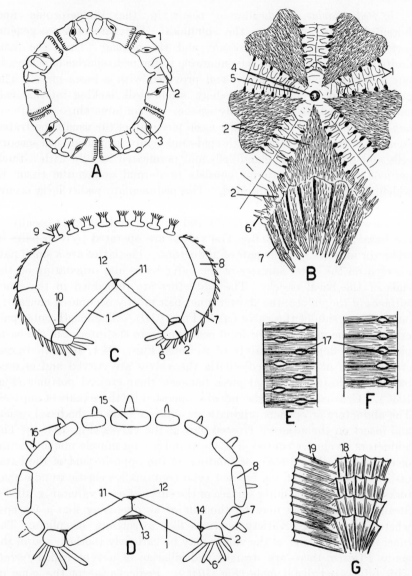

Fig. 102.—Endoskeleton (continued). *A*, peristomial ring of ossicles of ambulacral type, *Asterias* seen from the inside, (*after Chadwick*, 1923). *B*, peristomial ring of ossicles of the adambulacral type, *Astropecten*, seen from the outside. *C*, schematic section through the arm of a phanerozonic star. *D*, schematic section through the arm of a forcipulate star. *E*, scheme of ambulacral pores with two apparent rows of podia. *F*, scheme of the ambulacral pores with one row of podia. *G*, small part of adambulacral area of *Pteraster*, showing adambulacral fans. 1, ambulacral pieces; 2, adambulacral pieces; 3, pore for first podium; 4, mouth; 5, peristome; 6, adambulacral spines; 7, inframarginal plates; 8, supramarginal plates; 9, paxillae; 10, supra-ambulacral ossicles; 11, ambulacral ridge; 12, upper transverse ambulacral muscle; 13, lower transverse ambulacral muscle; 14, lateral transverse ambulacral muscle; 15. carinal ossicle; 16, tubercle; 17, ambulacral pore; 18, fan; 19, lateral membrane.

*b. Pedicellariae.*—Pedicellariae occur in the Phanerozonia and Forcipulata but are rare in the Spinulosa. They are of three general sorts: the *pedunculate,* the *sessile,* and the *alveolar.* Only the first, limited to the Forcipulata, is comparable to the pedicellariae of echinoids but differs in being two-jawed and provided with a basal piece. The pedunculate pedicellaria has a short, stout stalk lacking internal calcareous support or is practically sessile. It contains three calcareous ossicles, two jaws or valves, and a basal piece, all of the usual fenestrated construction. It is clothed with epidermis richly furnished with sensory cells and both kinds of gland cells and permeated basally with a thick nervous layer. The interior consists of dermal connective tissue in which the ossicles are imbedded. The pedunculate pedicellaria occurs in two varieties, the *straight* and the *crossed.* In the simpler straight type the valves are more or less straight and parallel and attached basally to the basal piece (Fig. 103*D*). The valves are operated by two pairs of adductor muscles and one pair of abductors. The latter are a small pair inserted on the outer surfaces of the valve bases and originating on the ends of the basal ossicle. The adductors are imbedded in the inner surfaces of the valves; the shorter inner pair mostly occupies a concavity on the inner side of the valve bases (Fig. 103*D*). The longer outer pair extends in the valve interior from near the tip to the interior of the basal piece and is detectable mainly in sections (Figs. 104*A*, 105*A*). In the crossed type of stalked pedicellaria the valves are curved and crossed basally, enclosing the basal piece between their crossed portions (Fig. 103*C*). Crossed pedicellariae are also operated by three pairs of muscles. The abductors or openers originate on opposite ends of the basal ossicle and insert on the adjacent crossed part of the valves (Fig. 103*C*). The adductors or closers consist of a short and a long muscle in the interior of each valve (Fig. 104*B*), originating on the opposite end of the basal ossicle. The stalk of the crossed type contains an elastic bundle that forks to attach to the outer surface of the curve of each valve (Fig. 103*C*). Straight pedicellariae may be thought of as operating like a forceps, whereas the crossed variety operates like a scissors or pliers. The inner surface and tips of the valves may be variously toothed, and in the genus *Pisaster* there are straight pedicellariae of a type called *furcate* with bifurcated distal ends (Fig. 104*C*). Pedicellariae of the same or similar structural type may occur in large and small sizes. Stalked pedicellariae may be scattered singly over the test, or a few to several may be mounted on a spine, especially spines near the ambulacral grooves (Fig. 97*D*), or they may be arranged in clusters; especially the crossed type is commonly found in numbers mounted on a retractile fleshy sheath that encircles spine bases (Fig. 97*E*). In *Pycnopodia* bouquets of pedicellariae on fleshy stalks occur in association with a spine

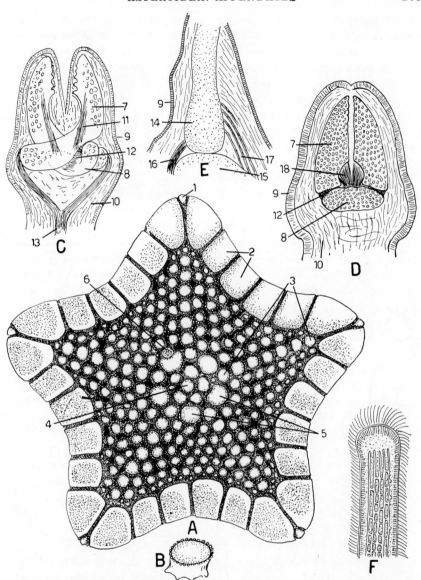

Fig. 103.—Endoskeleton (concluded), external appendages. *A, Tosia australis*, with primitive ossicle arrangement. *B*, one of the paxillae of *A*. *C*, crossed type of pedicellaria, *Asterias*. *D*, straight type of pedicellaria, *Asterias*. *E*, adambulacral spine, showing muscles. *F*, vibratile spine. (*E, F, after Cuénot*, 1887, 1891.) 1, terminal plate; 2, supramarginal plates; 3, row of carinals; 4, central plate; 5, interradial plates (corresponding to genitals); 6, madreporite; 7, valve; 8, basal piece; 9, epidermis; 10, connective tissue; 11, long adductor muscle; 12, abductor muscle; 13, ligament; 14, base of adambulacral spine; 15, adambulacral ossicle; 16, depressor muscle; 17, elevator muscle; 18, short adductors.

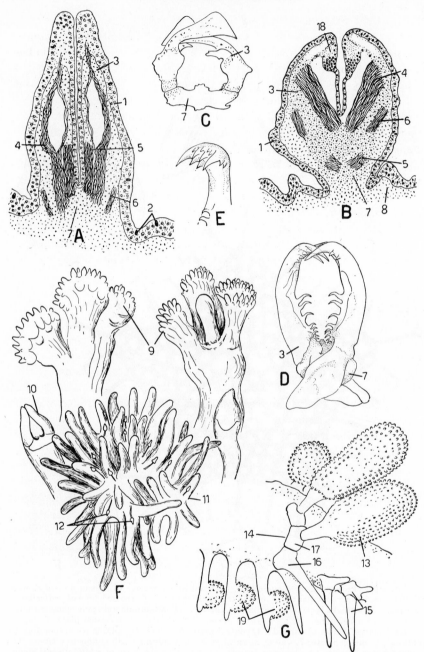

FIG. 104.—Pedicellariae (continued). *A*, longitudinal section of straight pedicellaria. *B*, longitudinal section of crossed pedicellaria. (*A*, *B*, *after Smith*, 1937.) *C*, furcate pedicellaria of *Pisaster* (*after Fisher*, 1930). *D*, strongly toothed crossed pedicellaria of brisingid *Labidiaster*. *E*, valve end of *D*. *F*, clusters of pedicellariae and branched papula of *Pycnopodia* (*after Fisher*, 1928). *G*, small bit of arm of brisingid, *Odinella nutrix*,

(Fig. 104*F*). Strands of pedicellariae (Fig. 105*C*) are found near the ambulacral groove in *Pisaster*. In the very curious, multirayed, antarctic brooding star *Odinella nutrix* (Fig. 150), belonging to the Brisingidae, many of the spines along the slender arms are completely encased in a fleshy sac covered with minute pedicellariae (Fisher, 1940). These large sacs form conspicuous bulbous projections along the arms (Fig. 104*G*).

Sessile pedicellariae, characteristic of the Phanerozonia, are simply groups of two or more movable spines attached directly by muscle and connective fibers to one or more skeletal ossicles. When formed of a cluster of spines borne on adjacent ossicles and meeting over the suture, they are termed *spiniform* if the spines are long and *pectinate* if they are short and curved (Fig. 105*D*), especially if arranged somewhat in two opposed rows (Fig. 105*E*). A pedicellaria formed of a cluster of spines borne on a single ossicle is called *fasciculate*. Sessile pedicellariae consisting of three jaws, simulating an echinoid pedicellaria, also occur. Sessile pedicellariae may become two-valved or *valvulate* by the sidewise fusion of groups of spinelets into two valve-like pieces.

Alveolar pedicellariae are similar to the foregoing but are partly sunk into an endoskeletal depression or alveolus that serves for the attachment of the muscle fibers operating the valves, generally two in number. In a common type, termed *bivalved*, found in *Hippasteria*, the two jaws are horizontally elongated and give the impression of a minute clam (Fig. 105*F*). In the *spatulate* type the jaws are longer and broadened at the ends (Fig. 105*H, J*). In the *excavate* type, characteristic of the Linckiidae (Fig. 105*G*), the elongated jaws resemble a pair of tongs and fit into depressions in the alveolus when opened. A type with erect, curved jaws and powerful muscles, also found in *Hippasteria*, has been described by Haubold (1933; Fig. 106*B*).

*c. Papulae.*—These are thin respiratory evaginations of the body wall that emerge between skeletal ossicles, either singly or in numbers, when sufficient space exists between adjacent ossicles. They may occur over the entire surface or be restricted to the aboral surface, as usually in Phanerozonia, or be limited to scattered papular areas or papularia (Fig. 98*A, C*). They are usually simple evaginations but sometimes branched, as in *Luidia* (Fig. 98*E*) or *Pycnopodia* (Fig. 104*F*). Histologically they resemble the body wall but differ in the thinness of the dermal layer and the lack of calcareous deposits; to the inner side of the dermis is found a muscle layer of outer longitudinal and inner circular fibers, con-

antarctic, showing clusters of pedicellariae. (*D, E, G, after Fisher*, 1941.) 1, epidermis; 2, gland cell; 3, valve ossicle; 4, long adductor muscle; 5, short adductor muscle; 6, abductor muscle; 7, basal piece; 8, connective tissue; 9, cluster of pedicellariae; 10, large straight pedicellariae; 11, papula; 12, small pedicellariae on papula; 13, pedicellariae on bulbous sheath of spines; 14, skeletal arch; 15, adambulacral ossicles and spines; 16, inframarginal ossicle and spine (sheath removed from latter); 17, supramarginal ossicle; 18, nervous expansion; 19, tufts of pedicellariae on adambulacral spines.

ferring contractility on the papulae.    The lumen is lined with coelomic flagellated epithelium.

*d. Podia.*—As already indicated, the podia occur in two or apparently four rows in each ambulacral groove. They are provided with well-developed terminal disks or suckers except in the phanerozonic suborders Cribellosa and Paxillosa (families Porcellanasteridae, Goniopectinidae, Astropectinidae, and Luidiidae), where they terminate with bluntly rounded tips.    According to Fisher (1911), the lack of terminal disks may not be regarded as an adaptation to life on muddy bottoms, and Tortonese (1947) states that *Astropecten* can climb glass walls and hang onto them for long periods, although more easily jarred loose than asteroids with suckered podia.    There is little histological difference between the two types of podia.    The row of podia ends in a terminal tentacle, and the last few podia before the terminal tentacle lack suckers and seem to act in a sensory capacity.    The podia, as evaginations of the body wall, share its histological construction but usually lack calcareous deposits (Fig. 106*A*).    Beneath the cuticle is an epidermis of elongated cells, each containing a supporting elastic fibril; the epidermal cells are interspersed with both types of gland cells and with sensory cells.    Below the epidermis lies a thick nervous layer of outer circular and inner longitudinal fibers, and these are further subdivided according to J. Smith (1937). The nervous layer forms a thickened strand along one side of the podium, the side facing the mouth, and also is thickened as a ring just below the sucker.    To the inner side of the nervous layer of the sucker is the usual connective-tissue layer that forms a flat plate in the center of the sucker, from which connective-tissue strands spray throughout the sucker in an arborescent manner, reaching into the epidermis up to the cuticle (Fig. 107*A*).    This spray of connective tissue is wanting in podia that lack suckers (Tortonese, 1947; Fig. 107*B*).    The connective-tissue layer is followed on its inner side by a stratum of longitudinal muscles that thins to a flat plate in the sucker.    Finally, the lumen of the podium is lined by peritoneum.

**6. Muscular System.**—As already related, the body wall contains on its coelomic side a muscular stratum of outer circular and inner longitudinal fibers (Fig. 99*G*).    These layers are on the whole rather thin and weak, but the longitudinal layer is thickened into a definite strand that extends from the disk center along the median aboral line of each ray, often splitting up into three strands in the more distal parts of the rays (Fig. 106*D*).    A system of muscles operates the ambulacral grooves. Each pair of ambulacral ossicles is connected by an *upper* or aboral and a *lower* or oral *transverse* muscle (Fig. 108*A,B*).    Contraction of the upper transverse muscle causes the outer ends of the ambulacral ossicles to diverge, thus widening the ambulacral groove, and contraction of the lower

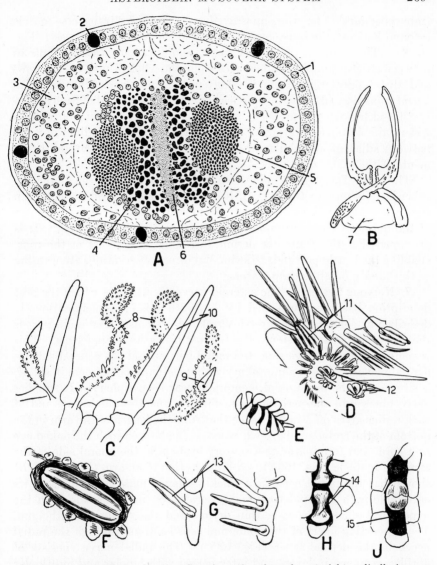

Fig. 105.—Pedicellariae (continued). *A*, section through a straight pedicellaria near base (*after Smith*, 1937). *B*, type of crossed pedicellaria of a brisingid. *C*, strands of pedicellariae of *Pisaster* (*after Fisher*, 1930). *D*, sessile pedicellariae of *Astropecten*. *E*, pectinate pedicellaria of *Astropecten*. *F*, bivalved pedicellaria of *Hippasteria* (*after Fisher*, 1911). *G*, tong-shaped pedicellariae of *Luidia*. *H*, spatulate pedicellaria of *Peltaster*, open. *J*, same as *H*, closed. (*D, E, H, J, after Fisher*, 1919.) 1, epidermis; 2, mucous gland; 3, section of valve, decalcified; 4, inner long adductor; 5, outer short adductor; 6, nervous cushion; 7, basal piece; 8, strand of pedicellariae; 9, large pedicellaria; 10, adambulacral spines; 11, spiniform pedicellariae; 12, pectinate pedicellariae; 13, tong pedicellariae; 14, valves of spatulate pedicellariae; 15, depression.

transverse muscles has the opposite effect. The lower transverse muscle is found between the hyponeural canals and the radial water vessel (Fig. 108*B*). There are further short *upper* and *lower longitudinal* muscles between adjacent ambulacral ossicles along the whole length of each row, and their contraction tends to shorten the ambulacral groove. The *lateral transverse* ambulacral muscles connect the outer end of each ambulacral ossicle with the adjacent adambulacral ossicle; their contraction widens the ambulacral groove. Finally, there are longitudinal muscles between adjacent adambulacral ossicles that would aid in lateral movements of the rays.

The family Benthopectinidae, comprising the whole of the phanerozonic suborder Notomyota (Ludwig, 1910), differs from all other asteroids in the presence of a pair of dorsal muscles in each ray, extending from some of the more proximal supramarginal plates to the tip of the ray. It is presumed that these muscles permit thrashing movements of the rays, enabling the benthopectinids to swim, but direct observations are wanting as this family inhabits deep waters.

**7. Nervous System.**—The asteroid nervous system, of which the best description has been furnished by J. Smith (1937), is conventionally described as comprised of three interrelated systems. The main part is the oral or ectoneural system, situated just beneath the epidermis. This is composed of the nerve ring, the radial nerves, and the general subepidermal plexus. The circumoral nerve ring, actually pentagonal in shape, is situated in the peristomial membrane near its periphery. It supplies nerve fibers into the peristomial membrane and the esophagus, and at each radius gives off a radial nerve that runs the length of the arm in the bottom of the ambulacral groove, where it can be seen with the naked eye as a cord, and terminates as a sensory cushion in the aboral side of the terminal tentacle (Fig. 106*E*). A cross section of an arm (Fig. 108*A*, *B*) shows that the radial nerve is a thick V-shaped mass continuous on its outer side with the epidermis and separated on its inner side from the hyponeural sinus only by a thin dermis and the coelomic epithelium. The supporting fibers of the epidermal cells continue through the radial nerve to the dermal layer (Fig. 100*C*). The radial nerve consists of fibrillae arranged in layers and interspersed with bipolar and multipolar ganglion cells. The radial nerves are continuous with a general subepidermal plexus spread throughout the entire body wall and innervating all the body-wall appendages. Its arrangement in the podia was already described. In general, according to Smith (1937), this plexus is very thin over most parts of the body but is thickened in connection with the various appendages.

At the outer margins of the ambulacral grooves at the location of the outer ends of the ambulacral ossicles, the subepidermal plexus is thickened into a cord extending the length of the arm on each side, called by Cuénot

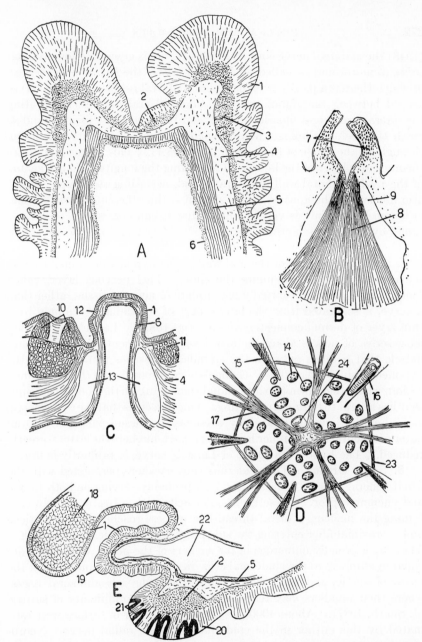

FIG. 106.—Appendages (continued), muscular system. *A*, longitudinal section through the tip of a podium of *Marthasterias glacialis* (*after Smith*, 1937, slightly altered). *B*, alveolate type of pedicellaria of *Hippasteria* (*after Haubold*, 1933). *C*, section through a papula (*after Cuénot*, 1887). *D*, aboral wall of disk of *Culcita*, seen from the inside (*after Ludwig*, 1880). *E*, longitudinal section through the terminal tentacle (*after Hamann*, 1883). 1, epidermis; 2, nervous layer; 3, nerve ring; 4, connective tissue; 5, longitudinal muscle layer; 6, coelomic lining; 7, valves of pedicellaria; 8, adductor muscles; 9, alveolus; 10, ossicles of tubercles; 11, endoskeletal ossicle; 12, papula; 13, ring cavity in dermis around base of papula; 14, papular areas; 15, interbrachial septum; 16, stone canal; 17, longitudinal muscle strands of median aboral wall of rays; 18, terminal ossicle; 19, terminal tentacle; 20, optic cushion; 21, pigment-cup ocelli; 22, end of radial water canal; 23, aboral haemal ring; 24, intestine.

(1948) the *marginal* nerve cord (Fig. 108*A*).    This gives off a longitudinal series of motor nerves, called by J. Smith (1937) the *lateral motor* nerves, of which there is a pair to each pair of ambulacral ossicles.    These nerves ascend between the ambulacral and adambulacral ossicles, innervating the lateral transverse muscles that extend between these ossicles, and so reach the coelomic lining where they form a plexus beneath this lining throughout the whole of the coelom (Fig. 108*A*).    This plexus innervates the muscular layer of the body wall, including the longitudinal thickening in the median aboral wall of the rays, and, according to Cuénot (1948), also innervates the gonads.    This system is thus the entoneural system, although it certainly is very doubtful that it can correspond to what is called by this name in crinoids.

There is further present a hyponeural system in the form of a nervous layer in the lateral part of the oral wall of the hyponeural sinus, beneath the coelomic epithelium lining the sinus.    This nervous layer, called *Lange's nerve*, although actually it is a plate of nervous tissue rather than a nerve, is separated from the lateral part of the radial nerve only by a thin layer of dermal connective tissue (Fig. 108*B*).    Lange's nerve gives off a series of nerves along the arm into the adjacent lower transverse muscle that extends between the ambulacral ossicles in the roof of the hyponeural sinus (Fig. 108*B*).    Lange's nerves continue to the peristomial region, where they form five interradial thickenings in the floor of ring sinus that lies aboral to the main nerve ring.    One perceives that the radial nerve, as in holothurians, is divided by a connective-tissue partition into an outer ectoneural and an inner hyponeural part, but here the latter is greatly reduced.    The hyponeural part, or Lange's nerve, is primarily motor.

**8. Sense Organs.**—The epidermis is everywhere permeated with the usual general type of neurosensory cell, probably serving as both tango- and chemoreceptor.    These are slender cells with a fusiform body containing the nucleus, a distal thread-like process reaching to the cuticle, and a proximal fiber entering the subepidermal nerve plexus (Fig. 100*C*). They are especially numerous in the suckers of the podia, where they are equal in numbers to the epidermal cells, in the thickened epidermis at the bases of spines and pedicellariae, and along the adambulacral region where their numbers may reach 70,000 per square millimeter of surface (J. Smith, 1937).    About 4000 per square millimeter of surface were estimated by this author in the epidermis over the radial nerve.    Neurosensory cells are also very abundant in the epidermis of the sides and oral surface of the terminal tentacle.

The only other sensory provision of asteroids is the optic cushion at the base of the oral surface of the terminal tentacle; the thick epidermis here contains numerous photoreceptors, which typically are of the sort called pigment-cup ocelli (Fig. 106*E*).    Each cup is covered externally

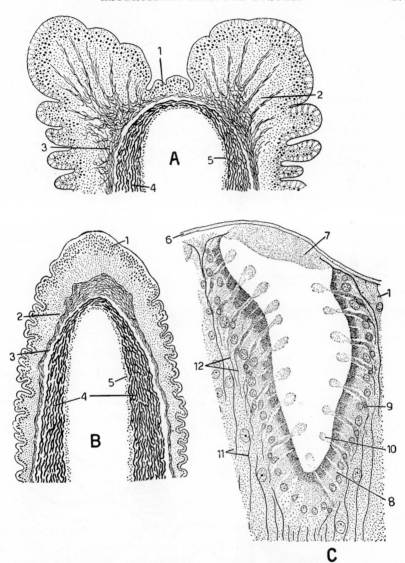

Fig. 107.—Appendages (concluded), nervous system. *A*, longutudinal section through the end of the podium of *Marthasterias*, showing connective-tissue spray. *B*, same as *A* for *Astropecten*, lacks sucker. (*A, B, after Tortonese,* 1947.) *C*, lengthwise section of one of the pigment-cup ocelli of the optic cushion of *Marthasterias* (*after Smith,* 1937). 1, epidermis; 2, location of nervous layer; 3, connective tissue; 4, longitudinal muscle layer; 5, coelomic lining; 6, cuticle; 7, lens; 8, pigment cells; 9, retinal cells; 10, end bulb of retinal cell; 11, epidermal fibrils; 12, nerve fiber.

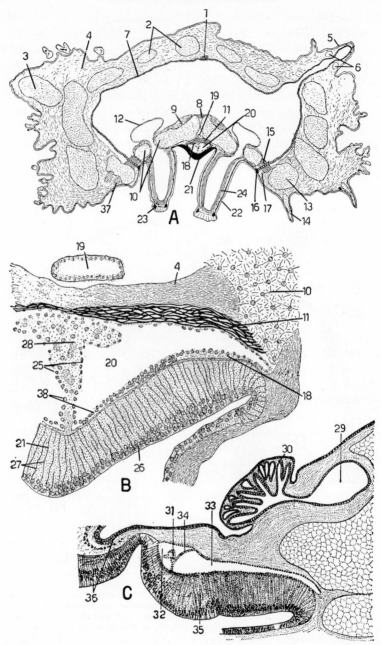

FIG. 108.—Nervous system (concluded), water-vascular system. *A*, section through the arm of *Marthasterias*, nervous system black, motor part cross-hatched. *B*, section through the radial nerve and associated parts of *A*. (*A*, *B*, *after Smith*, 1937.) *C*, section through the edge of the peristome of *Henricia*, mouth to left (*after Hayashi*, 1935). 1, longitudinal muscle thickening; 2, endoskeletal ossicles; 3, ossicle of tubercle; 4, connective tissue; 5, papula; 6, ring cavity at base of papula; 7, entoneural nerve plexus under coelomic

with a cuticle beneath which is found in many species a lens formed by the epidermis. The lens may be wanting. The cup wall consists of epidermal cells, altered into a shorter, stouter shape and filled distally with red pigment granules, and of retinal cells, disposed between the pigment cells. The retinal cells are elongated cells with a distal bulbous enlargement projecting into the cavity of the cup (Fig. 107*C*) and a proximal fiber passing into the underlying radial nerve. The number of ocelli in one optic cushion ranges from 80 to 200 in some common species and increases with age. In some asteroids, as *Astropecten*, pigment cups are lacking and the retinal cells are strewn throughout the cushion (Pfeffer, 1901). Photoreceptors are wanting in some asteroids of deep water, although present in others living at similar depths (Meurer, 1907). Peskin (1951) has shown that the pigment of the asteroid ocellus is photolabile, bleaching at certain wavelengths.

**9. Coelom and Coelomocytes.**—The interior of the asteroid is occupied by a spacious coelom that surrounds the digestive tract and gonads; there are also a number of minor coelomic compartments. The stone canal accompanied by the axial gland is enclosed in a tubular coelomic space, the *axial sinus,* and the latter is in turn enclosed in the inner edge of the interbrachial septum of that interradius (Fig. 113*A*). At its aboral end the axial sinus communicates with the ampulla of the stone canal (Fig. 112*B*) and terminates in the genital or aboral sinus, a tubular sinus in the form of a pentagon that is located on the inside of the aboral wall of the disk (Fig. 114*B*). The genital sinus gives off to each gonad a genital branch that enlarges into a sac enclosing the gonad. The genital sinus usually does not make a full circuit as it is incomplete in the region of the stone canal. At its oral end the axial sinus opens into a large tubular ring sinus that lies to the aboral side of the nerve ring and just to the inner side of the ossicles of the mouth frame (Fig. 108*C*). This oral ring sinus obviously corresponds to the peribuccal sinus of other echinoderms and is in fact the hyponeural ring sinus. It is divided by an oblique partition into a smaller inner and a larger outer ring (Fig. 108*C*), and it is the inner ring that receives the axial sinus. From the outer hyponeural ring sinus a radial hyponeural sinus is given off into each arm, and this, as already seen, lies to the aboral side of the radial nerve (Fig. 108*A, B*). The hyponeural radial sinus is bisected by a vertical partition continuous

---

lining; 8, upper transverse ambulacral muscle; 9, longutudinal ambulacral muscle; 10, ambulacral ossicle; 11, lower transverse ambulacral muscle; 12, ampulla of podium; 13, adambulacral ossicle; 14, adambulacral spine; 15, lateral transverse ambulacral muscle; 16, marginal nerve; 17, marginal sinus; 18, hyponeural nervous system; 19, radial water canal; 20, radial hyponeural sinus; 21, radial nerve; 22, podium; 23, nerve ring below sucker of podium; 24, muscle layer of podium; 25, septum dividing hyponeural radial sinus; 26, epidermis of radial nerve; 27, supporting epidermal fibers of radial nerve; 28, radial haemal sinus; 29, water ring; 30, Tiedemann's body; 31, oral haemal ring; 32, inner ring of hyponeural ring sinus; 33, outer ring of hyponeural ring sinus; 34, septum of hyponeural ring sinus; 35, nerve ring; 36, peristome; 37, longitudinal adambulacral muscles; 38, coelomic lining.

with the partition that subdivides the hyponeural ring sinus, but this is very imperfect, permitting ample communication between the two halves of the hyponeural radial sinus. Channels from the latter extend laterally to a marginal sinus (Fig. 108*A*) that runs lengthwise the arms on each side just aboral to the marginal nerve cord noted above. Fine channels also extend from the radial hyponeural sinus into the podia. There is also communication between these various channels and the spaces in the dermis of the body wall, although these latter spaces are not regarded as of coelomic origin since they are without definite lining. All the true coelomic spaces are lined with the same flagellated cuboidal epithelium.

The various tubular coelomic sinuses just mentioned are often regarded in books as constituting a "perihaemal" system. They do in fact enclose channels of the haemal system, but the term perihaemal is confusing and is here avoided.

Asteroids have a much less varied assortment of coelomocytes than do echinoids and holothuroids. There are two main types (Théel, 1919; Kindred, 1924; Lison, 1930): amoebocytes with ordinary slender pseudopods and amoebocytes with petaloid pseudopods. These are practically identical with the same types in echinoids (page 461). There is general agreement that the two sorts are phases of the same cell. This cell is highly phagocytic and will ingest injected ink or other inert particles and exit with them, mainly by way of the papulae (Durham, 1888). Coelomocytes with colorless spherules are also apparently present in asteroids in small numbers.

**10. Digestive System.**—The digestive tract of asteroids differs altogether from that of the preceding classes. It is straight and very short, extending from the oral to the aboral side of the disk. The mouth, situated in the center of the peristomial membrane, is provided with a sphincter muscle, also with radial fibers, derived from the circular and longitudinal layers, respectively, of the body-wall musculature. The mouth leads into a short, wide esophagus which in a few species gives off 10 esophageal pouches with greatly folded walls (Cuénot, 1887; Fig. 109*C*). The esophagus passes into the stomach, a broad sac that fills the interior of the disk and is typically divided by a horizontal constriction into a voluminous oral part, the *cardiac* stomach, with folded outpouched walls, and a much smaller, flattened aboral part, the *pyloric* stomach (Fig. 109*A*), to which are attached 10 glandular appendages, variously known as pyloric caeca, digestive glands, brachial caeca, hepatic caeca, etc. In some asteroids, as *Henricia* (Fig. 110*A*), the stomach is not very definitely divided into cardiac and pyloric portions, and in the Echinasteridae and Asterinidae in general the stomach sends out a pouch or diverticulum, known as Tiedemann's pouches, to the oral side of each of the pyloric caeca (Fig. 115*A*). In each radius the cardiac stomach is attached to the ambulacral ridge by two mesenteries (Fig. 109*D*), the *gastric ligaments.* These have a triangular shape with one short side extending centrally along the ridge and a longer side extending peripherally. The apex of the triangle is attached to the wall of the cardiac stomach by tough connective tissue forming what is called the *nodule* by Anderson (1954). Embryology shows that the gastric ligaments are of mesenterial nature, and histological examination proves that they consist mainly of connective tissue, with a small admixture of muscle fibers. Therefore they are clearly not retractor muscles, as usually stated, but act rather to anchor the cardiac stomach (Anderson, 1954). This author has shown that at the nodules the connective-tissue fibers concentrated at the free edges of the gastric ligaments pass into the stomach wall and run beneath the coelomic covering branching extensively, chiefly in the direction of the mouth, and contributing fibers to the muscular and connective-tissue layers of the stomach wall. Anderson has also found in *Asterias forbesi* a system of branching grooves on the internal surface of the stomach extending inward from the esophagus and more or less paralleling the fibrous system just mentioned. Besides the gastric ligaments, the stomach is attached to the disk walls and interbrachial septa by other, irregularly arranged mesenterial strands.

There are two pyloric caeca in each arm, each suspended from the aboral wall of the arm by two longitudinal mesenteries (Fig. 109*E*) that enclose between them a coelomic space continuous at its central end with the general coelom of the disk. The length of the caeca relative to arm length varies greatly in different asteroids. A large and conspicuous duct runs along each caecum and enters the pyloric stomach, either separately (Fig. 110*A*) or after union with its fellow duct of the same arm; in the latter case the five ducts opening radially into the pyloric stomach confer upon it a pentagonal shape. Each caecum is composed of a longitudinal series of lobules along both sides of the duct, and these are supplied by lateral branches of the duct. From the pyloric stomach the very short intestine ascends to the anus. Just as it leaves the stomach, the intestine is provided with diverticula or caeca, called the rectal or intestinal caeca, sometimes rectal sac, that lie upon the aboral surface of the pyloric stomach. These intestinal caeca vary from two- or three-branched appendages (Fig. 109*B*), as in *Asterias*, to numerous diverticula surrounding the intestine, as in *Henricia* (Fig. 110*A*); or five single or five pairs of interradial caeca may occur, as in *Culcita* (Fig. 110*B*), attached to the intestine by long ducts. By some the intestine distal to the caeca is termed rectum. Anus, intestine, and intestinal caeca are lacking in the phanerozonic families Porcellanasteridae and Luidiidae, and the anus, but not the intestine or caeca, is wanting in some genera of the Astropectinidae.

Histologically, the digestive tract resembles the body wall, and its layers are continuous with those of the peristomial membrane. Charac-

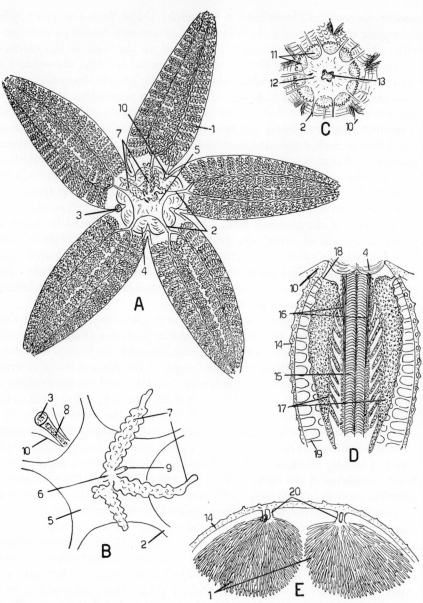

FIG. 109.—Digestive tract. *A*, dissection of *Asterias forbesi*, showing digestive tract, aboral view. *B*, enlarged view of pyloric stomach and intestinal caeca of *A*. *C*, *Echinaster* with esophageal pouches (*after Cuénot*, 1887). *D*, arm of *Asterias forbesi*, after removal of pyloric caeca, showing gonads and stomach ligaments, aboral view. *E*, section through arm of *Asterias forbesi*, aboral part, showing mesenteries of pyloric caeca. 1, pyloric caeca; 2, pyloric duct; 3, madreporite; 4, cardiac stomach; 5, pyloric stomach; 6, intestine; 7, intestinal caeca; 8, axial gland; 9, anus; 10, intrabrachial septum; 11, esophageal pouches; 12, stomach; 13, cut intestine; 14, cut body wall; 15, ambulacral ridge; 16, gastric ligaments; 17, gonad; 18, gonoduct; 19, skeletal arches; 20, mesenteries of pyloric caeca.

teristic of the latter are a tall epidermis, a well-defined subepidermal nervous layer continuous with the adjacent nerve ring, and a connective-tissue layer devoid of ossicles (Fig. 110*C*). Its muscle layer, thin peripherally, thickens toward the mouth, where its circular fibers become concentric with the mouth, forming the sphincter already mentioned, and its longitudinal fibers take on a radial disposition, acting to expand the mouth. The peristomial epidermis continues as the lining epithelium of the esophagus, composed of tall flagellated cells interspersed with mucous glands and granular glands similar to the muriform glands of the body surface. The nervous layer of the esophagus is broad and is said by some to be thickened here into a nerve ring. This is followed by the usual connective-tissue and muscular layers, covered on the coelomic side by the coelomic epithelium. The wall of the cardiac stomach (Fig. 110*D*) is similar, with a very tall epithelium containing mucous and granular glands and a thick nervous layer. Anderson (1954) notes that in the cardiac stomach of *Asterias forbesi* a lining epithelium of typical appearance is limited to the bottom of the grooves of the stomach wall, whereas the ridges between these grooves are clothed with an altered epithelium of cells provided with two to six flagella and very elongated dense nuclei and lacking a brush border. It is surmised that these altered epithelial cells may be of sensory nature. In the pyloric stomach the epithelium is decreased in height, gland cells are less numerous, the subepithelial nervous plexus is much diminished, and the muscle layers are weakened. This general diminution continues into the intestine (Fig. 111*B*), where, however, the connective-tissue layer is thickened.

The histology of the pyloric caeca is complicated and has been recently elucidated by Anderson (1953) in an article unfortunately illustrated only by microphotographs, not reproducible. The caecal wall consists of the same layers as the rest of the digestive tract but the lining epithelium composes most of the thickness of the wall (Fig. 111*A*). This is a very tall, flagellated epithelium that varies in thickness in various areas of the caecum and is made up of four types of cells. Some of the cells act only as current producers, and these are characteristic of the pyloric duct and its lateral branches. These current producers are liberally interspersed with mucous glands that also occur, less abundantly, everywhere throughout the caecum. The main tissue of the caecum, apart from the current-producing areas, is composed of granular and storage cells, with some mucous cells. The granular or secretory cells are densely filled basally with granules, believed to be of enzymatic nature. The storage cells are filled, except distally, with droplets of lipid substances and also contain a little glycogen and some sort of polysaccharide-protein complex. These food reserves in the storage cells disappear in animals subjected to prolonged starvation. The characteristic greenish-yellow color of the pyloric

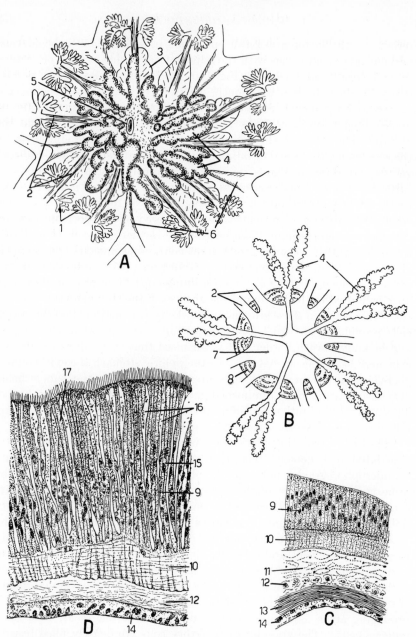

Fig. 110.—Digestive system (continued). *A*, dissected *Henricia*, aboral view, with many intestinal caeca and 10 pyloric ducts. *B*, digestive tract of *Culcita*, aboral view, with 10 pairs of intestinal caeca and 10 pyloric ducts (*after Ludwig and Hamann*, 1899). *C*, section through the peristome of *Henricia*. *D*, section through the stomach of *Henricia*. (*A, C, D, after Hayashi*, 1935.) 1, lobules of pyloric caeca; 2, pyloric ducts; 3, lobes of stomach; 4, intestinal caeca; 5, cut-off intestine; 6, interbrachial septa; 7, pyloric stomach; 8, cardiac stomach; 9, epidermis; 10, nervous layer; 11, connective tissue; 12, longitudinal muscle layer; 13, circular muscle layer; 14, coelomic epithelium; 15, lining epithelium; 16, mucous gland cell; 17, granular gland cell.

280

caeca is attributed by Anderson to a pigment in the distal part of the storage cells. Sections of the intestinal caeca (Fig. 111C, D) show a greatly folded epithelium containing mucous and other gland cells, while the remaining layers are rather reduced in width.

**11. Water-vascular System.**—This system has the same construction as in the previously considered Eleutherozoa. The madreporite, sunk into the periphery of the disk in an interradial position, is a rounded calcareous plaque marked with numerous furrows that give it a characteristic appearance (Fig. 113B) under magnification. In the bottom of these furrows are found a number of pores, each of which leads into a pore canal passing inward in the substance of the madreporite. There may be around 200 pores and pore canals. The latter unite to collecting canals that open into an ampulla beneath the madreporite (Fig. 112B). From the ampulla the stone canal proceeds in the oral direction and opens into the water ring. The water ring is located just to the inner side of the peristomial ring of ossicles and directly above (aboral to) the outer hyponeural ring sinus (Fig. 108C). To its inner side the ring canal gives off interradially five pairs of small, irregularly shaped bodies, called Tiedemann's bodies, that rest upon the peristomial ring of ossicles (Fig. 113A). They are present in all asteroids, but in some one is missing at the site of entry of the stone canal into the water ring, leaving a total of nine bodies. In many asteroids, the water ring also gives off to its inner side in the interradial positions one or more polian vesicles, similar to those of holothuroids, which hang freely into the coelomic cavity of the disk. A single polian vesicle may be present or one in each interradius, except that of the madreporite (CD), or two may occur in CD and one each in the other interradii, or two to four may be given off in each interradius (Fig. 113E, F). Usually those in one interradius spring from the water ring by a common canal. Polian vesicles are altogether wanting in the families Asteriidae and Echinasteridae. From its outer surface the water ring gives off a radial water canal into each arm that runs the length of the arm and terminates as the lumen of the terminal tentacle. In the arm the radial water canal runs immediately to the oral side of the ambulacral ridge, between this ridge and the lower transverse ambulacral muscles (Fig. 108A, B). Between successive muscles of this series, the radial water canal gives off on each side a lateral or podial branch, provided with a valve, for each podium. The podial branch, after reaching the ambulacral pore between successive ambulacral ossicles, forks at right angles to continue as the lumen of the podium, on one hand, and as the lumen of the ampulla of the podium, on the other hand (Fig. 160A). The ampullae are typically rounded sacs readily seen in one or two rows to either side of the ambulacral ridge in the opened asteroid. There is usually one sac to each podium, con-

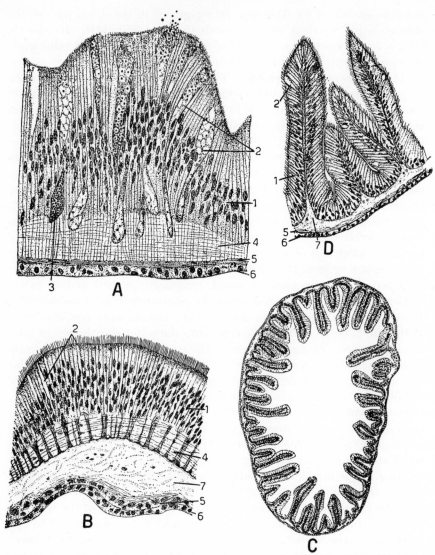

Fig. 111.—Histology of the digestive tract. *A*, section through the pyloric caeca. *B*, section through the intestine proximal to the intestinal caeca. *C*, section through one of the intestinal caeca. *D*, enlarged view of small part of *C*. (All of *Henricia, after Hayashi*, 1935.) 1, epithelial cells; 2, mucous glands; 3, granular glands; 4, nervous layer; 5, muscle fibers; 6, coelomic epithelium; 7, connective tissue.

tinuous with its podium through the corresponding ambulacral pore (Fig. 108*A*). However, in many asteroids the ampulla is bilobed to varying degrees (Fig. 113*H*), and the constriction may be carried so far that each podium appears to be supplied with two ampullae.

The madreporite is clothed externally with a tall, flagellated epithelium that continues into the furrows but diminishes to a cuboidal shape (Fig. 112*D*, *E*) in the pore canals; the stone canal is again lined with very tall flagellated cells (Fig. 112*C*) underlain by connective tissue heavily impregnated with calcareous deposits arranged to form rings. The stone canal is a simple tube in young asteroids, but later a ridge develops along one side of the interior; this may remain as a ridge (Fig. 113*C*) but usually develops further, commonly bifurcating into two vertical lamellae whose edges are more or less rolled into scrolls, so that in most asteroids a section through the stone canal appears, as in Fig. 113*G*. Other more complicated variations occur. The ridge may meet the opposite wall, dividing the interior into two tubes, and each of these may be provided with a pair of scrolls (Fig. 113*D*); or the lumen may become subdivided into a number of channels (Fig. 113*J*). Apparently these various arrangements are concerned with producing a circulation in the stone canal. The epithelium is said to be shorter, with shorter flagella, on the scrolls, ridges, and partitions than on the primary wall.

The polian vesicles are lined by a flattened epithelium, followed by a heavy layer of circular muscles; to the outer side of this occurs a stratum of connective tissue containing longitudinal muscle fibers in the larger vesicles, and the whole is clothed externally with coelomic epithelium. Tiedemann's bodies are hollow with a greatly folded interior (Fig. 108*C*). Svetlov (1916) investigated their structure in 16 species of asteroids and found that they are lined by a columnar to flattened epithelium, surrounded by connective tissue containing some muscle fibers and covered externally with coelomic epithelium. The lumen contains coelomocytes and coagulated fluid. The ring and radial water canals are lined by flagellated coelomic epithelium and consist otherwise of connective tissue generally devoid of muscle fibers but sometimes containing a few. On the other hand, the ampullae are highly muscular, having a layer of muscle fibers outside the lining epithelium. According to J. Smith (1947), the muscle fibers run circularly in the bifurcated ampullae of *Astropecten* (Figs. 113*H*, 160*B*) but longitudinally in the simple ampullae of *Asterias* (Fig. 160*A*). The muscle layer is followed by connective-tissue fibers running at right angles to the muscle fibers, and the surface is clothed with coelomic epithelium.

**12. Axial Complex.**—This complex is well developed in asteroids. The axial sinus is a thin-walled tubular coelomic cavity that contains the stone canal and the axial gland, both fastened to its wall close together by mesenteries. The whole complex is enclosed in or intimately attached to the interbrachial septum of interradius CD (Fig. 113*A*). At its oral end the axial sinus opens into the smaller inner ring of the hyponeural ring sinus, and at its aboral end it opens into the genital sinus, further into the ampulla of the stone canal (Fig. 112*B*). The axial gland is an

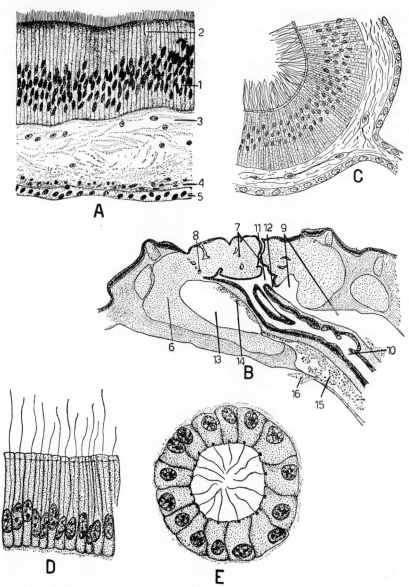

Fig. 112.—Digestive system (concluded), water-vascular system. *A*, section of distal part of the intestine (rectum). *B*, vertical section through the madreporite and under-lying parts. *C*, cross section through the stone canal (*after Hamann*, 1885). *D*, epithelium of madreporic groove. *E*, cross section of a pore canal. (*A*, *B*, *D*, *E*, *Henricia*, *after Hayashi*, 1935.) 1, epithelium; 2, mucous gland; 3, connective tissue; 4, muscle layer; 5, coelomic epithelium; 6, madreporite; 7, pore canals; 8, collecting canal; 9, axial sinus; 10, stone canal; 11, ampulla; 12, opening of ampulla into axial sinus; 13, dorsal sac; 14, process of axial gland in dorsal sac; 15, axial gland; 16, gastric haemal tufts.

elongated spongy body, mostly brownish or purplish in color, referred to in the literature by a variety of names, as heart, ovoid gland, dorsal organ, septal organ, brown gland, etc. At its oral end the axial gland thins and terminates in the septum that subdivides the hyponeural ring sinus. At its aboral end, the axial gland has an aboral extension or terminal process, similar to the terminal process of the gland in echinoids, that is lodged in a separate, closed sac, variously called *terminal sac, dorsal sac,* or *madreporic vesicle,* said to be contractile. This sac is situated under the madreporite, close to the ampulla of the stone canal, but has no communication with the ampulla.

The axial gland is clothed externally with peritoneum. The interior consists of connective tissue outlining numerous spaces that contain irregularly arranged cells of the nature of coelomocytes (Hamann, 1885; Cuénot, 1887; Fig. 114*D*). In *Henricia*, however, Hayashi (1935) found the coelomocytes scattered throughout the connective tissue (Fig. 114*C*). The color of the gland comes from granules in the coelomocytes.

**13. Haemal System.**—This system is inconspicuous in asteroids and has been elucidated mainly by means of serial sections. It is for the most part enclosed in coelomic spaces, whence, as already mentioned, the latter are often confusingly called perihaemal spaces or sinuses. The main or *oral haemal ring* runs in the septum that subdivides the hyponeural or peribuccal ring sinus (Fig. 108*C*). It gives off a *radial haemal sinus* into each arm, and this sinus is located in the septum that subdivides the hyponeural radial sinus of each arm (Fig. 108*B*). The radial haemal sinuses give off branches into the podia. From the oral haemal ring a haemal plexus ascends in the axial gland, the cavities of which are in effect haemal channels, and enters the *aboral haemal ring* which runs inside the aboral or genital coelomic sinus and gives off haemal branches to the gonads inside the coelomic branches to the gonads (Fig. 114*B*). Close to its junction with the aboral haemal ring, the haemal plexus of the axial gland receives haemal strands, known as the *gastric haemal tufts,* which come from sinuses in the wall of the cardiac stomach and cross the general coelom to reach the axial gland. There are generally two gastric haemal tufts, but they vary from one to four. They are the only part of the haemal system not enclosed in a coelomic channel. According to some authors (Cuénot, 1896, 1901) there is a haemal channel in the base of each of the two mesenteries that attach each pyloric caecum to the aboral wall of the arms, or a total of 20 pyloric haemal channels. These communicate with the plexus in the stomach wall and so with the axial-gland haemal plexus by way of the gastric haemal tufts (Fig. 163). This system would therefore convey products of digestion into the haemal system. It would appear that the haemal plexus of the axial gland is the center of the haemal system, so that its original designation as heart is not

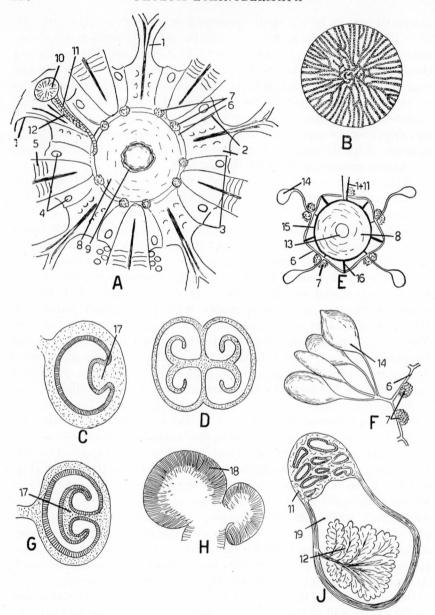

Fig. 113.—Water-vascular system (concluded). *A*, dissection of *Asterias forbesi*, aboral view of mouth frame and associated parts. *B*, madreporite of *Asterias forbesi*. *C*, section of stone canal of *Henricia* (*after Hayashi*, 1935). *D*, section of the stone canal of *Astropecten*. *E*, water ring and polian vesicles of *Asterina gibbosa*. *F*, one of the five clusters of polian vesicles of *Astropecten auranciacus*. *G*, section of the stone canal of *Asterias*. *H*, bifurcated ampulla of *Astropecten*. *J*, section of stone canal and axial sinus of *Culcita*. (*D, E, F, J, after Cuénot*, 1887). 1, interbrachial septum; 2, adam-

surprising. As already indicated, the terminal process of the axial gland is enclosed in a contractile sac. Contractions of the terminal process, the axial gland, the gastric haemal tufts, and the aboral haemal ring have been reported (Gemmill, 1914); hence there is little doubt that the fluid in the haemal system undergoes some movement.

The haemal channels have the usual histological construction (Fig. 114E), being essentially identical with the axial gland. Beneath the covering coelomic epithelium occurs a layer of connective tissue bounding internal channels containing coelomocytes.

**14. Reproductive System and Breeding Habits.**—There are typically ten gonads, two in each arm, lying free laterally in the proximal part of the arm (Fig. 109D). At its proximal end the gonad is attached near the interbrachial septum; the point of attachment indicates the location of the small gonopore, usually one to each gonad, although in some species a group of pores is present. Some asteroids with special breeding habits have ventrally located gonads that open orally (*Leptasterias, Asterina,* Fig. 115A). The gonads are numerous, occurring in a row along the side of each arm, each with a separate gonopore, in the Luidiidae, several genera of the Astropectinidae (*Leptychaster, Dipsacaster, Ctenopleura, Tethyaster, Thrissacanthias,* and one species of *Astropecten*), several genera of the Goniasteridae (*Rosaster, Mediaster, Peltaster, Anthenoides, Atelorias*), some Brisingidae (*Brisinga, Craterobrisinga, Brisingenes, Brisingaster, Freyellaster*), and no doubt others. Such a condition of the gonads is spoken of as *serial*. In some cases the gonad tufts are strung along one duct with one pore in the usual site. In several species of *Leptychaster*, the serial condition of the gonads is limited to males, whereas females have the usual pair in each interradius (Fisher, 1917).

The gonad appears as an elongated feathery tuft or tuft of tubules or bunch of grapes, whose size varies greatly according to the proximity of spawning time. When ready to spawn the gonads are greatly enlarged, often reaching to the tip of the ray; after spawning they are reduced to small tufts. At least in young stages the gonad can be seen to be enclosed in a genital sac of coelomic nature with a wall of muscle and connective fibers, covered externally with peritoneum (Fig. 115C). This genital sac is an outgrowth of the genital or aboral coelomic sinus. The gonad proper is lined by germinal epithelium, containing the germ cells, underlain by connective tissue.

The sexes are separate, although hermaphroditic specimens of normally dioecious species are sometimes found. Retzius (1911)

bulacral component of mouth frame; 3, ambulacral component of mouth frame; 4, podial pores on mouth frame; 5, ambulacral ridge; 6, water ring; 7, Tiedemann's bodies; 8, peristome; 9, cut esophagus; 10, madreporite; 11, stone canal; 12, axial gland; 13, mouth; 14, polian vesicle; 15, oral haemal ring; 16, radial haemal sinus; 17, ridge in stone canal; 18, circular muscle fibers; 19, axial sinus.

reported a specimen of *Asterias rubens* in which each gonad was partly male and partly female, and a similar specimen of *Marthasterias glacialis* .vas recorded by Buchner (1911).  Cuénot (1898) had an individual of the latter species with little islands of sperm in the ovaries.  A *Leptasterias groenlandica* with nine ovaries and one hermaphroditic gonad was reported by Lieberkind (1920).  Curious sexual conditions obtain in *Asterina gibbosa*, a common spinulose star of western Europe, which has ventrally located gonads and oral gonopores (Fig. 115*A*).  In the English Channel this species behaves as a protandric hermaphrodite, spawning as a male when young (*R* of 6 to 8 mm.), then becoming female for the rest of its life (Cuénot, 1898).  On the Mediterranean coast of France the relation of sex to size is less precise, and specimens with an *R* length of 7 to 18 mm. may spawn as males and those with an *R* length of 15 to 24 mm. as females; the largest specimens are all females.  At Naples (Bacci, 1949), individuals are either male, female, or hermaphroditic, without regard to size.  *Fromia ghardaqana* from the Red Sea is similarly a protandric hermaphrodite (Mortensen, 1938); young specimens are almost pure males with a few eggs in the testes, but with age more eggs develop in the gonads, and large specimens are nearly pure females, although some may function as males.  In *Asterina batheri*, Japan, most specimens are dioecious, but some hermaphroditic individuals occur (Ohshima, 1929).

The sexes usually cannot be distinguished externally except in the case of brooding females.  Color differences between the sexes at the height of breeding have been recorded in a few instances (Agassiz, 1877; Studer, 1880; Ludwig, 1882); very likely the color of the ripe gonads, which differs markedly in the two sexes, had affected the external coloration.  Testes are generally pale, ovaries pink or orange.  Studer claims that the sexes of *Oreaster nodosus*, Indo-Pacific, differ not only in color but also in the more strongly arched disk of the female.  The males of *Archaster typicus*, a common littoral phanerozonic star of the Indo-Pacific region, are possibly slightly smaller than the females (Ohshima and Ikeda, 1934; denied by Clemente and Anicete, 1949); but the difference, if any, is so slight as to necessitate recourse to statistical analysis.  A smaller size seems to obtain for males of *Leptasterias ochotensis* (Kubo, 1951).

A sort of copulation occurs in *Archaster typicus* (Boschma, 1923; Mortensen, 1931; Ohshima and Ikeda, 1934; Clemente and Anicete, 1949).  During the breeding season around Java and the Philippines, large numbers of pairs of this sea star may be seen lying on the bottom in shallow water, and investigation shows that the top member of the pair is invariably a male, the lower member a female.  The male lies with his oral surface pressed against the female's aboral surface and with his arms

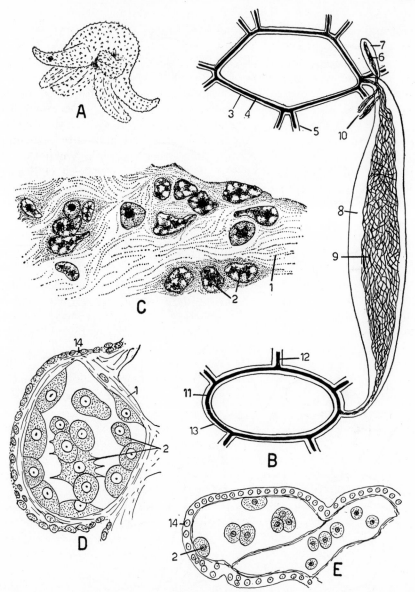

Fig. 114.—Haemal system, reproduction. *A*, brooding attitude of *Leptasterias hexactis* (*after Osterud*, 1918). *B*, scheme of the asteroid haemal system. *C*, section of the axial gland of *Henricia* (*after Hayashi*, 1935). *D*, section through the axial gland of *Asterias*. *E*, section through the aboral haemal ring. (*D*, *E*, *after Hamann*, 1885.) 1, connective tissue; 2, coelomocytes; 3, aboral or genital sinus; 4, aboral haemal ring; 5, genital branches; 6, head process of axial gland; 7, dorsal sac; 8, axial sinus; 9, axial gland; 10, gastric haemal tufts; 11, oral haemal sinus; 12, radial haemal channels; 13, hyponeural ring sinus; 14, coelomic epithelium.

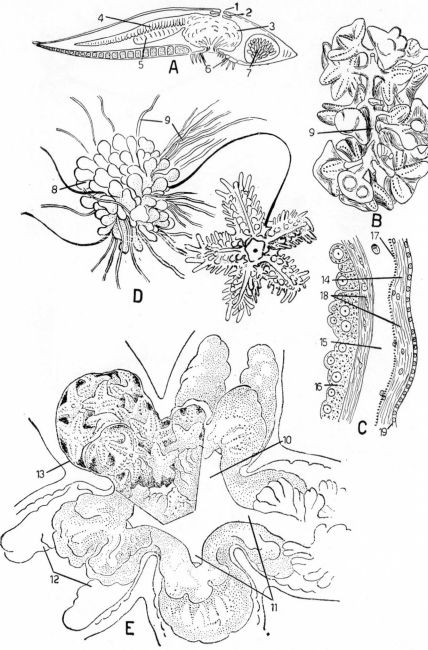

FIG. 115.—Reproduction (continued). *A*, radial section of disk and arm of *Asterina gibbosa*, showing oral gonad (*after Cuénot*, 1887). *B*, young of *Lysasterias belgicae* from brood chamber showing strands of attachment (*after Ludwig*, 1903). *C*, section through the ovary (*after Hamann*, 1885). *D*, central masses and attachment strands, only one baby star shown, of *Leptasterias arctica*. *E*, *Leptasterias groenlandica* with lobe of cardiac

alternating with hers. A similar behavior was reported for *Archaster angulatus* at Mauritius by Mortensen (1931). Gathering of males around ripe females with subsequent spawning has been noticed for *Asterina gibbosa*, Mediterranean (Ludwig, 1882), and *Leptasterias ochotensis*, Japan (Kubo, 1951). Gemmill (1914) for two British sea stars noted that spawning is induced in ripe specimens of either sex by the presence in the water of sex cells of the other sex. Mortensen (1938) recorded that when a number of ripe specimens of *Fromia ghardaqana*, Red Sea, were put together in an aquarium, they would spawn about the middle of the afternoon, with the males always preceding. However, isolated specimens of either sex, if ripe, may spawn in the laboratory. *Asterias forbesi* off the New England coast may be induced to spawn, presumably if the gonads are ripe, by a rise of temperature, even of only 2 or 3°C. (Galtsoff and Loosanoff, 1939). A peculiar behavior obtains for *Patiria miniata*, California, which will spawn when ripe if kept out of water in damp conditions (Newman, 1925).

The asteroids usually have one annual breeding period, and in the North Temperate Zone this usually falls in spring, probably evoked by the rising temperature. *Asterias vulgaris*, off the Atlantic Coast of Canada, spawns in May and early June (G. Smith, 1940), and *A. forbesi* on the New England coast in June (Mead, 1901). On the Pacific Coast of the United States, *Leptasterias pusilla* breeds in January (Fisher, 1930), and *Patiria miniata* in April and May (Newman, 1921), both in the Monterey Bay region; *Leptasterias hexactis* breeds in Puget Sound from February to April (Osterud, 1918); and *Pisaster ochraceus*, *Evasterias troscheli*, and *Pycnopodia helianthoides* are ripe in May at Vancouver Island (Mortensen, 1921). Similar times of breeding obtain for the common asteroids of the British Isles: *Asterias rubens* in April and May (Vevers, 1948); *Solaster endeca* in March and April (Gemmill, 1912); *Porania pulvillus* from April to June (Gemmill, 1915b); *Henricia sanguinolenta* from February to April (Masterman, 1902); *Leptasterias mülleri* in March and April (Mortensen, 1927); *Marthasterias glacialis* in summer (Mortensen, 1927); and *Astropecten gibbosa* in May and June (Cuénot, 1898). In Japan *Leptasterias ochotensis* breeds in April and May (Kubo, 1951), and Mortensen (1921) found several Japanese sea stars ripe in June. More irregularity of breeding season is shown by Mediterranean sea stars: thus here *Astropecten gibbosa* breeds from March to July, best in April and May (Mortensen, 1921; Ludwig, 1882); *Echinaster sepositus* in summer and fall (Löhner, 1913; Nachtsheim, 1914); and *Astropecten aurancianus* from February to June (Hörstadius, 1926a, 1939). Data

stomach opened to show baby stars inside. (*D, E, after Fisher*, 1930.) 1, anus; 2, intestinal caeca; 3, stomach; 4, pyloric caeca; 5, stomach extension; 6, adambulacral ossicles; 7, gonad; 8, central masses; 9, attachment strands; 10, pyloric stomach; 11, pyloric ducts; 12, gonads; 13, opened stomach pouch; 14, wall of genital sinus; 15, genital sinus; 16, germinal epithelium; 17, muscle layer; 18, connective tissue; 19, coelomic epithelium.

on the breeding times of tropical sea stars of the Indo-Pacific area are found in Mortensen's studies on echinoderm development (1921, 1931, 1937, 1938). In the Red Sea, some species were found ripe in April and May, others from July to September. At Java, *Archaster typicus* and *Acanthaster planci* gave ripe sex cells in April; at Mauritius, *Culcita schmiedeliana* was bred in September; and at Hawaii, *Asterope carinifera* in April. *Asterina exigua* on the Australia coast breeds from March to December and probably throughout the year (Whitelegge, 1889; Mortensen, 1921). One lone record is given for the West Indies, that of *Ophidiaster guildingi* breeding in April (Mortensen, 1921).

The sex cells are generally shed from the gonopores freely into the sea water, and the parents then go about their affairs; however, care of the young is not uncommon in asteroids. *Asterina gibbosa*, western Europe, *A. exigua*, Australia, and *Leptasterias ochotensis*, Japan, attach their eggs to objects, typically the undersurface of stones, and in correlation with this habit, have orally located gonads and gonopores (Whitelegge, 1889; Ludwig, 1882; Mortensen, 1921; Kubo, 1951). The eggs are very yolky and relatively large (0.5 mm. or more in diameter) and adhere by their surface membranes. The mothers here do not remain to protect the eggs, but the young may maintain contact with the empty membranes for a considerable period after hatching. Genuine brooding of the eggs is exhibited by a number of sea stars, all of which are limited to colder waters, chiefly in the Southern Hemisphere. Ludwig in 1903 listed the 16 brooding species known to that time and pointed out that only 5 inhabit northern waters, whereas the remaining 11 are antarctic and subantarctic species. Among the spinulose and forcipulate sea stars brooding occurs in the following manner. The mother arches the disk so that it becomes concave on the oral side and bends the arms ventrally so that the arm bases with the concavity of the disk form a considerable space (Fig. 114*A*) in which the egg mass is retained while development proceeds to the stage of tiny stars. During this period the mother does not feed. The eggs of such brooding stars are large and yolky (up to 2.5 mm. diameter) and strongly adherent into a compact mass closely pressed against the mother's peristome. In some cases the young developing from such masses are found attached at their mouth region to a common strand (Ludwig, 1903; Fig. 115*B*) or seemingly may be attached to the mother. In *Leptasterias arctica* (Fisher, 1930), each baby star is attached by a strand to one of several central soft masses (Fig. 115*D*).

The habit of brooding beneath the disk was discovered by Sars (1844, 1846) for two species of cold north European waters, *Henricia sanguinolenta* (Order Spinulosa) and *Leptasterias mülleri* (Order Forcipulata). It was then seen in a number of forcipulate sea stars from South American antarctic and subantarctic regions: *Anasterias antarctica*

(Phillipi, 1870; Perrier, 1891); *Lysasterias perrieri* (E. A. Smith, 1876, 1879); *Anasterias studeri, Diplasterias brandti* (= *lütkeni*), and *Neosmilaster steineni* (Perrier, 1891); *Lysasterias belgicae* and *chirophora* (Ludwig, 1903); *Cryptasterias turqueti* (Koehler, 1906); and *Diplasterias octoradiata,*

FIG. 116.—Brooding arctic star, *Leptychaster almus* (family Astropectinidae), Kamchatka (*after Fisher*, 1917).

*brucei,* and *meridionalis* (Fisher, 1940). Fisher (1940) remarks briefly on the brooding habit of asteroids of cold South American and adjacent antarctic waters and lists the following genera of the region as having been found carrying young beneath the disk: *Kampylaster* and *Rhopiella,* belonging to the Spinulosa, and *Anasterias, Lysasterias, Diplasterias, Cryptasterias, Neosmilaster,* and *Granaster,* belonging to the forcipulate family Asteriidae. He suspects that brooding will be found to occur in some additional genera: *Mirastrella* (Spinulosa) and *Anteliaster* and

*Psalidaster* (Forcipulata). Brooding species of Asteriidae are further found in the cold waters of the North Pacific from the Puget Sound region to the Aleutian Islands and Bering Sea, notably *Leptasterias hexactis* and *arctica* (Fisher, 1930). A study of *Leptasterias hexactis* in Puget Sound was made by Osterud (1918), who noted orally located gonopores. *Leptasterias pusilla* in the Monterey region of California has a more southerly location than the foregoing, but the water is permanently about as cold as in Puget Sound. This species is found carrying eggs and embryos in January (Fisher, 1930).

Brooding is occasionally found among the Phanerozonia, but members of this group are not able to form a suboral brood chamber because of the stiffness of their bodies and their generally short broad rays. In a few species the eggs lodge among the paxillae, and as the embryo increases in size, the paxillae are gradually pushed aside and the young star rests in a depression of the greatly thinned and stretched aboral body wall (Fig. 116). This type of brooding was discovered in *Leptychaster kerguelenensis*, from Kerguelen (Thomson, 1877, 1878). Other cases of this type of brooding are *Leptychaster almus*, Kamchatka (Fisher, 1917); *Leptychaster uber*, northwest Pacific (Djakonov, 1926), and *Ctenodiscus australis* (Lieberkind, 1926), off southern South America. The number of young carried by these sea stars is mostly below 30.

Still other methods of brooding the young are known. The antarctic *Odinella nutrix*, belonging to the Brisingidae, carries its young in the angles of the many rays (Fig. 150). The bases of the rays are abruptly swollen, so that their spines interdigitate, forming a sort of basket in which the large eggs, five to nine per basket, develop. Perhaps the most remarkable case of brooding in asteroids is that of the circumpolar *Leptasterias groenlandica* (Lieberkind, 1920; Fisher, 1930), in which the young develop in the pouches of the cardiac stomach (Fig. 115*E*), often found packed with baby stars. Here the gonopores open on the oral surface, as appears to be generally the case in *Leptasterias*. The eggs are few, large, and yolky. Something similar occurs in *Granaster nutrix*, south Georgia, in which, according to Studer (1885), development begins in the stomach pouches but is completed as usual in Asteriidae, in a brood chamber beneath the peristome.

Different from any of the foregoing is the type of brooding arrangement seen in the spinulose family Pterasteridae. Here a brooding or nidamental chamber is present between the aboral body wall and the supradorsal membrane supported by the crowns of the paxillae. The eggs pass from the gonopores directly into this chamber where development ensues. The embryos are aerated by the pumping of water in through the spiracles and out of the osculum. As the nidamental chamber is well developed in males, it seems probable that it was evolved

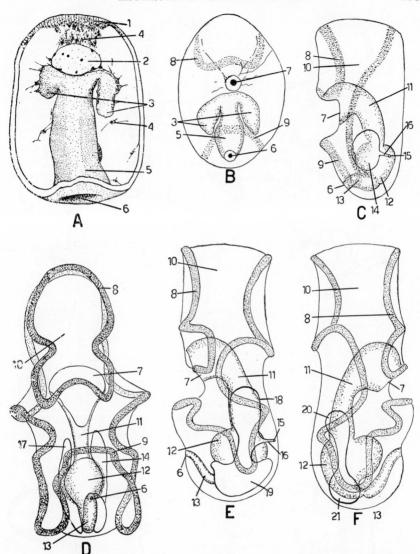

Fig. 117.—Embryology. *A*, stage of formation of coelomic sacs of *Patiria miniata* with sensory apical plate (*after Heath*, 1917). *B*, similar stage of *Astropecten auranciacus* with beginning ciliary band. *C*, 4-day stage of *A. auranciacus*, from the left side, with hydropore. *D*, 10-day stage of *A. auranciacus*, ventral view. *E*, same as *D*, left side. *F*, same as *D*, right side. (*B–F*, *after Hörstadius*, 1939.) 1, apical sensory plate; 2, dorsal sac; 3, coelomic sacs; 4, mesenchyme; 5, archenteron; 6, blastopore; 7, mouth; 8, preoral loop; 9, anal loop; 10, preoral lobe; 11, esophagus; 12, stomach; 13, intestine; 14, left coelom; 15, hydropore; 16, hydroporic canal; 17, right coelom; 18, left axohydrocoel; 19, left somatocoel; 20, right axchydrocoel; 21, right somatocoel.

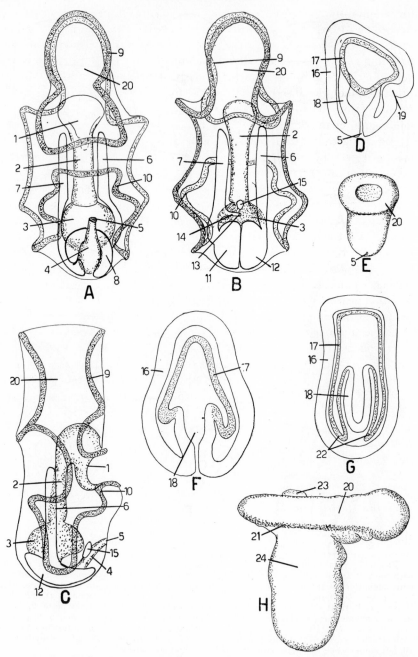

FIG. 118.—Embryology (continued). *A*, *Astropecten auranciacus*, 14 days, ventral view. *B*, same as *A*, dorsal view. *C*, same as *A*, right side. (*A–C*, *after Hörstadius*, 1939.) *D–H*, *Asterina gibbosa*. *D*, larva of 4 days, cutting off one large coelomic sac. *E*, similar to *D*, external view. *F*, similar to *D*, viewed from in front. *G*, later stage, coelomic sacs advancing posteriorly. *H*, 6-day larva, external view, showing attachment apparatus. (*D, F, G, after Ludwig*, 1882; *E, H, after MacBride*, 1896.) 1, mouth; 2,

for respiratory purposes and was secondarily utilized for brooding. According to Fisher (1940), probably all species of the pterasterid genera *Pteraster, Hymenaster, Euretaster,* and *Diplopteraster* brood. In non-brooding genera, as *Marsipaster, Calyptraster,* and *Benthaster,* the supra-dorsal membrane is delicate and poorly developed. Brooding in the Pterasteridae was discovered in 1856 by Danielssen and Koren in a *Pteraster* from Norwegian waters; 8 to 20 young were recorded in the nidamental chamber.

Brooding asteroids usually produce relatively few large, yolky, and opaque eggs, which develop without any free larval stage. The number of young often ranges from a few to 200, but some hundreds may be present in the mass carried beneath the peristome of forcipulates. Osterud (1918) counted a maximum of 1160 eggs in the egg mass of *Leptasterias hexactis* in Puget Sound, and Kudo (1951) 100 to 800 in *L. ochotensis,* Japan. On the other hand, the number of eggs discharged by nonbrood-ing species runs into millions. Thus Gemmill (1914) estimated that a female of *Asterias rubens* gave off 2,500,000 eggs during a spawning period lasting 2 hours, and such a female may spawn more than once during the breeding season. Mortensen (1913) estimated 200,000,000 eggs in the ovaries of *Luidia ciliaris.*

**15. Embryology.**—The embryology of asteroids has been well studied by a succession of investigators: Agassiz (1877) for *Asterias forbesi* and *vulgaris;* Ludwig (1882) and MacBride (1896) for *Asterina gibbosa;* Master-man (1902) for *Henricia sanguinolenta;* Gemmill (1912) for *Solaster endeca,* (1914) for *Asterias rubens,* (1915b) for *Porania pulvillus,* (1916) for *Asterias glacialis, Henricia sanguinolenta, Solaster endeca,* and *Stich-astrella rosea,* and (1920) for *Crossaster papposus;* Nachtsheim (1914) for *Echinaster sepositus;* Heath (1917) for *Patiria miniata;* Osterud (1918) for *Leptasterias hexactis;* Chadwick (1923) for *Asterias rubens;* Newth (1925) for *Astropecten irregularis;* Hörstadius (1926b) for *Luidia ciliaris* and *sarsi* and (1926a, 1939) for *Astropecten auranciacus;* and Kubo (1951) for *Leptasterias ochotensis.* There are further data about asteroid development and figures of asteroid larvae in Mortensen's studies on the larval development of echinoderms (1921, 1931, 1937, 1938). As in other echinoderms, there are two general types of development, the indirect, with a free larval stage, and the direct, in which a free stage is omitted. The latter is seen in asteroids with large, yolky eggs that are usually brooded in some manner or other and therefore may be regarded as a derived form of development. The indirect development will therefore be described first with special reference to the admirable

esophagus; 3, stomach; 4, intestine; 5, anus ( = blastopore); 6, right axohydrocoel; 7, left axohydrocoel; 8, ventral horn of left somatocoel; 9, preoral loop; 10, anal loop; 11, left somatocoel; 12, right somatocoel; 13, hydropore; 14, hydroporic canal; 15, dorsal sac; 16, ectoderm; 17, coelomic sac; 18, archenteron; 19, stomodaeum; 20, preoral lobe; 21, adhesive margin of preoral lobe; 22, somatocoels; 23, sucker; 24, primorium of sea star.

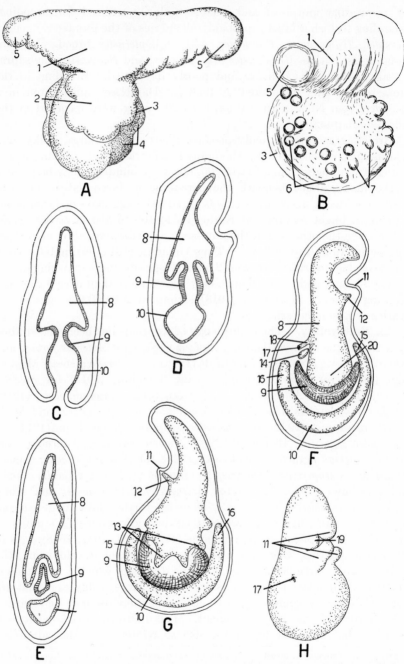

Fig. 119.—Embryology (continued). *A, Asterina gibbosa*, larva of 8 days, seen from the left side; is attached (*after MacBride*, 1896). *B, Asterina gibbosa*, 10-day larva, attachment apparatus degenerating (*after Ludwig*, 1882). *C–H, Solaster endeca* (*after Gemmill*, 1912). *C*, Beginning formation of coelomic sacs, 8 days. *D*, slightly later stage, blastopore

account of Hörstadius (1939); further valuable in that it contains a running review of preceding accounts.

Cleavage is total and practically equal, although in some species the average size of the blastomeres increases slightly toward the vegetal pole. In some species cleavage proceeds directly to the formation of a typical coeloblastula, whereas in others the blastula is for a time more or less solid or may have greatly infolded walls. A coeloblastula eventuates, however, in all cases. A typical embolic invagination ensues, with the production of a rather narrow archenteron. During the invagination the advancing tip of the archenteron gives off a limited amount of mesenchyme into the blastocoel. The blind inner end of the completed archenteron expands and cuts off on each side a coelomic sac, the hydro-enterocoel (Fig. 117$A$, $B$). These take up a position to the right and the left of the archenteron and gradually elongate in the plane of the long axis of the larva, invading its anterior region. The left hydroenterocoel puts out a narrow evagination toward the dorsal surface that forms a hydropore there (Fig. 117$C$), either with or without the participation of an ectodermal invagination. Meantime, on the opposite or ventral side of the larva, a stomodaeal invagination meets the archenteron, and a digestive tract is established. The blastopore, shifted somewhat ventrally, remains as the larval anus. The digestive tract soon differentiates into the usual three parts, esophagus, stomach, and intestine (Fig. 117$D$) and has the usual curved shape. The two hydroenterocoels continue to extend into the anterior end of the larva and eventually meet and fuse, so that the coelom as a whole has a U shape (Fig. 120$B$). Finally the posterior parts of the U are cut off as the right and left somatocoels (Fig. 120$B$).

In some asteroids the mode of formation of the coelom differs from the foregoing account. Thus in *Asterina gibbosa* the whole anterior half of the archenteron cuts off as a single coelomic sac (Fig. 118$D$), and this sends right and left extensions backward alongside the digestive tract, thus assuming the U form by a different and more direct route (Fig. 118$G$). Still more divergent is the mode of formation of the main coelomic sacs in the spinulose forms *Solaster endeca, Crossaster papposus, Henricia sanguinolenta*, and *Echinaster sepositus;* here the anterior half of the archenteron also cuts off as a large coelomic sac that represents all of the coelomic compartments except the left somatocoel. The left somatocoel forms separately by the cutting off of the posterior part of the

closed. *E*, coelomic sacs cut off from enteric sac, 9 days. *F*, embryo of 11 days, right side. *G*, same as *F*, left side. *H*, external view of stage similar to *F* and *G*. 1, preoral lobe; 2, hydrocoel with lobes; 3, dorsal surface future star; 4, beginnings of definitive arms; 5, adhesive ends preoral lobe; 6, terminal podium; 7, definitive podia; 8, main part of coelom; 9, primordium of digestive tract; 10, left somatocoel; 11, brachiolar arm; 12. coelomic extension into brachiolar arm; 13, hydrocoel lobes; 14, dorsal sac; 15, ventral horn of left somatocoel; 16, dorsal horn of left somatocoel; 17, hydropore; 18, hydroporic canal; 19, sucker; 20, right somatocoel.

archenteron (Fig. 119*C*, *D*), and the middle part of the archenteron then becomes the enteric sac (Fig. 119*E*). These asteroids have large and yolky eggs, and the larva does not feed, lacking a mouth and anus.

Sooner or later, in typical indirect development, the embryo escapes from the egg membrane, develops cilia (flagella?), and swims about as a larva. This may happen in the coeloblastula stage during the first day of development, as in *Asterias rubens* and other species of *Asterias*. With the completion of the digestive tract the larva begins to feed and in fact cannot develop further without food. Feeding is accomplished by means of powerful ciliary tracts in the walls of the stomodaeum. The food consists chiefly of diatoms. By the time of the separation of the coelomic sacs the larva has altered to a somewhat angular shape, and the previously uniform ciliation becomes concentrated into the usual locomotory band characteristic of eleutherozoan larvae. This forms a preoral loop around the ventral surface of the anterior end, passing in front of and above the mouth, then proceeds backward along the sides, and loops forward on the posterior part of the ventral surface, passing anterior to the anus as the anal (or postoral) loop (Fig. 117*D–F*). The preoral loop soons cuts off from the rest or in many cases is a separate, more or less circular, ciliary band from the start. The larva rapidly puts out projections bordered by the ciliary band, and these correspond to the arms of echinoid larvae and have received similar names (the names of the arms of echinoderm larvae originated with Mortensen, 1898). The arms increase in length and in some asteroids, especially the genus *Asterias*, eventually become quite long and slender (Fig. 123). The larva after the appearance of the ciliary band and the arm projections is termed *bipinnaria* and is the characteristic larval form of the Asteroidea. It bears a striking resemblance to the auricularia of the Holothuroidea. The beginning of the bipinnaria stage often appears during 4 to 6 days of development, but weeks are generally required for this larva to attain complete form (Fig. 121*A*, *B*). In the interior of the bipinnaria is seen the digestive tract and the various coelomic compartments.

In typical indirect development, the bipinnaria, after some weeks of free-swimming life, develops into a further stage, termed *brachiolaria*. This differs from the bipinnaria only in that a group of three additional arms, the *brachiolar arms*, has grown out from the anterior part of the ventral surface, anterior to the preoral loop (Fig. 123), which is carried along with the outgrowth of these arms. The brachiolar arms are relatively short and differ from the arms of the bipinnaria in containing a prolongation of the coelom and in being tipped with adhesive cells. One of the arms is anterior and median, and the other two are behind and lateral to this. Between the bases of the three arms is an adhesive glandular area, acting as a sucker; in fact, the brachiolar arms and the sucker together constitute an attachment device, and their appearance indicates that metamorphosis is imminent. It may be stated now that the brachiolaria soon attaches by the sucker, its anterior part, acting as a kind of stalk, degenerates and is absorbed, and the posterior part, that which contains the stomach and the somatocoels, alters into a baby star that detaches and begins independent existence. This happens in *Asterias rubens* about 2 months after the onset of development.

In many asteroids, development is more or less shortened by omission of larval stages. In the genus *Astropecten* the brachiolaria stage is omitted and the well-developed bipinnaria (Fig. 121*A*, *B*) metamorphoses after 2 to 3 months without attaching itself. In other cases, as in *Asterina gibbosa*, the bipinnaria stage is omitted; the larva does not swim until the third or fourth day of development, and then fails to differentiate a ciliary band or arms but instead puts out an adhesive apparatus, presumably corresponding to the brachiolar arms and sucker (Fig. 118*H*), and metamorphoses in about 10 days. A very peculiar bipinnaria, discovered by Sars in 1835 and named by him *Bipinnaria asterigera*, occurs in the genus *Luidia*. This has a long slender anterior part terminating in two broad arms, while the remaining arms are clustered around the posterior end where the young star develops (Fig. 124*A*). In *Luidia sarsi* at metamorphosis the bipinnaria, except for the primordium of the young star, is cut off and lives for some time, whereas in *L. ciliaris* the bipinnaria parts are absorbed as in other sea stars (Tattersall and Sheppard, 1934).

Returning now to the internal development, we shall follow first the history of the coelomic sacs. The axohydrocoels form a U in the anterior part of the larva alongside the esophagus, and this U near its posterior end on the left side bears the hydroporic canal (Fig. 120*A*, *B*). The axocoels do not definitely separate from the hydrocoels. In the posterior part of the body alongside the stomach lie the two somatocoels. Their time and degree of separation from the axohydrocoels varies much in different asteroids, and often the left somatocoel is larger than the right one and precedes the latter in separating from the axohydrocoel. The somatocoels expand and extend forward, and the left one puts out a transverse process to the ventral side of the stomach, in front of the intestine; this process, known as the ventral horn of the left somatocoel, fuses with the right axohydrocoel (Fig. 121*A*, *B*). The left somatocoel also emits a similar dorsal horn in the vicinity of the left hydrocoel that may fuse with the latter and thus reestablish a connection of the left somatocoel with the left axohydrocoel. By means of these and other expansions, the left somatocoel comes to embrace the rear part of the digestive tract and already reveals itself as the definitive coelom of the oral part of the disk. The plane of contact of the right and left somatocoels is originally the median sagittal plane of the bipinnaria, but as in other echinoderm larvae, this plane of contact, which is in fact the primary

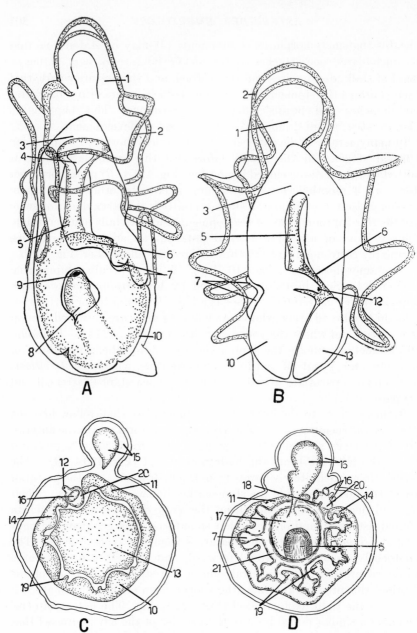

FIG. 120.—Embryology (continued). *A*, bipinnaria of *Astropecten auranciacus,* **70** days, ventral view. *B*, same as *A*, dorsal view. (*A, B, after Hörstadius,* 1939.) *C*, *Solaster endeca,* attached stage seen from the right or aboral side. *D*, earlier stage than *C*, seen from the left or future oral side. (*C, D, after Gemmill,* 1912.) 1, preoral lobe; 2, preoral loop; 3, fused anterior part of coelomic sacs; 4, mouth; 5, esophagus; 6, stomach; 7, hydrocoel lobes; 8, intestine; 9, anus; 10, left somatocoel; 11, ventral horn of left somatocoel; 12, hydropore; 13, right somatocoel; 14, dorsal horn of left somatocoel; 15, remains of preoral lobe and its coelom; 16, dorsal sac; 17, persistent part of anterior coelom; 18, cut-off first hydrocoel lobe; 19, diverticula to form outer ring of hyponeural ring sinus; 20, axial sinus; 21, water ring.

mesentery, gradually shifts and finally takes on a horizontal position, parallel to the oral and aboral surfaces of the future disk. In the meantime, that part of the left axohydrocoel that corresponds to the hydrocoel puts out the familiar lobes that become the coelomic lining of the five primary podia. These lobes lie upon the left side of the stomach (Fig. 121B). In some species all five lobes arise simultaneously; in others the middle ones precede and the end ones arise slightly later. In *Solaster endeca*, which has nine arms, after five hydrocoel lobes have arisen, four more are added (Fig. 120D), one by one, following lobe V (the most dorsal lobe is counted as I, and the stone canal opens between I and II, hence I and II are rays C and D). In the six-rayed *Leptasterias hexactis*, the sixth lobe also follows after V with some delay. In some asteroids the hydrocoel with its lobes is not as crescentic as in other echinoderms, but more of the shape of a disk, with, however, an indentation between lobes I and V. The larval stone canal arises as a groove in the wall of the left hydrocoel; this closes over to form a canal that continues from the inner end of the hydroporic canal.

Considerable attention is paid in the literature to the origin of the dorsal sac, also termed madreporic vesicle, which, it will be recalled (page 285), is a sac lying beneath the madreporite that contains the aboral end of the axial gland. In some asteroids the dorsal sac arises by the rearrangement of mesenchyme cells; in others it forms as an ectodermal invagination; and in still others it is cut off from the right axohydrocoel and hence classifies as a coelomic sac. The dorsal sac may perhaps be regarded as representing phylogenetically the right axocoel, as in echinoids. In the bipinnaria larva the dorsal sac exhibits rhythmic contractions and apparently maintains a circulation of fluid within the larva. It lacks inlet and outlet, but it is believed by observers of living larvae that fluid passes through its walls.

At about this stage of development the larva undergoes metamorphosis. In the case of brachiolariae, the three brachiolar arms feel about for a suitable substratum and accomplish temporary adhesion until the sucker attains a firm attachment. Such larvae remain attached during metamorphosis and what was the anterior half or more of the larva acts as a stalk. Where a brachiolaria is wanting as in *Astropecten*, the bipinnaria metamorphoses without attaching. Other modes are seen in cases of shortened development from large, yolky eggs, either brooded or not. Thus in the case of *Asterina gibbosa*, the anterior or preoral part of the larva puts out dorsal and ventral extensions to form an oval preoral lobe that gives the entire larva the shape of a T (Fig. 118H). In the concavity of this oval preoral lobe there develops a sucker that acts as the attachment organ. In *Solaster endeca* the larva, without any indication of a bipinnaria stage, puts out from the ventral surface of the elongated anterior region three short and plump brachiolar arms with

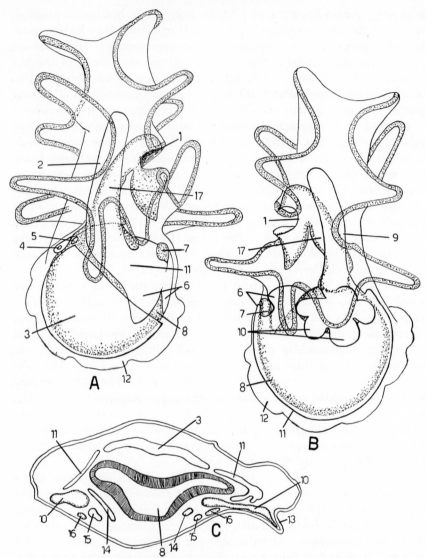

Fig. 121.—Embryology (continued).  *A*, bipinnaria of *Astropecten auranciacus*, 70 days, right side.  *B*, same as *A*, left side; compare with 120*A* and *B*.  (*A*, *B*, *after Hörstadius*, 1939.)   *C*, vertical section through metamorphosing *Solaster endeca*, showing coelomic divisions (*after Gemmill*, 1912); stage a little later than 120*D*.  1, mouth; 2, right axo-hydrocoel; 3, right somatocoel; 4, hydropore; 5, dorsal sac; 6, ventral horn of left somatocoel; 7, intestine; 8, stomach; 9, left axohydrocoel; 10, hydrocoel lobes; 11, left somatocoel; 12, aboral side of future star; 13, podium; 14, circumesophageal coelom; 15, inner hypo-neural ring sinus; 16, outer hyponeural ring sinus; 17, esophagus.

a sucker between their bases (Fig. 119*H*). The usual attachment by way of this sucker ensues. A similar story obtains for *Leptasterias hexactis*, except that here the arms are longer and more like those of a typical brachiolaria (Fig. 124*B*).

As already indicated, during metamorphosis the anterior half or more of the larva is absorbed and the definitive star forms from the rounded posterior region. What was the left side of this becomes the oral surface of the disk, and the right side is the aboral surface of the disk. It will be noticed that the young echinoderm is here formed without the aid of any vestibular invagination. As the anterior part of the larva degenerates, the lobulated hydrocoel is able to round out and makes a five-lobed disk obvious on the left side. Over this the ectoderm also lobulates correspondingly, and the five primary podia are thus delineated. From the aboral or right side five corresponding bulges are put out, and these represent the definitive arms. Additional podia arise in pairs proximal to the primary podia. As soon as the little star has acquired a few podia, it begins to attach these to objects and soon pulls itself loose from the sucker (which is left behind) and begins an independent life. The process of metamorphosis requires less than a day. The baby stars are of microscopic dimensions, less than 1 mm. across when developing from small non-yolky types of eggs, 1 to 2 mm. across when coming from large yolky eggs.

During metamorphosis the esophagus ruptures and most of it is absorbed. The stump reduces to a projection on the stomach. In *Asterias* this stump by torsion of the stomach is brought beneath the center of the hydrocoel ring and penetrates the middle of this to unite with an ectodermal invagination, forming the new and definitive mouth and esophagus. In other cases the esophagus is put out from the stomach without relation to the larval esophagus. The larvae of *Solaster* and *Henricia* lack mouth and esophagus, and here too the definitive esophagus arises as an evagination from the stomach. The stomach undergoes considerable histological reorganization, including ingestion of disintegrating tissues, and remains as the pyloric division of the adult stomach, soon putting out the pyloric caeca as evaginations. No definite statement has been found as to the origin of the cardiac division of the adult stomach. During metamorphosis the intestine ruptures from the anus and the anus and distal part of the intestine are absorbed. The stump remaining attached to the stomach eventually forms the proximal part of the adult intestine, including the intestinal caeca, but the distal part of the intestine is a new outgrowth from the old part. This outgrowth after some time makes contact with the aboral surface in interradius I/V or BC, establishing the anus, with the participation of a proctodaeum, at least in *Asterias*.

The history of the coelomic cavities is complicated. By means of the

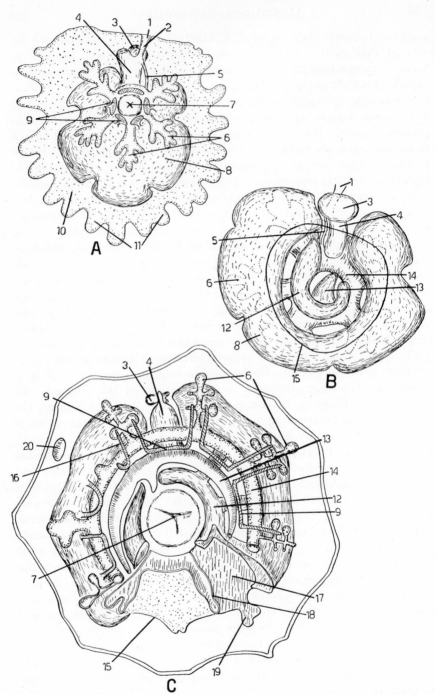

Fig. 122. Embryology (continued). *A, Astropecten auranciacus,* immediately after metamorphosis, oral view. *B,* same as *A,* aboral view, only coelomic compartments shown. (*A, B, after Hörstadius,* 1939.) *C, Solaster endeca,* oral view toward end of metamorphosis,

dorsal and ventral horns of the left somatocoel, communication exists for a time between all parts of the coelom except the right somatocoel. These communications permit flow of fluid that appears to be useful in expanding the left hydrocoel and its lobulations. During metamorphosis the absorption of the anterior part of the larva destroys the anterior parts of the coelom on both sides, except that the left axohydrocoel furnishes the axial sinus and the inner ring of the hyponeural ring sinus. This inner ring forms to the oral side of the hydrocoel either as a coelomic sac whose walls fuse into a ring shape or as outgrowths that curve into a ring and fuse. The inner hyponeural ring has therefore a common origin with the axial sinus, and this explains the adult relations, that is, the entrance of the oral end of the axial sinus into the inner hyponeural ring. The axial sinus is so formed as to include the stone and hydroporic canals. These canals are oriented end to end when the larval stone canal is formed and eventually fuse to become the definitive stone canal. By the same processes of absorption of the anterior part of the coeloms, the hydrocoel with its lobes that was in open communication with the left anterior coelom becomes completely cut off. In some species it is crescentic in form and the ends fuse to form the water ring and radial canals; in other species it is disk-like and apparently becomes a ring by the obliteration of the central part and fusion of the remaining walls. Through this ring, as well as through the ring that becomes the inner hyponeural ring, the esophageal outgrowth extends to the surface to become the definitive esophagus. Still another coelomic ring is formed here by the growth of the dorsal horn of the left somatocoel around the esophagus. This circular coelom lies between the hydrocoel and the left somatocoel and establishes a circular mesenterial contact with the right somatocoel. The remnants of this mesentery become the 10 gastric ligaments of the adult stomach. The left somatocoel puts out inter-radial lobes between the hydrocoel lobes, and each of these gives off two coelomic extensions toward the arms (Fig. 122). The lobes are cut off from the somatocoel and unite to form the outer ring of the hyponeural ring sinus. The extensions into the arms are the radial hyponeural sinus, the two halves of which originate from two adjacent lobes. This explains why the adult radial hyponeural sinus is subdivided; its septum is the wall of contact of the two outgrowths that contribute to this sinus and is therefore a mesentery. The main part of the left somatocoel

follows 120D (after Gemmill, 1912). 1, hydropore; 2, hydroporic canal; 3, dorsal sac; 4, axial sinus; 5, stone canal; 6, hydrocoel lobes; 7, mouth; 8, left somatocoel; 9, pouches of left somatocoel to form outer hyponeural ring sinus; 10, future aboral side of star; 11, indications of future arms; 12, dorsal horn of left somatocoel to form circumesophageal coelom; 13, primordium of inner hyponeural ring sinus; 14, water ring; 15, outline of right somatocoel; 16, radial branches of outer hyponeural ring sinus; 17, stomach; 18, cut edge of stomach; 19, beginning of pyloric caeca. In the lower left part of C, the left somatocoel has been cut away to show the stomach, and part of the stomach has been cut away to show the right somatocoel or aboral coelom.

becomes the coelom of the oral part of the disk, and the right somatocoel is the coelom of the aboral part of the disk.  As the pyloric caeca grow out, the right somatocoel sends out a pocket over each caecum, and the walls of these pockets come in contact and become the mesenteries that

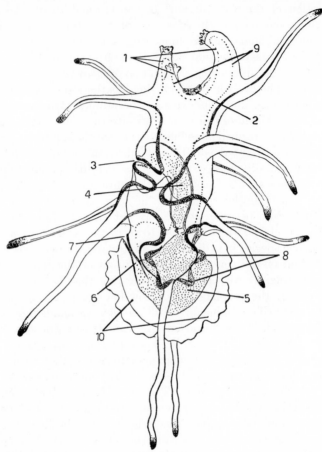

Fig. 123.—Embryology (continued).  Brachiolaria of *Asterias forbesi* (*after Mead*, 1901), seen from the left side.  1, brachiolar arms; 2, sucker; 3, mouth; 4, esophagus; 5, stomach; 6, intestine; 7, anus; 8, hydrocoel lobes; 9, coelomic extension into brachiolar arms; 10, definitive star.

suspend the caeca to the inside of the aboral wall of the ray.  The axial gland is a thickening in the wall of the axial sinus; its upper end pushes into the dorsal sac.

The origin of the gonads is not clearly explained in the literature. According to Gemmill (1914), the gonad in *Asterias rubens* arises as a group of primitive germ cells in or close to the wall of the dorsal horn of the left somatocoel.  This group of cells next grows into a compact mass that pushes out into the tissue between the dorsal sac and the axial sinus, carrying with it part of the dorsal horn that becomes the aboral or genital sinus. In this sinus, the gonad elongates into a genital rachis that forms a circle and gives off two branches enclosed in coelomic sacs into each interradius; after thus establishing the gonads the rachis

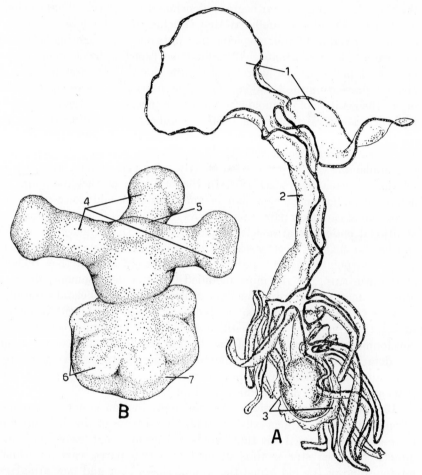

Fig. 124.—Embryology (continued). *A*, *Bipinnaria asterigera*, belonging to *Luidia ciliaris* (*after Tattersall and Shepherd*, 1934). *B*, larva of *Leptasterias hexactis*, taken from brood chamber, showing attachment apparatus and primordia of definitive star (*after Osterud*, 1918). 1, median arms; 2, preoral lobe; 3, primordium of definitive star; 4, brachiolar arms; 5, sucker; 6, hydrocoel lobes; 7, future aboral side.

disappears. Tissue from the axial gland, remaining in continuity with it, accompanies the genital rachis to become the aboral haemal ring and its genital branches.

The main parts of the ectoneural nervous system arise *in situ* as thickenings of the epidermis. Tiedemann's bodies are outgrowths of the water ring. The ampulla of the stone canal appears to arise as an expansion at the place of union of the stone and hydroporic canals. The numerous pores and pore canals through the madreporite are produced by subdivision of the original hydropore and hydroporic canal.

The skeleton appears rather late in development, generally about the time the young sea star begins independent existence. The development of the skeleton is similar to that of echinoids. Each ossicle begins as a minute rod or triradiate spicule that puts out anastomosing branches to form a fenestrated plate. In unmodified types of development there appear 11 pieces in the aboral side of the young star, first five radial pieces representing the terminals, then five interradial pieces corresponding to the genitals of echinoids, one of which incorporates the hydropore, and then a central plate (Fig. 126*B*). Spines, representing the future tubercles, put in an early appearance in relation to the terminals, generally a definite number to each terminal. On the oral side the first pairs of ambulacrals can be recognized shortly after attachment, one pair in relation to each hydrocoel lobe, to the oral side of the first pairs of definitive podia, and a new pair of ambulacrals is laid down after the formation of each new pair of podia. As the young star grows, numerous additional endoskeletal ossicles appear between the primary 11 aboral ossicles, so that in most cases the latter can no longer be recognized. These interpolated ossicles push the terminals out so that they remain at the arm tips. In the more modified types of development, there is often no definite pattern in the appearance of the endoskeletal ossicles.

It is to be understood that at the time of its detachment from the sucker the young sea star is still usually in a very imperfect state of development and that many of the changes recounted above occur after this detachment. As already indicated, the young stars are very minute and unlike their definitive appearance, having only slightly protruding arms and relatively large podia (Fig. 125*C*).

**16. Asexual Reproduction.**—Asexual reproduction is not uncommon among asteroids. It generally occurs by a splitting of the disk along a more or less preformed line that avoids ossicles and that leaves the arms intact. The sea star is thus divided into two parts, each of which retains some of the old arms; the wound closes over and new arms are regenerated. Such spontaneous fission in nature is common in the asteriid genera *Coscinasterias, Sclerasterias,* and *Stephanasterias* (Crozier, 1915, 1920; Fisher, 1925a, 1928; Bennett, 1927; Edmondson, 1935; Yamazi, 1950), and specimens are generally found with some large and some small rays (Fig. 155). *Coscinasterias tenuispina,* as observed by Crozier at Bermuda, usually has seven rays and one to five madrepores; fission through the disk produces three- and four-rayed specimens, each of which generally regenerates four arms. Fission is held in abeyance during the season of sexual reproduction (January to February). *Coscin-*

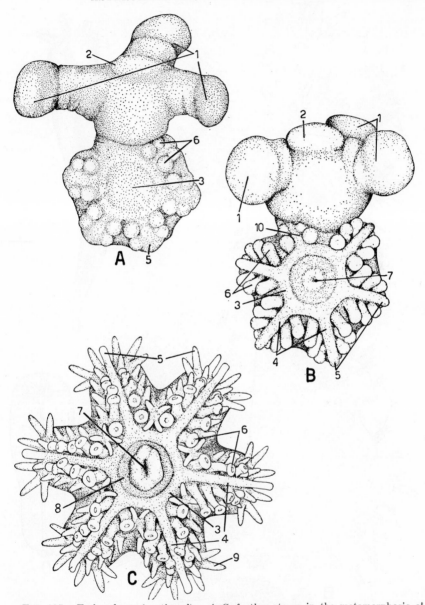

FIG. 125.—Embryology, (continued). *A–C*, further stages in the metamorphosis of *Leptasterias hexactis*, six-rayed brooding star (*after Osterud*, 1918). *A*, definitive podia forming. *B*, detachment apparatus degenerating. *C*, young star, oral side. 1, brachiolar arms; 2, sucker; 3, water ring; 4, radial water canals; 5, primary podium (terminal tentacle); 6, definitive podia; 7, mouth; 8, peristome; 9, spines; 10, sixth ray forming.

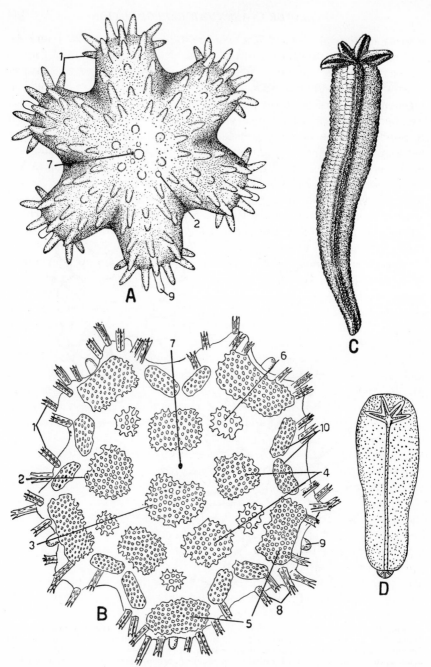

FIG. 126.—Embryology (concluded), regeneration. *A*, same as 125*C*, aboral side (*after Osterud*, 1918). *B*, young *Asterina gibbosa*, 16 days old, showing primordial skeleton (*after Ludwig*, 1882). *C*, comet state of *Linckia*, arm regenerating rest of body (*after Richters*, 1912). *D*, piece of arm of *Linckia* regenerating a star at each end (*after Edmondson*, 1935). 1, spines; 2, hydropore; 3, central plate; 4, primary interradial plates (genitals); 5, terminal plates; 6, interpolated plates; 7, anus; 8, spines; 9, primary podia; 10, plate pairs supposed to correspond to the first interambulacral plates of echinoids.

*asterias acutispina*, Japan, has four madreporites, two anal openings, and mostly eight rays, although the number of rays ranges from four to eleven. The disk splits in such a way as to leave four rays, two madreporites, and one anus in each half, and all these parts are doubled in regeneration. Fission in this species is stated to occur at all seasons, but usually only young specimens divide. In *Sclerasterias*, fission is limited to juveniles; these have six arms and four madreporites, evenly divided between the two halves, whereas the adults have five arms and one madreporite. The related genus *Allostichaster* is also fissiparous as has been observed in the New Zealand species *insignis* and *polyplax* by Farquhar (1895) and Bennett (1927). In *A. insignis*, with two to seven arms, a group of three arms generally grows out in each fission product, whereas in *A. polyplax*, mostly with eight arms, a group of four arms typically regenerates in each fission product.

Fission is also reported to occur in the spinulose family Asterinidae, in *Nepanthia* (Edmondson, 1935), and in *Asterina wega, anomala*, and *exigua* (Cuénot, 1887; Bennett, 1927). *Asterina wega* has usually seven rays and one madreporite, but examples with six and eight arms may be found. Fission usually results in products with three and four rays which typically regenerate four and three rays, respectively.

A different type of asexual reproduction obtains in the genus *Linckia* and seems to be practiced by all the species of this genus (Hirota, 1895; Monks, 1904; Kellogg, 1904; Richters, 1912; H. L. Clark, 1913; Edmondson, 1935). This genus has a habit of casting off arms, mostly at a more or less definite level about an inch from the disk, and these arms regenerate a complete sea star, something that is quite impossible in all other asteroids. No factors are known that bring on this autotomy. The process is a slow pulling apart, requiring up to 3 or 4 hours, and accomplished by the arm in question constantly pulling away from the rest of the animal. According to Edmondson, the rupture begins ventrally by the separation of ambulacral ossicles and spreads dorsally; tissues may be stretched as much as 2 inches before giving way. Of course the lost arms are also regenerated, and as a result of this habit, symmetrical specimens of *Linckia* are rarely found. Monks records only four in 400 specimens, no two of which were alike, varying in ray number from one to nine, in madreporic number from one to five, and in number of anuses from one to four. The cast-off arm generally regenerates a group of four or five arms at the torn surface, and such regenerating arms, presenting a curious appearance with a group of little arms at one end of a big arm, are called "comets" and are of common occurrence wherever species of *Linckia* abound (Fig. 126C).

**17. Regeneration.**—The occurrence of asexual reproduction in a number of asteroids indicates a high regenerative capacity in this group. Specimens of asteroids in process of regenerating one or more arms are very commonly found in nature.   King (1898, 1900) recorded that about 11 per cent of the specimens of *Asterias vulgaris* collected on the Massachusetts coast were in process of regenerating arms, almost always close to the disk, an indication that injured arms are cast off near the disk, generally at the level of the fourth or fifth pair of ambulacral ossicles. She found that *Asterias vulgaris* could be induced to cast off an arm by cutting off all of its podia and that the constriction occurred at the level indicated.   Several studies on the regenerative capacities of several species of asteroids are available in the literature (King, 1898, 1900, on *Asterias vulgaris;* Schapiro, 1914, on *Echinaster sepositus, Astropecten auranciacus* and *irregularis,* and *Marthasterias glacialis;* Nusbaum and Oxner, 1915, on *Echinaster sepositus;* and Zirpolo, 1916, 1921, 1922, on *Asterina gibbosa*).   In all species tested arms cut off at any level are readily regenerated, although the process is relatively slow.   Regeneration takes place in the same manner as postlarval growth; the tip of the arm, marked by the terminal plate and tentacle and the optic cushion, appears first, and other structures are then formed between this tip and the stump in a central direction with the youngest structures just proximal to the new tip.   The pyloric caeca are replaced by outgrowth from the old ones and similarly the radial water canal and radial nerve by outgrowth from the stumps of these structures.   The beginning stage of arm regeneration takes place at about the same time, usually several days up to 6 or 7 weeks in different species, regardless of the level of section, but outgrowth of the arm is more rapid the more proximal the level of section.   In some species more than a year may be required for complete replacement of an arm.   If an arm is split vertically, a double outgrowth usually results, producing a distally forked arm.   If an arm is split horizontally, the ventral half regenerates a complete arm, but the dorsal half merely rolls into a tube and does not regenerate.   Similarly if an arm is cut vertically through the side, the lateral piece will not regenerate an arm, while the larger piece, including the ambulacral groove and ridge, completes itself perfectly.   Pieces of body wall, madreporites, and other small structures are replaced.   Following removal of a rectangular piece cut completely through the arm but leaving the side walls intact, a new arm may be regenerated at the proximal cut surface of the rectangular hole (Fig. 127*D*) but not at its distal surface (Schapiro, 1914).   Fedotov (1934, 1935) removed the axial gland and gastric haemal tufts from *Asterias rubens* and found that they were replaced at some period between 2 and 6 months.   The axial gland regenerates from the oral haemal sinus and the gastric tufts from the haemal channels of the stomach wall.

Except in the genus *Linckia,* as already related, isolated arms are without any power of regeneration.   They must be accompanied by a

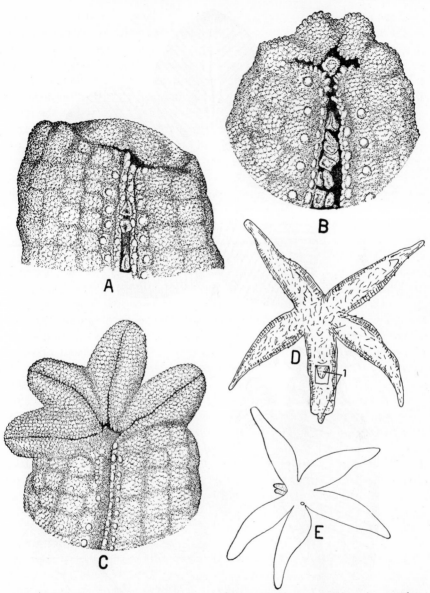

Fig. 127.—Regeneration (concluded). *A–C*, stages in the regeneration of a complete star by an arm of *Linckia* (*after Richters*, 1912). *A*, wound closed, leaving hole that becomes mouth. *B*, rays beginning to grow out, with ambulacral grooves extending from mouth. *C*, comet stage. *D*, *Echinaster sepositus*, regenerating arm at the proximal cut surface of a rectangular window cut through the arm (*after Schapiro*, 1914). *E*, *Asterias vulgaris* regenerating two extra arms from a cut through the disk at an interradius (*after King*, 1900). 1, regenerating arms.

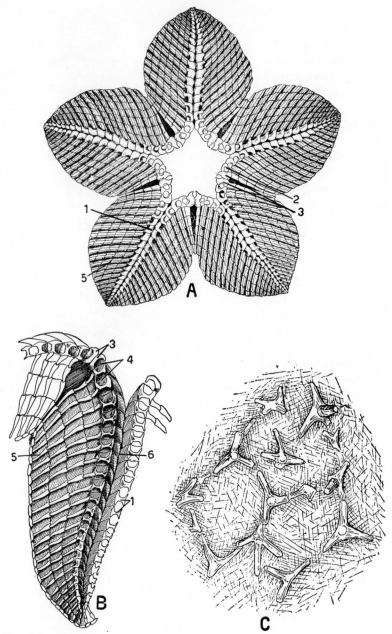

Fig. 128.—Somasteroidea. *A*, *Villebrunaster*. *B*, arm of *Chinianaster*. *C*, aboral skeleton of a somasteroid. (*All after Spencer*, 1951). 1, ambulacral ossicles; 2, mouth frame; 3, enlarged interradial pieces of mouth frame; 4, ambulacral pores; 5, virgalia; 6, ambulacral groove.

portion of the disk, and the amount of disk necessary varies in different species. In *Asterias vulgaris*, an arm accompanied by enough of the disk to include the madreporite and stone canal may sometimes regenerate an entire sea star, but at least one-fifth of the disk attached to the arm is necessary from areas outside the madreporite, and such portions often fail to regenerate. For certain regeneration a larger area of disk must remain attached to an arm in this species. In *Echinaster sepositus*, at least half of the disk is required; in *Astropecten* at least three-quarters of the disk, including the madreporite, must be left with the arm to ensure complete regeneration; and in *Marthasterias glacialis*, retention of the entire disk is necessary. An entire isolated disk will generally regenerate the entire animal in at least some of these species, but isolated parts of disks usually fail to regenerate. Partial cuts through the disk generally heal, but sometimes one or even two arms may grow out from the site of wound closure (King, 1900; Fig. 127E).

The special case of regeneration of the entire animal from a cast-off arm without any disk retention in *Linckia* has been treated in detail by Richters (1912) and Edmondson (1935). The wound closes over, leaving an opening that becomes the mouth, and after several weeks a crescentic ridge of new growth appears at the proximal end of the arm. This gradually grows out into four projections, each with an aboral groove continuous with the mouth (Fig. 127A–C). Even after a year these incipient arms are still very short and the comet form thus produced evidently lasts a long time. The more distal the proximal surface of the detached arm, the slower is its regeneration into a complete sea star. Pieces of arms with cut surfaces at both ends regenerated a disk at both ends in two cases out of several hundred in Edmondson's experiments (Fig. 126 D).

Details of the histology of regeneration have been furnished by Nusbaum and Oxner (1915) for *Echinaster sepositus*, using arms of which the dorsal wall had been removed. In 4 or 5 days the wound is covered by a delicate membrane consisting of connective tissue and coelomocytes. Large numbers of the latter are found at the cut surfaces, where they often fuse into syncytia. The epidermis then advances over the membrane from both sides with a thickened edge and eventually covers the surface. Damaged ossicles disintegrate, and the fragments are probably ingested by coelomocytes. The muscle layer of the body wall near the cut surface undergoes extensive change; old fibers may fall to pieces that are ingested by coelomocytes, and others dedifferentiate into a sarcoplasm containing nuclei. The new muscle fibers arise from this sarcoplasm.

**18. The Somasteroidea.**—Although Asteroidea were presumably very abundant in ancient seas, they preserve poorly as fossils because of the lack of a solid endoskeleton, and entire skeletons are seldom found.

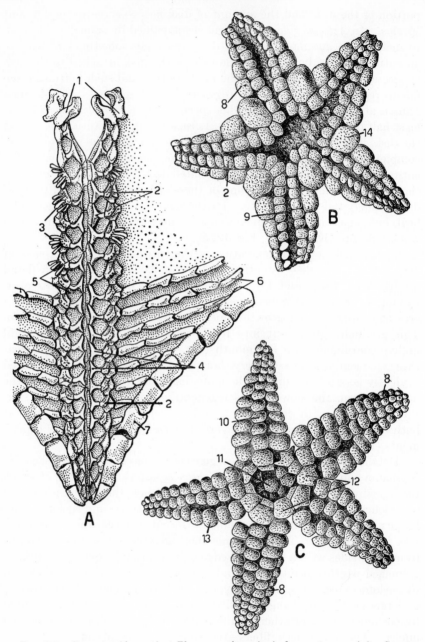

Fig. 129.—Somasteroida: extinct Phanerozonia. *A, Archegonaster* arm (*after Spencer*, 1951). *B, Hudsonaster*, oral view. *C, Hudsonaster*, aboral view. (*B, C, after Schuchert*, 1915.) 1, enlarged adambulacral ossicles of mouth frame; 2, adambulacral ossicles; 3, fans of adambulacral spines; 4, ambulacral ossicles; 5, ambulacral pores; 6, virgalia; 7, marginals; 8, inframarginals; 9, ambulacral groove; 10, coronals; 11, central plate; 12, primitive interradial ossicles; 13, supramarginals; 14, odontophore.

Some very archaic forms have recently been described by Spencer (1951) from the Lower Ordovician of southern France. The most primitive of these, *Villebrunaster* (Fig. 128*A*), has five short arms of petaloid shape with two rows of ambulacral ossicles, not forming a groove, along the center of each arm. The large and deep ambulacral pores lateral to the ambulacral ossicles suggest that the ampullae were more or less external. Adambulacrals are wanting, and the oral surface apart from the ambulacra is provided with hollow rod-shaped ossicles called *virgalia*, arranged in diagonal rows corresponding to the ambulacral ossicles. A ring of peristomial ossicles is lacking, and the large pentagonal peristome is bounded peripherally by a row of ossicles continuous with the ambulacral rows. At each interradius, a pair of these is enlarged, suggesting the future adambulacral type of mouth frame. The skeleton of the aboral surface consists of loose triradiate spicules (Fig. 128*C*), as in the first stage of embryonic formation of endoskeleton, somewhat arranged to form a mesh. *Chinianaster*, from the same stratum and locality, is very similar, but the arms are more definitely outlined and have ambulacral grooves (Fig. 128*B*); this genus is further provided with a madreporite, lacking in *Villebrunaster*, present on the oral side in an interradial angle. *Archegonaster*, from the Lower Ordovician of Bohemia, presents a more distinctly asteroid appearance; it has ambulacral grooves, adambulacral plates provided with fans of spines, and marginal plates, hence resembling a phanerozonic star (Fig. 129*A*). *Archegonaster* has an aboral madreporite, but aboral skeleton is apparently altogether lacking, and on the oral surface the rows of virgalia are limited to the distal parts of the arms. Adambulacrals and marginals apparently evolve from the innermost and outermost virgalia. These archaic asteroids appear to have been very flexible. Spencer is of the opinion that they lived partially buried in the mud with the arm tips bent aborally and protruding above the surface and that they fed after the manner of crinoids, by passing small food objects along the ambulacra to the mouth; but as they are supposed to have been oriented with the oral surface down, it is somewhat difficult to understand how the necessary ciliary currents could have been maintained.

Spencer, followed by other invertebrate palaeontologists (e.g., Ubaghs, 1953), unites the foregoing forms and a few others into a group, Somasteroidea, which he regards as a subclass coordinate with the subclasses Asteroidea and Ophiuroidea and ancestral to both of the latter. All three are then united into one class, Stelleroidea. As the author favors the separation of the Asteroidea and Ophiuroidea into distinct classes, this scheme has not been presented here. It appears that *Archegonaster*, at least, is distinctly asteroid.

**19. Order Platyasterida.**—This group, originated by Spencer (1951), includes a few fossils from the Ordovician and Devonian, characterized

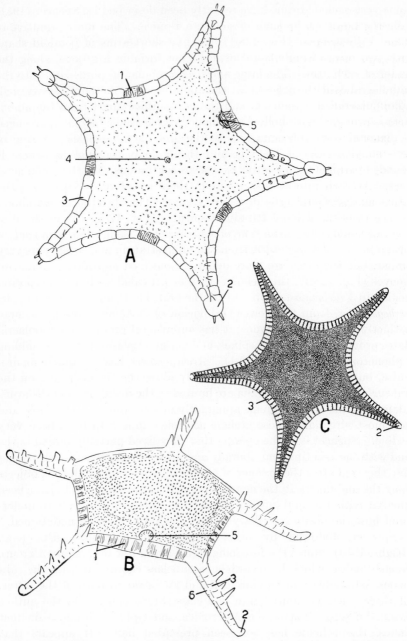

Fig. 130.—Phanerozonia: Porcellanasteridae, Astropectinidae. *A, Porcellanaster coeruleus*, at 2000 m., off New England (*after Sladen*, 1889). *B, Styracaster chuni*, at 2500 m., Gulf of Guinea (*after Lieberkind*, 1932). *C, Plutonaster agassizi*, 700 m., off Massachusetts; madreporite does not show. 1, cribriform organ; 2, terminal ossicle; 3, supramarginal plates; 4, epiproctal cone; 5, madreporite; 6, inframarginal plates.

by the widely open ambulacra, almost flush with the oral surface; adambulacrals are present but do not form an edge to the ambulacra. The dorsal surface is composed of paxillae and inframarginal plates edge the arms, hence in fact these forms may be regarded as archaic phanerozonians. The peristomial ring of ossicles is not well differentiated but is tending toward the adambulacral type with a pair of enlarged pieces at each interradial angle. The principal genus is *Platanaster* from the Ordovician of Great Britain.

**20. Order Hemizonida.**—In this group, also originated by Spencer in 1951 and also wholly extinct, ranging from the Ordovician to the middle Carboniferous, the ambulacral ossicles are insunk and definite ambulacral grooves have developed, bordered laterally by large, conspicuous adambulacrals. In some the rows of ambulacrals and adambulacrals form the whole of the oral surface of the arms; in others a row of inframarginals is added. The aboral surface is composed of paxillae or of ordinary ossicles. A madreporite is generally present, either orally or aborally located. The mouth armature is in about the same state as in the preceding order, with more or less developed pairs of pieces at the interradial angles. This order includes several families and a number of genera, among which may be mentioned *Taeniactis, Helianthaster, Lepidasterella, Palasterina, Schuchertia, Lepidactis, Lepidaster, Cnemidactis, Urasterella,* and *Arthraster.*

Contemplation of the characteristics of these ancient asteroids indicates that the original asteroid had petaloid arms without much in the way of an aboral skeleton, poorly defined ambulacral grooves, probably with more or less external ampullae, and an incipient mouth frame, tending to the adambulacral type. Such types appear to lead directly into the Phanerozonia, which may then be regarded as the most primitive of the three existing orders of Asteroidea.

**21. Order Phanerozonia.**—The members of this order are characterized by the conspicuous marginal plates, typically in two rows, infra- and supramarginal, that edge the arms and disk and confer upon the body great strength as well as considerable rigidity. Phanerozonic stars usually have five arms, and these are often short and broadly based (Fig. 103*A*). The aboral skeleton usually consists of paxillae, whose bases form a closely set mosaic (Fig. 101*A*), or of similarly arranged plates, a type of skeleton that increases the general body rigidity. Papulae are limited to the aboral surface bounded by the supramarginal plates. Pedicellariae when present are of the sessile or alveolar type. In existing forms the mouth frame is well developed, of the adambulacral type, with conspicuous pairs of spiny adambulacrals at the interradii, appearing like jaws (Fig. 102*B*). The podia are in two rows and may or may not be provided with suckers. This order began in the Lower

Ordovician and has flourished to the present time. It is divisible into five suborders, of which the first is wholly extinct: Pustulosa, Cribellosa, Paxillosa, Notomyota, and Valvata.

The name Pustulosa derives from the circumstance that the spines, which were small and slender, were mounted on hemispherical tubercles like those of echinoids; these tubercles are called pustules in this particular case, a very poor term. The Pustulosa lived from the Lower Ordovician into the Permian and include several families, well treated by Schuchert (1915). Of the most general interest is the genus *Hudsonaster*, probably the most primitive phanerozonic star. This was a very small form with five short, broadly based rays. Orally, the arm skeleton consists only of ambulacrals, adambulacrals, and inframarginals, which last form the margin on both sides, hence are visible aborally where in addition there is a row of supramarginals on each side and a median row of carinals (Fig. 129B, C). The ossicles of the aboral side of the disk show the primitive and embryonic arrangement, with a central piece, separated by some secondary plates from a ring of five large interradial pieces (genitals), one of which is associated with the madreporite, and a similar ring of five radial pieces which form the beginning of the row of carinals. A differentiated mouth frame is wanting, and the peristome is simply bordered by the unaltered ambulacral and adambulacral ossicles. Further evolution in the Phanerozonia consists in the interpolation of secondary plates, reduction in size of ossicles except the marginals, and differentiation of a mouth frame, changes that can be traced among the Pustulosa.

The suborder Cribellosa embraces the single family Porcellanasteridae, distinguished by the presence of cribriform organs. The members of this family typically dwell on mud bottoms, almost exclusively at great depths, and were first made known through the dredgings of the *Challenger* (Sladen, 1889). They are of stellate shape, with narrow, pointed arms, broadly based (Fig. 130A), and bordered by thin, marginal plates. The aboral surface generally appears membranous and is usually elevated centrally into a prominence, often long and tubular, often called epiproctal cone in works on asteroids, although it is not related to any anus. This family lacks anus, intestine, and intestinal caeca. On the oral surface the considerable areas between the proximal parts of the ambulacra are covered with scale-like plates. The podia are pointed, without suckers, and are provided with a simple ampulla. In the main genus *Porcellanaster* (Fig. 130A), there is a single cribriform organ in each interradius. *Eremicaster* has three such organs, one in the interradial angle and the others to each side of this. In *Styracaster* with three to nine cribriform organs along the sides of the arm bases from the interradial angle distally, the supramarginal plates meet along the median aboral

Fig. 131.—Phanerozonia: Goniopectinidae, Astropectinidae. Above, *Ctenodiscus crispatus*, oral side; note grooves between inframarginals continued between adambulacrals to ambulacral groove. Below, *Thrissacanthias penicillatus*, off Pacific Coast of the United States, 500 to 1600 m.

Fig. 132.—Phanerozonia: Astropectinidae, Luidiidae. Above, *Astropecten*. Below, *Luidia* (*from A. Clark*, 1953).

line of the long, slender rays, and there bear a median row of spines (Fig. 130*B*). *Hyphalaster* (Fig. 99*B*) has five to nine cribriform organs, short rays without a median aboral row of spines, and short adambulacral spines. The foregoing genera have large and conspicuous terminal plates armed with a few spines. In *Thoracaster*, with 14 cribriform organs, the terminal plate is small and inconspicuous, without spines. In addition to the Sladen report, the Porcellanasteridae have been especially treated by Döderlein (1921) and Lieberkind (1932, 1935).

In the suborder Paxillosa, the skeleton of the aboral surface consists of typical paxillae and the podia are devoid of suckers, as in the Cribellosa. The principal families here are the Goniopectinidae, Astropectinidae, and Luidiidae. The Goniopectinidae have the same general aspect as the Cribellosa, with a stellate body edged with conspicuous marginal plates. This family is further provided with a simplified type of cribriform organ in the form of a groove containing a few lamellae and bordered on each side by the scalloped edges of the marginal plates (Fig. 99*E*, *F*). There is one such cribriform organ between adjacent marginal plates along the whole length of the sides of the arms (Fig. 99*E*); the cribriform organs are further continued as simple channels lined with vibratile spines between the plates of the oral side of the arms up to the ambulacral grooves. The genus *Ctenodiscus*, formerly placed in the Porcellanasteridae, has in common with that family the lack of intestine, intestinal caeca, and anus, and the presence of an epiproctal cone. The common mud star *Ctenodiscus crispatus* (Figs. 94*C*, 131), is circumboreal, found throughout cold northern waters and extending southward to California, Cape Cod, and Japan. In *Goniopecten*, intestine, intestinal caeca, and anus are well developed.

Whereas the podia in the Goniopectinidae are provided with simple ampullae, these in the Astropectinidae and Luidiidae are deeply bifurcated. The Astropectinidae are a family of considerable extent, with a stellate body having conspicuous marginal plates and respiratory grooves between the marginal plates but no cribriform organs. Supra-ambulacral ossicles are present in the interior in the lateral angles of the arms (page 258). Intestine and intestinal caeca are almost always present, but an anus may be wanting. In the majority of the genera, the marginal plates are covered with little spines that increase in size to the margin, which is therefore bordered by a fringe (Fig. 101*D*). The main genus *Astropecten* was monographed by Döderlein (1917), who listed over 100 species. *Astropecten* (Fig. 132) is a flat, five-pointed star with a fringe of spines bordering the arms and with the elongated inframarginals meeting the adambulacrals to form the oral surface of the narrow rays. Some common species are *A. auranciacus* in the Mediterranean, often used for embryological studies, *A. irregularis* around the British Isles,

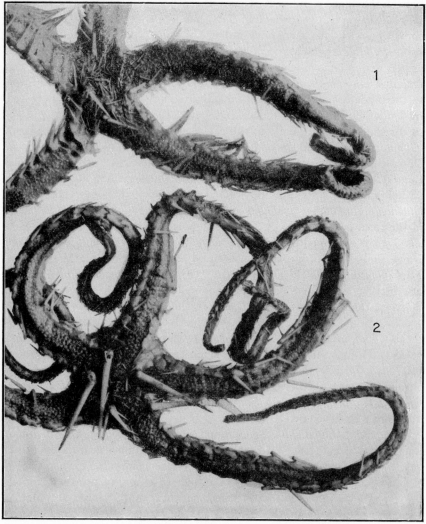

Fig. 133.—Phanerozonia: Benthopectinidae.  Two species of *Benthopecten*, deep water around Celebes (*after Fisher*, 1919, *courtesy U.S. National Museum.*)

*A. polyacanthus* in the Indo-Pacific, *A. armatus* in the Panamic region, and *A. californicus* off California.  The marginal fringe of spines is wanting in *Leptychaster*, also noted for its brooding habits (Fig. 116), whereas the spiny border is retained in most other astropectinid genera. The respiratory marginal grooves lined with vibratile spines occur in *Leptychaster*, *Psilaster*, and *Tethyaster* but are wanting in other genera to be mentioned.  Thick and block-like supramarginal plates occur in *Psilaster*, *Persephonaster* with ordinary gonads, *Thrissacanthias* (Fig. 131) with serial gonads, *Plutonaster* (Fig. 130*C*) with the madreporite concealed under special paxillae, and *Tethyaster* with a median aboral series of slightly enlarged paxillae; whereas the supramarginals are thin in *Dytaster*. The supramarginal plates are much smaller than the inframarginals in *Dipsacaster*, which also has paxillae covering the madreporite and serial gonads.

The family Luidiidae comprises the single genus *Luidia*, which has a very characteristic appearance (Fig. 132). *Luidia* lacks the stiff, star-like shape of the preceding Phanerozonia and instead has long flexible arms and a relatively small disk. It attains considerable size. Many of the species are five-rayed, but nearly half are multirayed with six to eleven arms. The arms are bordered with a spiny fringe. The paxillae of the aboral surface of the disk and of the median aboral area of the arms are small and irregularly arranged, but toward the sides of the arms they become larger, squarish or rectangular, and disposed in definite rows, producing a tesselated appearance. The supramarginals are reduced so as to appear identical with the adjacent paxillae, whereas the inframarginals are much elongated transversely and cover the greater part of the oral surface of the arms. The crowns of the paxillae consist of spinelets, and the inframarginals are covered with similar but larger spinelets. Pedicellariae are frequently present, usually of the two-jawed tong type (Fig. 105*G*), but bivalved and three-jawed varieties also occur. The papulae are branched (Fig. 98*E*). Anus and intestinal caeca are wanting, and the gonads occur in numerous tufts along the aboral sides of the rays. The genus is more or less characteristic of tropical and subtropical waters. It was monographed by Döderlein (1920), who lists 42 species. Among the more common species are *L. sarsi* and *ciliaris* from western Europe and the Mediterranean, *maculata* and *quinaria* from the Indo-Pacific, *clathrata* from the West Indies, *foliolata* from the Pacific Coast of North America, and *asthenosoma* from California.

The suborder Notomyota comprises the single family Benthopec-tinidae, limited to deeper waters. The members of this family have a characteristic appearance (Fig. 133), with slender, flexible rays, bordered with spines borne upon the rather small, oval marginal plates, of which the two rows more or less alternate. The aboral surface is covered with simple plates or with low paxillae, and these generally bear small spines. The adambulacral plates project into the ambulacral groove. The papulae are limited to papularia on the aboral side of the arm bases or are sometimes more extensive. Pedicellariae are chiefly of the pectinate type. The outstanding characteristic of this family is the pair of muscle bands on the inside of the dorsolateral surfaces of the arms, not occurring in any other family. In this and all subsequent families the podia are provided with the usual terminal disks or suckers. Anus, intestine, and

Fig. 134.—Phanerozonia: Benthopectinidae, Archasteridae. Above, *Nearchaster aciculosus*, off the Pacific Coast of North America, 600 to 1600 m. Below, *Archaster typicus*, littoral, Indo-Pacific.

intestinal caeca are present. The papularia are rounded, elevated areas in *Pontaster* and *Pectinaster* (Fig. 98C), bilobed and not elevated in *Cheiraster* and *Luidiaster*. In *Nearchaster*, the papularia extend as a band along the aboral surface of the rays and also spread over the disk, and the aboral surface is extremely spiny (Fig. 134). *Benthopecten* is characterized by the presence of an odd upper and lower marginal plate in the angle of the arms; the odd upper plate bears a conspicuous spine. In this genus the papularia are confined to the disk and ray bases.

The suborder Valvata includes all remaining phanerozonic families that have ordinary suckered podia. The ossicles of the aboral skeleton may be paxilliform or otherwise. In the small family Archasteridae with the single genus *Archaster*, the paxillae of the aboral surface of the arms are arranged in diagonal rows meeting a medial radial row. The general aspect of *Archaster* (Fig. 134) is similar to that of *Astropecten*, with a marginal fringe and transversely elongated inframarginals forming most of the oral surface of the arms. *Archaster typicus* is one of the most common asteroids of the Indo-Pacific region. The Odontasteridae are known by one or two large recurved spines pointing outward borne on each of the adambulacral wedges forming the interradial angles of the mouth frame. There are two such spines to each wedge in *Asterodon*, one in *Odontaster* and *Aconodonaster*. In *Odontaster* (Fig. 135) the crowns of the aboral paxillae consist of little erect spines, and the oral surface is densely covered with small spines. In *Acodontaster*, the general body surface bounded by the marginal plates is granular rather than spiny. A number of species of the Odontasteridae are characteristic of antarctic and subantarctic waters.

The Goniasteridae is the largest family of the Valvata, containing around 50 genera, of which only a few are here mentioned. Several genera are characteristic of Australia where (H. L. Clark, 1946) "the most brilliantly colored and beautiful sea stars are with a few exceptions goniasterids." Three genera, *Notioceramus*, *Pergamaster*, and *Chitonaster*, are limited to the antarctic (Fisher, 1940). The Goniasteridae are Phanerozonia of stellate form with broad disk and broadly based arms bordered by thick and massive marginal plates. The general body skeleton may be composed of paxillae but more often consists of simple plate-like ossicles of varied form, and often the skeletal ossicles are covered over with a smooth or granular membrane. In *Pseudarchaster*, *Mediaster*, and some other genera, the aboral surface is formed of paxillae, and these extend to the tips of the rays so that the supramarginals do not make contact aborally. In *Pseudarchaster* there is a tooth (not recurved) on each of the adambulacral wedges forming the interradii of the mouth frame; *Pseudarchaster parelii* is circumboreal, and *P. pusillus* (Fig. 137)

Fig. 135.—Phanerozonia: Odonasteridae. Above, *Odontaster hispidus*, off Rhode Island, aboral view. Below, left, paxillae of aboral surface, enlarged (*after Fisher*, 1911); below, mouth area enlarged, showing five large recurved spines.

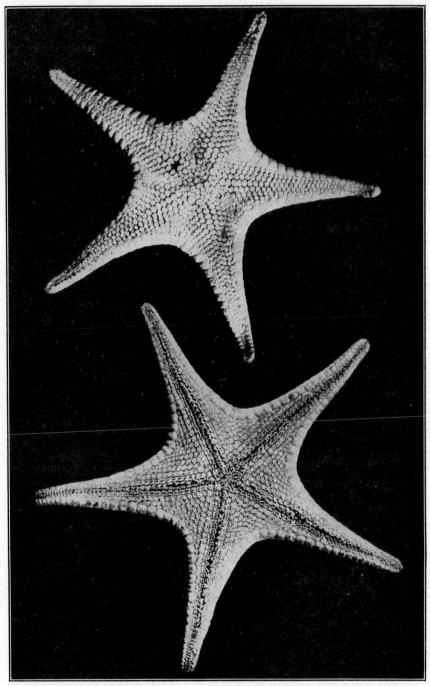

Fig. 136.—Phanerozonia: Goniasteridae. *Mediaster aequalis*, littoral, Pacific Coast of North America (*from Ulrey*, 1918); aboral view above; oral view below; note paxillae to ray tips on aboral side.

is common off California in waters of moderate depth. *Mediaster* lacks special teeth on the mouth frame and is covered with flower-like paxillae; the red *M. aequalis* occurs on the Pacific Coast from California to Alaska (Fig. 136). *Ceramaster* is a stellate short-rayed form with aboral surface composed of rounded plates covered with little granules (Fig. 137). *Rosaster* and *Nymphaster* (Fig. 138) have narrow rays on which the supramarginals meet aborally, or practically do so; both genera have a number of species in the Indo-Pacific region. *Amphiaster* is characterized by the blunt conical erect spines borne on both aboral and oral surfaces, also along the margins, whereas in *Calliderma* there are small sharp movable spines on the oral surface and on the inframarginals. In *Tosia* and *Pentagonaster* (Fig. 103A) spines are wanting, and the surfaces consist of rounded ossicles, bordered by a row of granules. The body is covered by a membrane obscuring the ossicles except the marginal ones in a group of genera including *Chitonaster*, *Anthenoides*, *Anthenea*, and *Stellaster*, all of which have bivalved pedicellaria. In *Anthenea* the whole oral surface, including the inframarginals, is beset with these bivalved pedicellariae, each encircled by granules. *Hippasteria* also has large bivalved pedicellariae (Fig. 105F) strewn over the oral surface (Fig. 139), but the marginal plates and sometimes the aboral surface are provided with tubercles.

The family Oreasteridae ( = Pentacerotidae) is characterized by the reticulate skeleton enclosing papular areas in its meshes. The members of the family are generally of a moderate to large size and of broad shape with short, broadly based arms, or almost none at all (*Culcita*, *Halityle*). Tubercles are typically borne on the nodes of the network, especially along the carinals, and may attain considerable size. Large marginal plates are present but are often concealed from surface view. The family is littoral in warm waters of the Indo-Pacific region; only the genus *Oreaster* is represented in the Atlantic. The Oreasteridae were monographed by Döderlein (1935), but he included in the family a number of genera regarded by Fisher (1911) as belonging to the Goniasteridae, and the more acceptable concept of the family corresponds to Döderlein's subfamily Oreasterinae, which he monographed in 1936. As thus understood, the family embraces *Oreaster*, *Pentaceropsis*, *Asterodiscus*, *Nidorellia*, *Culcita*, *Halityle*, and a few other genera. *Oreaster* ( = *Pentaceros*) was subdivided into two or three genera by Döderlein but is here used in the broad sense. In *Oreaster* the marginal plates are evident but not conspicuous, and the aboral surface bears immovable tubercles, including a carinal row. *Oreaster reticulatus* (Fig. 96), a large, handsome star, is common throughout the Florida–West Indies region, and *O. nodosus*, brilliantly colored red and blue, is abundant in the Indo-Pacific. *Pentaceropsis* lacks projecting tubercles, and the aboral surface is covered

Fig. 137.—Phanerozonia: Goniasteridae (continued). Above, *Pseudarchaster pusillus* littoral, California, aboral view. Below, *Ceramaster leptoceramus*, California, archibenthal, aboral view.

with convex ossicles of various sizes interspersed with papulae which here are not limited to definite areas. In *Nidorellia* there are high tubercles on the aboral surface, and the oral surface is also tuberculate. In *Asterodiscus* (Fig. 141) the body is covered with a warty skin, and the marginal plates are concealed except for two conspicuous ones on the aboral surface of the tips of the rays. *Culcita* and *Halityle* are plump pentagons with scarcely any arms (Fig. 95*C, D*); in *Culcita* the skeleton is concealed by the leathery surface bearing granules and more or less circular papular areas (Fig. 95*C*), whereas in *Halityle*, the marginals and reticulate skeleton are evident, and the papular areas have a triangular shape (Fig. 140).

The Asteropidae (= Gymnasteridae) is a small family in which the surface is also membranous, but the marginal plates are exposed and are more or less overlapping. There are two genera, *Petricia* in which the margins and aboral surface are devoid of spines and *Asterope* (= *Gymnasteria*) with a spiny margin and median row of spines along the aboral surface of the rays. *Asterope carinifera* (Fig. 141) is one of the most common sea stars of the Indo–West Pacific region.

The family Linckiidae (or Ophidiasteridae) is characterized by the small disk, long, flexible cylindroid arms, reduced and inconspicuous marginal plates, and mostly smooth surface although some species are warty. The skeleton consists of small rounded or squarish ossicles, closely placed to form a mosaic or pavement and usually covered with granules. The family is typical of shallow waters in tropical and subtropical zones. It was revised by H. L. Clark (1921), who recognized 20 genera, whereas Fisher in 1911 had recognized 12. The genera are distinguished chiefly on the basis of the distribution of papulae. In *Ophidiaster* (Fig. 142) the aboral ossicles are arranged in longitudinal rows and papulae occur in eight longitudinal bands on the arms. In the other genera to be mentioned, the aboral ossicles are irregularly disposed. Papulae occur on both surfaces of the arms, singly in *Fromia*, in small groups in *Nardoa* (Fig. 142). Papulae are limited to the aboral surface in *Linckia*, where they occur in rounded groups irregularly disposed (Fig. 98*A*), and in *Phataria*, where they are arranged in a band on each side of the arm (Fig. 166). *Linckia* is famous for the ability of its cast-off arms to regenerate a complete sea star (page 317). Of the several species of *Linckia*, the brilliantly blue *L. laevigata* is common in the Indo–West Pacific region and *L. guildingi* is circumtropical.

The family Poraniidae appears to be on the border line between the Phanerozonia and the Spinulosa. It has evident overlapping marginal plates, as in the Asteropidae, and the aboral surface is covered with a thick membrane. The body shape is stellate. Spines are wanting in *Dermasterias*, whereas in *Porania* and *Marginaster* they fringe the arms

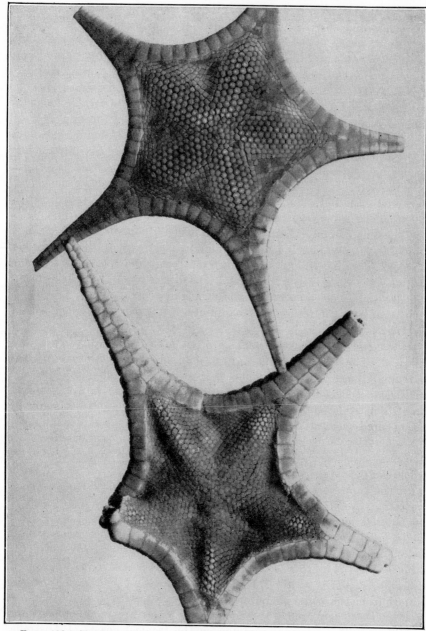

Fig. 138.—Phanerozonia: Goniasteridae (continued). Above, *Rosaster*. Below, *Nymphaster*. Note meeting of supramarginals on rays. Archibenthal, off the Philippines (*after Fisher, 1919, courtesy U.S. National Museum.*)

and in the latter also occur over the aboral surface. *Poraniomorpha* has some spines on the inframarginals, but they are insufficient to make a distinct fringe. The leather star *Dermasterias imbricata* (Fig. 143), purple with red markings, is found on the Pacific Coast from California to Alaska. *Porania pulvillus* and *Poraniomorpha hispidus* occur on north European coasts at moderate depths.

**22. Order Spinulosa.**—This order is not sharply separable from the Phanerozonia, although conspicuous marginal plates forming a broad vertical edge to the arms are usually wanting. The aboral skeleton is reticulate or imbricated and generally has low spines, not infrequently belonging to paxillae or pseudopaxillae. The mouth frame is of the adambulacral type, as in the Phanerozonia. The podia have the typical suckered form and occur in two rows in each ambulacral groove. Pedicellariae are rarely present.

The small family Ganeriidae (also called Radiasteridae) is again a borderline family, having distinct marginal plates and aboral paxillae; on the oral surface the plates are arranged in regular rows and bear one or two spines or a tuft of spinelets. The disk is broad, but the arms are usually somewhat elongated. Most of the genera of this family are limited to the antarctic and subantarctic (*Ganeria, Scotiaster, Cycethra, Perknaster*).

In the Asterinidae the body is often broadly stellate with a thin margin. The aboral surface is formed of scale-like, imbricated plates carrying groups or tufts of spinelets or granules, and the oral surface is also composed of imbricating plates bearing a tuft or fan of spinelets. In *Asterina* the main aboral plates are not crescentic and both surfaces are covered with tufts of small spines. *Asterina gibbosa* is a common sea star of western Europe, including the Mediterranean, and extends down the west coast of Africa to the Azores. In *Patiria* and *Patiriella* the aboral surface is covered with granules and the main plates are crescentic with the concave surface directed toward the disk, producing a pretty pattern. In *Patiria* the oral surface bears fan-like tufts of spines webbed together, whereas in *Patiriella* there are only one or two spines on each plate. *Patiria miniata*, typically red or orange but also occurring in other colors, is a well-known sea star of the Pacific Coast from California to Alaska (Figs. 144, 145). *Patierella* is limited to the Southern Hemisphere, where *P. exigua* is widely spread in the Indo–West Pacific. *Nepanthia* differs from the usual shape of the family in having a small disk and slender rays; here, too, the main aboral plates are more or less crescentiform. This genus is common on the tropical coasts of Australia. *Anseropoda* ( = *Palmipes*) is a very broadly pentagonal star remarkable for the wafer thinness of its body. On the aboral side there is a median crest along each ray, and both surfaces are provided with tufts of minute spinelets. *Anseropoda placenta* (Fig. 145) inhabits western Europe and the Mediterranean.

The Echinasteridae have a small disk and five slender cylindroid rays; the skeleton is reticulated with open meshes and single spines or a few

Fig. 139.—Phanerozonia: Goniasteridae (concluded). *Hippasteria equestris,* off Newfoundland, oral side; note numerous large bivalved pedicellariae.

small spines at the nodes. The members of this family are often red or orange. *Echinaster* (Fig. 94*A*), with a number of species in warmer waters, has single coarse spines at the nodes and lacks papulae on the oral surface. In *Henricia* there are small spines in groups or along ridges (Fig. 101*B*), and papulae occur on both surfaces. The blood star *Henricia sanguinolenta* is circumboreal (Fig. 146). *Poraniopsis* has wide skeletal meshes filled with numerous papulae and large single erect spines at the nodes.

Three small families, Mithrodiidae, Acanthasteridae, and Valvasteridae are separated from the Echinasteridae by their bifurcated ampullae. Each of these families contains a single genus, limited to warmer waters. *Mithrodia* has a very small disk, constricted from the bases of the narrow arms, and triangular skeletal meshes. *Acanthaster* is multirayed and very spiny (Fig. 97*A*). In *Valvaster* there are also triangular papular areas, but pedicellariae are present, and the suckers of the podia are supported by a skeletal rosette, rare in asteroids.

The Solasteridae or sun stars are multirayed stars (except for the five-rayed genus *Lophaster*), of characteristic appearance (Fig. 94*F*), with a broad disk continuous with the many, rather short tapering arms. The aboral skeleton is reticulated, beset with groups of spinelets resembling the crowns of paxillae. Some of the adambulacral spines tend to form transverse fans, as in the Pterasteridae. Main genera with up to 15 rays are *Crossaster*, with widely meshed skeleton and prominent groups of spinelets (Fig. 94*G*), and *Solaster*, with smaller skeletal meshes and shorter and more crowded bunches of spinelets. *Crossaster papposus* (Fig. 94*F*) is a very common circumboreal species. *Solaster endeca* (Fig. 147) is widely distributed in northern waters, and *S. stimpsoni* and *dawsoni* occur along the northern part of the Pacific Coast of North America. In *Heterozonias* prominent marginal paxillae are separated by longitudinally oriented plates bearing short spinelets; *H. alternatus* is found in deeper waters from Washington to California. The five-rayed *Lophaster* is represented by *L. furcilliger* in deeper waters from the Panamic region to the Bering Sea.

In the small five-rayed family Korethrasteridae, there are no prominent marginal paxillae and no plates on the oral side between the adambulacrals and the inframarginals; the spines on these two plate rows form continuous transverse series. *Korethraster*, with the paxilliform tufts of spinelets not webbed together, is known mainly by *K. hispidus* in Atlantic arctic waters, at moderate depths. In *Peribolaster*, the spines in the paxilliform tufts are webbed together; *P. biserialis* occurs at moderate depths off California.

The Pterasteridae, or cushion stars, present a very characteristic appearance, being plump, five-rayed asteroids with short broad arms. The aboral surface is composed of paxillae whose crowns are united by a supradorsal membrane which forms the apparent aboral surface and covers over the nidamental chamber. The supradorsal membrane is pierced by numerous small closable pores and a large central opening provided with a valve; there is, further, a row of openings into the nidamental chamber to the outer side of the adambulacral spines. On the oral surface there are no plates between the adambulacral and infra-marginal rows. In *Pteraster, Diplopteraster,* and *Retaster,* the adambu-lacral spines are webbed to form transverse fans, and the long outer adambulacral spines are united by a web into a longitudinal membrane

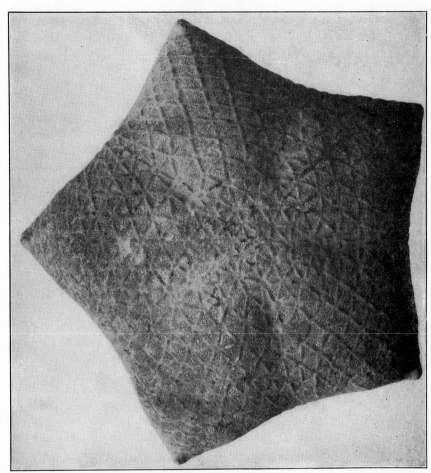

FIG. 140.—Phanerozonia: Oreasteridae. *Halityle,* littoral, near the Philippines *(after Fisher, 1919, courtesy U.S. National Museum.)*

that is not merged into the oral floor of the rays (Fig. 102*G*), but forms a projecting fringe. *Pteraster* lacks conspicuous muscle fibers in the supradorsal membrane. There are about 30 species (Fisher, 1940), of which *P. militaris, pulvillus,* and *obscurus* are circumarctic and *P. tes-selatus* (Fig. 95*B*) is found from Puget Sound to the Bering Sea. *Diplop-teraster* and *Retaster* have a prominent network of muscle bands in the supradorsal membrane, and the former is distinguished by the four rows of podia in the ambulacral grooves. *Diplopteraster multipes* appears to be circumboreal, and *Retaster insignis* is common in the Indo-Pacific region. In *Hymenaster*, with many species, the adambulacral spines are not webbed to form transverse fans, and the long outer adambulacral spines are merged into the oral floor. The genus inhabits mostly archibenthal and abyssal waters; *Hymenaster pellucidus* (Fig. 148) is common in arctic and boreal areas of the North Atlantic at depths of 15 to 2800 m.

**23. Order Forcipulata.**—The members of this order are distinguished from all other asteroids by the presence of typical pedicellariae provided with a basal piece and two valves. Generally they have a small disk and elongated tapering arms with rounded sides, hence are devoid of a definite margin and conspicuous marginal plates. The skeleton is reticular, usually arranged in the arms in transverse arches, corresponding to every second or third adambulacral, and mostly also showing more or less regular longitudinal series, as carinals and marginals (Fig. 101*E*). The mouth frame is usually of the ambulacral type. The podia occur in two or four rows in each ambulacral groove and are provided with simple ampullae. Papulae usually occur on all surfaces. Four families are recognized by Fisher (1928).

The deep-sea family Brisingidae presents a characteristic appearance, having a small, circular, well-delimited disk and numerous, slender bristly arms (Fig. 149). The aboral skeleton is weakly developed and is not reticulate, consisting of thin plates or of transverse arches separated by wide areas of body wall without ossicles. Only crossed pedicellariae are present (Fig. 105*B*), and there are but two rows of podia in each ambulacral groove. Fisher in 1928 listed 16 genera, and in 1940 he added the antarctic genus *Odinella* (Fig. 150), with interlocking spines at the ray bases forming brood pouches. In *Odinia* and *Odinella* numerous conspicuous papulae are present on the aboral surface of the disk and proximal parts of the rays, and in *Brisingenes* there is a circle of small papulae at the edge of the disk, two to each ray, but papulae are wanting in the remaining genera. The gonads are serial, that is, consist of numerous tufts in a row in the sides of the rays in *Brisingenes*, *Brisinga*, *Craterobrisinga*, *Brisingaster*, and *Freyellaster*, whereas in *Freyella* (Fig. 95*A*), *Asterostephane*, and some other genera, each ray contains the usual pair of gonads.

The Heliasteridae contains the single genus *Heliaster*, in which there is a very broad disk merged into numerous (20 to 44) short tapering rays. The skeleton is reticulate, and both straight and crossed pedicellariae are present. A single madreporite is present. Only the central part of the broad disk is the true disk, for the rays are continued inward by long interbrachial septa. The genus is peculiar in that at their inner ends the interbrachial septa are joined by a circular vertical wall (discobrachial

Fig. 141.—Phanerozonia: Oreasteridae; Asteropidae. Above, *Asterodiscus*. Below *Asterope carinifera*.

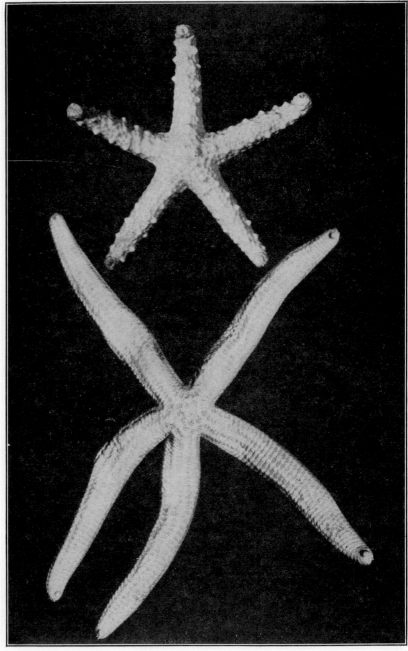

Fig. 142.—Phanerozonia: Linckiidae.  Above, *Nardoa tuberculata*, Philippines.  Below, *Ophidiaster ophidianus*, Mediterranean.  Note papular areas on both.

wall) which almost cuts off the coelom of the disk from that of the rays. *Heliaster* (Fig. 151), with several species, is confined to shallow waters in the Panamic region. The genus was monographed by H. L. Clark (1907), who has shown that *Heliaster* begins life with five rays and that additional rays are added in all the interradii except that which contains the madreporite.

The Zoroasteridae (reviewed by H. L. Clark, 1920) are deep-water forcipulates with a small disk and five long slender arms in which the plates are arranged in longitudinal rows. Pedicellariae, when present, are of the straight type only. There are mostly four rows of podia in each ambulacral groove. The aboral surface bears small delicate spines in *Zoroaster* (Fig. 152) with small papular areas and in *Myxoderma* with larger papular areas between the carinals and supramarginals. The aboral surface is devoid of spines and covered with a thick membrane in *Cnemidaster*. According to Fisher (1928) zoroasterids are abundant on muddy bottom in deep water off the Pacific Coast of the United States; there are also a number of Indo-Pacific species.

We come now to the large family Asteriidae which includes the majority of the forcipulates and is said by Fisher (1928) to be a polyphyletic aggregation of genera. Most members of this family have the general appearance made familiar to zoologists by the genus *Asterias*, with a disk of moderate size continued broadly into rounded tapering arms of moderate length, mostly five or six in number, but numerous in some genera, and with a reticulated bumpy or warty surface (Fig. 97*B*). The skeleton is reticulate, and in the arms the ossicles are more or less arranged in longitudinal series, as illustrated in Fig. 101*E*. Both crossed and straight pedicellariae are present, and there are typically four rows of podia in the ambulacral grooves. There are about 40 genera, subdivided by Fisher (1928) into seven subfamilies, later (1940) reduced to six. In 1930 Fisher provided very useful lists of genera, species, and synonyms for some of the subfamilies, especially the Asteriinae.

The subfamily Pedicellasterinae is characterized by the incomplete mouth frame, as the first pair of adambulacrals of each row do not meet medially; the crossed pedicellariae are scattered and do not occur in circlets around spines, and pedicellariae are wanting on the adambulacral spines. The members of this group have five or six rays and two rows of podia, at least distally; they are mostly confined to deeper waters. Conspicuous inframarginal spines are wanting in *Pedicellaster* and *Anteliaster*, present in *Tarsaster* and *Ampheraster*. *Pedicellaster* has two kinds of crossed pedicellaria with conspicuous spine-like teeth along the valves of the larger sort, whereas in *Anteliaster* the teeth of the crossed pedicellariae are terminal, numerous, and tiny. *Ampheraster* has curious straight pedicellariae with expanded tips provided with long spines that interclasp when the valves are closed (Fig. 158*A*); such are wanting in *Tarsaster*.

In the remaining subfamilies the mouth frame is of the usual ambulacral type, and there are nearly always four rows of podia per groove;

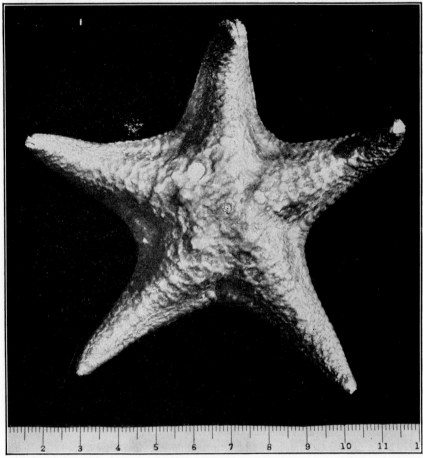

Fig. 143.—Phanerozonia (concluded). Poraniidae. *Dermasterias imbricata*, Pacific Coast of North America.

the adambulacral spines do not bear pedicellariae except in the last subfamily, the Asteriinae. The subfamily Neomorphasterinae is known only by the genus *Neomorphaster*, dredged by the *Challenger* (Sladen, 1889) near the Azores at about 1900 m. In this the primary larval plates of the aboral surface of the disk are retained as such, and the plates of the five arms occur in longitudinal rows, as in *Zoroaster*. These characters are wanting in the rest of the subfamilies, which further are provided with wreaths of crossed pedicellariae around spine bases. The

Fig. 144.—Spinulosa: Asterinidae. *Patiria miniata*, aboral view, common asterinid of the California Coast.

Labidiasterinae have numerous (9 to 50) long slender rays, prominent single inframarginal spines, and thick ruffs of crossed pedicellariae around both inframarginal and aboral spines. This subfamily consists of *Coronaster*, with 9 to 11 rays, *Rathbunaster* (Fig. 153) with 12 to 20, and *Labidiaster* with 25 to 50. The Coscinasteriinae present a spiny appearance with rows of spines along the median and lateral aboral surfaces of the rays and with two spines on each inframarginal plate; the aboral spines are encircled by a wreath of crossed pedicellariae. In *Astrometis*, *Sclerasterias*, *Astrostole*, *Coscinasterias*, and *Marthasterias* there is also a cluster of crossed pedicellariae around the outer of the two inframarginal spines. *Astrometis* and *Sclerasterias* have five rays in the adult; the latter is fissiparous when young (page 313), at which time it is provided with six rays. *Astrometis sertulifera* is common in shallow water off California and under the erroneous name of *Asterias forreri* was the subject of a famous study of behavior by Jennings (1907). *Astrostole* has seven to nine rays and is not known to undergo fission *Coscinasterias*, with seven to 12 rays and fissiparous habits, is represented by *C. tenuispina* (Fig.155) at Bermuda, *C. acutispina* around Japan, and *C. calamaria* in the Indo-Pacific. The nonfissiparous *Marthasterias glacialis* (Fig. 154) with five arms and much employed for experimental purposes is common on European coasts and also extends into the Mediterranean and down the west coast of Africa. In the genera *Stylasterias*, *Lethasterias*, and *Orthasterias*, both inframarginal spines carry a cluster of pedicellaria. *Notasterias*, confined to the antarctic, has a peculiar type of crossed pedicellaria with crossed tips (Fig. 158*B*, *C*), mostly rather large, reaching as much as 3 mm. in length. This genus was formerly made the type of the subfamily Notasteriinae, but in 1940 Fisher withdrew this subfamily, uniting it with the Coscinasteriinae. In the small subfamily Pycnopodiinae there is practically no aboral skeleton, so that the rays are soft and flexible; otherwise this family is similar to the Coscinasteriinae with two spines on each inframarginal plate and prominent sheaths of crossed pedicellariae around all of the spines. Of the few species in this group the most important is the 20-rayed star *Pycnopodia helianthoides*, a very large asteroid with mostly 15 to 23 soft rays and with the whole surface crowded with clumps of branched papulae and thick pompoms of crossed pedicellariae around spine bases. This species occurs from southern California to the Aleutian Islands on rocky bottom in shallow waters and is a conspicuous member of the fauna of Puget Sound.

The subfamily Asteriinae includes the majority of the Asteriidae. Here the adambulacral spines often bear pedicellariae, singly or in groups (Fig. 97*D*), and the general body armature is more of the nature of tubercles or warts than of spines. The genera are divided by Fisher (1930) into one group including those with pedicellariae on the adambulacral spines and another group without such pedicellariae. In the former are ranged the genera *Asterias*, *Evasterias*, and *Leptasterias*. The last is distinguished by the ventrally opening gonads in correlation with the brooding habit. *Leptasterias* is a genus of small five- or six-

FIG. 145.—Spinulosa: Asterinidae (concluded). Above, *Patiria miniata*, oral view. Below, *Anseropoda placenta*, aboral view.

FIG. 146.—Spinulosa: Echinasteridae. *Henricia sanguinolenta,* common blood star of circumboreal waters.

rayed stars with many species, subspecies, and varieties in cold northern waters, as *hexactis* (Fig. 94*B*), *arctica, polaris, groenlandica* (Fig. 115*E*), *camtschatika,* and so on. In *Asterias* and *Evasterias* the gonads open dorsally; *Asterias* has but one row of ossicles on the oral side between the adambulacrals and the inframarginals, so that the latter are distinctly on the oral surface, whereas in *Evasterias* there are three to six rows of ossicles lateral to the adambulacrals, so that the inframarginals occupy a lateral position. The genus *Asterias* (*Asteracanthion* or *Asteracanthium* in old literature), formerly made a catchall for a large number of species (close to 150), has now been restricted to a few forms of which the chief ones are *A. rubens* on north European coasts, *A. vulgaris* on the Atlantic Coast of North America from Labrador to Long Island Sound, *A. forbesi* from Maine to the Gulf of Mexico, and *A. amurensis* from the Bering Sea, Japan, and Korea northward. The principal species of *Evasterias* is *troscheli*, abundant from Puget Sound to Alaska (Fig. 156). Of the genera without pedicellariae on the ambulacral spines, the most important in the Northern Hemisphere is *Pisaster*, large, heavy, five- or six-rayed stars with a single spine on the adambulacral plates, two to five rows of plates between the adambulacrals and inframarginals, furcate pedicellariae (Fig. 104*C*), and strands of pedicellariae attached along the borders of the ambulacral grooves (Fig. 105*C*). *Pisaster ochraceus* (Fig. 157) is a characteristic sea star of the Pacific Coast from California to Alaska, and other species of *Pisaster* live in the same area, including *P. brevispinus*, one of the largest-known asteroids with an *R* of 320 mm., or about 2 feet from tip to tip. *Stephanasterias* (Fig. 155) is a genus of small, fissiparous stars with up to nine rays, two or three spines on each adambulacral ossicle, and no rows of plates on the oral side between the adambulacrals and inframarginals. *S. albula* is a circumpolar species. *Stichastrella* without rosettes of pedicellariae around the spines is represented by *S. rosea*, a rather large rose-colored star found on west European coasts. A number of asteriine genera, mostly with brooding habits, are limited to the antarctic, as *Anasterias, Lysasterias, Diplasterias, Cryptasterias, Neosomilaster, Smilasterias,* and *Granaster*.

**24. Ecology: Habits and Behavior.**—The sea stars are exclusively marine benthonic animals, inhabiting various types of bottom, mainly in the littoral zone, where they crawl about or may remain quiescent at times, either in the open or more or less concealed. Galtsoff and Loosanoff (1939) state that *Asterias forbesi* is found equally abundant on hard, rocky, sandy, or soft bottom and that its distribution is determined primarily by the abundance of bivalves, its main food. However, preference for a particular type of bottom is shown by many species. On the Pacific Coast of North America a number of species are limited to rocky bottom (Ricketts and Calvin, 1953): *Linckia columbiae, Astrometis sertulifera, Patiria miniata, Solaster dawsoni, Leptasterias aequalis, Henricia leviuscula, Dermasterias imbricata,* and *Pisaster ochraceus*. The common mud star *Ctenodiscus crispatus* inhabits soft, muddy bottom. *Asterina gibbosa* is typically found among stones. Species that live more or less buried in sand necessarily dwell on sandy bottom; this applies to *Anseropoda placenta*, most species of *Astropecten*, and some species of

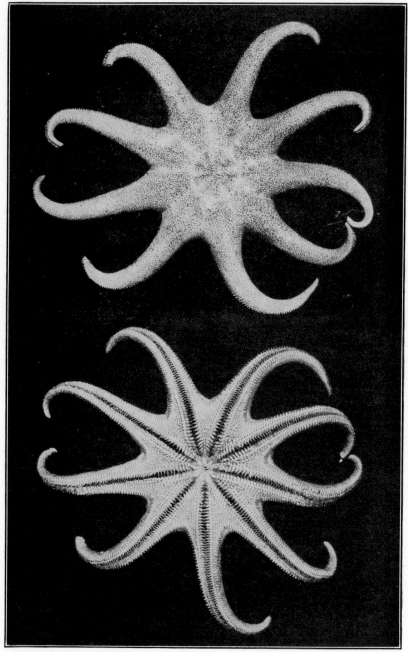

FIG. 147.—Spinulosa: Solasteridae.  Above, *Solaster endeca*, common northern sun star,
aboral view.  Below, *Solaster endeca*, oral view.

*Luidia* (Mangold, 1908a; Kenk, 1944; Mori and Matutani, 1952). In burying itself, *Astropecten* descends vertically, throwing the sand to both sides of each ray by outward flings of the podia and may cover itself within a minute.

The Benthopectinidae can possibly swim by thrashing the arms (page 270), but if so would presumably not be able to lift themselves much from the bottom. All others move by crawling on the bottom, mostly at a rather slow rate which varies with different species, somewhat inversely with size. The following figures on the rate of locomotion have been found in the literature: *Asterina gibbosa*, 2 to 5 cm. per minute (Mangold, 1908a; Crozier, 1935); *Asterias rubens*, 5 to 8 cm. per minute (Romanes and Ewart, 1881; Preyer, 1886); *Asterias forbesi*, 15 cm. per minute (Coe, 1912); *Oreaster nodosus*, 20 cm. per minute (Ohshima, 1940); *Astropecten auranciacus*, 30 to 60 cm. per minute (Preyer, 1886); *Astropecten spinulosus*, 60 cm. per minute (Tortonese, 1950a); and *Crossaster papposus* (small), 2 m. per minute (Milligan, 1916b), apparently the speed record for the group. According to Jennings (1907; also Diebschlag, 1938) asteroids explore their surroundings very thoroughly by means of the sensory podia on the ray tips and, when on the move, keep these stretched out. They tend to get started in one direction and to continue in this direction for some time before changing course, clambering over objects and climbing up the walls of aquaria in an obstinate adherence to a direction once started. They tend to remain in one locality and do not wander very far; the maximum distance covered by *Asterias forbesi* marked with a blue dye was 1 mile in 10 months (Galtsoff and Loosanoff, 1939). Similarly marked *Asterias vulgaris* migrated a maximum of 200 m., with an average of 20 m., in 4 months (G. Smith, 1940). Spärck (1932) noted that *Asterias rubens* failed in 4 summer months to repopulate oysters beds only 100 m. away from which they had been cleaned out.

Some consideration has been given in the literature to the question whether asteroids tend to move with some particular ray in advance; of course the rays can be identified only with reference to the madreporite. Preyer (1887) made observations on five species (*Luidia ciliaris, Astropecten bispinosus, pentacanthus,* and *auranciacus,* and *Marthasterias glacialis*) and considered that only *A. pentacanthus* exhibited any ray preference, in this case for rays D and E. Bohn (1909) reported that *Asterias rubens* shows some preference for advancing on rays A and D, but Diebschlag (1938) failed to find any ray preference in this species or in four other species (*Coscinasterias tenuispina* and *Astropecten irregularis, bispinosus,* and *spinulosus*). *Asterias forbesi* tends to move with ray D in advance (L. Cole, 1913), but no such ray preference could be found in *Echinaster crassispina* (Cowles, 1909, 1911). *Pteraster tesselatus*

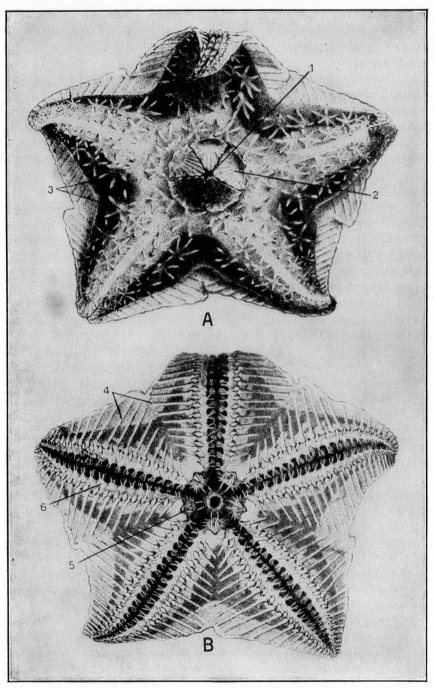

Fig. 148.—Spinulosa: Pterasteridae.  *A, Hymenaster pellucidus,* North Atlantic, aboral view.  *B,* same, oral view.  (*Both after Sladen,* 1889.)  1, osculum; 2, valves of osculum; 3, crowns of paxillae; 4, long adambulacral spines merged into oral surface; 5, adambulacral pieces of mouth frame; 6, adambulacral ossicles.

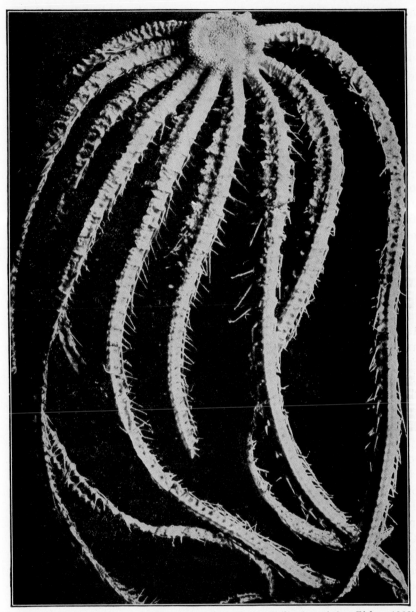

Fig. 149.—Forcipulata: Brisingidae. *Brisinga*, off the Philippines (*after Fisher*, 1919)

shows a distinct tendency to advance on ray E (Rodenhouse and Guberlet, 1946). The clearest case of morphological and physiological bilaterality in asteroids is that of *Pycnopodia helianthoides* (Kjerchow-Agersborg
1918, 1922), which invariably advances with what was ray E in the
newly metamorphosed star, that is, with the ray opposite the site of
formation of all the postnatal rays (page 247; Fig. 158*D*).

Light appears to play a considerable role in the life of asteroids;
most are negative to light, seeking shaded areas. The behavior of such
a negatively phototactic sea star was described by Jennings (1907) in
his study of *Astrometis sertulifera*. This species is aroused to activity
by light and moves away from it until it finds a shaded area, where it
comes to rest, reacting to the intensity of light and not to the direction
of the sun's rays. If placed under conditions where it cannot escape
strong light, it continues activity, appearing very disturbed, and finally
takes up a position of rest in which ventral structures and arm tips
are protected from light as much as possible by the rest of the body.
*Asterias forbesi* and *Henricia sanguinolenta* are also negative to light
(MacCurdy, 1912, 1913), retracting any parts subjected to sudden
illumination. Many sea stars, however, show a positive response to
light. Romanes and Ewart (1881) and Romanes (1885) reported that
*Asterias rubens, Crossaster papposus,* and *Astropecten auranciacus* are all
strongly positive to light, and Preyer (1887) found that *Marthasterias
glacialis, Echinaster sepositus,* and *Asterina gibbosa* would invariably
assemble at the lighted end of an aquarium and that the last, when
placed on a substrate marked off in white, gray, and black squares,
would come to rest on the white squares. Mangold (1909) observed
that *Asterina gibbosa* and *panceri* are positive to moderate light but
avoid both shade and direct sunlight, whereas *Pentagonaster placenta* is
positive to sunlight, despite the fact that it normally lives at 40 to 400 m.,
where dim light prevails. *Echinaster crassispina* moves from regions of
lower to regions of higher light intensity without regard to the direction
of the sun's rays, is also positive to all colors (Cowles, 1909, 1910, 1911),
and will select a white wall when placed in an otherwise black container
(Cowles, 1914); in its natural habitat (Tortugas) this species and also
*Astropecten duplicatus* lie on sandy or rocky bottom in shallow water
fully exposed to direct sunlight, and the same is true of *Oreaster reticulatus,*
observed by the author in the Bahamas. Variable results have been
reported for *Asterias rubens,* found by Bohn (1908) to be generally
negative to light, although readily altering its response; by Weel (1935)
to be positive to weak light; by Plessner (1913) to be positive to all
intensities; and by Romanes and Ewart and Ewart (above) and Just
(1927) to give a decided positive response. The claim of Just that
*A. rubens* when exposed to two opposite lights of equal intensity would

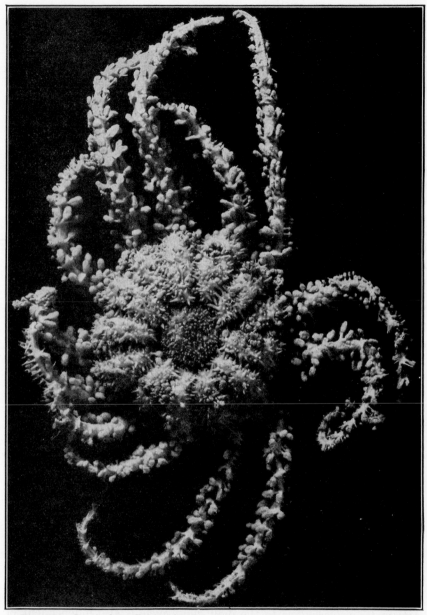

Fig. 150.—Forcipulata; Brisingidae (concluded). *Odinella nutrix*, antarctic brooding brisingid, with large clubs of pedicellariae and swollen ray bases whose interlocking spines act as brood chambers (*after Fisher*, 1940).

follow a resultant path between the lights was denied by Diebschlag (1938), who criticized Just's setup. According to Diebschlag, freshly collected specimens of *A. rubens* and *Astropecten irregularis* are nearly always positive to light and may be led around by shining a light on an arm tip, for about 15 minutes, after which they tire and become indifferent to light. He found that when exposed to two or more lights of equal intensity these stars would simply move directly toward one of them, ignoring the others. According to the resultant theory, these sea stars when surrounded by five lights of equal intensity should not move at all, but in fact they proceed toward one of the lights. Reports on *Asterina gibbosa* also appear rather discordant; Crozier (1935) declared that this species is indifferent to light, although Preyer and Mangold (above) obtained positive reactions. According to Kalmus (1929) only young specimens respond positively, moving directly to the lighted side of the container, choosing the brighter of two lights, selecting the lightest background, and changing direction when the direction of light is altered. *Pteraster tesselatus* is negative to bright light and to blue and yellow but is positive to moderate intensity and to green (Rodenhouse and Guberlet, 1946). Perhaps the most remarkable of all responses of asteroids to light is that of *Astropecten polyacanthus* (Mori and Matutani, 1952). This species lives buried in the sand most of the time but emerges twice daily to hunt food when the light reaches a certain intensity, toward morning and toward evening. It does not move about either in darkness or in strong light but only in a definite, rather low intensity. However, the tendency to emerge from the sand grows stronger as daylight approaches, and the time spent in activity on the surface of the sand is markedly lengthened in hungry animals. The rhythm with respect to light is retained for 2 or 3 days when the animals are kept in constant darkness, but is then lost.

Most of the investigators quoted above have considered the question whether response to light depends on the integrity of the ocelli in the optic cushion. It is to be noted that sea stars usually move about with the arm tips curved aborally, thus exposing the optic cushion and the terminal sensory podia. Results with regard to the role of the ocelli in light reactions are discordant. Romanes, Preyer, Just, Plessner, Kalmus, and Diebschlag found that a directive effect of light is abolished or rendered uncertain by removal of the arm tips, whereas Mangold and Cowles reported no effect of such removal; the rhythmic behavior of *Astropecten polyacanthus* to the daily light cycle is also independent of the presence of the ocelli. It would appear certain that in at least some species the ocelli are necessary for a directed response to light; for instance, Diebschlag's observation that an isolated arm of photopositive stars would move directly toward a light base forward (as usual in

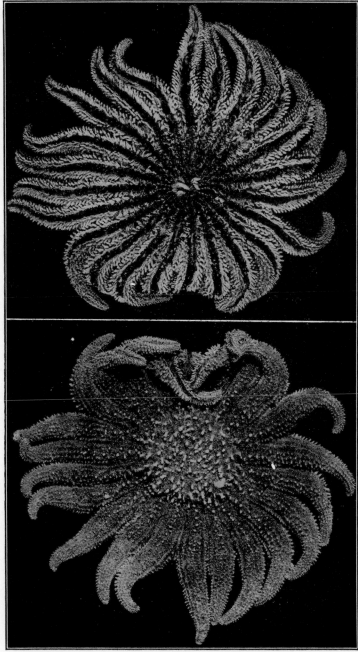

Fig. 151.—Forcipulata: Heliasteridae. *Heliaster kubiniji*, Panamic region; note numerous rays but single madreporite.

Fig. 152.—Forcipulata: Zoroasteridae. *Zoroaster evermanni*, off California, 400 to 1200 m.

isolated arms) but with the arm tip curved over the back so that the ocelli faced the light is rather convincing of a light-perceptive role of the ocelli. On the other hand, the general body surface of asteroids is undoubtedly sensitive to light. Sudden illumination of any part of *Asterias forbesi* evokes local contraction regardless of the presence of the ocelli (MacCurdy, 1912, 1913). Moore (1921) verified this result, that a flash of sunlight applied to the oral surface will cause the podia to retract and loosen hold and the groove to close locally; the podia do not respond to illumination of the aboral surface. The papulae and podia of *Oreaster reticulatus* contract and the ambulacral groove closes when spots of light or shadow are thrown on them (Cowles, 1910, 1911), and these reactions take place in the absence of ocelli. Similarly, in the absence of the ocelli, the podia of *Astropecten auranciacus* retract and the ambulacral groove closes locally if light is shone or flashed upon them, with a latent period dependent on the intensity of the light (Hess, 1914); the same reaction is given by isolated arms or pieces of arms, but no response follows illumination of the aboral surface.

Asteroids often clamber up rocks or ascend the walls of aquaria, but probably in response to factors other than gravity, often merely as an expression of a tendency to continue with great persistency in a direction once started. However, *Asterina gibbosa* is definitely negative to gravity (Mangold, 1909; Kalmus, 1929; Crozier, 1935); it will ascend a glass cylinder completely filled with water, coming to rest beneath the glass cover and so remaining for hours, and repeating the performance every time the cylinder is inverted. This behavior also occurs in the dark and will be carried out by one-fifth of the disk with an arm attached but not following removal of the nerve ring. It is generally believed that the pull of the body on the podia constitutes the means of perception of the direction of gravity. Crozier attached corks to the body so as to produce an upward pull and reported that under such circumstances *Asterina* descends.

Mechanical stimulation of the podia causes their retraction (Preyer, 1886; Mangold, 1908a; Kalmus, 1929), and this contraction may spread through the arm concerned, then to other arms, and finally to the entire animal; but such retraction of the podia is always followed by their extension. Stimulation of the sides of an arm causes the podia to point toward the stimulated spot, and this reaction may spread along the ray. Simultaneous stimulation of two points along the same side of a ray evokes pointing of the podia straight laterally, not toward the stimulated spots; simultaneous stimulation of opposite sides of the ambulacral groove results in bending of local podia to the stimulated spots, but the remaining podia of the ray point distally if the stimulation is slight, centrally if stronger. Retraction on contact and bending to lateral

Fig. 153.—Forcipulata: Asteriidae. *Rathbunaster californicus*, off California, 650 m. (*after Fisher*, 1928).

stimulation also occur in isolated arms. Mechanical stimulation of the aboral surface of an arm evokes local contraction of the podia to the oral side of the stimulated spot; but elsewhere the podia extend and the animal moves away. Preyer formulated the general rule that any stimulation of the oral or aboral surface of a ray evokes local contraction of the podia; in the case of oral stimulation such contraction may spread throughout the entire animal, but the contraction does not spread following aboral stimulation. In either case all contractions are followed by extension of the podia, apparently as a preliminary to flight. Transmission of stimuli from one arm to another is always by way of the radial nerves and nerve ring, never by way of the surface network. The podia of isolated arms react the same as when part of the intact animal. Moore (1920) discovered the *dorsal reflex*, that is, the dorsal flexure of an arm following stimulation of its aboral surface; this was verified by Mangold (1921). The dorsal reflex may be transmitted to the other arms, with resulting general curvature of the arms toward the aboral side, but only by way of the radial nerves and nerve ring. Isolated arms also give the dorsal reflex if their radial nerve is intact. Presumably dorsal curvature of the arms is brought about by contraction of the muscle strand in the middorsal wall of the rays. A special reaction to contact or mechanical stimulation is given by *Anseropoda placenta*. This species, it will be recalled, is very thin and flat and of pentagonal shape (Fig. 145). When at rest it lies in what seems to be a contracted condition, with the body wall between the rays indented, making the rays more evident. When stimulated to activity by touching the aboral surface, this animal first expands to the pentagonal shape, gives the dorsal reflex, and finally moves off in the expanded shape (Mangold, 1908b; Fröhlich, 1910). These reactions depend on the integrity of the radial nerves, and cuts indicate that transmission through the nerve net occurs only in the transverse direction; impulses will not go around a lateral cut as they will in echinoids.

Of all environmental relations of asteroids, contact is probably the most important. Keeping the oral surface, especially the podia, in contact with a substratum probably supersedes all other reactions, as shown by the fact that the righting reflex, that is, turning over into the normal position when placed on their backs, is given by all asteroids, with a facility depending on their body shape and flexibility. This reaction has been studied by a long succession of observers: Romanes and Ewart (1881), Romanes (1885), Preyer (1886), Jennings (1907), Moore (1910a, 1910b, 1920, 1921), L. Cole (1913), Russell (1919), Mangold (1921), Wolf (1925), Fraenkel (1928), Kalmus (1929), Diebschlag (1938), Ohshima (1940), and Tortonese (1950). The detailed movements involved in righting are often very variable, as noted by

Fig. 154.—Forcipulata: Asteriidae (continued). *Marthasterias glacialis.*

Jennings, but in general can be classified into three categories (Ohshima): somersaulting, folding over, and assuming the tulip form. When placed on its back, the asteroid usually lies quiescent for a brief period, then gives the dorsal reflex, bending the arm tips aborally. Some of the arm tips thus come in contact with the substratum; typically two then attach by the podia (Fig. 159A) and begin walking, so to speak, beneath the animal, bringing more and more podia into action. The rest of the sea star gradually rises up and eventually is lowered into the normal position, so that the animal in effect turns a somersault. If three arms attach, the two outer ones accomplish the righting, and the middle one becomes strongly bent under temporarily. If four or five arms take hold, righting is impeded until some let go. Folding over is a variant of somersaulting; the unattached part of the body, instead of elevating, doubles over on the attached part and then gradually slides into position. The assumption of the tulip form permits righting without much use of the podia; the animal rises up on the tips of the arms into a bud-like shape with the oral surface outward (Fig. 159B) and then just falls over. The inverted tulip form is also sometimes employed; here the tips of the arms are brought together above the animal with the aboral surface outward (Fig. 159C), and the animal than falls over and straightens out into the normal position. The more agile species usually right in less than a minute, often in 20 to 30 seconds, using the somersault method. *Echinaster sepositus* and species of *Astropecten* require 2 to 3 minutes, *Asterias forbesi* rights in 1 to 6 minutes, and *Marth. glacialis* in 8 or 9. The short-armed *Astropecten* species are apt to employ the tulip method (Fig. 159B). The large, heavy, and clumsy *Oreaster nodosus*, studied by Ohshima, may right in 2 to 90 minutes, usually requiring 6 or 7 minutes; it usually employs folding over or the tulip method as the podia are too weak to pull the heavy body over. Special methods are employed by plump pentagonal forms. Thus *Culcita* (Fig. 95C, D) rights by inflating half of the body, so that some podia can take hold, and then rolls over (Ohshima). In *Pteraster* (Fig. 95B) dorsal curvature of the rays permits some podia to take hold, and by slow deep inflations more are able to adhere, until finally the body falls over (Rodenhouse and Guberlet, 1946).

Some authors have endeavored to discover whether asteroids always turn on the same arms. Jennings found this to be the case in *Astrometis sertulifera*, which tends strongly to right on the arms adjacent to the madreporite, that is, C and D, and rarely employs the arms opposite the madreporite. The same arms that are directed forward in locomotion are also used to turn on in righting in *Pycnopodia helianthoides* (Kjerchow-Agersborg, 1918). The positively phototactic *Asterina gibbosa* is apt to employ the arms facing the lighted side of the container, so that the somersault brings the animal closer to the light source.

FIG. 155.—Forcipulata: Asteriidae (continued). Two small fissiparous asteriids, regenerating after fission. Above, *Stephanasterias albula;* below, *Coscinasterias tenuispina;* scale applies to both specimens.

364

Fig. 156.—Forcipulata: Asteriidae (continued). *Evasterias troscheli.*

Righting necessitates a coordinated action of all the arms and podia and is seriously delayed and interfered with if the nerve ring is cut through at one or more interradii or if the radial nerves are cut across at the arm base. The nervously isolated arms twist and turn without coordination, but righting may eventually be accomplished even if the nervous connections of all five arms have been severed. Isolated arms or pieces of arms will right if their shape permits. The short broad arms of *Astropecten* cannot right from mechanical difficulties but will do so if narrowed by slicing off their sides (Wolf).

Most of the investigations on righting have been directed toward the question of the nature of the stimulus that evokes righting. Upon this point there is much argumentation in the literature. Preyer (1886) claimed that sea stars suspended in water would right and that therefore righting results from a central impulse and does not depend on peripheral stimulation; and Jennings (1907) took much the same position. Moore (1910a, 1920) and Russell (1919) came to the conclusion that the positive stereotropism of the podia is the releasing factor for the reaction; the latter showed that righting does not occur unless the podia make contact with a sufficiently solid object and is not attempted if the available objects are too light. Mangold (1921) attributed the righting reaction to stimulation of the aboral surface and claimed that isolated arms or entire animals deprived of their aboral wall would not right. This statement appears to be incorrect, as Wolf (1925), Fraenkel (1928), and Diebschlag (1938) all observed righting under such conditions, although often much delayed. Wolf was of the opinion that the weight of the viscera against the aboral wall sets off the righting reaction; but Fraenkel in a critical review of the whole question found that asteroids would right after complete removal of both the aboral wall and the digestive tract, and this was verified by Diebschlag. Fraenkel denied that animals suspended in sea water would right but found that they give the dorsal reflex regardless of their orientation in the water. He returned to the view attributing righting to the stereotropism of the podia and found that animals whose podia had been removed would not attempt to right. But this is denied by Diebschlag, who states that asteroids will right following removal of the podia if the radial nerves are left intact. This author returned to the idea that the righting reflex is centrally originated; the animal is unable to move about or carry on any activities in the upside-down position, hence rights. As isolated arms can right, one must suppose that the central impulse can originate in the radial nerves as well as in the nerve ring. However, it is difficult to believe that the animal can be aware of its reversed position without some sort of information coming from peripheral structures. Positive stereotropism of the podia must be a potent factor in all asteroid activities.

Very little information is available concerning response to chemical stimulation. Romanes and Ewart (1881) and Preyer (1886) indicate that the reaction to chemical stimulation is similar to the response to mechanical stimulation. If acid is dropped upon the podia, they retract, the groove closes locally, the contraction may spread to other

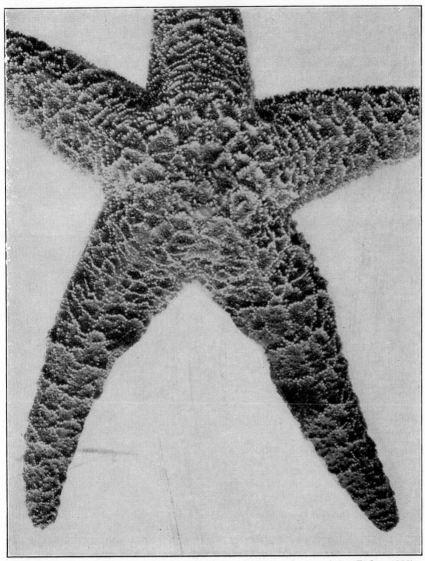

Fig. 157.—Forcipulata: Asteriidae (concluded). *Pisaster ochraceus* (*after Fisher*, 1930).

arms to a varying degree; extension then follows. Dropping of acid on the oral surface of the disk results in podial retraction in all arms, to a diminishing degree in the peripheral direction. Acid dropped on the aboral surface of an arm evokes momentary retraction of the podia to the oral side of the stimulated spot, and this is followed by general extension and activity of the podia, presumably indicative of a flight

reaction.   A drop of acid placed on the tip of a ray evokes strong contraction of the ray (Moore, 1920).   Dropping a salt crystal near a sea
star causes retraction of the nearest podia, closure of the grooves, and
flight away from the chemical (Mangold, 1908a; Kalmus, 1929).   The
ability of sea stars to detect food giving off juices is variously reported.
Romanes (1885) noted that freshly caught sea stars gave little response
to food, but that hungry aquarium specimens might be led about by a
piece of food held with a forceps,
although unfortunately the distance involved was not stated.
Isolated arms were also seen to
respond to food.   Removal of the
sensory podia at the arm tips was
said not to affect the food response.
Milligan (1915) saw specimens of
*Asterias rubens* move to dead fish
at distances of 1½ inches, 6 inches,
and 2 feet, respectively.   G. Smith
(1940) reported that *Asterias vulgaris* appeared to move directly to
food 12 m. away, requiring 2 days
in which to reach it.   It is well
known that sea stars will accumulate in lobster traps, feeding on
the bait therein, and presumably
could not so aggregate without
some perception at a distance of

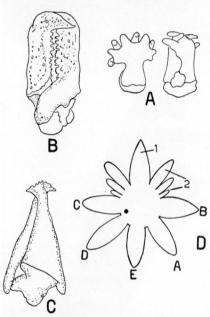

Fig. 158.—Forcipulata (concluded).   *A*,
clasping type of straight pedicellariae of *Ampheraster*.   *B*, *C*, pedicellariae of *Notasterias*
with crossed tips (*after Fisher*, 1940).   *D*,
scheme of formation of new rays in *Pyncopodia*.
(*A*, *D*, *after Fisher*, 1928.)   1, sixth ray early
formed; 2, new rays formed in succession between sixth ray and rays B and C.

the presence of food.   The Mac-
Ginities (1949) also claim distance
perception of food by asteroids.
Contrariwise, several observers
have reported poor ability of
asteroids to sense food.   Preyer
(1887) found no exact responses to food emanations; various species
moved away from bits of fresh food or did not react when these
were placed in close proximity, although food dropped upon an
ambulacral groove was carried to the mouth and sucked out.   Similarly, Kalmus (1929) noted that sea stars might wander toward an
area of crushed animal food but not in a definite fashion and often would
move about aimlessly after getting near the food area.   Galtsoff and
Loosanoff (1939) declared that *Asterias forbesi* displays poor ability to
detect food, ignoring pieces of oysters placed within 1 or 2 inches.   Apparently asteroids recognize food mainly on contact.

Most asteroids are carnivorous and feed voraciously on almost any available slowly moving or sessile animal, chiefly mollusks and other echinoderms, also corpses. There are two general methods of dealing with animal prey. In one method practiced by the Asteriidae and other asteroids with long flexible arms, the prey is held enclosed by the arms, the cardiac stomach is everted upon it, the more or less digested contents are sucked into the digestive tract of the asteroid, and the empty shell, test, or exoskeleton is left behind. Examination of the stomach contents of such asteroids therefore usually reveals no recognizable remains. Eichelbaum (1910) examined the stomachs of 85 *Asterias rubens* and found them empty and often everted. This species is known to feed on bivalves, gastropods, hermit crabs, which it can pull out of their shells, other crabs, fisherman's bait, and sickly fish (Milligan, 1915, 1916a). *Asterias forbesi* feeds primarily on bivalves, especially soft-shelled clams (*Mya*) and oysters (Galtsoff and Loosanoff, 1939), and also attacks sickly fish. In eating fish these asteriids evert the stomach over as much of the fish as possible and digest that, dropping the rest. Many asteroids, however, feed by the second method, swallowing their prey whole, probably mainly because their rays are too short and inflexible. It is clear that the Phanerozonia in general could not feed by the first method, because of their broad stiff rays; the lack of suckers on the podia in several families would also prevent them from maintaining the necessary hold on bivalve shells. Phanerozonia, nevertheless, are just as voracious as the Asteriidae. *Astropecten* species, said to have very distensible mouths, gobble incredible numbers of small animals. *Astropecten irregularis* was found by Eichelbaum (1910) to eat mainly bivalves, snails, young asteroids, ophiuroids, and to a lesser extent copepods, crustaceans, and polychaetes. One specimen had 19 identifiable bivalves in its stomach, besides numerous fragments of other bivalves. Hamann (1885) records a specimen of *A. auranciacus* that had swallowed 10 scallops, 6 *Tellina* (bivalve), 5 scaphopods, and several snails. Species of *Luidia* eat mainly other echinoderms, especially ophiuroids, all of which are ingested whole; one specimen of *Luidia sarsi* contained 26 entire ophiuroids, 5 small heart urchins, and numerous fragments of other echinoderms; another contained 53 ophiuroids, 1 heart urchin, and very numerous fragments of asteroids and ophiuroids; and still another yielded 73 small ophiuroids plus numerous fragments (Eichelbaum, 1910). *Crossaster papposus* and *Solaster endeca* are examples of other sea stars that eat mostly other echinoderms, especially asteroids (Bull, 1934). *Anseropoda placenta* is so thin and flat that one wonders how there is room inside for food, yet it swallows a variety of animals, mostly crustaceans, as amphipods, cumaceans, mysids, true crabs, and hermit crabs; further, mollusks and other echinoderms (Mortensen, 1927). Of interest is the food of a

form from deeper waters, *Psilaster andromeda*, belonging to the Astropectinidae, dredged up from 210 m. (Eichelbaum, 1910). This was
found to have eaten mainly bivalves, one specimen containing 24 of them;
further, other echinoderms, diatoms, and foraminiferans. It is to be

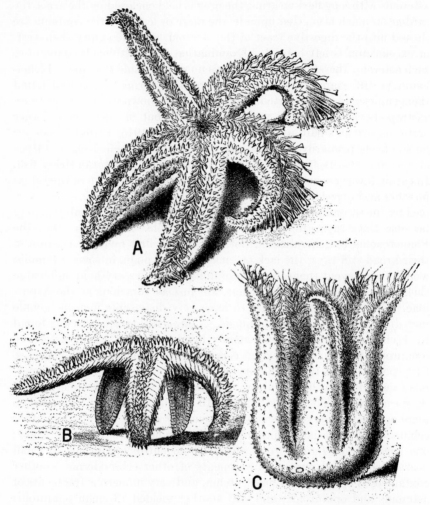

Fig. 159.—Righting reactions.  *A, Asterias rubens* righting by somersault method.
*B, Astropecten* righting by tulip method.  *C, Asterias rubens* in inverted tulip position as
result of cutting the nerve ring in all five interradii.  (*All after Romanes and Ewart*, 1882.)

understood that when prey is ingested whole, the fleshy parts are digested
by the sea star, and the empty shells, tests, exoskeletons, and so on, are
then ejected through the mouth.   Fisher (1928) records that a *Pycnopodia
helianthoides* that had swallowed whole some large purple urchins spewed

out the empty tests 24 to 36 hours later. However, A. H. Clark (1934) found a specimen of *Luidia clathrata* that had swallowed a keyhole urchin (*Mellita*) and had seemingly died thereof; the flesh of the urchin had been completely digested but the test appeared too large to pass the mouth frame. Whereas most asteroids eat a variety of foods, some are addicted to particular items. *Coscinasterias calamaria*, a common asteriid of the Indo-Pacific, is said by Young (1926) to feed primarily on brachiopods, opening them in the same manner as bivalves are opened by other Asteriidae. The spiny star *Acanthaster planci* eats coral polyps, crawling over the reefs and leaving a trail of empty cups in its wake (Mortensen, 1931). The food of the Pterasteridae is not known with certainty. Rodenhouse and Guberlet (1946) found that *Pteraster tesselatus* in Puget Sound would not eat any of the mollusk and crustacean foods favored by most sea stars but seemed to exist on sponges and anemones.

As bivalves are a preferred food item of asteriids that feed by everting the stomach into the prey, the question at once arises how they succeed in making the bivalves open. Bivalves close their valves tightly together at any disturbance or indication of danger and are provided with a powerful adductor muscle for keeping the valves closed. How the asteriid succeeds in causing the bivalve to open was investigated by Schiemenz (1896). The sea star grasps the bivalve with its podia and brings it toward the mouth, humping itself over the prey and bunching the basal parts of its arms around it while the distal parts of the arms maintain a firm hold on the substrate. It then manipulates the bivalve until the shell edges of the latter are brought in contact with the mouth and proceeds to pull upon the two valves by means of the firmly attached suckers of the podia. By means of attached weights Schiemenz determined that a sea star would let go of its prey under a pull of 1350 g., whereas a bivalve such as *Venus*, which has heavy valves, would begin to open in 5 to 25 minutes under a pull of only 900 g., and its adductor muscle would rupture in several hours or less under a continuous pull of 1000 to 2000 g. Schiemenz therefore concluded that the pull of the sea star's podia is more than ample to open a bivalve in the course of time sufficiently to permit the stomach to work itself into the interior. Oysters are a favorite food of asteriids, so much so that the latter are considered a menace to the oyster industry, but as oysters live permanently attached by one valve, it would seem difficult for the sea star to take the attitude necessary for obtaining a purchase on the valves. Schiemenz admits that sea stars can attack only oysters of small or moderate size and do so by taking a somewhat sidewise position. The results of Schiemenz were widely accepted and quoted until they were questioned by Reese (1942), who showed that bivalves can resist a far greater pull than stated by Schiemenz. Reese found that a pull of at least 10,000 g. is required to rupture the adductor muscle and that bivalves may withstand a pull of 1500 g. for 5 to 9 days. These findings bring us back to an old question, whether asteriids secrete some sort of toxin that paralyzes the prey. That such is the case was claimed by some early workers, but denied by Schiemenz, who stated that *Venus* and other mollusks removed from the grasp of asteriids were undamaged. However, toxic effects of the stomach secretion of *Asterias forbesi* were reported by Van der Heyde (1922), and Sawano and Mitsugi (1932) obtained a toxic action on the oyster heart from ground-up stomach of three out of five Japanese species of asteroids. The whole question of the opening of bivalves by sea stars must be regarded as still unsettled. It should perhaps be mentioned that fine photographs of a sea star opening a *Mytilus* were published anonymously in Kosmos (Stuttgart) for 1939; the entire process of opening the mussel and digesting out the contents required 10 hours.

In view of the general carnivorous and predatory habits of asteroids, it is surprising to find that some asteroids feed by the mucus-ciliary method. Gemmill (1915), investigating ciliary currents in asteroids, noticed that in *Porania pulvillus* all the ciliary currents of the oral surface converge to the mouth and that added particles, as carmine, become entangled in mucous strands and are carried into the digestive tract. He further found that specimens of *Porania* would live indefinitely and maintain their weight in jars of running sea water containing microscopic food, whereas under the same conditions the carnivorous *Asterias rubens* steadily lost weight and died after 8 weeks. The very sluggish mud star *Ctenodiscus crispatus* feeds primarily on mud, which is carried along the grooves that extend between the marginal plates from the aboral surface to the ambulacral grooves. Gislén (1924) states that mud particles stuck together with mucus are carried along these grooves to the podia and so into the mouth; carmine particles sprinkled on the aboral surface are eventually found in the digestive tract. When a specimen washed clean of mud was laid down on a natural mud bottom it ploughed halfway down into the mud, and when picked up again, the grooves were found filled with mud glued into strings by mucus, mud stuck together by mucus was present around the podia, and the mouth was covered by a veil of mucus leading into the stomach. Gislén is of the opinion that the cribriform organs of *Ctenodiscus* (page 253) serve primarily to sieve out coarser particles. Both Gemmill and Gislén suspect that some mucus-ciliary feeding may occur in other species as an adjunct to the taking of larger prey.

The secretion of mucus must be regarded as playing an important role in the biology of asteroids. Mucus protects the surface and serves to collect small particles which may then be swept by ciliary currents off the animal or into the digestive tract as the case may be. Excessive secretion of mucus was noted in *Pteraster tesselatus* by Rodenhouse and Guberlet (1946), who found that freshly dredged specimens were always covered with a thick layer of mucus; aquarium specimens lacked this mucous coat but would secrete mucus when handled.

Temperature and salinity are factors that contribute to the distribution of shallow-water asteroids in nature. The distribution of *Asterias vulgaris* and *forbesi* on the north Atlantic Coast of North America is probably controlled by temperature. *A. vulgaris* occurs from Labrador to Cape Cod in inshore waters and is killed by temperatures much above 25°C., so that in summer large populations may be wiped out by temperature rises (Huntsman and Sparks, 1924; G. Smith, 1940). *A. forbesi*, found from Maine to the Gulf of Mexico, will endure temperatures to 33.5°C., and this no doubt explains its greater range southward. Low salinity may also act as a limiting factor in asteroid distribution. The surface of asteroids appears freely permeable to water (Maloeuf, 1937), so that any decline in external salinity results in water intake and swelling, eventuating in death if carried to a sufficient extent. In their study of a brackish estuary on the coast of Maine, Topping and Fuller (1942) found that *A. vulgaris* remained at the mouth and would not ascend into the brackish water; according to G. Smith (1940) this species will not endure less than 14 parts salinity per thousand, and low salinities in winter may denude entire areas of this sea star. *A. forbesi* is somewhat more sensitive to lowered salinity and will not live indefinitely in salinities below 18 parts per thousand (a little more than half of normal salinity); this species will enter bays and estuaries but stops before reaching very brackish water, and entire populations may be wiped out by sudden influxes of fresh water (Loosanoff, 1945), from which they are unable to retreat in time because of their slow locomotion. Above the limiting concentration, salinity is of little importance. and large numbers of *A. forbesi* are found on the New England coast in a salinity range of 18 to 32 parts per thousand. A wide adaptability to salt content is shown by *Asterias rubens* on north European coasts; this species ranges from the North Sea with a salinity of 30 to 35 parts per thousand into the Bay of Kiel where the salinity is 17 parts per thousand and into very brackish parts of the Baltic down to salinities of 8 parts per thousand (Meyer, 1935; Bock and Schlieper, 1953). In the brackish waters of the Baltic, the animals take on a plump appearance, resulting from water intake, and are dwarfed in size. They are said not to reproduce sexually in the more brackish parts of their range.

Various tests have been made of the learning capacity of asteroids. Preyer (1887) marveled at the ability of sea stars to extricate themselves from various fetters and fastenings and stated that they freed themselves more readily after repeated trials. Ven (1922) performed similar experiments on *Asterias rubens* and reached the same conclusion. Jennings (1907), having observed that *Astrometis sertulifera* shows a very strong tendency to right by turning on rays C and D, adjacent to the madreporite, and rarely uses the opposite rays A and B, set out to train this species to right on rays A and B by preventing it from righting otherwise. After a large number of "lessons" of this sort, the animal would right on rays A and B and might retain the results of the training for a few days, up to five, without any lessons in the interval. Diebschlag (1938) tested the ability of *Astropecten bispinosus* and *spinulosus* to form associations. This author belongs to the same Marburg school that studied formation of associations in Protozoa (I, page 181) and in Turbellaria (II, page 219) and followed the same experimental procedure. The experiments consisted in training *Astropecten* to draw back from a boundary between two contrasting conditions by punishing the arm that had advanced over the boundary between the two conditions by pressing against it a battery of asteriid pedicellariae fastened to a needle. The contrasting conditions used were rough and smooth bottom, ribbed and plain glass, and light and dark. After a number of punishments the animal would in some cases draw back from the boundary without punishment, although the effects of such training were very evanescent. Success of this sort was attained in teaching the animal to remain on the smooth surface in contrast to rough or ribbed, but not the reverse; also with dark and light in either direction, using animals proved in advance to be indifferent to light. The available information indicates that asteroids possess some learning ability.

**25. Physiology.**—The body surface of asteroids, as in crinoids, echinoids, and ophiuroids, is ciliated (probably really flagellated), and studies on the direction of the currents have been made by Gemmill (1915a) and Gislén (1924) for a number of asteroid species and by Budington (1942) for *Asterias forbesi*. Details differ in different species but some generalities emerge. On the body appendages—papulae, pedicellariae, and spines—the current runs from base to tip, serving to carry away small particles. On the aboral surface the general flow is usually outward and on the arms from the center to the edges, thus also acting to deport debris. In some species, however, the aboral currents flow toward the anus, where the particles they carry are ejected with the feces. Other species, especially the Asteriidae, are so beset with appendages that the maintenance of .definite currents on the aboral surface is impractical. The madreporite is kept clean by currents from its center to its margin. On the oral surface, the currents also generally run outward, serving the same cleansing purpose, but in the ambulacral grooves and on the peristome generally run toward the mouth. However, the currents in the ambulacral grooves are very weak or wanting in species that do not ingest small particles and in such case may even run in the opposite direction, centrifugally. The currents are naturally otherwise than the foregoing in ciliary-mucous feeders, or, as Gislén terms them, detritus catchers. Here the currents in general tend toward the ambulacral grooves and thence to the mouth as described above (page 372). The direction of the currents is obviously related to their function, whether cleansing or food-catching; very likely the currents also have some respiratory value.

The physiology of the surface appendages has been much less studied in asteroids than in echinoids. The papulae collapse to mechanical stimulation (Jennings, 1907), also in some species to sudden illumination, sudden shadow, or both (Cowles, 1911; MacCurdy, 1913; J. E. Smith, 1945). The last author has shown that this reaction is prevented above a short lateral cut parallel to the long axis of the arm; the retraction of the papulae is therefore a reflex transmitted through transverse pathways in the ectoneural nerve net to the motor neurones in the marginal nerve cord (page 272) and back along motor axones to the muscle layer in the wall of the papulae. Any cut between the stimulated area and the marginal nerve cord prevents the transmission of the stimulation. A respiratory value of the papulae is indicated by their interior currents, passing to the tip along the periphery and back down the center, according to Budington (1942), up one side and down the other, according to Jennings (1907).

Only Jennings (1907) has studied the behavior of asteroid pedicellariae, employing a type of sea star (*Astrometis sertulifera*) provided with thick rosettes of pedicellariae around the spines as well as with large solitary pedicellariae. Jennings indicates that the main functions of the pedicellariae are protection of the papulae and the capture of small animals. Upon disturbance of the surface as by some small animal crawling over it, the papulae retract, the rosettes of the stimulated area erect themselves above the spine tips, the jaws of the pedicellariae open and close upon any projecting parts of the intruder, and the latter is then held immobile and eventually passed to the mouth. The erection of the rosette usually results only after repeated mechanical stimulation, and typically additional stimulation is necessary to elicit the opening of the jaws. The spines carrying the rosettes also bend toward a stimulated area, and the rosettes may curve down or reach out to a stimulated spot. A general disturbance of the entire animal results in the waving about of the rosettes and the repeated snapping of the pedicellariae. Mechanical stimulation of the outer surface of the jaws appears the cause of their opening, and their closure results from a touch on their inner surface. Once closed on an object, the pedicellariae remain closed for a long period; small crustaceans were held for 48 hours or more.

Pulling on the pedicellariae causes them to grip more tightly, but they will also hold for long periods onto lifeless objects. A pedicellaria closed on an object will not open to the usual stimuli. The strength of the hold is considerable, for a sea star may be lifted out of water by the pedicellariae closed on the hairs of the hand. Very weak chemicals may evoke erection of the rosettes and opening of the jaws, but most chemicals cause shrinkage and withdrawal of rosettes and papulae. Animal juice evokes a positive response and may facilitate subsequent response of the rosettes to mechanical stimulation. The large solitary straight pedicellariae appeared somewhat unresponsive and variable in their behavior. They might open to repeated touch or then close and remain closed despite repeated stimulation; once closed on an object they might hold on for long periods. The reactions of rosettes and pedicellariae appear mediated through the ectoneural nerve net, as these structures show the typical behavior on isolated pieces of body wall. The pedicellariae are nonpoisonous, as small animals that escape from them appear normal.

The reactions of the podia were already considered to some extent. Localized contraction can occur in either intact or isolated podia, and light stimulation applied to the side of a podium may elicit bending to the stimulated side, but in general various types of stimulation cause contraction of the podia. Isolated podia may show some extension and execute varied movements (Mangold, 1908a; Paine, 1929) but in general remain in a contracted state, although rise in temperature may bring about elongation. As podia are provided with longitudinal muscles only, it is evident that they are independently capable only of contraction, presumably by way of nervous arcs included within themselves. Relaxation of the longitudinal muscles would result in some elongation, but true extension of the podia cannot be obtained by direct stimulation, only by way of nervous arcs involving the ampullae. Explanation of the mechanism of podial locomotion has been deferred to this point because the mechanism has been best studied in asteroids, notably by J. E. Smith (1945, 1946, 1950). The same mechanism operates in other echinoderms in which the podia serve primarily a locomotory function, that is holothurians and echinoids, although the nervous connections have not been worked out. Ampullae, as repeatedly noted, are heavily muscularized (Fig. 160). Extension of the podia is brought about, probably exclusively, by contraction of their ampullae, forcing fluid into the podia. Contraction of the podium by its own musculature causes the fluid to run back into its ampulla. This behavior can be readily witnessed on an isolated preparation of a podium with its ampulla attached intact (Mangold, 1908a). Stimulation of the ampulla causes it to contract and discharge its fluid into the podium, which thereupon extends, and stimulation of the podium evokes its contraction and the fluid runs back into the ampulla, which thereupon expands again. The extension of a podium *cannot* be brought about directly. As shown by Smith, this mechanism operates by means of motor neurones located in the neck of the ampulla (Fig. 161) and sending fibers into its musculature. These motor neurones also make connections with Lange's nerves (page 272) and so with the radial nerves.

It was first pointed out by Jennings (1907) and verified by Kerkut (1953a) that the podia do not pull the sea star along (except when it is

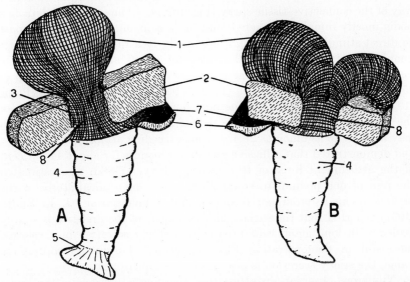

Fig. 160.—Ampullar structure. *A*, scheme of ampulla and attached podium of *Asterias rubens;* ampulla has lengthwise muscle fibers and podium ends in a sucker. *B*, scheme of ampulla and attached podium of *Astropecten irregularis;* ampulla is bifurcated and has circular muscles; podium lacks sucker. (*Both after J. E. Smith*, 1947.) Smaller fibers at right angles to muscle fibers represent connective-tissue strands. 1, ampulla; 2, ambulacral ossicle; 3, ambulacral pore; 4, podium; 5, sucker; 6, radial nerve cord; 7, hyponeural canal; 8, neck of ampulla.

climbing vertical surfaces), but their action is rather that of stepping, bringing the animal forward by a backward push. The details of the stepping process have been repeatedly described (Jennings, 1907; Hamilton, 1921). The podium extends forward ("points") in the direction of advance and applies the sucker to the substratum; the center of the sucker is pulled back, producing a vacuum cup; the podium then swings back, bringing the animal forward, and gradually contracts, finally releasing its hold on the substratum and extending forward again. Hamilton showed that in a sea star placed on its back stepping can be induced by laying thin pieces of celluloid on the suckers; stepping promptly ensues and the celluoid squares are "walked" backward.

Contact of the suckers with the surface film produces the same reaction. In a progressing sea star all the podia act in coordination, extending in the same direction although not simultaneously; such coordination necessitates the integrity of the radial nerves and nerve ring.

The presence of a vacuum cup in the center of the suckers can readily be seen in suckers attached to glass, and the inward pull producing the cup is caused by contraction of the longitudinal muscle fibers immediately beneath the sucker (Fig. 106A); but as no muscle fibers extend into the sucker, it would seem as if this pull must be transmitted to the sucker by way of the connective-tissue spray (Fig. 107A). The suckers of detached podia mostly remain contracted, may show some movements in response to direct stimulation, and may stick briefly to a rod, but in general are unable to attach (Paine, 1929). Those torn off and left attached in pulling off an attached sea star remain fastened for a short time, up to 15 minutes, and then fall off (Paine, 1929). It was shown by Paine (1926) that vacuum action alone does not explain the adhesive force of the suckers. She found that the pull of one podium of *Asterias forbesi* may amount to as much as 29.4 g., thus exceeding atmospheric pressure, and demonstrated that adhesive secretion accounts for about 44 per cent of the attachment force of the suckers. Preyer (1886) also estimated the pull of one podium to equal 25 g. In a histological study of the suckers of an asteroid, an echinoid, and a holothurian, J. E. Smith (1937) reported that the surface of attachment of the first two is simply loaded with long gland cells producing a sticky secretion but was less successful in demonstrating this in the holothurian. According to Paine, the sticky secretion is practically inexhaustible.

Numerous observations attest that coordinated actions of the podia depend on the integrity of the radial nerves and nerve ring. In the normal animal all the podia act in concert, that is, all step when the animal is progressing, even those not in a position to be effective, as in the case of an arm against the water film. Similarly in digging specimens of *Astropecten auranciacus* or *Anseropoda placenta*, all the podia engage in digging movements, including those on an arm that has not yet come in contact with the substratum (Mangold, 1908a, 1908b). This coordination is destroyed in any arm that is nervously isolated by cutting through the radial nerve at the arm base or through the nerve ring at the interradii adjacent to the arm base. Such an arm may step or dig but not in harmony with the other arms; it may dig when the other four arms are quiescent or may fail to dig when the others are so engaged. Detached arms live for a few days and can right and step, although stepping is slowed and less precise than normal. However, such detached arms always move with the proximal end forward (Hopkins, 1926; Diebschlag, 1938; J. E. Smith, 1945); but an arm with the disk attached

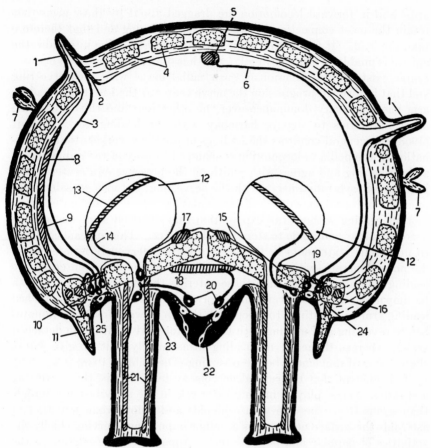

Fig. 161.—Scheme of neuromuscular connections in cross section of an arm of asteriid (*after J. E. Smith*, 1945). Diagonally hatched structures are muscles; black neurones are motor, white neurones sensory and associative. 1, papula; 2, muscle of papula; 3, motor nerve to papula; 4, ossicle of body wall; 5, median aboral muscle strand; 6, motor nerve to 5; 7, pedicellaria; 8, body-wall musculature; 9, motor nerve to 8 from marginal nerve cord; 10, marginal nerve cord; 11, adambulacral spine; 12, ampulla; 13, muscle layer of ampulla; 14, motor nerve to ampulla muscle from neck of ampulla; 15, ambulacral ossicle; 16, adambulacral ossicle; 17, upper transverse interambulacral muscles; 18, lower transverse interambulacral muscle; 19, lateral transverse ambulacral muscle; 20, motor neurones of Lange's nerve; 21, longitudinal muscle layer of podium; 22, radial nerve cord with sensory and association neurones; 23, motor center in neck of ampulla; 24, muscle for adambulacral spine; 25, sensory area over marginal nerve.

will move in the normal way with its tip forward until its radial nerve is severed at the arm base, whereupon the arm reverses and pushes the disk forward. Thus the normal arm movement with the tip forward depends on the presence of at least a part of the nerve ring. Any arm or arms nervously isolated by cutting through the radial nerve at the arm base or the nerve ring at the interradii are unable to cooperate with the other arms and in forward locomotion are dragged about by those arms that retain the most connection by way of the nerve ring and that therefore take the lead. If the nerve ring is cut through at all five interradii, the animal is unable to progress at all. Smith is of the opinion that a nervous center exists at the junction of each radial nerve with the nerve ring and that in forward progression the nerve center at the base of the leading arm has temporary dominance over the other four and thus causes the other four arms to step in harmony with the leading arm. Kerkut (1953b) in general confirms the findings of previous workers that coordination of the podia in locomotion is achieved by way of the radial nerves and nerve ring and agrees with Smith on the presence of a center at the junction of each radial nerve with the nerve ring; but also considers that muscle tensions transmitted directly play a role in coordinated locomotion, stating without full explanation that a cut-off arm can be sewn onto a sea star and made to step with the others. This appears contrary to numerous statements in the literature that nervously isolated arms do not cooperate with the others. That the impulses entering the leading arm are stronger than those entering the subordinated arms can be shown by cutting off arms during forward progression. The detached leading arm will continue to creep with the tip forward for 2 or 3 minutes before reversing and moving with the base forward (as usual in detached arms), whereas detached nonleading arms merely halt or give but a slight forward movement before reversing (Diebschlag, 1938).

It is evident that the central nervous system, that is, the nerve ring and radial nerves, plays a much greater role in the activities of asteroids than seems to be the case with echinoids and holothurians and that in asteroids the surface nerve net is of minor importance, serving chiefly the activities of papulae and pedicellariae. Apparently transmission in the nerve net occurs mainly in a direction transverse to the arms, and impulses will not be transmitted around cuts parallel to the arm axis. As already mentioned, Smith (1937) found that the nerve net is poorly developed over much of the body.

As the ambulacral system operates by means of hydraulic pressure, it obviously must be kept filled with fluid. It is usually believed that any water losses through the podia or ampullae are made good by fluid intake through the madreporite, although there does not seem to be any experimental proof of this assumption. Probably such water loss is very slight. Ludwig (1890) and Budington (1942) observed a definite inward current in the stone canal. Delage (1902a, 1902b) extirpated the madreporite, leaving in its place a permanent hole, and saw no effect upon the activities of the podia. No regeneration of the madreporite occurred within several months, although other authors state that the madreporite will regenerate.

The colors of asteroids are mostly of the nature of carotenoids, which are fat-soluble, non-nitrogenous substances responsible for most of the red, orange, and yellow colors in the animal kingdom; when united with proteins they also produce blue, green, violet, and purple colors. They consist of a long hydrocarbon chain with a benzene-ring complex at each end; those that contain no oxygen atoms are termed carotenes, and those with oxygen atoms are called xanthophylls if nonacidic or carotenoid acids when acidic in nature (Fox, 1953). In asteroids carotenoids occur as spherules in the epidermal cells; chromatophores appear generally wanting in the class. In addition to a number of older studies, carotenoids of sea stars have been investigated by Abeloos (1926), Lönnberg (1931, 1934a, 1934b), Lönnberg and Hellström (1931), Euler and Hellström (1934), Fox and Scheer (1941), Vevers (1952), and De Nicola and Goodwin (1954), and the whole subject of animal colors is treated in a recent book by Fox (1953), where additional references will be found. Carotenoids produce the red and orange colors common in asteroids, and when combined with proteins, also give rise to blue, green, and purple hues. Fox and Scheer, studying some California species that occur in pronounced color variants, as *Patiria miniata* and *Pisaster ochraceus*, found quantitative differences in the carotenoids correlated with the color variations. Abeloos showed that the violet tone of some specimens of the usually red *Asterias rubens* results from a loose combination of carotenoid with protein, and Vevers found that the brownish tint also seen in this species similarly depends on a protein combination of its main carotenoid, the carotene astaxanthin. Porphyrins, related to haemoglobin, also occur in *A. rubens* and other brown asteroids. The greenish color of the pyloric caeca and the orange and pink tints of asteroid ovaries are attributable to carotenoids. Several authors have remarked on a general similarity of the carotenoids of asteroids to those of decapod crustaceans.

The sterols, or higher unsaponifiable fats, of asteroids have been studied by Bergmann (1937), Bergmann and Stansbury (1943, 1944), and others, and the matter of echinoderm sterols has been given a general discussion by Bergmann (1949), where other references will be found. The sterols of asteroids differ from cholesterol, the most common animal sterol, and are called by the general name of stellasterols (Fig. 162), which include several related compounds. Stellasterols also occur in holothurians, but not in echinoids, which contain cholesterol. Batyl alcohol (page 219) is also common to asteroids and holothurians but is apparently wanting in echinoids.

Available data on the chemical composition of asteroids appear in the comprehensive volume by Vinogradov (1953). Figures on the water content range from 67 to 81 per cent. The skeleton is composed of 71 to 91 per cent of calcium carbonate, 8 to 14 per cent of magnesium carbonate, and small amounts of calcium phosphate and sulphate, as well as salts of aluminum, iron, and sulphur. Traces of many other elements are also present, as strontium, barium, copper, zinc, manganese, cobalt, nickel, and copper.

The papulae constitute the usual respiratory provision of asteroids but cannot be of supreme importance as they are few in number in many

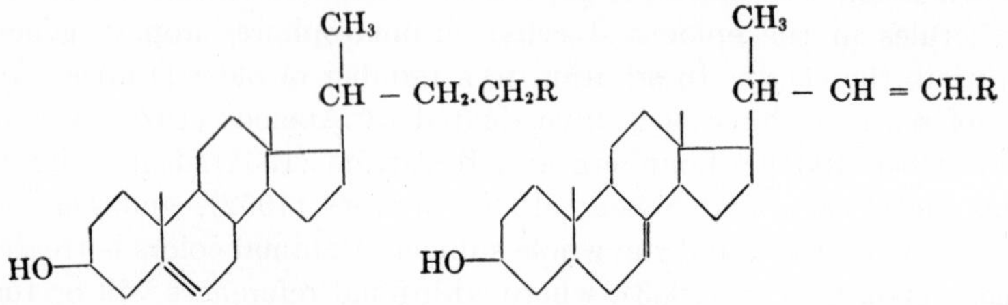

Fig. 162.—Sterols of echinoderms. Left, cholesterol, found in echinoids. Right, a stellasterol, found in asteroids. R stands for the group $CH_2CH(CH_3)_2$ in cholesterol; for $CH_3CHCH(CH_3)_2$ in stellasterol.

Phanerozonia and wanting in some cases. In the Porcellanasteridae, which mostly lack papulae, their place is presumably taken by the cribriform organs, assumed in the want of other evidence to have a respiratory function, as water currents pass between their lamellae. Possibly, however, they also serve as detritus catchers by the mucus-ciliary method, as is known to be the case in *Ctenodiscus* (page 372). The other family in which papulae are few or wanting, the Brisingidae, has numerous long and slender arms which would furnish plenty of surface for respiration by diffusion. The papulae are kept fully extended when the animal is undisturbed but, as already related, contract to any disturbance or to various stimuli. A special respiratory mechanism is seen in the family Pterasteridae provided with a respiratory and nidamental chamber between the aboral surface and the supradorsal membrane supported on the crowns of the paxillae. This chamber is rhythmically inflated and deflated by intake and outgo of water. The water enters through the contractile apertures in the supradorsal membrane, called spiracles, and also through a row of openings along each side of each ray adjacent to the adambulacral plates; and exits partly through the spiracles but chiefly through the large central opening or osculum in the supradorsal membrane. The papulae are found in the floor of the nidamental chamber and are said by Rodenhouse and Guberlet (1946) to expand with each inflation and retract with each deflation. These authors observed *Pteraster tesselatus* and found that when undisturbed this animal inflates about four times per minute and ejects about 65 cc. of water with each deflation. Any debris brought in with the respiratory current may be collected in mucus and expelled at the osculum by a vigorous deflation. Disturbance may evoke deeper and often convulsive inflations.

The main studies on actual oxygen intake of asteroids are those of Meyer (1935) on *A. rubens* and Maloeuf (1937) on *A. forbesi*. The former ascribed great respiratory importance to the podia and reported a decline in oxygen consumption if they are covered with some sort of adhesive, ranging from a 10 per cent decline if one groove is covered to a 60 per cent decline with all five covered. Meyer, Maloeuf, and Hyman (1929) agree that the oxygen intake of asteroids is dependent on the oxygen content of the water and rises and falls with the latter. Some adjustment is made to continued sojourn in high-oxygen water by a decline in the oxygen intake after a time, but the animals appear incapable of any adjustment to low oxygen content. According to Meyer the oxygen intake remains constant over a pH range from 5.5 to 7.8, is accelerated by increased alkalinity from 7.8 to 9.0, then falling off rapidly, and is depressed by increased acidity, ceasing below pH 4.5. The carbonate of the skeleton acts as a buffer against acidified sea water. Salinity also affects the oxygen intake. Maloeuf found that oxygen intake is lowered both in hypertonic sea water and in sea water diluted half with fresh water. According to Meyer, the oxygen uptake of North Sea specimens of *A. rubens* is higher than that of brackish specimens from the Baltic and is increased in the latter if they are placed in water of augmented salt content, up to about 25 parts per thousand, above which decline sets in. Bock and Schlieper (1953) verified this result on brackish *A. rubens* placed in water of increased salt content but found a similar rise in North Sea specimens placed in water of lowered salt content.

As in other echinoderms, asteroids have practically no power of osmotic regulation, and their coelomic fluid is therefore identical with sea water. This was shown by Duval (1924, 1925) for *A. rubens*, Parker and Cole (1940) for *A. vulgaris*, W. Cole (1940) for *A. vulgaris* and *Solaster endeca*, Bialaszewicz (1933) for *Astropecten auranciacus*, and by Robertson (1949) for *Marth. glacialis*. The last two authors, however, note a slightly higher potassium content and a slightly lower magnesium content in the coelomic fluid than in sea water. The coelomic fluid also contains protein (Griffiths, 1893). The coelomic fluid of asteroids is less alkaline than sea water, which is decidedly alkaline, usually having of pH of 8.2 or more. The pH of the coelomic fluid of *A. rubens* is given as 7.3 to 7.4 by Duval (1925), 7.6 to 7.8 by Verchowskaja (1931); of *A. vulgaris* as 7.2 (W. Cole, 1940), 7.54 (Parker and Cole, 1940); of *Solaster endeca* as 6.9 (W. Cole, 1940); and of *Patiria miniata* as 7.6 to 8 and of *Pisaster ochraceus* as 6.5 to 8.1 (Irving, 1926). The fluid in the water-vascular system of *Marth. glacialis* is practically identical with the coelomic fluid but contains still more potassium (Robertson, 1949).

The body wall of asteroids is freely permeable to water and hence these animals swell and grow turgid in diluted sea water and lose weight in sea water of augmented salinity (Meyer, 1935; Maloeuf, 1937; Loosanoff, 1945). They show considerable adaptability to salinity changes, but too long exposure to too low salinity is fatal. The body wall is also permeable to salts since weight is lost in sucrose solutions isotonic with sea water (Maloeuf). Alteration of shape and size and loss of reproductive capacity in *A. rubens* living in very brackish water were noted above (page 373).

The coelomic fluid circulates or at least is kept in motion by the flagella of the coelomic epithelium. In *A. forbesi*, Budington (1942) indicates a general internal flow toward the arm tips with a return current along the inner surface of the ray sides. Gemmill's (1915a) observations on several species give a varied picture and show chiefly that the coelomic fluid is subject to constant and thorough mixing. The coelomic fluid generally flows peripherally along the inner surface of the aboral wall and along the aboral surface of the pyloric caeca and centrally along the ventrolateral walls of the rays and the interbrachial septa.

As previously related, some asteroids feed by everting the cardiac stomach over the prey; this is accomplished by body-wall contraction exerting pressure on the coelomic fluid, while the gastric ligaments prevent too great eversion. Anderson (1954) has shown that acetylcholine evokes expansion and adrenalin closure of the mouth and that following injection of acetylcholine into the coelom the stomach of *Asterias forbesi* may be caused to evert by exerting pressure on the arms, something that cannot be done with the normal animal. Retraction of the stomach probably results from relaxation of the body wall plus contraction of muscle fibers in the stomach wall, including those in the fibrous strands that enter the stomach at the nodules of the gastric ligaments.

In asteroids that feed by stomach eversion the prey is digested outside into a sort of broth that is then ingested. It might be supposed that the channels of the cardiac wall described by Anderson (1954) in *Asterias forbesi* might function in the intake of the food broth, but on the contrary their currents are directed orally and they seem to serve for rejection of unwanted material. Other sea stars swallow their prey whole and digest it in the stomach lumen; it is not clear whether such species are incapable of everting the stomach, but probably some species may feed by either method. In any event, digestion is evidently mainly extracellular, and a powerful digestive fluid must be exuded upon the food from the stomach walls or the pyloric caeca, or both. Chapeaux (1893) found protease, amylase, and lipase in extracts of the pyloric caeca and the first two in stomach extracts; he thought digestion is extracellular except for fats which he believed to undergo intracellular digestion in the caecal epithelium as oil droplets could be found there after feeding oil. When fibrin mixed with carmine was fed, carmine particles were also seen later in the caecal epithelium. Stone (1897) detected a protease acting best in alkaline medium, a lipase, and a rapidly acting diastase in water extracts of the pyloric caeca. In *Asterias forbesi*, Van der Heyde (1922) reported that water extracts of both stomach and pyloric caeca would digest gelatin in alkaline, and egg white and gelatin in acid medium, but failed to find any lipase or amylase. Sugar and protein put into the stomach were well digested, and amino acids could be detected in the coelomic fluid of a specimen caught in the act of feeding on a bivalve. Oil, iron saccharate, and ammonium carminate injected into the stomach of *A. forbesi* pass into the pyloric ducts and are later found in the epithelium of the pyloric caeca; the carminate mostly passed through the epithelium and accumulated in the peritoneum of the caeca. This author (1923a) reported similar results for *Astropecten*—digestion of saccharose and protein in the stomach and ingestion of oil, iron saccharate, and ammonium carminate by the epithelium of the pyloric caeca. In similar experiments on *Echinaster sepositus* and *A. rubens*, carmine, blood corpuscles, and iron saccharate injected into the stomach were taken up by the caecal epithelium, but carbon particles only by the epithelium of the intestinal caeca (Van der Heyde and Oomen, 1924). Irving (1926) filled isolated caeca of *Patiria miniata* with gelatin solution and recovered products of protein digestion in the surrounding fluid. However, each pyloric caecum of *Patiria miniata* and other Asterinidae, also of Echinasteridae, is underlain on the oral side by an extensive stomach diverticulum (so-called Tiedemann's diverticulum, Fig. 115*A*), so that in Irving's experiments the gelatin solution went into this stomach diverticulum and the resulting digestion is probably to be attributed to the stomach. Proteolytic enzymes hydrolyzing gelatin, peptone, and polypeptides were found by Sawano (1936) in caecal extracts of *Distolasterias nipon*, further the intracellular proteolytic enzyme cathepsin in extracts of both pyloric and intestinal caeca. Anderson (1953) ascribed a zymogenic function to much of the epithelium of the pyloric caeca of *Asterias forbesi*.

The digestive activity of the pyloric caeca appears to take place in a medium more acid than sea water. Stone (1897) and Roaf (1910) reported slight acidity of the secretion of the pyloric caeca in *A. vulgaris* and *A. rubens*, respectively. Van der Heyde (1922) noted a pH of 7.1 to 7.7 in the stomach of *A. forbesi* and of 7.3 in the caeca. The pyloric enzymes of *Distolasterias nipon* are active at pH 7.1 to 8.4 (Sawano, 1936). Irving (1926) gave figures of 7.3 to 7.5 for the stomach of *Patiria miniata* and *Pisaster ochraceus*, and of 6.6 to 7.0 for the pyloric caeca. He found that excised pyloric caeca tend to alter the pH of the sea water to 6.7, the optimum for gelatin digestion and flagellary survival in these species, and that this acidification is accomplished by the carbon dioxide given off in respiration.

Strong flagellary currents are maintained in the digestive tract (Gemmill, 1915; Irving, 1924; Anderson, 1953). In the central digestive tract these run in general from mouth to anus but cause a circulation in

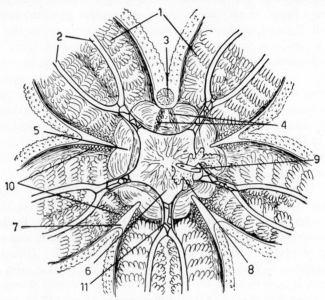

FIG. 163.—System of haemal channels of the digestive tract of *Asterias rubens* (after Cuénot, 1901). 1, pyloric caeca; 2, haemal channels along mesenteries of pyloric caeca; 3, madreporite; 4, gastric haemal tufts; 5, cardiac stomach; 6, pyloric stomach; 7, interbrachial septa; 8, intestinal caeca; 9, intestine; 10, gonads; 11, haemal plexus along pyloric ducts.

the stomach. They proceed distally in the caeca along their oral sides and back along their aboral sides to the stomach. Similar currents go into and out of the intestinal caeca. Anderson has shown that the cells lining the pyloric ducts and their side branches are specialized as current producers. Although the wall of the pyloric caeca contains a muscle stratum (Fig. 111*A*), no one has observed any movements of these structures. Budington (1927) saw rhythmic pulsations of the intestinal caeca of *Asterias forbesi*.

The evidence, while unsatisfactory, indicates that digestion occurs in both stomach and pyloric caeca and that food particles are swept into the latter and there undergo extracellular or intracellular digestion, or both. Digestion products may be passed through the caeca into the coelomic fluid or into the haemal system of the pyloric caeca described by Cuénot (1896; Fig. 163), which communicates with the main haemal system by way of the gastric haemal tufts, or may be stored in the epithelium of the caeca. According to Anderson (1953), much of this epithelium is devoted to food storage and contains glycogen, neutral fat, and a polysaccharide-protein complex resistant to diastatic digestion. Delaunay (1926) has identified glycogen in the caeca to the amount of 300 to 400 mg. per 100 g. of fresh weight and also suspected protein storage; he noted (1926) plumpness of the caeca during gonad decline and loss of weight from the caeca during maturation of the gonads.

The function of the haemal system of asteroids remains obscure. Verchowskaja (1931) removed the axial gland, which is in effect a haemal plexus in asteroids, and saw no effect on *A. rubens* except a slight enlargement of Tiedemann's bodies. Successful implantation of an extra axial gland resulted only in slight enlargement of the animal's own gland and of the gastric haemal tufts. No contractile movements have been seen in any part of the haemal system except the dorsal sac. This encloses the aboral end of the axial gland and by exerting pressure on this could possibly have some motile effect on the haemal system. One may note, however, that the haemal system contains an abundance of amoeboid, phagocytic coelomocytes that can move about in the absence of any haemal circulation. Very likely the coelomocytes transport absorbed food from the pyloric caeca along the haemal channels of the latter (Fig. 163). Van der Heyde (1922, 1923a) found that glucose and amino acids injected into the coelom disappear rapidly, being taken up largely by coelomocytes.

No function is known for Tiedemann's bodies. The supposition that they furnish coelomocytes does not appear to be supported by any evidence. Cuénot (1901) was unable to locate any site of formation of coelomocytes and concluded that these simply multiply by division. Kowalevsky (1889) injected carmine and Bismarck brown into the ambulacral system by way of a podium and found color throughout the ambulacral system, persisting longest in the Tiedemann's bodies. However, it may be pointed out that the ambulacral system, including the Tiedemann's bodies, is lined with coelomic epithelium, and this, as will appear shortly, has the general property of taking up foreign particles.

The asteroids lack a definite excretory system, and various observers have attempted to elucidate excretion in this group by the usual method of injecting colored foreign particles. Durham (1888) injected india ink and anilin blue into the coelom of *A. rubens* and noted that the particles are ingested by coelomocytes, which then pass to the exterior by way of the papulae and eventually disintegrate. This author also noticed that coelomocytes with refringent granules, probably of excretory nature, follow the same route and are found in numbers in the brownish slime covering the sea star in natural conditions. Similar observations were made by Chapeaux (1893), who, after injecting indigo carmine into the coelom, found that the colored particles are ingested by coelomocytes, which then exit through the pyloric caeca, the madreporite, and the papulae. Cuénot (1901) injected a variety of dyes into the coelom of *Marth. glacialis* and reported that they are taken up not only by coelomocytes but also by the peritoneum everywhere, including the lining of the ambulacral system and the hyponeural canals. This author saw masses of such colored coelomocytes aggregate in the tips of the papulae, where they might be eliminated by such tips constricting off. Some dyes might be taken up by the pyloric caeca and eliminated by way of the digestive tract. Lison (1930) also noted clumping of coelomocytes around injected carmine, prussian blue, or neutral red, and accumulation of such masses in the tips of the papulae which might then constrict off. The coelomocytes thus appear to constitute a principal mechanism for the elimination of unwanted materials in asteroids; possibly the pyloric caeca are also excretory in addition to their other functions.

Various workers have attempted to discover the form in which nitrogenous-waste products are excreted in asteroids. Griffiths (1888) reported uric acid but no urea in the stomach contents. Cohnheim (1901) could not detect any ammonia given off by several *Astropecten auranciacus* but found increased nitrogen in the water in which they had been kept for 40 hours. Fosse (1913) noted the presence of urea in water in which *A. rubens* had sojourned for 40 hours. Myers (1920) could detect no other nitrogenous excreta except a very little creatine and creatinine in the coelomic fluid of *Pisaster ochraceus;* that of *Pycnopodia helianthoides* gave only some urea and ammonia. Van der Heyde (1923c) reported the presence of uric acid in the coelomic fluid and pyloric caeca of *A. forbesi* but denied the presence of ammonia, urea, and creatine. A trace of uric acid was found in *Marth. glacialis* by Przylecki (1926). The most extensive investigations on this matter are those of Delaunay (1926, 1931), who found in the sea water in which *A. rubens* had lived for 24 hours mostly ammonia and other volatile bases, some amino nitrogen and urea, but scarcely any purine substances or uric acid; similar results were obtained with the coelomic fluid, freed from cells. Some urea, but practically no uric acid, was detected in the pyloric caeca which are high in amino nitrogen and purines, an indication of food digestion and storage. It is difficult to draw conclusions from these discordant results, but it seems probable that ammonia and urea are the chief nitrogenous wastes of asteroids and that only traces of uric acid are produced. The report of the presence of creatine and its derivative creatinine in asteroids is interesting, as these substances are typical of vertebrates, and echinoderms are among the invertebrates in which they have been reported.

**26. Ecology: Geographic Distribution.**—We begin with the northern part of the North Pacific, for unlike the state of affairs in the other echinoderm classes, this area is the center of greatest concentration of asteroids. Verrill (1909) remarks as follows: "No other part of the world, of similar extent, so far as known, has so many species of shallow water and littoral starfishes as the coasts of Alaska and British Columbia, including Puget Sound. Many of the species range from San Francisco to the Aleutian Islands, but the most favored region is from Puget Sound to southern Alaska. . . . The entire region has a very broken coast line, innumerable islands, bays, fiords and straits, giving a great extent of sheltered coast line, bathed in pure sea water and swept by strong tidal currents, all of which are very favorable to littoral marine life. . . . These favorable conditions are notably shown by the great abundance of individuals as well as species and also by the great size that many of the species attain." Fisher in the first part of his scholarly account of the asteroids of the North Pacific (1911, 1928, 1930) also states that "the west coast of North America is more prolific in species and individuals than any other part of the world." The area in question includes the Pacific Coast of North America from northern California northward, the Aleutian Islands, and the coast of Asia from Sahkalin and the Kurile Islands northward, that is, the boundaries of the Bering Sea. Although Fisher in his monograph also included southern California, this is best regarded as part of the Panamic region. It is to be noted that the coastal waters of the area in question are uniformly cold, even in the height of summer, and this no doubt constitutes an important factor in the rich development of littoral marine life along these coasts, especially where rocky substrate abounds. The author has seen no better display of littoral marine invertebrate life than that of Puget Sound, and the shores of Vancouver Island are said to be even richer in invertebrates. The majority of the asteroids of the area under consideration are endemic, that is, occur nowhere else. Fisher (1911) listed about 70 endemic species and seven endemic genera (*Thrissacanthias, Nearchaster, Myonotus, Gephyreaster, Dermasterias, Cryptopeltaster, Heterozonias*). In addition to the endemic species, the region includes a number of circumboreal and circumarctic species that have probably entered the area from the Arctic Ocean through the Bering Strait. There is also some invasion of the region by Panamic asteroids, and vice versa. The coast of Asia north of Japan is much poorer in endemic species than the North American side of the region but probably has not been exhaustively studied.

The only endemic phanerozonic species apt to be taken in shore collecting in the region is the leather star *Dermasterias imbricata* (Fig.

143), found sparingly on rocky bottom from Monterey Bay to Alaska, said (Ricketts and Calvin, 1953) to be delicately purple with red markings. The most common endemic shallow-water spinulose stars are the broad-armed *Patiria miniata* (Fig. 144), red, orange, buff, or mottled, the little blood-red *Henricia leviuscula* with slender rays, the sun stars *Solaster stimpsoni* and *dawsoni*, and the cushion star *Pteraster tesselatus* (Fig. 95B). The shallow-water endemic Asteriidae commonly seen include *Leptasterias arctica, camtschatika, hexactis* (Fig. 94B), *aequalis, alaskensis,* and *pusilla, Evasterias troscheli* (Fig. 156), *Orthasterias koehleri, Pisaster ochraceus* (Fig. 157), *giganteus,* and *brevispinus,* and *Pycnopodia helianthoides.* The prevalence of the genus *Leptasterias,* mostly small, often six-rayed asteroids, without striking coloration, is noticeable. They are especially common from Puget Sound northward and occur in a bewildering array of species, subspecies, and varieties. The genus *Pisaster* is also a typical shore asteroid of the Pacific Coast and often occurs in great numbers. *Pisaster ochraceus* is characteristic of rocky shores subject to heavy wave action and seems to remain in the same position for days firmly attached by rigid, contracted podia (Hamilton, 1921).

Mention may be made of some other species characteristic of the Pacific Coast from California to Alaska but limited to the deeper waters of the littoral zone, namely, *Leptychaster anomalus, Luidia foliolata, Mediaster aequalis* (Fig. 136), *Hippasteria spinosa,* and *Stylasterias forreri. Luidia foliolata,* grayish, is said by Fisher (1911) to be the commonest sea star of Monterey Bay, and *Mediaster aequalis* is notable for its billiant red color.

Circumboreal and circumarctic asteroids constitute an important element of the shallow-water asteroid fauna of the northern part of the Pacific Coast of North America. These have presumably invaded the area from the Arctic Ocean by way of Bering Strait. The most common among them are the phanerozonic stars *Ctenodiscus crispatus* (Fig. 131), *Leptychaster arcticus, Pseudarchaster parelii;* the spinulose species *Henricia sanguinolenta* (Fig. 146), *Solaster endeca* (Fig. 147), *Crossaster papposus* (Fig. 94F), *Lophaster furcifer* (includes *furcilliger*), *Pteraster militaris, pulvillus,* and *obscurus,* and *Diplopteraster multipes;* and the forcipulates *Asterias amurensis* and *Stephanasterias albula* (Fig. 155). These species in general range from the Bering Sea eastward by way of Greenland, the Faroes, Spitsbergen, Jan Mayen, the Barents Sea, and so on, to the northern coasts of Siberia; and from these arctic waters they extend southward along the shores of the continents to varying points. Thus *Ctenodiscus crispatus* ( = *corniculatus*) ranges from the Bering Sea south at least to California, through the Arctic Ocean to Greenland, and down the eastern coast of North America to Cape Cod, across the North Atlantic, with records at the Faroes, Iceland, Spitsbergen, and the

Norwegian coast, and into the Barents and Kara Seas (Fig. 164*A*); it lives on muddy bottom, mostly at depths of 35 to 80 m., but may descend to over 1000 m. The blood star *Henricia sanguinolenta* has an even more extensive range (Fig. 164*B*), for it completes the circle from

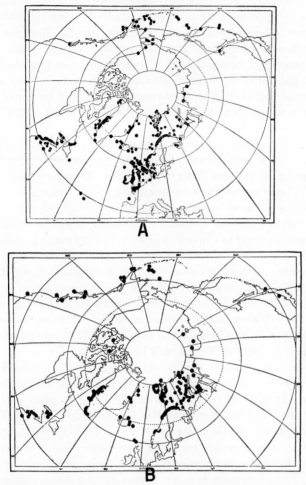

FIG. 164.—Maps of the distribution of two widely distributed northern asteroids (*after Hofsten*, 1915). *A, Ctenodiscus crispatus*, not quite circumboreal. *B, Henricia sanguinolenta*, circumboreal. Dotted line indicates Arctic Circle.

the Bering Sea through the Arctic and Atlantic Oceans to the Kurile Islands off the northeastern coast of Asia; on the Pacific Coast of North America it descends to Puget Sound, on the Atlantic Coast to the Carolinas, although only as far as Cape Cod in shallow water; and in the eastern Atlantic as far south as the Azores. In addition to these circumarctic and circumboreal species there are a number of northern species limited to the Atlantic, not found in Pacific waters. Some of the more common of these are *Pontaster tenuispinus, Pentagonaster granularis, Psilaster andromeda, Hippasteria phrygiana, Poraniomorpha hispida* and *tumida, Hymenaster pellucidus,* and *Leptasterias hyperborea* and *mülleri.* Strictly arctic species, that is, species limited to arctic waters where temperatures are constantly below freezing, include *Bathybiaster vexillifer, Korethraster hispidus, Poraniomorpha tumida, Tylaster willei, Icasterias panopla, Urasterias linckii,* and *Leptasterias hyperborea.* Such species are spoken of by some writers as "high arctic"; they are stenothermic forms that do not tend to range south along continental coasts. Main references on arctic asteroids are those of Ludwig (1900), Hofsten (1915), and Grieg (1928).

As indicated above, many of these northern asteroids range southward along continental coasts; hence they contribute largely to the asteroid fauna of the northern part of the Atlantic Coast of North America. Thus *Pontaster tenuispinus, Lophaster furcifer,* and *Leptasterias mülleri* descend as far as Nova Scotia and Newfoundland, and *Ctenodiscus crispatus, Solaster endeca, Crossaster papposus, Pteraster militaris,* and *Henricia sanguinolenta* to Cape Cod or even farther south in deeper water. Such species are clearly eurythermous, adaptable to considerable ranges of temperature. There are also endemic shallow-water sea stars along the Atlantic Coast of North America, chiefly *Asterias tenera,* from Nova Scotia to New Jersey, *A. vulgaris,* from Labrador to the Carolinas, and *A. forbesi* from Maine to the Gulf of Mexico. Main references on this area are those of H. L. Clark (1904) and Coe (1912), where references to earlier works, as those of Verrill, will be found.

Similarly arctic species contribute largely to the asteroid fauna of European coasts, descending along the Scandinavian peninsula and also by way of the Faroes to the British Isles. European asteroids are treated by Süssbach and Breckner (1911), Mortensen (1927), Mortensen and Lieberkind (1928), Koehler (1924), Lieberkind (1928), and Nobre (1938). Northern elements on north European coasts include *Psilaster andromeda, Pontaster tenuispinus, Hippasteria phrygiana, Ceramaster granularis, Poraniomorpha hispida, Crossaster papposus, Solaster endeca, Diplopteraster multipes, Henricia sanguinolenta,* and *Leptasterias mülleri.* Common endemic species often met with in the literature that do not extend into arctic waters include the phanerozonic stars *Astropecten irregularis, Luidia sarsi* and *ciliaris,* and *Porania pulvillus;* the spinulose forms *Asterina gibbosa* and *Anseropoda placenta* (Fig. 145); and the forcipulates *Marthasterias glacialis* (Fig. 154), *Asterias rubens,* and *Stichastrella rosea.*

Some of these species extend into the Mediterranean, notably *Asterina gibbosa, Anseropoda placenta, Luidia sarsi* and *ciliaris*, and *Marth. glacialis*, but in general the Mediterranean contains a different set of species, presumably requiring warmer waters. The asteroids of the Mediterranean have been reported by Ludwig (1897), Joubin (1928–1934), and Tortonese (1952), as well as in general works on European asteroids; excellent plates appear in the Joubin volume. Common shallow-water asteroids of the Mediterranean include, besides those just mentioned, the phanerozonic species *Astropecten auranciacus, bispinosus, spinulosus, jonstoni, platyacanthus,* and the *pentacanthus* variant of *irregularis, Ceramaster placenta, Tethyaster subinermis, Ophidiaster ophidianus* (Fig. 142), and *Hacelia attenuata*, the spinulose *Echinaster sepositus*, and the forcipulate *Coscinasterias tenuispina* (Fig. 155).

Many of the common asteroids of western Europe and the Mediterranean extend down the western coast of Africa to varying points. Thus *Henricia sanguinolenta* and *Asterina gibbosa* occur to the Azores, *Astropecten auranciacus* to Madeira and the Canary Islands, and *Psilaster andromeda, Astropecten irregularis, Luidia ciliaris* and *sarsi*, and *Marth. glacialis* to the Cape Verde Islands.

At the Asiatic end of the arctic there is the expected influx of ubiquitous far-northern asteroids southward into Japanese waters, and these form an important element of the asteroid fauna of Japan, at least of its northern parts. The Phanerozonia of Japan were extensively considered by Goto (1914), and the Spinulosa and Forcipulata by Hayashi (1940, 1943). Considerable information on Japanese asteroids also appears in Fisher's monograph of the North Pacific sea stars (1911, 1928, 1930). Arctic invaders include *Ctenodiscus crispatus, Leptychaster arcticus* and *anomalus, Pseudarchaster parelii, Crossaster papposus, Solaster endeca, Pteraster tessalatus*, a form of *Asterias amurensis* called *rollestoni*, and *Evasterias troscheli* and *echinosoma*. Japanese asteroids also include a number of species in common with those of the Bering Sea, Aleutian Islands, and Alaska, such as *Ceramaster japonicus, Hippasteria eliopelta, Solaster paxillatus, borealis, stimpsoni,* and *dawsoni, Poraniopsis inflata,* and *Leptasterias ochotensis* and *camtschatica*. To these are to be added endemic Japanese asteroids of which some common littoral species are *Astropecten scoparis* and several other *Astropecten* species, *Luidia maculata* and *quinaria, Asterina pectinifera* and *batheri, Coscinasterias acutispina,* species of *Lethasterias, Aphelasterias japonica, Leptasterias orientalis,* and *Distolasterias nipon*. Finally several of the most common Indo-Pacific asteroids extend into southern Japanese waters.

The Indo-Pacific may not be as rich in asteroids as the north Pacific but certainly suffers no dearth of these animals, which, moreover, are "conspicuous by reason of their brilliant colors" (H. L. Clark, 1921). This author found 41 shallow-water species in the Torres Strait region.

(which may be contrasted with the half dozen species found off the New England coast), and Fisher (1919) reported over 100 littoral species from the Philippines and adjacent waters. Main publications on the asteroids of this area are those of Döderlein (1896), Koehler (1910), H. L. Clark (1915, 1921), and Fisher (1919); for the Red Sea Tortonese (1936) and A. Clark (1952). Döderlein's reports (1916, 1917, 1920, 1924, 1935) on the extensive collections of the *Siboga* in Indonesia are very incomplete, being confined to a few genera and families. Some species range through the area from the Red Sea and Zanzibar through Indonesia and the Philippines to Japan and even Hawaii. Wide-ranging phanerozonic species include *Astropecten polyacanthus, monacanthus*, and *velitaris, Luidia maculata* and *savignyi, Archaster typicus* (Fig. 134) and *angulatus, Mediaster ornatus, Cheiraster inops, Pseudarchaster jordani, Oreaster* (or *Protoreaster*) *nodosus, Asterina* (or *Patiriella*) *exigua, Culcita novaeguineae, Fromia milleporella* and *monilis, Asterope carinifera* (Fig. 141), *Linckia laevigata, multifora*, and *guildingi*, and *Metrodira subulata;* of spinulose species may be mentioned *Echinaster purpurea* and *luzonicus, Asterina burtonii*, and *Acanthaster planci* (Fig. 97A). It will be noticed that the majority of the common widely ranging littoral sea stars of the Indo-Pacific are Phanerozonia; in fact of the 190 species described by Fisher (1919) for the Philippine area, about 70 per cent belong to the Phanerozonia. Especially characteristic of the area is the phanerozonic family Linckiidae (or Ophidiasteridae), with genera *Ferdina, Fromia, Nardoa* (Fig. 142), *Bunaster, Ophidiaster, Hacelia*, and *Linckia*. Perhaps the best-known of all Indo-Pacific shallow-water sea stars is the brilliantly blue *Linckia laevigata* (Figs. 98A, 165). Forcipulates are notably in the minority, and the large family Asteriidae has few representatives in littoral tropical waters, being characteristic of temperate and cold regions.

The asteroids of Australia have been exhaustively studied by H. L. Clark (1938, 1946), who lists 189 species, with as many as 38 species taken at a single locality; of these about 140 appear to be endemic, that is, so far not taken anywhere but Australia (and Tasmania), but many are known from only a single specimen. The remaining 50 species are in common with those of the general Indo-Pacific area and include most of the wide-ranging asteroids listed above. The northeastern coasts of Australia, including the Great Barrier Reef (asteroids here by Livingstone, 1932), may be reckoned as part of the Indo–West Pacific region.

The asteroids of the Hawaiian Islands were monographed by Fisher (1906) on the basis of extensive collections by the *Albatross*, and data from the *Tanager* collections were added (1925b). Sixty species are listed, but some of them are limited to deeper waters. Fisher states that the shore and shallow-water species are all tropical forms. About 12 of them come from the general Indo-Pacific area and include some of the widely distributed species repeatedly mentioned, as *Astropecten polyacanthus* and *velitaris*, *Archaster typicus*, *Linckia multifora* and *guildingi*, *Culcita novaeguinae*, *Mediaster ornatus*, *Pseudarchaster jordani*, *Acanthaster planci*, and *Asterope carinifera*. Two more species also

Fig. 165.—*Linckia laevigata*, one of the most common littoral asteroids of the Indo-Pacific region.

occur in the Panamic region (see below), and the remainder are endemic, although a number are closely related to Indo-Pacific species. The shallow-water asteroids of Hawaii have been considered by Ely (1942) and Edmondson (1946). The latter indicates that only a few of the 60 Hawaiian asteroids described by Fisher can be seen in shallow water and on the reefs. The most common of these are among the widely ranging

Indo-Pacific forms just listed; others include *Luidia hystrix, Ophidiaster lorioli* and *squameus, Dactylosaster cylindricus, Asterina anomala, Mithrodia bradleyi,* and *Coscinasterias acutispina.* The last is fissiparous (page 313).

As previously indicated, West Pacific and Hawaiian echinoderms tend to spread eastward to the eastern tropical Pacific or Panamic region, which extends from southern California to Peru and includes the Galapagos Islands; but the deep waters of the Pacific Ocean between the Hawaiian and South Pacific Islands on the one hand and the American coasts on the other form a formidable barrier devoid of land stops. Fisher (1906) listed with considerable reserve five asteroids as common to the Hawaiian and Panamic regions, but only two are valid, namely, *Nidorellia armata* and *Mithrodia bradleyi,* both common sea stars of the Panamic area. Further the common Indo-Pacific species *Linckia guildingi* occurs at the Galapagos Islands (H. L. Clark, 1920) and off Mexico (Caso, 1941). There is further an influx from the north of some common Pacific Coast species that range at least along Lower California, as *Mediaster aequalis,* and *tenellus, Ceramaster patagonicus, Patiria miniata,* and *Astrometic sertulifera; C. patagonicus* extends from the Magellanic area to the Bering Sea. Southern Californian species that extend at least throughout Lower California include *Astropecten armatus, ornatissimus,* and *californicus, Luidia foliolata* and *asthenosoma, Pseudarchaster pusillus, Echinaster tenuispinus,* and *Sclerasterias heteropaes.* The asteroids of southern California have been treated by Ulrey (1918); those of the Panamic region (omitting southern California) by H. L. Clark (1902a, 1910, 1913, 1920, 1923a, 1940), Ludwig (1905), Boone (1928), Ziesenhenne (1937), and Ricketts (1941). Some of these reports were based on dredgings and concern primarily the asteroids of deeper waters. Common littoral species, besides those already mentioned, include *Luidia bellonae* and *phragma, Phataria unifascialis* (Fig. 166), *Pharia pyramidata, Oreaster occidentalis, Othilia tenuispina, Acanthaster ellisii,* and *Heliaster kubiniji* (Fig. 151). The last is said by Ricketts to be by far the most common sea star on rocky shores in the Gulf of California, and in fact the genus *Heliaster* is confined to the Panamic region and the coast of Chile.

The littoral asteroids of the West Indian region were reported by Agassiz (1869), Döderlein and Hartmeyer (1910), H. L. Clark (1902b, 1919, 1933), and Boone (1933); the dredgings of the *Atlantis* (H. L. Clark, 1941) concerned mostly the species in moderate to considerable depths. The common shallow-water sea stars of the West Indies include *Astropecten duplicatus* and *antillensis, Luidia clathrata, alternata,* and *senegalensis, Oreaster reticulatus, Ophidiaster guildingi, Linckia guildingi, Asterina folium* and *minuta, Stegnaster wesseli, Echinaster sentus* and *echinophorus*, and *Coscinasterias tenuispina* (Fig. 155). The occurrence of *Linckia guildingi* is noteworthy, for this species was already indicated as common in the Indo-Pacific and Panamic regions; and as it is also found off the west coast of Africa it is definitely a tropicopolitan sea star. *Oreaster reticulatus* (Fig. 96A), a large, heavy sea star, is common and conspicuous in the Florida-Bahamas region and often collected as a 1urio. Any of these species may be expected to extend northward to the Carolinas and southward to Brazil; they also constitute the common littoral asteroids of the Caribbean (Engel, 1939). The littoral asteroids of Bermuda have been treated by H. L. Clark (1922, 1942), who reports that only one species is common there in shallow water, namely, *Coscinasterias tenuispina*. This is a typically Mediterranean species that presumably has been introduced into Bermuda and the West Indies, probably on the bottoms of ships.

The remaining tropical area, the eastern tropical Atlantic, comprising the central part of the western coast of Africa, is rather poor faunistically. The asteroids here were reported by Koehler (1914), who found only 15 littoral species, of which several were invaders from the Mediterranean and southwestern Europe. The presence here of *Linckia guildingi*, which thus completes its circle of the tropics, was already indicated. Two additional littoral west African asteroids occur in the West Indies, *Luidia senegalensis* and *Linckia bouvieri*.

Turning to the higher southern latitudes one finds in general a different set of asteroids. The asteroid fauna of South Africa was reported most fully by H. L. Clark (1923b) and Mortensen (1933). The former found that about half of the 35 littoral species then known are common Indo-Pacific sea stars; these, however, do not in general range farther south than the southern end of Mozambique, so that species from the coasts of South Africa proper are nearly all endemic. Mortensen listed 85 species from South Africa proper, but many of these came from deeper waters. The forms from moderate depths are for the most part endemic. *Ceramaster patagonicus*, which ranges from Cape Horn to the Bering Sea, is represented off South Africa in the littoral zone by a slight geographic variant. Rather surprisingly, the circumboreal *Diplopteraster multipes* is found off South Africa in its typical form, and *Marth. glacialis* extends down the west coast of Africa to the Cape as two geographic variants. Another species of the genus *Tylaster*, previously known only by the high arctic species *T. willei*, was found to occur in the South African seas at moderate depths. *Coscinasterias calamaria*, a common Australian–New Zealand star, has probably reached South Africa on ship bottoms. One may note the reappearance in these latitudes of members of the Asteriidae, mostly wanting in the littoral zone of tropical and subtropical seas.

Fig. 166.—*Phataria unifascialis* (family Linckiidae), very common littoral asteroid of the Panamic region; rows of depressions along arms are papular areas.

The asteroids of New Zealand and adjacent islands have been best considered by Mortensen (1925), Bennett (1927), and Fell (1953b). Of around 30 littoral species, nearly all are endemic; there is some invasion of a few common Indo-Pacific asteroids. The most common species are the endemic *Asterina regularis* and the Australian *Coscinasterias calamaria*. The asteroids of New Zealand include a notable number of fissiparous species (page 313).

The asteroids of antarctic and subantarctic regions, especially the southern end of South America and adjacent areas, have been extensively collected by a succession of expeditions, beginning with the *Challenger*, which during the years 1873–1876 twice visited the South American areas and secured a considerable percentage of the species now known to occur there, reported by Sladen (1889). Main reports on the asteroids of the various antarctic expeditions are those of Perrier (1891), Meissner (1904), Ludwig (1903, 1905), Bell (1908, 1917), Koehler (1906, 1908, 1911, 1912, 1917, 1920, 1923), Grieg (1929a, 1929b), Döderlein (1927), and Fisher (1940). The last in particular has given a very useful summary of our knowledge of the asteroids of the antarctic, unfortunately more or less excluding the subantarctic. He lists 33 genera as limited to the two areas; 15 of these belong to the family Asteriidae. The small spinulose family Ganeriidae consists largely of antarctic and subantarctic genera (*Scotiaster, Ganeria, Cycethra, Perknaster*). Among the asteriid genera limited to these areas may be mentioned *Labidiaster, Notasterias, Psalidaster, Anasterias, Diplasterias, Neosmilaster, Cosmasterias*, and *Granaster*.

These southern high-latitude areas have an extensive asteroid fauna that compares favorably with that of other areas. Fisher (1940) listed a total of 114 species of antarctic sea stars known to that date, but this list excluded many strictly subantarctic species, those of the Magellanic region and adjacent islands. However, only about 50 species on Fisher's list belong to the littoral zone, about 24 are abyssal, found only below 1000 m., and the remainder dwell in the archibenthal zone. The most common littoral species of the antarctic and subantarctic include the phanerozonic forms *Leptychaster kergulenensis* and *accrescens, Bathybiaster loripes* and its subspecies *obesus, Psilaster charcoti, Odontaster validus, meridionalis*, and *penicillatus, Asterodon singularis*, and *Ceramaster patagonicus;* the spinulose species *Ganeria falklandica, Cycethra verrucosa* (Fig. 167), *Perknaster fuscus, fuscus antarcticus, charcoti*, and *aurorae, Porania antarctica, Poraniopsis echinaster, Solaster regularis, Myoraster* (= *Lophaster*) *antarcticus, Patiriella fimbriata, Henricia pagenstecheri, Pteraster lebruni* and *gibber, Diplopteraster verrucosus*, and *Crossaster penicillatus;* and the asteriid forcipulates *Anteliaster scaber, Notasterias armata, Labidiaster annulatus* and *radiosus, Lysasterias perrieri* (= *victoriae*), *Diplasterias brucei, brandti* (= *loveni, lütkeni*), *meridionalis* ( = *studeri*), and *octoradiata, Cryptasterias turqueti, Anasterias antarctica, Neosmilaster steineni,* and *Granaster nutrix.* Fisher (1940) mentions a number of these species as notable for their large size, either in absolute terms or relative to other members of their genus; *Leptychaster*

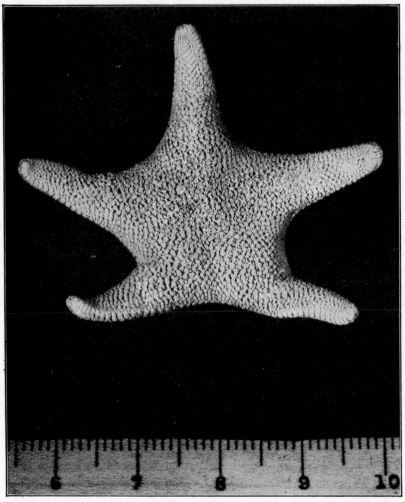

Fig. 167.—*Cycethra verrucosa* (family Ganeriidae), small spinulose star common in the Antarctic.

*flexuosus, Bathybiaster loripes obesus,* and *Labidiaster annulatus* attain diameters of around 70 cm., or over 2 feet, and several other species may be a foot or more across. A number of these species or of their strictly antarctic variants are indicated by Fisher as circumpolar, that is, found at high southern latitudes south of South America, Africa, and Australia and New Zealand, namely, *Leptychaster accrescens, Bathybiaster loripes obesus* (= *liouvillei*), *Perknaster fuscus antarcticus, Porania antarctica glabra, Psilaster charcoti, Solaster regularis subarcuatus, Myoraster antarcticus, Anasterias antarctica, Lysasterias perrieri,* and *Diplasterias brucei;* further several archibenthal species.

The asteroids of Kerguelen, an isolated island in the southern Indian Ocean at 50° south latitude, have been reported by E. A. Smith (1876, 1879), Koehler (1917), and Döderlein (1927). Koehler listed 35 sea stars as known from Kerguelen, of which 26 are littoral. Most of these have since been found widely distributed in the subantarctic. Perhaps the most familiar of the Kerguelen sea stars is *Leptychaster kerguelenensis,* described by Smith (1876) from collections made by a British party that went to the island in 1875 to observe the transit of Venus. Several specimens were also collected by the *Challenger* when it visited Kerguelen in 1874. The brooding habits of this phanerozonic star (page 294) were described by Wyville Thomson from *Challenger* material in his famous article (1878) on brooding in echinoderms of high southern latitudes. The species occurs not only at Kerguelen but also at Marion Island, a similar isolated island at about the same latitude but much nearer Africa, and what seems to be only a slight variant has been found off Tierra del Fuego.

A considerable similarity obtains between asteroids of high northern and southern latitudes. At least one species, *Ceramaster patagonicus,* exhibits "bipolarity," that is, is common to the two regions but lacking between. This species occurs from the Bering Sea to the Gulf of California and again in the Magellanic and Falkland Island region, and according to Fisher (1911, 1940) is identical in these locations. The genus *Pteraster,* with about 30 species, has 7 of these in the antarctic and 6 in the arctic. The circumboreal *Pteraster militaris* is scarcely distinguishable from the subantarctic *P. lebruni.* The mud star *Ctenodiscus crispatus,* which extends on the Pacific Coast of the Americas in its typical form from the Bering Sea to Panama, is represented in the subantarctic by two very similar species, *procurator* off Chile and in the Magellanic region and *australis* on the Atlantic side of the southern part of South America. Two common species of European coasts, *Astropecten irregularis* and *Marth. glacialis,* range down the western coast of Africa about as far as the Cape Verde Islands, then recur at the Cape of Good Hope as slight geographic variants. Many other cases of species similarity between the higher northern and southern latitudes could be cited. Of course it is always possible that the species crosses tropical areas in deeper water, but this does not seem to be the case.

Many littoral asteroids have not only a wide horizontal but also a great bathymetrical range, extend from the upper littoral or even intertidal zone to archibenthal or even abyssal levels. Data on bathymetrical range of common North American and European species are given in the works of Fisher (1911, 1928, 1930), Mortensen (1927), and Koehler (1924). The mud star *Ctenodiscus crispatus* occurs from the upper littoral zone to 1860 m., probably more; *Pteraster militaris* ranges from 10 to 1100 m.; *Hymenaster pellucidus* from 15 to 2800 m; and *Crossaster papposus* from the upper tide limit to 1200 m. On the other hand, a great many asteroids are limited to archibenthal and abyssal levels and are never seen except in the deep-water dredgings of collecting expeditions. The asteroid material collected by the *Porcupine* and some other ships in the general region of the British Isles, from the Faroes to Spain, was combined with the *Challenger* asteroids in the *Challenger* report by Sladen (1889). The *Challenger* dredged over a wide area, chiefly in the Southern Hemisphere, reaching depths of 5000 m. The North Atlantic has been extensively dredged. Its northern section from Norway to the Faroes was early investigated by the Norwegian North Atlantic Expedition (Danielsson and Koren, 1884), later by the *Michael Sars* North Atlantic Deep Sea Expeditions (Grieg, 1906, 1921); further information about Norwegian asteroids appears in Grieg (1928). The middle part of the North Atlantic, especially the Atlantic Coast of Africa from the Mediterranean to the Cape Verde Islands, was exhaustively dredged by a succession of voyages sponsored by the oceanographic station at Monaco (Perrier, 1896, Koehler, 1909), following the earlier report (Perrier, 1894) on the echinoderms dredged by the *Travailleur* and the *Talisman* in the same area. In the Indo-Pacific the main reports are those of Alcock (1893) and Koehler (1909) on the collections of the *Investigator* in the Bay of Bengal and the Arabian Sea, that of Fisher (1919) from the *Albatross* dredgings in the Philippine area, and that of Macan (1938) from the John Murray Expedition to the northern part of the Indian Ocean. The latest report on the deeper asteroids of the West Indies is that of H. L. Clark (1941). Main reports on the Panamic region are those of Ludwig (1905) and H. L. Clark (1913, 1920). The numerous antarctic and subantarctic collections have already been mentioned, and Fisher (1940) has summarized the knowledge of the asteroids of these areas in his *Discovery* report.

The extensive data thus made available show that the deeper ocean waters harbor a large asteroid fauna, but many of the species appear to be of limited distribution or at least have been taken only once or only in a restricted area; in the following account only common or widely distributed species are mentioned. One notices at once that the majority of deep-sea asteroids belong to the Phanerozonia; the families Porcellanasteridae and Benthopectinidae are almost exclusively found at considerable to great depths. Knowledge of the Porcellanasteridae was initiated by the *Challenger* collections which contained around 15 species, whereas the German Deep Sea Expedition took but 8 members of the family (Lieberkind, 1932), some the same as the *Challenger* species. *Porcellanaster coeruleus* (Fig. 130*A*) was discovered by the *Challenger* dwelling on blue mud at 2200 to 2400 m. off the eastern coast of the United States and is a regular member of the deep-water fauna there. *Eremicaster tenebrarius* is found from Alaska to the Galapagos and again off eastern Africa at depths of 2000 to over 5000 m., having been taken at 5121 m.; and *E. pacificus* inhabits similar depths off the Pacific Coast of North America and in the Panamic region. *Hyphalaster parfaiti* occurs from Norway to the Azores, also off Greenland, at depths of 2400 to 5400 m. Other porcellanasterids repeatedly taken in the eastern North Atlantic at depths greater than 4000 m. include *Styracaster elongatus, spinosus,* and *horridus,* and *Thoracaster cylindratus.* The deepest record for asteroids is that of the porcellanasterid *Albatrossaster richardi,* at 6035 m. near the Cape Verde Islands (Fig. 168*B*).

The Benthopectinidae appear to have no littoral representatives, being limited to archibenthal and especially abyssal waters. *Benthopecten armatus* (= *spinosus*) is spread throughout the whole North Atlantic to the West Indies. *Pectinaster filholi* (= *venustus*) is one of the most common abyssal species of the eastern Atlantic, and *P. agassizi* is common in the Panamic region and probably widely spread in the Indo-Pacific as slight variants.

The Astropectinidae contain a number of abyssal species, especially of the genera *Plutonaster, Dytaster, Psilaster, Bathybiaster,* and *Persephonaster.* *Plutonaster bifrons* and *notatus* are common in the eastern North Atlantic, and *agassizi* and *rigidus* occur throughout the North Atlantic to the West Indies; some other species of *Plutonaster* are characteristic of the West Indies. *Persephonaster patagiatus* is one of the most common abyssal species in the eastern North Atlantic, and *P. gracilis* has been taken in the Indo-Pacific at depths below 3000 m. at localities between Zanzibar and Japan. *Psilaster pectinatus* is a rather common abyssal species from the Bering Sea to Panama, and *Thrissacanthias penicillatus* is an archibenthal astropectinid in about the same region. *Dytaster gilberti* (includes *demonstrans*) is an abyssal Panamic species to over 4000 m. *Psilaster andromeda* is a common boreal species ranging from the upper littoral into the abyssal from the Murman coast to Greenland and southward to the Cape Verde Islands. *Bathybiaster vexillifer* (includes *robustus*) inhabits archibenthal and abyssal waters throughout the northern part of the North Atlantic.

In the Goniasteridae, the genera *Pseudarchaster, Paragonaster, Rosaster, Mediaster, Nymphaster,* and *Ceramaster* are the chief ones containing abyssal species. *Pseudarchaster annectans* is widely spread in

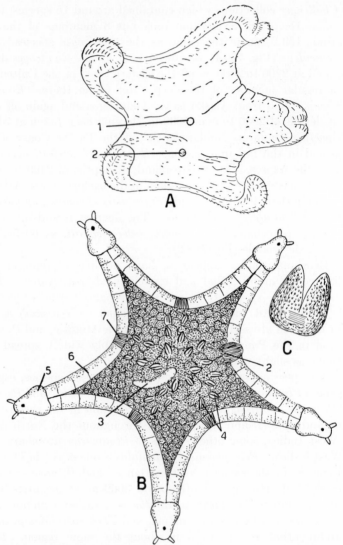

Fig. 168.—Abyssal asteroids.   A, high arctic phanerozonic star, *Tylaster willei* (family Asteropidae) (*after Danielsson and Koren*, 1884).   B, most abyssal known asteroid, *Albatrossater richardi* (family Porcellanasteridae) (*after Koehler*, 1909); note large two-jawed pedicellariae.   C, pedicellaria of B, enlarged.   1, anus; 2, madreporite; 3, epiproctal cone; 4, pedicellariae; 5, terminal ossicle; 6, supramarginal plates; 7, cribriform organ.

the North Atlantic, and *fallax* occurs in its northern part; *pectinifer* occurs throughout the Panamic region, and *jordani* and *mozaicus* are found in the Indo-Pacific.   *Paragonaster subtilis* under various names is common throughout the North Atlantic at depths of 2500 to 4700 m., and *stenostichus* is archibenthal in the Indo-Pacific.   *Rosaster alexandri* is an abyssal West Indian species to 3500 m. The genus *Mediaster* is represented in deeper waters mainly by *ornatus* found at archibenthal and abyssal depths at Hawaii and in the Indo-Pacific; *M. bairdii* occurs off the eastern coast of North America from 800 to 1300 m. *Nymphaster arenata* is common in the North Atlantic in archibenthal and abyssal waters; *N. diomedeae* is a characteristic Panamic species, and *N. moebii* is recorded from a number of deep localities in the Indo-Pacific. *Ceramaster granularis* appears widely spread in the North Atlantic from the littoral into the abyssal; *C. balteatus* is limited to the eastern part of this area. *Tylaster willei* (family Asteropidae) may be mentioned as a rare abyssal sea star of the high arctic (Fig. 168*A*).

Most of the Spinulosa from deeper waters belong to the Pterasteridae. Of other families may be mentioned *Henricia abyssalis* from the eastern North Atlantic at 1500 to 220 m., *Lophaster stellans*, archibenthal in the subantarctic, *Solaster abyssicola* off the eastern coast of North America at 1500 to 3800 m., and *Solaster borealis* in the North Pacific at 400 to 1800 m. The members of the Pterasteridae are typically inhabitants of archibenthal and abyssal waters, especially in higher latitudes. A number of abyssal species of *Hymenaster* have been recorded from antarctic and subantartic dredgings but mostly have been taken only once. Several *Hymenaster* species occur in deeper waters in the Panamic region (reviewed by H. L. Clark, 1920). Of several abyssal species in the eastern North Atlantic, the most common are *Hymenaster giboryi, rex,* and *roseus; H. pellucidus* (Fig. 148), common in far northern waters from Greenland to Siberia, descends to 2800 m. Some species of *Hymenaster* also inhabit deeper waters off the western coast of North America. Of the genus *Pteraster*, with about 30 species, mostly inhabiting littoral and archibenthal waters, may be mentioned *gibber* and *stellifer* in the subantarctic, *jordani* off the west coast of North America, and the abyssal *reductus* in the eastern Atlantic.

Among the forcipulates the families Brisingidae and Zoroasteridae are almost exclusively abyssal, with some ascent into the archibenthal. Some of the more common brisingid species are *Brisinga endecacnemos, Brisingella coronata*, and *Odinia robusta* in the eastern North Atlantic; *Freyella sexradiata* over the North Atlantic at depths of 4000 to 5000 m.; *Brisinga panamensis* and *Freyella insignis* in the Panamic area; and *Freyella fragilissima* and *Belgicella racovitzana* in the antarctic. *Freyella tuberculata* has a peculiar distribution in the Atlantic and Pacific Oceans, having been recorded from the Panamic region and the vicinity of the Cape Verde Islands. In the Zoroasteridae may be mentioned *Zoroaster fulgens*, found on both sides of the North Atlantic, and *Zoroaster ophiurus* and *evermanni* (Fig. 152) and *Myxoderma sacculatum* and *platyacanthum*, off the Pacific Coast of North America. Two forcipulates not belonging to these families are common in abyssal waters of the eastern North Atlantic, namely, *Neomorphaster talismani*, recorded to 5413 m., and *Pedicellaster sexradiatus*.

From this survey of the asteroids of deeper waters the impression is gained that they are surprisingly restricted in distribution, in view of the uniform conditions obtaining in the deeper parts of the oceans. A great many archibenthal and abyssal species occur in the eastern North Atlantic, ranging from various northern points southward along the Atlantic Coast of Africa, but few of these reach the western Atlantic or the West Indian region. Another group of species is limited to the Panamic region and rarely found elsewhere. A large number of archibenthal and abyssal asteroids are reported from the antarctic and subantarctic, but many seem to have been taken only once and most appear limited to definite localities. Most surprising of all is the general lack of widely spread asteroids in the deeper waters of the Indo-Pacific area, but insufficient collecting may account for this impression.

In perusing the taxonomic literature of asteroids one is struck by the great variability displayed by this group. Many species seem to spray out into an array of subspecies and geographic variants. Many of the species in the classical accounts of Sladen, Perrier, Koehler, and so on, have been shown to be founded on too small or too variable differences and have fallen into synonymy. The most experienced specialists not infrequently seem unable to decide whether specimens belong to distinct species or not. Adding confusion to this variability is the tendency for related species to hybridize, producing puzzling specimens. A number of cases of hybridization are reported in the works of Fisher.

**27. Ecology: Biological Relations.**—The Asteroidea are subject to the usual variety of parasites and commensals. However, only one internal protozoan parasite has been reported, *Orchitophyra stellarum*, belonging to the astomatous ciliates (I, page 189), which inhabits the gonads, destroying them. This creature was first noticed by Cépède (1907, 1910), who found it in only three males of hundreds of specimens of *Asterias rubens* examined (Fig. 170*A*). The idea that it infects males only was disproved later when the parasite was found in both sexes of *Asterias vulgaris* (G. Smith, 1936) and *A. forbesi* (Piatt, 1935; Burrows, 1936), although males seem to be more subject to infection. Several ciliates have been reported from the external surface of asteroids, and some of these belong to genera confined to a commensal existence. *Uronema digitiformis* and *Hemispeira asteriasi* were found by Fabre-Domergue (1885, 1888) on the aboral surface and papulae of *Marth. glacialis*. *Trichodina asterisci* and *Lichnophora asterisci* were noticed by Gruber (1884) on the aboral surface of *Asterina gibbosa*, Precht (1935) reported *Rhabdostyla arenaria* and *Trichodina astericola* on the podia and papulae of *Asterias rubens* in the Bay of Kiel, and still another *Trichodina* (*T. astropectinis*) occurs on *Astropecten bispinosus* (Chatton and Villeneuve, 1937).

A creeping ctenophore, *Coeloplana astericola*, slithers about on the surface of *Echinaster luzonicus*, but not other asteroids, at Amboina and the Kei Islands (Mortensen, 1927); its blotched red-and-white pattern contrasts conspicuously with the brown color of the sea star. Turbellarians of the family Umagillidae (II, page 140) are uncommon in

Fig. 169.—Commensals of asteroids. Polynoid polychaete *Achloe astericola* in the ambulacral groove of *Astropecten irregularis*, ready to participate in the meal as the *Astropecten* starts to ingest a bivalve; in the background an *Astropecten*, also with a commensal *Achloe*, is seen righting by the tulip method. According to Thorson, the worm actually puts its head into the host's stomach to steal food. (*Drawing by Poul H. Winther, courtesy of G. Thorson.*)

asteroids, being limited to one species, *Pterastericola fedotovi* (Beklemichev, 1916), inhabiting the intestine of three arctic species of *Pteraster* on the Murman coast.

Annelids of the polychaete family Polynoidae are well-known commensals of asteroids. *Achloe astericola* has long been known as an inhabitant of the ambulacral grooves of *Astropecten irregularis*, further on Mediterranean species of *Astropecten* (*auranciacus* and *bispinosus*) and on *Luidia ciliaris* (Cuénot, 1912). This author found as many as six specimens on one *Astropecten*, a large one in the ambulacral groove, and five small ones among the paxillae and marginal plates. Davenport (1953), making a special study of this polynoid on British coasts, found 75 per cent of *A. irregularis* infected, usually with one worm in an ambulacral groove.   Upon being removed from its host, the worm returns to it and also reacts positively to *Astropecten* tissues, also to those of other phanerozonic stars, especially *Luidia*, but not to parts of forcipulates; water coming from the host asteroid was not attractive to this worm. Another polynoid, *Harmothoe lunulata*, also occurs on *Astropecten irregularis* in British waters (McIntosh, 1874, 1900) and on species of *Astropecten* at Naples; *H. imbricata* is found in the ambulacral groove of *Asterias amurensis* off Japan (Okuda, 1938), and this same asteroid also harbors *Halosydnoides vittata*, further found on Californian asteriids. Species of *Arctonoe* occur on a number of Puget Sound asteroids, and the relationship of *Arctonoe fragilis* to *Evasterias troscheli* has been especially investigated by Davenport (1950) and Davenport and Hickok (1951). This polynoid is definitely attracted to its host star and can distinguish between water coming from an aquarium containing its host and water from other asteroids, or plain sea water.   Attractant water loses this property within a few hours after the host star is removed from it. Another type of polychaete, *Podarke pugettensis*, may occur in the ambulacral grooves of *Oreaster occidentalis* and other asteroids of the Pacific Coast of North America (Ricketts, 1941).   A myzostome, *Myzostoma asteriae* (von Marenzeller, 1895; Stummer-Traunfels, 1903), occupies an enlargement at the base of the pyloric caeca of one or more arms in deepwater species of the genus *Sclerasterias* in the eastern Atlantic.

Asteroids like other echinoderm groups are subject to attacks by parasitic snails, some living on the external surface, others in the interior. Parasitic snails of echinoderms have been well reviewed by Koehler and Vaney (1912), Vaney (1913), Pelseneer (1928), and Habe (1952).   They generally lack a radula and show other signs of parasitic degeneration. The genus *Thyca* (family Capulidae, related to the boat shell *Crepidula*) is exclusively parasitic on asteroids in warm waters and adheres to the host by a fixation disk in the center of which is found the mouth.   *Thyca crystallina, astericola, ectoconcha,* and *pellucida* are found in the ambulacral grooves of Indo-Pacific species of *Luidia*, and *Thyca stellasteris* (Fig. 170*C*) occurs fixed to the marginal plates of *Stellaster equestris*.   The Melanellidae (= Eulimidae), also ectoparastic, are represented by *Melanella astericola* on *Asterias solaris*, *M. breviuscula* on *Archaster typicus*, *M. asteriaphila* on an unidentified star, *M. equestris* on the marginal plates of *Stellaster equestris* with proboscis piercing the body wall into the interior (Fig. 170*B*), *M. astropectenicola* on the oral surface of *Astropecten polyacanthus* and *Luidia maculata*, and *M. robusta* also on the former.   The Stiliferidae are wholly parasitic, often endoparasitic, and have undergone varying degrees of parasitic degeneration, being often covered by a body fold, the pseudopallium.   Asteroid parasites of this family include *Mucronalia palmipedis* on *Anseropoda rosacea*

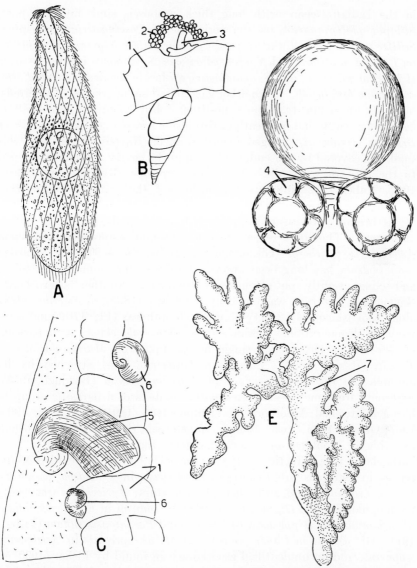

Fig. 170.—Parasites of asteroids. *A*, astomatous ciliate, *Orchitophrya stellarum*, from the gonads of *Asterias* species (*after Cépède*, 1910). *B*, *Melanella equestris*, parasitic snail on *Stellaster equestris*, with proboscis thrust through body wall into the interior. *C*, parasitic snail, *Thyca stellasteris*, one female and two much smaller males, on the aboral surface of *Stellaster equestris*. (*B*, *C*, *after Koehler and Vaney*, 1912.) *D*, copepod *Scottomyza gibberum*, parasitic on the surface of *Asterias rubens* (*after the Scotts*, 1895). *E*, parasitic barnacle, *Dendrogaster*, removed from the coelom of *Leptasterias groenlandica* (*after Fisher*, 1930). 1, marginal plates of sea star; 2, gonad; 3, proboscis of snail; 4, egg sacs; 5, female *Thyca*; 6, males of *Thyca*; 7, main part of barnacle.

in the Indian Ocean, with long thick proboscis sunk into the host, *Stilapex philippinarum* on the peristome of *Coscinasterias acutispina*, *Stilifer ovoideus* inside the arms of *Certonardoa semiregularis*, *S. linckiae* on *Linckia multifora* and *Nardoa pauciforis*, *S. utinomii* inside the arms of *Linckia guildingi*, and *S. ophidiastericola* inside the arms of *Ophidiaster cribrarium* and *lorioli*. Two other gasteropod endoparasites of asteroids, both of uncertain taxonomic position, merit mention. *Ctenosculum hawaiiense* was found by Heath (1910) inside a swelling of an arm base of *Brisinga evermanni*, dredged from 600 m. off Hawaii; the body of this snail was covered by a pseudopallium, and the cavity it occupied opened to the exterior by a slit. *Asterophila japonica* (Randall and Heath, 1912; Habe, 1952) inhabits the coelom of the arms of *Pedicellaster magister*, off Japan, and lacks communication with the exterior.

Arthropod parasites of asteroids include copepods, barnacles, and an amphipod. The occurrence of the parasitic asterocherid copepod *Asterocheres lilljeborgi* (Giesbrecht, 1899) on the surface of *Henricia sanguinolenta* has long been known; it moves about among the spines and clings tightly on attempts at removal. Another asterocherid, *Scottomyzon gibberum*, was found by the Scotts (1895) on *Asterias rubens* along Scottish coasts; its very plump cephalothorax (Fig. 170D) indicates parasitic degeneration. Designation of *Astericola clausii* as a parasite of asteroids is based on a single female taken on *Marth. glacialis* at Trieste (Rosoll, 1888). *Lichomolgus asterinae* lives attached by its antennae to the aboral surface of *Asterina gibbosa* (Bocquet, 1953). Asteroids are sometimes infested with members of a parasitic group of barnacles termed Ascothoracica (Knipowitsch, 1891, 1892; Roi, 1905, 1907; Okada, 1925; Yosii, 1931). In asteroids these live in the coelom as a highly lobulated or branched object (Fig. 170E) known to be a barnacle by its production of typical barnacle larvae. Recorded occurrences in asteroids are *Dendrogaster astericola* in *Crossaster papposus*, *Henricia sanguinolenta*, and other spinulose stars; *Myriocladus arborescens* in the phanerozonic *Dipsacaster sladeni; M. ludwigi* in *Echinaster fallax; M. arbusculus* in *Hippasteria californica* and *Poraniopsis inflata* (Fisher, 1911); *M. okadai* in *Coscin. calamaria; M. astropectinis* in *Astropecten scoparius;* and an unidentified ascothoracican found by Fisher (1930) in two cases in the coelom of *Leptasterias groenlandica*, where they had considerably damaged the host's gonads. A caprellid amphipod *Podalirus typicus* is a well-known associate of *Asterias rubens* (Cuénot, 1912), not very obvious on the host by reason of its small size and transparency. It occurs anywhere on the surface of the sea star, hanging on by the hooks at the ends of its appendages, and will not leave the host even when subjected to annoyance. Durham (1888) noted that the caprellid feeds on the surface slime of the sea star, for its digestive tract became blue following injection of a blue dye into the host. The most remarkable associate of asteroids is the pearl fish (page 243), which has several times been found inside the coelom of *Culcita* (Mortensen, 1922, 1931). It appears impossible for the fish to gain the coelom except by making a hole through the stomach wall.

Whether the stomach of sea stars secretes a toxic substance was considered above (page 372). C. Parker (1881) recorded that two cats that ate a *Crossaster papposus* soon became violently ill and died. However, sea stars are eaten by other animals, mostly other echinoderms, with impunity (Eichelbaum, 1910; Bull, 1934). Rodenhouse and Guberlet (1946) state that other invertebrates avoided the mucous secretion of *Pteraster tesselatus* and that gastropods, crabs, and a cucumber placed in a jar with such mucus died in 28 to 56 hours, but the conditions of the experiment are not clearly stated and apparently no control jar was set up. Apparently asteroids do secrete something that evokes reactions in other animals. Schiemenz (1896) noted that the snail *Natica* responds to contact with the podia of *Asterias rubens* by throwing a fold of skin over the shell, thus preventing the podia from getting a grip (Fig. 171*B*). Similarly another snail, *Nassa*, having been touched by the podia of *A. rubens*, takes flight by violent leaps (Fig. 171*A*). Scallops swim away on contact with asteroids, especially *Marth. glacialis* (von Uexküll, 1912; Lecomte, 1952); the latter author showed that other species are less or scarcely at all effective and that some chemical stimulus emanating from *M. glacialis* is at least partly responsible for the flight reaction, as flight is also evoked by application of ground material of this species but not of other asteroids. Bennett (1927) reported a marked reaction of *Haliotis* to contact with *Coscinasterias calamaria;* the abalone moves away at top speed, violently swinging its shell from side to side until it has shaken off the sea star. Bullock (1953) observed similar behavior of limpets (*Acmaea*) and other Californian gastropods to contact with the podia of several kinds of local forcipulates; they would rock their shells violently and move rapidly away. The reaction is evoked by dead podia and may occur before actual contact with the asteroid's podia, an indication of some sort of chemical emanation from the sea star. The common Californian spinulose star *Patiria miniata* does not evoke the behavior. The MacGinities (1949) record the retreat of sand dollars into the sand in the presence of *Pisaster brevispinus*.

Data are available on the growth of a few common species of asteroids. *Asterias forbesi* (Mead, 1901; Galtsoff and Loosanoff, 1939) spawns off the New England coast in June, and by the end of this month multitudes of minute stars 1 mm. or less in diameter may be found in the seaweeds. These increase to a maximum diameter of 10 to 11 mm. by the end of of July, 35 mm. by the end of September, and 50 to 80 mm. by the end of

October.   Growth declines during the winter but is resumed in early
summer, and spawning usually occurs in year-old specimens, even at a
size of 32 mm.   G. Smith (1940) states that *Asterias vulgaris* attains a
diameter of 35 mm. at the end of 1 year, 60 mm. at the end of its second
year.   Milligan (1916) noted that well-fed captive specimens of *Crossaster
papposus* grew from a diameter of 40 mm. to one of 90 mm. in slightly

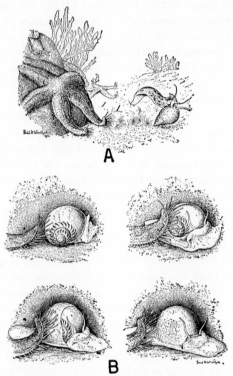

Fig. 171.—Flight reactions of snails to *Asterias rubens*.   A, *Nassa reticulata*, having
been touched by the podia of the sea star, escapes by leaping violently.   B, *Natica catena*,
on contact with the podia, draws a fold of the foot over itself, presenting a slippery surface
on which the podia cannot get a grip.   (*Drawings by Poul H. Winther, courtesy of G.
Thorson.*)

more than a year, or an increase of about 1 mm. per week.   Mortensen
(1927) is of the opinion that *Ctenodiscus crispatus* attains full size in 3
years, *Psilaster andromeda* in 4 years, and *Pseudarchaster parelii* in 4 years
or more.   Data on the growth of *Asterias rubens* have been furnished by
Orton and Fraser (1930), Bull (1934), Vevers (1949), and Barnes and
Powell (1951).   It is indicated that this species attains a diameter of
40 to 100 mm. during its first year of life, growing mostly in summer, and
generally spawns at 1 year of age.   At this rate of growth 6 or 7 years
would be required for this species to reach its maximum size of 70 cm. in
diameter.

## IX. CLASS ECHINOIDEA

**1. Definition.**—The Echinoidea are pentamerous eleutherozoan echinoderms of globose, oval, or discoid shape, oriented with the oral surface downward, provided with two to five, mostly five, gonads, and covered with spines borne on an endoskeletal shell or test of closely fitted calcareous plates arranged in 20 meridional rows, 10 ambulacral and 10 interambulacral, of which the former are pierced with pores for the passage of the podia.

**2. General Remarks.**—The echinoids include marine animals commonly known as sea urchins, heart urchins, and sand dollars. As ubiquitous and conspicuous inhabitants of the sea, the echinoids were known to the ancients, and several different kinds were described by Aristotle, who applied to the common Mediterranean urchin the name *echinos*, meaning literally a hedgehog, and surviving in the name of a common genus, *Echinus*, whence the name of the class. However, scientific knowledge of the group began about 1825 and progressed vigorously throughout the nineteenth century, but interest has somewhat declined in recent decades and most zoologists are aware of echinoids chiefly as a source of eggs for experimental purposes. General accounts of the class are given by J. W. Gregory (1900) in Lankester's *A Treatise on zoology*, by H. Ludwig and O. Hamann (1904) in Bronn's *Klassen und Ordnungen des Tierreichs*, and by L. Cuénot (1948) in Grassé's *Traite de zoologie*. The two-volume work of Jackson (1912), *Phylogeny of the Echini*, remains a classical reference. The colossal *Monograph of the Echinoidea* by Mortensen (1928–1951) in 15 volumes, primarily a systematic work, was fortunately completed before the author's death, but a further volume, intended to contain a general account of the class, has not been published. Valuable articles on echinoid morphology are those of Lovén (1874), Koehler (1883), Hamann (1887), Prouho (1887), Cuénot (1891a), and Chadwick (1900). Agassiz's (1881) report on the echinoids collected by the *Challenger* began a long series of reports on the echinoids taken on marine collecting expeditions that have added much to our knowledge, especially of the systematics, of the group. A large literature, much of it not pertinent here, also exists on the experimental embryology of echinoids.

Because of their possession of a continuous calcareous theca or test, echinoids preserve well as fossils and occur in abundance in the rocks, beginning in the Middle Ordovician. Consequently, there is also available a large literature on fossil echinoids; extinct forms together with pertinent literature are included in Mortensen's monograph. The following account concerns only the existing echinoids, and the definition given above also excludes the fossil members. Consideration of fossil echinoids will be limited to the systematic survey.

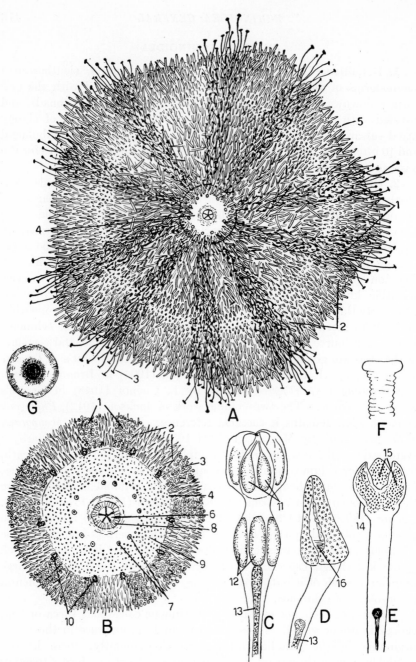

Fig. 172.—External features of regular echinoids. *A–G. Tripneustes ventricosus* (from life, Bahamas). *A*, oral view. *B*, enlarged view of peristome. *C*, globiferous pedicellaria with stalk glands. *D*, tridentate pedicellaria. *E*, ophiocephalous pedicellaria. *F*, buccal podium from side. *G*, buccal podium from top. 1, ambulacrum with double row of podia; 2, interambulacrum; 3, podia; 4, peristome; 5, spines; 6, mouth occupied by five teeth of masticatory apparatus; 7, buccal podia; 8, mouth rim; 9, pedicellariae on peristome; 10, gills; 11, glands of head; 12, glands of stalk; 13, skeletal rod; 14, jaws; 15, valve or endoskeletal piece of jaws; 16, adductor muscle.

414

A count in Mortensen's monograph reveals that there are about 750 described existing echinoids.

**3. External Characters.**—The echinoids are subdivided into regular and irregular groups, and it is desirable to consider these separately. The regular echinoids, equivalent to sea urchins, are typically of globose shape, usually more or less flattened at the poles, but some are oval. They present differentiated oral and aboral surfaces and, as in the Eleutherozoa in general, they move upon the oral surface, which is consequently more or less flattened or even concave, whereas the aboral surface is moderately to highly arched. The most conspicuous external feature of a sea urchin is the armature of thickly placed spines. The spines may be all of approximately one size (Fig. 172*A*), but usually those of the oral and aboral areas are shorter than those around the sides, and generally, also, the armature consists of an intermingling of large and small spines definitely arranged (Fig. 173*C*). In some the spines are generally short (Fig. 172*A*), in others long; and some diadematids have short spines on the oral surface and very long and sharply pointed ones aborally (Fig. 176*D*), reaching up to a foot in length.

In addition to the spines, one notices on the external surface of regular urchins, especially live ones, the five double rows of podia extending in a perfect pentaradiate arrangement from the oral to the apical region of the animal (Fig. 172*A*). The podia thus define five ambulacral areas, and between these lie the five interambulacral areas, usually wider than the ambulacra. The podia, usually provided with terminal disks, although these may be wanting on the aboral podia, are very slender and extensile and can be elongated to protrude beyond the spines. Both spines and podia are used by sea urchins in locomotion.

In the center of the oral surface is found the mouth, from which there generally protrude the five hard *teeth* belonging to the chewing apparatus (*lantern of Aristotle*). The mouth is surrounded by a circular, more or less soft and membranous area, the *peristome*, which usually edges the mouth opening with a thickened rim or *lip*. Near the mouth the peristome bears a circlet of five pairs of altered podia, the *buccal podia* (Figs. 172*B*, 173*B*), probably of chemoreceptive nature; they are usually short and stout and provided with a circular, oval, or reniform disk (Fig. 172*F*, *G*). The peristome may be more or less naked but usually is provided with small spines and pedicellariae (Figs. 172*B*, 173*B*) and contains embedded plates for the support of the buccal podia. At the edge of the peristome in the interambulacral areas are borne five pairs of little bushy structures, the *gills*, presumably of respiratory nature (Figs. 172*B*, 173*B*, *F*). Gills and differentiated buccal podia are wanting in the order Cidaroidea. In the cidaroids (Fig. 173*E*) and also in the family Echinothuriidae (Fig. 222*C*) the podial rows and their supporting plates continue over the peristome to the mouth lip.

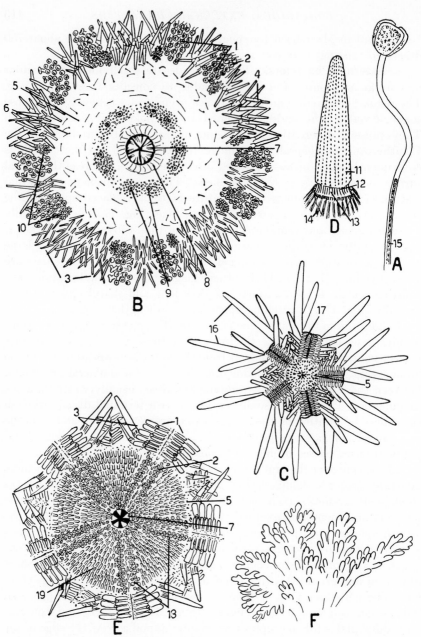

Fig. 173.—External features of regular echinoids (continued). A, triphyllous pedicellaria of *Tripneustes*. B, oral view of *Arbacia punctulata*. C, a cidaroid urchin, *Eucidaris tribuloides*. D, a primary spine of C. E, oral surface of *Eucidaris*. F, gill of *Tripneustes*. (All from life, Bahamas.) 1, ambulacrum with double row of podia; 2, podia; 3, interambulacrum; 4, spines; 5, peristome; 6, pedicellariae; 7, mouth with five teeth of chewing apparatus; 8, mouth rim; 9, buccal podia; 10, gills; 11, shaft; 12, collar; 13, milled ring; 14, cylinder of muscle fibers; 15, skeletal rod; 16, primary spines; 17, secondary spines; 18, ambulacra of perisotome; 19, interambulacra of peristome.

At the aboral pole there also occurs a membranous area, the *periproct*, usually containing one to many imbedded endoskeletal plates, commonly provided with small spines and pedicellariae. The anus is located somewhere in the periproct, often near its center but also often in a markedly excentric position. In the regular echinoids, the oral-aboral axis, extending from the mouth to the center of the periproct, forms an axis of symmetry around which most of the body parts are pentamerously arranged.

Between the peristome and the periproct the body wall is rendered hard and unyielding by a continuous endoskeletal *shell* or *test* made of closely and immovably fitted calcareous plates that support the spines, except in the family Echinothuriidae and some members of the Diadematidae in which the plates of the test are imbricated, so that the body is leathery and more or less flexible. Viewed from either the oral or aboral surface, the circumference of the test, called the *ambitus*, is generally circular, although sometimes slightly pentagonal (Fig. 172*A*), and regularly oval in some genera as *Echinometra* (Fig. 228*A*). The echinoid test is undoubtedly comparable to the theca of extinct Pelmatozoa.

In the irregular echinoids the periproct, including the anus, has moved out of the center of the aboral surface, and the line of its retreat along one of the interambulacra establishes an axis of bilateral symmetry that obtains throughout the irregular forms. Anterior and posterior ends are thereby also established; the interambulacrum bisected by the plane of bilateral symmetry becomes posterior, since it houses the periproct, and in the opposite direction the symmetry plane bisects one of the ambulacra that thereby becomes the anterior ambulacrum (Fig. 174*A*, *B*). This anterior ambulacrum is numbered III on Lovén's system (explained later), universally used by echinoid systematists, and the posterior interambulacrum is 5 on this system; they correspond to ambulacrum D and interambulacrum AB on the Carpenter system adopted here. The ambitus in irregular echinoids varies from oval or cordiform (Figs. 174*A*, 175*B*) to practically circular (Fig. 177*A*). The body is flattened orally and may be arched aborally (Fig. 175*A*) or more or less flattened aborally, greatly so in sand dollars (Fig. 177*C*). With the retreat of the periproct from the center of the aboral surface, the plates of the test close together here, maintaining an aboral center, but this is often shifted anteriorly (Fig. 174*A*) or posteriorly (Fig. 231*H*). From it the five ambulacra radiate over the aboral surface. Their proximal parts aborally are nearly always altered to a petal-like shape, so that on the aboral surface of irregular echinoids the petals or *petaloids* of the ambulacra form a flower-like figure (Fig. 175*B*). The podia of the petaloids are altered for respiratory purposes and are not employed

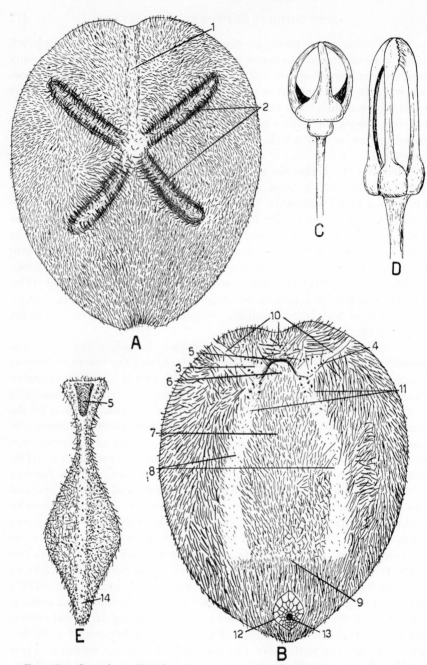

FIG. 174.—Irregular echinoids. *A*, a spatangoid, *Meoma ventricosa*, West Indies, aboral view. *B*, same, oral view. (*A B*, from a dry specimen.) *C*, rostrate pedicellaria. *D*, tridentate pedicellaria of *Meoma*. (*C, D, after Boone*, 1933.) *E*, pourtalesiid urchin, oral view, *Echinosigra (after Mortensen*, 1907). 1, anterior ambulacrum; 2, petaloid ambulacra; 3, phyllodes; 4, pores for penicillate podia of phyllodes; 5, peristome; 6, labrum; 7, plastron; 8, posterior ambulacra; 9, anterior part of subanal fasciole; 10, trivium; 11, bivium; 12, periproct; 13, anus; 14, posterior end.

in locomotion.   On the oral surface of irregular echinoids the mouth and peristome may occupy a central position (Fig. 177*B*) or may be displaced anteriorly, often greatly so (Fig. 174*B*).   The ambulacra continue over the ambitus to the edge of the peristome wherever that may be located. Gills are wanting in all irregular echinoids.

The main groups of existing irregular echinoids are the *spatangoids* and the *clypeastroids*.   In the spatangoids, or heart urchins, the ambitus is oval or cordiform (Fig. 174*A, B*) and the aboral surface more or less arched (Fig. 175*A*).   The aboral center may be shifted anteriorly or posteriorly, but as the peristome is always displaced anteriorly, the three anterior ambulacra take a shorter course over the ambitus to the peristome than do the two posterior ambulacra (Fig. 174*B*), as the latter must curve around the posterior end and then extend forward.   The three anterior ambulacra are often spoken of as the trivium, and the posterior ones as the bivium, but these do not correspond morphologically to the trivium and bivium of holothurians.   The anterior ambulacrum is generally not altered into a petaloid in spatangoids but forms a narrow band of even width bearing on each side a single row of podia.   On the aboral surface the other four ambulacra, often called the paired ambulacra, form petaloids that may be flush with the surface or more or less indented (Fig. 174*A*).   The periproct, supported by a number of small plates, is located in the posterior interambulacrum at or near the posterior end on either aboral or oral surface (Fig. 174*B*).   The peristome, also filled with small plates (Fig. 184*A*), is displaced well forward and is bordered posteriorly by a lip-like projection of the posterior interambulacrum, called the *labrum* (Fig. 175*A*).   The presence of the labrum forces the peristome into an oval or somewhat crescentic shape (Fig. 192*A;* the peristome plates are missing from this specimen).   The oral ends of the ambulacra surround the peristome, alternating with the much narrower interambulacra, and are somewhat expanded into a petal-like shape, called a *phyllode* (Figs. 174*B*, 192*A*).   The phyllodes are pierced by large pores for the passage of special modified podia (see later).   On the oral or ventral surface the two posterior ambulacra are very long and narrow (Figs. 174*B*, 192*A*) and enclose between them a long and fairly wide part of the posterior interambulacrum that is called the *plastron* (or *sternum*) and may be provided with a special spination.   The plastron extends from the labrum in front to the periproct behind.   Shortly in front of the periproct, the posterior ambulacra broaden, and each is provided with a single row of a few large podia, the *subanal* podia, the pores for which are shown in Fig. 192*A*.   Apart from these the podia along the ambulacra between the phyllodes and the petaloids are usually much reduced, and even rudimentary, and generally limited to a single row on each side.   Spatangoids lack locomotory podia but have sev-

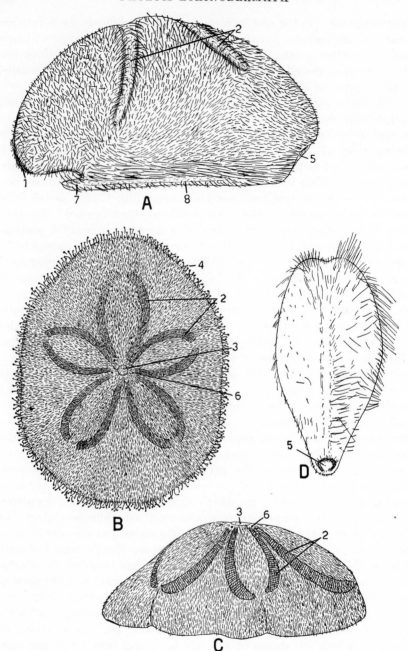

Fig. 175.—Irregular urchins (continued). *A, Meoma ventricosa*, spatangoid, from the side (from a dry specimen). *B*, clypeastroid, *Clypeaster roseaceus*, West Indies, aboral view. *C*, same as *B*, side view. (*B, C*, from life.) *D, Pourtalesia*, aboral view (*after Mortensen*, 1907). 1, anterior ambulacrum; 2, petaloid ambulacra; 3, madreporic plate; 4, podia; 5, periproct; 6, gonopores; 7, labrum; 8, plastron.

eral other kinds, altered for a variety of nonlocomotory functions (see later).

The spatangoids are clothed with spines of small to moderate length, often showing size and shape patterns with reference to body regions (Fig. 235*A*, *B*) and usually curved and held parallel to the body surface, appearing as if combed back. Peculiar to spatangoids are narrow bands composed of thickly set minute spines called *clavules* that are shaped something like a miniature tennis racket (Fig. 187*G*) and are heavily ciliated basally. The clavules are said to maintain a water current and to assist in removing sand grains from the test. The tracts of clavules are called *fascioles*, and there are several of these fascioles among spatangoids, named according to location as follows: the *peripetalous* fasciole, encircling the petaloids and crossing the anterior ambulacrum (Fig. 191*E*); the *internal* fasciole, enclosing the aboral apex and much of the anterior ambulacrum (Fig. 235*D*); the *subanal* fasciole enclosing the posterior part of the plastron anterior to the periproct on the aboral surface and also embracing the subanal podia (Fig. 192*A*); the *anal* fascioles, running from the angles of the subanal fasciole back along either side of the periproct (Fig. 192*A*); the *marginal* fasciole along the ambitus; and the *lateral* or *lateroanal* fascioles that extend from the posterior angles of the peripetalous fasciole backward toward the posterior end (Fig. 236*B*). No one spatangoid has all the possible kinds of fascioles, but many have two or three, and the kind of fasciole present furnishes an important generic distinction. The most common kinds of fascioles are the subanal and the peripetalous.

Among the spatangoids, the family Pourtalesiidae is notable for peculiarities of shape. Although some members are of simple oval form, most are triangular or pyramidal or bottle-shaped, with a short (*Pourtalesia*, Fig. 175*D*) or long (*Echinosigra*, Fig. 174*E*) neck. In both, the periproct is situated on the aboral surface of the narrowed end, and the peristome is located on the oral surface of the broad end near the margin. The Pourtalesiidae lack petaloids and phyllodes, but as both aboral center and peristome are moved anteriorly, the ambulacra show the typical spatangoid differentiation into short anterior and long posterior groups. Labrum, plastron, and subanal fasciole are present. The Pourtalesiidae inhabit deep waters and are known only from the collections of dredging expeditions. They were first seen by Pourtalés while dredging at 600 m. off the Tortugas (reported by A. Agassiz, 1869) and astonished zoologists by their strange shape and fragile, transparent test.

The clypeastroids include the types of irregular echinoids known as sand dollars or cake urchins. They usually have an oval or circular ambitus and typically are greatly flattened in the oral-aboral direction, although members of the family Clypeastridae are not infrequently arched dorsally, as the common West Indian sea biscuit *Clypeaster rosaceus* (Fig. 175*B*, *C*). The more typical flat sand dollar shape is shown in profile in Fig. 177*C*. The body is covered with a fur of very short spines. The aboral apex is generally centrally located and is surrounded by five petaloids (Fig. 177*A*), often showing bilaterally symmetrical size inequalities. The peristome occupies the center of the oral surface (Fig. 177*B*), and the periproct is also usually on the oral side, occurring anywhere along the line of symmetry of the posterior interambulacrum from the peristome to the ambitus. The oral side also bears grooves radiating from the peristome to the ambitus. When there are five simple grooves, as in *Clypeaster* (Fig. 176*A*), they occur along the center of the ambulacra. When the furrows branch, as in *Mellita* (Fig. 177*B*) and *Rotula* (Fig. 178*B*), they are not very definitely related to the ambulacra, except at the peristome, and spread over into the interambulacra. Phyllodes, fascioles, and other peculiarities of spatangoids are wanting in clypeastroids.

In several genera of sand dollars, the test is perforated with two or more round to elongated holes, the *lunules*, that typically arise as marginal indentations and become enclosed by the growth of the test; but in some cases they form *in situ* by local resorption of the test. The keyhole urchins of the genus *Mellita* are familiar examples of clypeastroids with lunules (Fig. 177*A*, *B*). Another variant is seen in the genus *Rotula*, with a number of permanent indentations along the posterior margin of the test (Fig. 178*A*, *B*).

The Echinoidea are in general animals of small to moderate size. The smallest forms occur among the sand dollars, some of which are no more than 10 mm. in diameter. Among the regular echinoids, the larger species attain a diameter of 10 to 15 cm., exclusive of the spines. Some large forms occur among the spatangoids, where the common West Indian *Meoma ventricosa* (Fig. 174*A*) may reach a length of 18 cm. The largest urchins belong to the deep-sea family Echinothuriidae, the members of which tend to a large size. The largest existing echinoids occur in this family, viz., *Hygrosoma hoplacantha*, Indo-Pacific, with a test diameter of 28 cm., and *Sperosoma giganteum*, Japan, of which the only known specimen has a test diameter of 32 cm. (a little over 1 foot).

Echinoids are usually colored uniformly in plain, dark shades, most commonly green, olive, brown, purple, and black, although some are pale or nearly white, and there are a few red urchins. Typically, the spines and body show the same coloration although contrasting in some species. The spines are sometimes prettily cross-banded in a contrasting color or may have contrasting tips. The common *Diadema antillarum* of the West Indies (Fig. 176*D*) is uniformly dark purple or almost black

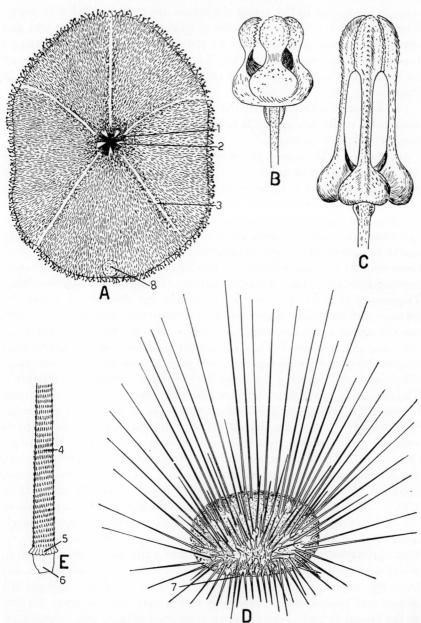

FIG. 176.—External features (continued). *A, Clypeaster rosaceus*, West Indies, oral view (from life). *B*, ophiocephalous pedicellaria of *A*. *C*, tridentate pedicellaria of *A*. (*B, C, after Boone*, 1933.) *D, Diadema antillarum*, side view (from life, Bahamas). *E*, base of spine of *D*. 1, peristome; 2, teeth of masticatory apparatus; 3, grooves marking center of ambulacra; 4, shaft with circles of thorns; 5, milled ring; 6, base; 7, oral side; 8, periproct,

when mature, but in the young the spines are cross-banded with white. The young of this species are able to change the color of the test and spine bases to pale grey and white by the contraction of the melanophores that contain the black pigment (Millott, 1952). Color in echinoids may be localized in such pigment cells or may occur as masses of granules in the dermis.

**4. External Appendages.**—These comprise the spines, pedicellariae, sphaeridia, podia, and gills. It is to be understood that in life all of these are covered with epidermis.

*a. Spines.*—The spines, never wanting, are one of the most characteristic features of echinoids. They are usually differentiated into two main sizes, the larger, or *primary*, spines (also called radioles) and the smaller, or *secondary*, spines; very small spines are termed *tertiary* or *miliary*. In regular urchins the primary spines occur in meridional rows extending over the test from periproct to peristome, and the secondary spines are also more or less arranged in a pattern. These patterns are more evident by examining the tubercles on a denuded test. Whereas in many common genera of regular urchins, as *Echinus*, *Strongylocentrotus*, *Tripneustes* (Fig. 172*A*), there is no striking size difference between the primary and secondary spines and intermediate sizes may occur, in others the difference is conspicuous. Notably, the cidaroids have very large and stout primary spines (Fig. 173*C*), whereas the secondaries are reduced to small flattened spines encircling the base of each primary spine (Fig. 179*B*) and also covering the areas between the meridians of primaries. The regular family Echinometridae also often shows an extreme contrast between the primary and secondary spines, as in *Heterocentrotus mammillatus*, with large club-shaped primary spines and secondary spines reduced to short, flat-topped structures forming a mosaic over the surface (Fig. 178*D*, *E*). In another echinometrid genus, *Colobocentrotus*, all the aboral spines are reduced to this short, thick, flat-topped shape, bordered at the ambitus with a circle of broad, flattened spines (Fig. 178*C*). The spination of *Colobocentrotus* is considered an adaptation to life on rocky shores beaten by surf. Secondary spines are poorly developed in the family Arbaciidae and are wanting in the genus *Arbacia*. Both primaries and secondaries show size variations with respect to position on the test. Usually in regular urchins all spines increase in size from the poles to the ambitus that therefore customarily bears the largest and longest spines; but spine length may increase from the oral to the aboral surface, as in *Diadema antillarum* (Fig. 176*D*). Spines are usually longer and more numerous on interambulacral than on ambulacral areas.

Less size variation is seen in irregular urchins, where the spines are generally short, especially in clypeastroids. Primaries are often evident

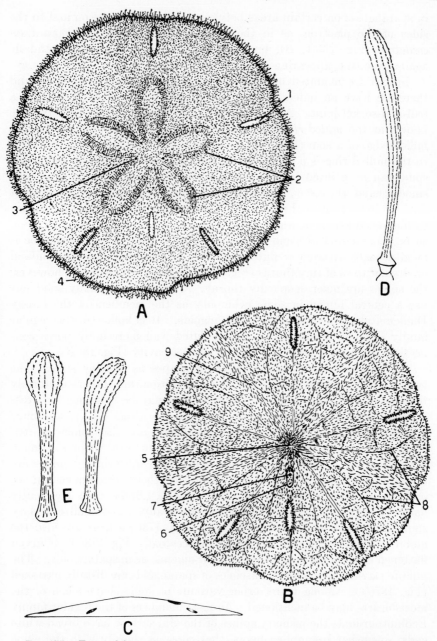

Fig. 177.—External features of irregular echinoids. *A*, a keyhole sand dollar, *Mellita sexiesperforata*, aboral view. *B*, oral view of *A*. *C*, profile view. *D*, oral spine of *Mellita*. *E*, aboral spines of *Mellita*. (All from life, Bahamas.) 1, lunule; 2, petaloid; 3, gonopores; 4, podia; 5, peristome; 6, periproct; 7, anus; 8, furrows; 9, interambulacrum.

in spatangoids on certain areas between the petaloids and on and to the sides of the plastron, as in the common heart urchin *Echinocardium cordatum* (Fig. 235*A*, *B*), but these larger spines are curved and lie against the test, appearing as if combed back.

Spines are mounted on tubercles of the test, considered later, and therefore have an indented base that fits over the tubercle to form a ball-and-socket joint. Above the base there is a projecting circular ledge known as the *milled ring*, marked by grooves so that it resembles the milled edge of a coin (Fig. 173*D*). Extending from around the tubercle to the milled ring is a circle of longitudinal muscle fibers by which the spine can be pointed in any direction. Above the milled ring a short smooth band, the *collar*, may be present, and distal to that the main part of the spine is termed the *shaft*. Although the shaft may appear smooth to the naked eye, it is nearly always found on microscopical examination to be ornamented in some fashion or other. Very often the surface is longitudinally striated or fluted and may be provided with longitudinal or circular rows of tiny thorns (Figs. 173*D*, 176*E*). Sometimes, however, the spines are macroscopically thorny. The spine is usually solid but has a central lumen in some echinoids, as the members of the family Diadematidae, as well as most spatangoids. It is hollow in the regular family Echinothuriidae, with a thin fluted wall pierced by pores connecting the surface grooves with the interior cavity (Fig. 180*B*).

Spines occur in a great variety of shapes as well as sizes. The typical spine is straight, circular in cross section, and tapers uniformly to a pointed or blunt tip. However, spines may be triangular in cross section, as in the arbaciid genus *Coelopleurus* (Fig. 180*E*); the huge primary spines of *Heterocentrotus* (Fig. 178*D*) are also somewhat triangular in section. Spines are often curved, notably so in the much figured species *Plesiodiadema indicum*, in which the primary spines are exceedingly long, slender, and curved, so that their tips, widened on the oral spines, touch the ground (Fig. 223*E*). Spines are frequently flattened, either throughout their length or distally. The small secondary spines of cidaroids are much flattened (Fig. 173*C*, *E*), as are also the ambital spines of the curious genus *Colobocentrotus* (Fig. 178*C*). Curved flattened types of spines may be used for digging, as in spatangoids. The minute clavules borne on the fascioles of spatangoids are distally flattened (Fig. 187*G*). Among many other variants of spine shape some of the most bizarre may be mentioned. In most members of the regular family Echinothuriidae, the primary spines of the oral surface have broad white ends, somewhat resembling hoofs, that contrast sharply with the spine shaft (Fig. 179*J*). In the cidaroid *Cidaris blakei*, the aboral primaries are widened into an oar-like or fan-like shape (Fig. 179*E*), and in another cidaroid, *Goniocidaris clypeata*, the primary spines at the aboral ends of

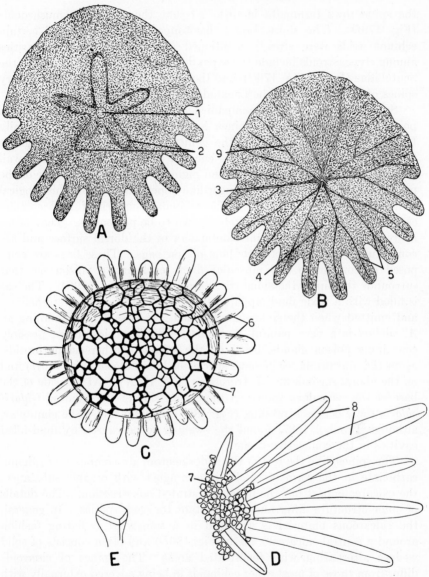

Fig. 178.—Irregular echinoids, spines. *A*, scutellid sand dollar, *Rotula orbiculus*, Africa, aboral view. *B*, same as *A*, oral view. *C*, *Colobocentrotus atratus*, Africa, aboral view. *D*, part of *Heterocentrotus mammillatus*, Indo-Pacific, aboral view. *E*, one of the flat-topped spines of *D*. (All from dry specimens.) 1, madreporite; 2, petaloids; 3, peristome; 4, periproct; 5, furrows; 6, flat ambital spines; 7, flat-topped spines; 8, large primary spines; 9, interambulacrum.

the spine rows terminate in disks so that they resemble mushrooms (Fig. 179*D*). The short, broad, flat-topped aboral spines of certain echinometrids were already mentioned (Fig. 178*C*, *E*). Peculiarities among clypeastroids include the expanded tips of the aboral spines of the Scutellidae (Figs. 177*E*, 179*C*), and the terminal crowns of the secondary spines of the oral side of the Laganidae (Fig. 179*F*).

Spines are sometimes accompanied by glandular tissue, usually of a poisonous nature. Poison spines are best developed in the family Echinothuriidae, especially in the genus *Asthenosoma*. In this genus the aboral spines are more or less encased in a thickening of body-wall tissues. This thickening, ringed and pigmented, covers the whole of the primary spines, giving them a finger-like appearance, but its histological structure is not well known. The secondary spines of *Asthenosoma*, especially *A. varium*, are definitely known to be poisonous. They occur in five double rows in the interambulacra of the dorsal surface and are conspicuous by reason of their blue poison bags. These bags are composed of connective and muscular fibers enclosing a poison sac that surrounds the tip of the spine (the Sarasins, 1888, Fig. 179*G*). The sac is filled with a toxic fluid, apparently secreted by the lining epithelium, and emitted when the spines are touched. It is said that handling an *A. varium* is a very painful experience. Similar thickenings, possibly containing poison glands, occur on the spines of other echinothuriids, as on the oral primaries of some species of *Phormosoma* (Fig. 179*H*) and on the aboral secondaries of *Araeosoma* (Fig. 179*K*). At one side of the base of the secondary spines on the aboral side of the cidaroid *Cidaris cidaris* there occurs a swelling (Fig. 180*F*), usually said to be glandular, although Prouho (1887) found the swelling to be caused by fluid-filled cavities in the connective tissue.

The spines, like the rest of the endoskeleton, are composed of calcium carbonate in the form of calcite intermingled with organic substance; the calcareous part has the usual fenestrated construction. The details of spine structure differ and are constant for each species. In general, the calcareous material is arranged in a somewhat radiating fashion around a central calcareous mesh (Fig. 180*D*) and often consists of solid wedges alternating with fenestrated areas. The spines of cidaroids differ from those of most other echinoids in being covered externally with an extra layer in the form of a thin hard cortex that carries the external ornamentations (Fig. 180*A*) and also bears hair-like projections. These form a felt on the surface of cidaroid spines that gives them a characteristic woolly appearance and that permits the attachment of all sorts of debris and of other organisms. A cortex like that of cidaroids may be present on the spines of Arbaciidae, usually limited to a cap over the spine ends (Fig. 180*C*).

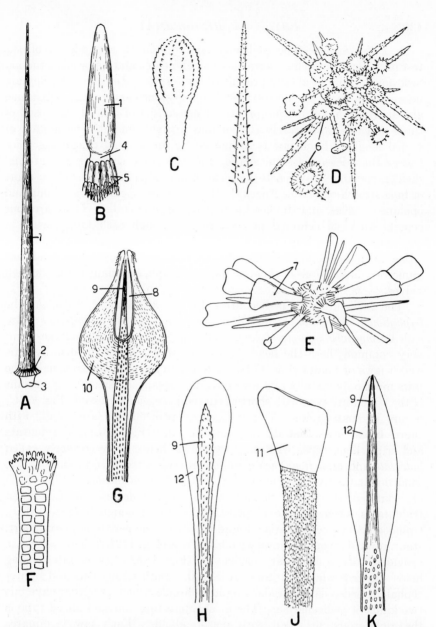

Fig. 179.—Spine variations.  *A*, ordinary primary spine of a regular urchin.  *B*, primary spine of a cidaroid, encircled at base by secondary spines.  *C*, aboral spine of scutellid *Encope*.  *D*, *Goniocidaris clypeata* with mushroom-shaped aboral spines.  *E*, *Cidaris blakei*, with fan-shaped aboral spines.  *F*, oral spine of *Laganum* with crown end.  *G–K*, spines of Echinothuriidae.  *G*, aboral poison spine of *Asthenosoma varium* (*after the Sara-sins*, 1888).  *H*, primary oral spine of *Phormosoma* with end covered by bag of tissue.  *J*, primary oral spine of *Araeosoma* with hoof-shaped end.  *K*, secondary aboral spine of *Araeosoma* with end enclosed in tissue.  (*D, E, G–K, after Mortensen, Monogr.*; others from dry specimens.)  1, shaft; 2, milled ring; 3, base; 4, collar; 5, secondary spines; 6, mush-room-shaped spine; 7, fan-shaped spines; 8, poison bag; 9, spine tip; 10, sheath of muscle and connective tissue; 11, hoof end; 12, tissue bag around end of spine.

*b. Pedicellariae.*—The pedicellariae are minute appendages of the test peculiar to the echinoderm classes Echinoidea and Asteroidea and are best developed and always present in the former. In echinoids they are borne abundantly on the test between the spines and on the peristome, also sparingly upon the periproct. They consist of a head composed of three movable jaws (rarely two or four or five), mounted on a stalk of varied length. Each jaw is supported by an internal calcareous piece (*valve*) that determines its shape, and the stalk contains an internal skeletal rod that may reach the head or stop short of it, leaving a short or long stretch of flexible "neck." The jaws are operated by closing and opening muscles, and the head is movable on the stalk. There are four general kinds of echinoid pedicellariae, although each kind occurs in numerous shape and size variants; in fact, Mortensen regards the pedicellariae as important taxonomically in species discrimination and has numerous illustrations of them in his monograph, especially of the cleaned valves.

The fours kinds of pedicellariae are the *tridentate* or *tridactyle*, the *triphyllous* or *trifoliate*, the *ophiocephalous*, and the *globiferous* (also called *gemmiform* and *glandular*). The tridentate type is the largest and very common; here the head consists of three elongated, distally narrowed jaws or blades (Fig. 172*D*), often with serrated edges; usually the jaws meet only distally and are separated basally by spaces. A variant of the tridentate type with shorter, curved jaws, called *rostrate* (Fig. 174*C*) occurs in spatangoids. The triphyllous pedicellariae are small, with short, broad jaws that do not meet distally (Fig. 173*A*). Tridentate and triphyllous types with only two jaws, hence more correctly called *bidentate* and *biphyllous*, are common in clypeastroids, especially in the sand dollar family Scutellidae (Fig. 181*B*). *Quadridentates* (Fig. 181*C*) are found in the family Saleniidae, and *quinquedentates*, or five-jawed tridentates, occur in the clypeastroid family Laganidae (Fig. 181*D*). Ophiocephalous pedicellariae, found chiefly on the peristome, have short, stout, inwardly concave jaws with blunt tips (Fig. 172*E*); their valves are provided with a basal arc or handle (Fig. 181*A*) whose interlocking holds the grip when the jaws are closed. Both triphyllous and ophiocephalous pedicellariae are lacking in cidaroids, which therefore have but two kinds of pedicellariae. The most interesting and specialized type is the globiferous, provided with poison glands. Each jaw terminates distally in a sharp tooth bent inward, or a group of teeth, and has a rounded, plump appearance because of the presence of a single or bilobed or double glandular sac in its wall to the outer side of each valve (Fig. 181*E*). The glandular sac is filled with a toxic secretion that discharges by one or two ducts opening just proximal to the terminal tooth or teeth. In many urchins, the globiferous pedicellariae are furnished with poison sacs, not only in the head but also encircling the stalk (Fig. 172*C*), and provided with individual exit pores. The presence of such stalk glands may lead to atrophy of the head, resulting in a *claviform* pedicellaria, consisting only of the stalk with its three poison sacs (Fig. 182*E*). Stages in the degeneration of the head occur as in *Plesiodiadema* (Fig. 182*D*). It appears that claviform pedicellariae may derive from ophiocephalous as well as from globiferous types. The globiferous pedicellariae of cidaroids differ from those of other echinoids in that the poison sacs are lodged in cavities in the valves (Fig. 181*G, H*) and lack a muscular sheath. Globiferous pedicellariae are wanting in spatangoids and in a number of families of regular urchins, as Echinothuriidae, Saleniidae, Arbaciidae, Aspidodiadematidae, and Micropygidae. Generally in globiferous pedicellariae, the supporting rod extends throughout the stalk up to the head, so that a flexible neck region is wanting. In other types of pedicellariae such a flexible neck of varying length is usually present between the base of the head and the top of the skeletal rod.

A very peculiar type of pedicellaria, called *dactylous*, is found in the Echinothuriidae and may be a variant of the globiferous type as it possesses poison sacs. The dactylous type reaches its extreme development in species of *Araeosoma*, where it consists of four or five jaws drawn out into a long narrow shape, topped by a terminal disciform expansion (Fig. 183*B*). These unique pedicellariae were first made known by Thomson (1874) from the deep-sea dredgings of the *Porcupine* in the North Atlantic off western Europe. Stages in the evolution of the dactylous type that are less modified from ordinary pedicellariae also exist, as in *Araeosoma thetidis* (Fig. 183*A*), in which the valves are beginning to lengthen and show spoon-shaped ends.

The function of the pedicellariae is discussed under physiology. Here it may be said that they bite intruders, possibly catch small animals as food, and deport unwanted particles off the test.

*c. Sphaeridia.*—These are minute, glassy or transparent, hard, solid bodies of oval or spherical shape borne on the ambulacral areas of all echinoids except cidaroids. They were discovered by Lovén (1874), who gave a considerable account of them, especially of their number and location in different echinoids. They are situated in the center of the ambulacrum or at its sides near the podia and extend from the edge of the peristome toward the ambitus (Fig. 183*C*), or if numerous, even around on the aboral surface to the periproct. When only one is present in each ambulacrum, as in *Arbacia*, it is found close to the edge of the peristome. Usually in regular urchins there are several to many sphaeridia, arranged alternately on the two rows of plates of each ambulacrum and extending from the peristome to varying distances depending on their number. In the irregular echinoids the sphaeridia are commonly

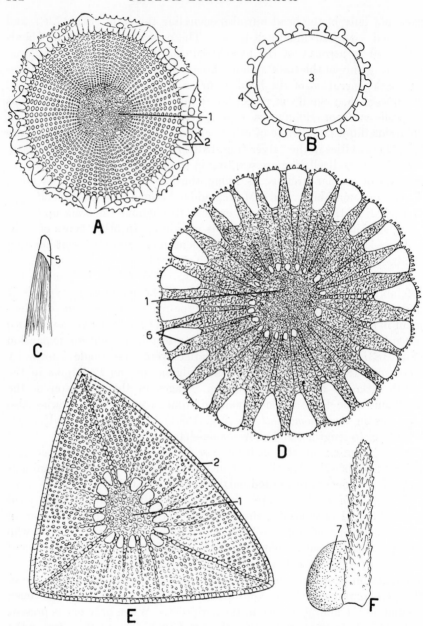

Fig. 180.—Spines.  *A*, cross section of a cidaroid spine.  *B*, cross section of an echinothuriid spine.  *C*, oral spine of *Arbacia punctulata*, showing cap or shoe of cortex.  *D*, cross
section of a spine of *Arbacia*.  *E*, cross section of a spine of *Coelopleurus*.  *F*, aboral secondary spine of *Cidaris cidaris* with glandular ampulla at base (*after Mortensen*, 1903).  (*A, B,
D, E, after Mortensen, Monogr.*)  1, central mesh; 2, cortex; 3, hollow interior; 4, surface
flutings; 5, cortical cap; 6, radiating wedges; 7, glandular ampulla.

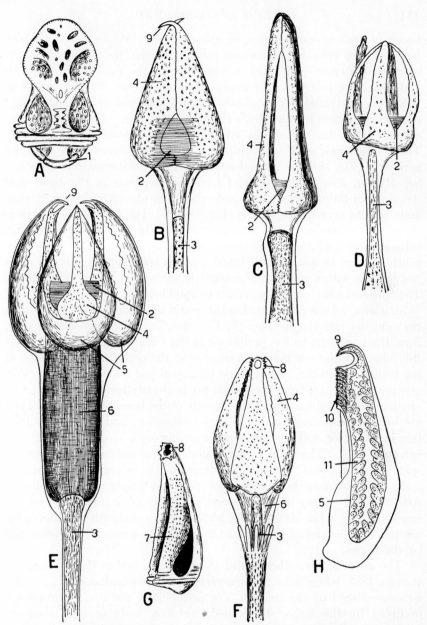

Fig. 181.—Pedicellariae. *A*, valve of ophiocephalous pedicellaria of *Tripneustes ventricosus*, to show handle. *B*, bidentate pedicellaria of sand dollar, *Echinarachnius parma*. *C*, quadridentate pedicellaria of *Salenia*. *D*, quinquedentate pedicellaria of laganid *Peronella* (*after Mortensen*, 1918). *E*, globiferous pedicellaria of *Strongylocentrotus*. *F*, globiferous pedicellaria of a cidaroid, *Eucidaris*. *G*, single valve of *F*. *H*, longitudinal section of a jaw of globiferous pedicellaria of *Cidaris cidaris* to show poison sac (*after Prouho*, 1887). (*A–C*, *E–G*, *after Mortensen*, *Monogr.*) 1, handle; 2, adductor muscle; 3, skeletal rod of stalk; 4, valve; 5, poison sac; 6, flexor muscle; 7, bulge containing poison sac; 8, aperture surrounded by teeth; 9, terminal tooth; 10, ciliated cells occupying aperture in valve; 11, glandular lining of poison sac.

433

borne in grooves, depressions, or almost closed cavities, each of which harbors one, two, or several of them. Among the spatangoids the sphaeridia are usually situated in depressions on the plates of the phyllodes and along the two posterior ambulacra that border the plastron (Fig. ¹84A, B). In some species of *Lovenia* each sphaeridium is enclosed in a rounded elevation opening by a slit (Fig. 184C, D). Among the clypeastroids, also, the sphaeridia are usually almost completely enclosed. There is a single such sphaeridium in each ambulacral area near the peristome (Fig. 184E) in a number of genera, as *Echinarachnius, Dendraster, Mellita, Encope, Rotula,* and *Laganum;* whereas in *Clypeaster* and *Arachnoides* there are two enclosed sphaeridia at the beginning of each ambulacrum near the peristome (Fig. 185A). The sphaeridia are borne on minute tubercles of the test and are usually provided with a stalk supported by an internal calcareous mesh (Fig. 184F). This mesh may continue more or less into the interior of the sphaeridium, but the main body of the latter consists of concentric calcareous layers (Fig. 183E). The sphaeridia are probably organs of equilibrium.

d. *Podia.*—In regular urchins the podia are arranged in five double rows on the ambulacra (Fig. 172A), extending, symmetrically spaced, from the peristome to the periproct; in the Cidaroidea and the Echinothuriidae, the rows of podia continue over the peristome to the edge of the mouth (Fig. 173E), so that special buccal podia are wanting in these two groups. Apart from the buccal podia already mentioned, the podia or tube feet of regular urchins are mostly of the locomotory type. They are long and slender, capable of great extension, and provided with a terminal disk or sucker supported internally by a circle of several calcareous pieces. The stalk of the podium is strengthened by calcareous spicules, mostly of C shape. Not infrequently in regular urchins, the podia of the aboral side lack terminal disks and simply taper to a bluntly rounded end. They are therefore papillate podia, serving sensory functions. In cidaroids the podia, although provided with terminal disks, are not well developed for locomotion, which is accomplished primarily by the spines.

The greatest diversification of the podia is seen in the spatangoids (Lovén, 1883) where none of the several sorts serve for locomotion as this is accomplished by the spines. The petaloids of the aboral surface are occupied by the large, thin-walled, leaf-like, more or less lobulated branchial podia (Fig. 186D), devoid of skeletal support and believed to serve respiratory purposes. The frontal podia of the nonpetaloid anterior ambulacrum vary from a simple tapering shape to types topped with a more or less scalloped or stellate disk (Figs. 185B, 186A). The podia of the phyllodes, corresponding to the buccal podia of regular urchins, are greatly altered to a type termed *penicillate,* in which the expanded end is

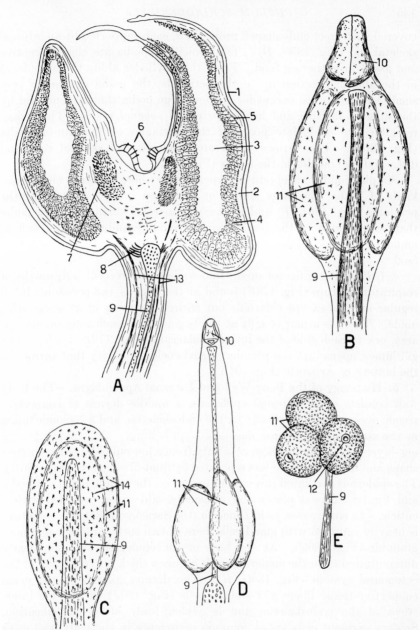

Fig. 182.—Pedicellariae (continued). *A*, longitudinal section of a globiferous pedicellaria of *Sphaerechinus* (after *Hamann*, 1887). *B*, ophiocephalous pedicellaria of diadematid *Astropyga* with poison glands on stalk. *C*, claviform pedicellaria of diadematid *Centrostephanus*. *D*, ophiocephalous pedicellaria of aspidodiadematid *Plesiodiadema*, stage of degeneration to claviform condition. *E*, claviform pedicellaria of *Colobocentrotus* (after *Agassiz*, 1908). (*B–D*, after *Mortensen*, *Monogr.*) 1, epidermis; 2, dermis; 3, poison sac; 4, glandular lining of poison sac; 5, muscle sheath of poison sac; 6, sensory hillock; 7, adductor muscle; 8, flexor muscle; 9, skeletal rod of stalk; 10, head of ophiocephalous pedicellaria; 11, poison glands of stalk; 12, gland aperture; 13, nerves; 14, pigment cells.

covered with erect club-shaped projections, each supported by an internal skeletal rod (Fig. 185C, D). The penicillate podia are chemoreceptive and assist in gathering food. From the phyllodes along the ambulacra in the aboral direction up to the petaloids, the podia decline to very small, slender forms, except for the few large podia that are enclosed by the subanal fasciole and hence are called *subanal* podia. These may resemble the penicillate podia of the phyllodes or the frontal podia (Fig. 186C). The various types are supported by skeletal rods and disks and by spicules in the stalks (Fig. 186A–C).

Simpler conditions obtain in clypeastroids where there are mostly two kinds of podia, the large simple or lobulated branchial podia of the petaloids (Fig. 186E, F) and the very numerous, small, suckered podia that cover much of the test, occurring on interambulacral as well as ambulacral areas. They assist the spines in locomotion and also gather food.

*e. Gills.*—The gills are small, thin-walled, arborescent outgrowths of respiratory nature (Fig. 173F) found at the edge of the peristome in all regular urchins except cidaroids but entirely wanting in irregular echinoids. There is a pair of gills at the beginning of each interambulacral area, one to each side of the interambulacrum (Figs. 172B, 173B). The gill lumen opens into the peripharyngeal coelomic cavity that surrounds the lantern of Aristotle (Fig. 194A).

**5. Histology of the Body Wall and External Appendages.**—The body wall consists of an external epidermis, a middle dermis of connective tissue, occupied almost wholly by the endoskeleton, and a coelomic lining in the form of a flattened flagellated epithelium. The epidermis is a one-layered epithelium whose cells vary from a low cuboidal to a columnar shape and may be more or less separated by fluid-filled spaces (Fig. 186H). The epidermis is ciliated throughout except on the terminal disks of podia and similar exposed places and is usually said to be provided with a cuticle. In some cases, as in *Diadema* (the Sarasins, 1887), the epidermis is heavily supplied with gland cells, here of two sorts, granular and nongranular (Fig. 186G). At the base of the epidermis and not clearly differentiated from the epidermal cells occurs a thick nervous layer of the ectoneural system (Fig. 186G, H). The dermis consists of the usual connective-tissue fibers and stellate cells (Fig. 186J); it fills the interstices of the endoskeleton and is evident only after decalcification. Spidery pigment cells are of common occurrence in the body wall in or beneath the epidermis; color may also reside in heaps of granules in the dermis. As the presence of the test makes the body wall rigid and immovable, a regular body-wall musculature is superfluous and is absent except in the curious family Echinothuriidae (see later). In other echinoids muscles are limited to the movable appendages of the

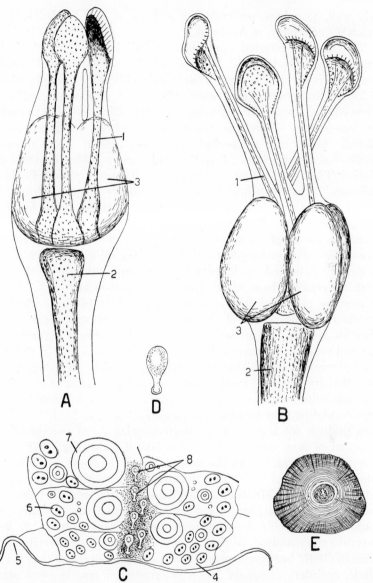

Fig. 183.—Pedicellariae (concluded), sphaeridia. *A*, dactylous pedicellaria of *Araeosoma thetidis*. *B*, more advanced type of dactylous pedicellaria of *Araeosoma violaceum*. (*A*, *B*, *after Mortensen, Monogr.*) *C*, part of the peristome edge of *Toxopneustes*, showing sphaeridia along the center of the ambulacrum. *D*, sphaeridium enlarged. *E*, cross section through a sphaeridium. (*C–E*, *after Lovén*, 1874.) 1, valve; 2, skeletal rod; 3, poison sac; 4, ambulacral plates; 5, gill 'ut; 6, pores for podia; 7, spine tubercles; 8, sphaeridia.

body wall, as spines, pedicellariae, and so on, and to the masticatory apparatus or lantern of Aristotle.

The various external appendages have the same histological construction as the body wall. The spines in life are clothed with epidermis except where a cortex is present, as in cidaroids (Fig. 180*A*) in which the epidermis disappears as the cortex differentiates. The epidermis is more or less ciliated, especially in young spines; the ciliation tends to disappear with age except around the spine base which generally remains fully ciliated. Gland cells are probably generally present. The bases of the clavules of the fascioles of spatangoids are notable for their heavy ciliation (Fig. 187*G*). Chromatophores are typically present in the spine epidermis. The ectoneural or subepidermal nervous layer forms a ring around the spine base, innervating the epidermis there for sensory purposes and also the spine musculature. This nervous layer often ascends to the tip of the spine, especially in particularly sensitive spines, as the clavules of spatangoids and the rotating spines of *Centrostephanus*. As already indicated, each spine is borne on a tubercle of the test on which its concave base fits to form a ball-and-socket joint. In many urchins the center of the tubercle bears a deep pit into which there extends from the center of the spine base an elastic ligament. Such tubercles are termed *perforate*. Beneath the nervous layer the spine base and tubercle are encircled by two muscle cylinders (Fig. 187*A*) that differ physiologically. The outer cylinder consists of ordinary muscle fibers that by local contraction cause the spine to point in the direction of the stimulus. The inner cylinder belongs to a physiological type called cog musculature that by means of tonus increase can hold the spine in a given position for a long time. Both muscles are of the smooth type, composed of long slender fibers with frayed ends (Fig. 187*C*). Their outer ends are attached to the milled ring of the spine, and their inner ends are continuous with the connective tissue of the interstices of the plates of the test. Mention has been made of the rotating spines of the diadematid *Centrostephanus longispinus*. These are primary spines around the periproct, of conspicuous violet coloration, that are kept in constant rotary motion, so that their club-shaped ends describe a circle. Hamann (1887) has investigated their histology and found that the outer muscle cylinder, composed of cross-striated fibers, is very strongly developed, extending halfway up the shaft, whereas the inner cylinder is scarcely evident. The epidermis of these rotating spines is poorly ciliated but frequently thickened into sensory hillocks provided with stiff sensory hairs (Fig. 187*E*).

The pedicellariae are morphologically equivalent to spines and are similarly constructed and related to the test. The base of the supporting rod of the stalk is articulated to a minute tubercle of the test by a ball-

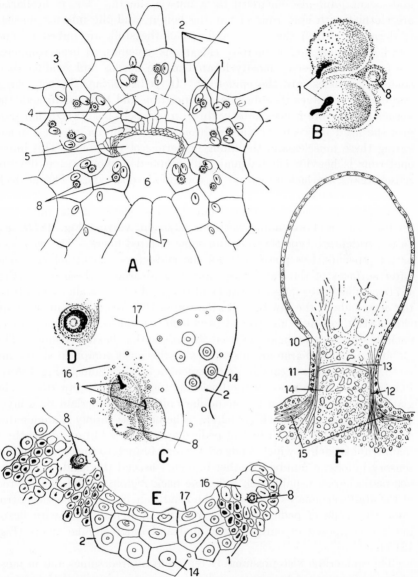

Fig. 184.—Sphaeridia (continued). *A*, peristome region of spatangoid *Echinocardium*, showing sphaeridia, spine tubercles omitted. *B*, small part of *A* enlarged, showing two podial pores and one sphaeridium. *C*, small part of peristome edge of spatangoid *Lovenia* showing enclosed type of sphaeridium. *D*, sphaeridium of *C*, opened. *E*, small part of peristome edge of clypeastroid *Encope* with single sphaeridium (opened) in each ambulacrum. (*A–E, after Lovén*, 1874.) *F*, longitudinal section of decalcified sphaeridium (*after Hamann*, 1887). 1, podial pores; 2, interambulacrum; 3, phyllode (= ambulacrum); 4, plates of peristome; 5, mouth; 6, labrum; 7, plastron; 8, sphaeridium; 9, spine tubercles; 10, covering epidermis; 11, pigment; 12, muscle cylinder; 13, ball-and-socket joint; 14, tubercle of test; 15, nerve ring; 16, ambulacrum; 17, peristome edge.

and-socket joint also encircled by a muscle sheath. The pedicellariae are clothed with epidermis of varying height, and the interior consists of dermis in which the valves and rod of the stalk are imbedded and which also contains numerous calcareous spicules. Chromatophores are frequently present, mostly located in the dermis and sending their spidery processes into the epidermis. In pedicellariae, the ectoneural nervous layer leaves its subepidermal position and courses through the dermis as separate nerves, mostly three in number (Fig. 187*D*) that pass into the head between the valves through the adductor muscles, innervating these muscles and the lining epidermis of the jaws. This lining epidermis is heavily ciliated and well supplied nervously, but definite sense organs are lacking except in the globiferous type. The pedicellariae in general are provided with three sets of muscles. The *adductors*, or jaw-openers, are three short, stout bundles located on the inner side of the jaws and extending between adjacent valves (Fig. 187*D*, *F*). In the tridentate type they contain some striated fibers. The *abductors* or jaw openers, less powerful than the adductors, are attached to the outer surfaces of the valve bases and extend around these bases (Fig. 187*D*). The flexor muscles that bend the head on the stalk extend from the outer side of the jaw bases to the top of the skeletal rod in the stalk (Fig. 181*E*). When this rod ends well below the head, the flexor muscles encircle the central ligament that traverses this flexible region. The globiferous pedicellarae are histologically the most complicated, having on the inner surface of each jaw a conspicuous sensory hillock (Fig. 188*A*); in some cases three more such hillocks are found near the jaw tips. The gland sacs are lined by a tall glandular epithelium underlain by a layer of circular muscle fibers (Fig. 182*A*). The nervous supply is augmented as compared with other types of pedicellariae. In addition to the three main trunks, each of which sends off a strong branch to the corresponding sensory hillock, a number of other branches ascend the head. Globiferous pedicellariae usually lack a flexible neck region, as the skeletal rod of the stalk terminates just below the head, but in the Strongylocentrotidae this type of pedicellaria has a highly muscular neck with flexor muscles composed of outer longitudinal and inner circular fibers (Fig. 181*E*).

The sphaeridia also presumably represent altered spines and in most urchins are mounted by a short stalk on a minute tubercle of the test by way of a muscle sheath (Fig. 184*F*). The whole is clothed with a ciliated epidermis underlain at the stalk base by a nervous ring. In clypeastroids, however, the sphaeridia are immovable and lack a nerve ring, according to Cuénot (1891a), although supplied with nerve fibers.

The locomotory podia terminate in a disk which is usually circular but sometimes scalloped (Fig. 188*C*); the disk is supported by skeleton

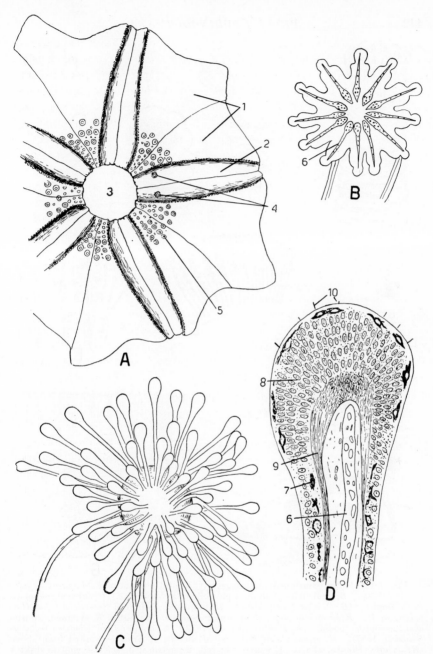

FIG. 185.—Sphaeridia (concluded), podia. *A*, peristome area of clypeastroid *Arach-noides* with two concealed sphaeridia in each ambulacrum, opened in only one; note absence of interambulacra (*after Lovén*, 1874). *B*, frontal podium of *Spatangus*. *C*, penicillate podium of *Spatangus*. *D*, longitudinal section of one of the projections of *C* (*B–D, after Hamann*, 1887.) 1, ambulacral plates; 2, ambulacral grooves; 3, peristome; 4, sphaeridia; 5, spine tubercles; 6, skeletal rod; 7, pigment cells; 8, epidermis; 9, nervous layer; 10, sensory bristle.

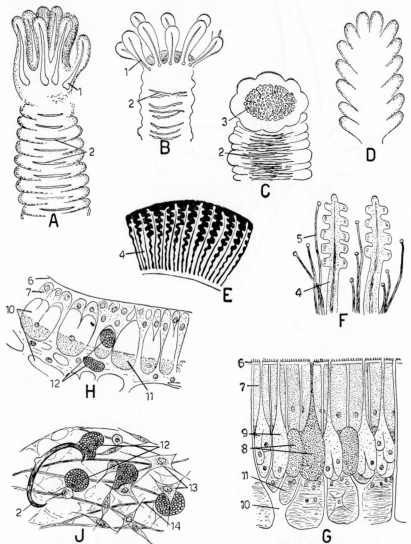

Fig. 186.—Podia (concluded), histology.  *A*, frontal podium of *Echinocardium* (*after Perrier*, 1870).   *B*, penicillate podium of phyllode of *Palaeotropus*.   *C*, subanal podium of *Palaeotropus*.   (*B, C, after Lovén*, 1883.)   *D*, branchial podium of *Spatangus* (*after Hoffmann*, 1871).   *E*, branchial podia of *Clypeaster rosaceus*.   *F*, part of *E*, enlarged, showing also locomotory podia.   (*E, F, after Agassiz*, 1872.)   *G*, epidermis of *Diadema* (*after the Sarasins*, 1887).   *H*, epidermis of *Echinus*.   *J*, dermis of *Echinus*, viewed from above.  (*H, J, after Prouho*, 1887.)   1, supporting rod; 2, spicules; 3, skeletal ring in disk; 4, branchial podium; 5, locomotory podia; 6, cuticle; 7, epidermal cells; 8, granular gland cells; 9, nongranular gland cells; 10, fluid-filled spaces; 11, nervous layer; 12, coelomocytes with spherules; 13,   connective-tissue cells; 14, fibers of nerve net.

in the way of a ring of four to seven fenestrated pieces resting on an underlying frame (Fig. 188*C*, *D*). The podia are covered with a tall epidermis of slender cells ciliated except on the terminal disk and well furnished with gland cells. Beneath the epidermis there runs on one side a strong nervous strand that forms a thickening, externally evident, shortly below the disk (Fig. 188*B*). From this thickening two nerves proceed, one to each side of the disk, where they join a nerve ring in the disk margin. There is also a thin nervous stratum in the epidermis throughout the disk. The lumen of the podium is lined by coelomic epithelium underlain by a layer of longitudinal muscle fibers that terminates below the center of the disk (Fig. 188*B*). The rest of the podium is filled with fibrous connective tissue, typically containing numerous crescentic or trifid calcareous spicules and of denser consistency next the muscular layer. The connective tissue sprays out in the disk into numerous strands that penetrate the epidermis (Fig. 188*B*) and were formerly mistaken for muscle fibers. Papillate and buccal podia are similar histologically to locomotory podia except that the former lack terminal skeletal support. The histology of one of the projections of a penicillate podium is shown in Fig. 185*D*.

The gills are evaginations of the peristome and hence have the same histological construction as the body wall in general. There is a very columnar ciliated epidermis of attenuated cells, a dermis containing a skeletal lattice, and a lining of flagellated coelomic epithelium. Coelomocytes abound in both epidermis and dermis.

**6. Morphology of the Test.**—The Echinoidea differ from all other Eleutherozoa and resemble the Pelmatozoa in that the body wall contains a continuous endoskeleton of closely fitted calcareous plates, leaving only the peristome and periproct free. In all existing echinoids this shell or test consists of 20 curved rows of plates, five ambulacral areas of two plate rows each alternating with five interambulacral areas, also of two plate rows each. The ambulacral areas are usually narrower than the interambulacral ones and are also conspicuously differentiated from the latter through being pierced with pores for the passage of the podia. Echinoidea are the only echinoderms, living or extinct, in which the pores for the podia pass *through* the ambulacral plates.

The cleaned test of the regular echinoids is a beautifully symmetrical object. Upon it the numerous tubercles that in life bear the spines and pedicellariae are conspicuous and are seen to be arranged in a more or less definite pattern (Fig. 189*A*, *C*). The largest or primary tubercles occur in meridional rows with the smaller tubercles more or less definitely disposed between the rows of primaries. Often each plate of the test bears one primary tubercle (Fig. 189*A*, *B*), but a few to many may be present more or less horizontally arranged (Fig. 189*C*, *D*). Typically, the tuber-

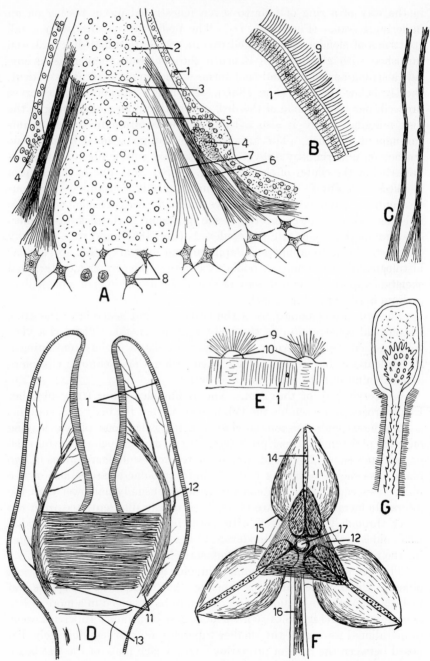

Fig. 187.—Histology of body-wall appendages (continued). *A*, longitudinal section through a spine base and tubercle of *Strongylocentrotus*. *B*, epithelium of spine of *Sphaerechinus*, showing cilia and sensory hairs. *C*, muscle fibers from a spine base. *D*, longi-

cles are largest and most numerous at the ambitus and decrease in size and number regularly toward the poles; further, the tubercles are larger on the interambulacral than on the ambulacral plates. Each tubercle consists of a basal part, the *boss*, having the shape of a low truncate cone, surmounted by a terminal knob, the *mamelon*, that articulates with the spine (Fig. 189*B*). The mamelon is perforate (page 438) in the cidaroids and the families Echinothuriidae and Diadematidae. Around the base of the mamelon is a more or less definite narrow circular area, sometimes marked by crenulations. The boss is encircled by a bare area, the *areole*, to which are attached the muscles operating the spine. Around the areole in cidaroids is seen a ring of secondary tubercles called *scrobicular* tubercles that bear the small secondary spines (*scrobicules*), protectively encircling the base of the primary spine in this group (Fig. 189*B*).

The plates of the regular test are commonly largest at the ambitus and decrease in size toward the poles. They are elongated horizontally and are five-sided with more or less straight horizontal edges (Fig. 189*B*). The plates of the two rows of each double row alternate, and as their inner edges along which they meet are shaped like an arrow head, the plates dovetail and present a zigzag line of meeting (Fig. 189*A*); the outer edges are more or less straight. All the plates are rigidly and immovably fitted closely together by ligamentous material except in the Echinothuriidae and a few others (see later).

At the aboral end of the test surrounding the periproct is found a special system of plates called the *apical system* (Fig. 189*A*, *C*). This consists of five larger *genital* plates in line with the interambulacra, each pierced by a gonopore, and five smaller *terminal* (or *ocular*) plates in line with the ambulacra, each pierced by a small pore for the emergence of the altered terminal podium. One of the genital plates is larger than the others and is peppered with numerous pores, thus revealing itself as the madreporic plate or madreporite. The madreporite constitutes the only departure from pentamerous symmetry noticeable on the external surface of regular urchins. The genital plates always border the periproct; some or all of the terminal plates may or may not touch the periproct. Those that do are said to be *insert*, those that do not are *exsert*. Great importance is placed by echinoid taxonomists on the relation of the terminals to the periproct, but as it may alter during growth and shows a certain amount of variation in adult specimens, its value in species recognition is

tudinal section of a decalcified pedicellaria of *Echinus*, showing muscles and innervation. *E*, epithelium of base of a rotating spine of *Centrostephanus*. (*A–E, after Hamann*, 1887.) *F*, open globiferous pedicellaria of *Echinus*, showing adductor muscles (*after Koehler*, 1883.) *G*, clavule from the fasciole of a spatangoid (*after Ludwig and Hamann*, 1904.) 1, epidermis; 2, spine base; 3, ball-and-socket joint; 4, nerve ring; 5, tubercle; 6, outer muscle sheath; 7, inner muscle sheath; 8, cells of dermis; 9, sensory hairs; 10, sensory hillocks; 11, nerves; 12, adductor muscle; 13, small portion of abductor; 14, valve; 15, poison sac; 16, skeletal rod of stalk; 17, top of skeletal rod.

questionable. A cidaroid in which all the terminals are insert, alternating with the genitals to form a genitoterminal ring encircling the periproct, is shown in Fig. 189*A*. Other arrangements with some or all of the oculars exsert are shown in Figs. 18*C* and 190*A–D*. According to Jackson (1912) all terminals are exsert in young regular urchins, and this is clearly the primitive condition. When during ontogeny terminals alter from the exsert to the insert position they do so in a more or less regular sequence. The plates of the apical system are provided with spines, pedicellariae, and tubercles. Comparison of the apical system of echinoids with the calyx plates of crinoids as done by some authors appears illusory. The term *corona* is applied to the test minus the apical system.

The periproct, although retaining flexibility, is strengthened with plates that also usually bear small spines and a few pedicellariae. Considerable variation is shown by the plates of the periproct. In the family Saleniidae the periproct is occupied by one plate (Fig. 190*A*) that pushes the anus to one side, and it appears that in many regular urchins the endoskeleton of the periproct begins as one plate (Fig. 190*C*). Comparison of this single plate with the centrodorsal of crinoids lacks sufficient basis. In the Arbaciidae there are four plates in the periproct (Fig. 190*B*). In most regular urchins the periproct membrane is more or less filled with many small plates (Fig. 190*D*). The anus varies from a central position in the periproct to a very excentric location.

The peristomial edge of the test shows at each side of each ambulacrum a marked indentation or slit-like incision, known as the *gill cut* (Fig. 183*C*), wherein is lodged a gill. These of course are wanting in cidaroids. On the inner side of its peristomial edge the test has a calcareous ridge called the *perignathic girdle* that serves for the attachment of the muscles of the masticatory apparatus. In cidaroids (Fig. 190*G*) this ridge is best developed at the interambulacra, where it has a pair of projections called *apophyses*. In all other echinoids the perignathic girdle is best developed at the ambulacra (Fig. 190*E*, *F*, *H*) similar projections are called *auricles*. The pair of auricles may meet over the ambulacrum to make an arch.

The peristome, like the periproct, is strengthened by imbedded plates that support spines, the buccal podia, and pedicellariae, especially the last, that usually occur in great numbers on the peristome (Fig. 172*B*). Each buccal podium is underlain by an ambulacral plate belonging to the regular series of ambulacral plates and pierced by a pair of pores for the passage of the podium. In cidaroids both the ambulacral and interambulacral plate series continue in the peristome to the edge of the mouth (Fig. 173*E*), but the plates are reduced in size and either overlap or do not meet each other, so that the peristome remains flexible. In the family Echinothuriidae, the ambulacral, but not the interambulacral, series similarly continues in the peristome to the mouth (Fig. 222*B*).

As already indicated, the test is flexible in the Echinothuriidae as the plates overlap instead of meeting (Fig. 222*B*). The test is further movable by a set of body-wall muscles wanting in all other echinoids. This set consists of 10 crescentic sheets ascending on the inside of the body wall from the auricles (here forming arches) to the periproct, fastened to the outer edges (edges next the interambulacra) of the ambulacral plates. These muscle sheets project into the coelom at right angles to the inner surface of the body wall, and their free inner edge consists of a tendon to which the diagonal muscle bundles composing the muscle sheet converge (Fig. 190*J*). These muscles were discovered by the Sarasins (1888), who called them the motor muscles of the corona; they are variously referred to in the subsequent literature as longitudinal, somatic, or vertical muscles, but *meridional* muscles would seem to be a more exact appellation. There is also present in echinothuriids a pair of *peristomial* muscles extending from each auricular arch along the inner surface of the peristome, inserting on the ambulacral plates there (Fig. 190*J*).

Each ambulacral plate is pierced with pores for the passage of the podia. For each podium there are typically two pores in the plate, since in echinoids, unlike other echinoderms, two canals run through the ambulacral plate connecting the podium with its ampulla (Fig. 195*A*). Each pair of pores is situated in a small oval area. Primitively, as still in cidaroids, there is one pair of pores to each ambulacral plate, and such plates are spoken of as *primary*. In cidaroids, therefore, the ambulacral plates are very narrow in the meridional direction, and there are several and often many of them to each interambulacral plate (Fig. 189*B*). In other regular echinoids the ambulacral plates are *compound*, that is, composed of two or three or more primary plates and therefore pierced with a corresponding number of pore pairs, arranged in an arc or a zigzag manner. Plates bearing two or three pore pairs are called *oligoporous*, and those with more than three pore pairs, *polyporous*. The compound plates vary in composition, that is, in the number of primary plates (indicated by the number of pore pairs) involved in their formation. These primary plates may retain full size reaching from the outer to the inner edge of the compound plate, or through growth pressure some may be reduced to *demiplates* that do not reach the inner edge. There are three main types of compound plates (Fig. 191*A–C*): the *diademoid*, consisting of three full-sized primary plates; the *arbacioid*, composed of a median primary plate with a demiplate to either side of the outer part of this; and the *echinoid*, made of two primary plates with a demiplate inserted between their outer ends. Polyporous types of compound plates arise by the insertion of more demiplates into these three types (Fig. 191*D*). The echinothuriid type appears distinctive with demiplates inserted between the primary plates in the meridional direction (Fig. 223*B*, *C*) but has been shown to be a variant of the diademoid type.

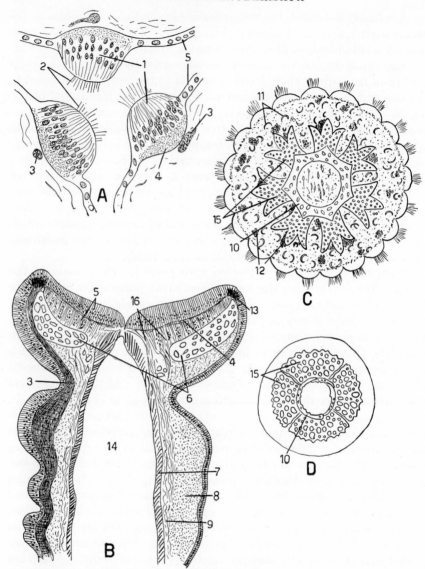

Fig. 188.—Histology of body-wall appendages (concluded). *A*, horizontal section through a globiferous pedicellaria of *Strongylocentrotus*, to show the three sensory hillocks. *B*, longitudinal section of a locomotory podium of *Echinus*. (*A, B, after Hamann*, 1887.) *C*, disk of a locomotory podium of *Paracentrotus* (*after Hoffmann*, 1871). *D*, disk of locomotory podium of *Echinoneus*, viewed from the inside (*after Lovén*, 1883). 1, sensory hillock; 2, sensory hairs; 3, nerve; 4, nervous layer; 5, epidermis; 6, supporting skeleton of disk; 7, longitudinal muscle fibers; 8, dense connective tissue; 9, loose connective tissue; 10, frame; 11, spicules; 12, coelomocytes; 13, marginal nerve; 14, lumen of podium; 15, pieces of skeletal rosette in disk; 16, connective-tissue strands in disk.

In ambulacral plates the pore pairs are almost always near the outer edges adjacent to the suture with the interambulacral plates, so that the ambulacral plates are divisible into poriferous and nonporiferous portions.

The alterations of the test seen in the irregular urchins appear to have been initiated by the retreat of the periproct, establishing an axis of bilateral symmetry that bisects an anterior ambulacrum and a posterior interambulacrum, now containing the periproct. With the withdrawal of the periproct from the aboral center or apex, the plates of the apical system close together, maintaining the aboral center. Therefore the regular urchins are also called *endocyclic*, in reference to the enclosure of the periproct by the apical system, while the irregular urchins are *exocyclic*, since the periproct lies outside the apical system. The composition of the aboral center after withdrawal of the periproct varies considerably among the irregular urchins. Usually the retreat of the periproct along the posterior interambulacrum destroys the gonad and the genital plate of that interradius, although these may reappear in later evolved forms. The four remaining genital plates then close together to become the center of the apical system, either symmetrically, or more often asymmetrically, with the enlarged madreporite extending inward to occupy the central position (Fig. 191*G*), while the terminals still encircle the genitals (*ethmophract* condition). However, the madreporite tends to follow the periproct along the posterior interambulacrum and continues to extend backward, finally emerging from the terminal system (*ethmolytic* condition, Fig. 191*F*). This condition obtains in many common spatangoids. The four genital plates are symmetrically arranged at the aboral apex, each with a gonopore; the elongated madreporite without a gonopore extends back along the posterior interambulacrum, outside the terminal system, and the five small terminal plates occupy the angles between the genitals (Fig. 191*F*). Often in irregular urchins there is considerable fusion among the genitals, and only three or even two gonopores may persist. The madrepores, also, are subject to variation and in place of being confined to one of the genital plates may spread onto others or onto all of the genital plates or can be reduced to a few pores. In clypeastroids in general, the genital plates are fused to one central pentagonal plate, pierced throughout with madrepores and with the reduced terminal plates pressed against the centers of the sides of the pentagon (Fig. 192*C*, *D*). The gonopores may occur at the angles of the pentagon but often are removed some distance along the interambulacra, as in *Clypeaster rosaceus* (Fig. 192*D*).

The test of the irregular urchins lacks the patterned arrangement of conspicuous tubercles that makes the regular test such an attractive object. For the most part it is covered with innumerable small to minute tubercles, although in some spatangoids larger tubercles occur

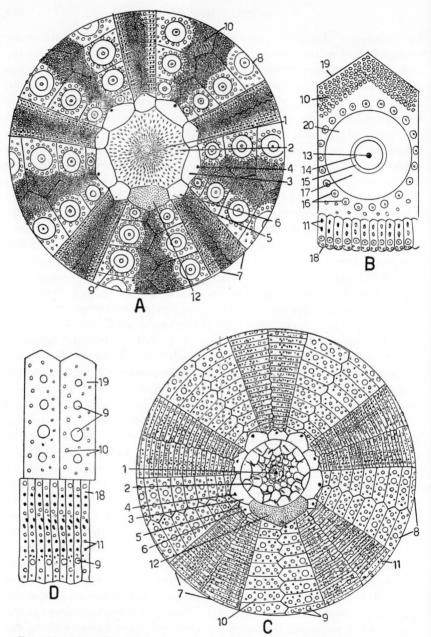

Fig. 189.—Morphology of the test. *A*, aboral side of the test of a cidaroid, *Eucidaris tribuloides*. *B*, ambulacral and interambulacral plates of *A*. *C*, aboral side of the test of *Tripneustes ventricosus*. *D*, ambulacral and interambulacral plates of *C*. (All from specimens, Bahamas.) 1, anus; 2, periproct; 3, genital plate; 4, gonopore; 5, terminal plate; 6, pore for terminal podium; 7, ambulacrum; 8, interambulacrum; 9, tubercle of primary spine; 10, tubercles of secondary spines; 11, pore pairs; 12, madreporite; 13, perforation; 14, mamelon; 15, ledge at base of mamelon; 16, scrobicular tubercles; 17, boss; 18, ambulacral plates; 19, interambulacral plate; 20, aerole.

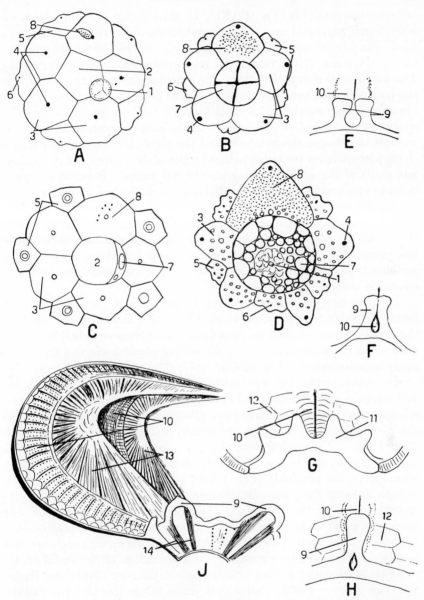

Fig. 190.—Morphology of the test (continued). *A*, periproct and apical system of *Salenia*. *B*, periproct and apical system of *Arbacia*. *C*, periproct and apical system of young *Strongylocentrotus*. *D*, same as *C* in adult. (*A*, *C*, *after Lovén*, 1874.) *E–H*, perignathic girdle of one ambulacrum of various echinoids. *E*, *Arbacia*. *F*, *Strongylocentrotus*. *G*, cidaroid. *H*, *Echinometra*. *J*, part of interior of echinothuriid *Asthenosoma*, showing two of the ten meridional muscle sheets (*after the Sarasins*, 1888). 1, anus; 2, central plate of periproct; 3, genital plates; 4, gonopore; 5, terminal plates; 6, pore for terminal podium; 7, plates of periproct; 8, madreporite; 9, auricles; 10, ambulacrum; 11, apophyses; 12, interambulacrum; 13, meridional muscle sheet; 14, peristomial muscles.

between the petaloids (Fig. 191*E*).  In spatangoids, the ambulacra are often much narrowed and the interambulacra are correspondingly widened, aborally by the horizontal elongation of their plates (Fig. 191*E*). Orally there are a few very large interambulacral plates (Fig. 192*A*). The ambulacral plates of spatangoids are all simple primary plates.  In the petaloids each bears a conspicuous pore pair; the two pores of a pair are often widely separated but usually connected by a groove, a condition spoken of as *conjugate*.  The plates of the anterior ambulacrum and of the others between the petaloids and the phyllodes usually bear only a single pore each, for the much reduced podia of these areas and the penicillate podia of the phyllodes may also be uniporous.  Between the phyllodes in spatangoids, the interambulacra reach the peristome by only a single narrowed plate, except for the posterior interambulacrum that forms the posterior border of the peristome by a plate called *labrum* (Fig. 192*A*).  Posterior to this the plastron meets the labrum by one or two plates (Fig. 192*A*); whether one or two is considered an important systematic character.  In nearly all existing spatangoids, the two-plate condition obtains (Fig. 192*A*).

In some irregular urchins, especially members of the order Cassiduloida, the single interambulacral plates meeting the peristome between the phyllodes are swollen to conspicuous prominences called *bourrelets*, which with the somewhat sunken alternating phyllodes form a flower-like figure called a *floscelle* (Fig. 229*A*).

In clypeastroids, the interambulacra are much narrower than the ambulacra Fig. 192*B*) and tend to disappear on the oral side, being represented or not around the peristome.  Pore pairs are limited to the petaloids, where the two of a pair are usually widely spaced and conjugate (Fig. 193*B*).  The ambulacral plates of the petaloids may be simple primary plates, but in the Clypeastridae primary plates and demiplates alternate in the petaloids (Fig. 193*B*).  The demiplates are only wide enough to carry the pore pair, whereas the primary plates extend to the central suture of the petaloid.  The clypeastroids are provided with numerous small suckered podia, emerging through single pores on both surfaces and on both ambulacra and interambulacra, although not uniformly distributed.  In a study of the distribution of the podia on the common sand dollar *Echinarachnius parma*, Gregory (1911) and Parker and Van Alstyne (1932) found that podia fringe the ambitus thickly, occur in many patches on the aboral surface and in two thick bands along the aboral ambulacra, including the center of the petaloids, and on the oral surface are concentrated along the furrows.  Examination of the furrows shows that they are devoid of spine tubercles but thickly pierced with pores for the podia.  The podia of sand dollars are of little value in locomotion, apparently functioning to gather food particles that are passed along the furrows to the mouth.

The test of spatangoids is often thin, while that of clypeastroids may be very thick and heavy and supported by internal calcareous beams and columns (Fig. 193*A*). In sand dollars the two surfaces are strongly united in the periphery of the test, leaving only a central area available to the viscera (Fig. 202*A*).

**7. Orientation.**—The orientation of regular echinoids with respect to other echinoderms presents some difficulty as only the madreporite occupies an asymmetrical position and hence can serve as a guide. Lovén (1874), in his classical studies of echinoids, developed a system of naming the rays that has been universally adopted by other echinoid specialists. Lovén took the spatangoids as his point of departure, counting the rays with reference to the spatangoid bilateral axis. If the spatangoid is held oral surface up and the interambulacrum containing the periproct is considered posterior, then the ambulacra are numbered I to V, beginning to the left (animal's right) of the posterior interambulacrum and proceeding in a clockwise manner (Fig. 193*D*). The interambulacra are numbered 1 to 5, beginning to the left of ambulacrum I and also proceeding clockwise. The anterior ambulacrum bisected by the plane of symmetry is thus III, and the madreporite primitively has a right anterior position, immediately to the right of ambulacrum III if the aboral side is up, only later by displacement becoming symmetrically placed in the posterior interambulacrum. Lovén further applied his system to the regular echinoids. As the two plate rows of both ambulacra and interambulacra alternate, it follows that at the peristome edge, one plate of each double row is necessarily smaller than the other of that row in order to make a smooth edge at the peristome (Fig. 183*C*). According to Lovén, the arrangement of the large and small plates around the peristome is such that it is bilaterally symmetrical with only one ambulacrum, namely the one that, when the aboral side is up, has the madreporite immediately to the right of its aboral end, or the same as ambulacrum III in spatangoids.

Although the size arrangement of the end plates at the edge of the peristome appears generally throughout echinoids to conform to Lovén's report, his axis is not the only one that is symmetrical with these size differences (Fig. 219*C*). Further, any system of orientation should be based on the regular echinoids as the irregulars are obviously of derivative nature. The orientation of echinoids should be brought in harmony with that of the other echinoderm classes. On these grounds it is preferable to adopt the system of Carpenter already utilized for crinoids and holothuroids. On the Carpenter plan, with the oral surface up, in the pelmatozoan position, the interambulacrum that contains the madreporite becomes CD and the ambulacrum opposite this is the anterior ambulacrum or A. The rays A, B, C, D, and E of Carpenter correspond to V, I, II, III, and IV of Lovén. When a spatangoid is similarly oriented

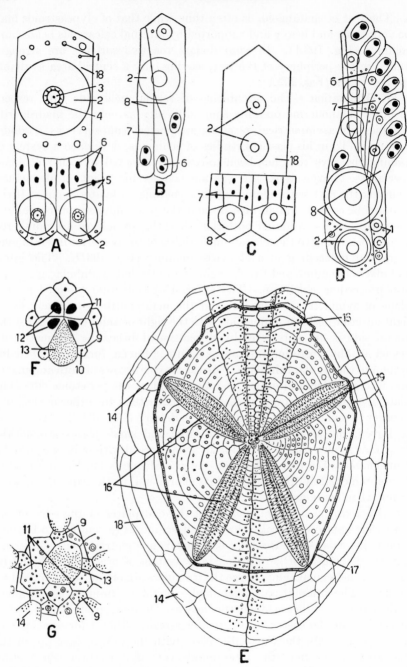

FIG. 191.—Morphology of the test (continued). A plates of *Diadema*, showing diahematoid arrangement. B. ambulacral plate of *Echinus*, showing echinoid arrangement. C, ambulacral and interambulacral plates of *Arbacia*, showing arbacioid arrangement:

with the oral surface up and the interambulacrum that contains the madreporite (in its original position to the left of D from the oral view or the right of D from the aboral view) is taken to be CD, then it is clear that the axis of elongation of a spatangoid does not correspond to the bilateral axis (based on the madreporite) of a regular echinoid (Fig. 193C, D). Consequently the bivium and trivium of spatangoids do not correspond with those of holothurians.

**8. Nervous System.**—The nervous system is similar to that of holothurians. The main system belongs to the ectoneural category and consists of the circumoral nerve ring, the radial nerves, and the subepidermal plexus. The circumoral or peripharyngeal nerve ring encircles the beginning of the pharynx (Fig. 194A) just internal to the mouth and inside the lantern of Aristotle and is attached to the pharynx by connective-tissue bands. The nerve ring supplies nerves to the mouth region and also gives off nerves, mostly 5 or 10, that ascend the digestive tract and form a nervous layer beneath its lining epithelium. From the nerve ring arise five radial nerves that pass out through the muscle fibers of the lantern between the pyramids (Fig. 194A) and ascend the inner surface of the body wall, along the mid-line of the ambulacra. Each radial nerve is a flat band of nerve cells and fibrils that is bounded to its outer side, between itself and the ambulacral plates, by the epineural sinus, and to its inner side by the hyponeural sinus (Fig. 195A). The radial water canal forms the innermost structure here, and between it and the hyponeural sinus is found a channel of the haemal system (Fig. 195A). Relations here are the same as in holothurians except that the radial nerve represents only the ectoneural system. Toward the mouth region the hyponeural sinus disappears, while the epineural sinus continues and becomes a ring sinus lying to the oral side of the nerve ring and corresponding to the peribuccal sinus of holothurians.

In their course along the inner surface of the test the radial nerves give off a podial nerve to each podium (Fig. 195A) that, as already noted, ascends along one side of the podium and spreads out into a nervous layer in the terminal disk; and they also give off nerves that pass with the podial nerve through the pores of the ambulacral plates and spread out in the body wall to the outer side of the plates of the test, forming there an extensive subepidermal plexus. As already mentioned, this plexus has a ring around the base of each spine and pedicellaria, and nerve

---

note lack of secondary tubules. *D*, polyporus ambulacral plate of *Strongylocentrotus*. *E*, aboral view of test of spatangoid, *Plagiobrissus grandis*, West Indies. *F*, apical system of *E*. *G*, apical system of *Holectypus*, extinct. 1, secondary tubercles; 2, primary tubercle; 3, perforate mamelon; 4, crenulations; 5, three primary plates composing ambulacrum; 6, pore pairs; 7, demiplate; 8, primary plate; 9, terminal; 10, pore for terminal tentacle; 11, genital plate; 12, gonopores; 13, madreporite; 14, ambulacra; 15, anterior ambulacrum; 16, petaloids; 17, peripetalous fasciole; 18, interambulacra; 19, apical system.

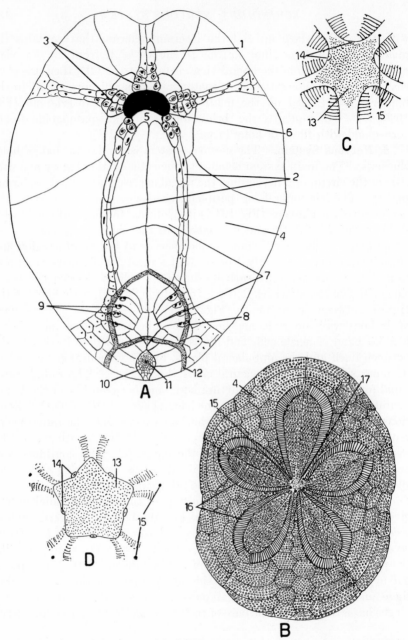

FIG. 192.—Morphology of the test (continued). *A*, oral view of the test of *Plagio-brissus grandis*. *B*, aboral view of test of clypeastroid, *Clypeaster rosaceus*, West Indies. *C*, apical system of keyhole urchin, *Mellita*. *D*, apical system of *B*. 1, anterior ambula-crum; 2, other ambulacra; 3, phyllode; 4, interambulacra; 5, labrum; 6, peristome; 7, plastron; 8, subanal fasciole; 9, pores for subanal podia; 10, periproct; 11, anus; 12, anal fascioles; 13, pentagonal madreporite of fused genitals; 14, terminals; 15, gonopores; 16, petaloids; 17, apical system.

fibers also ascend these structures. At its aboral end each radial water canal terminates by a single reduced podium, often called the terminal tentacle, that passes through the pore in the corresponding terminal plate (Fig. 194B). The radial nerve, accompanied by the epineural, but not the hyponeural, sinus passes out also in the wall of the terminal tentacle and terminates in its epidermis.

The hyponeural or deeper oral system is represented in echinoids that are provided with an Aristotle's lantern. It consists of five plaques of nervous tissue situated on the aboral surface of the nerve ring in the radial positions. These plaques send strong nerves into the lantern, presumably to its muscles.

An aboral or entoneural nervous system has been found in a few regular echinoids in the form of a nerve ring in the inner surface of the aboral body wall around the periproct. It gives off nerves to the gonads and their ducts.

**9. Sense Organs.**—It is to be assumed that every spine, podium, and pedicellaria acts in a sensory capacity. The heavy nervous supply of these structures was already noted; further, the presence of a subepidermal nervous plexus throughout the external surface. According to Hamann (1887), the epidermal cells are everywhere interspersed with the usual very attenuated neurosensory cells or tangoreceptors. Conspicuous hillocks of such tangoreceptors appear limited to the inner surface of the jaws of globiferous pedicellariae (Fig. 188A) and a few other places. The sphaeridia are probably equilibratory organs; this would seem at least to be a necessary conclusion for those that are almost completely enclosed. Other special sensory organs appear lacking, except for the "eyes" of the Diadematidae. In this family, especially in the genera *Astropyga*, *Diadema*, and *Chaetodiadema*, the test is ornamented with brilliant blue spots, resembling sapphires. They occur on the genital plates, in rows along the interambulacra, often on the peristome, sometimes also on the ambulacra. They are fused into stripes in some cases. The structure of these blue spots was first investigated by the Sarasins (1887) for *Astropyga radiata*, who compared them to the compound eyes of insects and who gave figures showing them to consist of a number of six-sided prisms surrounded basally by heavy pigment granules and underlain basally by a thick nervous stratum. Later investigators have been more moderate in their statements; Mortensen in his monograph confirmed the presence of units filled with transparent material (Fig. 194C) but found no pigment accumulations, and Millott (1953a) denied any histological resemblance to eyes in the blue spots of *Diadema antillarum*. The blue spots reach their greatest development on the oral side of *Astropyga radiata* where each is stalked and does in fact resemble a compound eye (Fig. 194D). Döderlein (1885), examining

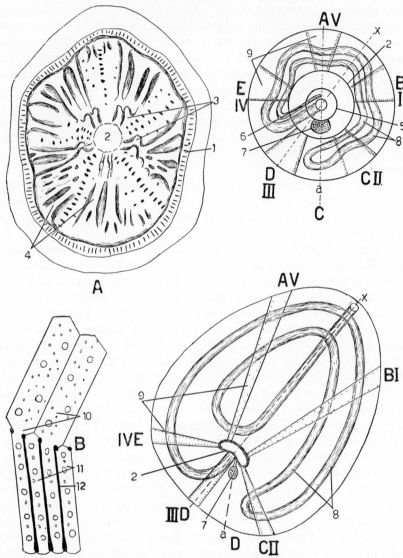

Fig. 193.—Morphology of the test (concluded). *A*, interior of test of *Clypeaster rosaceus*, showing calcareous supports. *B*, plate arrangement of *Clypeaster*. *C*, scheme of orientation of test of regular echinoid, oral view. *D*, scheme of orientation of test of spatangoid, oral view. (*C*, *D*, based on *Cuénot*, 1891a.) 1, broken edge; 2, peristome; 3, auricles; 4, calcareous supports; 5, periproct seen through peristome; 6, anus; 7, madreporite; 8, intestine; 9, ambulacra; 10, primary ambulacral plates; 11, demiplates; 12, conjugated pore pair; a, Carpenter axis; x, Lovén axis; A–E, rays on Carpenter plan; I–V, rays on Lovén plan.

freshly collected *Diadema setosum*, declared that the blue spots are luminescent, but this has not been verified by others, and probably this author mistook iridescence for luminescence. Whether the spots in question actually are photoreceptors cannot be decided on present evidence.

**10. Coelom and Coelomocytes.**—In the regular urchins the interior of the test is occupied by a spacious coelom, partly encroached upon by the gonads and the festoons of the intestine. There are also several minor coelomic compartments completely or partly closed off from this main coelomic cavity. Chief among these is the peripharyngeal cavity, corresponding to the cavity of the same name in holothurians. This in echinoids provided with an Aristotle's lantern completely encloses the lantern, beginning around the esophagus where it emerges from the lantern and extending over the sides of the lantern to the perignathic girdle (Fig. 194*A*). It is entirely closed off from the general coelom by a delicate coelomic membrane consisting of two ciliated epithelia enclosing between them connective tissue and some muscle fibers. The peripharyngeal cavity is continuous at the edge of the peristome with the lumina of the gills. Its membrane forms on the aboral surface of the lantern five little *dental sacs* in the interradial positions for the growing ends of the teeth of the lantern; in the cidaroids and the Echinothuriidae there are, further, in the radial positions five elongated and conspicuous sacs known as Stewart's organs that project into the main coelom as appendages of the peripharyngeal sinus (Fig. 196*A*, *B*). These seem to act as expansion chambers for the fluid in the peripharyngeal cavity and its adjuncts. In echinoids that lack a lantern the peripharyngeal cavity is present in the same location but greatly reduced. Other minor coelomic cavities occur at the aboral pole. In regular echinoids the rectum is attached to the edge of the periproct by a coelomic membrane, thus cutting off a *periproctal sinus* from the main coelom. Around the anus is a ring sinus, the *perianal sinus*. The wall of both of these sinuses contains muscle fibers. Still another ring-shaped sinus occurs on the inner surface of the apical system of plates; this, called the *aboral* or *genital* sinus (Fig. 197*A*), runs between the gonoducts, encloses a haemal network supplying the gonads, and makes contact with the aboral nerve ring. These several aboral sinuses are more or less wanting in irregular echinoids, being fused into a single sinus (Fig. 204*B*).

The coelomic spaces are filled with a fluid similar to sea water and containing the usual coelomocytes that also wander freely throughout the body tissues and organs. The coelomocytes of echinoids have been studied by a long list of investigators (Geddes, 1880; Cuénot, 1891b; St. Hilaire, 1897; Kollmann, 1908; Théel, 1920; Kindred, 1921, 1924; Behre, 1932; Boliek, 1935; Kuhl, 1937; Bookhaut and Greenberg, 1940; Liebman, 1950; Schinke, 1950). In general six types of cells are found

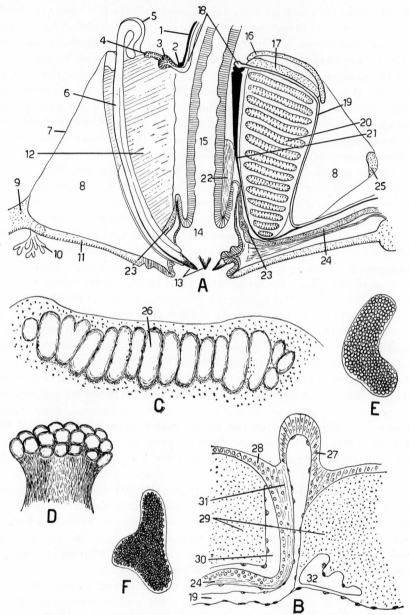

Fig. 194.—Nervous system, sense organs, coelom. *A*, vertical section through the lantern and peripharyngeal cavity of *Paracentrotus lividus*. *B*, vertical section through a terminal tentacle of *Echinocyamus pusillus*. (*A, B, after Cuénot*, 1891a.) *C*, section through a compound eye of *Diadema setosum*. *D*, compound eye from the oral surface of *Astropyga pulvinata*. (*C, D, after Mortensen, Monogr.*) *E*, amoebocyte with colorless inclusions, *Arbacia*. *F*, amoebocyte with red inclusions, *Arbacia*. (*E, F, after Kindred*, 1921.)  **1**, haemal channel to axial gland; **2**, haemal ring; **3**, spongy body; **4**, compass muscle;

in echinoids: amoebocytes with ordinary pointed pseudopodia (Fig. 195*C*); amoebocytes with petaloid pseudopodia (Fig. 195*B*), that is, the pseudopodia are broad, thin, membranous flaps; amoebocytes filled with colorless spherules (Fig. 194*E*); those filled with greenish or yellowish spherules; those filled with reddish spherules (Fig. 194*F*; and vibratile cells, small round cells provided with a long, thin process, apparently a flagellum in at least some cases (Fig. 195*D*). The first two types are phagocytic and are called leucocytes by some authors; it is probable that they represent different phases of the same cell. The three types with spherical inclusions lack phagocytic power but are able to move slowly by putting out blunt pseudopods. The reddish inclusions are so colored because of the presence therein of echinochrome, a common echinoid pigment. It has been shown for *Diadema antillarum* that the colorless spherules contain precursors and enzymes that produce a black melanin pigment on breakdown of the amoebocytes containing them (Millott and Jacobson, 1951). As regards the vibratile cells, Liebman (1950) suggests that they are detached cells of the coelomic lining and has seen them lose their flagellum and become amoeboid. The experiments of Schinke (1950) show that the coelomocytes originate from the mesenchyme (dermis) of the body wall. This author finds in *Psammechinus miliaris* a total of 3800 coelomocytes per cubic millimeter of fluid: 1910 phagocytic amoebocytes, 910 with colorless inclusions, 500 with reddish inclusions, and 480 vibratile cells. Henri (1906) gave the following figures per cubic millimeter for *Paracentrotus lividus:* 4400 to 7080 phagocytes, 40 to 600 brown amoebocytes, 40 to 680 colorless amoebocytes, and 120 to 240 vibratile cells; for *Spatangus* the figures were 900 phagocytes, 190 brown amoebocytes, 240 colorless amoebocytes, and 5600 vibratile cells. In *Arbacia punctulata*, about half the coelomocytes are of the phagocytic type, the rest amoebocytes with inclusions (Liebman, 1950).

**11. Digestive System.**—The mouth usually lies in the center of the aboral surface but is shifted anteriorly in spatangoids. In regular echinoids it is usually encircled by a lip-like eminence (Fig. 173*B*) and here leads into a small buccal cavity encircled by the main nerve ring and pierced by the teeth of the masticatory apparatus (Fig. 194*A*). From the buccal cavity the pharynx (often called esophagus) ascends vertically through the center of the masticatory apparatus to which it is

5, dental sac; 6, tooth; 7, coelomic membrane enclosing peripharyngeal cavity; 8, peripharyngeal cavity; 9, edge of test; 10, gill; 11, peristomial membrane; 12, pyramid; 13, free ends of teeth; 14, buccal cavity; 15, pharynx; 16, compass; 17, rotule; 18, water ring; 19, radial water canal; 20, comminator muscle; 21, radial haemal sinus; 22, connective-tissue support of pharynx; 23, nerve ring; 24, radial nerve; 25, piece of auricle; 26, unit of eye; 27, terminal tentacle; 28, epidermis; 29, terminal plate of test; 30, epineural canal; 31, termination of radial nerve; 32, aboral coelomic sinus.

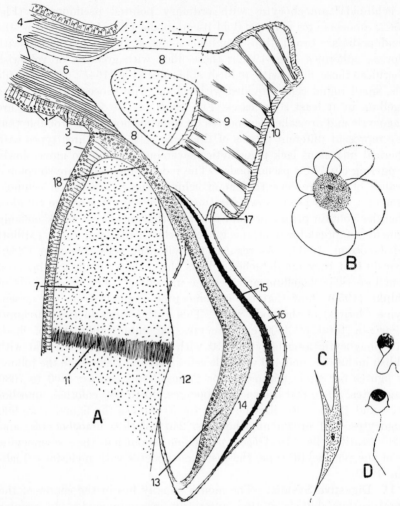

FIG. 195.—Nervous system, coelom (continued).  *A*, section through the test (decalci-fied) across an ambulacrum, *Paracentrotus lividus* (after *Cuénot*, 1891*a*.)  *B*, petaloid coelomocyte, *Arbacia*.  *C*, phagocytic amoebocyte, *Arbacia*.  (*B*, *C*, after *Kindred*, 1921.) *D*, vibratile cells, *Arbacia* (after *Liebman*, 1950).  1, base of podium; 2, epidermis; 3, nerv-ous layer; 4, connective tissue; 5, longitudinal muscle of podium; 6, lumen of podium; 7, ambulacral plate; 8, two pore canals through the ambulacral plate; 9, ampulla; 10, muscle strands in ampulla; 11, median suture of ambulacrum; 12, epineural sinus; 13, radial nerve; 14, hyponeural sinus; 15, radial haemal sinus; 16, radial water canal; 17, valve between water canal and ampulla; 18, nerve accompanying podial canal through ambulacral plate.

attached by strands.   The masticatory apparatus, usually called from its discoverer the *lantern of Aristotle*, is present fully developed only in the regular echinoids and is reduced or wanting or evidenced only in young stages in irregular echinoids except clypeastroids.   When fully developed the lantern is an admirable complex of muscles and calcareous pieces that serves to grasp and chew up food.   It is a pentamerous object of general conical shape with its apex formed by the five teeth usually seen protruding from the mouth opening. The lantern is formed of five main interradial pieces, the pyramids (Fig. 196C), each of which consists of two pieces, the half pyramids, closely joined by a suture. The pyramids are separated from each other by a short space filled with short transverse muscle fibers forming the *interpyramidal* or *comminator* muscles by which the pyramids can be rocked upon each other. At the upper or aboral end of each pyramid is usually found a bar, the *epiphysis;* in some echinoids the two epiphyses of each pyramid remain separate, but in most they are sutured to form a continuous bar along the aboral end of the pyramid. On the aboral surface of the lantern, corresponding to the base of the cone, there radiate from the esophagus in the radial positions, that is in line with the comminator muscles, five slender pieces called *compasses* (Fig. 197C), and beneath them five more, somewhat stouter pieces, the *rotules* (Fig. 196D). Each compass is composed of two pieces, an inner and an outer half, and the outer half often terminates in a forked end. The pyramids act as a support for the teeth, long calcareous bands ascending in the interior spaces of the pyramids. At its lower end each tooth is formed of especially hard calcareous material. This hard oral end of the five teeth projects into the buccal cavity beyond the oral ends of the pyramids and is protrusible through the mouth. As they ascend in the interior of the pyramids, the teeth become softer, and their aboral ends, quite soft and often curled, lie upon the aboral surface of the lantern, each enclosed in the dental sac, already mentioned, which is a coelomic sac evaginated from the general peripharyngeal cavity (Fig. 200C). The teeth grow continually from these soft aboral ends, and thus the wearing away of the oral end through use is compensated. The foregoing account shows that the fully developed lantern consists of 40 skeletal pieces: 5 teeth, 10 half pyramids, 10 epiphyses, 5 rotules, and 10 pieces that form the compasses.

An equally complex system of muscles (Fig. 197C) is necessary to operate this apparatus. The comminator muscles between the pyramids were already mentioned. The *protractors* of the lantern are a pair of flat bands extending from the epiphyses to the perignathic girdle at the interambulcra. They serve to push the lantern outward, thus exposing the teeth. The *retractor* muscles that pull the lantern back and also open the teeth originate on the auricles of the ambulacral areas and insert on the lower ends of the pyramids. Small *external* and *internal rotular* muscles connect the epiphyses with the corresponding rotule, and as the epiphyses are articulated to the half pyramids, movements of the epiphyses through these rotular muscles are transmitted to the teeth.

The compasses and their muscles do not function in mastication but are part of the respiratory apparatus. It will be recalled that the entire lantern and its muscles are enclosed in a coelomic membrane that attaches

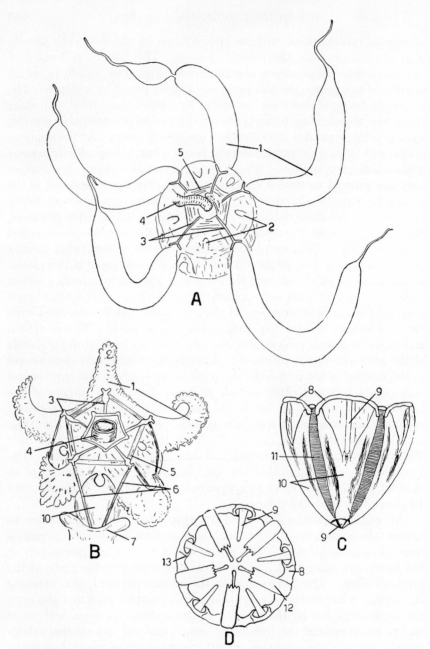

Fig. 196.—Coelom, lantern. *A*, top of lantern of *Asthenosoma*, showing Stewart's
organs (*after the Sarasins*, 1888, slightly altered). *B*, top of lantern of *Cidaris cidaris*,
showing Stewart's organs (*after Stewart*, 1879). *C*, side view of lantern of *Tripneustes
ventricosus*, cleaned. *D*, top of lantern of *C*, with compasses removed to show rotules. 1,
Stewart's organs; 2, dental sacs; 3, compasses; 4, esophagus; 5, elevator muscle of compasses; 6, depressor muscles of compasses; 7, auricles; 8, epiphyses; 9, tooth; 10, pyramid;
11, comminator muscles; 12, rotule; 13, projections of epiphyses to hold tooth.

to the perignathic girdle and that the coelomic cavity so enclosed is continuous with the lumina of the gills. In that part of this coelomic membrane that covers the aboral surface of the lantern there runs around the emerging esophagus a flat, pentagonal muscle that attaches to the compasses (Fig. 197*C*). This muscle, the *elevator of the compasses*, on contraction raises the compasses, thus increases the volume of the peripharyngeal cavity, and so draws fluid out of the gills. From the outer end of each compass two slender muscles run along the outer surface of the lantern protractors to originate on the perignathic girdle at the interambulacra. There are thus two of these *depressors of the compass* to each compass, and these diverge to adjacent interambulacra (Fig. 197*C*). Their contraction depresses the compasses and thus forces fluid into the gills.

The structure of the skeletal part of the lantern is of great importance in the systematics of regular echinoids. Those in which the two epiphyses for each pyramid are widely separate and in which the teeth lack a keel are termed *aulodont* (Fig. 198*C, E*). The principal existing aulodont families are the Aspidodiadematidae and the Diadematidae. Regular echinoids in which the epiphyses are still separate but the teeth are keeled (that is, have a median crest along their inner surface) are termed *stirodont*. The main existing stirodont families are the Saleniidae and the Arbaciidae. Most regular urchins (as the Toxopenustidae, Echinidae, Strongylocentrotidae, Echinometridae) are *camarodont*, that is, the epiphyses are joined to form a bar across the top of the pyramid (Fig. 196*C*). The teeth are keeled (Fig. 198*D*) and are often held in place by a pair of curved processes extending inward from the epiphysis (Fig. 196*D*).

In irregular urchins a lantern is wanting throughout ontogeny in spatangoids and is present only in the young of the existing members of the small groups of holectypoids and cassiduloids. It is present, however, in the clypeastroids, although it cannot be protruded through the mouth, whence the necessity of the feeding ambulacral grooves of the oral surface in this group. The compasses and their muscles are wanting in clypeastroids, as gills are absent in all irregular echinoids. The form of the lantern in clypeastroids is quite different from that in regular echinoids (Fig. 198*A, B*). The lantern is low but very broad and has the general outline of a pentagonal star with the points at the radii. It is composed almost wholly of the greatly enlarged pyramids, which are strongly fluted. They are usually of uneven size and the teeth are correspondingly unequal. The epiphyses and rotules are reduced to minute rods between the aboral ends of the pyramids. On their oral surfaces the pyramids have one or two deep depressions or fossae that fit over the auricles of the perignathic girdle. Comminator, retractor, and protractor muscles are present as in regular urchins and have the

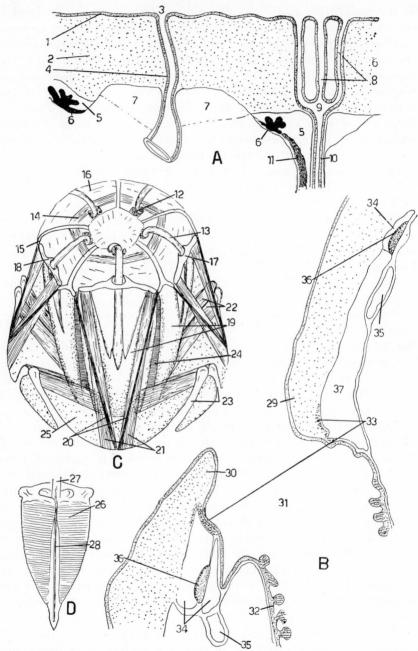

Fig. 197.—Coelom (concluded), lantern. *A*, section through the periproct region of *Sphaerechinus*. *B*, longitudinal section through the peristome of *Spatangus*. (*A, B, after Hamann*, 1887.) *C*, lantern of *Tripneustes ventricosus*, in place. *D*, pyramid of same, seen from the inside. 1, epidermis; 2, skeletal plates; 3, anus; 4, rectum; 5, aboral or genital

same functions.   On account of the broad shape of the lantern and the very small extent of the peristome in clypeastroids, the teeth are but slightly protrusible.   The best and most detailed account of the lantern in clypeastroids is that of Lovén (1892).

The pharynx, pentagonal in section and attached by membranes (Fig. 200*D*) to the inner edges of the pyramids, emerges from the top of the lantern and passes at once into the esophagus.   This descends orally, often making a considerable loop (Fig. 198*F*), and enters the intestine. A blind pouch or caecum is generally present at the junction of esophagus and intestine.   The intestine is usually arranged in festoons fastened to the inner surface of the test by mesenteries (Fig. 198*F*) but may lie horizontally.   It first curves around the inside of the test in a counter-clockwise direction as viewed from the aboral surface; after making a nearly complete circuit of the interior it turns back upon itself and makes another almost complete circuit in the clockwise direction, lying aboral to its first circuit (Fig. 198*F*).   The terminal part of the intestine or rectum then ascends to the underside of the periproct and opens there by the anus, encircled by the perianal and periproctal coeloms already mentioned.   The two circuits of the intestine are called stomach and intestine by some writers, inferior and superior intestine by others, but perhaps are preferably designated small and large intestine.   As shown in Fig. 198*F*, the festoons of the intestine are usually enlarged into pouches at the places of attachment to the test by mesenteries.   In most echinoids, but not in cidaroids, the inner border of the small intestine is constricted off as a slender tube, the *siphon*, that extends from the beginning of the small intestine at the caecum nearly to the turn (Fig. 203). A current of water constantly passes along the siphon from its proximal to its distal end.   This, according to Cuénot (1948), represents water removed from the food, accomplishing concentration of the food for digestion in the small intestine.   The arrangement of the intestine is definitely related to the body pentamery, as shown in Fig. 193*C*.

In spatangoids, as a lantern is wanting, the esophagus proceeds directly from the mouth, and a considerable caecum is present along the proximal part of the small intestine (Fig. 199*A*).   The intestine makes the usual two circuits, but the rectum, in place of ascending aborally, proceeds posteriorly to the anus (Fig. 199*A*).   The usual siphon is present, but in certain genera (*Schizaster, Brissus, Brissopsis*) there are

sinuses; 6. aboral haemal ring inside the aboral sinus; 7, periproctal sinus; 8, canals through madreporic plate; 9, ampulla; 10, stone canal; 11, axial gland; 12, spongy bodies; 13, aboral ends of teeth; 14, elevator of compasses; 15, compass; 16, coelomic membrane; 17, epiphysis; 18, prongs of epiphysis around tooth; 19, pyramid; 20, depressor of compass; 21, lantern protractors; 22, lantern retractors; 23, auricles; 24, comminator muscle; 25. peristomial membrane; 26, ridges for attachment of comminator muscles; 27, tooth; 28, keel of tooth; 29, upper lip; 30, lower lip; 31, buccal cavity; 32, esophagus; 33, sphincter; 34 oral haemal ring; 35, water ring; 36, nerve ring; 37, noncoelomic space.

two siphons; the secondary or accessory siphon accompanies the proximal part of the small intestine, and the main siphon its distal part (Fig. 200*A*). According to Eichelbaum (1910), a second caecum occurs at the junction of large intestine and rectum in some spatangoids (Fig. 199*B*). The digestive tract is simplified in clypeastroids in that the intestine, after making the first circuit, turns and proceeds backward to the anus (Figs. 201*A*, 202*A*). The first circuit or part of it is much widened and may perhaps properly be called stomach.

Histologically the digestive tract has the usual layers (Hamann, 1887, Bonnet, 1925). It is lined by a mostly ciliated epithelium of very tall, slender cells, followed by a layer of connective tissue and then a thin muscle layer of mostly circular fibers; on the coelomic side the digestive tract is covered with the flagellated peritoneum. Gland cells may be present in the lining epithelium, especially in the pharynx (Fig. 199*C*); they also occur in the esophagus of *Echinus* (Chadwick, 1900) and other regular urchins (Hamann, 1887) but appear wanting in the intestine. Bonnet (1925) was unable to find any gland cells in the intestine of several regular echinoids investigated. In place of typical gland cells, glandular crypts may occur in the esophagus (Fig. 199*D*) and appear regularly present in the esophagus of spatangoids (Fig. 200*B*). Longitudinal muscle fibers may occur to the inner side of the circular ones but are generally sparsely developed in echinoids. Connective tissue permeates the muscle layers and by some is regarded as constituting an external connective-tissue layer. The siphon resembles the small intestine histologically.

**12. Water-vascular System.**—This system follows the usual echinoderm plan. The digestive tube on emergence from the lantern (when present) is encircled by the main water ring (Fig. 194*A*) from which the stone canal ascends vertically through the coelom to the madreporic plate, accompanied throughout by a conspicuous axial gland (Fig. 200*C*). The water ring further gives off in each interradius in line with the aboral ends of the teeth a branch to a small body that lies on the aboral surface of the lantern just beneath the coelomic membrane covering the latter (Fig. 197*C*). These five small bodies are often called polian vesicles, but as they seem rather to be of lymphoid nature, they are perhaps better designated *spongy bodies*. They are generally present in echinoids having a lantern, but in cidaroids, probably echinothuriids, and some clypeastroids, there is, in place of the spongy bodies, a continuous spongy ring intimately associated with the water and haemal rings.

From the water ring are given off in the radial positions the five radial water canals. These run beneath the rotules and descend the sides of the lantern along the outer surface of the comminator muscles (Fig. 194*A*). They then proceed along the inner surface of the peristome,

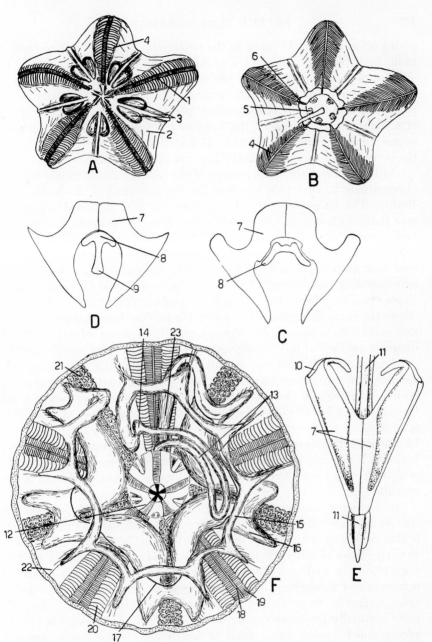

Fig. 198.—Lantern (concluded), digestive system. *A*, lantern of *Clypeaster*, oral view. *B*, same as *A*, aboral view. *C*, cross section through a pyramid, aulodont type. *D*, cross section through a pyramid, camarodont type. (*C*, *D*, *after Lovén*, 1892.) *E*, pyramid of a diadematid (*after Mortensen, Monogr.*), showing small, separated epiphyses. *F*, dissection of *Tripneustes ventricosus*, seen from the oral side. 1, comminator muscles; 2, pyramid; 3, fossae that fit over auricles; 4, flutings; 5, spongy bodies; 6, location of rotules and epiphyses; 7, half pyramid; 8, section of tooth; 9, keel of tooth; 10, epiphysis; 11, tooth; 12, lantern, detached; 13, esophagus; 14, caecum; 15, small intestine; 16, large intestine; 17, haemal sinus; 18, radial water canal; 19, podial branches of radial water canal; 20, ampullae; 21, gonad; 22, mesenterial supports of intestinal festoons; 23, rectum.

giving off an unpaired branch to the two buccal podia of their respective radii, and, passing under the arch of the auricles or between the two auricles of each radius if these are not fused to an arch, ascend on the inner surface of the test to the terminal plates. Here each radial canal passes through the pore of its terminal plate and terminates as the lumen of a slight protrusion called the *terminal tentacle* (Fig. 194*B*). In their course along the inner surface of the test the radial water canals lie to the inner side of the hyponeural sinuses of the radial nerves (Fig. 195*A*).

As they ascend the inner surface of the test the radial canals give off alternatingly to each side branches for the ampullae of the podia (Fig. 198*F*). The ampullae in regular urchins are thin, flattened, elongated sacs that lie closely packed in two rows along the coelomic side of each ambulacrum where they are readily noticed in the opened test (Fig. 198*F*). The radial canal gives off a branch, usually guarded by a valve, into each ampulla, and from the ampulla two canals pass through the corresponding ambulacral plate by the pore pair and then unite to a single canal that forms the lumen of the podium (Fig. 195*A*). In young stages the ampulla communicates with the podium by a single canal, and this condition is maintained throughout life in many of the podia of irregular echinoids; but usually calcareous growth later subdivides the pore. Connection between ampulla and podium by two canals is seemingly of respiratory significance, as a water current is maintained in a circuit by way of these canals. The water-vascular system is lined throughout by a flattened ciliated epithelium of coelomic nature. This is followed by a connective-tissue layer covered externally by peritoneum. In the ampullae there is in addition a layer of circular muscle fibers between the lining epithelium and the connective tissue; and strands of these muscle fibers covered with epithelium also cross the lumen of the ampulla (Fig. 195*A*).

In regular echinoids the stone canal extends vertically between the madreporite and the water ring. The opening through the madreporite is always by way of a chamber or ampulla situated beneath it (Fig. 201*C*). In early stages of echinoids there is but a single pore through the madreporic plate, the hydropore of echinoderm embryology, and this condition is maintained throughout life in some clypeastroids (Fig. 205*B*). In all other echinoids, however, the number of pores through the madreporic plate gradually increases during ontogeny. The stone canal is closely accompanied by the axial gland to which it is bound by a common mesentery that more orally also includes the esophagus (Fig. 200*C*). The pore canals through the madreporic plate are lined by a ciliated epithelium, and this is also the case with the stone canal. According to Hamann (1887), each of the cells lining the stone canal bears a single cilium that should properly be regarded as a flagellum. External to

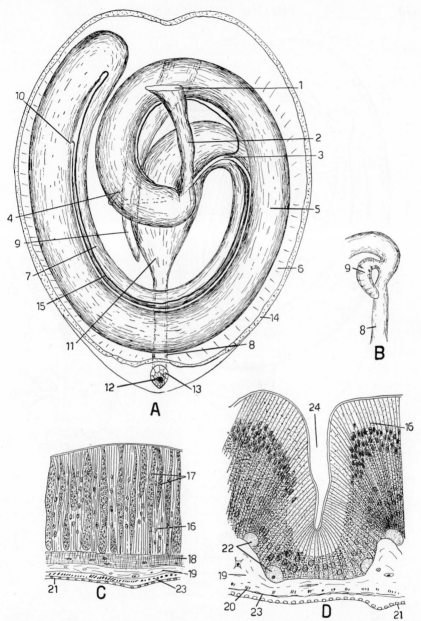

Fig. 199.—Digestive system (continued). *A*, dissection of the spatangoid *Meoma ventricosa*, viewed from the oral side. *B*, *Echinocardium cordatum*, showing second caecum at junction of large intestine and rectum. *C*, longitudinal section of the pharynx of *Centrostephanus*. *D*, transverse section of the esophagus of *Sphaerechinus*. (*C*, *D*, *after Hamann*, 1887.) 1, mouth; 2, esophagus; 3, siphon; 4, opening of siphon into beginning of small intestine; 5, small intestine; 6, mesentery; 7, large intestine; 8, rectum; 9, caecum; 10, distal end of siphon; 11, junction of small intestine with rectum; 12, anus; 13, periproct; 14, broken edge of test; 15, inner marginal sinus; 16, epithelial cells; 17, gland cells; 18, nervous layer; 19, connective tissue; 20, longitudinal muscle fibers; 21, coelomic epithelium; 22, nerves; 23, circular muscle fibers; 24, glandular crypt.

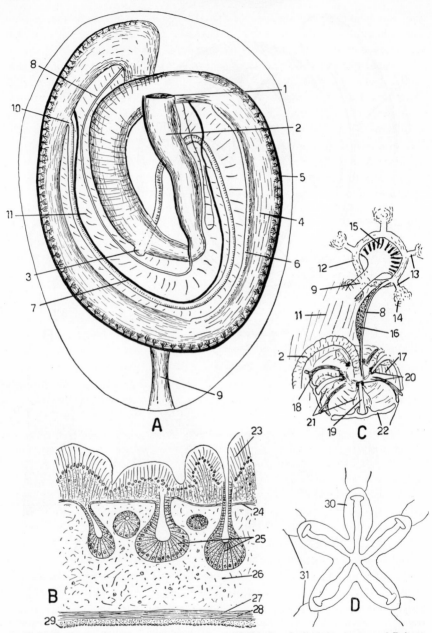

Fig. 200.—Digestive system (continued), axial gland.  A, digestive system of *Brissus*, to show the two siphons.  B, section of the esophagus of *Spatangus purpureus*, near the beginning of the siphon, showing glandular crypts.  (A, B, after Koehler, 1883.)  C, dissection of *Tripneustes ventricosus* to show axial gland in place.  D, cross section of the pharynx of *Echinus* (after Chadwick, 1910).  1, mouth; 2, esophagus; 3, beginning of primary siphon; 4, small intestine; 5, outer marginal sinus; 6, accessory siphon; 7, inner

the lining epithelium the wall of the stone canal consists of connective tissue heavily impregnated with calcareous spicules, and external to this the surface of the stone canal is clothed with peritoneum.

In spatangoids there are two calcareous ridges on the inside of the test beneath the madreporic plate, and the pore canals pass through one of these directly into the stone canal without the intervention of an ampulla. The stone canal is here also closely attached to the axial gland, and at about the middle of this gland it loses its characteristic epithelium and calcareous stiffening and passes into a mesh of water canals closely applied to one side of the axial gland. From this mesh a water channel finally emerges on the oral side and enters the water ring. In the absence of a lantern in spatangoids the water ring is found on the inner surface of the test around the edge of the peristome in close association with the nerve ring and the haemal ring (Fig. 204*A*).

**13. Axial Gland.**—This is an obvious, elongated, dark-colored body of spongy appearance that in regular echinoids accompanies the stone canal from near the aboral surface of the lantern to the vicinity of the madreporite (Fig. 200*C*). It is variously called in the literature heart, kidney, ovoid gland, brown gland, and other names and has given rise to a surprising amount of argument and disagreement as to its structural relationships and function. The clearest accounts of its relations to other parts are those of Hamann (1887) and Leopoldt (1893). The gland is not enclosed in any coelomic cavity, or in other words, an axial sinus is lacking in echinoids. The gland is of fusiform shape, widest through its middle region, tapering to the ends. It is hollow, containing an extremely irregular cavity that ends blindly in the oral direction and represents a coelomic cavity, that of the right axocoel. Consequently the lumen of the gland is lined by coelomic epithelium. At its aboral end the gland often narrows abruptly into a finger-shaped process with which it terminates. This process projects into a coelomic space (Fig. 201*C*) shown by embryological studies to represent the right axocoel. It is claimed by some authors that the aboral end of the axial gland communicates with the ampulla of the water-vascular system, whereas others do not record any such connection; however, the existence of such a connection is indicated by experiment (see under physiology). A large haemal channel (originally mistaken for a duct of the gland) ascends from the haemal ring at the top of the lantern into the axial gland and forms a complicated mesh of haemal spaces over its surface.

---

marginal sinus; 8, stone canal; 9, rectum; 10, end of primary siphon; 11, mesentery; 12, aboral or genital sinus; 13, gonoducts; 14, aboral ends of gonads; 15, strands of periproctal sinus; 16, axial gland; 17, top of lantern; 18, compasses; 19, aboral ends of teeth; 20, spongy bodies; 21, dental sacs; 22, epiphysis, 23, epithelium; 24, basement membrane; 25, glandular crypts; 26, connective tissue; 27, longitudinal muscle fibers; 28, circular muscle fibers; 29, coelomic epithelium; 30, pentagonal pharynx; 31, strands of attachment of the pharynx.

In spatangoids the gland is shorter and begins farther away from the oral surface, at the end of the digestive caecum, to which it is attached by a mesentery.  A haemal and a water channel ascend from the haemal and water rings, respectively, around the peristome and run along one side of the gland, breaking up into networks, although the main haemal channel remains recognizable.  According to Hamann (1887), haemal and water channels here communicate with each other.  After the stone canal emerges from the water network it accompanies the gland to the aboral surface.  At the aboral center the three ring-shaped coelomic sinuses present in regular echinoids are represented in spatangoids by one pentagonal space (Fig. 204*B*) in which the narrowed aboral end of the axial gland terminates while the stone canal proceeds through a calcareous ridge to the madreporite (page 473).  In this aboral coelomic space the blood sinuses communicate with the termination of the axial gland.

Histologically the axial gland in regular echinoids consists of a connective-tissue meshwork enclosing coelomocytes in its meshes (Fig. 202*B*, *C*).  Around the periphery is a network of blood spaces, and the external surface is clothed with coelomic epithelium.  The peripheral part of the gland also contains numerous brown inclusions, whence the name brown gland employed by Cuénot and others.  The axial gland of spatangoids is similar, except that the blood spaces are more confined to one side and there are fewer cells in the connective-tissue meshes. The function of the axial gland remains uncertain, although an excretory role appears probable (see later under physiology).

The opinion of Cuénot (1948) that the axial gland of echinoids (and other Eleutherozoa) is not homologous with the structure of the same name in crinoids and therefore should be called by some other name, as brown gland, is not accepted by other workers.

**14. Haemal System.**—Accounts of this system are based chiefly on the researches of Perrier (1875), Hamann (1887), and Bonnet (1925). In regular echinoids a haemal ring encircles the esophagus on the aboral surface of the lantern (Fig. 203).  This gives off in each interradius a branch to the corresponding spongy body and in each radius a radial haemal sinus that passes down the outer surface of the pharynx inside the lantern (Fig. 194*A*) and then proceeds onto the inner surface of the peristome.  It then passes under the arch formed by the auricles and continues in the radial position along the inner surface of the test, being located between the hyponeural canal of the radial nerve and the radial water canal (Fig. 195*A*).  Branches are given off into the podia that accompany the podial branches of the water canal.

The other main channels of the haemal system are the two conspicuous sinuses that accompany the festoons of the small intestine.  The larger of these, the *inner* or *ventral marginal* sinus, springs from the

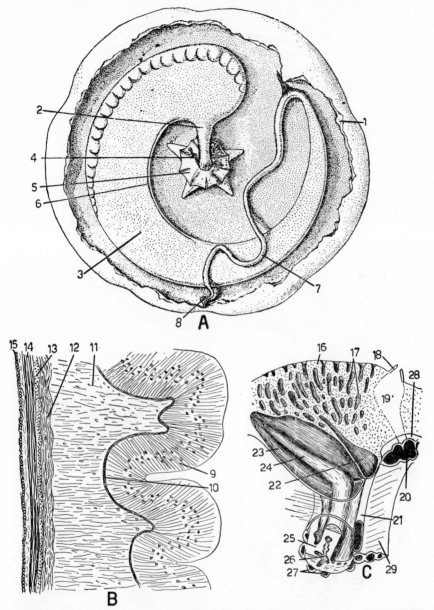

Fig. 201.—Digestive tract, axial gland (continued). *A*, dissection of sand dollar, *Echinarachnius parma*, seen from the aboral side (*after Coe*, 1912). *B*, cross section of the small intestine of *Spatangus purpureus* (*after Koehler*, 1883). *C*, longitudinal view through the madreporite of *Sphaerechinus granularis*, showing terminal process of the axial gland (*after Leipoldt*, 1883). 1, cut edge of test; 2, esophagus; 3, small intestine (stomach); 4, stone canal; 5, aboral surface of lantern; 6, siphon; 7, large intestine; 8, rectum; 9, epithelium; 10, basement membrane; 11, connective tissue; 12, dense connective tissue; 13, longitudinal muscle fibers; 14, circular muscle fibers; 15, coelomic epithelium; 16, madreporic plate; 17, canals through madreporic plate; 18, genital papilla; 19, gonoduct; 20, aboral haemal sinus; 21, stone canal; 22, ampulla; 23, coelomic cavity (right axocoel) in which axial gland terminates; 24, terminal process of axial gland; 25, body of axial gland cut open; 26, lumen of axial gland; 27, haemal lacunae around axial gland; 28, aboral sinus; 29, mesentery.

475

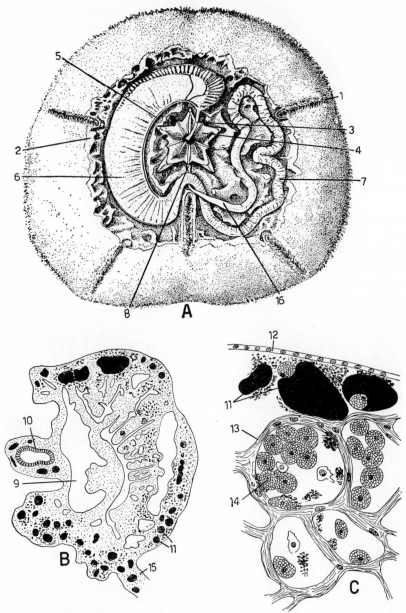

Fig. 202.—Digestive tract, axial gland (concluded). *A*, dissection of keyhole sand dollar, *Mellita* (*after Coe*, 1912). *B*, cross section of the axial gland of *Arbacia lixula*. *C*, enlarged portion of *B*. (*B, C, after Hamann*, 1887.) 1, lunule; 2, broken surface of test; 3, esophagus; 4, aboral surface of lantern; 5, siphon; 6, stomach; 7, intestine; 8, anus; 9, lumen; 10, stone canal; 11, haemal lacunae; 12, coelomic epithelium; 13, connective-tissue mesh; 14, coelomocytes; 15, mesentery; 16, rectum.

haemal ring, runs along the esophagus, and accompanies the inner side of the festoons of the intestine, branching richly into the intestinal wall (Fig. 203). The *outer* or *dorsal marginal* sinus is found along the other side of the festoons of the small intestine; its origin is uncertain, but apparently it branches from the same channel that supplies the axial gland. It also gives off a rich network into the intestinal wall. The inner sinus continues along the large intestine but the outer one gradually dies away. In a few genera of regular urchins (*Echinus, Psammechins, Sphaerechinus,* Bonnet, 1925), there is present an additional *collateral* sinus that lies free in the coelom between the lantern and the intestine and connects with the outer marginal sinus by about 10 widely spaced channels (Fig. 203). The collateral sinus has been observed to show contractions. The sinus for the axial gland arises from the haemal ring, branches richly over the surface of the gland, and then reforms at the aboral end of the gland into a channel that enters the aboral haemal ring. This latter is enclosed in the aboral coelomic sinus (Fig. 197*A*) and gives off branches into the gonads.

The haemal system of spatangoids is similar except that the oral haemal ring, closely associated with the nervous and water rings, lies along the inner surface of the peristome edge and gives off the five radial sinuses directly (Fig. 204*A*). The intestine is also here supplied by an inner and an outer marginal sinus, both of which give off a rich vascularization into the caecum. A branch from the haemal ring ascends to the axial gland from which channels reach an aboral network inside the general aboral sinus; this aboral network also supplies the gonads.

The haemal sinuses or lacunae lack a definite lining and consist of connective tissue covered externally by peritoneum. Scanty longitudinal muscle fibers and sometimes also circular fibers are present beneath the coelomic covering in those sinuses that are capable of contraction, especially the inner marginal sinus and the collateral sinus. No statements have been found concerning the circulation.

In older works the hyponeural sinus is called pseudohaemal or sometimes perihaemal canal and an air of mystery is thereby thrown around this space. The hyponeural sinus or canal is not part of the haemal system except in the sense that the contained fluid differs little between haemal and other spaces but is simply a coelomic canal that, like the epineural sinus, cushions the radial nerve cord and presumably also supplies it with nutrition. According to Hamann (1887), both epineural and hyponeural sinuses are lined by coelomic epithelium, but embryology shows that only the latter is of coelomic origin.

**15. Reproductive System and Reproductive Habits.**—In regular echinoids the reproductive system consists of five gonads, sometimes more or less fused, suspended by mesenterial strands along the inner surface of the interambulacra. When ripe they are quite voluminous, lobulated bodies that occupy the available space between the intestinal festoons and extend from the aboral center almost to the lantern (Fig. 205*A*). At its aboral end each gonad narrows to a short gonoduct that exits by the gonopore in the corresponding genital plate of the apical system. The gonoducts are closely associated with the aboral nerve ring of the entoneural nervous sytem, the aboral haemal ring, and the aboral coelomic sinus. In a few echinoids the gonopores are mounted on papillae in males or in both sexes. In most irregular urchins there are only four gonads (Fig. 204*B*), as the retreat of the periproct along interradius AB usually destroys the gonad of that interradius, although the gonad has returned in some clypeastroids and a few others. In at least some species of the spatangoid genera *Abatus, Schizaster,* and *Lovenia,* there are but three gonads, as that of interradius CD has also vanished; and in *Schizaster canaliferus* the number of gonads is further reduced to two (Fig. 204*C*) by the disappearance of the gonad of interradius DE.

The echinoids are strictly dioecious, and hermaphroditic specimens occur only as rare anomalies. Gadd (1907) reported a female specimen of *Strongyl. dröhbachiensis* with one male gonad. Viguier (1900) found a hermaphroditic individual of *Sphaerechinus granularis,* and Neefs (1954) reported one with two testes and three ovotestes. Several cases of hermaphroditism in *Par. lividus* are on record: Herlant (1918) had one with three normal testes, one atrophied testis, and one ovotestis; Gray's specimen (1921) was mainly female, with three ovaries and two ovotestes; the specimen of Drzewina and Bohn (1924) was also a female with four ovaries and one testis; and of the seven specimens of Neefs (1937), four were mainly female with one testis or ovotestis or with patches of sperm on the ovaries, and the gonads of the other three were male proximally, female distally. A hermaphroditic specimen of *Arbacia punctulata* with four ovaries and one ovotestis was reported by Heilbrunn (1929), another with four testes and one ovary by Shapiro (1935), and still another with five ovotestes by Harvey (1939). Reverberi (1940, 1947) recorded a total of six hermaphroditic specimens of *Arbacia lixula,* two with four ovaries and one testis, two with four testes and one ovary, one with three testes and two ovaries, and one with one testis, one ovary, and three ovotestes. This same author also had a *Psammechinus microtuberculatus* with three ovaries and two testes. H. B. Moore (1932) found a hermaphroditic *Echinus esculentus* with four ovaries and one testis and later (1935) recorded an *Echinocardium cordatum* with ovotestes. Needham and A. H. Moore (1928) had a sand dollar (*Dendraster excentricus*) in which each gonad was half male and half female. A Japanese urchin, *Strongyl. pulcherrimus,* with one ovary and four ovotestes was reported by Okada and Shimoizumi (1952). The sex cells of hermaphroditic urchins are commonly self-fertile, but development is frequently abnormal.

In most echinoids the sexes cannot be distinguished externally except in the case of brooding females, but an external sexual dimorphism

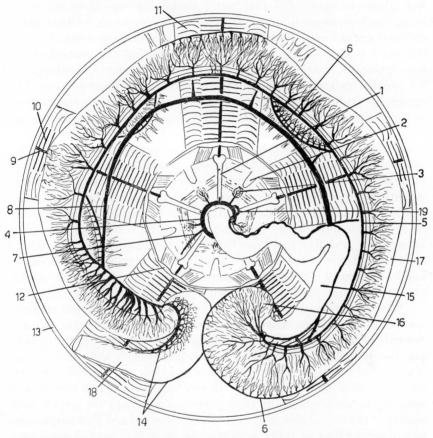

Fig. 203.—Haemal system of *Echinus* (*after Perrier*, 1875). 1, compass; 2, aboral end of tooth; 3, spongy body; 4, haemal ring; 5, inner marginal sinus; 6, outer marginal sinus; 7, branch to axial gland; 8, collateral sinus; 9, radial sinus; 10, branches of radial sinus to podia; 11, ampullae; 12, perignathic girdle; 13, cut edge of test; 14, extensions of marginal sinuses onto large intestine; 15, esophagus; 16, caecum; 17, small intestine; 18, beginning of large intestine; 19, junction of inner marginal sinus with haemal ring.

obtains in a few species. In *Psammechinus miliaris* the gonopores are mounted on short papillae in the males but not in the females, and in *Echinocyamus pusillus* such genital papillae occur in both sexes but are much longer in males (Marx, 1929). Claims of sex difference in test shape in various echinoids (Studer, 1880; Ikeda, 1931a) have been disproved by broader studies (Cascia, 1930; Mortensen, Monogr.). In brooding spatangoids the deeper excavation of the petaloids in females distinguishes them from males even when not brooding.

The eggs and sperm are shed directly into the sea water and fertilization and development ensue immediately. Little information is available concerning the factors inducing spawning. Fox (1924b) observed that the presence of a spawning *Par. lividus* induces other individuals to spawn and that water containing eggs or sperm would cause ripe individuals to spawn, with the males preceding. Direct application of egg or sperm water to the gonads or gonoducts proved ineffective. The same author (1922, 1924a, 1924b) reported that *Diadema setosum* at Suez spawns at the full moon during its breeding season and recuperates its gonads by the next full moon. However, he observed only two spawnings (July, August), and Mortensen, working with the same species in the Java Sea during April and May, was not able to confirm lunar periodicity. Yoshida (1952) reported that this species breeds at Japan from May to September and that spawning, especially in females, shows some correlation with the full moon. Spawning with reference to external factors has not been noticed in other species, and various external conditions tried proved ineffective in *Echinometra lacunter* (Tennent, Gardiner, and Smith, 1931) and in *Arbacia punctulata* (Palmer, 1937). The former simply spawns when ripe shortly after being brought into the laboratory. Possibly zoologists have not been interested in the natural spawning of echinoids because in this group artificial fertilization is highly successful. Sex cells obtained directly from the ripe gonads almost invariably yield normal development.

A curious method of inducing spawning is known for the common urchin of the western Atlantic, *Arbacia punctulata*. If a cut is made around the peristome or the ambitus of a ripe specimen of this species and the animal placed aboral side down in a dish, it will spawn immediately, but not if placed oral side down, unless very severely injured. The analysis of Palmer (1937) has shown that this reaction results from some substance produced by the injury that can reach the gonads more readily if the aboral side is down. She further showed that suspensions of ground urchins or other echinoderms or of disrupted *Arbacia* eggs and sperm (but not undamaged sex cells) or of ground frog or fish muscle induce spawning when applied to the gonads of *Arbacia*. Calcium and potassium salts are also effective. It is not clear, however, what relation any of these findings would have to natural spawning.

It has been noticed in a few cases that urchins tend to move inshore and aggregate when about to spawn. Orton (1914) states that *Psamm. miliaris* tends to associate in pairs, most of which consist of opposite sexes, at spawning time, and Tennent (1910) saw *Lytechinus variegatus* aggregating preparatory to spawning. The spring inshore migration of *Echinus esculentus* in British waters is related to spawning (Elmhirst, 1922b).

The gonads consist of an outer coelomic epithelium, a middle layer of muscle fibers and connective tissue, and a lining of germinal epithelium

(Fig. 205*D*). Spawning is directly caused by the contraction of the muscle fibers. Palmer (1937) observed this contraction on the application of extracts of injured tissues to the surface of the gonads. It is difficult to understand how this contraction is mediated since in most urchins there appears to be no direct nerve supply to the gonads. Palmer saw no effect on injury of the nerve ring or radial nerves.

It is probable that most echinoids have an annual breeding cycle, extending over a few to several months at a definite time of the year. Following spawning the gonads are retrogressed and much reduced in size and must build up again for the next spawning period. This annual cycle has been described by Caullery (1912, 1925) for the common heart urchin of western Europe (*Echinocardium cordatum*). In the fall the gonads begin developing a new lot of sex cells, spawning occurs from April to June, with the males ripening before the females, and any remaining sex cells are phagocytized by reserve tissue that grows and reforms sex cells.

In the Northern Hemisphere most echinoids spawn in spring and summer, usually earlier the more southern the latitude; this indicates some relation of rise of temperature to the onset of spawning. The same species may spawn at a different time in different geographical regions. The common urchin of the New England coast, *Arbacia punctulata*, is ripe in spring and summer. Off Carolina, *Lytechinus variegatus* spawns in June and July (Tennent, 1910), whereas the same species in the West Indies is ripe in March and April (Mortensen, 1921). Several other common West Indian echinoids also spawn in March and April (Mortensen, 1921): *Diadema antillarum, Tripneustes ventricosus, Echinometra lacunter,* and *Mellita sexiesperforata*. At Bermuda, however, *Diadema antillarum* is ripe in July (Mortensen, 1931). On the Pacific Coast of North America, *Strongylocentrotus franciscanus* and *Dendraster excentricus* were found ripe in May and June at Vancouver Island by Mortensen (1921). In Puget Sound, *S. franciscanus* and *purpuratus* are reported as breeding in March and April (Johnson, 1930), whereas at Pacific Grove, California, ripe specimens of *S. purpuratus* may be obtained from January to July, best during February and March, and of *S. franciscanus* from February to July, best during April and May (Newman, 1923). Mortensen (1921) found ripe echinoids at Panama in October, December, and January. *Psammechinus miliaris*, one of the most common regular urchins of western Europe, may be found with ripe gonads from February to November (Orton, 1923a), with the maximum breeding period varying somewhat with locality, and *Echinus esculentus*, another common urchin of this region, is ripe from February to August (Elmhirst, 1922a), best from March to June, with a maximum in May. The annual cycle of the latter at the Isle of Man has been described by Stott (1931) and H. B. Moore (1934); here the males show some sperm by late autumn, but the females are not in spawning condition

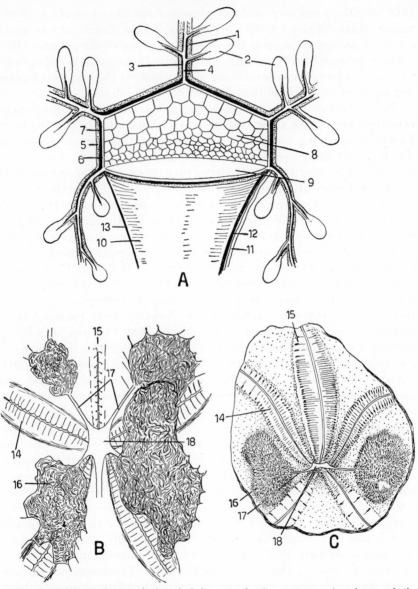

Fig. 204.—Haemal system (concluded), reproductive system. *A*, scheme of the peristome of a spatangoid (*after Koehler,* 1883). *B*, aboral side of test viewed from inside, showing the four gonads, spatangoid, *Meoma ventricosa;* the two left gonads are fused. *C*, aboral side of test of *Schizaster canaliferus*, viewed from the inside, showing the two gonads (*after Koehler,* 1883). 1, radial nerve; 2, ampullae; 3, radial haemal sinus; 4, radial water vessel; 5, nerve ring; 6, water ring; 7, haemal ring; 8, plates of peristome; 9, mouth; 10, esophagus; 11, stone canal; 12, inner marginal sinus; 13, outer marginal sinus; 14, inner side of petaloid; 15, anterior ambulacrum; 16, gonad; 17, gonoduct; 18, aboral sinus.

until February, and spawning takes place mostly from March to May; in this region the gonads are spent by the end of June. The common heart urchin of western Europe, *Echinocardium cordatum*, breeds from April to June on the English Channel (Caullery, 1912, 1925), from May to August off Scotland (MacBride, 1914; Elmhirst, 1922a), from August to September off Sweden (Mortensen, 1937), and from October to April in the Mediterranean (Lo Bianco, 1888). According to the last reference, many of the common echinoids around Naples breed from late fall to March, some possibly throughout the year. Selenka (1879) reported the most common Mediterranean echinoids—*Psammechinus miliaris*, *Sphaerechinus granularis*, *Paracentrotus lividus*, *Arbacia lixula*, and *Echinocardium cordatum*—as ripe in April. In pursuing his studies on echinoderm development in many parts of the world at various seasons, Mortensen (1921, 1931, 1937, 1938) never failed to find some echinoids in breeding condition. Many species were found ripe in the Red Sea from April to June, others from July to September; good development was obtained of several species at Mauritius in September and October, off Japan from April to July, at Hawaii in April, at Panama in December and January, in the Java Sea in May, and at Port Jackson, Australia, in February. A number of Japanese species were bred in July and August by Onoda (1936). *Salmacis bicolor* at Madras is said by Aiyar (1934) to breed throughout the year.

A number of echinoids, chiefly cidaroids and spatangoids, brood their young, and as in other echinoderms, this habit is particularly prevalent in the antarctic. The eggs, generally large and yolky, develop on the peristome or around the periproct in cidaroids (Fig. 205C), sometimes in an annular sunken area; in spatangoids, deepened petaloids serve as brood pouches (Fig. 206). Adjacent spines crisscrossed over the brooding area help keep the young in place. Apart from cidaroids, only one regular urchin is known to brood its young, *Hypsiechinus coronatus* (Mortensen, 1903), belonging to the Temnopleuridae. This species is limited to the far northern part of the North Atlantic. It is sexually dimorphic in that females have an elevated periproct around the base of which on the apical system of plates the young are carried. Brooding is common among cidaroids. Thomson (1878) reported two antarctic brooding cidaroids: *Ctenocidaris nutrix* from Kerguelen that carries its young on the peristome and *Austrocidaris canaliculata* from the South American antarctic (Fig. 205C) that broods around the periproct. Two additional brooding cidaroids from the antarctic were reported by Mortensen (1909) from the collections of the German South Polar Expedition: *Rhynchocidaris triplopora* and *Notocidaris gaussensis*. Both carry the young on the peristome protected by spines and in the former species lodged (35 counted) in a circular depression. Still another

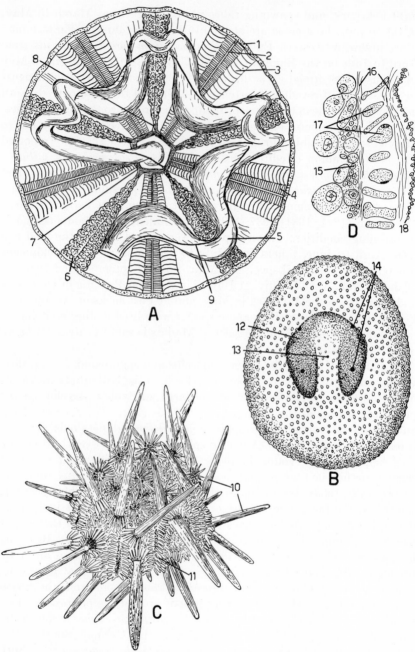

Fig. 205.—Reproductive system, brooding. *A*, aboral half of the test of *Tripneustes ventricosus*, seen from the inside, showing the gonads.  *B*, brooding sand dollar, *Fibularia nutriens*, with brooding depression on the aboral surface; note lack of petaloids (*after Mortensen, Monogr.*).  *C*, brooding antarctic cidaroid, *Austrocidaris canaliculata*, Falk-

antarctic brooding cidaroid, *Ctenocidaris spinosa*, with peristomial brooding, was found on the Australasian Antarctic Expedition (Koehler, 1926), and two more on the British, Australian, New Zealand Antarctic Research Expedition (Mortensen, 1950). These last were *Ctenocidaris perrieri* and *geliberti*, brooding on the peristome, which is sunken around the edge in the second species. Other cidaroids with peristomial brooding are

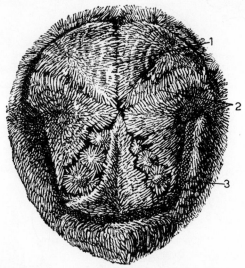

FIG. 206.—Brooding spatangoid from Kerguelen, *Abatus cordatus*, with young in the posterior petaloids (*after Thomson*, 1878). 1, anterior ambulacrum; 2, petaloids; 3, peripetalous fasciole.

*Goniocidaris umbraculum* from New Zealand (Mortensen, 1926) and *Aporocidaris milleri* from deep water off Panama (Mortensen, 1927a).

Among the irregular echinoids two brooding species belonging to the order Cassiduloida are known. These include *Anochanus sinensis* (Grube, 1868), off China, and *Tropholampas loveni*, off South Africa (H. L. Clark, 1923). The former is the first brooding echinoid discovered and no other specimen has been found; the insunken aboral center acts as a brood pouch in both species. Brooding is common among spatangoids, and Mortensen is of the opinion that all antarctic spatangoids brood, usually in the deepened petaloids. Apparently all members of the closely related genera *Abatus*, *Amphineustes*, and *Tripylus*, limited to antarctic and subantarctic regions, have the brooding habit. The well-known

land Islands (*after Thomson*, 1878). *D*, section of the ovary of *Arbacia* (*after Palmer*, 1937). 1, broken edge of test; 2, radial water canal; 3, ampullae; 4, podial branches of water canal; 5, large intestine; 6, gonad; 7, aboral sinus plus aboral haemal ring; 8, gonoduct; 9, inner marginal sinus; 10, primary spines; 11, secondary spines; 12, brooding depression; 13, hydropore; 14, gonopores; 15, germinal epithelium with ova; 16, connective tissue; 17, cross sections of muscle fibers; 18, coelomic epitheluim.

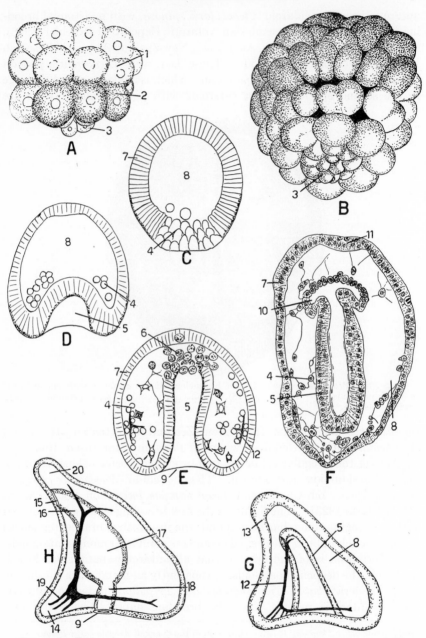

Fig. 207.—Embryology.  A, cleavage stage, 32 cells.  B, later cleavage of *Psam-mechinus microtuberculatus*, showing group of micromeres at the vegetal pole (*after Selenka*, 1883).  C, blastula, giving off primary mesenchyme.  D, beginning gastrulation.  E, gastrulation completed, secondary mesenchyme coming off.  (A, C, D, E, *Paracentrotus lividus, after Boveri*, 1901; heavy stippling indicates orange band.)  F, section of gastrula of *Echinus esculentus*, giving off the coelomic sacs (*after MacBride*, 1903).  G, young pluteus,

brooding spatangoid from Kerguelen reported by Agassiz (1876) and Thomson (1878) under the name *Hemiaster* is identified by Mortensen as *Abatus cordatus* (Fig. 206). Brooding in the deeply insunken aboral center is suspected by Mortensen (1950) for another antarctic spatangoid, *Plexechinus nordenskjöldi*. One sand dollar is known to brood in a crescentic sunken aboral area, *Fibularia nutriens* (Fig. 205B) found off New South Wales.

**16. Development.**—The eggs of echinoids (except brooding species) are mostly small and transparent and when shed into the sea water generally sink, although a few are floating. Cleavage progresses rapidly and is of the holoblastic, equal type up to the eight-cell stage, whereupon the four vegetal cells each give off a small micromere at the vegetal pole, being then themselves known as macromeres, as by this unequal division they are left slightly larger than the cells of the animal half or mesomeres that continue to divide equally (Fig. 207A, B). The micromeres undergo further divisions, producing a group of small cells at the vegetal pole, and the macromeres and mesomeres proceed with a number of successive cleavages that are approximately equal. There results a coeloblastula of about 800 to 1000 cells that are more or less equal except for the small cells at the vegetal pole. Details of the cleavage have been published by Selenka (1883) for *Paracentrotus lividus*, *Sphaerechinus granularis*, and *Psammechinus microtuberculatus*, by Fleischmann (1888) for *Echinocardium cordatum*, by Morgan (1894) for *Arbacia punctulata*, by Boveri (1901) for *Paracentrotus lividus*, and by MacBride (1903) for *Echinus esculentus*. As the accounts agree for the various species, it may be assumed that the cleavage follows the same pattern throughout the group. The egg of *Paracentrotus lividus* has been a favorite object of embryological investigation because it has a band of orange pigment in the vegetal hemisphere. The orange pigment can be followed during development, and by this means, together with many ingenious experiments (reviewed by Hörstadius, 1939), it has been learned that the micromeres furnish the primary mesenchyme, the mesomeres and the upper part of the macromeres are ectodermal, and the lower macromeres, those adjacent to the micromeres, invaginate as archenteron. The echinoid egg is therefore organized with respect to the future embryo, and hence its development belongs to the determinate or mosaic type.

The cells of the blastula soon put out flagella, and the blastula begins

---

*Anthocidaris. H*, slightly older pluteus, *Anthocidaris*, arms beginning, digestive tract differentiated. (*G, H, after* Onoda, 1931.) The orientation of *G* and *H* is the same as of *E*, to show relation of pluteal axis to gastrular axis. 1, mesomeres; 2, macromeres; 3, micromeres; 4, primary mesenchyme; 5, archenteron; 6, secondary mesenchyme; 7, epidermis; 8, blastocoel; 9, blastopore; 10, coelomic sacs; 11, apical sensory thickening; 12, primary spicule; 13, oral lobe; 14, postoral arm; 15, mouth; 16, esophagus; 17, stomach; 18, intestine; 19, three branches of spicule to form lattice rod in postoral arm; 20, anterolateral arm.

rotating within the fertilization membrane that ruptures, setting the embryo free. This stage, the swimming blastula, is generally reached within 12 hours. The vegetal pole of the blastula flattens, and the cells here begin proliferating mesenchyme into the interior (Fig. 207C). This primary mesenchyme, which is descended from the micromeres, gathers in the vegetal part of the blastocoel and secretes on each side a triradiate calcareous spicule (Fig. 207E). Meantime a typical embolic invagination is in progress, establishing a rather long, narrow archenteron (Fig. 207E). The advancing tip of this continues to proliferate mesenchyme, the secondary mesenchyme. A large space, occupied by mesenchyme, remains between the archenteron and the gastrular wall. The inner end of the archenteron promptly cuts off as a coelomic sac that at once divides into two sacs, the right and left hydroenterocoels, or the coelomic sac is bilobed before separating from the archenteron (Fig. 207F). The gastrula stage is completed within 1 to 2 days. In either the blastula or gastrula stage there is established at the apical pole the usual sensory patch provided with long cilia (Fig. 208A).

The gastrula alters into a characteristic larval type, the *pluteus;* as both ophiuroids and echinoids have a pluteus larva, that of echinoids may be referred to when necessary as *echinopluteus.* The transformation of the gastrula into the pluteus begins by the elongation of the former into a conical shape (Fig. 207G). The apex of the cone represents the animal pole, and the base of the cone is the flattened vegetal surface with the blastopore in its center. One side of the gastrula, destined to become the oral surface, flattens. The apex of the conical gastrula rounds into an oral lobe that inclines toward the flattened side. Just under the oral lobe on this flattened side a stomodaeal invagination breaks through into the archenteron, which now, if not previously, differentiates by constrictions into esophagus, stomach, and intestine (Fig. 207H). The digestive tract and hence also the larval axis thus form a curve from the original blastoporal side to the present oral surface (Fig. 207H). The blastopore remains as the larval anus. The larva begins to put out slender projections, known as arms, supported by skeletal rods secreted by the primary mesenchyme. There first appears on the oral end opposite to the oral lobe a pair of *postoral* arms and then in the oral lobe a pair of much shorter *anterolateral* arms. These arms are supported by the two original spicules whose rays have lengthened into long rods that extend into the arms and also to the posterior end of the pluteus as well as transversely into the body (Fig. 208B). The pluteous generally reaches this four-armed stage in one to a few days and swims about near the surface but usually develops no further unless it obtains food, mostly diatoms and other microscopic planktonic organisms. If nourished, it grows and puts out additional arms, a *posterodorsal* pair

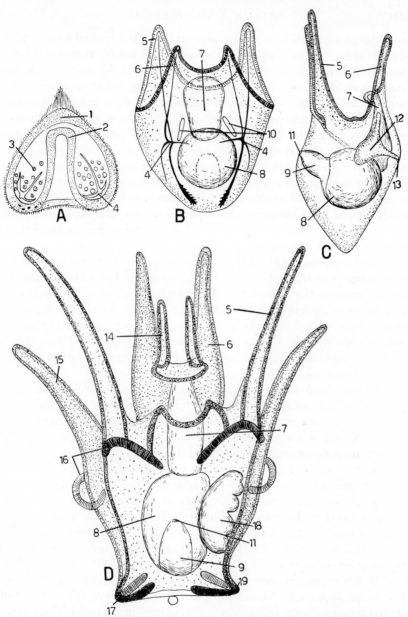

Fig. 208.—Embryology (continued). *A*, beginning pluteus of *Diadema*, showing apical sensory plate (*after Mortensen*, 1931). *B*, four-armed stage of the pluteus of *Strongyl. franciscanus*. *C*, four-armed stage of the pluteus of *Psammechinus miliaris*, seen from the left side (*after MacBride*, 1903). *D*, fully developed pluteus of *Strongyl. franciscanus*, seen from in front. (*B, D, after Mortensen*, 1921.) 1, sensory plate; 2, archenteron; 3, mesenchyme; 4, primary spicule; 5, postoral arms; 6, anterolateral arms; 7, esophagus; 8, stomach, 9, intestine; 10, hydroenterocoels; 11, anus; 12, left hydroenterocoel; 13, hydropore; 14, preoral arms; 15, posterodorsal arms; 16, anterior epaulettes; 17, posterior epaulettes; 18, echinus rudiment; 19, posterolateral processes.

near the postoral arms, a *preoral* pair on the oral lobe oral to the antero lateral arms, an *anterodorsal* pair near the latter, and sometimes a *posterolateral* pair at the sides of the posterior end (Fig. 208D). The last-named pair is well developed in spatangoids (Fig. 209C) and some others but usually is very short, often indicated only by a pair of eminences, called the posterolateral processes. Thus a fully developed echino-pluteus may have six pairs of arms, but usually there are only five pairs because of the lack of development of the posterolateral pair, and many have only four through failure of appearance of the anterodorsal pair. The later arms are also supported by calcareous skeletal rods that arise from independently formed spicules, secreted like the first pair of spicules by groups of primary mesenchyme cells; in fact, the formation of the larval skeleton is the sole function of the primary mesenchyme. The preoral arms are supported by the branches of an unpaired skeletal rod called the *dorsal arch* (Fig. 210A) that also gives off supporting rods into the anterodorsal arms when present. A corresponding unpaired *posterior transverse rod* in the posterior end of the pluteus gives off the supporting rods into the posterolateral arms when these are sufficiently developed. In the pluteus the cilia (or flagella?) that completely covered the blastula and gastrula become limited to a band edging the arms, disappearing elsewhere, and the apical sensory patch is indistinguishably incorporated into this band.

The formation of the larval spicules has been studied by Woodland (1905), Prenant (1926), and von Ubisch (1937), who find that the spicule begins as a granule in a mesenchyme cell or in a clear cytoplasm formed by the partial union of several mesenchyme cells (Fig. 210C). This granule soon becomes three-angled and rapidly grows into a triradiate spicule by means of mesenchyme cells grouped along its rays; apparently the rays are deposited in a clear plasm produced by partial fusion of strands of mesenchyme cells. Experiment has shown that the arms are predetermined in the ectoderm but grow out only in the presence of an influence emanating from the adjacent primary mesenchyme (Hörstadius, 1939). In the absence of a skeletal rod arms may begin to protrude but do not progress very far.

The echinopluteus occurs in an infinite variety of shape and structure. The plutei of a large number of echinoid species have been beautifully figured by Mortensen (1921, 1931, 1937, 1938) in his splendid studies of the larval forms of echinoderms, made on living material in near and far corners of the earth. The arms are usually long and slender but may be short and broad, and their angles with the main body of the pluteus vary widely in different species. As already indicated, plutei may have four, five, or six pairs of fully developed arms, and these are often beauti-fied by pigment cells of varied colors. The curious plutei of *Diadema* remain in the four-armed stage, and the postoral arms gradually shift to a horizontal position, also elongating greatly. These peculiar *plutei transversi* (Fig. 209*A*, *B*) were known long before they could be assigned generically. Spatangoid plutei are distinguished by a median posterior projection, the *aboral spike,* supported by a skeletal rod (Fig. 209*C*).

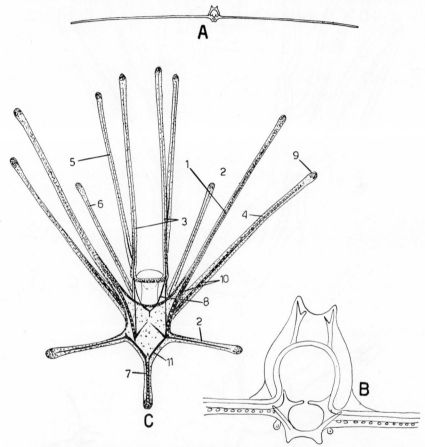

FIG. 209.—Embryology (continued), types of plutei. *A*, transverse pluteus of *Diadema,* width about 1 mm. *B*, body of *A* enlarged. (*A*, *B*, *after Mortensen, Monogr.*) *C*, spatangoid pluteus (*Echinocardium cordatum, after Mortensen,* 1931). 1, postoral arms; 2, posterolateral arms; 3, preoral arms; 4, posterodorsal arms; 5, anterolateral arms; 6, anterodorsal arms; 7, aboral spike; 8, dorsal arch; 9, red pigmented tips; 10, fenestrated rods; 11, posterior transverse rod.

The form of the skeletal rods is distinctive for each species. The rods may be simple or thorny or fenestrated or variously branched or with thickened club-like ends, often thorny. There may be numerous branches anastomosed into a sort of basketwork. Fenestrated or lattice rods, limited to postoral and posterodorsal arms (Fig. 210*A*), are formed from three parallel branches that become united by cross bars (Fig. 210*D*).

The locomotory provision is also subject to variation in different

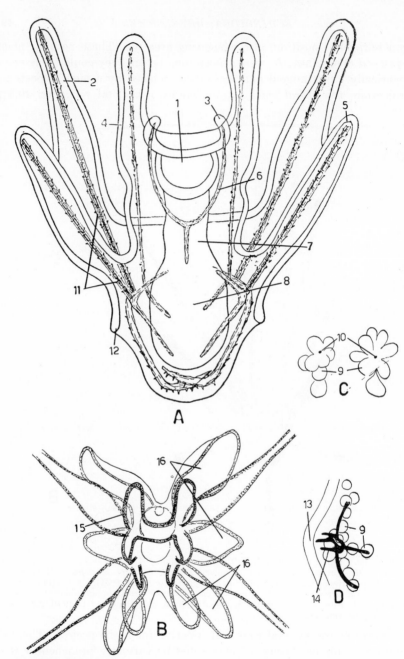

Fig. 210.—Embryology (continued). *A*, temnopleurid larva to show skeleton (*after Tennent*, 1929). *B*, cidarid larva seen from above to show ciliated lobes (*after Mortensen*, 1938). *C*, beginning formation of a calcareous spicule. *D*, beginning formation of a lattice rod. (*C, D, after von Ubisch*, 1937.) 1, oral lobe; 2, postoral arms; 3, preoral arms; 4, anterolateral arms; 5, posterodorsal arms; 6, dorsal arch; 7, esophagus; 8, stomach; 9, mesenchyme cells; 10, calcareous granule; 11, fenestrated rods; 12, posterolateral processes; 13, beginning of arm; 14, three spikes to form lattice rod; 15, ciliated band; 16, ciliated lobes.

genera. In certain genera, especially *Echinus*, *Sphaerechinus*, *Psammechinus*, and *Strongylocentrotus*, portions of the ciliated band, mostly in four places, between the arm bases, become thickened and arched and provided with especially long cilia, being then called *epaulettes* (Fig. 208*D*). These separate from the ciliated band, which heals together after this separation, and become the chief locomotory organs of the larva. There may be one circle of epaulettes, anteriorly situated, or another posterior set, and in each case they may be more or less united into a ring. In other genera, as *Arbacia* and *Cidaris*, the pluteus may put out special ciliated lobes, between the arm bases, independent of the ciliated band edging the arms. These lobes are termed variously vibratile lobes, auricular lobes, or auricles (Fig. 210*B*).

The pluteus is a tiny creature of microscopic dimensions, swimming about in the surface waters, where it can be obtained by means of a plankton net. Weeks or months may be required for the pluteus to attain full external development. Meantime, of course, changes are proceeding internally, especially as regards the hydroenterocoels. Accounts of the later development are given by Bury (1889, 1895) for *Psammechinus microtuberculatus*, Théel (1892) for *Echinocyamus pusillus*, MacBride (1903) for *Echinus esculentus* and (1914, 1918) for *Echinocardium cordatum*, von Ubisch (1913b) for *Paracentrotus lividus*, and Onoda (1931, 1936) for *Anthocidaris crassispina* (not a cidaroid) and a number of other species.

The two coelomic sacs or hydroenterocoels lie as elongated sacs to either side of the digestive tract. Each soon divides into an anterior and a posterior sac. The left anterior coelom enlarges to an ampulla and puts out a water canal to the surface that opens there on the left dorsal side by a hydropore. It further extends posteriorly as a tubular outgrowth terminating in a bulbous enlargement. The tubular outgrowth is the primordium of the stone canal and the bulbous enlargment of the rest of the water-vascular system (Fig. 211*A*). The left anterior coelom then divides behind the ampulla, so that there are then three coelomic sacs on the left side, the ampulla, corresponding to the axocoel, the primordium of the water-vascular system or hydrocoel, and the posterior coelom or somatocoel. On the right side the anterior coelomic sac also divides much later into two vesicles, but these remain in a rudimentary state. In the older literature the rudimentary right axocoel is called the dorsal sac. An ectodermal invagination now occurs on the left side over the bulbous part of the hydrocoel (hereafter called simply hydrocoel). This invagination quickly enlarges to a sac whose inner side becomes closely applied to the hydrocoel (Fig. 211*B*). The ectodermal invagination continues until it has reached a considerable size and then cuts off from the ectoderm as a flattened sac with a thin outer wall and a thick inner wall applied to the hydrocoel. Although this sac is called in the literature amniotic sac and its thin outer wall amnion, it is self-evident that we are here dealing with the vestibule already met with in crinoid and holothuroid development. As in these classes, the combined vestibular floor and hydrocoel produce the oral side of the adult, which here is located on the left side of the pluteus. Meantime the right and left somatocoels have elongated and broadened to flattened sacs applied to the digestive tract on either side (Fig. 211*B*).

The hydrocoel enlarges and flattens and puts out the familiar five lobes that represent the five radial water canals and the five primary podia (Figs. 208*D*, 212*A*). These lobes butt against the thick vestibular floor and cause it to project into the vestibular cavity as the ectodermal coverings of the five podia. The hydrocoel curves around the adjacent digestive tract, establishing the water ring. The left somatocoel extends anteriorly, encircling the hydrocoel and the stomach. It pushes its way between the five lobes of the hydrocoel as five alternating lobes, the *dental sacs*, which represent the primordium of the lantern, and these also push against the thick vestibular floor and cause it to bulge into the vestibular cavity as five blunt lobes alternating with the five primary podia (Fig. 211*C*). The vestibular floor between the primary podia, that is, over the dental sacs, thickens into five *epineural* ridges or folds that elevate and spread laterally, hence appearing T-shaped in section, finally uniting to make a secondary floor to the vestibule external to the original floor and consisting of two thin ectodermal layers (Fig. 212*B–D*). The space between these two layers fills with mesenchyme cells that later secrete the plates of the oral part of the test. There is also a cavity left between the inner epineural layer and the original vestibular floor. This cavity takes the form of a central space and five canals in the radial positions. These canals become the epineural canals external to the radial nerves, and the central space becomes the epineural ring sinus. Thus the epineural system of canals is not of coelomic nature, and its formation is a phylogenetic reminiscence of the closure of the ambulacral grooves in the evolution of echinoids. The nerve ring and radial nerves arise in position by proliferation from the inner surface of the original thick vestibular floor (Fig. 213*B*). The dental sacs cut off from the left somatocoel, and a tooth begins to form in each as a thickening of the wall. Each dental sac puts out a tubular canal that becomes the hyponeural ("perihaemal") canal found in the adult to the coelomic side of the radial nerve and thus shown to be of coelomic nature. Lobulations from the dental sacs work themselves around the parts of the hydrocoel and fuse to form a continuous coelomic cavity except centrally where the esophagus will break through. In this cavity the lantern differentiates.

The differentiation of the lantern has been described by Devanesen (1922) and Prenant (1926); the account of the former, based on specimens

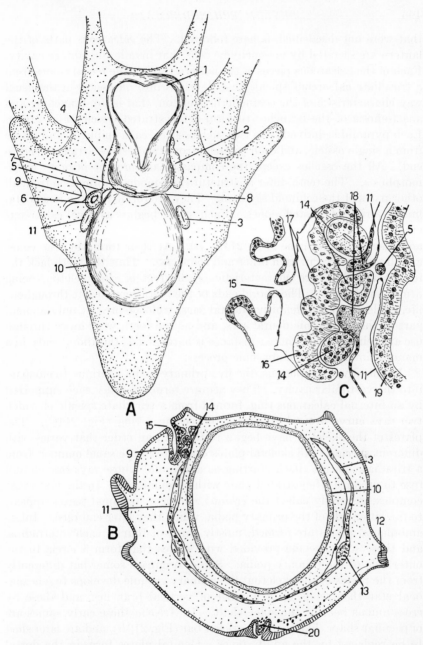

FIG. 211.—Embryology (continued). *A*, pluteus of *Psammechinus*, seen from behind, showing the coelomic compartments (*after Bury*, 1889). *B*, cross section through a pluteus of *Echinus* (*after MacBride*, 1903), showing vestibular invagination. *C*, section of the echinus rudiment of *Paracentrotus lividus* with the vestibular invagination still open (*after von Ubisch*, 1903). 1, esophagus; 2, right axohydrocoel; 3, right somatocoel; 4, left axocoel; 5, stone canal; 6, left hydrocoel; 7, hydroporic canal; 8, hydropore; 9, vestibular invagination; 10, stomach; 11, left somatocoel; 12, ciliated band; 13, muscle fibers; 14, primary podia; 15, opening of vestibular invagination; 16, floor of vestibular cavity; 17, beginning of epineural folds; 18, dental sacs; 19, wall of stomach; 20, pedicellaria.

that were not decalcified, is here followed. The calcareous parts of the lantern are secreted by mesenchyme cells that invade the lantern cavity. Each of the calcareous pieces of the lantern (except the teeth) comes from a triradiate calcareous spicule that develops into an ossicle in the usual way characteristic of the echinoderm skeleton, that is, by branching and anastomosis of the branches to form a fenestrated ossicle (Fig. 216*E*). Each pyramid is derived from two such ossicles, each epiphysis and rotule from a single ossicle, and each compass from two ossicles arranged end to end. All the ossicles except the compasses are present prior to metamorphosis. The teeth differ in structure and mode of formation from all other parts of the echinoid skeleton. They are formed by the fusion of a linear series of nested cones. Each cone begins as two calcareous granules that increase in size to become triangular pieces; these curve and fuse to form a cone (Fig. 214*A*, *B*). At their formation the cones are already nested in each other and soon fuse. Thus the teeth lack the fenestrated structure characteristic of the rest of the skeleton, being firmer and harder. The aboral ends of the teeth remain soft throughout life, enclosed in the definitive dental sacs, which represent only a small part of the embryonic dental sacs, and as the teeth wear away through use at their oral ends, more substance is hardened at the aboral ends, in a manner similar to the embryonic process.

In the advanced pluteus, the five primary podia continue to elongate into the vestibular cavity. They acquire terminal disks, each supported by an internal calcareous ring, formed from a triradiate spicule of which two rays curve around and meet to become a ring (Fig. 214*C*). The plates of the skeleton have begun to form, in an order that varies with different species. All skeletal plates originate in the same manner, from a triradiate spicule (itself starting as a granule) whose rays branch and fuse to produce a fenestrated plate with large meshes. In the vestibular complex, generally called the *echinus rudiment*, terminal plates appear, to the outer side of the primary podia, which they later embrace. Interambulacral plates are formed, mostly three or four in each interradius, and these soon become provided with spines that form a circle to the outer side of the primary podia. Spines originate somewhat differently from the plates of the skeleton; the primary granule develops to a hexagonal star that sends up a number of vertical branches, and these by cross unions become the spine shaft. In *Arbacia* these early spines are of peculiar shape, like that of a cricket bat (Fig. 219*B*) and are later shed to be replaced by the adult spines. Genital plates form in the dorsal surface of the pluteus, not in the echinus rudiment (Figs. 215*B*, 217*E*). Some genitals and some terminals arise from skeletal material at the inner ends of the rods of the pluteus arms; one of the genitals (genital 2) invariably arises from one end of the dorsal arch, and this genital embraces

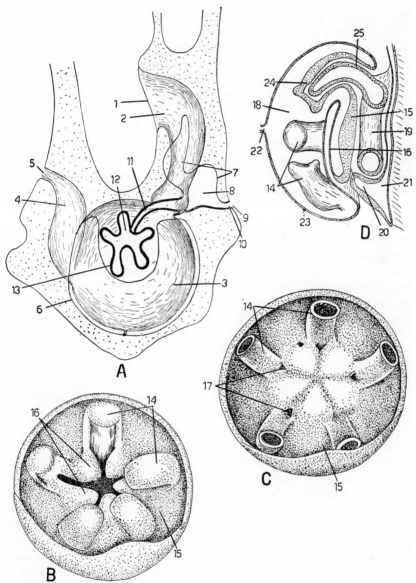

FIG. 212.—Embryology (continued). *A, Psammechinus* pluteus seen from the left side, showing echinus rudiment (*after Bury,* 1889). *B,* scheme of formation of the epineural folds. *C,* similar to *B,* later stage, folds closed. (In *B* and *C,* the roof of the vestibule is cut away.) *D,* section through the echinus rudiment showing formation of the epineural folds. (*B–D, after von Ubisch,* 1913.) 1, mouth; 2, esophagus; 3, stomach; 4, intestine; 5, anus; 6, left somatocoel; 7, left axocoel; 8, definitive ampulla; 9, hydropore; 10, hydroporic canal; 11, definitive stone canal; 12, hydrocoel; 13, five hydrocoel lobes to form primary podia; 14, primary podia; 15, floor of vestibule; 16, epinural folds; 17, epineural canals; 18, vestibular cavity; 19, water ring; 20, dental sac; 21, left somatocoel; 22, place of closure of vestibular invagination; 23, roof of vestibule; 24, ectodermal part of podium; 25, lining layer of podium derived from hydrocoel.

the hydropore and becomes the madreporite of the adult (Fig. 215*B*). Other genitals and terminals develop independently from triradiate spicules. Pedicellariae, mostly three or four in number, appear on the dorsal surface attached to some of the genital plates (Fig. 217*E*) and may develop prior to these plates. Their development indicates that each valve represents a spine. These early pedicellariae are very short, almost without a stalk. In the echinus rudiment, ambulacral plates and 10 buccal plates put in an appearance and the lantern is in process of formation. A pair of definitive podia may have developed to the oral side of each of the primary podia. The skeletal support in the terminal disk of the definitive podia originates otherwise than does the skeletal ring of the disk of the primary podia; three spicules form the circle of skeletal pieces in the disk and six more below this produce the frame (Fig. 214*D*).

In the interior of the advanced pluteus the digestive tract remains as in earlier stages with widely open mouth overhung by a flap, esophagus now muscularized and capable of peristalsis, large stomach sac, and intestine curving forward to parallel the stomach and leading to the larval anus (blastopore) on the ventral side on a level with the echinus rudiment. The latter occupies a large part of the left side of the pluteus, pressing against the stomach. The somatocoels retain their positions at the sides of the digestive tract; the left one has outgrown the right in producing the dental sacs. The two somatocoels meet posteriorly, establishing a mesentery, which, however, eventually breaks through. Sooner or later the two meet above and below the digestive tract to establish a mesentery. As a result of the development of skeleton, the pluteus becomes heavier and sluggish and gradually sinks to the bottom.

Some 4 to 6 weeks or more after the onset of development, depending on temperature, food supply, and species, the pluteus undergoes metamorphosis into a young urchin. This event usually occupies only an hour or less. The outer wall of the vestibule (so-called amnion) ruptures and shrinks back, so that the primary podia and spines and any additional podia that have developed now emerge to the exterior (Fig. 213*C*). The central part of the two epineural layers (*epineural veil* of MacBride) also ruptures and shrinks. The covering of the larval arms is absorbed back into the general body surface, and the skeletal rods supporting the arms break off and are discarded (Fig. 219*A*). The larval mouth and anus close over. The baby urchin, mostly less than 1 mm. in diameter, walks about by means of the primary podia. As indicated above, it is already provided with genital and terminal plates, the first ambulacral and interambulacral plates, buccal plates, a few pedicellariae, a number of spines, and a more or less developed lantern. The spines may be of juvenile type, discarded later, or partly of juvenile and partly of adult type. In *Arbacia*, all the spines at metamorphosis are of juvenile type,

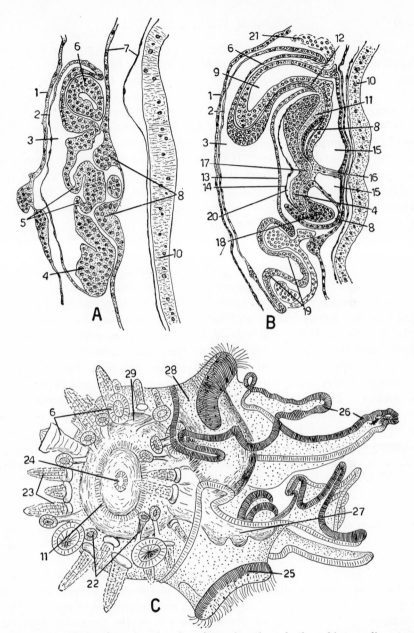

Fig. 213.—Embryology (continued). *A*, section through the echinus rudiment of
*Paracentrotus*, showing epineural folds closing. *B*, section through the echinus rudiment
later, epineural folds closed. (*A, B, after von Ubisch*, 1913.) *C*, pluteus of *Psammechinus*
in process of metamorphosis; vestibular roof and epineural veil have ruptured (*after
MacBride*, 1903). 1, surface ectoderm; 2, roof of vestibule; 3, vestibular cavity; 4, floor of
vestibule; 5, epineural folds; 6, primary podium; 7, left somatocoel; 8, dental sacs; 9, radial
water canal; 10, wall of stomach; 11, nerve ring; 12, radial nerve; 13, outer epithelium of
epineural fold; 14, inner epithelium of epineural fold; 15, water ring; 16, place of breakthrough of definitive pharynx; 17, beginning of stomodaeum; 18, primordium of tooth; 19,
primordia of spines; 20, epineural canal; 21, masses of mesenchyme cells; 22, definitive
podia; 23, spines; 24, stomodaeum; 25, epaulettes; 26. remains of pluteal arms; 27, esophagus; 28, intestine; 29, stomach.

the so-called spatulate or bat-shaped spines that form a circle around the
ambitus (Fig. 219*B*).   In other urchins there may be juvenile three- and
four-pronged spines on the aboral surface, which are later shed (Fig.
215*B*).   Exhaustive accounts of the development of the spines and
skeletal plates in regular urchins have been published by von Ubisch
(1913a) and Gordon 1926a, 1929) for several different species.   The
newly metamorphosed urchin retains the larval digestive tract but lacks
mouth, anus, and periproct.   It will be perceived that the oral surface of
the young urchin comes from the left side of the pluteus by way of the
echinus rudiment, while the aboral surface is the right side of the larva.
However, the proportions of the two sides of the pluteus contributing to
the urchin vary in different species.

Following metamorphosis, development continues.   The definitive
podia, of which five pairs may be present at metamorphosis, arise in pairs
to the oral side of the primary podia which are forced more and more
aborally and eventually degenerate to mere bumps.   The terminal
plates have meantime grown around them so that they emerge through a
pore in the latter.   More and more ambulacral and interambulacral
plates form, to the aboral side of those already present, between the
latter and the apical system, so that the corona gets more and more
extensive, while the apical system of plates, which at metamorphosis
covers the entire aboral surface, comes to cover a smaller and smaller area
of surface.   The ambulacral plates are laid down to the aboral side of the
developing definitive podia in such a way as to leave a single pore for
each podium; but later this pore becomes divided into two pores by
calcareous growth.   A single circular plate appears in the small space
at the apical pole between the genitals and increases in size for a time,
establishing the periproct (Fig. 218).   It then decreases by resorption
and small plates appear in the spaces thus provided; but in *Arbacia* the
four periproct plates form as such.   The peristome expands in part by
resorption of skeletal material around its edge.   It appears that primitively each interambulacrum terminates at the peristome by a single
plate, but this is usually resorbed later.

The digestive tract undergoes great changes, beginning with the
absorption of the esophagus.   The center of the original vestibular floor
sinks inward to form a new mouth and a stomodaeum that unites with a
slight process put out by the stomach to become the definitive pharynx.
The stomach elongates and becomes the first circuit of the intestine; it
further constricts off the siphon along its inner side.   The larval intestine
which has long curved back along the stomach elongates in the same
direction to become the second circuit of the intestine or large intestine
that eventually grows along the mesentery to reach the center of the
aboral surface, then establishing an anus (Fig. 217*A–D*).   Most accounts

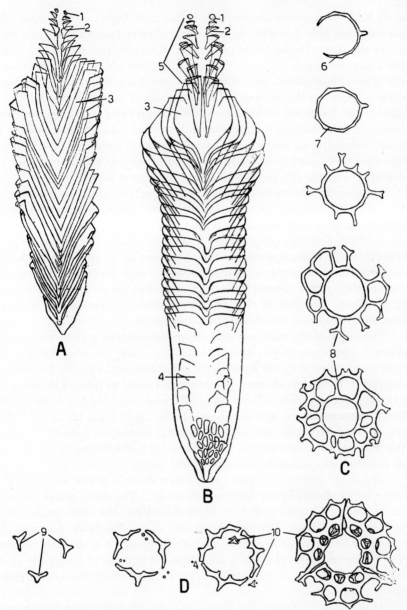

FIG. 214.—Embryology (continued). *A*, stage in the development of a tooth. *B*, later stage of tooth. (*A, B, after Devanesen*, 1922.) *C*, five stages in the formation of the end disk of the primary podia. *D*, four stages in the development of the end disk of a definitive podium. (*C, D, after Gordon*, 1926.) 1, granule stage of cone; 2, triangular stage of cone; 3, cones formed; 4, cones fused to form hard end of tooth; 5, aboral formative end of tooth; 6, triradiate spicule; 7, spicule united into ring; 8, formation of fenestrated plate; 9, three triangles to form end disk; 10, frame forming.

state that the anus breaks through rather late, but Gordon (1926a) discovered that it is probably present soon after metamorphosis, concealed under the central plate of the periproct. The alterations in the digestive tract involve much degeneration and phagocytosis, by amoebocytes of the original epithelium, that formed the larval digestive tract, and regeneration from remaining cells. In the change of orientation at metamorphosis, the formerly vertical mesentery supporting the digestive tract takes on a horizontal orientation and is much altered and broken up later, remaining as the strands attaching the festoons of the definitive intestine to the test. The left somatocoel becomes the oral part of the definitive coelom, the right somatocoel the aboral part.

The gonads develop from the genital stolon, a strand of cells budded off from the left somatocoel, although it is not clear whether the actual primordial germ cells in the strand have this origin. The strand accompanied by a coelomic evagination of the left somatocoel that soon separates from the latter approaches the aboral surface in the interradius that contains the madreporite. Genital stolon and accompanying genital coelom then curve around beneath the genital plates and each forms a ring. From this genital ring the five gonads are budded off into the interambulacra and the stolon then disappears.

The origin of the main parts of the water-vascular system was already given. The stone canal, early formed as a sort of stem for the left hydrocoel, fuses with the hydroporic canal leading to the hydropore and derived from the left axocoel; the combined canal so formed becomes the definitive stone canal. The ampulla derived from the left axocoel (Fig. 211A) remains as the ampulla beneath the madreporic plate into which the adult stone canal opens. The original hydropore persists as one of the pores of the madreporite, and additional pores derive by subdivision of the original hydropore and hydroporic canal.

The axial sinus or coelomic space that surrounds the axial gland in other echinoderms is wanting in echinoids. The axial gland develops in the wall of a vesicle called by MacBride (1903) the madreporic vesicle and by von Ubisch (1913b) the dorsal sac. MacBride thought this vesicle to be the right hydrocoel, but undoubtedly it is the right axocoel. The lumen of the axial gland is therefore the remains of the cavity of the right axocoel and so is the coelomic cavity into which the aboral end of the gland extends.

Muscle fibers, connective tissue, and coelomocytes apparently originate from the secondary mesenchyme and further from mesenchyme constantly given off during development from the walls of spaces of coelomic nature. The haemal system seems to arise simply as spaces in the mesenchyme.

It has been illuminatingly pointed out by von Ubisch (1913b) that in

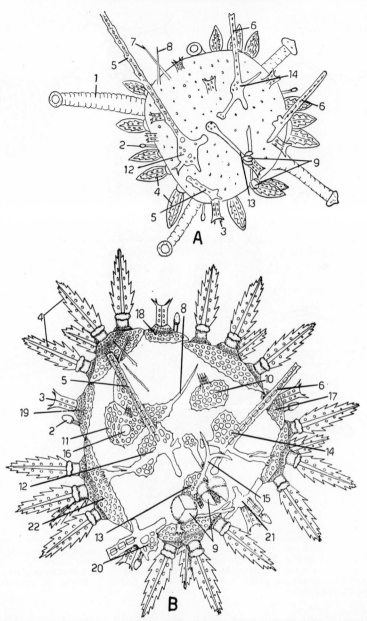

Fig. 215.—Formation of test. *A, Mespilia globulus,* just after metamorphosis, aboral view. *B,* same, later, aboral view. (*A, B, after Onoda,* 1936.) 1, primary podium; 2, sphaeridium; 3, four-pointed juvenile spines; 4, definitive spines; 5, remains of postero-dorsal rod; 6, remains of postoral rod; 7, remains of anterolateral rod; 8, remains of preoral rod; 9, pedicellariae; 10, genital plate 1; 11, genital plate 2; 12, genital plate 3; 13, genital plate 4; 14, genital plate 5; 15, remains of posterior transverse rod; 16, hydropore; 17, terminal plate I; 18, terminal II; 19, terminal III; 20, terminal IV; 21, terminal V; 22 interambucral plate. Plate numbers after Lovén's system.

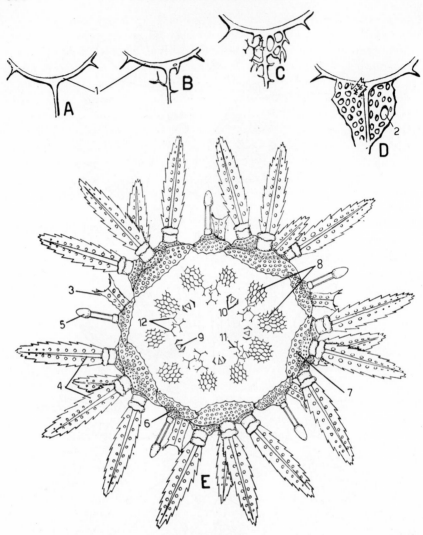

Fig. 216.—Formation of test (continued). *A–D*, your stages in the formation of genital plate 2 from the dorsal arch (*after Onoda*, 1931). *E*, young *Mespilia globulus*, oral view of same specimen as Fig. 215*B* (*after Onoda*, 1936). 1, dorsal arch; 2, hydropore; 3, four-pointed juvenile spines; 4, definitive spines; 5, sphaeridium; 6, ambulacral plate; 7, primordial interambulacral plate; 8, plates for buccal podia; 9, tooth; 10, pyramids; 11, rotule; 12, epiphyses.

the newly metamorphosed urchin the skeletal plates have a bilateral arrangement (Fig. 218) that agrees neither with the Lovén nor the Carpenter scheme of orientation. This axis passes through Lovén's ambulacrum II or Carpenter's C and through Lovén's interambulacrum 5 or Carpenter's AB. Von Ubisch's diagram (Fig. 219*C*) further shows that the arrangement of large and small ambulacral plates around the peristome is more symmetrical with respect to his axis than with respect to Lovén's axis.   In both the von Ubisch and Lovén schemes the madreporic plate is to one side of the bilateral axis, whereas in the Carpenter scheme it is symmetrical with regard to the bilateral axis.   It appears acceptable to regard the von Ubisch bilateral axis as representing the original axis of symmetry and the asymmetrical position of the madreporic plate as explicable on the undoubtedly correct assumption that there were originally two madreporic plates, symmetrically paired, of which the present one is the surviving left plate.   This original axis of symmetry represents a torsion of 90 degrees from the plane of symmetry of the pluteus.   This torsion is obviously due to the suppression of the right side during echinoderm development, so that the left side of the pluteus becomes the oral surface of the adult.

The chief articles on the development of irregular echinoids are those of Théel (1892) on the sand dollar *Echinocyamus pusillus* and of MacBride (1914, 1918) on the heart urchin *Echinocardium cordatum;* Gordon has also described the development of the skeleton of *Echinocardium cordatum* (1926b) and of the sand dollar *Echinarachnius parma* (1929). Up to metamorphosis the development of irregular echinoids is identical in all essential points with that of regular urchins.   In *Echinocardium* the primary podia are rudimentary from the beginning and there is no trace of a lantern.   In sand dollars, the primary podia are well developed, and the lantern arises as in regular urchins except that compasses are entirely wanting.   The periproct in newly metamorphosed irregular echinoids is centrally located inside the apical system of plates.   All the changes in shape and the migrations of the periproct and peristome in irregular echinoids occur after metamorphosis by processes of differential growth.

In echinoids that brood their young and apparently also in a number of other species, as judged by their large and yolky eggs, development is "direct," that is, a free larval stage is more or less omitted, and metamorphosis may occur after 2 or 3 days of development.   The best-described case is that of the echinometrid *Heliocidaris erythrogramma* (Mortensen, 1921) with an oval, uniformly ciliated larva, devoid of a hydropore and a larval skeleton.   The vestibule never closes, and therefore the primary podia and spines soon protrude through the opening and widen it, thus accomplishing metamorphosis.   Several strange peculiarities of development are ascribed by Mortensen (1921) to the sand dollar *Peronella lesueuri*, in which the larva does not get beyond the two-armed stage.   The larval mouth and esophagus are said to have no connection with the stomach, so that the larva cannot feed, and to serve as vestibule so that the young urchin emerges through the mouth.   It is presumable that brooding species omit the pluteus stage and proceed directly to metamorphosis, but no information is available.

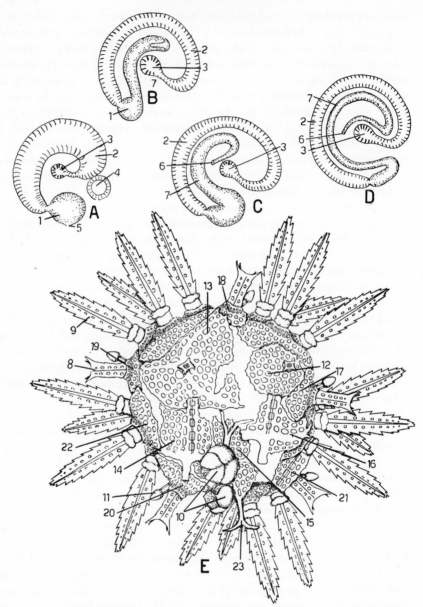

Fig. 217.—Embryology (continued). *A–D* four stages in the postmetamorphic transformation of the digestive tract (*after MacBride*, 1903). *E, Mespilia globulus*, aboral view, 20 days after metamorphosis, showing further development of the test (*after Onoda*, 1936). 1, larval intestine; 2, stomach; 3, definitive mouth and stomodaeum; 4, position of larval mouth; 5, position of larval anus; 6, definitive anus; 7, definitive intestine; 8, juvenile spines; 9, definitive spines; 10, pedicellariae; 11, sphaeridium; 12, genital plate 1; 13, genital 2; 14, genital 3; 15, genital 4; 16, genital 5; 17, terminal plate I; 18, terminal II; 19, terminal III; 20, terminal IV; 21, terminal V; 22, interambulacral plate; 23. remains of posterior transverse rod. Plate numbers after Lovén's system.

**17. Regeneration.**—All the external appendages—spines, pedicellariae, and podia—readily regenerate, and damage to the test is repaired, but apparently sphaeridia are not replaced (Delage, 1903). Spines broken off complete themselves (Borig, 1933); a calcareous mesh covers the broken surface, and then the spine begins to elongate as in normal growth. The regenerated part is much more slender for a time than the original stump, but gradually the size difference is eliminated. Upon removal of an entire spine a new one arises on the same tubercle, and the tubercle by resorption reduces in size to fit the newly forming spine, which is much more slender than the definitive spine (Borig, 1933). Probably if a spine breaks off too near the tubercle, the stump will be shed and an entire new spine formed (Krizenecky, 1916). Under unfavorable conditions urchins may shed most or all of their spines and regenerate a new set (Chadwick, 1929; Hobson, 1930), which are more slender for a time than usual in the species. Such fine-spined individuals have been collected in nature by students of echinoids. Swan (1952) found that regenerated spines may differ from nonregenerated ones in microscopic details, especially the number of wedges in the cross section. Damages to the test are temporarily repaired by the filling of the wound with coelomocytes, after which calcareous deposition sets in (Cuénot, 1906). Kindred (1924) cut out pieces of the test 1 cm. square and found that the opening was gradually closed by a membrane, growing from the cut margins and covering the hole in about 2 weeks. This membrane, delicate at first but firmer later, was found to consist of a syncytium composed of phagocytic coelomocytes to which were added dermal cells from the adjacent body wall. The spaces of the mesh were occupied by large numbers of amoebocytes with spherules, possibly carrying nutrition. During the third and fourth weeks following the operation, calcareous material was laid down in several centers in the membrane, without relation to the old calcareous material. According to the experiments of Okada (1926), removed plates of the test are replaced by irregularly arranged plates or a number of small plates so that the normal plate pattern is not reproduced. Crozier (1919) has noted that when the lunules of *Mellita* are broken open by loss of the test margins (probably bitten off by fishes), they are closed again by concrescence of the growing edges of the test.

**18. Extinct Echinoids of Uncertain Position.**—Before beginning the systematic account, it appears desirable to dispose of certain fossils of enigmatic position. *Bothriocidaris*, of which about a dozen specimens are known, comes from Ordovician strata in the Baltic region. The small globular test, reaching a maximum diameter of 18 mm., is composed of hard, thick plates inflexibly united in meridional rows (Fig. 220*A*). The ambulacra consist of two rows of alternating plates, each provided

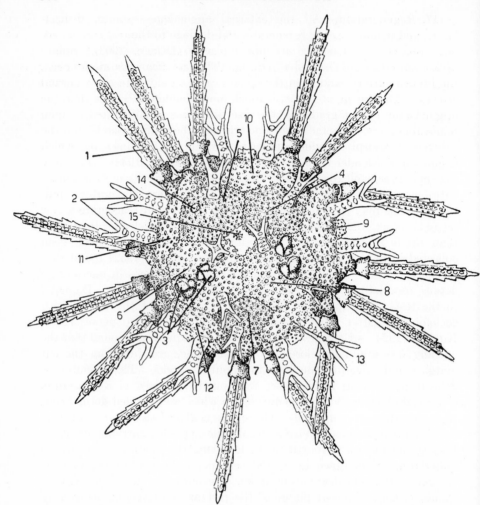

Fig. 218.—Embryology (continued), formation of test. *Psammechinus miliaris*, shortly after metamorphosis (*after Gordon*, 1926). Note bilateral symmetry of apical system, with reference to von Ubisch's primordial axis. 1, definitive spines; 2, juvenile spines; 3, pedicellariae; 4, genital plate 1; 5, genital 2; 6, genital 3; 7, genital 4; 8, genital 5; 9, terminal I; 10, terminal II; 11, terminal III; 12, terminal IV; 13, terminal V; 14, hydropore; 15, beginning of central plate of periproct. Plate numbers after Lovén's system.

with two perforated spine tubercles and pierced by a pore pair from which extended what seems to be a podium, well preserved in one specimen (Mortensen, 1930). The test differs, however, from that of all other echinoids in that the interambulacra consist of but a single row of plates, lacking spine tubercles. The periproct was covered by several small plates and encircled by the terminals, one of which is a madreporite, hence in a radial position (Fig. 220*B*). In no other echinoderm does the madreporite occupy a radial position. There appear to have been no genital plates, and gonopores have not been found; there are, further, no terminal pores in the terminal plates. The interambulacra do not reach the peristome, and the ambulacra terminate at the peristome by a single plate each, devoid of a pore pair. These five ambulacral plates alternate at the peristome edge with five other small plates, of uncertain nature, possibly continuations of the interambulacral rows after an interruption. Whether a lantern was present has not been definitely ascertained.

The systematic position of *Bothriocidaris* has been the subject of argument between leading echinoid specialists. Jackson (1912, 1929) maintains that *Bothriocidaris* is the most primitive known echinoid and ancestral to the entire class. This position was rather generally accepted until it was attacked by Yakovlev (1922) and Mortensen (1928, 1931, Monogr. II, V). Mortensen finally reached the conclusion that *Bothriocidaris* is not an echinoid at all but a cystid. This position was successfully refuted by Hawkins (1929, 1931) and Bather (1931). They have pointed out that *Bothriocidaris* cannot be a cystid as it lacks food grooves and brachioles. In its possession of spines, tubercles, and ambulacral plates pierced by pore pairs, *Bothriocidaris* appears distinctly echinoid. Its several peculiarities—radial position of the madreporite, lack of genital plates and gonopores, single row of interambulacral plates— throw grave doubts on Jackson's belief that it is *the* ancestral echinoid. Mortensen has pointed out that equally old fossil echinoids of more typical structure are now known. One may conclude that *Bothriocidaris* is a blind offshoot of very early echinoid stock and should be placed by itself in a separate order or even subclass of Echinoidea.

*Eothuria* (MacBride and Spencer, 1938) bears a close resemblance to lepidocentroids such as *Aulechinus* and *Ectinechinus* (see below) and comes from the same geological era. The test is somewhat elongated with two rows of ambulacral plates, wide interambulacral areas composed of many, irregularly arranged plates (Fig. 220D, E), and a periproct of many small plates without any definite apical system except for the madreporite, interradially placed. There were ambulacral grooves, open to the exterior, closed to the interior. *Eothuria* has two peculiarities that differentiate it from recognized groups of echinoids. Each ambu-lacral plate is pierced with many pores (Fig. 220C) for the passage of the podia, and a typical lantern is wanting, being represented by 10 thin plates united in pairs and possibly interpretable as teeth (Fig. 220D). The original describers regarded *Eothuria* as a holothuroid intermediate between holothuroids and echinoids, but it is difficult to conceive of a holothuroid with a complete theca of plates. *Eothuria* would seem to be some sort of echinoid not assignable to any of the recognized orders.

**19. Subclass Regularia and Order Lepidocentroida.**—As already learned, the echinoids are divisible into two subclasses, the regular or endocyclic forms and the irregular or exocyclic ones. In the former the test generally has a rounded profile and is pentamerously symmetrical with regularly alternating ambulacra and interambulacra, the peristome and periproct occupy central positions at the oral and aboral poles, respectively, and the periproct is encircled by the apical system of plates. The regular urchins begin with the order Lepidocentroida, which includes the most primitive known true echinoids (extinct), probably ancestral to all other echinoids or at least typifying the characters of an ancestral form. The order includes two families, the Lepidocentridae, entirely extinct, and the Echinothuriidae. The outstanding features of this order are the flexibility of the test, resulting from the imbrication of the plates, and the continuation of the ambulacral plates on the peristome to the edge of the mouth, a condition recalling the complete theca of Pelmatozoa. In the Lepidocentridae the number of rows in each ambulacrum varies from 2 to 20, and the interambulacra consist of 3 to over 40 rows; in the most primitive forms the plates are irregularly arranged, not disposed in rows. The primordial interambulacral plate (noted above as present in the newly metamorphosed urchin but usually disappearing later) persists although the interambulacra may be excluded from the peristome. The ambulacra are deeply grooved centrally (Fig. 221*B*), a condition recalling the food grooves of Pelmatozoa, and the radial water canals are imbedded in the test, being excluded from contact with the coelom by inner projecting ridges from the ambulacra (Fig. 221*D*). A well-developed lantern has been found in many cases. Small, slender spines were present, but pedicellariae have been discovered to only a limited extent. The apical system of plates appears to have been imperfect, not yet having reached the typical echinoid condition, or perhaps has failed to preserve as well as the rest of the test. Over 20 genera (listed with characters in Piveteau's treatise, 1953) of the Lepidocentridae have been described, of which two or three are of especial interest. *Aulechinus* from the Upper Ordovician of Scotland (MacBride and Spencer, 1938) probably depicts for us the general appearance of an ancestral echinoid. The five ambulacra, of two rows of plates each, run symmetrically over the small, flexible, globular test, and between them the wide interambulacra consist of a number of irregularly arranged plates (Fig. 221*A*). The periproct is composed of a considerable number of small plates, some of which form a sort of anal pyramid for the slightly excentric anus. The apical system is not differentiated; the five end plates of the ambulacra represent the terminals, although not differentiated as such; there are no genitals except the madreporite found in the typical interradial position (Fig. 221*A*). The center of each ambulacrum is grooved. On the peristome each ambulacral plate bears two podial pores but only one pore on the test, located near the groove, from which

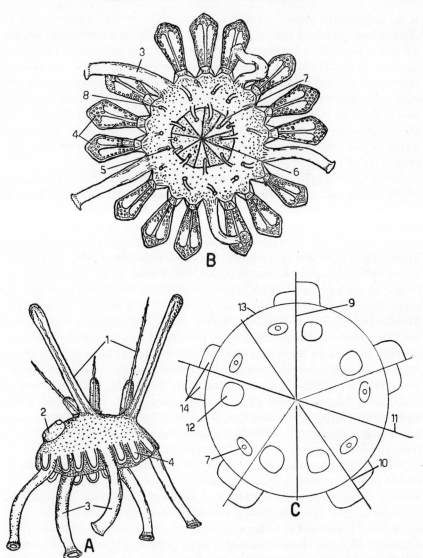

FIG. 219.—Embryology (concluded). *A, Arbacia punctulata* in process of metamor phosis. *B, Arbacia punctulata*, shortly after metamorphosis, oral view. (*A, B, after Garman and Colton*, 1883.) *C*, scheme of symmetry of young urchin (*after von Ubisch*, 1913b). 1, remains of pluteal arms; 2, oral lobe of pluteus; 3, primary podia; 4, juvenile spines; 5, peristome; 6, teeth; 7, buccal podia; 8, definitive podia; 9, Lovén's axis; 10. Carpenter's axis; 11, von Ubisch's primordial axis; 12, buccal plates; 13, edge of peristome: 14, large and small ambulacral plates at peristome edge.

it is imperfectly closed off (Fig. 221*B*). The radial water canals of *Aulechinus* run along the bottoms of the ambulacral grooves and are cut off from the coelom by inward projections of the ambulacra that meet medially (Fig. 221*D*). Writers on *Aulechinus* consider that this condition represents a stage in the alteration of the radial water canals from the external condition found in most echinoderms to the internal condition peculiar to the echinoids. Disappearance of the internal projections of the ambulacral plates as found in *Aulechinus* would leave the radial water canals free on the inner surface of the test, as in present echinoids (Fig. 221*C–E*).

Some other Lepidocentridae of interest are the genera *Ectinechinus, Myriastiches,* and *Palaeodiscus. Ectinechinus* (MacBride and Spencer, 1938) was elongated along von Ubisch's primordial plane with anterior peristome and posterior periproct (Fig. 222*A*) but was otherwise very similar to *Aulechinus* with two rows of ambulacral plates, numerous irregular interambulacral plates, periproct of numerous plates, no definite apical system except the madreporite, and radial water canals shut off from the coelom by inward projections of the ambulacral plates. It came from the same stratum as *Aulechinus. Myriastiches* from the Middle Ordovician of England (Sollas, 1899) was similarly constructed with two rows of ambulacral plates, pore pairs *between* these plates, not through them, very numerous small interambulacral plates in more than 40 rows, and ambulacral grooves. In *Palaeodiscus* (Hawkins and Hampton, 1927), also from the same strata as the foregoing, with two rows of ambulacral plates pierced by pore pairs and eight columns of interambulacral plates at the ambitus, the internal projections of the ambulacral plates that in the preceding genera cut off the radial water canals from the coelom are in process of disappearance.

The Echinothuriidae are a family of mostly deep-sea echinoids of rather large size with a flexible leathery test of which the plates either overlap or are separated by strips of leathery body wall (Fig. 222*B*). Ambulacra and interambulacra consist of two plate rows each. The ambulacral plates are of a characteristic type, considered a variant of the diadematoid type, compounded of a large primary plate flanked on each side by a demiplate (Fig. 223*B, C*); the demiplates may undergo considerable displacement during ontogeny. The primordial interambulacral plate at the peristome edge persists throughout life, and the ambulacral plates continue in the peristome to the mouth edge (Fig. 222*B*). The periproct of numerous small plates is usually encircled by a typical apical system, sometimes breaking up into many small plates in later life. The gonopores are mounted on papillae. The hollow spines (Fig. 180*B*) are borne on perforate tubercles and on the oral side may have hoof ends (Fig. 179*J*) or may be covered with a glandular bag

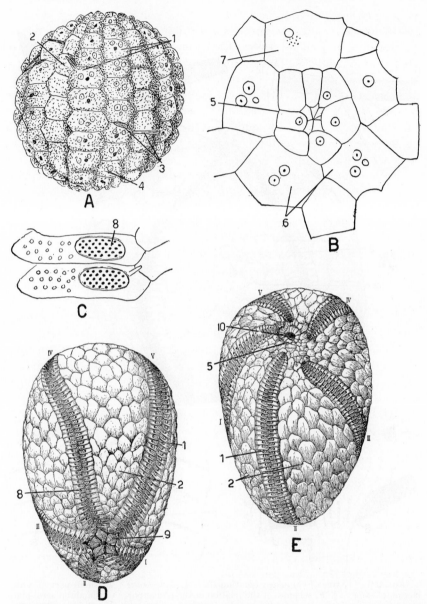

Fig. 220.—Archaic Echinoidea. *A, Bothriocidaris.* *B*, apical system of *Bothriocidaris.* (*A, B, after Mortensen,* 1930.) *C*, two ambulacral plates of *Eothuria*, showing pore areas. *D, Eothuria*, showing peristome. *E, Eothuria*, showing periproct. (*C–E, after MacBride and Spencer,* 1938.) 1, double row of ambulacrum; 2, interambulacrum; 3, remnants of spines; 4, pore pair; 5, periproct; 6, terminals; 7, madreporite; 8, pore area; 9, mouth plates; 10, anus. Ambulacra numbered I to V in *D* and *E* after Lovén's system.

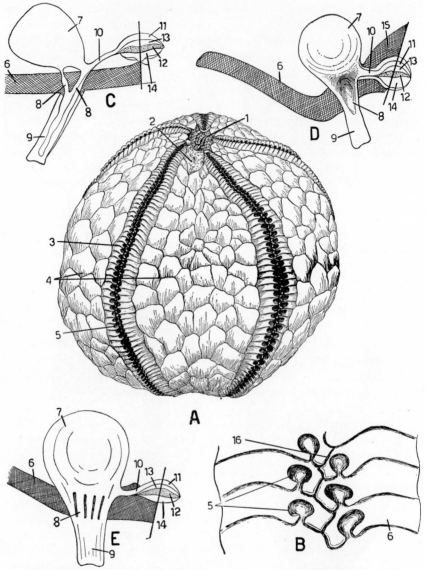

Fig. 221.—Extinct Echinoidea (continued).  *A, Aulechinus.*  *B,* small part of ambulacrum of same.  *C–E,* schemes of the relation of the podial pores to the ambulacral plate. *C,* ordinary urchin.  *D, Aulechinus.*  *E, Eothuria.*  (*All after MacBride and Spencer,* 1938.)  1, periproct; 2, madreporite; 3, ambulacrum; 4, interambulactum; 5, ambulacral pores; 6, ambulacral plate; 7, ampulla of podium; 8, canals through ambulacral plate; 9, podium; 10, podial branch of radial water canal; 11, radial water canal; 12, radial nerve; 13, hyponeural sinus; 14, epineural sinus; 15, inner ridge of ambulacral plate; 16, ambulacral groove.

(Fig. 179*H*, *K*); spines tipped with poison bags (Fig. 179*G*) very toxic to man are common in this family. The family is richly provided with pedicellariae, including the special dactylous type (Fig. 183*A*, *B*). Features of the internal anatomy are the meridional muscle sheets (Fig. 190*J*) and the large sausage-shaped Stewart's organs (Fig. 196*A*). This family has been especially treated by the Sarasins (1888) and Schurig (1906).

Representative echinothuriid genera are *Phormosoma*, with very deep areoles to the oral spine tubercles; *Tromikosoma* ( = *Echinosoma*), with no or rudimentary gills; *Araeosoma*, with dactylous pedicellariae; *Asthenosoma*, with thick aboral poison bags (Fig. 179*G*); *Calveriosoma* (Fig. 222*C*), without poison bags or dactylous pedicellariae; and *Sperosoma*, with eight rows of ambulacral plates orally, caused by displacement of poriferous and separation of nonporiferous areas.

**20. Order Melonechinoida.**—This wholly extinct order from the lower Carboniferous comprises a single family, the Palaeechinidae, with a high, mostly spherical, rigid test. Within the family the ambulacra evolve by displacement of the original two rows of primary plates into a condition of many small plates (Fig. 223*A*). There are four, six, or more (up to 11) rows of interambulacral plates. As in the preceding order, the ambulacra continue to the mouth. Gills were wanting.

**21. Order Cidaroidea.**—This is a very distinctively characterized group. The hard, rigid, and beautifully symmetrical test, of small to moderate size, is of globular shape, somewhat flattened at the poles. The intact cidaroid (Fig. 173*C*) is recognized at once by the large, widely separated, primary spines, contrasting markedly with the numerous small, secondary spines, some of which, the scrobicular spines, form a protecting circle around the base of each primary spine (Fig. 179*B*). Examination of the cleaned test shows that these primary spines are borne on the interambulacra only, one to each interambulacral plate (Fig. 189*A*, *B*). Each of the latter therefore carries a large, conspicuous tubercle, with a perforate mamelon, crenulations around the mamelon base, and wide areole, encircled by the small tubercles for the scrobicular spines (Fig. 189*B*). The ambulacral plates are all of the simple, primary sort, each with a pore pair and with numerous small tubercles (Fig. 189*B*). Both ambulacra and interambulacra continue on the peristome to the mouth edge (Fig. 173*E*). The apical system has the typical construction, and the periproct is provided with small plates; studies of young cidaroids have shown that these plates are not preceded by one large plate (Mortensen, 1927), as is often the case in other regular echinoids. The primary spines differ from those of other echinoids in being provided with a cortical layer (Fig. 180*A*), often covered with woolly hairs to which foreign particles and organisms adhere. Cidaroids have but two kinds of pedicellariae, the tridentate and globiferous types,

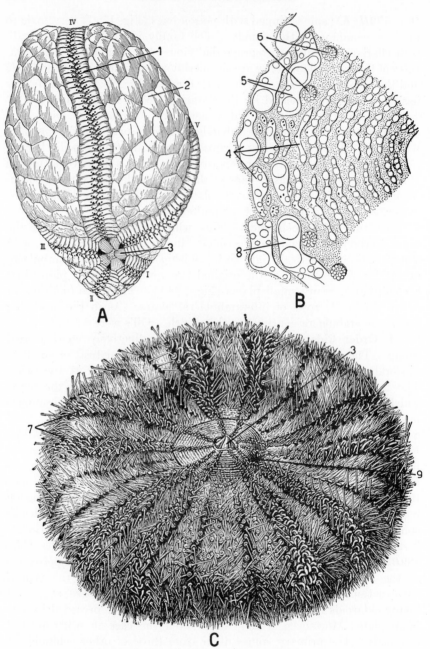

Fig. 222.—Extinct Echinoidea (concluded), Echinothuriidae.  A, Ectinechinus (after MacBride and Spencer, 1938).  B, peristome of echinothuriid Calveriosoma hystrix.  C, Calveriosoma hystrix, oral view.  (B, C, after Thomson, 1878.)  1, ambulacrum; 2, interambulacrum; 3, teeth of lantern; 4, ambulacral plates; 5, interambulacral plates; 6, gills; 7, podia; 8, premordial interambulacral plate; 9, peristome.

and the latter differ from the globiferous pedicellariae of other echinoids in that the poison glands are lodged in cavities in the skeletal valves (Fig. 181*G*, *H*). The perignathic girdle is distinctive in that the main projections for attachment of lantern muscles (apophyses) are interradial in position (Fig. 190*G*). Gills and sphaeridia are wanting. A distinctive feature of the internal anatomy is the presence of five bushy Stewart's organs appended to the lantern (Fig. 196*B*).

All the existing genera are included in the one family Cidaridae, with the characters of the order. Of the considerable number of extinct and living genera, only some of the more common of the latter are mentioned here. *Histocidaris* is distinguished by the absence of globiferous pedicellariae. On the other hand, tridentate pedicellariae are wanting in *Aporocidaris*, *Ctenocidaris*, and *Notocidaris*, and the globiferous pedicellariae of these genera lack an end tooth, having a large subterminal pore to each valve bordered by serrations. In *Notocidaris* the primary spines are often more or less flattened, and this character is notably present in the recently discovered antarctic species *N. remigera*, which has wide paddle-like primary spines (Fig. 224*D*, Mortensen, 1950). These genera include brooding antarctic species. *Goniocidaris*, one of the largest genera of the family, with about 15 species, is characterized by the terminal disks on the ends of some of the aboral spines (Fig. 179*D*). In *Stereocidaris* the most aboral primary tubercles are rudimentary. The following genera possess tridentate pedicellariae and large and small types of globiferous pedicellariae. In *Cidaris* the large globiferous pedicellariae are provided with an end tooth, whereas in *Stylocidaris*, *Eucidaris*, and *Prioncidaris* this is wanting, and instead there is a large subterminal pore bordered by small teeth. *Phyllacanthus* is distinguished by the semicircular shape of the scrobicular tubercles.

The family Cidaridae includes a number of fossil genera, and there is further an entirely extinct cidaroid family, the Archaeocidaridae, with two genera. These had a flexible test with imbricating plates and four to many rows of interambulacral plates, but plainly show the typical large primary tubercles characteristic of the order.

It should be mentioned that there are a number of generic names among echinoids (nearly 35) ending in *cidaris* that do not belong to the Cidaroidea.

**22. Order Aulodonta.**—This order begins the systematics of the more typical regular urchins. The coronal plates do not continue onto the peristome where plates of the ambulacral system are represented only by the 10 buccal plates, supporting the buccal podia. The ambulacral plates of the corona are generally compound, of the diadematoid type (Fig. 191*A*). Gills and broad gill cuts are present. The spine tubercles are perforate; the spines lack a cortex and are solid or provided with a

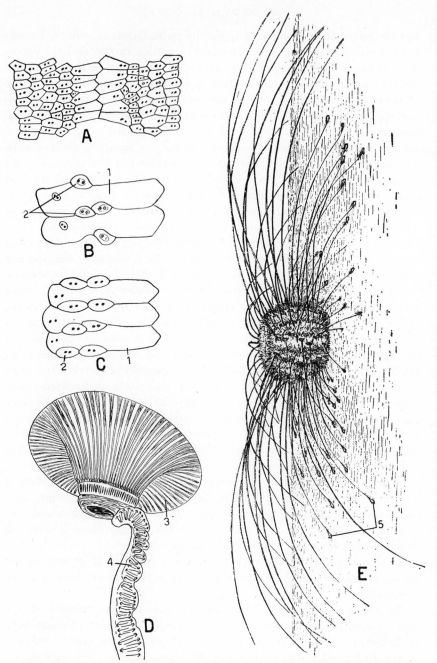

Fig. 223.—Echinothuriidae, Melonechinoida, Aspidodiadematidae, Micropygidae. *A*, ambulacrum of *Melonechinus* (*after Jackson*, 1912). *B*, *C*, echinothuriid ambulacral plates (*after Mortensen, Monogr.*). *D*, umbrella podium of *Micropyga* (*after Döderlein*, 1906). *E*, *Plesiodiadema indicum* (*after Mortensen*, 1923). 1, primary plate; 2, demi-plates; 3, spicules supporting umbrella; 4, anchor spicules of stalk; 5, expanded tips of oral spines.

narrow lumen. Globiferous pedicellaria are frequently wanting, but the other three types are abundantly represented. When present the globiferous pedicellariae lack the large terminal teeth or fangs characteristic of the globiferous pedicellariae of many cidaroid genera. Sphaeridia occur along the whole length of the ambulacra. The name of the order derives from details of the lantern. The epiphyses are small and do not meet above the tooth, leaving a large open space in each pyramid, and the teeth lack keels. Small auricles, more or less separated, are present on the perignathic girdle.

The order includes four families, of which one is chiefly extinct. The Aspidodiadematidae are characterized by the very long, slender, downwardly curved primary spines whose tips, widened in the case of those of the oral side, touch the ground (Fig. 223E). The test is high and generally delicate and fragile. The spines are solid but peculiarly constructed, having numerous transverse partitions connected by vertical strands. Each plate of the corona bears one large primary tubercle. The terminal plates of the apical system are all insert, so that this system forms a continuous ring around the periproct. Globiferous pedicellariae are wanting, but poison glands occur on claviform types derivable from the ophiocephalous category. The two existing genera, *Plesiodiadema* and *Aspidodiadema*, are distinguished by the ambulacral plates that are simple in the former, compound of the diadematoid type in the latter. The several species of each of these genera inhabit deeper waters and hence are known chiefly from the dredgings of collecting expeditions. The striking natural appearance of these urchins is indicated by Mortensen's (1923) much copied figure of *Plesiodiadema indicum* (Fig. 223E), drawn by him from life from a specimen dredged at 290 m., off the Kei Islands.

The family Pedinidae is mostly extinct, represented by only one existing genus, *Caenopedina*, with about 10 species, mostly limited to deeper waters. This genus differs from the preceding genera in the flatter test, exsert terminals, and spines of ordinary construction; the primaries are solid and the others have a narrow lumen. In the two remaining families all the spines are hollow. The family Micropygidae, with one genus *Micropyga*, containing two species, is distinguished by the remarkable alteration of some of the podia, those emerging from the outermost pore pairs of the ambulacra. In these (Fig. 223D) the terminal disk is enormously expanded, resembling an umbrella, and supported by special radiating spicules, arranged like spokes. The highly extensile stalks of these podia contain anchor spicules. The outer surface of the umbrella disks appears of glandular nature and probably secretes an adhesive substance. The two species of *Micropyga* inhabit deeper waters in the Indo-Malay region.

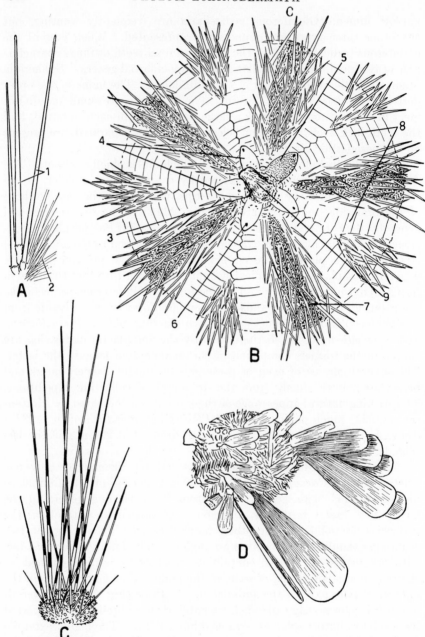

FIG. 224.—Cidaridae, Diadematidae, Saleniidae.  *A*, small bit of *Echinothrix diadema*, Indo-Pacific, showing contrast of aboral primary and secondary spines.  *B*, *Astropyga pulvinata*, Panamic region, showing spineless areas of test.  *C*, *Salenia goesiana*, West Indies.  *D*, *Notocidaris remigera*, antarctic (*after Mortensen*, 1950).  1, primary spines; 2, secondary spines; 3, periproct; 4, genital plates; 5, madreporite; 6, gonopore; 7, ambulacral areas; 8, interambulacral areas; 9, anal cone.

The Diadematidae is the most important and familiar aulodont family; its members live mostly in littoral and sublittoral zones in tropical and subtropical areas as the Indo-Pacific, the West Indies, and the California-Panamic region. This family is distinguished by the slender, fragile, hollow spines, often very long, armed with whorls of minute teeth (Fig. 176E). The terminals are generally insert. Globiferous pedicellariae are mostly wanting, but the other types are usually richly developed, especially the claviform variety. Diadematid urchins are generally of large size and purple or black in color with, in some genera, spots or streaks of a brilliant blue color along the aboral interambulacra. The main genus *Diadema* (= *Centrechinus*)[1] is noted for its very long primary spines that may reach a foot in length. These spines are very dangerous, as the sharp tips easily penetrate the skin and further sting badly, causing intense pain; apparently some sort of toxin accompanies the penetration of the spine tip, although the source of this is not clear. The terminals next the madreporite are exsert and the periproct is naked with a conspicuous anal cone. Very common species are *D. setosum* and *savignyi* from the Indo-Pacific and *D. antillarum* (Fig. 176D) from the West Indies and Florida. The test is somewhat flexible in *Astropyga*, *Chaetodiadema*, and two other diadematid genera, because of imbrication of the plates, but this fact does not relate the Diadematidae to the Echinothuriidae. The test of *Astropyga* is large and flattened, and the elongated genital plates give a star-like appearance to the aboral center, heightened by the fact that a sunken spineless interambulacral area continues from each genital plate toward the ambitus, soon bifurcating. The bright-blue spots are located on these naked areas. *Astropyga radiata* is widespread in the Indo-Pacific region, and *A. pulvinata* (Fig. 224B) inhabits shallow waters on the Pacific shores of tropical America. In *Chaetodiadema*, the test is also large, flattened, and somewhat flexible, with naked interambulacral areas on the aboral side. In the only common species, *C. granulatum*, Indo-Malay region, there are well-developed spines only around the ambitus, so that much of the oral and aboral surfaces contrast with the ambitus by reason of their short, fine spines. In *Centrostephanus* with rather large, flattened, but inflexible, test without spineless aboral interambulacral areas, long aboral primary spines are often present, as in *Diadema*. *Centrostephanus* differs from other diadematid genera in having globiferous pedicellariae, mostly with stalk glands. The most common species, *C. longispinus*, found in the Mediterranean and eastern Atlantic, is provided aborally with the brightly colored rotating spines already mentioned (page 438). In

---

[1] The long *Diadema-Centrechinus* controversy between Mortensen and other specialists on echinoids has finally been settled by the International Commission on Zoological Nomenclature in favor of *Diadema*, thus supporting Mortensen.

*Echinothrix* with firm, flattened test, large spines are confined to the broad interambulacra, and the narrow ambulacra bear only fine spines (Fig. 224*A*), elongated aborally and capable of inflicting severe wounds. The spines of this genus are often beautifully banded.   The two species, *Echinothrix calamaris* and *diadema*, are of wide occurrence in the Indo–West Pacific area.

**23. Order Stirodonta.**—In this order, as in the Aulodonta, the epiphyses of the lantern are small and do not unite above the teeth, but the teeth are keeled.   The test is always inflexible and not much flattened at the poles.   The perignathic girdle gives rise to auricles in the radial positions and is reduced to a ridge or wall in the interradii.   The spines are solid with or without a cortex, and globiferous pedicellariae are generally wanting.   The ambulacral plates when compound are of the diadematoid or arbacioid types.   The stirodonts are mostly extinct, consisting of four wholly extinct families, two others each represented by only one living species, and two families, the Saleniidae and Arbaciidae, which contain a number of living members.

The Saleniidae have rounded tests of rather small size; among the extinct members are found some of the smallest echinoids known, with a test diameter of 1 to 3 mm.   The outstanding characteristic of the family is the large plate (badly called suranal plate) that occupies the aboral pole and presents a concavity toward the periproct that is thus pushed markedly to one side (Fig. 190*A*).   The peristome is covered with small imbricating plates.   The spination reminds one of cidaroids; the primary spines are long, slender, and more or less thorny, covered with a cortex, whereas the secondaries are small and flattened, without a cortex.   The existing saleniids belong to two genera, *Salenocidaris* with simple ambulacral plates and *Salenia* with ambulacral plates composed of two full-length primary plates.   In both genera each plate of the corona carries one large primary tubercle.   Members of both genera inhabit deeper waters and are obtained only by dredging.   The best-known saleniid is *Salenia goesiana* ( = *pattersoni*) from the West Indies at depths of 90 to 540 m., a pretty and very small urchin, white with long aboral primary spines, banded in red and white (Fig. 224*C*).

The outstanding characteristic of the Arbaciidae is the provision of the periproct with four (sometimes five) large plates that act like valves for the central anus (Fig. 190*B*).   The members of this family are of small to moderate size with a rough or papillate test, bearing chiefly primary spines of moderate length.   Secondary spines are scanty or wanting.   The primary spines of the oral side are usually covered at the tip with shiny cortex forming a cap (Fig. 180*C*).   The ambulacral plates are of the arbacioid type (Fig. 191*C*).   The primordial interambulacral plate persists at the peristome edge throughout life.   The sphaeridia

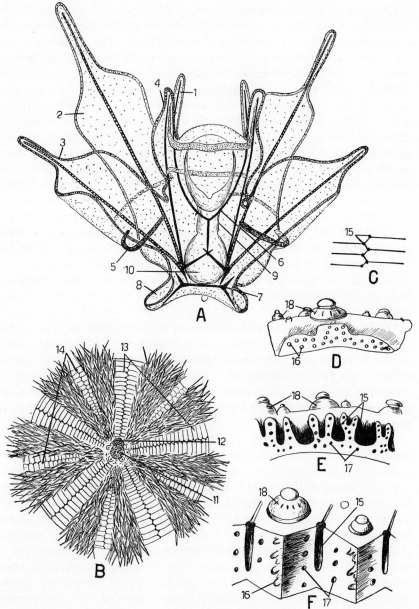

FIG. 225.—Temnopleuridae. *A*, pluteus of a temnopleurid (*after Mortensen*, 1937). *B*, *Mespilia globulus*, Indo-Pacific. *C*, some plates of *Mespilia*, showing pits at angles. *D*, interambulacral plate of *Temnopleurus toreumaticus*, showing dowels. *E*, ambulacral plate of same, showing pits and holes for dowels. *F*, interambulacral plates of *Salmacis bicolor*, showing pits, dowels, and holes. (*D–F, after Duncan*, 1883.) 1, preoral arms; 2, posterodorsal arms; 3, postoral arms; 4, anterolateral arms; 5, epaulette; 6, dorsal arch; 7, posterior transverse rod; 8, posterolateral processes; 9, esophagus; 10, stomach; 11, periproct; 12, madreporite; 13, bare interambulacral areas; 14, bare ambulacral area; 15, pits; 16, dowels; 17, holes for dowels; 18, spine tubercles.

are housed in pit-like depressions along the center of the ambulacra. The genus *Arbacia* is provided with primary spines only and has one sphaeridium at the oral end of each ambulacrum. The members of this genus are mostly littoral forms and are among the most familiar regular urchins. The most common species are *A. punctulata*, found from Cape Cod to Florida and throughout the West Indies, *A. lixula* ( = *pustulosa*) in the Mediterranean and along the Atlantic Coast of Africa, and *A. stellata*, from Lower California to Peru. The genus *Coelopleurus* differs in having 6 to 12 sphaeridia in a row along the center of each ambulacrum. Members of this genus are somewhat larger with longer spines than *Arbacia* species and are conspicuously red or purple. The primary spines are angled, being triangular in cross section (Fig. 180*E*). *Coelopleurus* inhabits deeper waters than *Arbacia* and hence is less familiar. *C. floridanus* occurs from Carolina to the West Indies, mostly at depths of 100 to 500 m., although descending to 2380 m. Another arbaciid that may be mentioned is the black urchin *Tetrapygus niger*, the largest existing arbaciid, reaching a diameter of 75 mm., differing from *Arbacia* in the presence of secondary spines on the interambulacra. This urchin is common in the littoral zone of the coasts of Peru and Chile.

The Stomopneustidae with a periproct of small plates are represented by only one living species, *Stomopneustes variolaris*, a rather large black or violet urchin with polyporous ambulacral plates, common in shallow waters in the Indo-Pacific region. The Phymosomatidae are also extinct except for one species, *Glyptocidaris crenularis*, with oval periproct of small plates and polyporous ambulacral plates, a littoral species found in Japanese waters.

**24. Order Camarodonta.**—In this order the enlarged epiphyses are fused across the top of each pyramid, forming a sort of bar in front of the tooth (Fig. 196*C*) and demarcating a large cavity in the upper half of the pyramid; the teeth are keeled (Fig. 198*D*). In the young the periproct is often occupied by a large plate, as in the Saleniidae, later usually absorbed in part and more or less replaced by small plates. The ambulacra are of the diadematoid or echinoid types, or polyporous variants of these types. The spines are solid without a cortex. All four types of pedicellariae are abundantly present, and the globiferous type is often provided with stalk glands. The auricles of the perignathic girdle generally form arches over radial structures passing onto the corona. Most of the common and familiar regular urchins of the littoral zone belong to this order. The existing species fall into six families: Temnopleuridae, Toxopneustidae, Echinidae, Strongylocentrotidae, Parasaleniidae, and Echinometridae.

In the Temnopleuridae the test is more or less sculptured by pits and

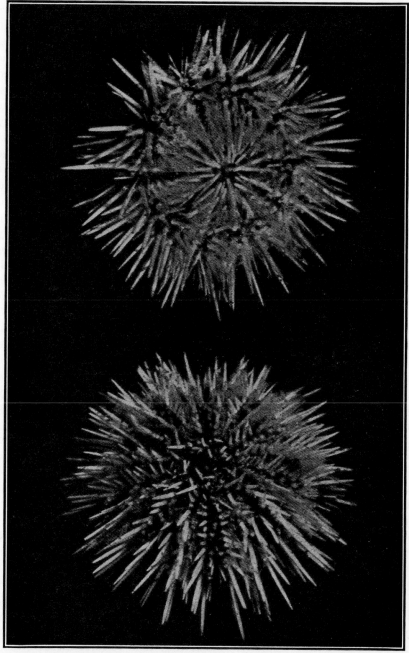

Fig. 226.—Toxopneustidae. *Lytechinus variegatus*, oral view above, aboral view below. *(Photographed alive by Dr. Ralph Buchsbaum, at Beaufort, North Carolina.)*

depressions along the sutures and on the plates, and the plates are sutured together by a system of pits and knobs (Fig. 225C–F). The gill cuts are mostly shallow. The pluteus of this family is notable for the wide, flattened, postoral and posterodorsal arms (Fig. 225A). The Temnopleuridae are mostly small urchins with short, brightly colored or brightly banded spines, limited to tropical and subtropical regions, except the eastern Pacific. *Temnopleurus* with pits on the plates of the aboral part of the corona is exemplified by *T. toreumaticus*, widely distributed in the Indo–West Pacific region. *Salmacis* has the pits reduced to minute pores at the sutural angles of the coronal plates; the most common species, *S. bicolor*, from the Indian Ocean, has very short spines banded in red and yellowish green. In both *Microcyphus* and *Mespilia* there are naked (spineless) areas along the interambulacra, and in the latter they form broad bands extending from the apical system to the oral side. *Mespilia globulus*, a common littoral form of the Malay region, presents a curious appearance from the aboral view with naked radiating interambulacral areas alternating with areas covered with numerous short, red-banded spines (Fig. 225B). In *Amblypneustes*, mostly from Australian coasts, these areas bear small spines. *Pseudechinus*, with a number of species in the Australia–New Zealand and subantarctic region, lacks test sculpture and pores at the plate angles. *Temnotrema*, a genus of small, short-spined urchins with about 12 species on tropical coasts from Japan through the Indo-Pacific area to Hawaii, has conspicuous oblong pits along the plate angles and horizontal plate sutures. The test is heavily sculptured in *Trigonocidaris*, exemplified by *T. albida*, a very small, almost white urchin from moderate depths in the West Indies.

In the Toxopneustidae the test lacks sculpturing and is well covered with spines of short to moderate length. The ambulacral plates are of the echinoid type or a polyporous variant thereof, and the gill cuts are sharp and deep (Fig. 227G). *Nudechinus* and *Lytechinus* have echinoid ambulacral plates, each with a single primary tubercle. The former with naked peristome includes several very small species, confied to the Indo–West Pacific area. *Lytechinus* with heavily plated peristome is of moderate to large size and includes the familiar species, *L. variegatus*, a whitish green urchin of some size (Fig. 226), very common in the West Indies and extending northward to the Carolinas. Other species, also of pale coloration, occur on the west coasts of the Americas in tropical and subtropical waters. In *Toxopneustes* a primary tubercle occurs on every other ambulacral plate only; the three pore pairs of these plates are placed somewhat horizontally, so that they tend to form three vertical series (Fig. 227A). The genus is notable for the excessively numerous globiferous pedicellariae, of two sizes, both with stalk glands. The

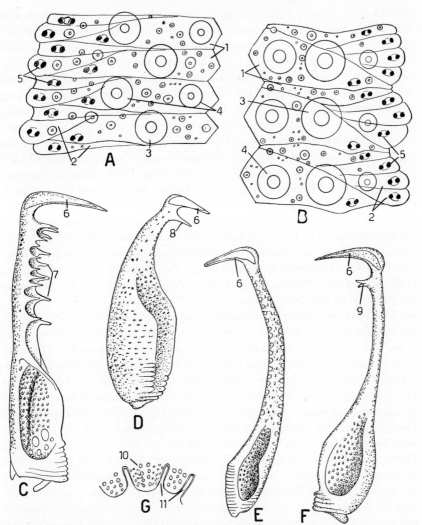

Fig. 227.—Various Camarodonta. *A*, ambulacral plates of *Toxopneustes*. *B*, ambulacral plates of *Sphaerechinus*. *C*, valve of globiferous pedicellaria of *Psammechinus*. *D*, valve of globiferous pedicellaria of *Echinometra*, with one lateral tooth. *E*, valve of globiferous pedicellaria of *Strongylocentrotus*, without lateral teeth. *F*, valve of globiferous pedicellaria of *Echinus*, with unpaired tooth below the end tooth. (*C, F, after Mortensen*, 1903; *ethers after Mortensen, Monogr.*) *G*, edge of peristome of *Tripneustes*, showing sharp, narrow gill cuts. 1, primary plate; 2, demiplates; 3, primary spine tubercles; 4, secondary spine tubercles; 5, pore pair; 6, end tooth; 7, side teeth; 8, side tooth; 9, median tooth; 10, ambulacrum; 11, gill cut.

smaller type, usually held wide open, covers the test, producing a flower-like effect, intensified by a white border, due to densely placed spicules, that edges the valves.  The most common species is *T. pileolus*, widely distributed in the Indo–West Pacific region; on American coasts the genus is represented by *T. roseus*, rose or light purple, in the Panamic region.  The genus *Tripneustes* comprises rather large urchins with long narrow ambulacral plates (Fig. 189*D*), so that primary tubercles occur on every two to four plates and the three pore pairs are horizontally placed, forming distinct vertical (meridional) rows.  In this genus the epiphyses of the lantern throw out a pair of curved processes around each tooth (Fig. 196*D*).  *Tripneustes ventricosus* (Fig. 172*A*) is one of the most common littoral urchins of the West Indian region, and *T. gratilla* is equally common in the western tropical Pacific as far as Hawaii.  *Sphaerechinus* and *Pseudocentrotus* are large urchins with polyporous ambulacral plates bearing four to seven pore pairs in each arc (Fig. 227*B*).  The former has but one species, the well-known *Sphaerechinus granularis*, found in the Mediterranean and along the west coast of Africa to the Gulf of Guinea.  *Pseudocentrotus*, distinguished by the oral widening of the ambulacra also has but one species, *P. depressus*, Japan.

The four remaining camarodont families have smooth tests without sculpturing, shallow gill cuts, compound ambulacral plates of the echinoid type, and solid spines borne on imperforate tubercles.  The four families are distinguished mainly by details of their globiferous pedi-cellariae.  In the Echinidae, each valve of the globiferous pedicellariae bears a single poison sac, has one to several teeth along its sides, and terminates in a single large pointed tooth (Fig. 227*C*).  In *Echinus* and *Psammechinus* the ambulacral plates are *trigeminate*, that is, with three pore pairs, whereas in *Paracentrotus* there are five pore pairs on each plate.  Mortensen recognizes 17 species of *Echinus*, of which two, *esculentus* and *acutus*, are common along north European coasts; they are urchins of considerable size with short spines.  *Echinus esculentus* is said by Mortensen to be very beautiful when alive, having an intensely red test with spines shading to purplish distally.  There are no littoral species of *Echinus* along American shores, but several species occur in the western Atlantic in ·deeper waters.  *Psammechinus miliaris*, of a general green color, occurs from Norway and Iceland along north Euro-pean coasts and along the west side of Africa as far as the Cape Verde Islands, but does not enter the Mediterranean where the genus is repre-sented by *P. microtuberculatus*, greenish brown in color.  *Paracentrotus lividus*, with dark green test and violet, brown, or green spines, is another common and well-known Mediterranean echinoid, extending down the west coast of Africa.  This is a rock-boring species and in some regions the rocks are honeycombed with depressions containing this urchin.

The Strongylocentrotidae are regular echinoids of moderate to large size with polyporous ambulacral plates (Fig. 191D). Their globiferous pedicellariae are characterized by a long muscular "neck" and valves without teeth except the terminal one (Figs. 181E, 227E). The main genus *Strongylocentrotus* is represented by several familiar littoral species. The green species, *S. dröbachiensis*, with typically five pore pairs on each ambulacral plate, is distributed throughout polar and cold northern waters, extending south on North American shores to Chesapeake Bay and Puget Sound. The purple species, with at least eight pore pairs on typical aboral plates, are familiar littoral animals of the Pacific Coast of North America. The smaller species with the shorter spines is *S. purpuratus*, and the large one, to 6 inches in test diameter, with long pointed spines, is *S. franciscanus*, a splendid species.

In the small family Parasaleniidae with one existing genus *Parasalenia*, the test is oval with trigeminate plates. The globiferous pedicellariae are provided with stalk glands, wanting in the two preceding families, but lack a muscular neck; the valves are armed with end teeth only. The two species of *Parasalenia* inhabit the Indo-Pacific area.

The Echinometridae, the last regular family, are small to large forms, with round or oval test, with three or more pore pairs on the ambulacral plates. The ambulacra tend to widen gradually in the oral direction. The globiferous pedicellariae have double poison sacs and may be provided with stalk glands; the distinguishing character is the presence of one unpaired tooth near the end tooth of each valve (Fig. 227D). *Echinostrephus*, with pentagonal ambitus, three or four pore pairs on each ambulacral plate, and aboral tuft of longer spines, is limited to the Indo–West Pacific region. The Australian genus *Heliocidaris* has a rounded ambitus and seven to ten pore pairs in each plate. The other echinometrid genera to be mentioned—*Echinometra, Heterocentrotus,* and *Colobocentrotus*—all have oval or elliptical tests, but the plane of elongation corresponds neither to Lovén's nor to Carpenter's plane (Fig. 228A), although almost at right angles to the latter. All three genera have polyporous ambulacra with up to 16 pore pairs per plate. *Echinometra* with ordinary spines is represented by *E. lacunter* (Fig. 228A) in the West Indies, extending also to Brazil and the west coast of Africa, and by *E. mathaei*, widely spread throughout tropical and subtropical waters. *Heterocentrotus* is easily recognized by the large, heavy primary spines, cylindrical or keeled, contrasting with the short secondary spines with flat ends forming a sort of mosaic (Fig. 178D). The primary spines of *Heterocentrotus mammillatus*, the slate pencil urchin, widely distributed in the Indo-Pacific, were once used for writing on slates. Of even more peculiar appearance is *Colobocentrotus*, in which all the aboral spines are short and flat-topped, forming a mosaic edged by a fringe of short, flat spines at the ambitus (Fig. 178C). More ordinary spines occur on the oral side. This genus is supposed to be adapted for life on rocks in

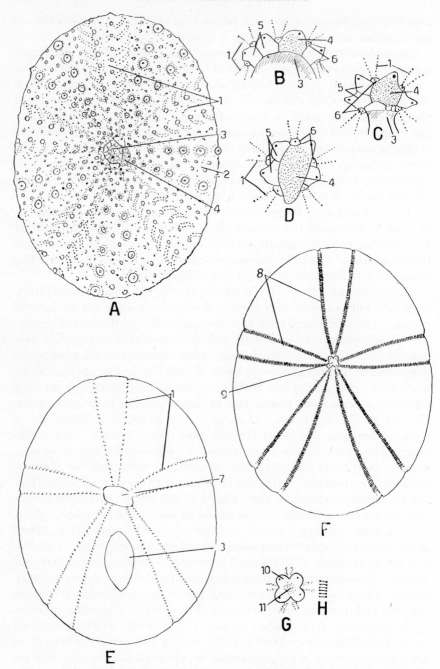

Fig. 228.—Echinometridae, Holectypoida. *A, Echinometra lacunter,* West Indies, aboral view of test. *B–D,* apical region of various extinct holectypoids (*after Hawkins, 1913*). *B,* periproct still in contact with opened apical system. *C,* periproct has lost

heavy surf. The most common species, *C. atratus*, is found in the intertidal zone subject to wave action around various Pacific islands.

**25. Subclass Irregularia or Exocyclica and Order Holectypoida.—**
This subclass includes all echinoids in which the periproct including the
anus has moved outside the apical system of plates. The periproct
regresses along one particular interambulacrum, AB on the Carpenter
plan, that thereby becomes posterior. Fossil forms exemplify stages in
the retreat of the periproct (Fig. 228*B–D*) and in the migration of the
madreporite from its original position to the right of base of the anterior
ambulacrum (III on Lovén's system) to a symmetrical location in the
posterior interambulacrum, as in Fig. 191*F*. The irregular urchins are
arranged by Mortensen into four orders, two of which are mostly extinct.

The Holectypoida are a group of mainly extinct echinoids, which have
been especially studied by Hawkins (1912a, 1912b, 1920). The extinct
members had tests of regular shape, circular or pentagonal at the ambitus,
simple ambulacra without petaloid differentiation, and centrally located
peristome and apical system. They had gills cuts and therefore gills, a
perignathic girdle with auricles not connected by ridges, and a lantern,
although its structure is not known. Therefore the more primitive
holectypoids differed from a regular echinoid primarily in the removal of
the periproct from within the circle of the apical plates. In the most
primitive genera *Pygaster* and *Plesiechinus* (Hawkins, 1917), the anterior
edge of the oval periproct has remained in contact with the semicircle
of apical plates (Fig. 228*B*). In other genera the periproct shows various
degrees of removal toward the posterior edge of the test and in *Holectypus*
has moved around to the oral side. The apical plates then close together
to form a new, mostly asymmetrical apical center, and the madreporic
plate gradually shoves itself into a central position (Fig. 228*C, D*). There
are often but four genital plates and gonopores, but the fifth one may be
restored after the periproct has regressed sufficiently. The order contains
one living family, the Echinoneidae, which differs from the fossil holectypoids in having taken on an oval shape (as regards all the existing
members) and in having lost the lantern and perignathic girdle, further
gills and gill cuts. It was discovered by Agassiz (1909) that a lantern
and teeth of the stirodont type are present in young echinoneids at
metamorphosis but soon disappear without leaving a trace. The
periproct is on the oral side close behind the oblique peristome. There
are two existing genera, *Echinoneus* with two species and *Micropetalon*

---

contact with genital plates; madreporite extending centrally. *D*, periproct altogether
withdrawn; madreporite in central position. *E, Echinoneus cyclostomus*, oral view of test.
*F*, same, aboral view. *G*, apical system of *E, cyclostomus*. *H*, bit of petaloid, with conjugated pores. 1, ambulacra; 2, interambulacra; 3, periproct; 4, madreporite; 5, genital
plates; 6, terminal plates; 7, peristome; note asymmetry; 8, petaloids; 9, apical center; 10,
fused genital plates; 11, madreporic pores.

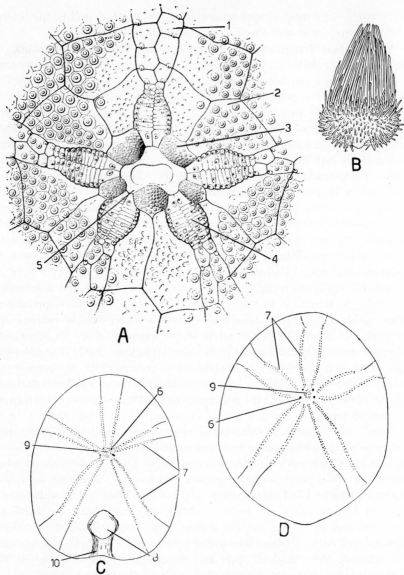

Fig. 229.—Cassiduloida, Echinometridae. *A*, peristome of *Cassidulus*, showing the floscelle (*after Lovén*, 1875). *B*, *Echinostrephus aciculatus*, Indo-Pacific. *C*, *Apatopygus recens*, New Zealand, aboral view of test. *D*, *Echinolampas ovata*, Indo-Pacific, note unequal length of pore rows of petaloids. 1, ambulacrum; 2, interambulacrum; 3, bourrelet; 4, phyllode; 5, peristome; 6, gonopores; 7, petaloids; 8, periproct; 9, madreporic pores; 10, groove leading to periproct.

with one; of these the last is rare, but *Echinoneus cyclostomus* is common in the West Indies and in fact is circumtropical, and *E. abnormalis* appears distributed throughout the tropical Pacific. The three species were monographed by Westergren (1911). *Echinoneus cyclostomus* (Fig. 228*E*, *F*) is a small oval species of pale coloration, uniformly covered with short dense spines, living concealed beneath stones, coral slabs, and the like.

**26. Order Cassiduloida.**—This is another mostly extinct order. The test varies from round to oval in profile with apical system and peristome central or slightly anterior. On the aboral surface the ambulacra are more or less petaloid, and around the peristome they typically form phyllodes alternating with well-developed bourrelets (page 452) to produce floscelles (Fig. 229*A*). The periproct varies from contiguity with the apical system to an oral location near the peristome and may be sunk into a groove. In a few extinct forms a fully developed lantern is present in the adult, but in most cassiduloids the lantern disappears during juvenile stages. The family Echinobrissidae with separate genital plates is represented by one existing genus, *Apatopygus*, with two species, of which one, *A. recens* (Figs. 229*C*, 230*A*), is not uncommon around New Zealand (Mortensen, 1921). In the Cassidulidae the four genital plates are fused with the madreporite; the test is rounded or oval with fairly developed petaloids open at their distal ends and conspicuous bourrelets (Fig. 229*A*). There are six existing species in this family, of which may be mentioned *Cassidulus caribaearum* in the West Indies and *C. pacificus* in the tropical eastern Pacific. The Echinolampadidae have open petaloids with the peculiarity that the two pore rows of each petaloid are of uneven length (Fig. 229*D*); the periproct, posteriorly located on the aboral side, is covered with three large plates. There are a number of existing echinolampadids limited to tropical and subtropical waters, living mostly in waters of moderate depth. The Neolampadidae with several existing species differ from other cassiduloids in the absence of petaloid and phyllode development, although well-formed bourrelets are present. The ambulacra are peculiarly simple with only single pores or none. The periproct is at the posterior end of the test. There are generally three, sometimes two or four, gonopores, and in two species of this family, *Tropholampas loveni* and *Anochanus sinensis*, the peristome of the female is insunken to serve as a brood pouch for the young.

It may be said that in general the existing cassiduloids resemble sand dollars, and some have the same burrowing habits; they differ from sand dollars in the imperfect development of the petaloids, the presence of bourrelets, and the want of a lantern.

**27. Order Clypeastroida.**—The clypeastroids or sand dollars naturally follow from the preceding order. The test is usually flattened, oval or

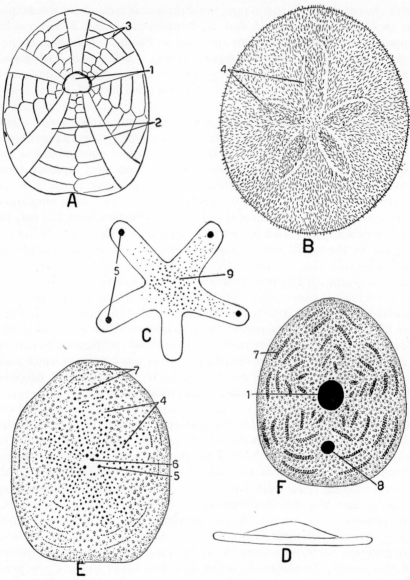

Fig. 230.—Cassiduloida (concluded), Clypeastroida. *A*, *Apatopygus recens*, oral view of test. *B*, *Peronella lesueuri*, Australia, aboral view. *C*, apical system of *Peronella*. *D*, profile of *Peronella*. *E*, *Echinocyamus pusillus*, Europe, aboral view. *F*, same, oral view. (*E*, *F*, *after Mortensen*, 1907.) 1, peristome; 2, ambulacra; 3, interambulacra; 4, petaloids; 5, gonopores; 6, hydropore; 7, arcs of podial pores; 8, periproct; 9, madreporic pores.

rounded or somewhat angled at the ambitus, and is often very substantial with heavy internal skeletal supports (Fig. 193*A*). The peristome and apical system are usually central; the latter generally consists of a porous pentagonal plate composed of fused genitals and madreporite, accompanied by very small terminals (Fig. 192*D*). On the aboral side the ambulacra form five well-developed petaloids (Fig. 192*B*) with conjugate pore pairs; elsewhere there are large numbers of small uniporous podia emerging not only along the ambulacra but often along the interambulacra also. Phyllodes and bourrelets are wanting. The periproct varies in position in the posterior interambulacrum but is never in contact with the apical system. There are no gills or gill cuts. The test is usually covered densely with small spines (Fig. 176*A*). A large lantern with broad flattened pyramids is present (Fig. 198*A*, *B*), but the compasses are lacking. Globiferous pedicellariae are usually wanting, but the three other types occur, although not conspicuously. There is a single concealed sphaeridium (sometimes two) along each ambulacrum near the peristome (Fig. 184*E*). The sand dollars are arranged into five families by Mortensen.

In the Clypeastridae the petaloids are formed of primary plates alternating regularly with demiplates (Fig. 193*B*). The two pores of each pair are widely separated, connected by a furrow. The ambulacra are much broader than the interambulacra (Fig. 192*B*) and on the oral side intervene between the first interambulacral plate adjacent to the peristome and the rest of the interambulacrum; hence the latter is said to be discontinuous. On the oral side the ambulacra usually show a simple central furrow (Fig. 176*A*). The apical system is central, consisting of a porous rounded or pentagonal plate with five minute terminals and five gonopores, placed at the plate angles or removed somewhat from the plate (Fig. 192*B*, *C*). The periproct covered with small plates is found on the oral surface near the posterior margin (Fig. 176*A*). This family contains but one existing genus, *Clypeaster*, with many species in tropical and subtropical waters, living on or buried in sandy bottom. Whereas most species of *Clypeaster* conform to the concept of sand dollar, being flattened with a more or less circular outline, others are decidedly oval or with a high test. One of the most common species is *C. rosaceus* from the West Indies, locally known as sea biscuit. This is a rather large, oval form with a thick, heavy test covered with a dense fur of short, dark-brown spines (Figs. 175*B*, *C*, 176*A*, 192*B*, 193*A*). Some other common species are *europacificus* and *rotundus* from the tropical eastern Pacific, Gulf of California to the Galapagos, *telurus* and *australasiae* from Australian coasts, *rarispinus* and *reticulatus* from the Indo–West Pacific area, *humilis* from the Red Sea, extending into the Malay region, and *japonicus* in Japanese waters.

The Arachnoididae differ from the Clypeastridae, with which they share the plate arrangement in the petaloids, in having but four gonopores and in the arrangement of the tubercles and podial pores (except those of the poriferous part of the petaloids) in oblique rows. They are of moderate to large size with typical flattened, thin-edged test. The members of this family are confined to the Australian–New Zealand–Malay region, where the common species is *Arachnoides placenta* with aboral periproct.

In the remaining three families the plates of the petaloids are all primary. The Fibulariidae are mostly small, oval forms with less distinctly formed petaloids than the foregoing. The interambulacra are continuous on the oral side. The apical system forms a fused plate with four gonopores and usually a single hydropore, although sometimes a few to several. There are two existing genera, *Echinocyamus* with internal radial partitions in the test and *Fibularia* without them. The former genus is best known by *E. pusillus*, common on north European shores, in the Mediterranean, and along Africa to the Azores. It is a little, somewhat egg-shaped creature with short, straight-sided petaloids, one hydropore surrounded by four gonopores, and periproct on the oral side (Fig. 230*E, F*). The genus *Fibularia* is represented by several species in the Indo–West Pacific region; one of these, *F. nutriens*, from the coast of New South Wales, broods its young in a U-shaped depression of the aboral surface (Fig. 205*B*, H. L. Clark, 1909).

The Laganidae are sand dollars of mostly small to moderate size, with a thick-edged, flattened test of circular, ovoid, or angled outline. On the aboral surface the ambulacra are distinctly petaloid and the interambulacra terminate between them by one large plate. The apical system is fused into one pentagonal plate (Fig. 230*C*). The periproct is situated on the oral surface, which also bears five simple ambulacral furrows not reaching the edge of the test. The small (miliary) spines terminate in a crown (Fig. 179*F*), as is also the case in the Fibulariidae. The laganids are inhabitants of sandy bottoms in shallow waters in the Indo–West Pacific region. There are two existing genera, *Laganum* with five gonopores and madreporic pores sunken in lines or pits (Fig. 231*A–D*) and *Peronella* with four gonopores and madreporic pores not so sunken (Fig. 230 *B–D*). Each has a number of species in the region indicated.

The typical sand dollars belong to the family Scutellidae, relatively large forms with a very flat, thin-edged, discoidal test, provided with distinct petaloids aborally and branching furrows orally. The interambulacra are generally discontinuous on the oral surface and terminate aborally with two small plates. Genitals and madreporic plate are fused into one pentagonal plate with four or five gonopores (Fig. 192*C*), whereas the terminals remain more or less separate. The tips of the miliary

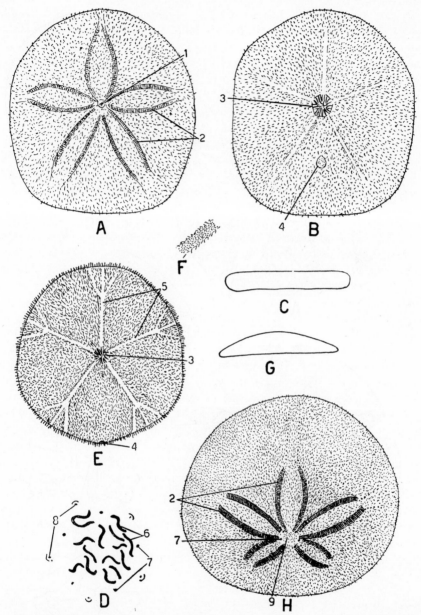

FIG. 231.—Clypeastroida (continued), Laganidae, Scutellidae. *A, Laganum laganum,* Indo-Pacific, aboral view. *B,* same oral view. *C,* same, profile. *D,* same, apical region, showing vermiform madrepores. *E, Echinarachnius parma,* New England coast, oral view. *F,* ambulacral furrow of same, showing podial pores. *G,* profile of *E, parma.* *H, Dendraster excentricus,* Pacific Coast of North America, aboral view. 1, apical center; 2, petaloids; 3, peristome; 4, periproct; 5, ambulacral furrows; 6, worm-like madrepores; 7, gonopores; 8, terminal pores; 9, madreporic pores.

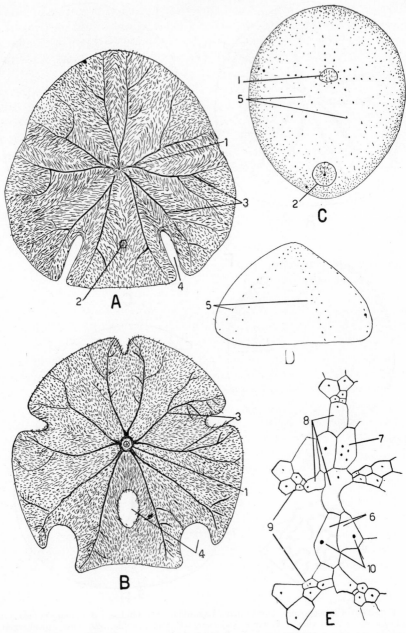

Fɪɢ. 232.—Scutellidae (concluded), meridosternous spatangoids. *A, Echinodiscus auritus,* Red Sea, oral view. *B, Encope grandis,* Gulf of California, oral view. *C, Urechinus loveni,* Gulf of California, oral view. *D,* profile of *Urechinus loveni. E,* apical system of *Urechinus (after Lovén,* 1883). 1, peristome; 2, periproct; 3, ambulacral furrows; 4, lunules; 5, pores marking ambulacra; 6, genital plates; 7, madreporic plate; 8, terminal plates; 9, ambulacra; 10, gonopores.

spines of the aboral side are usually encased in a bag of glandular tissue. In this family pedicellariae are mostly small and scarce, and the tridentate and triphyllous types are reduced to the small two-valved condition (Fig. 181*B*). The geographical distribution of the Scutellidae is peculiar in that they are limited to American and Japanese waters.

The genus *Echinarachnius*, in which the furrows bear only one pair of branches near the margin, has but one good species, *E. parma* (Fig. 231*E–G*), the common sand dollar of the North Atlantic Coast of the United States as far south as New Jersey; what seems to be the same species is also found in the North Pacific from Vancouver to Japan. *Scaphechinus*, limited to Japanese waters, differs in that the ambulacral furrows soon fork into two branches, each with small side branches. *Dendraster* is easily recognized by the posterior position of the apical system, so that the three anterior petaloids are much longer than the posterior ones. *Dendraster excentricus* (Fig. 231*H*) is very common buried in the sand of sheltered flats on the Pacific Coast from Lower California to Alaska. The remaining scutellid genera are readily distinguished by the presence of lunules. *Echinodiscus*, a large, very thin and flat scutellid, somewhat widened posteriorly with a truncate posterior margin, has two lunules, one in each posterior ambulacrum (Fig. 232*A*). The common species, *auritus* and *bisperforatus*, occur in the Indo-Malay region and along the east coast of Africa. The very large *E. auritus*, varying in color from yellow to purple, is called sea pancake by some authors. The genus *Mellita* is provided with lunules in the four paired ambulacra and in the posterior interambulacrum, also in some species in the anterior ambulacrum. The species with five lunules, *M. quinquiesperforata*, is found from Nantucket to Brazil and into the West Indies as far as Puerto Rico, and that with six lunules, *M. sexiesperforata* (Fig. 177*A*, *B*), occurs from the Carolinas to Patagonia, including the West Indies. *Encope* has six lunules, but the ambulacral lunules remain as open notches, so that the only closed lunule is that of the posterior interambulacrum (Fig. 232*B*); it further has five gonopores whereas *Mellita* has four. These are a number of species of *Encope*, limited to tropical and subtropical coasts of the Americas. *Rotula* is easily recognized by the numerous deep notches of the posterior margin of the test, presumably representing incomplete lunules. This genus is limited to the tropical part of the west coast of Africa, where there are two species, *orbiculus* without lunules (Fig. 178*A*, *B*) and *augusti* with a lunule in each anterior ambulacrum.

**28. Order Spatangoida.**—The spatangoids or heart urchins are irregular echinoids of mostly oval shape, usually elongated, with the structures of the test arranged symmetrically with respect to the axis of elongation. The anterior ambulacrum is often indented at the ambitus, giving the test a cordiform outline.    The ambulacra, except the anterior one, are generally petaloid aborally and may be flush with the surface or more or less deeply insunk.    Phyllodes are generally present, but bourrelets are wanting.    On the oral side the posterior interambulacum is often slightly elevated and forms a plastron.    The peristome is displaced anteriorly, so that the three anterior ambulacra are shorter than the two posterior ones.    The apical system consists of separate plates with two to four, mostly four, gonopores.    The spines are mostly short and slender and the larger ones are usually curved and held parallel to the surface of the test, appearing as if combed back, and often arranged in tracts (Fig. 235*A*, *B*).    Peculiar to the spatangoids are the fascioles, narrow bands composed of closely crowded minute tubercles that support special tiny ciliated spines.    The location of the fascioles was described above (page 421).    A masticatory apparatus is completely wanting and consequently the structures usually located on the aboral surface of the lantern are found encircling the inner edge of the peristome.    The spatangoids are typically burrowers, and many of their peculiarities are adaptations for this form of life.    The existing spatangoids are divided by Mortensen into the meridosternous forms in which the labrum abuts posteriorly with a single plate of the plastron (Fig. 233*A*) and the amphisternous forms in which it abuts on two plates (Fig. 192*A*).    A more primitive group of protosternous spatangoids in which the posterior interambulacrum was not differentiated at all into a plastron is wholly extinct.

The meridosternous group also contains a number of extinct genera and is represented by three existing families, the Urechinidae, the Calymnidae, and the Pourtalesiidae.    The Urechinidae are deep-water echinoids of ovoid form with a thin, fragile test with short spines.    Petaloids and phyllodes are not differentiated, and the ambulacra consist of simple, uniporous plates (Fig. 232*D*, *E*).    In the apical system the terminals of the two anterior paired ambulacra meet at the center, separating the anterior from the posterior genital plates (Fig. 232*E*).    The periproct is near the posterior margin on either the aboral or oral surface.    In *Plexechinus* the posterior end of the plastron, bearing a well-formed subanal fasciole, projects conspicuously, whereas there is no such projection and a fasciole is wanting or indistinct in the other existing genera, *Urechinus* and *Pilematechinus*.    The Calymnidae are represented by only one species, *Calymne relicta*, dredged near Bermuda at 4845 m. by the *Challenger* (Agassiz, 1881).    Only fragments were preserved, but from the description at the time of collecting, it appears that the test was oval, fragile, and pale green in color with a conspicuous marginal fasciole.

The peculiarities of the Pourtalesiidae were already indicated (page 421).    The test is thin, fragile, and usually bottle-shaped, with the

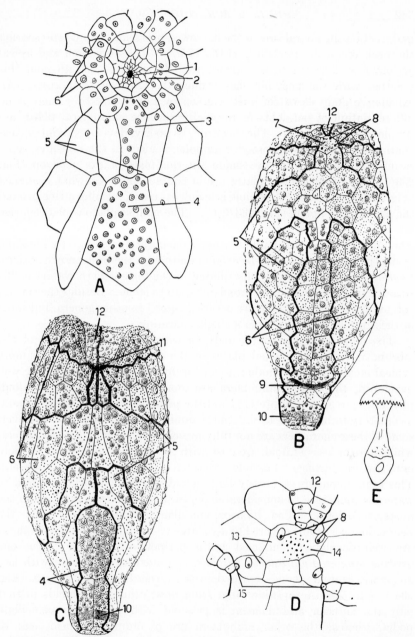

Fig. 233.—Meridosternous spatangoids (concluded). *A*, peristome of *Plexechinus*. *B*, test of *Pourtalesia*, aboral view. *C*, test of *Pourtalesia*, oral view. *D*, apical system of *Pourtalesia*. (*B–D, after Lovén*, 1883; ambulacra heavily outlined.) *E*, jaw of ophiocephalous pedicellaria of *Pourtalesia*. (*A, E, after Mortensen, Monogr.*) 1, mouth; 2, peristome; 3, labrum; 4, plastron (single plate meets labrum); 5, ambulacra; 6, interambulacra; 7, apical center; 8, gonopores; 9, position of periproct; 10, subanal fasciole; 11, position of peristome; 12, anterior ambulacrum; 13, genital plates; 14, madreporite; 15, terminal plates.

periproct on the aboral side of the narrowed posterior region, representing the neck of the bottle (Figs. 174$E$, 175$D$). The peristome and apical system are displaced to a position near the anterior margin, and this together with the peculiar shape much distorts the plate rows. An exhaustive analysis of the test is given by Lovén (1883). There is no differentiation of petaloids or phyllodes and the ambulacral plates are simple and uniporous. The plastron is poorly developed and is discontinuous, as the two posterior ambulacra meet in the mid-line, separating the labrum from the single anterior plate of the plastron (Fig. 233$C$). The four genital plates are in contact and somewhat coalesced (Fig. 233$D$). A subanal fasciole is usually present, forming a ring around the neck of the bottle (Fig. 233$B$, $C$). The ophiocephalous pedicellariae are of a characteristic type with expanded, toothed tips (Fig. 233$E$). The Pourtalesiidae are all inhabitants of deep water, collected by dredging at depths ranging from 440 to 5850 m., although the best-known species, *Pourtalesia jeffreysi*, widely distributed in the far northern waters of the Atlantic, may occur at moderate depths, up to 50 m. Besides the several species of *Pourtalesia*, there are others assigned to other genera, but most of these are known only from a single collecting.

The amphisternous spatangoids, in which the posterior end of the labrum abuts on two equal plates of the plastron, comprise the more typical members and include a wealth of forms. Fascioles are here well developed, the paired ambulacra are more or less obviously petaloid, phyllodes are generally present, and the podia occur in a variety of non-locomotory forms (page 434). In the family Palaeopneustidae, however, some of these characters are not fully present. Especially the ambulacra, while more or less petaloid, are flush with the surface and continue widely onto the oral surface. Fascioles are often absent or indistinctly present. This family consists of mostly large ovoid or rounded forms, limited to waters of moderate to considerable depth, and hence not familiar to the average zoologist. The Palaeostomatidae are characterized by the pentagonal peristome covered by five large triangular plates; the petaloids are well developed, encircled by a peripetalous fasciole. The one existing species, *Palaeostoma mirabile*, is a small ovoid urchin with two gonopores, found at moderate depths in the Indo-Malay area (Fig. 234$A$, $B$). The Aeropsidae differ from most other spatangoids in that only the anterior ambulacrum is petaloid with very large penicillate podia, whereas the other ambulacra are of ordinary appearance; all the ambulacral plates are simple with a single pore pair. There are two existing genera, *Aeropsis* (Fig. 234$E$) with shallow and *Aceste* (Fig. 234$C$) with deeply sunken anterior ambulacrum, both in deep waters. The family Toxasteridae contains but one existing species, *Isopatagus obovatus*, in which all five ambulacra are distinctly petaloid and fascioles are lacking. This is a large urchin with a high test, known only from the Sulu Sea, taken at 890 m. In the Hemiasteridae, the usual four paired ambulacra are petaloid, and fascioles are represented by the peripetalous kind only; there is but one existing genus, *Hemiaster*, with a few species, also inhabiting deeper waters. Of these *Hemiaster expergitus* is the best known, distributed over the North Atlantic as far south as the West Indies and the Azores.

The remaining families include the more familiar spatangoids with the typical characters of the order: four petaloids closed at their ends, projecting labrum, phyllodes, and one or more fascioles. The Spatangidae are known by the presence of only the subanal fasciole; the apical system is ethmolytic, that is, the madreporite has moved into a symmetrical posterior position with reference to the four genitals (Fig. 191*F*). In the genus *Spatangus* the test is large, aborally arched, and cordiform with petaloids flush with the surface, and with a spiny plastron. The most common species, *S. purpureus*, of violet color, distinguished by the broad shape of the fasciole, is found along western European coasts, in the Mediterranean, and down the west side of Africa (Fig. 234*D*). In *Maretia* the plastron and adjoining ambulacra are almost devoid of spines. In the most common species, *M. planulata*, widely distributed in shallow waters in the Indo–West Pacific region, this naked area is raised as a sort of keel. In *Paramaretia* with four and *Pseudomaretia* with three gonopores, the pore pairs are degenerate along part or all of the anterior side of the anterior petals.

The family Loveniidae differs from all other spatangoids by the presence of an internal fasciole that encloses the apical system and much of the anterior ambulacrum (Fig. 235*C*, *D*). The test is of moderate to large size, rather low, and of cordiform outline. The four petaloids are well developed, flush with the test. On the aboral side between the petals there are often large tubercles with deeply sunken areoles; these tubercles in life carry long curved spines directed backward. The apical system is ethmolytic, as in the Spatangidae, with nearly always four gonopores. The main genera are *Lovenia* and *Echinocardium* with internal and subanal fascioles and *Breynia* with, in addition, a peripetalous fasciole. Of the several species of *Lovenia* there may be mentioned *L. elongata* (Fig. 235*D*) from the Indo-Pacific with narrowed posterior end and *L. cordiformis* from California to the Galapagos with an altogether rather narrow test. *Echinocardium* differs from both *Lovenia* and *Breynia* in lacking the large aboral spine tubercles with deep areoles. *Echinocardium cordatum*, the common heart urchin, is one of the best studied echinoids (Fig. 235*A*, *B*). It appears to have a nearly cosmopolitan distribution, occurring on north European coasts from Norway and Ireland into the Mediterranean, also off South Africa, from Carolina

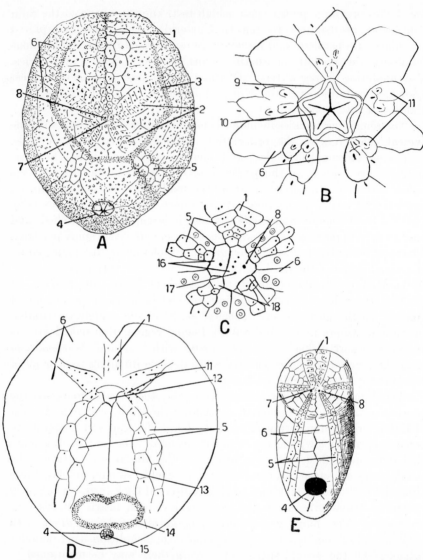

Fig. 234.—Amphisternous spatangoids. *A, Palaeostoma mirabile.* *B,* peristome of *A.* *C,* apical system of *Aceste.* (*A–C, after Lovén,* 1883.) *D, Spatangus purpureus,* Europe, oral view of test. *E, Aeropsis rostrata,* northeastern coast of North America (*after Mortensen,* 1907). 1, anterior ambulacrum; 2, petaloids; 3, peripetalous fasciole; 4, periproct; 5, ambulacra; 6, interambulacra; 7, apical center; 8, gonopores; 9, peristome; 10, five valves of peristome; 11, phyllodes; 12, labrum; 13, plastron (two plates meet labrum); 14, subanal fasciole; 15, anus; 16, genital plates; 17, madreporic pores; 18, terminal plates.

to Brazil, further along Australia, New Zealand, and Japan. Some other species are *E. flavescens*, along European coasts and down the coast of Africa to the Azores; *E. mediterraneum* in the Mediterranean; and *E. pennatifidum* in northern European waters from Bergen to the English Channel. The genus *Breynia* (Fig. 235C) is limited to Australian shores and the Malay region.

The family Pericosmidae is characterized by the combination of peripetalous and marginal fascioles; a subanal fasciole is wanting and the peripetalous fasciole bends inward markedly between the petaloids. The single existing genus *Pericosmus* has sunken petaloids and the frontal ambulacrum is also usually sunken, forming a notch. The several species of *Pericosmus* have been taken sporadically in the tropical Indo-Pacific.

Still another combination of fascioles occurs in the family Schizasteridae; here there is typically a peripetalous fasciole from whose posterior angles a lateral fasciole proceeds backward to either side of the periproct. However, fascioles are wanting in the antarctic genus *Amphineustes*, which is a brooding species with deeply sunken petaloids in the females. A similar restriction to cold southern and antarctic waters and a similar deepening of the petaloids in females for brooding purposes also pertain to the genera *Abatus* (Fig. 206) with peripetalous but no lateral fascioles and *Tripylus* with both. A number of species of all three genera have been taken on antarctic expeditions. In *Brisaster* the apical system with three gonopores is much displaced posteriorly, so that the posterior petaloids are very short and the test is high at the rear (Fig. 236D, E). The lateral fascioles may be present or more or less reduced. *Brisaster fragilis* is common on Norwegian coasts and adjacent areas of the North Atlantic, and *B. townsendi* and *latifrons* are found from Alaska to the Gulf of Panama. The test is high in *Schizaster* with deeply sunken anterior ambulacrum bordered laterally by crests formed of the adjacent interambulacra; here, too, the apical system is posterior with very short posterior petaloids, but there are only two gonopores, and the lateral fascioles are distinctly developed. *Schizaster canaliferus* is a well-known Mediterranean species that often serves as an illustration of an echinoid with only two gonads (Fig. 204C). In *Moira* also the test is high with deeply insunken narrow petaloids and anterior ambulacrum; although the apical system is approximately central, the posterior petaloids are very short. The lateral fasciole is well developed beginning at about the middle of the anterior petaloids and extending back to make a deep bend below the periproct which is situated well up on the truncate posterior end. *Moira atropos*, a rather small species, to 57 mm. in length, occurs from Carolina to Texas and in the West Indies, living buried in mud (Fig. 236A, B).

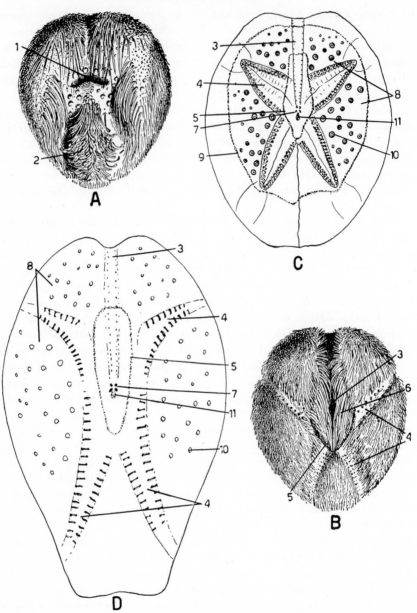

Fig. 235.—Amphisternous spatangoids (continued), Loveniidae. *A, Echinocardium cordatum,* Europe, oral view. *B,* same, aboral view. (*A, B, after MacBride,* 1906.) *C, Breynia australasiae,* Australia, aboral view of test. *D, Lovenia elongata,* Indo-Pacific, aboral view of test. 1, peristome; 2, plastron; 3, anterior ambulacrum; 4, petaloids; 5, internal fasciole; 6, aboral spine tuft; 7, gonopores; 8, interambulacra; 9, peripetalous fasciole; 10, large spine tubercles; 11, madreporite.

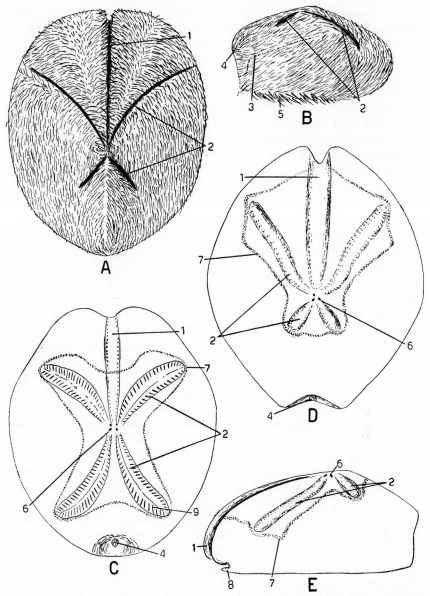

Fig. 236.—Amphisternous spatangoids (continued), Schizasteridae, Brissidae. *A*, *Moira atropos*, West Indies, aboral view. *B*, same from the side. *C*, *Brissopsis pacifica*, Panamic region, aboral view. *D*, *Brisaster latifrons*, California, aboral view. *E*, same as *D*, side view. 1, anterior ambulacrum; 2, petaloids; 3, lateral fasciole; 4, periproct; 5, spines of plastron; 6, gonopores; 7, peripetalous fasciole; 8, labrum; 9, conjugated pore pairs.

The last spatangoid family, the Brissidae, is known by the combination of peripetalous and subanal fascioles; anal branches from the latter along the sides of the periproct are generally present. The petaloids are usually not much sunken, and this also applies to the anterior ambulacrum. The genus *Brissopsis* includes rather large forms with equal petaloids and anal branches forward from the subanal fasciole. *Brissopsis lyrifera* is a well-known species along northern European coasts, extending into the Mediterranean and down the west African coast; *B. luzonica* occurs throughout the Indo–West Pacific region from the Red Sea to Japan and Hawaii; and *B. pacifica* (Fig. 236*C*) in the Panamic region. *Plagiobrissus* is also rather large with long, narrow petaloids, anal branches from the subanal fasciole, narrow ambulacra bounding the plastron, and well-marked peripetalous fasciole that does not bend inward between the petaloids. *Plagiobrissus grandis* (Figs. 191*E*, *F*, 192*A*), from Florida and the West Indies, is one of the largest spatangoids with a very handsome test. *Brissus* is characterized by the anteriorly located apical system, the lack of anal fascioles, the kidney-shaped subanal fasciole, and the inbending of the peripetalous fasciole between the petals. *Brissus unicolor* is common in the warmer waters of the Atlantic, on both its eastern and western coasts (Fig. 237*B*, *C*), and *B. latecarinatus* is widely distributed in the Indo–West Pacific from the Red Sea and Mauritius to the Marquesas and Hawaii. The genus *Meoma* includes two species of very large size with arched test having narrow, sunken petaloids; the peripetalous fasciole bends sharply inward between the petaloids; the subanal fasciole is imperfect in the adult and there are no anal branches from it. *Meoma ventricosa* (Figs. 174*A*, *B*, 175*A*) is a well-known, very large spatangoid from the West Indies, and *Meoma grandis*, slightly smaller with large spine tubercles between the petaloids, occurs from the Gulf of California to the Galapagos. In *Metalia* the peripetalous fasciole does not bend inward markedly between the petaloids, and the shield-shaped subanal fasciole gives off anal branches; large tubercles are wanting. The several species are found mostly in the tropical West Pacific, except *M. nobilis* from the Panamic region.

**29. Ecology: Habits and Behavior.**—The echinoids are exclusively marine benthonic animals, and therefore their activities and adaptations are correlated with an existence on the ocean bottom. All echinoids keep the oral surface in contact with the substratum and if turned over are generally able to right themselves. The regular urchins generally inhabit rocky or partially rocky or other types of hard bottom, although they may be found on sand. Coral reefs also constitute a favorable habitat for large numbers and kinds of regular urchins. In suitable spots along ocean shores urchins may be present in such numbers that their spines touch and it is impossible to step between them. Regular urchins often occupy depressions or crevices in rocks, and in the case of certain species it is known that these depressions are deepened by the activities of the animals themselves. The main rock-boring urchins are *Psammechinus miliaris* and *Paracentrotus lividus* on western European coasts, *Strongylocentrotus purpuratus* on the Pacific Coast of the United

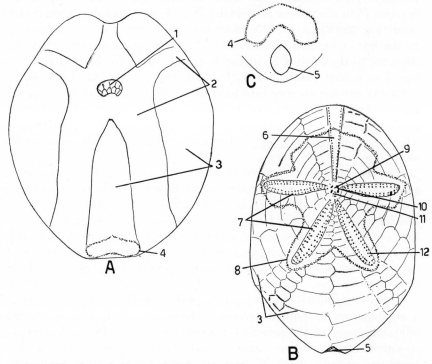

FIG. 237.—Spatangoids (concluded). *A, Brissopsis pacifica*, oral view. *B, Brissus unicolor*, aboral view. *C, Brissus unicolor*, rear end from oral side, showing fasciole. 1, peristome; 2, ambulacra; 3, interambulacra; 4, subanal fasciole; 5, periproct; 6, anterior ambulacrum; 7, petaloids; 8, peripetalous fasciole; 9, apical center; 10, gonopores; 11, madreporite; 12, pore pairs.

States, and the echinometrids *Echinostrephus aciculatus* and *molaris* in the Indo–West Pacific and *Evechinus chloroticus* off New Zealand (Farquhar, 1894). The best-known rock borer is *P. lividus*, whose activities may honeycomb rocky walls. When the burrows are shallow the urchins may leave them to feed when the state of the tide is suitable, but the animals appear to remain permanently in deep burrows and in fact are often unable to get out of the narrow entrance made when they were younger and smaller. In such cases they must depend for food on material washed into the burrows by waves and tides. The matter of rock-boring urchins has been reviewed by Otter (1932), who states that boring is a protection against waves and therefore is limited to localities subject to excessive wave action. After reviewing all the evidence Otter concludes that boring is accomplished by a rotary action of the spines, widening an already existing depression, while the teeth are probably employed in deepening the burrow by a gnawing action. The two *Echinostrephus* species, both small urchins, make smooth cylindrical burrows 75 to 100 mm. or more in depth, and the short spines around their sides (Fig. 229*B*) are said by Mortensen (Monogr.) to be an adaptation to the boring habit. When undisturbed the *Echinostrephus* sits at the entrance to the burrow but when disturbed drops to the bottom of the hole and cannot be dislodged (H. L. Clark, 1921). All doubt of the ability of urchins to bore into hard materials is dispelled by the recent finding (Irwin, 1953) of extensive damage to steel pilings on the coast of California by the boring activities of *Strongyl. purpuratus*, numbers of which were found nestling in the concavities they had made in the steel.

Another type of adaptation to wave action is seen in the echinometrid genus *Colobocentrotus*, said by Mortensen (Monogr.) to be the most highly specialized of all regular urchins. The flattened or concave oral surface, provided with especially large, strong podia and fringed at the ambitus by a circle of broad flat spines, acts like a sucker, enabling the animal to adhere tightly to rocks subject to powerful wave action, while the short, flat-topped spines that cover the aboral surface (Fig. 178*C*) break the force of the waves.

Regular echinoids move by means of their podia or their spines or by a combination of both. Vertical surfaces are climbed solely by the adhesive power of the terminal disks of the podia. Podial locomotion was given as 22 mm. per minute in *Arbacia punctulata*, increasing to 35 to 40 mm. if hurried (H. W. Jackson, 1939); as 150 mm. per minute in *Echinus* (Romanes and Ewart, 1881). Locomotion on the spine tips is much more rapid, e.g., 5 to 7 cm. per 2 seconds in *Centrostephanus longispinus* (von Uexküll, 1900a). Romanes and Ewart (1881) and Gemmill (1912) noted that *Echinus* out of water can progress by use of the lantern; the teeth are dug into the substratum, the animal erects itself on the closed teeth, and, pushing with the teeth and spines, falls forward, thus advancing by a series of lurches. Regular urchins move with any ray forward and can reverse their direction without turning around. In a study of the locomotion of *Lytechinus variegatus*, Parker (1936) noted an extremely slight preference for locomotion with Lovén's ray III forward when the podia were in use but not when the spines were employed; however, the axis of forward locomotion was frequently changed. The echinometrid *Anthocidaris crassispina* usually (but not invariably) has much shorter spines on one side of the body and when climbing vertical surfaces keeps the short spines directed down (Onoda, 1933); this species also shows a tendency to move with Lovén's ray III directed forward, although Mortensen (Monogr.) notes that the area of short spines does not necessarily correspond with this ray.

Regular urchins right themselves when placed on the aboral surface; this is done by attaching suitable podia, which thereupon shorten, pulling the test first into a vertical position and then slowly lowering it with more and more podia finding attachment (Romanes and Ewart, 1881). These authors also reported that vertical halves and even a meridional fifth would right. Kleitman (1941) gave the time of righting of *Lytechinus variegatus* as $1\frac{1}{2}$ to 2 minutes at moderate temperatures; this species would right repeatedly without showing fatigue. *Echinus*, forced to attach to a vertical surface by its aboral podia, generally rights by rotating downward and obliquely, gradually turning over as it goes (Romanes and Ewart, 1881). The righting reaction is held in abeyance if an urchin placed on its aboral surface is rotated in a vertical plane (Romanes, 1883).

In general the regular echinoids are negative to light and tend to retreat into shaded areas or retire under objects. Many have the habit of covering the aboral surface with pieces of plants, shells, small stones, and other objects, held on by the podia, and it is generally believed that protection from light is the object of this behavior rather than concealment from enemies. Dubois (1913) reported that *P. lividus*, exposed to strong light in an aquarium, would cover itself with disks provided, placing them at right angles to the incident rays; transparent disks might be utilized but would be replaced later by opaque ones. A fairly definite negative response to light is given by some species. Thus *Arbacia* (Mangold, 1909; Holmes, 1912), when exposed to a bright light, waves its spines and feet vigorously but aimlessly at first. Soon the spines on the illuminated side stop in a lowered state, those of the opposite side erect, those of the sides begin to move against the bottom like oars, the podia of the illuminated side retract, those of the opposite side stretch out, and the urchin moves away from the light into a shaded area. In addition to the general negativity to strong light, some species give a definite spine response to sudden increases and decreases of illumination. The shadow reflex or response to sudden or considerable decrease of illumination consists in the erection of the spines and is clearly a defense reaction. It is given by *Centrostephanus longispinus* (von Uexküll, 1896b), *Arbacia lixula* (Mangold, 1909), *Arbacia punctulata* (Holmes, 1912), species of *Diadema* (von Uexküll, 1900b; Millott, 1950), and no doubt other diadematids. The reaction appears to be the most precise in *Diadema* in that the spines converge and point toward the object casting the shadow, and the reaction is given to any decrease, without the necessity of a sharp shadow. The latent period for the shadow reflex is about 1 second for *Diadema antillarum* (Millott, 1950), even less (0.6 to 0.7 second) in *Centrostephanus longispinus* (von Uexküll, 1896b), which altogether is one of the most sensitive and reactive urchins. The shadow reflex is given by isolated pieces of shell if these contain a radial nerve and its branches to the spines, but the presence of the nerve ring is not necessary. According to Millott the receptors for the shadow reflex are located on the surface of the test, especially along the ambulacra, and not on the spines themselves. The role played in this reaction by the eyes of diadematids has not been tested, but it is evident that the eyes are not necessary for the response. The foregoing species also respond to sudden illumination by spine erection or pointing of the spines toward the direction of illumination. This reaction is also given by isolated pieces of test, and the presence of the radial nerve is not necessary for the response. Thus the shadow reflex is mediated by the radial nerves, whereas the reaction to increased illumination is mediated by the sub-epidermal nerve net on the external surface of the test.

Responses of regular urchins to mechanical and chemical stimulation have been described by Romanes and Ewart (1881), von Uexküll (1896a, 1896b, 1900a), and Holmes (1912). In general, any weak or moderate mechanical stimulation of spines or the test surface evokes a defense reaction: adjacent spines point to the stimulated spot. The spread of this reaction varies with the strength of the reaction but is limited, and the spines soon swing back to the normal position. Stronger or longer or repeated intermittent stimuli may cause the spines to "freeze" for some time in the defense position, and during this period other stimuli are ineffective. In *Diadema antillarum* and no doubt other diadematids, the long poisonous aboral spines bunch together and point to any source of disturbance. The spines of the diadematid *Centrostephanus longispinus* are especially sensitive and give the defense reaction to weak mechanical stimulation with a latent period of only 0.2 to 0.3 second. In this urchin mechanical or other stimulation evokes rotation of the short aboral rotating spines if they are at rest, or causes them to rotate faster if in motion. Strong mechanical stimulation may cause the spines of regular urchins to point away from the stimulated spot, thus permitting the pedicellariae to come into action.

Not much information is available regarding response to chemical stimulation, and such response is not as definite or as regularly obtained from different species as is response to mechanical stimulation. Weak chemical stimulation may evoke pointing of the spines to the place of application, stronger solutions, a pointing away. According to von Uexküll, caffein is a particularly effective chemical agent and evokes pointing away of the spines in all concentrations. Placing of urchins in sea water to which weak chemicals as acids have been added causes intense activity of all the spines.

It is evident that the spines in general constitute the defense mechanism of the animal; the spines are erected or pointed toward a source of disturbance. In case of sufficient disturbance the animal reacts by flight, in which spines and podia coordinate to carry it away from the source of danger.

Some species of regular urchins are definitely negative to gravity, especially *Psammechinus miliaris* (Bolin, 1926; Lindahl and Runnström, 1929), which will climb the walls of aquaria and ascend a glass plate, even if held at an angle of only 45 degrees, reversing if the plate is reversed. *Diadema antillarum* is also negatively geotactic (Parker, 1922).

Regular urchins in general feed by moving on top of the food, holding it with spines and podia and chewing it into bits with the lantern. If food falls on the aboral surface, it is pushed toward the mouth by the coordinated action of spines and podia and its advent is relayed to the mouth and lantern along the nervous tracts; for the mouth is directed toward the approaching food and opened and closed repeatedly, while the teeth are repeatedly thrust out and withdrawn (Roaf, 1910). Living food coming in contact with the urchin is first attacked and stupified by the pedicellariae, and these also act to hold on to food. Milligan (1916a) has reported the behavior of hungry aquarium specimens of *Psammechinus miliaris*. The food (algal fronds) is detected at a considerable distance, and the urchin indicates such detection by extending and waving the podia on the side nearest the food. It then moves directly toward the food from distances up to 19 inches, clambering over obstacles in the path, protruding the lip and opening and closing the teeth. An urchin that was 21 inches from the food started for it in a roundabout path, but after getting within 15 inches took a straight course toward it. When a bunch of algal fronds was suspended in the aquarium out of reach of hungry urchins, they would clamber up rocks near the food, stretching out their podia toward it. Urchins might require 2 or 3 weeks to chew up a bunch of seaweeds and would remain in the same spot during the process.

The food of regular urchins has been ascertained by a number of investigators, chiefly by examining the contents of the digestive tract. The available information to date, together with a detailed account of his own researches on the matter, is given by Eichelbaum (1910). It appears that most urchins will eat almost anything, but some tend to a carnivorous, others to a herbivorous, diet, although in lack of preferred items they will ingest the bottom material, and in fact act as general scavengers. Urchins with carnivorous tastes can capture live animals, if these are moribund or very sluggish, but usually they subsist abundantly on sessile and encrusting organisms such as hydroids, bryozoans, barnacles, sponges, tubicolous polychaetes, and the like. Such organisms are chewed up, shells and all, and in fact the teeth appear able to cope with any sort of shelly material. *Psammechinus miliaris* appears to be mainly carnivorous, eating chiefly, according to Eichelbaum, hydroids and tubicolous polychaetes, secondarily other animals and detritus; Milligan (1916a), keeping this species in an aquarium for 3 years, saw it eat ascidians, dead fish, fish eggs, raw beef, crustaceans, barnacles, dead crabs, crustacean legs, soft parts of mollusks, snail eggs, bryozoans, tube worms, hydroids, sponges, seaweeds, and coralline algae, as well as all sorts of empty shells and exoskeletons. *Echinus esculentus* is another carnivorous species, eating mainly other animals, as tube worms, echinoderms, crustaceans, and hydroids. *Echinus acutus* was found by Eichelbaum to feed mainly on crustaceans and mollusks. Cidaroids and diadematids also have carnivorous habits (Mortensen, Monogr.). Cidaroids tend to eat animals with hard exoskeleton, as bryozoans, mollusks, serpulids, and foraminiferans, which they crush with their powerful teeth, and diadematids, living mostly among coral reefs, browse off corals and their incrusting organisms. *Arbacia punctulata* and *Strongyl. dröbachiensis* and *purpuratus* are examples of herbivorous urchins. The first eats mostly plant material, but also animal corpses, and was observed to catch small weakened fish, holding them against the aquarium walls with spines and podia while chewing them up with its teeth (Parker, 1932). The food habits of *S. dröbachiensis* seem to vary with locality: in Puget Sound it eats mostly seaweeds and resorts to animal material only when plant material is not available (Weese, 1916); also on the eastern Canadian coast this species eats mainly seaweeds and similar material scraped from rocks plus fish refuse from adjacent canneries (Dawson, 1868); but Eichelbaum's specimens from the Baltic contained chiefly diatoms, tube worms, and hydroids, with smaller quantities of other animals. *Strongyl. purpuratus* in nature feeds on algae and other plants but in the laboratory would eat fresh and cooked vegetables, boiled eggs, fruit, and meat (Lasker and Giese, 1954). *Sphaerechinus granularis* is herbivorous, scraping algae and other material from rocks (Krumbach, 1914). Many regular urchins are scavengers and will gather in numbers to feed on dead fish or other animal corpses. They can also capture weakened or sluggish animals by fastening the terminal disks of the podia to their bodies and drawing them within reach of the teeth. In this way the crustacean *Squilla* was captured by urchins in the same aquarium (Dohrn, 1875). Urchins may be able to extract live snails from their shells (Milligan, 1916a). Deep-water forms, as the Echinothuriidae and Aspidodiadematidae, necessarily feed chiefly on the bottom ooze.

The spatangoids and clypeastroids differ altogether in their habits from the regular urchins. They live buried in sandy bottoms and no doubt their many peculiarities of structure are correlated with this habit. Not only are these animals organized morphologically with respect to an anteroposterior axis but also physiologically. They move with the anterior end forward (and this is true also of sand dollars that have a circular outline) and they are unable to move with any other ray forward or to progress backward. Spatangoids such as *Echinocardium cordatum* and *flavescens* and *Spatangus purpureus* dwell in cavities in the sand connected by a canal with a surface hole which betrays the presence of the animal. *E. cordatum* lives several inches below the surface (Robertson, 1871; Cuénot, 1912), whereas *E. flavescens* may stay close to the

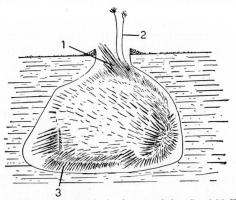

FIG. 238.—*Echinocardium flavescens* in its burrow (*after Gandolfi-Hornyold*, 1910). 1, aboral tuft of spines; 2, frontal podia extended above surface of sand; 3, spines of plastron.

surface with its tuft of long aboral spines projecting from the hole (Gandolfi-Hornyold, 1910, 1913, Fig. 238). The walls of the burrow and canal are plastered with mucus secreted by the mucous glands of the spines and thus retain their shape, so that they do not touch the animal and sand does not fall upon it. If the spatangoid is placed on the surface of the sand, it erects itself on its oral spines and begins to throw the sand sidewise by means of its curved lateral spines, burying itself in a few minutes. If these lateral spines are removed, the animal cannot burrow. The large, strong spines of the plastron do not participate in burrowing but keep up a water circulation through the burrow by rowing movements. The feeding habits of spatangoids, so far as observed, are remarkable. The pencillate podia of the phyllodes, which are very extensile, are thrust out through the surface hole and with widely opened terminal processes explore the sand surface, picking up small food particles by way of adhesive secretion. They then retract and deliver the food particles to the spines of the upper lip and labrum that direct them to the mouth. Eichelbaum (1910) reported that the digestive tract of several spatangoids examined (*E. cordatum, E. flavescens, Spatangus purpureus, Brissopsis lyrifera, Schizaster fragilis*) was invariably stuffed with bottom material, containing an abundance of diatoms and foraminiferans, as well as fragments of worms, coelenterates, mollusks, and echinoderms. Lafon (1953), studying sandy areas on the Channel coast of France, found the digestive tract of *E. cordatum* filled with bottom material, extremely poor in organic contents; and, similarly, the author noted that *Meoma ventricosa* in the Bahamas ingests nothing but coral sand, very low in nutritive value. It would appear that these large spatangoids must subsist on very scanty fare.

Sand dollars live buried directly in the sand, close under the surface. They always move with Lovén's ray III forward, chiefly or wholly by the spines, which in *Echinarachnius parma* are longest along the anterior edge and decrease in length posteriorly. In a study of the activities of this sand dollar, Parker (1927) and Parker and Van Alstyne (1932) found that the animal buries itself by piling up sand into a mound in front of itself by means of the podia, then shoving itself into this mound with the spines while the podia continue to cover it with sand. The burying process requires about 15 to 20 minutes. The animal may continue to move about under the sand or come to a stop. It will also move about on top of the sand at a maximum rate of 18 mm. per minute. On meeting an obstacle, the animal will rotate on its oral-aboral axis and start off in another direction. *Echinarchnius* can right itself, in an hour or so, when buried oral side up, or in several hours when placed oral side up on the top of the sand. In righting, the animal by means of its spines works its anterior edge into the sand and gradually erects itself into a vertical position, from which it falls over into the normal orientation. Following the ablation of the sphaeridia, the animals are usually able to right themselves, but the reaction is much slowed and less efficiently accomplished. The Pacific sand dollar, *Dendraster excentricus*, lies buried in an oblique or nearly vertical position with the anterior edge down and the posterior third protruding (H. L. Clark, 1901; Ricketts and Calvin, 1953); it leans away from a current at an angle that is similar throughout the bed. On suitable sand flats this species may occur in enormous numbers.

Some information on the activities of keyhole scutellids has been furnished by Crozier (1920), Ikeda (1941), and Kenk (1944). The *Mellita* with six lunules lives at Bermuda buried in the sand, preferably in the path of tidal currents, and digs deeper in stormy weather. It buries itself by rotating the test from side to side, and thus slides itself under the sand in about 15 minutes, aided by the action of spines and podia. In the West Indies the five-lunuled *Mellita* lies buried in a slightly oblique position with the posterior edge exposed and may move continuously through the sand at a rate of 11 to 26 mm. per minute. If put on top of the sand in the normal orientation, it simply advances into the sand, disappearing in 1 to 4 minutes. According to Kenk, this species cannot right, but the inverted position is unstable and waves soon turn the animal over. Ikeda is of the opinion that the lunules are essential in burrowing and righting of *Astriclypeus manni*. In burrowing, this sand dollar takes a slanting position and buries itself in 10 minutes by driving sand through the anterior lunules through the action of the large spines bordering the lunules. If placed on its back, it will right itself in about 3 hours. Because of its shape, the test slants forward, sand is driven through the anterior lunules and piles up behind the animal, gradually raising the test into a vertical position, whereupon it falls over. Burying is greatly delayed if the lunules are filled with soft paraffin, and the animal cannot right itself if the large spines bordering the lunules are also removed.

Information on the feeding behavior of sand dollars is scanty. The MacGinities (1949) state that mucous strands in which tiny particles and organisms are entrapped are carried by ciliary currents into the furrows of the oral surface and so into the mouth. Gislén (1924) reported that the intestine of the Japanese sand dollar, *Astericlypeus manni*, contained sand grains, bits of plants, detritus, diatoms, foraminiferans, tiny copepods, flagellates, rotifers, annelid and acarid bristles, and bits of siphonophores.

A few urchins are known to change color with reference to light conditions. *Arbacia lixula* is black in daylight, brown in the dark (von Uexküll, 1896b; Kleinholz, 1938), and this change occurs in about an hour. Parker (1931) could not find any color change in *Arbacia punctulata* with alterations of light conditions. Color change is most marked among the diadematids. *Centrostephanus longispinus* is dark purple in daylight, but after even half an hour in the dark becomes light grey (von Uexküll, 1896b). This result was verified by Kleinholz (1938), who also found that isolated tube feet, brownish red in the light, turn pinkish white after several hours in darkness. Young *Diadema antillarum* are intensely black by day or in strong light but in darkness turn pale gray in 60 to 90 minutes and show a brilliant white star with iridescent blue edges encircling the periproct and extending along the interambulacra to the ambitus (Millott, 1950, 1952). This reaction is given by small isolated pieces of test scraped clean of tissue on the coelomic side. In fact, all the above observers agree that the color changes of echinoids are independent of the nervous system and result from a direct action of light on black chromatophores which expand their spidery processes in light and contract to balls in darkness. In *Diadema* contraction of the black chromatophores exposes white chromatophores (iridophores), and diffraction of light by these is mainly responsible for the blue spots and stripes seen in this genus under certain conditions (Millott, 1953a). The blue pattern corresponds to the distribution of the iridophores, and Millott is therefore of the opinion that the blue spots are not of the nature of photoreceptors and are not of taxonomic importance. The color change of *Diadema antillarum* is exhibited only by young specimens, disappearing as the animal ages, and shows a daily rhythmicity in young animals even when these are kept in total darkness.

**30. Physiology.**—The physiology of spines, pedicellariae, and podia has been investigated by Romanes and Ewart (1881), Romanes (1883), and especially von Uexküll (1896a, 1896b, 1900a). It will be recalled that each spine is operated by a double muscle circlet (Fig. 187*A*) of which the inner circlet acts as a cog musculature that serves to "lock" the spine in a certain state of tone (tension). It is this cog musculature that keeps the spines in their typical state of erection at approximately right angles to the surface of the test. If urchins are anesthetized, as by carbon dioxide, the spines fall flaccidly against the test. The action of the cog musculature can be demonstrated by placing the finger on the tip of a spine and attempting to move the spine; one then finds that the spine is immovable, as the stimulus has brought the cog musculature into action and thus set the spine in a given position. If one now stimulates the adjacent test surface, the spine becomes freely movable, as the cog musculature is now inhibited. Thus any stimulus evoking spine movements must first inhibit the cog musculature. However, the spines of *Centrostephanus longispinus* are so sensitive that any touch upon them finds them freely movable; this is perhaps only another way of saying that the inhibition of normal tension is very rapid. Jarring the urchin is another way of bringing the cog musculature into action and setting the spines into a fixed position temporarily. Typical spine reactions, erection, or pointing toward or away from the source of stimulation are given by spines on isolated pieces of test that have been cleaned of all tissue on the coelomic surface. This proves that the stimulus to ordinary spine reactions is transmitted through the subepidermal nerve net on the external surface of the test. This may also be demonstrated by making a circular cut through the surface tissues down to the calcareous plates of the test; the spines enclosed by this cut will respond to a stimulus applied within the circle but not to one applied outside it. A stimulus also will generally not be transmitted around the end of a short straight cut through the surface tissues (Romanes and Ewart, 1881); but in the very sensitive *Centrostephanus* this does happen (von Uexküll, 1900a). In such case, however, the spine does not point toward the stimulated spot but toward the end of cut around which the stimulus reaches the spine. In short, the rule seems to be that a spine points toward the direction from which the stimulus reaches it through the nerve network, and therefore adjacent spines all point in the same direction. In case of spines pointing away from a locus of stimulation as to a chemical, the stimulus may be transmitted by the descending spines striking against those farther out that are still erect, and hence this kind of reaction may be transmitted across a cut. The general bending of spines seems to occur more readily in the oral than in the aboral direction. General reactions involving all the spines as locomotion are not affected by cuts through the subepidermal network, and hence are mediated by way of the radial nerves. Thus if the area mentioned above which is isolated by a circular cut is sufficiently stimulated, all of the spines come into action and the animal moves away. One may say that the spines operate entirely by way of the subepidermal network to ordinary stimuli, but if the situation appears threatening, the radial nerves enter the picture, all of the spines are brought into coordinated action, and the animal retreats.

Information concerning the behavior of pedicellariae comes almost entirely from the well-known article by von Uexküll (1899), although Romanes and Ewart (1881) contributed some observations. The pedicellariae are highly independent structures, operating by way of the nervous ring in their base and the nervous tissue within their stalk and head. The tridentate and ophiocephalous pedicellariae act to bite objects that come within their reach. The former respond the most rapidly as their adductor muscles contain striated fibers, but soon open, whereas the ophiocephalous pedicellariae hang on more tenaciously when closed. Both respond positively to a weak stimulus, and the ophiocephalous type is also positive to a stronger stimulus whereas the tridentates bend away. On an isolated piece of test the tridentates are found swinging about with open jaws. A slight jarring causes all of them to close. A light touch on the inner surface of the jaws evokes instant closure; stroking the outer surface causes the jaws to open. These reactions occur in isolated tridentates. Chemicals brought near the tridentate and ophiocephalous types cause them to snap several times and render them insensitive to simultaneous mechanical stimulation. In the normal urchin these two types of pedicellariae act as defense weapons and also assist in capturing live food by hanging onto the hairs of crustaceans, and so on. The trifoliate pedicellariae have a cleansing function, and their ordinary activity consists in mouthing over the test surface and spine bases to remove small particles. Larger particles are moved off the test by the spines, but if fine material falls upon the test the trifoliates come into action, spreading it out thinly or biting it into smaller particles so that the cilia of the epidermis can remove it. Isolated trifoliates are not very reactive and remain for some time closed and motionless; but if they finally open, a mechanical or chemical stimulus evokes closure. In none of the foregoing three types is there any evidence of the existence of definite receptors such as occur on the globiferous pedicellariae in the form of sensory hillocks (Fig. 188*A*).

The globiferous pedicellariae are weapons of defense; whereas the tridentate and ophiocephalous types draw away from sufficiently strong stimuli, the globiferous forms react positively, viciously attacking intruders. As already noted, the spines also bend away from such stimuli, allowing the globiferous pedicellariae free play. Their toxic bite usually succeeds in driving away a foe, even a starfish; but as the heads easily detach and remain in the foe, the starfish by repeated attacks may exhaust the supply of globiferous pedicellariae of the urchin, which then falls prey to the enemy. Battles of this kind between starfish and urchin have been witnessed by Prouho (1890) and von Uexküll. The negative reaction of the spines to such stimuli is wanting in the case of urchins such as *Arbacia* which lack globiferous pedicellariae. The use of the globiferous pedicellariae is generally followed by flight, so that the same stimulus successively brings into play withdrawal of the spines, action of the globiferous pedicellariae, and extension of the podia away from the source of stimulation.

Isolated globiferous pedicellariae usually remain open or can be caused to open by lightly stroking the tip or the outer surface. Any touch on the sensory hillocks evokes wider opening, but if chemical stimulation is simultaneously applied, as a grain of salt or a starfish podium, closure occurs. Following such chemical stimulation of the test surface, the globiferous pedicellariae bite at mechanical objects of stimulation but do not eject their poison. The ejection of the poison is relatively independent of jaw closure, but follows if the jaws close upon a source of chemical stimulation, as the podia of a starfish. The emission of the toxin can be evoked without jaw closure by laying a bit of chemical on the opened jaws. Apparently the globiferous pedicellariae must first be sensitized by chemical stimulation before they will react by closure to mechanical stimulation.

The toxin is of unknown nature but acts by paralyzing small animals. Extracts of all four types of pedicellariae are toxic to small animals, such as crabs, fish, or lizards, when injected, but frogs and other echinoderms are more or less immune (Henri and Kayalof, 1906; Pérès, 1950). Paralysis immediately follows injection, and death generally ensues in one-half to several hours. Although the extract of the globiferous pedicellariae is the most effective, the other types are also toxic, as are in a lesser degree the body fluids and the axial gland (Pérès, 1950). Fujiwara (1935) reported that the bites of seven or eight pedicellariae of *Toxo-*

*pneustes pileolus* into his finger evoked severe pain, followed later by dizziness, some facial paralysis, and difficulty of respiration.

The functions of the sphaeridia have not been definitely ascertained. The negative geotropism of *Psammechinus miliaris* continues after ablation of the sphaeridia, although some individuals may show disturbance of this reaction and the general tone of the animal appears upset (Bolin, 1926). Delage (1902) noted that urchins would continue to climb after ablation of the sphaeridia, but the righting reaction was greatly slowed, seemingly from a lack of coordination among the podia.

As might be inferred from their innervation, the podia are operated by the radial nerves in response to surface stimulation. Weak mechanical stimulation evokes stretching out of the podia, stronger stimulation, their retraction. Jarring of the urchin causes the podia to adhere so tightly that they will be torn off rather than release their hold. Weak chemical stimulation, as with acid, evokes retraction of the podia, extension of the opposite ones, and a moving away from the source of stimulation. The podia are also employed as feelers, being stretched out in the direction of advance to test the environment.

No evidence of participation of the nerve ring in urchin behavior appears in the foregoing account. Romanes and Ewart (1881) divided urchins at the ambitus into oral and aboral halves that were freed of viscera (including, one supposes, the lantern and nerve ring, although this is not clearly stated) and reported that such halves would live for some time and move about, giving normal responses of spines, podia, and pedicellariae. Following a circular cut in the peristome, isolating the nerve ring from communication with the test, the podia can still be protruded and will adhere, anchoring the urchin. The animal can move about but does not show determinate advance, constantly changing direction and often rotating in one spot; it can also climb, but in a weakened manner. The outstanding effect of the operation is the loss of coordinated movement as a whole. The animal is incapable of flight, as in response to an injurious stimulus it will move indifferently in any direction, even toward the source of injury. Most of such operated animals do not right, although some may. While the spines show their usual reactions and after a time recover, so that they will bristle up over the whole animal in response to a strong stimulus, their locomotory function is permanently destroyed, because of a lack of coordination in their movements. Von Uexküll (1900b) and Bolin (1926) also found that the normal reactions of external appendages can be elicited after destruction of the nerve ring, but the animal is in general immobilized and inactive. Holmes (1912) indicates that *Arbacia punctulata* will continue to move about after the nerve ring is sectioned in several places but does not show negative phototaxis. In general, the reactions of the animal as a whole, such as directed advance and flight response, are obliterated in the absence of the nerve ring, from a lack of coordination among the locomotory appendages. The pedicellariae are wholly unaffected by destruction of the nerve ring.

The surface ciliary currents of echinoids are reported by Gislén (1924). In regular urchins these currents run toward the mouth, in general. In the sand dollar *Echinocyamus pusillus*, the aboral surface ciliates toward the edge, the oral surface toward the mouth. The ciliary currents of spatangoids in general run toward the margin, and particles of mud gather in the fascioles where they are glued together by mucous secretion and then plastered onto the burrow walls by the penicillate podia and spine tufts.

Available information about the chemical composition of echinoids has been assembled by Vinogradov (1953). Meyer (1914) analyzed *Echinus esculentus* and found 73.5 per cent water; the dry substance was composed of 8.37 per cent protein, 7.11 per cent carbohydrate, 0.68 per cent fat, and 83.31 per cent ash, most of which of course is the calcium carbonate of the skeleton. The same author gave the following figures for *Spatangus purpureus:* 55.01 per cent water, and 44.99 per cent dry substance, consisting of 9.07 per cent protein, 1.62 per cent fat, 6.64 per cent carbohydrate, and 78.58 per cent ash. It would appear that the skeleton forms a much larger proportion of the fresh weight in the heart urchin than in the regular urchin. The calcium carbonate of the skeleton is in the form of calcite, as in all echinoderms. A tabulation of the available analyses in Vinogradov, mostly from Clarke and Wheeler (1922), shows the skeleton to consist of 83 to 95 per cent calcium carbonate, 3 to 14 per cent magnesium carbonate, and small quantities of phosphate, aluminate, and calcium sulphate and other forms of sulphur. The composition of the spines, lantern, and test is not identical; the test is highest in magnesium carbonate. The spines consist of crystals of calcite arranged parallel so as to give the impression of one large crystal (Garrido and Blanco, 1947). Traces of the following elements have also been found in echinoids: iron, manganese, strontium, barium, copper, zinc (Phillips, 1922; Webb, 1937).

Much interest has been shown by biochemists in the pigments of urchins. The red or purple pigments common in many regular urchins, not only in the spines and test but also in the podia, pedicellariae, gonads, and coelomocytes, belong to the category of naphthoquinones (review in Lederer, 1940). They are divisible into echinochromes and spinochromes, only slightly different chemically, and related to certain vitamins. Echinochrome was first studied and named by MacMunn (1885) in the red coelomocytes of *Paracentrotus lividus* and *Echinus esculentus*. Its chemical structure was elucidated by Kuhn and Wallenfels (1939, Fig.

239); other chemical studies have been made on these pigments by Ball (1936), Lederer and Glaser (1938), Fox and Scheer (1941), and Goodwin, Lederer, and Musajo (1951). They have the general formula $C_{12}H_{8-10}O_{7-8}$. Echinochromes and spinochromes are apparently wanting in irregular urchins (Goodwin and Srisukh, 1951). The black pigment of *Diadema antillarum* and no doubt of other black urchins is melanin (Millott and Jacobson, 1951, 1952a, 1952b; Jacobson and Millott, 1953). These authors have shown that the melanin comes from the coelomocytes

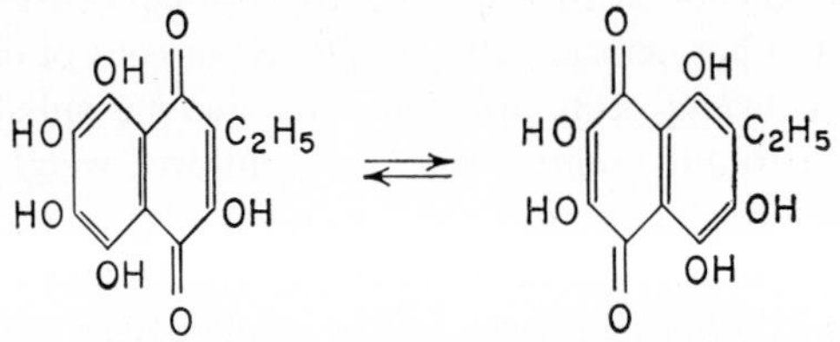

Fig. 239.—Formula of echinochrome.

with colorless spherules. These cells or their spherules contain both the precursor of the melanin and the enzyme (phenolase) necessary to transform the precursor into melanin. The coelomoctyes in question wander to the epidermis where they deposit the melanin in the large melanophores (black pigment cells) found there. The coelomic fluid contains an inhibitor of the transformation process, and this explains the lack of melanin deposition as long as the coelomocytes remain in the coelomic fluid. Some carotenoid pigments occur in echinoids (Lönnberg, 1931, 1934a; Fox and Scheer, 1941; Fox, 1947; Lederer, 1938), but in less quantity than in other echinoderm classes, and appear not to contribute to surface coloration. Large amounts of carotenoid were found in the gonads of the heart urchin by Goodwin and Srisukh (1951) and determined as a mixture of beta carotene, echinenone (provitamin A), and lutein. Echinenone was first isolated from *Paracentrotus lividus* and appears widely distributed in marine invertebrates. Small amounts of carotenoids, including xanthophylls, carotene, and echinenone, were found by Fox and Scheer (1941) in all of three regular urchins and one sand dollar investigated on the California coast.

Considerable phylogenetic importance is attributed by Bergmann (1949) in his studies of sterols to the fact that cholesterol is the principal sterol of echinoids and is not found in asteroids or holothuroids.

The composition of the coelomic fluid of echinoids (minus the coelomocytes) has been determined by a number of workers, but their reports disagree slightly. Some as Geddes (1880), Griffiths (1893), Robertson (1939), and Cole (1940) report the salt content as identical with that of sea water, whereas Bethe and Berger (1931) found all salts in *Echinus esculentus* in higher amounts than in sea water, especially potassium and calcium, and Parker and Cole (1940), using *Strongyl. dröbachiensis*, reported more potassium and chloride than in sea water. The presence of a trace of protein in the coelomic fluid was asserted by Geddes (1886), Cuénot (1891b), Robertson (1939), and others, whereas Cohnheim (1901), Myers (1920), and Van der Heyde (1923c) denied its presence. Reducing sugar up to 62 mg. per cent wet-body weight occurs in the coelomic fluid of *Strongyl. purpuratus* but quickly disappears in starvation (Lasker and Giese, 1954). The best analysis of the coelomic fluid appears that of Myers, who obtained for *Strongyl. dröbachiensis* 96.52 per cent of water, 3 per cent of salts, and 0.48 per cent of organic material, some of which consists of nonprotein nitrogenous substances. Lasker and Giese (1954) found about 5 mg. per cent wet weight of nonprotein nitrogen, at least part consisting of amino acids, in the coelomic fluid of *Strongyl. purpuratus*. (See also page 569.) The coelomic fluid so far as tested is less alkaline than sea water; Cole (1940) reported a pH of 6.9 in *Echinarachnius parma* and 7.2 to 7.84 for *Strongyl. dröbachiensis* off Maine, whereas in Puget Sound figures of 7.35 to 8.15 are given for the latter by Weese (1926).

In general, echinoids have practically no power of ionic regulation, that is, of maintaining in their body fluid an ionic concentration other than what results from passive equilibrium with the medium. Placed in diluted sea water they imbibe water and gain weight, but not if the difference in osmotic pressure is compensated by the addition of sugar (Henri and Lalou, 1903); salts did not pass out within the time limits of the experiment (2 hours). Echinoids apparently avoid brackish water; in a study of the fauna of a brackish estuary on the Maine coast, Topping and Fuller (1942) noted less adaptation of echinoderms to brackish water than of other marine invertebrates. *Strongyl. dröbachiensis* was limited to the mouth of the estuary where the salinity was but slightly less than that of the sea.

All observers agree that the coelomic fluid clots shortly after shedding and that the clot consists of the phagocytic types of coelomocytes whose pseudopods more or less fuse to a mesh in which the other amoebocytes become entangled (Geddes, 1880; Nolf, 1909; Kindred, 1921; Donellon, 1938; Bookhaut and Greenburg, 1940; Millot, 1951). The coelomic fluid minus the cells will not clot. Clotting is accelerated by extracts of the tissues of urchins or other marine invertebrates, by salts of the alkaline earth series, especially potassium, and by hypertonic solutions, but is delayed by magnesium salts and by calcium precipitants as oxalate. The work of Donellon shows that some injury substance is normally responsible for clotting, and this explains why the cells do not clot while in the coelom; but if a needle is thrust through the peristome and the inner surface of the test scratched, a clot will form at the scratch. In the clot the coelomocytes break down, releasing their inclusions, and in *Diadema antillarum* the clot slowly turns black, as melanin is formed, after the manner already described (Millott, 1951).

The nature of the inclusions in the coelomocytes has not been definitely ascertained. Cuénot (1891b) and St. Hilaire (1897) thought that the colorless inclusions contain albuminoid and some fatty substances. The former found that coelomocytes would take up peptone, but this is not significant, as they also take up inert particles. Liebman (1950) was unable to arrive at any satisfactory results on the nature of the inclusions by means of histochemical tests, but nevertheless concluded that the coelomocytes aggregated in the gonads were carrying food supplies to the developing germ cells. It is more likely that they were on their way to the exterior with waste matters. Bookhaut and Greenburg (1940) found that the red coelomocytes of *Mellita* contain fatty material but did not ingest injected fat droplets. The phagocytic types of coelomocytes will take up almost any kind of material injected into the coelom, as carmine, carbon, indigocarmine, fat droplets (Awerinzew, 1911; Kindred, 1921; Bookhaut and Greenburg, 1940), and according to Awerinzew they carry them to the exterior. Probably the coelomocytes convey both food materials and waste and foreign substances and are also concerned in pigment deposition at the surface, as already indicated for *Diadema*. Awerinzew found that the color of *Strongyl. drôbachiensis* varies with the kind of plant food ingested and results from the conveyance to the surface by coelomocytes of the pigments of ingested plants.

Kollmann (1908) could find no evidence of a production of coelomocytes by the axial gland; and the experiments of Schinke (1950) have shown that the coelomocytes originate in the general dermis of the body wall. Schinke drained out the coelomic fluid of *Psamm. miliaris*, replacing it with sea water, and found that 60 per cent of the coelomocytes are reformed in 1 day and all of them in 2 to 4 days. Repetition of the experiment following removal of the axial gland gave the same result, and in fact, after removal of all the internal organs, the coelomocytes are still readily replaced. This author is of the opinion that the amoebocytes with colorless and red inclusions originate directly by transformation of dermal mesenchyme cells, but that the phagocytic coelomocytes derive from the type with colorless inclusions.

Digestion in echinoids was studied by Weese (1926), using *Strongyl. dröbachiensis*, and by Lasker and Giese (1954), using *S. purpuratus;* data are also furnished by Roaf (1910) on *Echinus esculentus* and Van der Heyde (1922) on *Arbacia punctulata*. Roaf found that the food reaches the beginning of the small intestine in 4 hours and of the large intestine in 24 hours and in its passage is formed into rounded pellets enclosed in mucus that gradually become transparent. Lasker and Giese report that starved urchins continue to pass fecal pellets for about 2 weeks. Roaf added indicators to the food and concluded that the food becomes more acid at first and later turns alkaline, but Weese rejected Roaf's procedure as unreliable and could find no correlation between pH and location in the digestive tract. The pH varied from 6.2 to 7.55 without definite reference to the amount of food present or level of the intestine. Van der Heyde found a pH of 7.2 to 7.8 in the intestine of *Arbacia*, and Lasker and Giese one of 7.2 to 7.3 in *S. purpuratus*. Several investigators have tested extracts of echinoids' digestive tracts for enzymes. Cohnheim (1901) reported finding a strong diastase and a weak invertase but no protease. Scott (1901) detected protease and diastase, acting in neutral or alkaline media, but no lipase. Van der Heyde (1922) found a weak protease, a very weak invertase, and no lipase in *Arbacia*. Weese determined the presence of a protease acting on egg white at pH 2.4, another acting on gelatin at pH 7.0, best at 8.0, and an amylase working best at 7.5, but noted no lipase. Amylase and invertase, but no protease, were reported by Bertolini (1930, 1932) in extracts of the siphon and both circuits of the intestine, and this author thinks the siphon is a digestive gland. In extracts of ground entire digestive tracts of *S. purpuratus*, Lasker and Giese proved the presence of protease and amylase, but found no evidence of the ability of the urchin to digest many of the constituents of the algal food of this species and suggested that perhaps the bacteria in the urchin gut might assist in the digestion of the algae, as the food pellets in the large intestine are covered with a transparent membrane lined with bacteria. The large caecum of spatangoids appears definitely of digestive nature; it contains a brownish, slightly acid fluid rich in amylase and also able to digest egg white, fibrin, and gelatin (Henri, 1903c). The existence of a current through the siphon of regular urchins was confirmed by Henri (1903b), who in the opened specimen observed rhythmic contractile waves, originating in the esophagus, passing along the siphon at intervals of 10 to 12 seconds in the direction of the small intestine; methylene blue injected into the esophagus could be seen moving along the siphon and into the intestine.

Little is known of the fate of the digested food. The rich vascularization of the intestinal wall would indicate absorption into the haemal system, but evidence is wanting. Awerinzew (1911) injected carmine, carbon, and indigocarmine into the intestinal lumen of *S. dröbachiensis* and reported that the last was retained in the intestinal wall but the other two substances reached the coelom and were taken up by coelomocytes that, loaded with particles, would leave the urchin, or might deposit the particles in the body wall. Van der Heyde (1922) noted amino acids in the coelomic fluid of feeding *Arbacia* and found amino acids in this fluid after injecting proteins into the digestive tract; similar experiments with sugar failed. Kindred (1926) saw droplets, apparently of digested food, in the connective tissue of the intestine picked up by phagocytic coelomocytes and concluded that amoebocytes with colorless inclusions represent phagocytic coelomocytes stuffed with food; Schinke (page 565) reached a different conclusion. The experiments of Lasker and Giese (1954) evidence the passage of the products of digestion into the coelomic fluid. They showed that the sugar in the coelomic fluid disappears in starvation but rises after a meal containing carbohydrates, and similarly the nonprotein nitrogenous content of the coelomic fluid rises after a high protein diet, decreasing again to a normal value in about 3 days and not declining further with starvation. They noted a rapid disappearance of glucose injected into the coelom of a starving urchin and reported glycogen storage in all tissues but especially in the intestine. The glycogen content of a male *S. purpuratus* was found to be 472 mg. per cent on the basis of dry weight. Stott (1931) reported glycogen storage in the gonads of both sexes of *Echinus esculentus* with a large decrease just prior to spawning. Whether coelomocytes distribute digested food and whether their inclusions represent stored food must remain unsettled as regards echinoids.

The role of the compass apparatus (page 465) in respiration in echinoids was discovered by von Uexküll (1896c), whose work indicates that the respiratory movements of the apparatus are controlled by the nerve ring as they may be invoked by stimulation of the nerve ring. The movements are not rhythmic but occur only when an oxygen need is felt; the increased carbon dioxide content then acts as a stimulant to the nerve ring. As acetic acid applied to the nerve ring is also effective, the stimulating action of carbon dioxide must be attributed to its acidity. The only data that have been found on oxygen consumption are those of Koller and Meyer (1933), whose figures indicate a utilization of 0.11 mg. of oxygen per gram of weight per hour for the smaller and 0.08 for the larger specimens used. The finding of these authors that exclusion of the podia by taping them up eliminates all oxygen intake appears incredible. Lasker and Giese (1954) give the average oxygen intake of the intestine of *S. purpuratus* as 0.7 cu. mm. per mg. per hour; it was not affected by addition of glucose or yeast extract to the medium.

The mode of operation of the water-vascular system was considered under Asteroidea, and the account there presumably applies to echinoids also. Some work has been done on the role of the madreporite and stone canal in echinoids. Ludwig (1890) noted an inward current in the removed madreporite with stone canal attached. According to Bamber (1921) the current flows out along the center and in along the periphery of the stone canal. The madreporite appears to be kept clean by ciliary action, as a cloud of particles added to the water does not settle on the madreporic plate (Bamber, 1921). Krüger (1932) fastened a manometer tube over the madreporite and found that water will pass through the latter if sufficient pressure is applied, under which circumstances a colored fluid will extend throughout the water-vascular system. Ordinarily, however, there is no continuous inflow of sea water through the madreporite into the water-vascular system (Bamber, 1921, Krüger, 1932). Added color usually gets no farther than the axial gland, which thus seems from the results of these workers to open definitely into the watervascular system. Perhaps such connection serves primarily for the exit of excreta or of coelomocytes loaded with excreta (see below).

Attempts have been made to solve the problem of excretion in echinoids by injecting inert particles and by chemical analysis. Kowalevsky (1889) noted that injected carmine accumulated thickly in the axial gland. Awerinzew (1911) found that carmine or carbon particles are ingested by the coelomocytes and that such loaded coelomocytes would leave the body by way of the gills or elsewhere or might deposit the granules in the body wall. Three days after the injection the gills were covered with outwandered coelomocytes filled with injected particles. This author also indicates a phagocytic power on the part of the coelomic epithelium. Kindred (1921) noted that carmine and carbon particles injected into the coelom of *Arbacia* are taken up by the phagocytic coelomocytes. Similar observations were made on *Mellita* by Bookhaut and Greenburg (1940), who reported that half an hour after the injection of carmine into the coelom, carmine particles are found in both types of phagocytes and in the amoebocytes with brown inclusions. Durham (1892) noticed that dark-brown material can be wiped off the gills of *Echinus* and that this is found on examination to be composed of amoebocytes with yellow or brown inclusions. Similarly he found cells with brown or black spheres on the surface, on the madreporite, and around the podia of the phyllodes in spatangoids. It would seem to be established that the coelomocytes, or some of them, ingest foreign particles and convey them to the exterior; presumably metabolic wastes would be treated in the same manner. It further appears probable that the axial gland is a way station in the elimination of excretory material as foreign colored material accumulates there (Kowalevsky, 1889; Krüger, 1932). This gland as already described is full of coelomocytes of the types with inclusions, and this fact is difficult to explain on any other basis. The walls of the gland also contain numerous granules suggestive of excretory matters. Further, an exit route is available by way of the stone canal and madreporite. It seems probable, therefore, that in echinoids the axial gland serves an excretory function.

Identification of the form in which the nitrogenous wastes of echinoids are eliminated has been attempted by a number of biochemists, chiefly by analysis of the coelomic fluid (freed from cells) or tissue extracts. Cohnheim (1901) found that the coelomic fluid contains five or six times as much nonprotein nitrogen as sea water, about 3 mg. per 100 cc., and identified therein urea, amino nitrogen, ammonia nitrogen, and purine bases, but noted scarcely any uric acid. Sanzo (1907) reported 2.24 to 3.69 mg. of urea per 100 g. of coelomic fluid of several regular urchins. Myers (1920) examined the coelomic fluid of *Strongyl. franciscanus* and detected creatine, creatinine, a trace of uric acid, some urea, and ammonia nitrogen, but no amino nitrogen. Uric acid was the only nitrogenous waste found by Van der Heyde (1923c) in the coelomic fluid of *Arbacia punctulata*, and as this substance was also present in the intestine, this author concluded that nitrogenous excretion occurs by way of the intestine. Przylecki (1926) detected only a trace of uric acid in echinoids, 0.5 mg. per 100 g. of tissue. In sea water in which *Paracentrotus lividus* had lived for 24 hours, Delaunay (1931, 1934) detected ammonia nitrogen, amino nitrogen, urea, and a trace of uric acid. In the coelomic fluid was found 5.7 mg. of nonprotein nitrogen per 100 cc. as compared with 0.4 mg. in sea water, and analysis showed this to include 0.24 mg. of ammonia N, 2.40 of amino nitrogen, and 0.12 of urea, but no uric acid. Florkin and Duchateau (1943) have pointed out that the breakdown from uric acid to ammonia by way of allantoin and urea requires a specific enzyme at every stage; if uricase is wanting, uric acid is excreted, but in the presence of uricase the breakdown proceeds mostly to ammonia. As urchins possess uricase, it may be expected that they will excrete chiefly urea and ammonia. The foregoing data show that in most cases uric acid is absent or present only in traces and that amino and ammonia nitrogen are the most common end products in echinoids. Baldwin (1947) places importance on the finding of creatinine and creatine in echinoderms, as these are typical nitrogenous products of vertebrates and among invertebrates occur only in echinoderms.

**31. Ecology: Geographical Distribution.**—The echinoids inhabit all seas and all types of bottom, extending from the intertidal zone to depths of around 5000 m. but appear absent from the deepest ocean abysses. They are most common in the littoral zone, that is, from the upper tide limit to the edge of the continental shelf, although many occur or extend into waters of considerable depth. As already indicated, regular littoral urchins are rather addicted to rocky or hard bottom, whereas the irregular forms are usually associated with sandy or partly sand substrates. Deeper-water forms necessarily live on the bottom ooze.

The littoral echinoids occur most richly in the Indo-Pacific area, centering in the Indo-Malay part of this great region and from there radiating to Australia, Japan, the eastern coast of Africa, and even as far eastward as the Hawaiian Islands. The main reports on the littoral

Indo-Pacific echinoids are those of Döderlein (1902) from Semon's expedition to Australia and the Indo-Malay Archipelago, De Meijere (1904) from the *Siboga* Expedition to the Netherland East Indies (now Indonesia), Koehler (1914, 1922, 1927) on the echinoids of the Indian Museum, Roxas (1928) on Philippine littoral echinoids, H. L. Clark (1946) in his book on the echinoderms of Australia, and Mortensen (1948) on the *Albatross* collections from the Philippines and adjacent areas. The scientific names given here are those that appear in Mortensen's monograph, where preceding synonyms will be found.

According to Mortensen (1930), the cidaroids center in the Indo-Pacific, where most of the known species occur. There are, however, only a few common littoral cidaroids in the Indo-Pacific, namely, *Eucidaris metularia, Phyllacanthus imperialis,* and *Plococidaris verticillata;* slightly less common are *Prionocidaris baculosa* and *bispinosa.* The Echinothuriidae are represented by *Asthenosoma varium,* common throughout the Indo-Pacific in shallow waters to 100 m. depth. The Arbaciidae are represented by *Coelopleurus maillardi.* Diadematids, notable for their poisonous spines, are common in the Indo-Pacific, especially *Chaetodiadema granulatum, Diadema setosum* and *savignyi, Echinothrix diadema* and *calamaris,* and *Astropyga radiata.* The Temnopleuridae are well represented in the Indo-Pacific by the very common species *Temnopleura toreumaticus* and *reevesii, Salmacis bicolor,* and *Mespilia globulus;* other common forms are *Salmacis sphaeroides, belli,* and *virgulata,* and *Temnotrema siamense, pulchellum,* and *reticulatum.* Among the most common of Indo-Pacific littoral echinoids are the two toxopneustids *Toxopneustes pileolus* and *Tripneustes gratilla.* There appear to be no common littoral echinids in the Indo-Pacific, but the strongylocentrotids are represented by the two rock-boring species *Echinostrephus aciculata* and *molaris.* Echinometrids are especially characteristic of the Indo-Pacific area where the species *Echinometra mathaei* and *Heterocentrotus mammillatus* are very common, especially the former, said to be the most common urchin in the world, occurring in great numbers on coral reefs and reef flats. The strange echinometrid *Colobocentrotus atratus* (Fig. 178C) is limited to intertidal surf-beaten rocks of various islands from Ceylon to Hawaii.

Turning now to the irregular urchins one finds the holectypoid *Echinoneus cyclostomus* widely distributed in the Indo-Pacific. Sand dollars of all the common genera are abundant in the area, especially *Clypeaster reticulatus, Arachnoides placenta, Echinocyamus crispus* and *provectus, Fibularia ovulum* and *cribellum, Peronella lesueuri, orbicularis,* and *macroproctes, Laganum decagonale, laganum,* and *depressum,* and *Echinodiscus auritus.* There is no dearth of littoral spatangoids, either, of which the most common Indo-Pacific species are *Maretia planulata*

(= *ovata*), *Lovenia elongata*, *Breynia elegans*, *Schizaster lacunosus*, *Brissopsis luzonica*, *Brissus lateocarinatus*, and *Metalia sternalis* and *spatagus*.

Many of the common littoral Indo-Pacific echinoids extend northeastward into southern Japan by way of the Ryukyu (or Liu Kiu) Islands and form a familiar element of the fauna of shallow waters there. In addition to this element, however, Japan has a number of endemic echinoids, that is, species not found elsewhere (Japanese echinoids in Döderlein, 1885, 1887, 1906; Yoshiwara, 1906; Mortensen, 1929; Ikeda, 1940). There appear to be no common cidaroids along the coasts of Japan, but endemic species of *Goniocidaris*, *Stereocidaris*, and *Stylocidaris* are characteristic of waters of moderate depths. Typical endemic littoral species are the stirodont *Glyptocidaris crenularis*, the temnopleurid *Temnotrema sculptum*, the strongylocentrotids *Strongyl. intermedius*, *nudus*, and *polyacanthus*, and *Hemicentrotus pulcherrimus*, the toxopneustid *Pseudocentrotus depressus*, and the echinometrid *Anthocidaris* (= *Heliocidaris*) *crassispina*. There are a number of characteristic sand dollars, as *Scaphechinus* (= *Echinarachnius*) *mirabilis*, *griseus*, and *tenuis*, *Clypeaster virescens* and *japonicus*, *Astriclypeus manni*, *Fibularia acuta*, and *Peronella rubra*. The genera *Astriclypeus* and *Scaphechinus* are exclusively Japanese. Endemic Japanese spatangoids found in shallow water include *Brisaster owstoni*, *Moira lachesinella*, and *Brissus agassizii*.

The echinoid fauna of Australia, exhaustively considered by H. L. Clark (1938, 1946), is also a mixture of Indo-Pacific and endemic species. The Australian fauna is especially rich in echinoderms and includes 135 of the known existing species of echinoids, most inhabiting shallow waters at depths of not more than 20 m. The characteristic endemic Australian cidaroid is *Goniocidaris tubaria* found along the entire coast. There are endemic diadematids, *Centrostephanus rodgersii* and *tenuispina*, and endemic temnopleurids, notably the genera *Amblyneustes* and *Holopneustes*, limited to Australia and Tasmania. The echinometrid *Heliocidaris erythrogramma* is common on Australian coasts, probably not found elsewhere. Endemic clypeastroids include *Clypeaster australasiae* and *telurus*, *Arachnoides tenuis*, *Ammotrophus cyclius*, *Peronella peronii* and *tuberculata*, *Fibularia plateia* and the brooding *nutriens*, and *Echinocyamus platytatus* and *planissimus;* scutellids are somewhat wanting from the Australian fauna. There appear to be only two endemic Australian spatangoids, *Breynia australasiae* and *Eupatagus valenciennesii*, a brooding species.

The echinoids of New Zealand include a few species also found on Australian coasts and in the Indo-Pacific, but of the 22 littoral species (Farquhar, 1894, 1898, 1926; Mortensen, 1921), no less than 14 are endemic. These comprise two cidaroids, *Goniocidaris umbraculum* and *Ogmocidaris benhami*, five species of the temnopleurid genus *Pseudechinus*, the rock-boring echinometrid *Evechinus chloroticus*, *Apatopygus recens*, which is one of the two surviving species of the cassiduloid family Echinobrissidae, the sand dollars *Arachnoides zelandiae*, *Peronella hinemoae*, and *Echinocyamus polyporus*, and the spatangoids *Spatangus multispinus* and *Brissopsis zealandiae*.

The Indo-Pacific echinoids also extend onto the eastern and southern coasts of Africa; in fact, there may be recognized a large faunal unit termed by Ekman (1953) the Indo–West Pacific, which extends from the Red Sea and the east coast of Africa through the Australian and Indo-Malay regions as far east as the Hawaiian Islands. H. L. Clark (1923) found that of 23 littoral echinoids reported in his study of South African echinoderms, only two are endemic; the others are mostly common Indo-Pacific species. Turning to the eastern boundary of the great Indo–West Pacific area, one finds that also many of the littoral echinoids of the Hawaiian Islands are common Indo-Pacific species (Agassiz and Clark, 1907b, 1909; H. L. Clark, 1912, 1914, 1917, 1925). Some littoral endemic species of the Hawaiian Islands are the cidaroids *Histocidaris variabilis*, *Acanthocidaris hastigera*, *Prionocidaris hawaiiensis*, and *Chondrocidaris gigantea*, the diadematid *Diadema paucispinum*, the sand dollars *Clypeaster lytopetalus* and *Echinocyamus australis*, and the spatangoid *Lovenia hawaiiensis*. It is worthy of remark that one of the three existing holectypoids, *Micropetalon purpureum*, of which only three specimens are known, is endemic to the Hawaiian Islands.

A region rich in echinoderms, comparable to the Indo-Pacific, is the West Indies–Florida area (Döderlein and Hartmeyer, 1910; H. L. Clark, 1933). There is one species here in common with the Indo-Pacific, the holectypoid *Echinoneus cyclostomus*, said to be the only circumtropical echinoid. Other familiar littoral echinoids of the West Indies, many already mentioned and figured, are the cidaroid *Eucidaris tribuloides*, the diadematid *Diadema antillarum*, the arbaciid *Arbacia punctulata*, the toxopenustids *Lytechinus variegatus* and *Tripneustes esculentus*, the echinometrid *Echinometra lacunter*, the sand dollars *Clypeaster rosaceus* and *ravenelii*, *Mellita quinquies-* and *sexiesperforata*, and *Encope emarginata* and *michelini*, and the spatangoids *Moira atropos*, *Meoma ventricosa*, *Plagiobrissus grandis*, and *Brissus unicolor* (= *brissus*). Taxonomic similarity of many of the foregoing with common Indo-Pacific species, as *Eucidaris metularia*, *Diadema setosum*, *Tripneustes gratilla*, *Echinometra mathaei*, and *Brissus latecarinatus*, may be noted. The West Indian echinoid fauna extends southward along Brazil and northward along the Atlantic Coast of the United States. *Lytechinus variegatus*, *Moira atropos*, and *Mellita quinquiesperforata* are distributed northward as far as the Carolinas, and the last and also *Arbacia punctulata* occur to Cape Cod although the *Mellita* is somewhat uncommon north of the Carolinas. The sand dollar *Echinarachnius parma* is a characteristic echinoid of the Atlantic Coast from Maryland to Labrador, and the green urchin *Strongyl. dröbachiensis* is the common littoral urchin from Cape Cod northward to the north coast of Greenland, within the Arctic Circle. It should be noted that there are no cidaroids north of Florida or thereabouts, and in fact there is a general dearth of cidaroids throughout the entire Atlantic. This cannot be attributed to lower temperatures as cidaroids are common in the antarctic.

Another tropical and subtropical area comparable in general environmental conditions to the Indo-Pacific and West Indian regions is the eastern tropical Pacific or Panamic area extending from southern California to Peru and including the Galapagos and other outlying islands. The littoral echinoids of this region have been reported by H. L. Clark (1910, 1948), and a general resemblance to those of other tropical areas is evident although there are no species in common. One of the commonest and most characteristic urchins of the tropical eastern Pacific is *Eucidaris thouarsii*. Other common littoral urchins are the diadematids *Diadema mexicana*, a big black urchin with long poisonous spines, *Astropyga pulvinata*, and *Centrostephanus coronatus*, *Arbacia stellata*, the toxopneustids *Toxopneustes roseus* and *Tripneustes depressus*, the largest urchin of the region to 150 mm. in diameter, and *Echinometra vanbrunti*, violet with an oval test, the most abundant species of the eastern tropical Pacific. Sand dollars include several species of Clypeaster and 11 species of *Encope*, and spatangoids are represented by *Brisaster townsendi*, *Moira clotho*, *Brissopsis pacifica*, *Brissus obesus*, *Meoma grandis*, *Agassizia scrobiculata*, *Lovenia cordiformis*, *Metalia nobilis*, and *Plagiobrissus pacificus*. The echinoids of the Galapagos Islands are in general Panamic species or species from the coasts of Peru and Ecuador; however, of 23 species recorded from these islands, four are endemic. Some characteristic Peruvian littoral echinoids that do not extend northward are the edible echinid *Loxechinus albus* and the arbaciids *Arbacia spatuligera* and *Tetrapygus niger*. The Gulf of California is liberally populated with echinoids, but all of the 22 species recorded from there are definitely Panamic except one, the cidaroid *Hesperocidaris perplexa*.

Some of these Panamic species extend into southern California waters, notably *Centrostephanus coronatus* and *Lovenia cordiformis*, and the spatangoid *Brisaster townsendi* ranges from Panama to Alaska, but in general the Panamic species are replaced along the Pacific Coast of the United States and Canada by a different set of urchins. No cidaroid is found north of Lower California. Some species are limited to southern California and the adjacent part of Lower California, notably the two toxopneustids *Lytechinus anamesus* and *picta*, but most range from California or Lower California to Alaska. The characteristic species of this range are the two purple urchins *Strongyl. purpuratus* and *franciscanus* and the sand dollar *Dendraster excentricus;* two North Atlantic echinoids, *Strongyl. dröbachiensis* and *Echinarachnius parma*, extend from Puget Sound far northward. A general survey of the echinoids of the eastern Pacific is given by Grant and Hertlein (1938).

Some general facts about the echinoid fauna of the coast of the Americas and their outlying islands emerge from the foregoing account. There are no cidaroids north of subtropical waters. There is an almost complete absence of the large family Temnopleuridae, which is essentially an Indo-Pacific group, although two temnopleurids occur in the West Indies, further evidence of a relation of the West Indian to the Indo-Pacific echinoids. The sand dollar family Scutellidae is notably developed in American (also Japanese) waters, and the genera *Mellita* and *Encope* are exclusively American, occurring on both sides of these continents. *Mellita* is better represented in the West Indies–Florida area although there are two uncommon Panamic species, whereas *Encope*, as Mortensen remarks, shows an amazing richness of species and varieties in the Panamic area.

A familiar group of echinoids occurs along north European coasts from Norway and Iceland through the British Isles. Surprisingly enough this includes the well-known cidaroid *Cidaris cidaris* (= *Dorocidaris papillata*), although this is not found above 50 m. of depth. The typical shallow-water forms of this area are *Echinus esculentus* and *acutus*, especially the variety *acutus norvegicus*, with *E. elegans* below 50 m., *Psammechinus miliaris*, the inevitable *Strongyl. dröbachiensis*, the little sand dollar *Echinocyamus pusillus*, and the spatangoids *Spatangus purpureus*, *Echinocardium cordatum* and *flavescens*, and *Brissopsis lyrifera* (Süssbach and Breckner, 1911; Mortensen, 1927; Koehler, 1927; Grieg, 1928; Mortensen and Lieberkind, 1928; Lieberkind, 1928). The fauna of this area is more or less continuous with that of the eastern North Atlantic in general, extending into the Mediterranean and down the Atlantic Coast of Africa. Common Mediterranean echinoids (Mortensen, 1913; Tortonese, 1949, 1952) include *Cidaris cidaris* and *Stylocidaris affinis*, *Arbacia lixula*, the diadematid *Centrostephanus longispinus*, the echinids *Echinus acutus* and *melo*, *Psammechinus microtuberculatus*, and *Paracentrotus lividus*, the temnopleurid *Genocidaris maculata*, the toxopneustid *Sphaerechinus granularis*, the sand dollar *Echinocyamus pusillus*, and the spatangoids *Spatangus purpureus* and *inermis*, *Brissopsis lyrifera* and *atlantica*, *Brissus unicolor*, *Metalia costae*, *Schizaster canaliferus*, and *Echinocardium cordatum*, *flavescens*, *mediterraneum*, and *mortenseni*. One may note as characteristic of the littoral echinoids of European waters the presence of a number of members of the family Echinidae, a general lack of Temnopleuridae, the absence of sand dollars except for the one very common species belonging to the Fibulariidae, and the presence of a good assortment of spatangoids, lacking on North American coasts of corresponding latitude. Whereas heart urchins are common objects on European coasts, they are almost unknown to students of zoology in the United States.

As might be anticipated, many of the littoral echinoids of the Mediterranean and the adjacent North Atlantic extend down the west coast of Africa either in the typical form or as an African subspecies. This west African coast constitutes the fourth great tropical-subtropical faunistic area, the eastern tropical Atlantic, which broadly extends from Gibraltar to the lower end of the Gulf of Guinea. Ekman (1953) remarks that this area is faunistically the poorest of all the tropical-subtropical regions as the sandy bottom prevents the formation of coral reefs, and the lack of rocky bays and other irregularities is unfavorable for the development of a rich fauna. In addition to containing a number of Mediterranean and southwest European species, the echinoid fauna here has many species in common with the West Indies (Koehler, 1914; Mortensen, 1951). Some of the most characteristic West Indian urchins, as *Diadema antillarum*, *Tripneustes ventricosa*, and *Echinometra lacunter*, are also found on the tropical African coast, and *Eucidaris tribuloides* is represented there by an African subspecies. There are also a number of corresponding species between the two areas, as the West Indian *Plagiobrissus grandis* and the African *P. africanus*. The sand dollar genus *Rotula* with two species (Fig. 178*A*, *B*) is confined to the tropical west coast of Africa.

Common echinoids of north European and northern North American coasts may extend into arctic and subarctic regions, and hence there are no echinoid species distinctive of far-northern waters. *Psammechinus miliaris*, *Echinus esculentus*, and *Echinus acutus norvegicus* continue along the Norwegian coast to its northern limits, and the last is also found in the Barents Sea at 74° north latitude. *Strongyl. dröbachiensis* is a circumpolar species inhabiting both the North Atlantic and Pacific, reaching its most northerly distribution in Discovery Bay, north of Greenland, at 81° north latitude; it is also found north of Russia and Siberia and at Jan Mayen. *Echinocyamus pusillus* extends along the Norwegian coast to 70° north latitude, and a similar distribution obtains for *Spatangus purpureus* and *Echinocardium cordatum; Schizaster fragilis* continues into the Barents Sea at 73° north latitude. The fauna of the North Pacific is less well known, but here also *Strongyl. dröbachiensis* is the most northerly ranging species, being found in the Bering Sea; *Strongyl. franciscanus* and *Echinarachnius parma* go as far as Kodiak Island, and

*Dendraster excentricus* to Unalaska in the Aleutians.   It is thus clear that all the littoral echinoids of arctic and subarctic waters range south to varying degrees and are not characteristic of the area (Döderlein, 1905).   There is further no resemblance between arctic and antarctic echinoids.

The antarctic, especially the South American antarctic, has been explored by a succession of expeditions, following that of the *Challenger*, which passed through the Strait of Magellan.   Antarctic echinoids have been reported by Koehler (1901) from the Belgian expedition, Koehler (1908) from the Scottish expedition, Mortensen (1909, 1910) from the German and Swedish South Polar expeditions, respectively, Koehler (1912) from the second French exploration, Bell (1917) from the British antarctic expedition, Koehler (1926) from the Australasian expedition, Mortensen (1936) in the *Discovery* reports, and Mortensen (1950) in the reports of the British, Australian, and New Zealand antarctic expedition. From these accounts it appears that the littoral echinoids of the South American antarctic are mostly limited to the cidaroid, echinid, and spatangoid groups.   The antarctic is relatively rich in cidaroids, many of them with brooding habits, but they all belong to a limited number of related genera, namely, *Notocidaris, Ctenocidaris, Rhynchocidaris*, and *Austrocidaris;* further, it appears that all the species of these genera (about 13) are limited to the antarctic and subantarctic.   One arbaciid, *Arbacia dufresnii*, is a characteristic species of the southern tip of South America, extending northward along both the Argentinian and Chilean coasts.   All five species of the echinid genus *Sterechinus* are antarctic or subantarctic, and *Loxechinus albus* extends from the Strait of Magellan to Peru and up the Argentine coast.   Although the Temnopleuridae are characteristic of the Indo-Pacific area, the genus *Pseudechinus* is mostly limited to colder waters, and one species, *P. magellanicus*, is definitely antarctic.   There is a considerable variety of spatangoids in the South American antarctic, many of them with brooding habits, including all species of the genera *Abatus, Amphineustes, Tripylaster*, and *Tripylus*, totaling 22 species.   Other antarctic spatangoids are *Brisaster moseleyi* and *Plexechinus nordenskjöldi*.   Species typical of Kerguelen Island include *Ctenocidaris nutrix, Sterechinus diadema*, and *Abatus cordatus*.

There has been little investigation of the echinoids of the eastern coast of South America, but recently Bernasconi (1947, 1953) has reported on Argentinian echinoids, finding them to be a mixture of a few species descending from warmer waters to the north with a majority of antarctic and subantartic forms spreading up the coast from the south.

We may now turn from the littoral species to the echinoids of deeper waters.   The existence of a rich echinoid fauna, in general specifically different from the littoral fauna, in the archibenthal zone, that is, roughly from 200 to 1000 m., was revealed by numerous dredging expeditions, as well as a variety of deeper forms, ranging to 5000 m. Among the early famous dredging expeditions was that of Wyville Thomson (1874) in the *Porcupine* which dredged the North Atlantic from the Faroes to Gibraltar and brought to light for the first time members of the curious family Echinothuriidae; echinoids were found at all depths between 1000 and 4000 m. Prior to his report (1881) on the echinoids collected by the *Challenger*, A. Agassiz (1869, 1879, 1880) had studied the echinoids taken by the *Blake* in its dredgings in the Caribbean, Gulf of Mexico, Florida, and the West Indies. Echinoids were dredged from the Atlantic from Spain to the Azores by the yacht *Hirondelle* belonging to the marine station at Monaco (Koehler, 1898). In 1904 A. Agassiz reported on the echinoids of deep water in the Panamic region, and De Meijere published an account of the echinoids collected by the *Siboga* in the Netherland East Indies. The echinoids of the German Deep Sea Expedition were treated by Döderlein (1906), and Mortensen (1903, 1907) gave an extended description of the echinoids taken by the Danish ship *Ingolf* in the North Atlantic between Jan Mayen, the Faroes, Iceland, and Greenland. The North Atlantic was again dredged by the *Michael Sars* in 1910 (echinoids by Grieg, 1921). Sixty years after the *Blake* expeditions, the West Indian echinoids were again dredged by the *Atlantis* (H. L. Clark, 1941). Echinoids from the dredgings of the *Albatross* in the Philippines and adjacent areas were described by Mortensen (1927, 1940, 1948). The many antarctic expeditions mentioned above have added much to our knowledge of the echinoids of deeper waters.

The assembled information shows that the cidaroids are predominantly archibenthal forms. The genera *Histocidaris*, *Hesperocidaris*, *Goniocidaris*, *Stereocidaris*, and *Stylocidaris* consist almost wholly of archibenthal species, most with a limited distribution. Widely ranging archibenthal species include *Stylocidaris affinis* found in the Mediterranean, the tropical eastern Atlantic, and the West Indies; *Cidaris abyssicola* occurring in the North Atlantic from Martha's Vineyard to the West Indies; *Porrocidaris purpurata*, a characteristic urchin of the North Atlantic from Iceland and the Faroes to the Canary Islands, *Stereocidaris indica*, throughout the Indo-West Pacific from the east coast of Africa to Japan; and *Stereocidaris ingolfiana* over the North Atlantic from Iceland to the West Indies and the Cape Verde Islands. An example of a cidaroid with limited distribution is *Cidaris blakei* with oar-like aboral spines (Fig. 179*E*), restricted to the West Indies at 315 to 420 m., one of the finds of the *Blake* dredgings. There are also a few abyssal cidaroids, as *Aporocidaris milleri*, which with its geographic variants is probably distributed throughout the deep Pacific from the antarctic to Alaska and Kamchatka at depths of 3000 to 4000 m.; and *Notocidaris hastata* from the antarctic at 2450 to 2725 m.

The entire family Echinothuriidae is archibenthal and abyssal, except the genus *Asthenosoma*, mainly littoral. One of the most common deep-water species is *Phormosoma placenta*, first found by Thomson in the dredgings of the *Porcupine*, distributed all over the North Atlantic from Iceland and Greenland to the West Indies and the Azores at depths to 2500 m.; *Phormosoma bursarium* occurs throughout the Indo–West Pacific in the archibenthal zone to 1600 m. Other echinothuriids ranging from the archibenthal into the abyssal over wide areas of the North Atlantic are *Sperosoma grimaldii*, *Hydrosoma petersii*, *Calveriosoma hystrix*, and *Aerosoma fenestratum*. Strictly abyssal are two Panamic species, *Tromikosoma hispidum* and *panamense*, *Hemiphormosoma paucispinum* off the Philippines to nearly 4200 m., and *Kamptosoma asterias*, from the central Pacific, at depths of 3890 to 4950 m., thus one of the most abyssal of all echinoids.

The small family Saleniidae also comprises mainly archibenthal or abyssal members. In this category belong all of the species of *Saleno-cidaris*, of which may be mentioned *varispina* and *profundi*, widely distributed in the tropical and subtropical Atlantic, and *hastigera*, common in the Indo-Pacific. The species of *Salenia* are inhabitants of the deeper littoral and archibenthal zones. *Salenia goesiana* ( = *pattersoni*, Fig. 224C) is limited to the West Indies, and the other species occur in the Indo-Pacific area. There are a few abyssal arbaciids, mostly known from one or a few specimens, as *Dialithocidaris gemmifera* from the Panamic region at 3255 m. and *Pygmaeocidaris prioniger* from the Indo-Malay region to 2860 m.; *Coelopleurus floridanus* is mainly archibenthal, although occurring to 2380 m. in the West Indies and extending along the coast to the Carolinas.

The family Aspidodiadematidae is also characteristically archibenthal and abyssal. All members of the genus *Plesiodiadema* inhabit the abyssal zone except the archibenthal Indo-Malay species *indicum* (Fig. 223E); *globulosum* and *horridum* are Panamic species to over 3000 m., and *antillarum* occurs throughout the tropical and subtropical Atlantic from the Caribbean and Brazil to the Canaries and St. Helena, descending to a depth of 3000 m. The several species of *Aspidodiadema* belong to the archibenthal of the Indo–West Pacific area.

The Pedinidae are for the most part archibenthal, although they extend to 2000 m. *Caenopedina cubensis* is found throughout the warmer North Atlantic from the West Indies to Nantucket and the west African coast. *C. indica* and *annulata* are spread throughout the Indo-Malay region at moderate depths, and two further species occur at the Hawaiian Islands. In the Micropygidae, *Micropyga tuberculata* is common in the Indo-Malay region at depths to 1340 m.

Although the Temnopleuridae are for the most part littoral urchins, the genera *Prionechinus, Hypsiechinus, Opechinus, Trigonocidaris, Orechinus,* and *Lamprechinus* are typically archibenthal, with some extension into the upper abyssal. *Trigonocidaris albida* is widely distributed from the West Indies to the eastern tropical Pacific, and *Orechinus monolini* is a widely spread Indo–West Pacific form to 2300 m.

The clypeastroids in general belong in the littoral zone, but many species extend their range into deeper waters, and a few appear limited to the archibenthal and upper abyssal, notably *Echinocyamus macrostomus,* widely distributed in the North Atlantic from the West Indies to the Mediterranean, Azores, and Cape Verde Islands, at depths of 1600 to 2300 m. There are many abyssal forms among the spatangoids. The family Urechinidae is wholly abyssal, and some of the deepest records for echinoids occur in this family. In the genus *Urechinus,* confined to deep waters, may be mentioned *naresianus,* distributed throughout the Atlantic from Greenland to the antarctic at 770 to 4400 m., *drygalskii* in the antarctic at 3423 m., *loveni* from the Panamic region to the Bering and Okhotsk Seas at 3000 to 3600 m., and *wyvillei* in the subantarctic at 3000 to 3600 m. The genus *Pilematechinus* is also wholly abyssal, occurring off Panama and in the antarctic at depths of 2000 to over 4000 m. *Plexechinus* is on the whole somewhat less abyssal with one well-known littoral species in the antarctic, *P. nordenskjöldi,* but *P. spectabilis* is again extremely abyssal, judging by the single record of 4163 m. in the Sulu Sea. The only species in the Calymnidae, *Calyme relicta,* comes close to the depth record, being found in the Atlantic near the Bermudas at 4845 m. The Pourtalesiidae are also typically abyssal although some species ascend into the archibenthal and even the littoral zone. Common species are *Pourtalesia miranda,* found throughout the North Atlantic from the West Indies to Greenland and Iceland at depths of 450 to 3220 m., *P. jeffreysi* in the far North Atlantic, around Spitsbergen, the Faroes, and Greenland, and into the Kara Sea, at 50 to 2450 m., and *Echinosigra phiale* (Fig. 174E) from the depths of the Atlantic. A number of Pourtalesiidae appear limited to the abysses of the antarctic and subantarctic, as *Pourtalesia hispida, aurorae,* and *debilis, Helgocystis carinata* (3656 to 4790 m.), *Spatagocystis challengeri* and *Ceratopyga ceratophysa* (3165 to 4030 m.).

The typical or amphisternous spatangoids also extend into deeper waters. The family Palaeopneustidae is typically archibenthal, spreading into the abyssal and less commonly into the littoral, mainly in tropical and subtropical areas. Some species appear limited to the West Indian region, as *Palaeopneustes cristatus, Arachaeopneustes hystrix, Linopneustes longispinus,* and *Homolampas fragilis.* Others are characteristic of the deeper waters of the Indo–West Pacific, as *Linopneustes murrayi* and other species of this genus, *Argopatagus vitreus,* and *Palaeo-*

*trema loveni.* One paleopnuestid, *Delopatagus brucei*, is found in the antarctic abyssal, at 4435 m. The small family Aeropsidae, with genera *Aceste* and *Aeropsis*, consists wholly of abyssal species, with records to 5200 m., the depth record for the echinoids. The Hemiasteridae are archibenthal and abyssal, represented by *Hemiaster expergitus*, common throughout the North Atlantic from Iceland and Greenland to the West Indies and Cape Verde Islands, at depths of 950 to 3200 m. The genus *Brisaster* is rather confined to archibenthal and abyssal waters; the more common species are *B. fragilis*, subarctic, extending from the Barents Sea and the Murman coast to Bergen and the Faroes to 1300 m. depth; *B. townsendi* and *latifrons* (Fig. 236D), from Panama to Alaska to 1800 or 1900 m.; and *B. moseleyi* from the Strait of Magellan. The genus *Brissopsis* is also rather addicted to deeper waters; a characteristic species is *B. columbaris* in the Panamic region to 2280 m.

From the foregoing survey it is evident that there are no cosmopolitan species of urchins. The heart urchin *Echinocardium cordatum* has the widest distribution, occurring, outside its typical home from Norway and Ireland along north European shores into the Mediterranean and along Morocco, also around South Africa, Japan, Australia, Tasmania, and New Zealand, and in the Atlantic from Brazil to North Carolina. Also of wide distribution is the common Indo-Pacific species *Echinometra mathaei*, which with its geographic variants extends from the Red Sea, east coast of Africa, and Madagascar throughout the entire Indo–West Pacific region, including Japan and Australia, to the Hawaiian Islands, and even to Clarion Island several hundred miles west of Mexico. An even wider distribution in tropical seas is shown by *Echinoneus cyclostomus* which, in addition to occurrence throughout the Indo–West Pacific in its broadest sense, is also common in the West Indies; but it is wanting from the eastern tropical Pacific and the west coast of Africa (eastern tropical Atlantic). There appear to be no species common to the Atlantic and Pacific Coasts of the Americas outside of polar and subpolar areas (as *Strongyl. dröbachiensis* and *Echinarachinius parma* in the north). It has been noticed that there are many species in common in the warmer parts of the eastern and western Atlantic, but this is not true of the Pacific. There are no species in common between the Indo-Pacific and the tropical eastern Pacific. The distance, of course, here is very great, but the true reason is the existence between Polynesia and Hawaii, on the one hand, and the western coasts of the Americas, on the other, of a wide stretch of deep water without islands that cannot be passed by warm-water littoral species, thus constituting what Ekman (1953) terms the East Pacific Barrier. As already indicated, many of the Indo-Pacific littoral species manage to get as far as the Hawaiian Islands, and one, *Echinometra mathaei*, has even arrived at Clarion Island, but none has reached American shores.

Wide range of horizontal distribution is often associated with the formation of distinct geographic races. One of the most variable species is *Echinus acutus*, with one variety in the Mediterranean, another off the French coast, and a third along the coast of Norway. On the other hand, some widely distributed species, as *Strongyl. dröbachiensis* and *Echinocardium cordatum*, appear morphologically identical wherever found. Many echinoids also have an extensive vertical distribution. While it is to be expected that archibenthal species will range into the abyssal, as there is no sharp boundary between these two zones, it is rather surprising to find many species extending from the intertidal zone well into the abyssal. This is true for a number of common echinoids of European coasts, as *Echinus esculentus, acutus,* and *melo*, which are distributed from shallow waters to depths of between 1000 and 2000 m. *Strongyl. dröbachiensis* ranges from the intertidal zone to 1150 m. Great vertical range is also shown by the spatangoids *Brisaster fragilis*, 40 to 1300 m., and *Brissopsis lyrifera*, 15 to 1400 m.

Hybridization between closely related species is not uncommon, and a number of instances are recorded by Mortensen in his monograph as between the common European species of *Echinus*. In Puget Sound, the three species of *Strongylocentrotus* may interbreed (Swan, 1953), and hybrids may be found to the extent of one specimen among several thousand.

**32. Ecology : Biological Relations.**—Despite their armature of spines and poisonous pedicellariae, echinoids may be eaten by other animals, as crabs, sea stars, large fish, mammals, and birds; the last may crack them by flying up with them and dropping them on rocks. The gonads when ripe are highly nutritious and are eaten, either raw or after roasting in the half shell, by man in various parts of the world. Echinoid gonads are commonly eaten in the Mediterranean, especially those of *Paracentrotus lividus*. Along the coasts of Peru and Ecuador there is much eating of the gonads of *Loxechinus albus*, roasted in the half shell. Ricketts and Calvin (1953) record that Italians along the California coast eat raw the gonads of the big purple urchin (*Strongyl. franciscanus*). *Tripneustes ventricosus* is eaten in the West Indies, and *Evechinus chloroticus* is extensively used as food by the natives of New Zealand.

As already mentioned, some urchins, especially members of the families Echinothuriidae and Diadematidae, are provided with poisonous spines that are capable of inflicting severe injury, and diadematids when approached bunch these spines and point them at the intruder. Mortensen in his monograph states that many animals, especially crustaceans and small fish, may seek shelter and protection among the spines of diadematids.

Echinoids serve as hosts to a variety of commensal and more or less parasitic animals. The spines of cidaroids, being devoid of a living epidermis and often having a woolly surface, are usually overgrown with a variety of sessile organisms, as algae, sponges, hydroids, zoanthids, anemones, bryozoans, brachiopods, tubiculous polychaetes, barnacles, and the like.

It has long been known that the digestive tract, chiefly the large intestine, of many urchins harbors entocommensal ciliates, often in great numbers. These are mostly holotrichous ciliates (I, page 183) and do not appear to have undergone any morphological alteration in correlation with their mode of life. Jacobs (1914) found that the ciliates of the intestine of *Diadema antillarum* would survive only 24 to 30 hours in a dead urchin, and in the removed intestinal contents plus a little sea water would die in 2 or 3 hours to 2 days, depending on the species; the four different species harbored by this urchin thus exhibit different capacities for survival outside the host, although all live under the same environmental conditions within the host. A considerable number of different species of ciliates, all taxonomically distinct from free-living species, have been found in urchins, and no doubt many more remain to be discovered. Maupas (1883) described *Cryptochilidium echini* from *Paracentrotus lividus* in the Mediterranean, refound by Powers (1933), who also found two other species in this urchin. *Strongyl. dröbachiensis* harbors seven different kinds of ciliates (Madsen, 1931; Powers, 1933; Beers, 1948, 1954), namely, *Entodiscus borealis*, also found in *Echinus esculentus* (Hentschel, 1924) and *Psammechinus miliaris* (Madsen, 1931), further, *Madsenia indomita*, *Biggaria gracilis*, *Cyclidium stercoris*, *Plagiopyla minuta*, *Euplotes balteata*, and a species of *Trichodina*. Both the *Trichodina* and the *Euplotes* also occur on seaweeds and on the surface of the urchins, and the former is present in such small numbers that it may be regarded as a chance inhabitant of the urchin intestine, but the other five species are obligatory entocommensals, and the first three are almost invariably present, often in enormous numbers, up to 1000 individuals of each in 0.1 cu. cm. of intestinal fluid. The ciliates are usually limited to the large intestine. In a detailed study of *Entodiscus borealis* Powers (1933) reported that it swims about or clings to the walls of the large intestine or in its folds and might live outside the urchin for 15 to 23 days in hanging drops. Some pass out in the fecal pellets and young urchins probably get infected by eating these. Some other holotrichous ciliates found in European urchins are *Colpidium echini* (Russo, 1914) and *Anophrys echini* (Di Mauro, 1904) in *Paracentrotus lividus*, the latter also in *Arbacia lixula* and *Sphaerechinus granularis*.

The ciliate inhabitants of Japanese urchins were investigated by Uyemura (1934) and Yagiu (1933, 1934, 1935). The common Japanese echinometrid *Anthocidaris crassispina* is said to harbor at least 12 distinct species of ciliates, of which, however, there are described only *Entori-*

*phidium fukui, Cryptochilidium sigmoides, minor,* and *ozakii, Cyclidium ozakii,* and *Strombilidium rapulum,* an oligotrich. *Cryptochilidium ozakii* was also found in other common Japanese echinometrids and in *Temnopleurus toreumaticus. Conchophthirius striatus* occurs in great numbers in Japanese strongylocentrotids; further, in *Pseudocentrotus depressus* and *Mespilia globulus.*

Lynch (1929, 1930) began a study of the ciliates of California *Strongylocentrotus,* which unfortunately was never completed. He reported 12 species in the intestine of *S. purpuratus,* some of which also occur in *S. franciscanus,* but named and described only five, *Entorhipidium echini, tenue, pilatum,* and *multimicronucleatum,* and *Lechriopyla mystax,* all holotrichs.

Urchins of the Bermuda–West Indies–Carolina area have been examined for ciliates by Biggar (1932), Lucas (1934), and Powers (1933, 1935). Characteristic of echinoids of this area, not so far reported elsewhere, are heterotrichous ciliates of the genus *Metopus* (I, page 193). *Metopus circumlabens* is extremely abundant in *Diadema antillarum,* which also harbors *M. rotundus; M. brevicristatus* is limited to *Clypeaster rosaceus* and *M. histophagus* to *Clypeaster subdepressus.* Apparently all the common shallow-water echinoids of this area, except *Eucidaris tribuloides,* are infected with intestinal ciliates, and most species of these are found in more than one kind of urchin, although usually most common in some particular species. *Lytechinus variegatus* is the main host of *Cryptochilidium bermudense, Anophrys vermidiformis, elongata,* and *aglycus,* and *Colpoda fragilis. Cryptochilidium echinometris* is most common in *Echinometra lacunter,* and *Cohnilembus caeci* in *Tripneustes ventricosus. Entodiscus subularis* appears limited to species of *Clypeaster.* Other holotrichs found by Powers are *Cyclidium rhabdotectum* and *stercoris.*

Other Protozoa associated with echinoids include acephaline eugregarines of the genera *Lithocystis* and *Urospora* (Goodrich, 1915), ubiquitous in the coelom of European spatangoids, such as *Echinocardium cordatum* and *Spatangus purpureus.* Cuénot (1912) mentions a little flagellate, *Oikomonas echinorum* (probably incorrectly named), common in the coelomic fluid of urchins on the French coast, apt to be confused with the vibratile cells of this fluid.

There seem to be no genuine cases of association of echinoids with coelenterates apart from the mere use of spines as attachment sites by hydroids and small anemones. The ctenophore *Coeloplana bannworthi* was found creeping on the spines of *Diadema savignyi* in the Gulf of Suez (Krumbach, 1933), and *Coeloplana echinicola* similarly on *Toxopneustes pileolus* off Japan (Tanaka, 1931).

Notable entocommensals, or possibly semiparasites, of echinoids are the rhabdocoel flatworms of the family Umagillidae (II, page 140), of which new species continue to be discovered (Westblad, 1953). These are less common in echinoids than in holothuroids, but the first described species, *Syndesmis echinorum*, inhabits the intestine of common European urchins, as *Echinus esculentus* and *acutus*, *Paracentrotus lividus*, *Sphaerechinus granularis*, and *Strongyl. dröbachiensis*. Another species, *Syndesmis* ( = *Syndisyrinx*) *franciscana* (II, page 141) lives in the intestine of *Diadema antillarum* and *Strongyl. franciscanus*. Recently a species of *Syndesmis*, *S. dendrastorum*, has been described from the Pacific Coast sand dollar *Dendraster excentricus* (Stunkard and Corliss, 1951). This is the first finding of an umagillid in an irregular echinoid, but soon thereafter Westblad (1953) reported *Marcusella atriovillosa* in the intestine of *Spatangus purpureus* in the English Channel. Heart urchins are also hosts to acoel flatworms of the genus *Avagina* (II, page 131); *A. incola* occurs in the intestine of *Echinocardium flavescens* (Leiper, 1904) and *A. glandulifera* in that of *Spatangus purpureus* (Westblad, 1953). Two polyclads, a leptoplanid, *Ceratoplana colobocentroti*, and a stylochid, *Discostylochus parcus*, have been found sheltering under the surf-dwelling echinometrid *Colobocentrotus atratus* (Bock, 1925), and this is the regular habitat of at least the former species. Mortensen (1921) records that off Japan *Mespilia globulus* "is very generally infected with a trematode living in its genital organs and destroying these more or less completely."

An amazingly large dracunculoid nematode, *Philometra grayi*, of which the females reach a length of 150 cm., was described by Gemmill and von Linstow (1902) from the coelom of *Echinus esculentus* off Britain. Up to four individuals might be found coiled in the coelom. This occurrence is rather puzzling as there seem to be no further records of the finding of the nematode in this very common urchin and as the species of *Philometra* regularly parasitize fish (III, page 370).

Some other echinoderms appear more or less constantly associated with echinoids. A peculiar synaptid cucumber, *Taeniogyrus cidaridis*, has twice been found on cidaroids in different Indo-Pacific localities and seems to live with the posterior part of its body coiled around their primary spines (Ohshima, 1915; Mortensen, Monogr.). Several cases of commensalism of ophiuroids with echinoids have been reported. Campbell (1921), studying Californian intertidal ophiuroids, often found *Ophiopteris papillosa* attached around the mouth of *Strongyl. purpuratus*, but Ricketts and Calvin (1953) do not mention any such association. Mortensen (Monogr.) remarks that an ophiuroid "is not rarely found attached to the apical spines" of the cidaroid *Schizocidaris assimilis*. In 1933 he reported finding a minute ophiuroid, with a disk 0.5 mm. in diameter, *Nannophiura lagani*, attached oral side down to the oral side of a large sand dollar, *Clypeaster latissimus*, in the Sunda Strait.

*Ophiosphaera insignis* was taken by Mortensen (1933) in association with *Toxopneustes pileolus* and *Diadema setosum* in the Indo-Malay region. This is one of those ophiuroids in which the small male lives permanently attached to the female (page 623).

Several cases of association of polychaete annelids with echinoids are on record. Marenzeller (1895) found that the spines of *Cidaris cidaris* brought up from the deeper waters of the Mediterranean often bear the curved tubes of the little hermellid polychaete *Phalocrostemma cidariophilum*, which apparently does not live elsewhere. Cuénot (1912) reported that a polychaete, *Siphonostoma dujardini*, is constantly present on *Psammechinus miliaris* and that a polynoid, *Malmgrenia castanea*, is often found near the mouth of *Spatangus purpureus*. In Mortensen's monograph mention is made of the finding of *Flabelligera affinis* on *Echinus esculentus*, of a polynoid worm on several specimens of *Schizocidaris assimilis*, and of many specimens of *Haplosyllis spongicola* between the spines on the oral side of an individual of *Asthenosoma varium*. The data are too few to establish the existence of a definite commensalism in most of these cases. No doubt the annelids rob the echinoids of food.

Echinoids share with other echinoderms relations, usually disadvantageous, with mollusks. Little bivalves of the genus *Montacuta* may be found on the oral spines of *Spatangus purpureus* or living in the burrows of *E. cordatum*. Another related small bivalve, *Scioberetia australis*, may occupy the brood pouches of the antarctic brooding spatangoid *Tripylus excavatus* (Bernard, 1896). Echinoids are preyed upon by the little parasitic snails of the families Melanellidae and Stiliferidae, especially by the stiliferid genus *Pelseneeria*. These snails may bore into the base of the primary spines of cidaroids, inducing a gall, often of grotesque shape, in which one or more snails dwell, also stunting the growth of the spine (Rathbun, 1885; Koehler, 1924; Koehler and Vaney, 1925). Other species of these snails live on the surface of common urchins, as *Strongyl. dröbachiensis* and species of *Echinus*, and fasten their egg masses to the test (Jeffreys, 1864; Koehler and Vaney, 1908; Koehler, 1909; Ankel, 1938). Several snails and up to 40 egg masses containing 50 to 100 eggs each may be found on one urchin. These snails presumably feed on the surface tissues of the urchin, and some of them live with the proboscis tip, which in *Pelseneeria* lacks a radula, fixed in the test or inserted into the interior. This is the case with species of *Mucronalia* and *Stilifer* (Stiliferidae) found attached to various urchins in the Indo-Pacific area (Kükenthal, 1897; Schepman and Nierstrasz, 1909). Habe (1952) reported species of *Melanella* and *Pelseneeria* on various Japanese echinoids, *Peronella japonica*, *Anthocidaris crassispina*, *Pseudocentrotus depressus*, and *Diadema setosum*. The temnopleurid *Salmacis bicolor* is

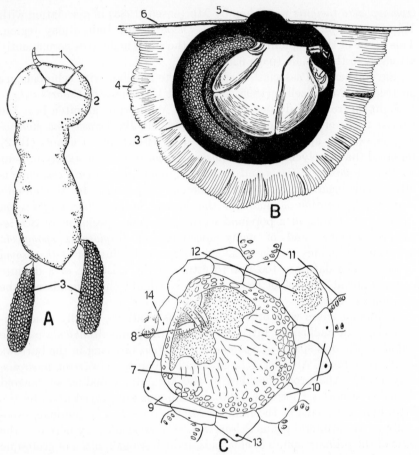

Fig. 240.—Crustacean parasites of echinoids. *A, Dichelina phormosomae,* parasitic copepod (*after Stephensen,* 1933). *B, Prionodesmotes phormosomae,* copepod in gall projecting into coelom from underside of test (*after Brian,* 1912). *C,* crab *Fabia chilensis* lodged in sac of rectum of *Caenocentrotus gibbosus* (*after Jackson,* 1912). 1, antennae; 2, brain; 3, egg sacs; 4, wall of gall; 5, external opening of gall; 6, cut edge of test; 7, periproct; 8, feet of crab; 9, genital plates; 10, terminal plates; 11, ambulacra; 12, madreporite; 13, gonopore; 14, terminal pore.

subject to attacks by a parasitic gastropod that attaches itself and its egg masses to the test halfway between the ambitus and the apical system, causing a narrowing of the test there.

Echinoids are often infested with parasitic copepods. Some of these differ but little from free-living members and retain complete motility; they feed on the host by piercing its tissues with their mouth parts. In this category belong *Asterocheres violaceus* and *minutus,* attacking common European urchins, where up to 20 may occur around the periproct (Claus, 1889; Giesbrecht, 1899; Cuénot, 1912); other recorded species are *Asterocheres echinocola* (Giesbrecht, 1899) and *Lichomolgus maximus* (Scott, 1896) on *Echinus esculentus,* and *Pseudanthessius sauvagei* on *E. cordatum* (Claus, 1889). Other copepods reside permanently in or on echinoids and have undergone some degree of parasitic alteration. Echinothuriids are especially subject to attack. Most specimens of *Hygrosoma petersii* are infested with the copepod *Pionodesmotes phormosomae* (Fig. 240*B*) which evokes large spherical galls, 5 to 30 per test, on the oral side projecting into the interior; these contain one female and some much smaller males, all imprisoned for life (Koehler, 1898; Brian, 1912; Bonnier, 1898). Similar galls are made on the spines of the same urchin by *Calvocheres oblongus* (Koehler, 1898) and of *Calveriosoma gracile* (Hanson, 1902) and *Sperosoma quincunciale* by *Calvocheres globosus* (Agassiz and Clark, 1909). Species of *Phormosoma* are infested with another parasitically altered copepod, *Dichelina phormosomae* (Fig. 240*A*), which seems to live in the intestine (Stephensen, 1933, 1935).

Various other crustaceans have been taken in association with echinoids. An ostracod was found by Lönneberg (1898) on the spines around the anus of *Strongyl. dröbachiensis.* Brattström (1936) reported that 50 to 90 per cent of *E. cordatum* in the Öresund are badly infested with a barnacle *Ulophysema öresundense* that resembles a sac attached to the inner surface of the test with an opening to the exterior through which the cypris larvae escape. These sacs project among the gonads which may be so damaged as to render the heart urchin sterile. It is well known that an amphipod *Urothoe marina* dwells in the burrows of *E. cordatum* as an inquiline (Giard, 1876), and Parker (1936) noticed another amphipod, *Amphilocus neapolitanus,* previously known as a free-living form, persistently clinging to the distal parts of the aboral spines of *Lytechinus variegatus* at Bermuda; the creatures resisted removal from the spines and would return at once to them when freed. An alphaeid shrimp, *Arcte dorsalis,* red brown with three pale longitudinal bands, resembling the host in color, was found on *Echinometra lacunter* at Djibouti by Coutière (1897); the occurrence of similar protectively colored shrimps on crinoids may be recalled (page 118). Another shrimp, the palaeomonid *Stegopontonia commensalis,* clings to the spines of diadematids in the Indo-Pacific but is not protectively colored (Mortensen, Monogr.). Various observers have noticed the presence of a crab, *Pinaxodes* (= *Fabia*) *chilensis,* in the rectum of two common littoral urchins of Peru and Chile, *Loxechinus albus* and *Caenocentrotus gibbosus,* especially in the latter, of which nearly all specimens are infected (Jackson, 1912). Apparently the crab when small forces its way into the anus, dilating and deforming the rectum into a sac that may reach to the peristome and in which the crab sits with claws protruding (Fig. 240*C*).

In *C. gibbosus*, but not in *L. albus*, the presence of the crab distorts considerably the aboral part of the test. *L. albus* may also harbor a porcellanid crab, *Petrolithes patagonicus*, that lives between the oral spines (Porter, 1926). Rectal invasion also obtains in the crab *Eumedon convictor*, of which the females (males unknown) inhabit large rectal pouches of *Echinothrix diadema* and may evoke some test distortion (Bouvier and Seurat, 1905). Little grapsoid crabs of the genus *Dissodactylus* regularly dwell on the oral surface of sand dollars, grasping the spines by their bifurcated claw ends. *D. mellitae* is found on the five-lunuled *Mellita* from Vineyard Sound to Florida (Rathbun, 1918), and *D. encopei* lives attached to *Encope emarginata*, Honduras (Rathbun, 1902). In the Panamic region the species *D. lockingtoni, nitidus, xanthusi, smithi*, and *glasselli* occur on one or more of the sand dollars *Mellita longifissa* and *Encope micropora, grandis*, and *californica* (Glassell, 1935, 1936; Ricketts, 1941; Rioja, 1944). *D. lockingtoni* is said by Glassell (1935) to remain attached near the posterior lunule of *Encope* and to clear away spines so as to make a roadway for itself to the anus, since these crabs seemingly feed on the feces of the sand dollars; other species run about on the sand dollars. A representative of the Halacaridae, a family of marine mites containing some parasitic members, was described by Viets (1938) from the intestine of *Plesiodiadema indicum*.

Some data are available on the growth and longevity of urchins. As urchins measure around 1 mm. in diameter at metamorphosis, one supposes that the larger species must require several years to attain full size. The following data on the growth of *Psammechinus miliaris* under laboratory conditions are furnished by Bull (1938): newly metamorphosed specimens, slightly over 1 mm. in diameter, test 10 mm. in diameter at 8 months, 20 mm. at 1 year, 26.2 at 2 years, 29.2 at 3 years, 30.3 at 4 years, 37 at 5 years, and 38.7 at 6 years. According to Mortensen this species may breed when 1 year of age. The rate of growth is seen to be somewhat irregular and the ratio of the diameter to the height of the test also varied. A somewhat more rapid rate of growth is recorded by Grieg (1928) for specimens of *Strongyl. dröbachiensis* collected off the Norway coast: 0.5 mm. across at metamorphosis, 5 to 6 mm. across at 1 year of age, 15 mm. at 2 years, 24 at 3 years, 40 at 4 years, 50 at 5 years, and 60 at 6 years. The largest specimens, 78 mm. in diameter, were presumed to be about 8 years old. A similarly rapid rate of growth is evidenced in Elmhirst's data (1922b) on *Echinus esculentus*, which is 20 mm. across at 6 months of age, 40 mm. at the end of its first year, when it may spawn, 40 to 70 at the age of 2 years, 70 to 90 at 3 years, and 90 to 110 at 4 years of age, probably the limits of its life. The diameter of *Mellita sexiesperforata* at Bermuda was given by Crozier (1920) as 32 mm. at 6 months of age, 57 at 18 months, 70 at 3 years, and 100 at 4 years.    This species probably lives about 4 years, reaching a maximum diameter of 120 to 130 mm.    These data indicate that in nature echinoids grow rather rapidly, may spawn at the end of their first year, and live from 4 to 8 years, depending on the size of the species.    The findings of Orton (1923b) suggest that urchins grow about as well at Spitsbergen with a year-round temperature of about 4°C. as along British coasts.

## X. CLASS OPHIUROIDEA

**1. Definition.**—The Ophiuroidea are Eleutherozoa of stellate form with slender simple or branched arms sharply separated from the disk and of relatively solid construction, being supported by an internal row of ossicles representing fused ambulacral ossicles, without ambulacral grooves, with podia reduced to small papillae not provided with ampullae, without anus or intestine or (rare exceptions) digestive extensions into the arms, and typically with 10 genitorespiratory pouches in the periphery of the disk, opening orally at the sides of the arm bases by 10 or 20 slits.

**2. General Remarks.**—The Ophiuroidea are commonly known as serpent stars from the snaky appearance of the arms, or as brittle stars from the tendency of the arms to break off readily.    The name of the class derives from *ophis*, snake, and *ura*, tail, in reference to the resemblance of the arms to the tail end of a snake.    Although less conspicuous than other eleutherozoans from their small size, they are nevertheless common and familiar animals of the seashore.    They were recognized as distinct from asteroids early in the eighteenth century, although Linnaeus combined both types under the name *Asterias*, by which he meant stellate echinoderms in general.    They were first made into a separate group of echinoderms by Forbes (1841), and in 1842 Müller and Troschel divided the serpent stars into two groups, the Ophiurae with simple arms and the Euryalae with branched arms, an arrangement that still seems the most satisfactory.    The name Ophiuroidea as an echinoderm division separate from Asteroidea originated with Norman (1865).    As in the case of other echinoderm classes, knowledge of the Ophiuroidea was greatly enhanced by the study of the materials secured by the numerous collecting and dredging expeditions beginning in the latter part of the nineteenth century and continuing, although with diminished frequency and scope, into the present time.

Main accounts of ophiuroids are those of Lyman (1882) in the *Challenger* reports, Gregory (1900) in Lankester's *A treatise on zoology*, Ludwig and Hamann (1901) in Bronn's *Klassen und Ordnungen des Tierreichs*, and Cuénot (1948) in the *Traité de zoologie*.    Apart from taxonomic works, ophiuroids appear in zoological literature chiefly as material for studies of behavior.

According to H. L. Clark (1946), there are about 1600 existing species

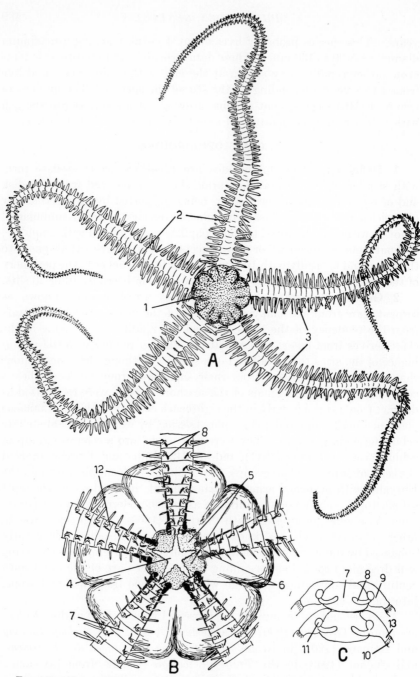

Fig. 241.—Types of Ophiuroidea. *A, Ophiocoma*, West Indies, type with spiny arms.
*B*, oral view of same. *C*, oral view of two arm joints. 1, disk; 2, arms; 3, arm spines; 4,
mouth; 5, jaws; 6, bursal slits; 7, oral arm shield; 8, podia ("tentacles"); 9, lateral arm
shields; 10, spine base; 11, tentacle scale; 12, arm bases in disk; 13, spine tubercle.

of ophiuroids; this class thus surpasses in number of surviving species the other classes of echinoderms, except asteroids. It may be regarded as the most successful echinoderm group living today, and this is probably to be attributed to the smaller size and greater agility of its members.

**3. External Characters.**—The ophiuroids lack the variety of external appearance seen in the other eleutherozoan groups. With the exception of the few euryalous forms with branched arms they all look alike. They have a small flattened disk of rounded, pentagonal, or scalloped contour, sharply separated from the five (rarely six or seven) symmetrically placed long, slender, smooth, or spiny arms. In those euryalous forms known as basket stars the disk is larger and the arms branch repeatedly, producing a bewildering maze of intermingled branches (Fig. 243).

The aboral surface of the disk may be smooth and leathery, or covered with granules or small spines, or may show a number of imbedded plates. In juvenile specimens there is usually seen the primitive plate arrangement already described for juvenile asteroids and echinoids, namely a central plate surrounded by other primitive plates disposed in concentric circles of five each. The outermost circle consists of the terminal plates, and these, as in asteroids, come to occupy the arm tips as the arms grow out. The primitive arrangement is still retained on the disk in some adults (Fig. 244B) but usually, as in asteroids, is lost by the interpolation of secondary plates or the deposition of granules concealing the original plates. Thus the aboral surface of the ophiurous disk often presents a complete coverage of small plates of irregular shapes and sizes (Fig. 244D). Most conspicuous of the secondary plates and apparently always present, although sometimes concealed from view by granules, is a pair of *radial shields* at the base of each arm (Fig. 244C, D). These are typically of considerable size and may become so large as to extend from the periphery of the disk to its center, like spokes of a wheel. In the euryalous ophiuroids the aboral surface of the disk is usually naked or may bear a few granules or spines, or may be covered with granules or spines or small scales; the radial shields are here spoke-like, reaching the center of the disk, although they may be obvious only in dried specimens (Fig. 244E). In the basket stars (family Gorgonocephalidae) the disk is much larger than in other ophiuroids, and in some species the granules or spines are limited to the rib-like radial shields.

The arms are always long relative to the disk diameter and very long (Fig. 242D) in some species. The arms may be smooth or show varying degrees of spininess. They present a jointed appearance recalling that of crinoids because they are protected typically by four longitudinal series of calcareous plates or shields that may be obvious in life or more or less concealed by skin. Each arm "joint" (corresponding to an internal

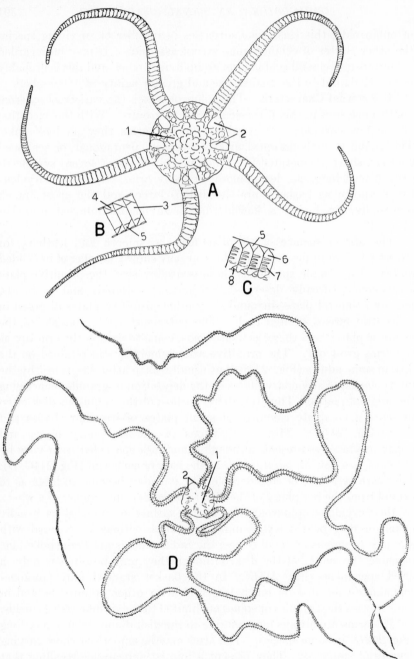

Fig. 242.—Types of Ophiuroidea (continued). *A*, *Ophiolepis elegans*, West Indies, with smooth arms. *B*, bit of oral surface of an arm, showing shields. *C*, side view of bit of arm, showing small, appressed spines. *D*, *Orchasterias columbiana*, British Columbia, with exceptionally long arms. 1, disk; 2, radial shields; 3, oral arm shield; 4, oral end of lateral arm shields; 5, interpolated oral piece; 6, lateral shield; 7, spines; 8, tentacle scales.

ossicle) is covered aborally by an aboral arm shield, on each side by a lateral arm shield, and orally by an oral arm shield; these shields may be of about equal size, but often the aboral and oral shields are greatly reduced concomitant with enlargement of the lateral shields; or the aboral shields may break up into a number of small plates or become part of a mosaic of interpolated pieces. The lateral shields are the more fundamental of the arm coverings and may meet above and below, as in *Ophiomusium* (Fig. 247*A*, *D*), forcing the small aboral and oral shields apart. It is unanimously acknowledged that the lateral arm shields correspond to the adambulacral ossicles of asteroids, and hence it is not surprising to find that the arm spines, when present, are borne upon them.

The arm spines, varying in number from 2 or 3 to about 15 on each lateral arm shield, form a vertical row. They may stand out at right angles to the arm axis, giving the animal a spiny appearance, as in *Ophiocoma* (Fig. 241*A*) and *Ophiothrix*, and in such case are borne along the center of the lateral shield on a low ridge (Fig. 245*E*). They may also spring from the distal edge of the shield and are then usually small and appressed to the side of the arm (Fig. 247*D*), reducing its flexibility. The spines are mostly alike in shape throughout the arms of a given species, but they often vary in length along each vertical row. The most aboral member of the row may be the longest and the length gradually decrease in the oral direction (Fig. 245*E*); or the longest spines may occur somewhere within the row and the length decline in both directions from these. Among the ophiurous forms much variation in spine shape is found in different species. The spines may be short or long, pointed or blunt, slender or stout, rounded in section or flattened, smooth or thorny, and so on. Slender thorny spines of a peculiar glassy texture characterize the family Ophiothrichidae (Fig. 245*F*). Glandular spines, possibly poisonous, occur in addition to ordinary spines in the genera *Ophiomastix*, *Ophiocreas*, and *Asteroschema* (Hamann, 1889). These have thick, fleshy, club-shaped ends composed of an extraordinarily thick epidermis of very attenuated epithelial cells interspersed with gland cells (Fig. 248*A*) and richly innervated. Some of the spines of each arm joint are webbed into transverse fans in the genus *Ophiopteron* (Ludwig, 1888); the most oral spines are thick and thorny, but the remaining spines (10) of each vertical row are long and slender, increasing in length aborally and united by membrane into a vertical fan (Fig. 245*C*). Mortensen (1932) also studied those fans and found that the supporting spines are provided basally with strong musculature. This finding suggests that the fans might be waved so as to enable the animal to swim, but Mortensen (1922) observed many live *Ophiopteron* in the Indo-Pacific region (Amboina) and never saw any swimming activity, reporting, on the contrary, that the animals are rather sluggish.　This author further found that a number of species of *Ophiothrix* possess such fans when young, but later the webs disintegrate, setting the spines free.　The function of these fans, either in the adult *Ophiopteron* or in the ophiopteron stages of *Ophiothrix*, remains problematical.　Spines altered into hooks are common among ophiuroids; thus in *Ophiothrix* the most oral member of each vertical

Fig. 243.—Types of Ophiuroidea (continued).　Basket star, *Gorgonocephalus*, North Atlantic, to 1500 m. (*after Koehler*, 1909); note greatly branched arms, orally located spines on arms.

row of spines is transformed into a hook (Fig. 245*F*) along the distal parts of the arms.　Parasol spines, resembling a minute parasol, are found distally on the arms of the related genera *Ophiohelus* and *Ophiotholia* (Lyman, 1882), replacing distally the ordinary spines altogether in the former genus (Fig. 245*D*), accompanying them in the latter.

The Ophiuroidea contrast with other echinoderms in the total lack of anything resembling ambulacra or ambulacral grooves on the body surface.　Podia are, however, present as small papillae, commonly called *tentacles* in the literature.　There is a pair of such podia to each arm joint on its oral surface; one emerges on each side between the lateral and oral arm shields and is usually protected by one or more altered spines known as *tentacle scales*, usually immovable, and mostly of a rounded shape. In the genus *Ophiopsila*, the more oral of the two tentacle scales retains the spine shape, is heavily flagellated, and is provided with a muscle by which it can lean over the oral surface of the arm, crossing its fellow of the opposite side (Reichensperger, 1908a; Fig. 246*A*). The arm surface between the bases of these flagellated spines is also strongly flagellated, and a current is therefore maintained along the oral surface of the arms, in the direction of the disk. At the end of the ophiuroid arm is found the usual terminal podium, called tentacle, that here lacks a photoreceptor. The podia serve primarily sensory functions, although participation in locomotion by the gripping of objects has been observed.

The foregoing account applies chiefly to the order Ophiurae in which the arms, provided with well-developed shields, are capable of sidewise movement only, in the horizontal plane. In the Euryalae the longer and much more flexible arms are movable in the vertical plane and can be coiled around objects. In a number of euryalous genera the arms are simple, in some they branch only at a considerable distance from the disk, and in others, especially *Gorgonocephalus* and *Astrophyton* (Fig. 243), they fork at the periphery of the disk and continue to branch repeatedly, in *Astrophyton* at very short intervals. Disk and arms in the Euryalae are covered with a thick skin and hence the scalation of the arms is more or less concealed, although in fact less developed than in the Ophiurae. All four series of shields may be present, but often the aboral or oral rows or both may be reduced or wanting or broken up into irregular mosaics. Arm spines are limited to the oral arm surface and are generally greatly reduced, perhaps representing tentacle scales, otherwise absent. Toward the arm ends the spines often develop hooks, and in the smaller branches and twigs of *Gorgoncephalus* these hooks are incorporated into rings of granules bearing microscopic hooks (Fig. 246*C*).

On the oral side, the arms, imbedded in the disk, continue to the mouth angles with all their parts—oral and lateral shields, spines, podia, and tentacle scales—retained, except the aboral shields (Fig. 247*A*, *B*). To each side of each arm base is seen a slit, the *bursal slit*, entrance to a pouch of inturned body wall, the *bursa*, with genitorespiratory functions. In the genus *Ophioderma*, each bursal slit is subdivided into a central and a peripheral slit (Fig. 246*D*). In *Ophioschiza monacantha*, Bering Sea, there is a single bursal slit in each interradius, transversely placed near the adoral shield (H. L. Clark, 1911) but the state of the bursae is unknown. In *Ophiopus arcticus* from the boreal Atlantic the bursae are reduced to slight depressions, and each of the 10 sacciform gonads opens independently by a pore in the oral interradial areas (Mortensen, 1893). Bursae and slits are altogether absent in *Ophiactis virens* (Cuénot,

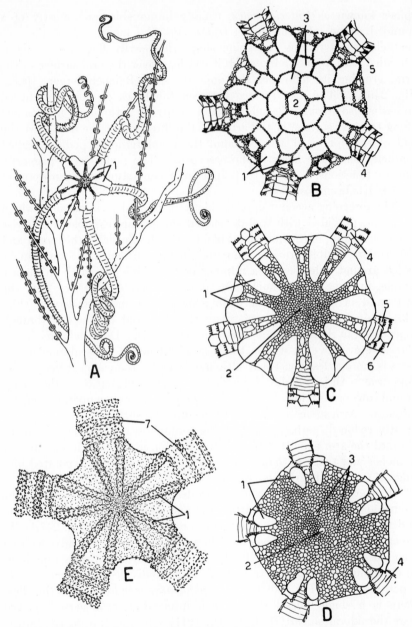

Fig. 244.—Types of Ophiuroidea (concluded), disk scalation.  A, euryalous type with
simple arms, *Asteronyx excavata*, Panamic region, with arms coiled around the branches
cf an antipatharian coral.  B, disk of *Ophiolepis* with concentric arrangement of plates.
C, disk of *Ophiomusium* with large radial shields.  D, disk of *Ophiura* with many small
plates.  E, disk of euryalous form, *Asteroschema*, with naked disk, except for thorny
rib-like radial shields.  1, radial shields; 2, central plate; 3, primary concentric plates;
4, aboral arm shields; 5, lateral arm shields; 6, appressed spines; 7, thorny bands.

1891a), *Ophiocanops fugiens* (Mortensen, 1932), and other species and not infrequently are very rudimentary. The oral surface of the disk between the arm bases forms fleshy, triangular interradial areas that in general have the same skeletal provision as the aboral surface of the disk.

In the center of the oral surface of the disk is seen a large five-angled aperture loosely called mouth, although actually a sort of preoral cavity leading to the true mouth. It is surrounded by five interradial wedge-shaped jaws that form a mouth frame comparable to the adambulacral type of asteroids. Only the triangular oral ends of the jaws are visible on the oral surface. These are edged by little scallops or teeth called the *oral papillae*, wanting in some genera. At the jaw point to the aboral side of the terminal oral papilla may be seen a group of *tooth papillae*, also wanting in some ophiuroids. These are continued inward by larger and heavier projections, the teeth, mostly in one row, more or less visible if the jaws are widely open. When tooth papillae are absent the vertical row of teeth extends to meet the oral papillae. The jaws consist of two main fused pieces, the half jaws, of which the oral ends may usually be seen in part on the exposed triangular surface of the jaw (Fig. 247*A*, *B*). Between these and the jaw tip is usually exposed the oral end of a narrow elongated vertical piece, the *maxiller* or *jaw plate* (torus angularis), through which pass the muscles operating the teeth. The greater part of the oral surface of the jaws is covered over by a conspicuous rounded plate, the *oral* or *buccal* shield, bordered to either side by a smaller, elongated *adoral* shield (Fig. 247*A*, *B*). One of the buccal shields acts as a madreporite, being pierced by usually one pore, sometimes more, but is generally impossible to recognize as such externally. Buccal and adoral shields are poorly developed or wanting in the Eurylae and here there may be a hydropore in each interradius. The bursal slits, extending usually from the disk periphery to the buccal shields, are supported on each side by an elongated *genital* shield, of which the one next the arm base usually does not show at the surface. At their outer ends the genital shields meet the radial shields; their inner or oral ends do not as a rule reach the buccal shields, and the gap is filled by one or more small *genital scales*. The edges of the bursal slits may be smooth or thrown into small scallops, the *genital papillae*. The first two pairs of podial pores are usually hidden in the sides of the jaws, but the second pair is exposed on the surface in *Ophiura* (Fig. 247*B*) and some other genera. The disk scalation is often obscured in life by membrane or a layer of granules (Fig. 246*D*).

The ophiuroids are mostly small animals with a disk 10 to 30 mm. across and arms typically three to five or six times the disk diameter in length; however, species with small disks may have very long arms (as in Fig. 242*D*). The basket stars (Gorgonocephalidae) are very much

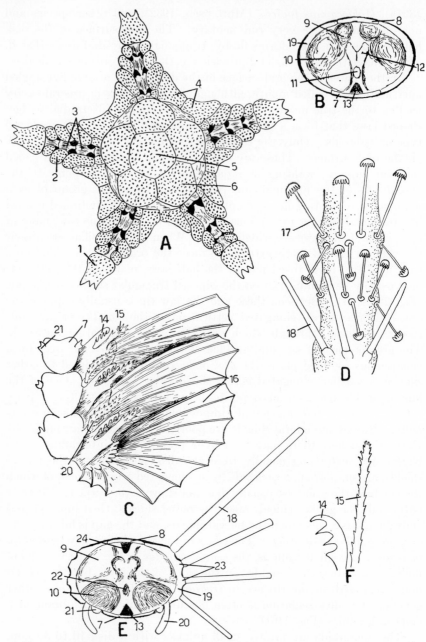

Fig. 245.—Scalation, spines. *A*, young specimen of *Asteronyx*, showing primitive plates (*after Mortensen*, 1912). *B*, distal surface of arm joint, showing surface shields and vertebral ossicles, *Ophiocoma*, spines omitted. *C*, three arm joints of *Ophiopteron*, seen from the oral side, showing fans or wings formed by webbing of spines (*after Ludwig*, 1888). *D*, parasol spines from distal part of arm of *Ophiohelus* (*after Lyman*, 1882).

larger than the run of ophiuroids, having disks up to 10 cm. across and long branching arms of which the length is not apparent as they are always much coiled (Fig. 243).

In general the coloration of ophiuroids is on the sober side and bright colors when present are not very effective because of the small size of the animals. Common colors of the disk are cream, yellow, green, olive, gray, brown, maroon, purple, and black, but often the color is not uniform, being relieved by contrasting spots and bands, and the arms are often of a lighter or different hue from the disk. Epizoic species may show adaptive coloration.

**4. Histology of the Body Wall and Its Appendages.**—The body surface is covered with a cuticle and is for the most part devoid of ciliation or flagellation. Cilia (flagella?) do, however, exist around the bursal slits and apparently are often present over much of the oral surface of the disk and arm bases in at least some species, as Gislén (1924) described currents here in several of the forms that he studied (see under physiology). The heavy flagellation of the inner tentacle scales of *Ophiopsila* was mentioned above, and in this genus there are also present flagellated streaks on the oral surface of the disk and transverse flagellated tracts along the oral surface of the arms (Fig. 246A). A definite cellular epidermis appears wanting in most ophiuroids in the adult condition (Cuénot, 1888, 1891a), except in certain areas, especially the bursal slits and sites of nerve endings. An epidermis is evident on the disk and proximal parts of the arms of the Euryalae and is fairly developed in the genus *Ophiomyxa* where it also contains gland cells everywhere (Reichensperger, 1908c; Fig. 247C). Otherwise gland cells are generally wanting in ophiuroids, except on the podia (see below) and in connection with luminescence (see under physiology). It is stated by Cuénot that an epidermis is present in young ophiuroids but during ontogeny becomes invaded by mesenchyme and reduced to a granular state (Fig. 247C, F). In any case a definite basement membrane is always lacking so that the syncytial epidermis is continuous with the dermis. The latter is for the most part occupied by the endoskeletal shields already described; the remainder is gelatinous or fibrous with scattered cells and contains the pigment responsible for the surface colors, as fine granules or sometimes in amoeboid cells. In the ophiurous forms

*E*, arm joint of *Ophiocoma*, seen from proximal end, showing spine arrangement (one side only) and vertebral articulations. *F*, thorny spine and hooked spine from distal part of arms of *Ophiothrix*. 1, terminal ossicle; 2, lateral arm shield; 3, vertebral ossicles; 4, adoral shields; 5, central plate; 6, primary radial plates; 7, oral arm shield; 8, aboral arm shield; 9, upper intervertebral muscles; 10, lower intervertebral muscles; 11, central articulating knob (umbo); 12, articulating projections; 13, oral canal for radial nerve and water vessel; 14, hooked spine; 15, thorny spines; 16, fan; 17, parasol spine; 18, ordinary spines; 19, lateral arm shield; 20, podia; 21, tentacle scale; 22, depression to receive umbo; 23, tubercles of lateral arm shield for spine attachment; 24, aboral canal.

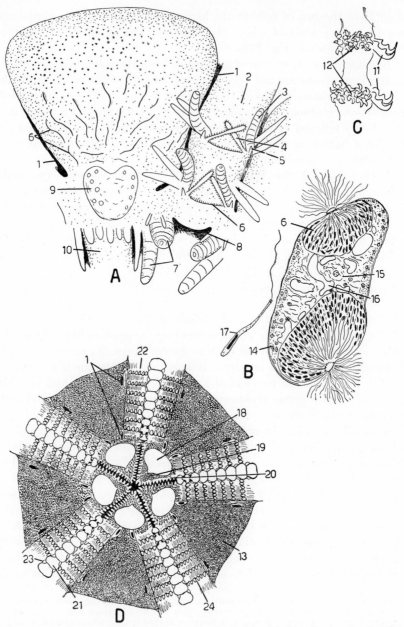

FIG. 246.—External features, spines. *A*, part of disk of *Ophiopsila* showing flagellated spines and flagellated areas of disk. *B*, section through a flagellated spine; the flagellated cells occur in spiral tracts. (*A, B, after Reichensperger*, 1908a.) *C*, distal bit of arm of *Gorgonocephalus*, showing girdles of hooks. *D*, oral surface of the disk of *Ophioderma*, with two slits to each bursa. 1, bursal slit; 2, arm base; 3, podia; 4, flagellated tentacle scale; 5, ordinary tentacle scale; 6, flagellated tracts; 7, buccal podia; 8, mouth angle; 9,

the body wall lacks a muscle stratum and the dermis rests directly on the coelomic epithelium; but in the euryalous ophiuroids a muscle stratum is present in the wall of the disk (Fedotov, 1926a). The coelomic lining is definitely cellular in some places, in others only vaguely indicated.

Pedicellariae and respiratory protrusions are entirely wanting in ophiuroids and therefore the external appendages comprise only spines and podia. Spines are of minor importance here; as already indicated, they are generally confined to the lateral arm shields, although sometimes occurring on the disk also, and vary in size, shape, and surface characters. They consist of an internal calcareous support covered thinly by the epidermal-dermal combination described above and containing a central lumen filled with connective tissue. At least the larger spines are movable, being mounted on an endoskeletal tubercle as in echinoids, by way of a cylindrical ligament and a central muscle that originates in a depression in the side of the tubercle. The tubercle is further perforated by a hole through which a nerve passes and ascends the connective-tissue axis of the spine, ramifying therein; this nerve springs from a ganglion located at the tubercle base (Fig. 248C). Mention was already made of the glandular spines of certain genera, covered with a thick epidermis of elongated epithelial and glandular cells (Fig. 248A).

The podia are reduced to small papillae, whose histological structure (most recently described by J. E. Smith, 1937) is, however, similar to that of the podia of other Eleutherozoa. The podia are clothed with a definite columnar epidermis, typically thrown into numerous papillae; this is underlain by a thick nervous stratum followed by connective tissue, a longitudinal muscle layer, and the lining coelomic epithelium (Fig. 248D–F). In some species, connective tissue occurs to both sides of the nervous stratum. The papillae consist of exceptionally elongated epithelium cells which at the tips of the papillae are liberally interspersed with deeply staining elements thought by earlier workers to represent sensory endings but shown by Reichensperger (1908c) and Smith to be adhesive gland cells (Fig. 249A).

**5. Endoskeleton.**—This is roughly divisible into superficial and deeper parts. The elements of the former are called shields and were described above. On the arms the superficial endoskeleton is constituted of the aboral, lateral, and oral arm shields located close to the surface and generally externally visible because of the poor development of the epidermis. The interior of the arm is occupied by a longitudinal series of ossicles belonging to the deeper skeleton and called *vertebral ossicles* or

madreporite (oral shield); 10, basal part of a jaw; 11, main hooked spines; 12, girdle of hooked granules; 13, granules; 14, epidermis; 15, connective tissue; 16, holes left by decal-cification; 17, one of the flagellated cells; 18, oral shield; 19, jaw; 20, oral papillae; 21, oral arm shield; 22, lateral arm shield; 23, tentacle scale; 24, spines.

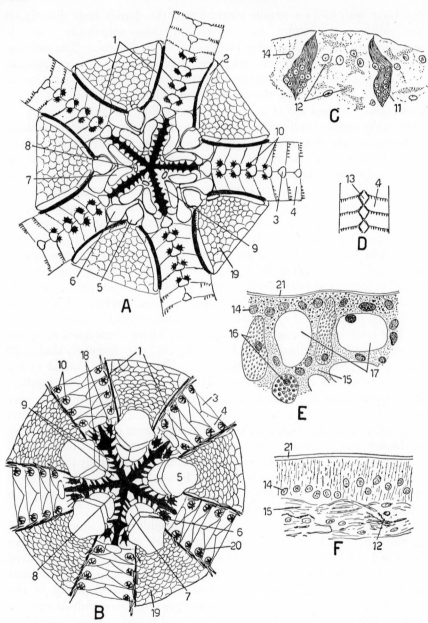

Fig. 247.—Scalation, epidermis.  *A*, oral view of the disk of *Ophiomusium*, showing scalation; in this genus podial pores and podia are limited to the arm bases.  *B*, oral view of the disk of *Ophiura;* second podial pores appear on surface.  *C*, epidermis of *Ophiomyxa* with gland cells *(after Reichensperger, 1908c).*  *D*, aboral arm scalation of *Ophiomusium.* *E*, epidermis of *Ophiactis (after Cuénot, 1891).*  *F*, epidermis of *Ophiomyxa* with indications of cells *(after Hamann, 1889).*    1, bursal slit; 2, genital plate; 3, oral arm shield; 4, lateral

*vertebrae* from a fanciful resemblance to the vertebrae of vertebrate animals. The vertebral ossicles are somewhat disk-like, thicker through the middle and thin laterally (Fig. 249D); these thin lateral wings furnish attachment sites for the intervertebral muscles. Toward the arm ends the vertebral ossicles become reduced and cylindroid and the terminal ossicle is trough-like with an oral groove to house the terminal podium. Medially the oral surface of each vertebra is deeply notched, and the succession of notches forms a groove in which runs the radial nerve cord (Fig. 249B, C). In this groove there are present to each side of the median line two small holes in each vertebra that lead into fine canals in the substance of the vertebra. The more proximal pair of holes houses a pair of nerves for the upper intervertebral muscles; the more distal pair conveys the podial branches of the water-vascular system. There is also a median aboral groove along the vertebrae but this does not house any particular structure. The two ends of each vertebral ossicle, that is, its proximal surface facing in the direction of the mouth and its distal surface facing the arm tip, differ from each other. In most ophiuroids the proximal surface bears a series of depressions and a median projection and these fit into corresponding projections and a median depression on the distal surface (Fig. 249B, C), forming an articulation that in general permits only sidewise movements of the arms, in the horizontal plane (*zygospondylous* articulation). A different type of articulation (*streptospondylous*) obtains in the euryalous ophiuroids. Here both vertebral ends bear a projection shaped somewhat like an hourglass, but this is oriented vertically on the proximal surface, transversely on the distal surface (Fig. 249E, F). Hence the vertebrae can roll upon each other and the arms can be coiled and entwined around objects (Figs. 243, 244A).

It is to be understood that each vertebral ossicle corresponds to an external arm "joint" and is covered over with one set of arm shields (Fig. 245B). It is established that each vertebra is formed by the fusion of one pair of ambulacral ossicles, and in a few species the line of fusion remains evident throughout life. One visualizes the ophiuroid type of arm as derived from a type with open groove by the closing over of the ambulacral groove and the relegation of the ambulacral ossicles to the interior of the arm followed by their fusion in pairs to form the vertebral ossicles.

As the scalation of both sides of the disk was described above, it remains to consider the deeper parts of the mouth frame. The mouth

arm shield; 5, oral shield; 6, adoral shields; 7, half jaws; 8, maxiller; 9, oral papillae; 10, podial pores; 11, gland cells; 12, pigment cells; 13, aboral arm shield; 14, epidermal nuclei; 15, dermis; 16, coelomocytes; 17, spaces left by decalcification; 18, second pair of podial pores; 19, scales of disk; 20, tentacle scales; 21, cuticle.

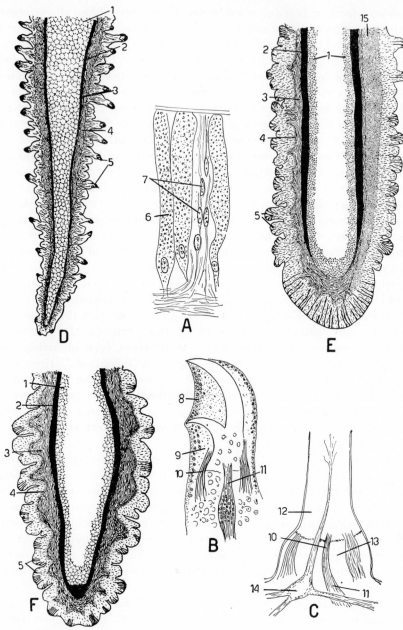

Fig. 248.—Body-wall appendages. A, epidermis of glandular spine of *Ophiomastix annulosa*. B, hooked spine of *Ophiothrix* with muscular and ligamentous attachments. (A, B, after Hamann, 1889.) C, spine of *Ophiocoma* with nerve supply (after Cuénot, 1891). D, longitudinal section of podium of *Ophiothrix fragilis*. E, longitudinal section of podium of *Ophiocomina nigra*. F, longitudinal section of podium of *Ophiura texturata*.

frame, as already indicated, consists of five wedge-shaped pieces or jaws that are compounded of the first two ambulacrals, the first two adambulacrals, and surface shields. As each jaw occupies an interradial position it is evidently composed of ossicles from two adjacent arm bases, and therefore formed of two half jaws. Each half jaw consists of a larger piece representing the second ambulacral ossicle and a smaller piece representing the first adambulacral ossicle (lateral arm shield) fastened to the oral side of the larger piece and bearing the teeth, which are modified adambulacral spines. As already indicated, there is generally present here as an additional support for the teeth a small interpolated maxiller or jaw plate, composed of a vertical row of pieces. On the oral surface the half jaws may be partially visible but are usually more or less concealed from view by the oral and adoral shields; the adoral shields are easily seen to be in line with the regular lateral arm shields and in fact represent the second adambulacrals. They carry some of the oral papillae. The first pair of ambulacrals is formed into two elongated pieces, called *peristomial plates*, that occupy the aboral surface of the jaws (Fig. 249*G*) and hence are not visible from the oral side. The two peristomial pieces of adjacent rays meet diagonally at the interradius and thus seem to act as stays. The homologies of the parts of the mouth armature of ophiuroids were worked out by Ludwig (1878a), whose diagram is reproduced in Fig. 250*A*. As already indicated, there are two podial pores through each half jaw, a fact in itself proving that two pairs of ambulacral ossicles are involved in the formation of each jaw. These podial pores are usually hidden in the interior of the mouth cavity, but in some genera, as *Ophiura*, the second pairs are visible on the surface (Fig. 247*B*). The podia of the mouth armature are often spoken of as buccal podia or buccal tentacles.

**6. Musculature.**—As stated above, the body wall of ophiuroids lacks a muscle layer except in the Eurylae, and hence in most members musculature is limited to discrete bundles for operating the arms, the jaw apparatus, the spines (already described), and the teeth. There are two pairs of intervertebral muscles between successive vertebral ossicles, an upper or aboral and a lower or oral pair (Fig. 245*B*, *E*), although the two of the same side may be merged into each other. They extend between the thin lateral parts of the vertebral ossicles and consist of fibers running parallel to the arm axis. The aboral and oral pair are not necessarily in the same vertical plane (Fig. 250*B*). By suitable combinations of contractions the intervertebral muscles could move the arms

---

(*D–F, after J. E. Smith*, 1937.) 1, coelomic lining; 2, longitudinal muscle layer; 3, nervous layer; 4, connective tissue; 5, papillae; 6, gland cell; 7, neurosensory cells; 8, epidermis; 9, dermis; 10, ligament; 11, muscle; 12, spine base; 13, tubercle of lateral arm shield; 14, nerve ganglion; 15, main podial nerve.

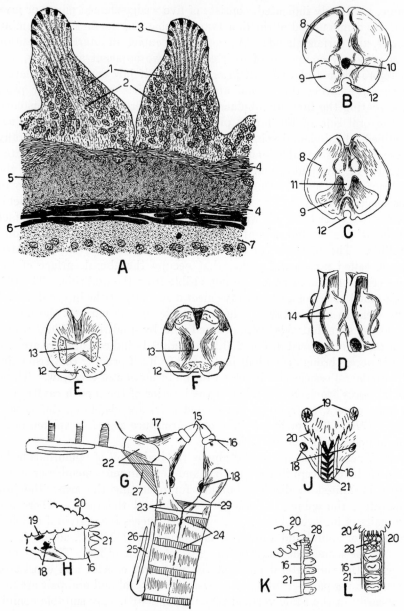

FIG. 249.—Appendages (concluded), endoskeleton. *A*, two papillae of a podium of *Ophiothrix fragilis* (*after J. E. Smith*, 1937). *B*, vertebral ossicle of *Ophiolepis*, proximal surface. *C*, same as *B*, distal surface. *D*, side view of vertebral ossicles of *Ophiarachna* (*after Ludwig*, 1878); proximal surface to left. *E*, distal surface of vertebral ossicle of *Astrophyton* with transverse hourglass articulation. *F*, proximal surface of *E* with vertical hourglass articulation. (*B, C, E, F, after Lyman*, 1882.) *G*, one sector of the jaw apparatus and one arm base of *Ophiomusium*, seen from the aboral side, after removal of the aboral

in any direction, but as already explained, the articulating surfaces of the vertebral ossicles of most ophiuroids are so constructed that movement is feasible only in the horizontal plane.

The jaw apparatus is operated by two concentric series of muscles of which the best available descriptions are those of Simroth (1876) and Teuscher (1876). The largest and most important of the jaw muscles are the *external interradial* muscles that run between the half jaws of two adjacent radii, hence occupy an interradial position (Fig. 251A). The two half jaws of the same radius are bound together by two muscles, a *superior* or *aboral* and an *inferior* or *oral radial* muscle, often more or less merged. The fibers of these 15 muscles of the external circle run concentric with the mouth and hence their contractions bring the jaws together so that the teeth make contact. The inner circle of muscles consists of the *superior* or *aboral* and *inferior* or *oral internal interradial* muscles. These muscles are situated one above the other between the maxiller and the adambulacral parts of the half jaws. The fibers of the inferior muscles run circularly and act to approximate the central ends of the jaws. The fibers of the superior muscles run radially; they pass through openings in the maxiller to attach to the teeth and accomplish movements of the latter (Fig. 253B).

**7. Nervous System.**—The main nervous system (exhaustively described by Hamann, 1889) is subepidermal in position, as in asteroids, in the young ophiuroid, but like the ambulacral system becomes displaced internally during ontogeny by the closure of the ambulacral grooves (Cuénot, 1891a). The nerve ring occupies a groove close to the aboral surface of the jaw apparatus, being somewhat concealed by the peristomial plates (Fig. 250C). On the side toward the esophagus the nerve ring is bounded by a cavity, the epineural sinus, and on the opposite side by another cavity, the hyponeural sinus. The nerve ring gives off esophageal nerves, mostly 10 in number, into the esophagus, where they form a plexus in the Euryalae (Cuénot, 1891a). The nerve ring further supplies a nerve directly to each of the buccal podia belonging to the first ambulacrals (main piece of each half jaw); these podia are in fact situated very close to the nerve ring. In each interradius there springs from the nerve ring a pair of nerves or a nerve that promptly forks; one goes to

disk wall. *H*, jaw of *Ophiomusium;* lacks tooth papillae. *J*, jaw of *Ophiura;* lacks tooth papillae, has two rows of teeth. *K*, jaw of *Ophiocoma*, with tooth papillae. *L*, same as *K* seen from the mouth side. 1, papilla; 2, epidermis; 3, gland cells; 4, connective tissue; 5, nervous layer; 6, longitudinal muscles; 7, coelomic epithelium; 8, fossa for upper intervertebral muscles; 9, fossa for lower intervertebral muscles; 10, central depression; 11, central projection; 12, canal for radial nerve; 13, hour-glass projection; 14, holes for passage of podial canal; 15, tooth; 16, maxiller; 17, half jaw; 18, pore for first pair of podia; 19, pore for second pair of podia; 20, oral papillae; 21, teeth; 22, peristomial plate (first pair of ambulacrals); 23, third pair of ambulacrals; 24, upper interambulacral muscles; 25, genital plates; 26, location of bursal slit; 27, external interradial muscle; 28, tooth papillae; 29, aboral radial muscle.

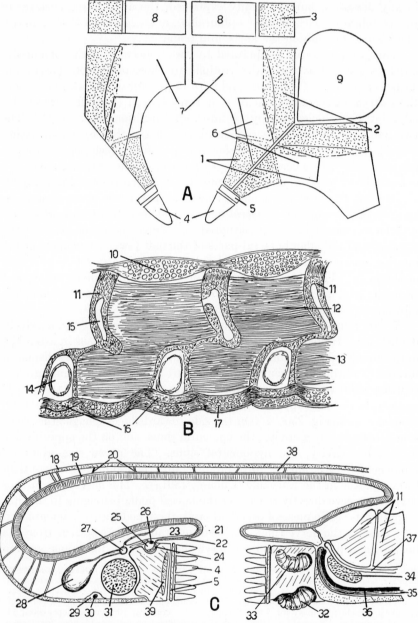

FIG. 250.—Endoskeleton (concluded), muscular and nervous systems.  *A*, scheme of jaw composition, adambulacrals stippled, ambulacrals plain (*after Ludwig*, 1878a).  *B* vertical section through the side of an arm (*after* Simroth, 1876).  *C*, schematic vertical section through the disk, an interradius on the left, radius with arm base on the right (*after Ludwig*, 1880).  1, first pair of adambulacrals; 2, second pair of adambulacrals ( = adoral shields); 3, third pair of adambulacrals ( = lateral arm shields) ; 4, tooth; 5,

the external muscles of the jaw apparatus and the other to the internal muscles, including branches to the teeth. These interradial muscle nerves generally present a ganglionic swelling before entering the muscles.

In each radius, the nerve ring gives off a radial nerve that descends to the oral side of the arm base in the disk and proceeds along the arm to its tip, running in the groove already mentioned that is present in the median line along the oral faces of the vertebral ossicles (Fig. 249*B, C*). The radial nerve, as in other echinoderms, is accompanied by tubular cavities, an epineural sinus to its oral side, and a hyponeural sinus to its aboral side (Fig. 251*A, B*). The radial nerves of ophiuroids are more complicated than those of other echinoderms; they have a ganglionic enlargement at each vertebral ossicle (Fig. 253*A*) and give off a number of branches that also may bear ganglionic swellings. A podial nerve is given off from the radial nerve into each podium, including the second set of buccal tentacles. This podial nerve at once forms a ring ganglion around the base of the podium, and from this ganglion a nerve proceeds into the podium along its medial side between the epidermis and the longitudinal muscle layer (Fig. 251*B*). From the podial ganglion there are given off, at least in some species, nerves into the oral wall of the arm, and these may meet to form a small median ganglion from which the body-wall branches arise (Fig. 251*B*). Close behind the podial nerves there springs in each arm joint a pair of main lateral nerves that ascend in the lateral parts of the arms giving off branches into the body wall; when spines are present this nerve gives off a branch into each spine and this enlarges to a ganglion before entering the spine (Fig. 252*B*). Minor lateral nerves to the body wall are present in some species. The foregoing nerves are mainly sensory and spring from the radial nerve between its ganglionic enlargements. These ganglionic enlargements are somewhat bilobed or paired because of the presence of a median haemal channel. At the ganglionic enlargement there is given off in each arm joint a strong pair of motor nerves that supply the intervertebral muscles (Fig. 252*A*).

The nerve ring and radial nerves are in reality double, consisting of two superimposed systems, an outer thick ectoneural and an inner thin hyponeural system. The former is sensory and motor, the latter purely

maxiller; 6, first pair of ambulacrals ( = peristomial plates); 7, second pair of ambulacrals (main part of jaw); 8, third pair of ambulacrals ( = vertebral ossicle); 9, buccal shield; 10, aboral arm shield; 11, vertebral ossicles; 12, aboral intervertebral muscles; 13, oral intervertebral muscles; 14, podium; 15, podial canal in vertebra; 16, lateral arm shield; 17, oral arm shield; 18, wall of disk; 19, stomach; 20, mesenterial attachments of stomach; 21, mouth; 22, peristome; 23, peristomial or periesophageal coelomic cavity; 24, nerve ring; 25, hyponeural ring canal; 26, oral haemal ring; 27, water ring; 28, polian vesicle; 29, aboral coelomic sinus; 30, aboral haemal ring; 31, external interradial muscle; 32, first pair of podia (buccal tentacles); 33, second pair of podia; 34, lower radial muscle; 35, radial nerve; 36, radial haemal channel; 37, radial water canal; 38, coelom; 39, internal interradial muscle.

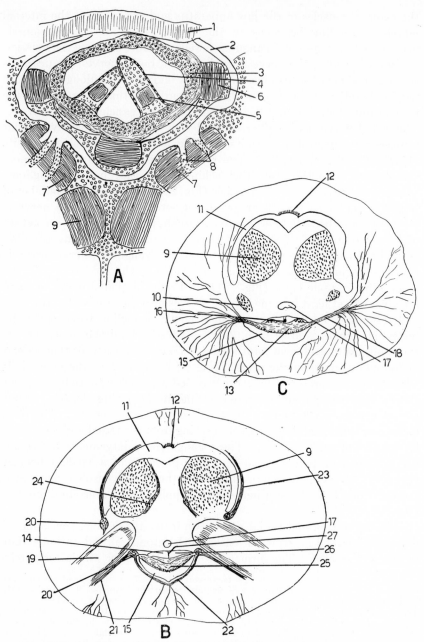

Fig. 251.—Muscular system (concluded), nervous system. *A*, horizontal section through the disk at the level of the aboral end of the jaw apparatus (*after Simroth, 1876*). *B*, cross section of arm at level of podia. *C*, cross section of arm at level of main lateral nerves. (*B, C, after Hamann, 1889.*) 1, stomach wall; 2, water ring; 3, nerve ring; 4, tooth; 5, aboral internal interradial muscle; 6, aboral radial muscle; 7, external interradial

motor, and it is from it that the nerves to the intervertebral muscles spring. The two systems are separated only by a thin membrane (Fig. 252*C*). An entoneural system appears wanting, unless it is represented by the genital nerve supply, discovered by Cuénot (1891a). Genital nerves are given off from a nerve ring on the inner surface of the aboral wall of the disk. This genital system is said by Cuénot to be connected with the main nervous system.

The epineural sinuses are only external spaces that became enclosed when the ambulacral grooves fused over. They are not lined by epithelium and are not coelomic cavities. They terminate blindly at each end, having no connections with other parts. On the other hand, the hyponeural sinuses are coelomic canals formed as in echinoids. They are subdivided, as in asteroids, by a very delicate septum that contains a haemal channel.

The ophiuroids are devoid of special sense organs, but the rich innervation of the body wall, podia, and spines indicates the presence of numerous sensory endings.

**8. Water-vascular System.**—The water ring occupies a groove on the aboral surface of the jaw apparatus, immediately to the outer side of the nerve ring (Fig. 251*A*). At each interradius, except that which contains the stone canal, the water ring gives off a polian vesicle of typical appearance. In *Ophiactis virens*, which has regularly six arms and lacks bursae, a main polian vesicle and one or two subsidiary ones are present in each interradius, including CD, and they are accompanied by a number (up to 15) of long slender tubular appendages, discovered by Simroth (1876) and hence sometimes called Simroth's appendages, that spring from the water ring or the stem of the main polian vesicle and insinuate themselves among the viscera (Fig. 252*D*). The water ring also supplies the buccal podia directly, giving off 10 (or 12 in case of six-armed species) branches that bifurcate, passing through the main jaw ossicle. One fork of each branch goes into the corresponding buccal tentacle of the first set and the other into that belonging to the second set. The stone canal springs from the water ring in an interradius that thereby becomes CD and, accompanied by the axial gland, descends to the oral side where it terminates in an ampulla. As in asteroids, stone canal and axial gland are enclosed in the axial sinus that also opens into the ampulla (Fig. 253*B*). Usually a single pore canal, often provided with lateral out-

---

muscle; 8, branches from water ring to buccal podia; 9, aboral intervertebral muscle; 10, oral intervertebral muscle; 11, coelom of arm; 12, band of tall coelomic cells; 13, radial nerve; 14, hyponeural sinus; 15, epineural sinus; 16, radial haemal channel; 17, radial water canal; 18, main lateral nerve; 19, base of podia; 20, podial ring ganglion; 21, main podial nerve; 22, nerves from podial ganglion to oral wall; 23, nerves from podial ganglion to aboral wall; 24, muscle nerves with ganglia from podial ganglia; 25, ectoneural part of radial nerve; 26, hyponeural or motor part of radial nerve; 27, septum.

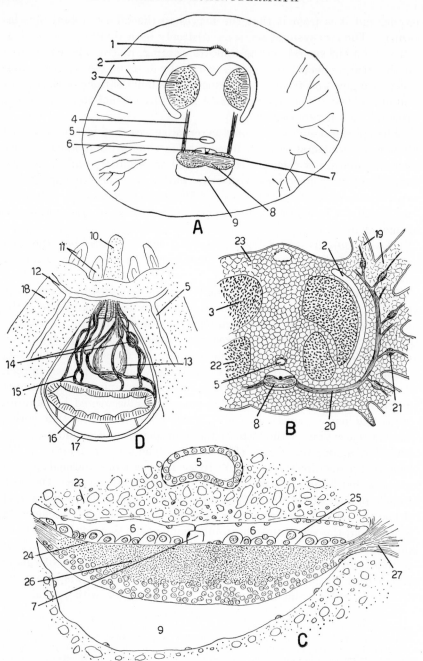

FIG. 252.—Nervous system (continued), water-vascular system.  *A*, cross section of arm at the level of the motor nerves to the intervertebral muscles (*after Hamann*, 1889). *B*, section through arm at level of main lateral nerves. showing spine ganglia (*after Cuénot*,

pouchings, leads from the ampulla to the hydropore located in the oral shield of interradius CD. Some species, however, have several pores (up to 12) and corresponding pore canals through the oral shield. *Ophiactis virens*, in addition to the peculiarities of its water-vascular system just mentioned, may have up to five madreporites and a corresponding number of oral shields altered into madreporites. This species is fissiparous; it starts life with five arms and one stone canal and madreporite, and the multiplication of the last two and increase to six arms result from fission. Among the Euryalae the presence of a madreporite in each interradius is not uncommon, especially in the genus *Astrophyton*. Some species of this genus have a single madreporite, perforated with as many as 250 pores, whereas others possess five madreporites, each with a few, up to 15 or 20 pores (Ludwig, 1878b). In *Trichaster elegans* there is a single hydropore in each interradius, not associated with any skeletal element (Ludwig, 1878b). In these cases a stone canal leads inward from each madreporite or hydropore. Tiedemann's bodies appear wanting in typical ophiuroids, although Fedotov (1926a) reported some insignificant radial protrusions of the water ring in *Ophiocten sericeum* that he interpreted as such. This same author discovered in *Gorgonocephalus* the presence of a bunch of blind, branching tubules appended to the water ring in each radius and is inclined to interpret these as homologues of Tiedemann's bodies.

From the water ring a radial canal departs in each radius and descends toward the oral side (Fig. 250C) where it enters the arm base and proceeds along the arm to its tip, terminating as the lumen of the terminal tentacle. The radial water canal runs in the substance of the vertebral ossicles of the arm in an uncalcified area of connective tissue that is located immediately aboral to the hyponeural canal of the radial nerve (Fig. 252C). In each vertebral ossicle the radial water canal shows an enlargement from which springs a pair of podial canals for the pair of podia of that arm joint (Fig. 253D). The podial canals may pass directly through the substance of the vertebral ossicle to the base of the podia or they may ascend in the ossicle and then descend, making a V-shaped curve before passing into the podium. There are no ampullae. The entrance of the podial canal into the podium is provided with a valve. As already

---

1888, *slightly altered*). C, enlarged view of cross section of the radial nerve at the level of the main lateral nerves (*after Hamann*, 1889). D, sector of disk of *Ophiactis virens*, showing water-vascular appendages (*after Cuénot*, 1891a). 1, strand of tall coelomic epithelium; 2, arm coelom; 3, aboral intervertebral muscles; 4, motor nerves; 5, radial water vessel; 6, hyponeural radial sinus; 7, radial haemal channel; 8, radial nerve; 9, epineural radial sinus; 10, tooth; 11, buccal podia; 12, water ring; 13, main polian vesicle; 14, secondary polian vesicles; 15, Simroth's appendages; 16, wall of stomach; 17, body wall; 18, arm base; 19, spine base; 20, main lateral nerve; 21, ganglia of 20 for spines; 22, oral intervertebral muscle; 23, decalcified vertebral ossicle; 24, partition between ectoneural and hyponeural parts of radial nerve; 25, hyponeural (motor) part of radial nerve ( = Lange's nerve) ; 26, ectoneural part of radial nerve; 27, base of main lateral nerves.

described, the podia are reduced to small inconspicuous papillae that, protected by one or more tentacle scales, project on the oral surface between the oral and lateral arm shields.

The water-vascular system is lined throughout with a low flagellated coelomic epithelium that becomes cuboidal in the pore canals and columnar in the stone canal. This is underlain in many cases or in some regions by muscle fibers followed by a hyaline elastic membrane that seems to constitute the main support of the wall. In projecting parts, as the polian vesicles, this membrane is followed externally by connective tissue and then a covering coelomic epithelium, also flagellated.

**9. Digestive System.**—This system is of the simplest possible construction in ophiuroids. The peristomial membrane is attached to the aboral surface of the jaw apparatus close to the nerve and water rings; hence the long five-angled cavity bounded by the jaws is not exactly the mouth, although often loosely so called. The true mouth is a circular opening in the center of the peristomial membrane (Fig. 250C). It leads into a very short esophagus that is encircled by a peristomial cavity (Fig. 250C) in the surrounding mesenchyme, and in some species an additional but smaller circular cavity is present to the inner side of the larger one. The wall of this smaller cavity is provided with muscle fibers (Hamann, 1889), and possibly both cavities are concerned in the opening and closure of the mouth. The esophagus leads into the sacciform stomach that fills the interior of the disk not occupied by other parts and completes the digestive tract, for there is neither intestine nor anus. The aboral wall of the stomach is closely applied to the inner surface of the aboral wall of the disk, to which it is further attached by mesenteric strands. The periphery of the stomach is scalloped into pouches, typically 10 in number, fitting between the bursae (Fig. 257A) and does not extend into the arms except in the curious species *Ophiocanops fugiens*, Indo-Pacific, with very small disk and very long arms, in which the stomach sends out a diverticulum into each arm, for about two-thirds of its length (Mortensen, 1932). This diverticulum is accommodated in a large space in the aboral part of the arms, aboral to the vertebral ossicles, and is there supported by a transverse mesentery (Fig. 255A). The stomach wall consists from the inside out of a flagellated epithelium, much taller aborally than orally, and provided with a brush border, a nervous stratum best developed near the esophagus, a thin layer of connective tissue, muscle fibers running circularly, and the flagellated cuboidal coelomic covering (Fig. 253C). Definite gland cells have not been observed.

**10. Bursae.**—The bursae are 10 sacciform invaginations of the oral wall of the disk alongside the arm bases (Fig. 247A, B). Except in the genus *Ophioderma*, each bursa opens by an elongated slit located close

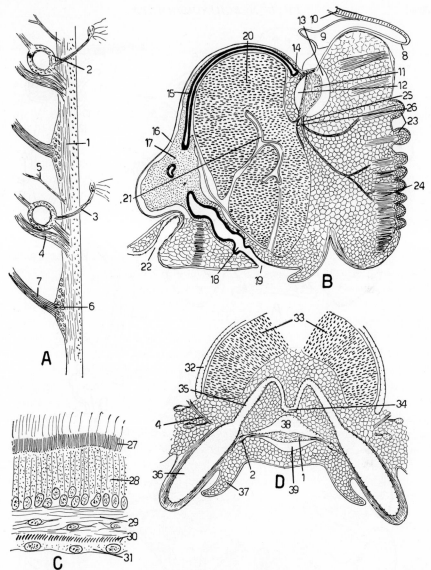

FIG. 253.—Nervous, digestive, and water-vascular systems. *A*, side view of radial nerve, schematic, with main branches, oral end above. *B*, vertical section of disk of *Ophiothrix* through the stone canal (*after Cuénot*, 1888). *C*, section through the stomach wall (*after Hamann*, 1889). *D*, partial section of arm to show podial water canals (*altered after Cuénot*, 1888). 1, radial nerve; 2, ring ganglion at base of podium; 3, nerve to oral wall of arm; 4, main lateral nerve; 5, minor lateral nerve; 6, motor ganglion of hyponeural system; 7, main motor nerve to intervertebral muscles; 8, peristome; 9, peristomial ring sinus; 10, stomach wall; 11, nerve ring; 12, epineural ring sinus; 13, hyponeural ring sinus; 14, water ring; 15, stone canal; 16, axial sinus; 17, axial gland; 18, ampulla; 19, hydropore; 20, external interradial muscle; 21, bursal extension into 20; 22, bursal slit; 23, teeth; 24, superior internal interradial muscles to teeth; 25, nerve from nerve ring to 24; 26, nerve to 20; 27, brush border; 28, stomach epithelium; 29, connective tissue; 30, muscle layer; 31, coelomic epithelium; 32, arm coelom; 33, intervertebral muscle; 34, radial water canal; 35, podial branches of 34; 36, podium; 37, tentacle scale; 38, hyponeural radial sinus; 39, epineural radial sinus.

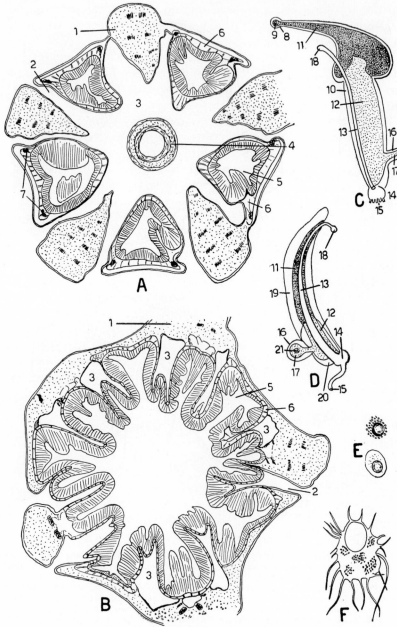

Fig. 254.—Bursae, coelom.  *A*, transverse section of the disk of *Gorgonocephalus* through the esophagus, showing fusion of the bursal sacs.  *B*, more aboral transverse section of *Gorgonocephalus* disk, through the stomach.  (*A*, *B*, *after Fedotov*, 1926.)  *C*, scheme of the axial complex of the Euryalae (*after Fedotov*, 1924).  *D*, scheme of the axial complex of the Ophiurae (*after J. Smith*, 1940).  *E*, *F*, types of coelomocytes (*after Cuénot*,

to the arm base and supported on each side by a genital shield. In *Ophioderma* the edges of the middle part of each slit have fused together, leaving a short opening at either end (Fig. 246*D*), and hence there are two openings to each bursa. The bursae project into the interior of the disk, occupying the spaces between the stomach outpouchings. They are usually well developed but reduced in a number of species and altogether lacking in some. In the genera *Ophiothrix* and *Ophiocoma* the bursae send out a simple or ramifying diverticulum into the corresponding external interradial muscle of the jaw apparatus (Cuénot, 1891a; J. E. Smith, 1940). The latter author finds in *Ophiothrix fragilis* two pairs of bursae to each interradius or 20 in all, of which one pair sends a simple diverticulum into the external interradial muscle. In *Gorgonocephalus*, and presumably the Eurylae in general, the bursae undergo a remarkable expansion (Fedotov, 1915, 1926a), the reasons for which are not apparent. They spread throughout the disk coelom and fuse wherever practical, forming a ring space around the esophagus and insinuating themselves between the stomach pouches and between the stomach and the disk wall, uniting to larger spaces (Fig. 254*A*, *B*), except where prevented by the mesenterial attachments of the stomach. Similar bursal fusions are not unknown in the Ophiurae. In *Ophiomitrella corynephora* and *Ophiacantha densispina* (Mortensen, 1933a, 1936), the two bursae of each ray are coalesced to the aboral side of the arm base, making five large bursae, and in *Ophiomitrella hamata* all the bursae are fused into one large circular space to the oral side of the stomach (Mortensen, 1933a).

The bursal wall histologically resembles the body wall, but its epidermis is better developed and strongly flagellated, at least in places, especially along the slits. The epidermis is underlain by a thin dermis that may contain calcareous deposits, and on the coelomic side the bursa is clothed with peritoneum. Bursae are peculiar to ophiuroids and important in their biology. A water current constantly circulates through the bursae for respiratory purposes, and some species pump water in and out of them by movements of the aboral disk wall. The bursae further serve as outlets for the sex cells and in brooding species act as brood chambers.

**11. Coelom and Coelomocytes.**—The coelom occupies such space in the interior of the disk as remains around the stomach, gonads, and bursal sacs. As just indicated, it is still further reduced in the Euryalae by the expansion and fusions of the bursal sacs. The strands attaching

1888). 1, arm base; 2, bursal slit; 3, cavity formed by fusion of bursal sacs; 4, section of esophagus; 5, stomach pouch; 6, true coelom; 7, gonad; 8, hyponeural ring sinus; 9, main haemal ring; 10, axial sinus; 11, dark oral part of axial gland; 12, light aboral part of axial gland; 13, stone canal; 14, ampulla; 15, madreporite; 16, aboral sinus; 17, aboral haemal ring; 18, water ring; 19, left axial sinus; 20, right axial sinus; 21, genital stolon.

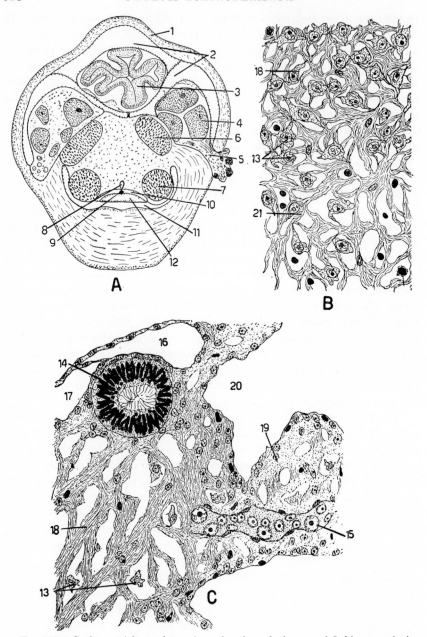

FIG. 255.—Coelom, axial complex.   A, section through the arm of *Ophiocanops fugiens* (*after Mortensen*, 1932).   B, section through the axial gland of *Ophiothrix*.   C, section through the aboral part of the axial gland of *Ophiothrix*, showing origin of the genital stolon.   (B, C, after J. Smith, 1940.)   1, body wall; 2, arm coelom; 3, stomach diverticulum in arm coelom; 4, gonad in arm coelom; 5, gonoduct; 6, upper intervertebral muscle; 7, lower intervertebral muscle; 8, radial water canal; 9, radial haemal channel;

the stomach and other viscera to the inner surface of the disk wall represent remnants of mesenteries, and as the one or two peristomial cavities that encircle the esophagus are of coelomic nature, their bounding walls constitute horizontal mesenteries.    The coelom also continues into the aboral part of the arms as a narrow space appearing crescentic in cross section that lies between the vertebral ossicles and the aboral and lateral arm shields (Fig. 251B, C).    In *Ophiocanops fugiens* (Mortensen, 1932) this arm coelom is greatly enlarged and subdivided by mesenteries into an aboral channel that contains the stomach extension already mentioned and two lateral channels that house gonads (Fig. 255A). There are further present in ophiuroids the following minor cavities of coelomic nature.    The five hyponeural radial sinuses to the aboral side of the radial nerve cords give off a branch into each podium, and their central ends enter the hyponeural ring sinus that lies adjacent to the nerve ring.    The axial sinus and the genital or aboral sinus with its branches around the gonads complete the list of coelomic cavities.

The coelomocytes of ophiuroids are mentioned briefly by Cuénot (1888).    The coelomic fluid and haemal and water-vascular systems contain very active granular amoeboid cells with slender pseudopods that tend to anastomose into networks (Fig. 254F).    The granules of these cells are believed by Cuénot to be of enzymatic nature.    This author further noted small rounded cells with or without granulations (Fig. 254E) in the polian vesicles and axial gland and believes the latter to be a site of formation of coelomocytes.    The presence of rounded coelomocytes in the axial gland is generally reported.

**12. Axial Complex.**—This is well developed in ophiuroids and has been exhaustively described by Fedotov (1924) from a study of sections of a number of species.    Its parts and relations are similar to those of asteroids, except that the axial complex turns orally instead of aborally because of the location of the madreporite on the oral surface in ophiuroids.    The axial sinus extends from the hyponeural ring sinus to the ampulla of the water-vascular system beneath the madreporite.    The axial sinus is nearly filled with the axial gland, which is attached to its wall in such a way as to divide its cavity into right and left portions (Fig. 254C, D).    According to Fedotov, and his views are strongly supported by J. E. Smith (1940), the left part of the axial sinus represents the left axocoel and the right part the right axocoel; hence the left part corresponds to the entire axial sinus of asteroids, the right part to the dorsal sac or madreporic vesicle.    At its oral end, corresponding to the

10, hyponeural radial sinus; 11, epineural radial sinus; 12, radial nerve; 13, coelomocytes; 14, stone canal; 15, genital rachis; 16, left part of axial sinus; 17, right part of axial sinus; 18, aboral part of axial gland; 19, aboral haemal ring; 20, aboral sinus; 21, oral part axial gland.

aboral end in asteroids, the left axial sinus communicates not only with the ampulla but also with the genital (or aboral) sinus, whose peculiar course in ophiuroids was discovered by Ludwig (1880). This sinus loops outward in five places that are located aborally beneath the radial shields and then descends orally along the interradii to form five inter-radial loops located near the buccal shields (Fig. 256A). The genital sinus contains the aboral haemal ring and the genital rachis and gives off a coelomic sac around each gonad. The stone canal, shortly after leaving the water ring, enters the left part of the axial sinus and, closely adherent to the axial gland, accompanies the latter to the ampulla (Fig. 254C, D).

The axial gland consists of two regions, a darker and thicker aboral part (corresponding to the whole of the axial gland of asteroids) and a lighter, more slender oral part (corresponding to the terminal process of the gland in asteroids that occupies the dorsal sac). As in asteroids and echinoids, the gland is essentially a haemal mesh. It consists of a network of connective tissue containing rounded amoebocytes in its spaces (Fig. 255B). There is little histological difference between the darker and lighter portions, but the latter contains fewer amoebocytes.

**13. Haemal System.**—As in asteroids, the haemal channels, except those of the digestive tract, are enclosed in tubular coelomic channels, often called perihaemal canals in the literature. The main oral haemal ring is found inside the hyponeural ring canal (also called oral perihaemal ring), located to one side of the nerve ring. The oral haemal ring is attached to the wall of the hyponeural ring canal opposite the nerve ring, with the main cavity of this canal between the two structures (Fig. 250C). One end of the axial sinus originates from the hyponeural ring canal, and the axial gland is continuous with the oral haemal ring. The latter gives off a radial haemal channel into each arm; this lies in the hyponeural radial canal situated to the aboral side of the radial nerve (Fig. 252C). The hyponeural radial canal is sometimes or in places subdivided by a very short vertical partition, and the radial haemal channel is located in this when present. Haemal channels are given off from the radial channel into the podia. The aboral haemal ring lies inside (Fig. 257C) the genital or aboral coelomic sinus described above, and the axial complex has the same relations to these as to the oral haemal ring and hyponeural ring sinus, that is, the axial sinus is continuous at its so-called aboral end with the aboral coelomic sinus, and the axial gland is continuous with the aboral haemal ring. The axial gland is therefore a haemal center connecting the oral and aboral haemal rings. The aboral haemal ring gives off channels to the bursal walls and gonads and receives in each radius a gastric branch from the stomach. These gastric branches are the only parts of the haemal system not enclosed in coelomic canals.

The haemal channels, also called blood lacunae, are of simple histological construction. In the smaller channels the wall is made of a nucleated membrane, in the larger ones, of a thin layer of connective tissue (Fig. 256$B$). The channels are filled with a fluid containing a few amoebocytes similar to those in the axial gland.

**14. Reproductive System and Reproductive Habits.**—The gonads are little sacs attached to the coelomic wall of the bursae, mostly near the bursal slits or directly to the slit walls. The gonads therefore project into the coelom, still further reducing the space available for the latter. The gonads originate from a genital rachis that runs inside the aboral haemal ring, and this in turn is enclosed in the genital or aboral coelomic sinus (Fig. 257$C$). As the aboral haemal ring is continuous with the oral (corresponding to aboral in asteroids) end of the axial gland, the genital rachis appears to originate from the latter (Fig. 255$C$), actually that part of the axial gland belonging to the right part of the axial sinus. The sinuous course of the genital sinus was described above (Fig. 256$A$). The aboral or outer loops of the genital sinus pass along the interradial sides of the bursae and supply the radial sides of the bursae by means of a branch (Fig. 256$A$); at these contacts coelomic sacs are budded from the genital sinus and a branch from the genital rachis enters each such coelomic sac and expands therein to form the gonad. Hence the gonad is a sac of coelomic nature containing germinal tissue. The genital rachis is a cylindrical strand separated by a sheath of flattened cells from the surrounding aboral haemal ring. It contains the primordial germ cells recognizable as such by their large round nuclei provided with a central nucleolus.

The number and arrangement of the gonads varies. There may be a single large gonad appended to each bursa or two per bursa, one on its radial and one on its interradial side, or a number of smaller gonads, variously disposed, sometimes in clusters, sometimes in rows (Fig. 256$D$). The gonads are very numerous in *Gorgonocephalus*, up to several thousand (Mortensen, 1923a). In *Ophiocanops fugiens* with very small disk devoid of bursae, the gonads are found in the proximal two-thirds of the arms, roughly one pair to each arm joint; they are lodged in the lateral compartments of the very large arm coeloms of this peculiar species (Mortensen, 1932; Fig. 255$A$), and discharge through the adjacent body wall. In *Asteroschema*, belonging to the Trichasteridae (Euryalae), each of the 10 long tubular gonads makes a loop extending far into the arm coeloms (Fedotov, 1926a).

The manner of discharge of the gonads into the bursae is not clearly stated in the literature. Presumably, when ripe each gonad discharges by a rupture or temporary opening into the bursa to which it is attached. The sex cells are emitted through the bursal slits in most ophiuroids.

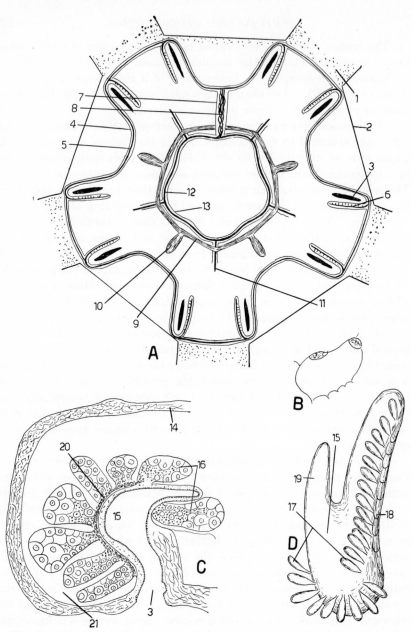

FIG. 256.—Haemal system, reproductive system. *A*, scheme of the ophiuroid haemal system (*based on Hamann*, 1889). *B*, section through a radial haemal channel. *C*, section of a bursal sac of *Ophioglypha* with attached ovaries. (*B*, *C*, *after Hamann*, 1889.) *D*, bursa of *Ophioglypha* with attached gonads, external view, outer end below, interradial side to right (*after Ludwig*, 1878a). 1, arm base; 2, edge of disk; 3, bursal slit; 4, aboral sinus; 5, aboral haemal ring; 6, branch of 4 and 5 to radial side of slit; 7, axial sinus; 8, axial gland; 9, water ring; 10, polian vesicle; 11, radial haemal channel; 12, haemal ring; 13, hyponeural ring sinus; 14, disk wall; 15, bursa; 16, ovaries; 17, gonads; 18, interradial side of bursa with genital scales; 19, aboral diverticulum of bursa; 20, genital rachis; 21, coelom.

In a detailed study of the reproductive system of *Ophiothrix fragilis*, J. E. Smith (1940) found that each of the 10 gonads narrows to a definite ciliated gonoduct that opens onto the side of the bursal slit. In species lacking in bursae, the gonads emit their products directly through the body wall.

The gonad consists chiefly of germ cells in various stages of development that at times of sexual ripeness almost occlude the lumen. The mass of germ cells is surrounded by a connective-tissue layer containing some muscle fibers and covered externally with coelomic epithelium. The presence of muscle fibers indicates that contraction plays a role in the discharge of ripe germ cells. The gonad may be more or less subdivided by partitions from the layer of connective tissue.

The great majority of the Ophiuroidea are dioecious, but the sexes cannot usually be distinguished externally unless the differing colors of the ripe gonads affect the usual coloration. There are, however, four species known that exhibit pronounced sexual dimorphism, having dwarf males that cling to the much larger female. Mortensen (1933a) discovered this state of affairs in *Amphilycus androphorus*, Portuguese East Africa, at first thought to be carrying a young specimen over its mouth. Investigation showed that the supposed young animal is really a male and that the male remains permanently in this position, with his mouth pressed against the female's and his arms alternating with hers (Fig. 258A). Mortensen then bethought himself of two similar cases reported by Koehler (1930) in which an adult was thought to be carrying a young animal mouth to mouth. Study of these species, *Ophiosphaera insignis* and *Ophiodaphne materna*, proved that here, too, the couples consist of a female and a dwarf male. Still another example was reported by Mortensen (1936) from the antarctic where the females of the gorgonocephalid *Astrochlamys bruneus* are mostly found with a smaller male riding on their aboral surface.

A considerable number of ophiuroids are normally hermaphroditic, a fact discovered by Metschnikoff (1869) in the cosmopolitan species *Amphipholis squamata*. In this species there is generally present one ovary on the interradial side and one testis on the radial side of each bursa, although irregularities occur (Fig. 257E). As there is less space on the radial side of the bursa because of the presence of the arm base, the testis is usually displaced aborally. Since this first report, hermaphroditism has been found to obtain in a number of other ophiuroids, all belonging to the Ophiurae. The latest list of these appears in Mortensen's *Discovery* report (1936), where 36 species are stated to be known hermaphrodites, although one of these, *Ophioscolex nutrix*, is sometimes dioecious. About one-fourth of the hermaphroditic species are protandric, and the gonads are first male and later female; *Ophioceres*

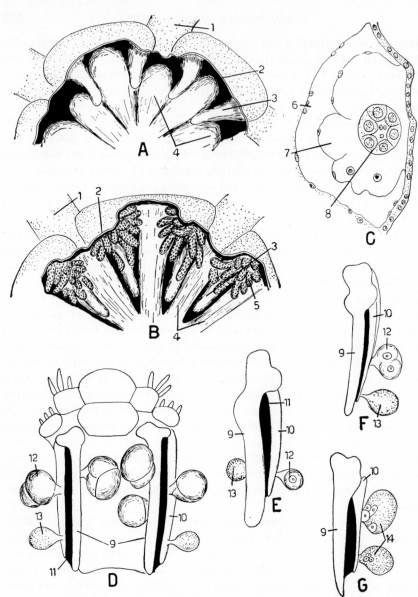

FIG. 257.—Reproductive system (continued).   *A*, immature specimen of *Ophioglypha*,
aboral disk wall removed.   *B*, same as *A*, sexually mature, with gonads.   (*A*, *B*, *after
Ludwig*, 1878a.)   *C*, cross section through the aboral sinus with enclosed aboral haemal ring
and genital rachis (*after Hamann*, 1889).   *D*, gonad arrangement in *Stegophiura vivipara*.
*E*, gonad arrangement of *Amphipholis squamata*, testis on radial, ovary on interradial side
of bursal slit.   *F*, *Amphiura constricta*, both gonads on the interradial side.   *G*, *Ophiomitrella
clavigera*, with two hermaphroditic gonads per bursa, both on interradial side.   (*D–G*,
*after Mortensen*, 1920.)   Larger of two genital plates is always on the radial side; contact
of genital plates is toward arm base.   1, arm base; 2, cut aboral wall of disk; 3, bursal sac;
4, stomach pouches; 5, gonads; 6, aboral ring sinus; 7, aboral haemal ring; 8, genital rachis;
9, genital plate of radial side; 10, genital plate of interradial side; 11, bursal slit; 12, ovary;
13, testis; 14, hermaphroditic gonad.

*incipiens* is suspected by Mortensen (1936) of undergoing several such changes of sex. In other hermaphroditic species the gonads may be ovotestes, and in still others there are separate testes and ovaries, usually definite in number and location. Often there are one radial testis and one interradial ovary per bursa, as in *Amphipholis squamata*, but other conditions are described by Mortensen (1920, 1933a, 1936). Thus in *Amphiura monorima*, which lacks bursae and bursal slits, there is one ovotestis in each interradius, and this discharges through a gonopore near the buccal shield. *Amphiura borealis* has also one interradial gonad per bursa, which is first a testis, then an ovary. In *Amphiura constricta* the ovary and testis of each bursa are both on its interradial side (Fig. 257*F*). In *Amphiura magellanica* there are two to four interradial and one or two radial gonads, of variable nature. *Ophiura meridionalis* has one or two testes radially, and one or two ovaries interradially, to each bursa. In *Ophiolebella biscuticera* the gonads are ovotestes, two on the interradial side, one on the radial side per bursa. Two testes and one ovary are present on the interradial side of each bursa and sometimes an additional testis on the radial side in *Stegophiura nodosa*, and in *S. vivipara* (Fig. 257*D*) there are present one ovary and one testis interradially and one or two ovaries radially to each bursa. Irregularities obtain in *Ophionotus hexactis*, which has up to three radial testes, depending on age, and three to five ovaries, even as many as eight in one specimen, on the interradial side of each bursa. All hermaphroditic ophiuroids brood their young, but not all brooding species are hermaphroditic. Anomalous hermaphroditic specimens of normally dioecious species are sometimes found; thus Thorson (1934) had two hermaphroditic *Ophiocten sericeum;* in one of these (the other was lost) one bursa bore ovaries, another testes, and the other three mixed gonads. Mortensen (1936) suspects three antarctic species of existing in the female state only, hence of having parthenogenetic development. Nearly 300 specimens of all sizes of one of these, *Ophiacantha vivipara*, were all females, although testes had been seen in previous material.

Ophiuroids commonly spawn directly into the sea water, discharging their sex cells through the bursal slits. Spawning usually takes place during spring and summer and thus may be related to rise of temperature. Spawning in response to temperature rise was noted by Mortensen (1938) and Olsen (1942b); further, following injury to arms or disk or pressure on the disk. However, ripe specimens often spawn without evident cause when brought into the laboratory, either in a short time or during the evening or night of the same day. Spawning at twilight or night appears characteristic of a number of species. Males usually spawn first, followed by other males, and then by females, but sometimes females initiate spawning. In several species the brittle star raises itself on its arms above the substratum to spawn (Grave, 1916; Mortensen, 1920; Olsen, 1942b; the MacGinities, 1949; Fig. 258*B*).  Although the spawning period of a given species usually extends over a month or more, probably each ripe individual discharges all of its mature sex cells at one spawning, sometimes with short pauses.

Breeding data are available for a number of brittle stars.  The common *Ophioderma brevispina* of the Atlantic Coast of North America

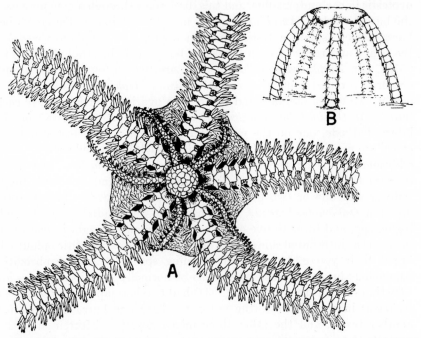

Fig. 258.—Reproductive habits.  *A*, female *Amphilycus androphorus* carrying dwarf male mouth to mouth (*after Mortensen*, 1933a).  *B*, *Amphiura filiformis* in spawning attitude (*after Mortensen*, 1920).

spawns in summer.  The circumboreal daisy brittle star *Ophiopholis aculeata* breeds in August off the coast of Maine (Fewkes, 1886), in June and July around the British Isles (Mortensen, 1927), from April to August in the North Sea (Mortensen and Lieberkind, 1928), and in April and May on the coast of Norway (Olsen, 1942b).  Other data from the last two references and localities are *Ophiura albida*, May to June and August and September; *Ophiocomina nigra*, June to August; *Ophiothrix texturata*, July; *Amphiura chiajei*, fall and winter; and *Amphiura filiformis*, summer and fall.  Common species at Plymouth, England, breed in summer (MacBride, 1907; Narasimhamurti, 1933).  Plutei of *Ophiura albida* and *texturata, Amphiura filiformis, Ophiocomina nigra,* and *Ophiothrix fragilis* were taken in the tow on the Baltic coast of

Sweden by Mortensen (1931) in August and September. In tropical waters, also, ophiuroids commonly spawn in spring and summer. Thus Mortensen (1937) noted spawning of several species on the Red Sea in April and May and on another occasion (1938) in July. This author (1921) saw spawning of *Ophionereis squamulosa* at Tobago, British West Indies, in April and (1931) of *Ophiocoma echinata* at Bermuda in July.

Not all brittle stars spawn into the sea water. Fell (1941) described an unidentified New Zealand ophiuroid that sticks a plate of 20 to 200 very yolky eggs to the underside of small stones or sometimes into rock crevices or onto seaweeds; this species lays during August at or near high tide. A considerable number of viviparous ophiuroids brood their young in the bursae or in a few cases viviparous development occurs in the ovaries. Bursal brooding in brittle stars was discovered by Quatrefages (1842) in the cosmopolitan *Amphipholis squamata*. Since that time instances of the brooding habit in brittle stars have been reported in increasing numbers. This topic was reviewed by Ludwig (1904) and Mortensen (1920, 1933a, 1936). In his 1936 report on antarctic and subantarctic ophiuroids, Mortensen was able to add 25 new instances of brooding in this group, making a total of 54 species with brooding habits known to that date. Others have since been reported and no doubt the number of brooding brittle stars will be considerably augmented in the future. As in other echinoderm classes, brooding ophiuroids are especially prevalent in the antarctic and subantarctic; Mortensen notes that 31 species or about half of the known ophiuroids from these regions are viviparous. However, brooding brittle stars are not limited to cold waters, as some well-known forms with this habit dwell in the tropics, notably *Amphiura stimpsonii*, in the West Indies (Mortensen, 1921). Only one brooding euryalous ophiuroid is known, the antarctic *Astrochlamys bruneus*.

In brooding ophiuroids the eggs are discharged as usual into the bursae but remain there until they have developed into juveniles, often so large that one wonders how they are able to escape through the narrow bursal slits. In some cases the developing young are enclosed in sacciform expansions of the bursae (Murakami, 1941). There are generally only one or two young in each bursa, but Murakami (1941) reported up to a total of 70 young in the bursae of *Stegophiura sculpta* and Mortensen (1936) found about 200 embryos in each bursa of the viviparous gorgonocephalid *Astrochlamys bruneus*. Brooding species usually have a more extended breeding period than do oviparous ones. Thus the common *Amphipholis squamata* breeds throughout the year (MacBride, 1892, Naples; Fell, 1941, New Zealand), and developmental stages may be found in the bursae at any time. In other brooding species the brooding period seems to extend over about half a year. Murakami

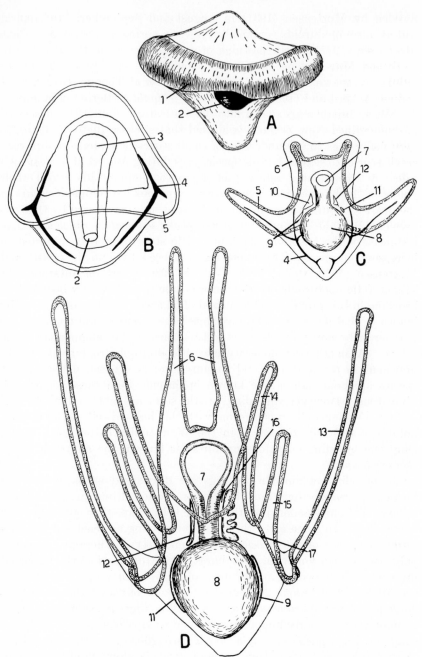

Fig. 259.—Embryology.  *A*, late gastrula of *Ophiothrix fragilis* with ciliated band (*after MacBride, 1907*).  *B*, early pluteus of *Ophiopholis aculeata* with beginning arms and skeletal rods (*after Olsen, 1942*).  *C*, later pluteus with two pairs of arms, *Ophiocomina*

(1941) reported that *Stegophiura sculpta*, Japan, breeds from January to July and contains juveniles from May to July. Similarly, Ricketts and Calvin (1939) record that *Ophioplocus esmarki*, California, is found with the bursae swollen with eggs in January and containing young in July. These data indicate that some 6 or 7 months elapse between the discharge of eggs into the bursae and the emergence of juveniles.

It is not clear to what extent brooding ophiuroids are genuinely viviparous, that is, contribute nourishment to the developing embryos during their sojourn in the bursae. In *Amphipholis squamata* the bursal wall puts out a stalk that attaches to the embryo, but Fell (1946) is of the opinion that no nutrition passes along this stalk. He notes that when an embryo is present therein, numerous haemal sinuses, absent in the unoccupied bursa, develop in the bursal wall; further, that the attachment stalk disappears before the main growth processes set in. The embryos of *Amphipholis squamata* are therefore probably nourished by the bursal wall, for the yolk present in the small eggs of this species appears insufficient as a food supply for the entire intrabursal development. Fell (1940) found that embryos removed from the bursa would survive only a few days unless furnished with nutriment. Other brooding ophiuroids have such large yolky eggs that the yolk supply may be sufficient for the entire development.

Presumably true viviparity obtains among the antarctic brittle stars in which eggs develop inside the ovaries. For years the only known case of this kind was *Ophionotus hexactis*, but in 1936 Mortensen noted several others with this habit. In *O. hexactis* (Mortensen, 1921) the ovaries have the shape of hollow vesicles. Usually only one egg ripens at a time and this falls into the lumen of the ovary, remaining there and undergoing development, with subsequent distension of the ovarian wall and degeneration of the other ovocytes that presumably are used as nutrition by the growing young. There is usually but one young in each ovary, but sometimes two or three are found and on one occasion six were noted. The young develops to a juvenile of quite large size with a disk about 8 mm. in diameter and arms about 20 mm. long before liberating itself from the mother, apparently through the bursal slit. Following this liberation the ovarian sacs shrink considerably and regenerate a new ovary.

In general, brooding and viviparous ophiuroids have large and yolky eggs that undergo an altered and shortened type of development, with the omission of a free-swimming larval stage. It is probable that in

*nigra*. D, fully developed pluteus of *C*, skeletal rods omitted. (*C*, *D*, *after Narasim-hamurti*, 1933.) 1, ciliated band; 2, blastopore; 3, archenteron; 4, skeletal rods; 5, beginning posterolateral arms; 6, anterolateral arms; 7, esophagus; 8, stomach; 9, left somatocoel; 10, left axohydrocoel; 11, right somatocoel; 12, right axohydrocoel; 13, posterolateral arms; 14, postoral arms; 15, posterodorsal arms; 16, left axocoel; 17, left hydrocoel with lobes.

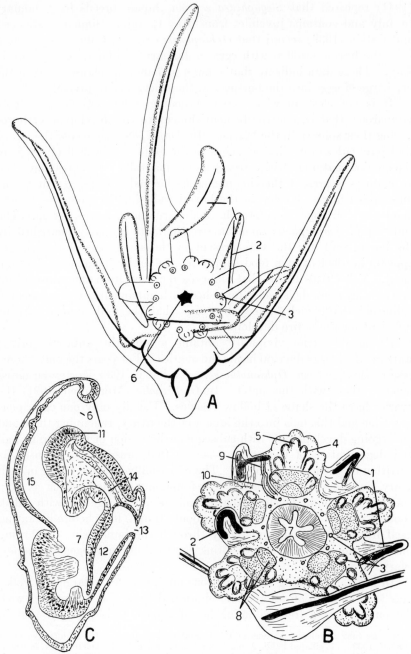

FIG. 260.—Embryology (continued). *A*, metamorphosing pluteus of *Ophiura albida* with young ophiuroid developing (*after* Mortensen, 1931). *B*, late stage of metamorphosis of *Ophiopholis aculeata*, pluteal arms degenerating; only bases of posterolateral arms shown.

many cases the more advanced embryos devour, or in some way utilize as food, eggs and earlier stages. Because of the ease of obtaining an ample supply of stages, many of the studies on ophiuroid embryology have concerned brooding species.

**15. Embryology.**—Species with small eggs shed into the sea water undergo an indirect type of development with a swimming larva having the characters of a pluteus that metamorphoses into a juvenile ophiuroid; those with larger yolky eggs that are brooded or attached to objects omit a swimming larval stage and develop more or less directly by a shortened and altered method. Artificial fertilization generally fails in ophiuroids and hence material for studies of indirect development must be obtained from natural spawnings. This difficulty explains the few available accounts of indirect development in ophiuroids. Only three such accounts in fact appear in the literature: that of MacBride (1907) on *Ophiothrix fragilis*, that of Narasimhamurti (1933) on *Ophiocomina nigra*, and that of Olsen (1942b) on *Ophiopholis aculeata*. As the indirect type of development is undoubtedly the less modified, the account will begin with this.

The egg undergoes holoblastic, practically equal cleavage, and a typical blastula results within 24 hours. This ruptures the fertilization membrane and starts a free existence; it is completely ciliated (flagellated?) and swims about with the animal pole forward. From the vegetative pole, ingression of cells occurs to form the primary mesenchyme, and this event is followed by a typical embolic invagination. The gastrula is completed within 2 or 3 days. The epidermis of the animal pole thickens and becomes vacuolated, apparently acting as a floating device, but there is no indication of an apical sensory tuft. The advancing tip of the archenteron proliferates the secondary mesenchyme. After the gastrulation is completed, the tip of the archenteron differentiates as a thin-walled coelomic sac (Fig. 259B). This either cuts off as a vesicle that subsequently divides into the two coelomic sacs or it develops a lobe on each side that separates as a coelomic sac. The two coelomic sacs move to a position along the sides of the archenteron. The gastrula meantime has broadened its blastoporal surface and flattened one surface that becomes ventral. From the ventral surface near the animal pole a stomodaeal invagination unites with the archenteron to establish the usual L-shaped digestive tract that soon differentiates into esophagus, stomach, and intestine; the blastopore remains

---

*C*, longitudinal median section of pluteus in early metamorphosis showing digestive tract *Ophiopholis aculeata*. (*B, C, after Olsen,* 1942.) 1, degenerating pluteal arms; 2, skeletal rods; 3, buccal podia; 4, definitive podia; 5, terminal tentacle; 6, mouth; 7, stomach; 8, vertebral ossi les; 9, hydroporic canal; 10, stone canal; 11, thickened ciliated area of esophagus; 12, intestine; 13, anus; 14, ventral horn of left somatocoel; 15, esophagus.

as the larval anus (Fig. 260*C*).   The cilia (or flagella?) become limited
to a broad band that encircles the part of the gastrula at right angles to
the gastrular axis (Fig. 259*A*).

The larva now begins to put out arms and gradually develops into a
pluteus very similar to the echinopluteus; to distinguish it from the
latter the name *ophiopluteus* is applied.   The ciliated band accompanies
these outgrowths and edges them as in other larvae.   The vacuolated
ectodermal crest of earlier stages returns to an ordinary epithelial
condition.   There first appears a pair of posterolateral arms (Fig. 259*B*);
mesenchyme wanders into these and in each secretes a three-rayed
skeletal rod for the support of the arm.   At about the fourth day the
anterolateral arms, supported by a branch from the same skeletal rod,
grow out from the anterior (original animal) part of the larva.   The pair
of skeletal rods also sends posterior extensions into the now projecting
rounded posterior end of the larva (Fig. 259*C*).   At about 10 days of age
the postoral arms arise opposite the anterolateral arms, and these also
are supplied by branches from the same skeletal rods as the others.
Finally, at about 18 days the fourth and last arm pair, the posterodorsal
arms, puts in an appearance (Fig. 259*D*), and these like the others are
supported by the same pair of skeletal rods, now four-branched and with
a posterior extension.   The arms continue to lengthen for a few days,
and the ophiopluteus reaches its full development in about 3 weeks.
The posterolateral arms are often very long, especially in *Ophiothrix* and
other Ophiothrichidae.   The posterodorsal arms are sometimes wanting.
In some species a pair of epaulettes develops at the base of the posterolateral arms.   Ophioplutei were noticed in the plankton and described
before their relationship to ophiuroids had been discovered.   Numerous
figures of ophioplutei appear in Mortensen's studies of larval echinoderms
(1921, 1931, 1937, 1938).

Meantime the internal development has continued along familiar
lines.   The two coelomic sacs elongate, retaining their position along
either side of the digestive tract (Fig. 259*D*).   They give off muscle
fibers to the stomodaeum which has a very wide aperture heavily provided with cilia and which, now invested with a muscular layer, is able
to take in food.   Each coelomic sac divides into an anterior and posterior
portion; either before or after this division the left one puts out a tube
that meets an ectodermal invagination, thus establishing the hydropore
and its canal (Fig. 262*A*).   The posterior part of the left anterior coelom
(axohydrocoel) constricts off as the hydrocoel; the constricting part is
drawn out into a canal that becomes the stone canal.   In *Ophiopholis*
Olsen insists that the hydrocoel arises from the anterior part of the left
somatocoel; if this is not a mistake it would indicate that the plane of
constriction of the original left coelomic sac varies in different ophiuroids.

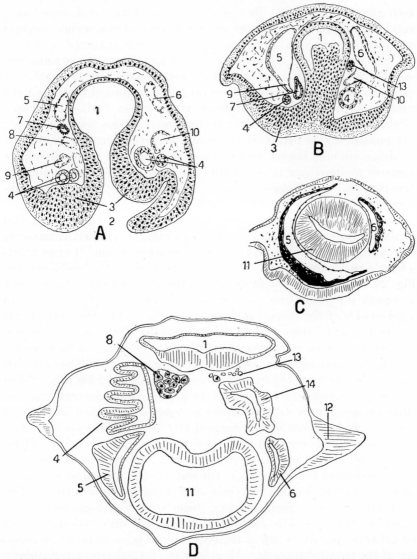

Fig. 261.—Embryology (continued). *A–C*, three sections through a stage similar to Fig. 259*C* (*after Olsen*, 1942). *A*, through the level of the mouth. *B*, through the level of the esophagus. *C*, through the level of the stomach. *D*, frontal section of similar stage, *Ophiothrix fragilis* (*after MacBride*, 1907). 1, esophagus; 2, mouth; 3, ciliated thickenings around mouth; 4, hydrocoel lobes; 5, left somatocoel; 6, right somatocoel; 7, stone canal; 8, left axocoel; 9, dorsal horn of left somatocoel; 10, ventral horn of left somatocoel; 11, stomach; 12, arm bases; 13, right axocoel; 14, right hydrocoel.

Olsen further states that in *Ophiopholis* the stone canal arises as a protuberance from the hydrocoel and subsequently forms an opening into the left anterior coelom. In all cases there is also formed a right hydrocoel that later degenerates. The left hydrocoel soon puts out the usual five lobes, each of which represents a definitive radial water canal. In *Ophiothrix* the madreporic vesicle or dorsal sac is formed from the right anterior coelom as in other echinoderms, but in *Ophiopholis* Olsen surmises that it arises from the left somatocoel. This does not appear very probable in the light of the generally accepted homology of this sac.

Metamorphosis begins with the appearance of the primordia of the definitive skeleton (see later) around the sides of the stomach and the curvature of the hydrocoel around the esophagus. The pluteus continues to swim during the metamorphosis. The hydrocoel continues to encircle the esophagus, at the same time undergoing a rotation, and eventually its ends fuse to form the water ring. The left somatocoel puts out a dorsal and a ventral horn and these fuse around the esophagus to form a coelomic ring that lies to the aboral side of the hydrocoel ring (Fig. 261*A*, *B*). In *Ophiopholis* this coelomic ring puts out a tubular outgrowth into each arm, and these outgrowths are the hyponeural radial sinuses of the arms. In *Ophiothrix* (Fig. 262*A*) MacBride states that only four of these sinuses are outgrowths of the left somatocoel whereas the fifth one comes from the left anterior coelom or axohydrocoel; whereas Narashimhamurti finds that in *Ophiocomina* the fifth outgrowth is also a derivative of the left somatocoel. Epineural folds (Fig. 264*A*) arise as in echinoids and close over to produce the epineural ring and radial sinuses, which may be taken to represent enclosed ambulacral grooves. The nervous system formed of ectodermal thickenings (Fig. 263*A*) also becomes enclosed by the fusion of the epineural folds. There is some indication that the hyponeural or motor part of the nervous system is derived from the cells of the wall of the hyponeural sinus, and the intervertebral muscles may also come from the same source. The hydrocoel lobes have elongated to a finger shape and begin to put out paired side branches (Fig. 263*B*, *C*) that push out the ectoderm to form the definitive podia; the tip of the original lobe remains as the coelomic part of the terminal tentacle. Meantime the pluteal arms are gradually shortening and their contained skeletal supports break off and are discarded (Fig. 260*A*, *B*).

The anus closes and the intestine degenerates, as does also the esophagus for the most part. There is of course no anus or intestine in the adult. Stomach and mouth move to the definitive position. The stomach fills up with folds and cells but later hollows out again and differentiates into the definitive stomach. The accounts are unclear as to the fate of the larval mouth, but apparently the larval mouth persists

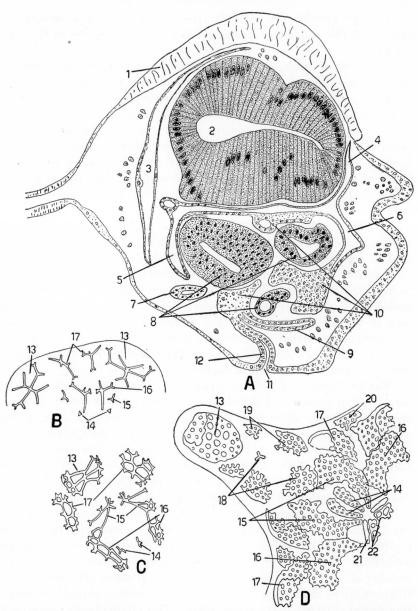

Fig. 262.—Embryology (continued). *A*, section through the stomach of *Ophiothrix fragilis* in early metamorphosis, showing origin of the hyponeural ring canal (*after MacBride*, 1907). *B–D*, three stages in the development of the jaw skeleton (*after Ludwig*, 1882), *Amphipholis squamata*. 1, vacuolated area of ectoderm; 2, stomach; 3, right somatocoel; 4, left somatocoel; 5, dorsal horn of left somatocoel; 6, ventral horn of left somatocoel; 7, right hydrocoel; 8, sections of three hydrocoel lobes; 9, left axocoel; 10, primordia for hyponeural ring sinus; 11, hydropore; 12, hydroporic canal; 13, terminal plate; 14, ambulacral 1; 15, ambulacral 2; 16, adambulacral 1; 17, adambulacral 2; 18, oral arm shields; 19, lateral arm shields; 20, buccal shield; 21, maxiller; 22, teeth.

as the adult mouth, or at least the latter forms in the same location.   A portion of the esophagus appears to persist and give rise to the adult esophagus.

The oral or hypogastric part of the definitive coelom is usually derived from the main part of the left somatocoel in echinoderms; but in ophiuroids it seems that the periesophageal ring coelom formed by the fusion of the dorsal and ventral horns of the left somatocoel contributes largely or in part to the hypogastric coelom.   In any case the latter puts out five outgrowths, solid at first, but hollow later, that become the arm coeloms and are the first indication of the formation of the adult arms. Covered by the adjacent ectoderm they begin to grow out as rounded bulges that are in line with the hydrocoel lobes, now bearing one or two pairs of lateral podia in addition to the terminal tentacle, and fuse with them.   The right somatocoel furnishes the aboral or epigastric part of the main coelom, but in *Ophiopholis* both right and left somatocoels contribute to this.   By breakdown of the walls of contact the general main coelom of the adult is formed, with remnants of the walls persisting as the strands supporting the stomach.   Still another periesophageal coelomic ring sinus is formed and presumably is the peristomial ring sinus seen in the adult.   This originates, according to Narasimhamurti and MacBride, as a tubular outgrowth of the left somatocoel that insinuates itself aboral to the water ring; according to Olsen it arises by the appearance of a lumen among cells of coelomic nature.

The development of the axial complex is complicated and the available accounts are unclear and discrepant.   It appears established, however, that the ampulla comes from the left axohydrocoel.   As already indicated, the dorsal sac which becomes the right part of the adult axial sinus probably originates from the right axohydrocoel.   The source of the main or left part of the adult axial sinus is not clearly explained in the literature, except that it is of coelomic nature.   The axial gland develops from the coelomic wall covering the stone canal and soon spreads and enlarges until it occupies the greater part of the axial sinus.   The stone canal unites end to end with the hydroporic canal, and the original hydropore remains as the definitive pore through the madreporite. Additional pores and pore canals when present presumably arise by subdivision of the original ones.   The primordial germ cells become distinguishable by their large nuclei as a group of cells in the wall of the left somatocoel adjacent to the stone canal.   This group of cells elongates to become the genital rachis; this grows out into a coelomic diverticulum that originates from the coelomic wall adjacent to the stone canal, hence also presumably part of the left somatocoel, and becomes the genital or aboral sinus.

The development of the skeleton has been particularly studied by

Ludwig (1882), Murakami (1937, 1940, 1941), and Fell (1941). As in other echinoderms each skeletal element begins as a calcareous granule that rapidly becomes a triradiate spicule and this develops into a perforated plate by the usual process of putting out branches that anastomose. The vertebral ossicles arise by the fusion of a pair of such plates, but each of the arm shields comes from a single embryonic plate. The primary skeleton of the aboral side of the disk closely resembles that of echinoids and asteroids. Five radial and five terminal plates arise along the radii and a central plate is added a little later. The five terminals move distally as the arms grow, always remaining at the arm tip, and new vertebrals and arm shields are laid down immediately to the oral side of the terminals. The buccal shields soon appear in the interradii and one of them grows around the hydropore; at first they are found on the aboral surface of the disk but gradually become shifted to the oral surface, according to Ludwig and Fell. Murakami states that only the oral shield surrounding the hydropore makes this shift and that the others arise in place on the oral surface. The original arrangement of the plates of the aboral surface of the disk is usually disrupted by the interpolation of secondary plates. On the oral surface, the mouth armature develops from five groups of four pairs of spicules each (Fig. 262B), two pairs of adambulacrals and two pairs of ambulacrals. In each group the first adambulacral and second ambulacral rapidly increase in size and fuse to form the main part of a half jaw (Fig. 262C, D). The maxiller and teeth arise as independent ossifications that attach to the oral end of the first adambulacrals. The second adambulacrals also increase rapidly in size and develop spines; they become the adoral shields and their spines alter into oral papillae. The first ambulacrals lag in growth and retain an elongated shape. According to Ludwig, whose account is usually followed, they displace aborally and remain as the peristomial plates. Murakami states that in the species studied by him the first ambulacrals diminish and disappear, but he fails to explain the origin of the peristomial plates. Fell verifies Ludwig's account but refrains from identifying the plates in question as ambulacrals. Fell further questions the homology of the teeth with adambulacral spines.

In the meantime larval arms and skeletal rods have continued to be absorbed or discarded, and the gradually increasing weight of the skeleton causes the larva to sink to the bottom where it takes up adult habits of life.

Varying degrees of modification from the foregoing account are seen in the development of species with yolky eggs. Grave (1899, 1916) described the embryology of *Ophioderma brevispina* which has relatively farge, yolky eggs, although these are shed into the sea. The main leature of its development is the lack of a typical pluteus. The larva

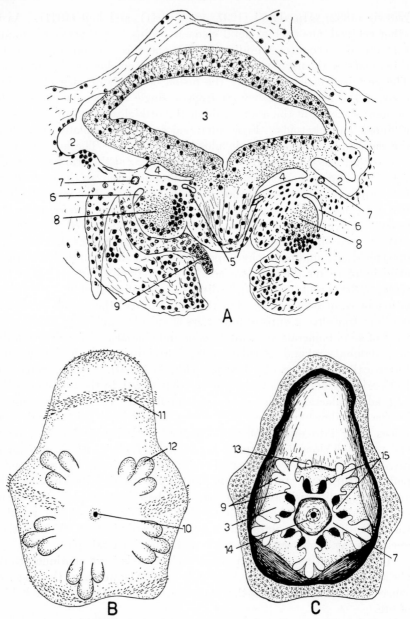

Fig. 263.—Embryology (continued). *A*, section through the mouth of *Ophiocomina nigra*, late metamorphosis (*after Olsen*, 1942) to show coelomic cavities around the esophagus. *B*, larva of *Ophioderma brevispina* with rudiment of ophiuroid. *C*, same as *B*, with wall removed to show internal structures. (*B, C, after Grave*, 1899.) 1, right somatocoel; 2, left somatocoel; 3, stomach; 4, peristomial ring coelom; 5, hyponeural ring sinus; 6, hyponeural radial sinuses; 7, water ring; 8, nerve ring; 9, buccal podia; 10, mouth; 11, ciliary ring; 12, terminal podium; 13, stone canal; 14, cut edge of esophagus; 15, protrusions of left somatocoel to form the hyponeural ring sinus.

becomes uniformly ciliated and swims at 36 hours of development but never grows out any pluteal arms. Instead the cilia become limited to four circles on the cylindroid larva that thus resembles a doliolaria (Fig. 263B); rudiments of the pluteal spicules are, however, formed, and other developmental details are similar to those described above with the occurrence of typical epineural folds (Fig. 264A). A similar sort of larva without pluteal arms and with four ciliated rings was observed by Mortensen (1921, 1938) in *Ophionereis squamulosa* and *Ophiolepis cincta*. Probably the resemblance to a doliolaria is coincidental and the larva in these cases is simply an aborted pluteus. Much greater deviation of development was made known by Fell for an unidentified species called Kirk's ophiuroid that attaches its large, yolky eggs to stones (Fell, 1941) and for the viviparous *Amphipholis squamata* (Fell, 1946). In the former the eggs undergo total but unequal cleavage into a blastula with a small blastocoel. Gastrulation combines emboly and epiboly, but the archenteron is small and the blastocoel filled with cells. Soon the archenteron disappears and the solid embryo takes on a pentagonal shape with a central blastopore which becomes the site of an inwardly progressing cavity (Fig. 264B). Near the periphery 10 equally spaced rounded ectodermal bulges represent the first podia (Fig. 264C). These elongate, and splits developing in their interior and in the central mesenchyme become the lumina of the podia and the water ring, respectively. At this stage (20 days of age), the embryo hatches from the egg membrane and begins moving about on its peg-like podia but cannot feed as it lacks a digestive tract. The cavity from the blastopore continues to progress inward and produces the digestive tract, with the blastopore retained as mouth. The main coelom and subsidiary coelomic spaces as the hyponeural ring and radial sinuses arise by splits in the mesenchyme.

A somewhat similar story obtains for *Amphipholis squamata* which develops to a juvenile stage inside the bursal sac. Usually a single egg is shed directly from the ovary into the adjacent bursa; this species is hermaphroditic, but it is not known whether self-fertilization obtains. Cleavage and gastrulation were not observed, but the gastrula is nearly filled with cells. In this mass of cells the stomach arises by the formation of a cavity around which the cells organize into an epithelium and a stomodaeal invagination grows inward to meet the stomach, thus establishing the definitive digestive tract. The hydrocoel, the right coelomic sac, and the left somatocoel originate as cell balls that hollow out into vesicles (Fig. 264D). The hydrocoel undergoes the usual development into the water-vascular system, but the other two coelomic sacs degenerate, and the definitive coelom is formed by the union of splits in the mesenchyme. Meantime the embryo has become attached to the bursal wall by a stalk-like outgrowth from the latter. A rudi-

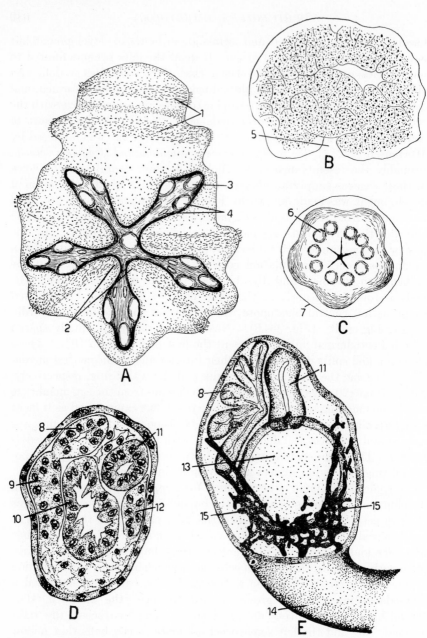

Fig. 264.—Embryology (continued). *A*, later stage of larva of *Ophioderma brevispina* (*after Grave*, 1899), showing epineural folds. *B*, gastrula of Kirk's ophiuroid. *C*, later stage of *B*, from ventral surface, showing beginning of definitive ophiuroid. (*B, C, after Fell*, 1941.) *D*, embryo of *Amphipholis squamata*, showing primordia forming from mesenchyme. *E*, later stage of *D*, with attachment stalk and pluteal skeleton. (*D, E, after Fell*, 1951.)   1, ciliary bands; 2, epineural folds; 3, terminal podium; 4, buccal podia; 5, blastopore; 6, primordia of podia; 7, egg membrane; 8, hydrocoel; 9, left somatocoel; 10, archenteron; 11, esophagus; 12, right coelomic sac; 13, stomach; 14, attachment stalk; 15, skeletal rods.

mentary and transitory pluteal skeleton is secreted in that part of the
embryo near the attachment stalk (Fig. 264*E*).   The hyponeural and
epineural sinuses also form as splits above and below the nerve ring and
cords.   The nerve ring is differentiateα from deeper-lying ectodermal
cells closely associated with the stomodaeal invagination.   About the
time that the embryo takes on a pentagonal shape (Fig. 265*A*) with the
formation of additional podia, the embryonic attachment atrophies and

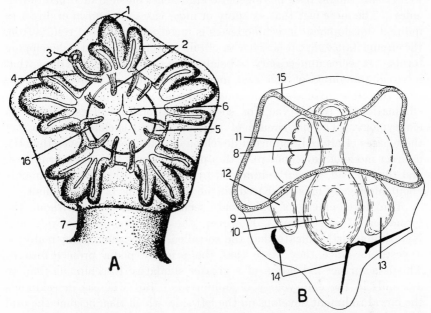

Fig. 265.—Embryology (concluded).   *A*, later stage of *Amphipholis squamata* with
ophiuroid established (*after Fell*, 1951).   *B*, aborted pluteus of *Ophionotus hexactis*, removed
from ovary (*after Mortensen*, 1921).   1, terminal tentacle; 2, buccal podia; 3, hydropore;
4, hydroporic canal; 5, water ring; 6, beginning of jaw; 7, attachment stalk; 8, esophagus;
9, stomach; 10, intestine; 11, hydrocoel; 12, left somatocoel; 13, right somatocoel; 14,
pluteal rods; 15, ciliated band; 16, nerve ring.

the embryo continues its development lying free in the bursal cavity.
After attaining a considerable size, the young ophiuroid works its way
out of the bursa through the bursal slit.   In the one escape observed by
Fell, the young animal had attained 15 arm joints and required 3 hours
to work its way out of the slit.

   Incomplete information on other species with viviparous development
is given by Mortensen (1921).   In the large yolky eggs (0.5 mm. in
diameter) of *Amphiura vivipara*, West Indies, only the nuclei divide and
these accumulate at one area where the main structures differentiate
while the large yolk mass remains unaltered, serving as a food supply;
there is here no trace of a pluteus or pluteal skeleton.   On the other hand,

the development of *Ophionotus hexactis*, which takes place inside the ovary, is surprisingly normal. A stage similar to a young pluteus with a ciliated band and skeletal rods (Fig. 265*B*) is passed through, although the arms fail to grow out, and the general course of internal development appears typical except that an anus is wanting.

The foregoing deviations from typical echinoderm development are certainly very striking, but the author is at a loss to understand why Fell (1945) should base phylogenetic arguments on such modified ontogenies. The mere fact that as many or more cases are known of direct as indirect development in echinoderms is inconsequential and results from the circumstance that it is easier to obtain material of directly developing forms. It seems unnecessary to belabor the point, as Fell has done, that increasing amounts of yolk and increasing degrees of protection of the embryo result increasingly in shortened and altered development with elimination of free larvae, for such correlation is well established in embryology. The occurrence of aborted pluteal skeletons in most of these cases of altered ophiuroid development sufficiently proves that the indirect mode of development with a pluteus larva is the more primitive, and this, indeed, is tacitly admitted by Fell. It is clear that arguments about phylogeny must be based on the indirect type of development.

The development of ophiuroids seems to take place without the formation of a vestibule. However, the accounts of MacBride and Narasimhamurti indicate that the so-called stomodaeum must really be a vestibule since they state that the primary podia project into it. This is a further indication of a greater similarity to echinoids than to asteroids in the embryology of ophiuroids. But whereas in echinoids the larval rudiment develops on the left side, which then become the oral side of the adult, in ophiuroids the larval rudiment is located on the ventral surface of the larva, that is, the surface bearing the mouth and blastopore. Thus the definitive oral surface corresponds to the ventral surface of the larva and the definitive aboral surface to its dorsal surface. The anterior part of the ophiopluteus corresponds to the preoral lobe of other echinoderm larvae and, as in these, degenerates, while only the posterior part of the larva is continuous with the definitive animal.

**16. Asexual Reproduction.**—The occurrence of fission in ophiuroids was well known to older workers, e.g. Lütkin (1872) and Simroth (1877). Fission appears limited to very small, six-armed species with a disk diameter of not more than 3 mm. and may be restricted to young animals or may continue throughout life. There is no preformed fission plane and the disk may divide in any direction, but division almost invariably takes place in such a way that each product is left with three arms and half the disk. Consequently, fissiparous species are commonly found with three longer and three shorter arms, and in fact fissiparity is often ascribed to species on the mere finding of a few specimens of this sort. Division into products with four and two arms, respectively, rarely occurs. Skeletal and internal structures may be torn in any possible way. Fission is especially common in the genus *Ophiactis* and was exhaustively studied in *O. virens* in the Mediterranean by Simroth (1877), who states that of over 150 specimens collected, all but one showed evidence of fission by the condition of the arms. Some of the peculiarities of *O. virens* (page 613), especially the multiplication of madreporites, stone canals, and polian vesicles, result from repeated fissions. Other species of *Ophiactis*, said by Lütken to be fissiparous, include *savignyi* (= *sexradia, krebsii, virescens*) and *mülleri;* to these may be added *O. arenosa*, California (the MacGinities, 1949) and *O. modesta*, Japan (Yamazi, 1950). In the Ophiothrichidae, *Ophiothela danae* (= *isidicola*), Japan, is reported as fissiparous (Kamazi, 1950), and in the Ophiocomidae, *Ophiocoma pumila* and *valenciae* reproduce asexually. Mortensen (1933a) remarked that fissiparity obtains in three members of the Amphiuridae: *Amphiodia dividua*, Mauritius, *Amphipholis torelli*, arctic, and *Amphiura sexradiata*, Gulf of Siam. *Ophiostiba hidekii* is a fissiparous ophiomyxid (Matsumoto, 1917). A few Euryalae are also fissiparous: *Astrogymnotes catasticta* (H. L. Clark, 1914), *Astrocharis ijimai* and *virgo* (Matsumoto, 1917), and *Astroceras annulatum* (Yamazi, 1950).

The process of regeneration in the fission products was reported by Simroth (1877) in minute detail for *Ophiactis virens*, but this lengthy article is far from clear and allowance must be made for the state of histological knowledge at the time of writing. In general the torn edges of the stomach adhere to those of the adjacent disk wall, and to the inner side of this adhesion the torn edges of the coelomic lining also close together. Contraction aided by tissue growth closes the wound, which is also lessened by adjustment of the three arms to fill the gap. A streak of coelomocytes (mesenchyme cells?) from the broken ends of the water ring fills in the gap here, and a channel forming through this material completes the water ring. The multiplication of coelomocytes (presumably also mesenchyme cells from the dermis) furnishes material for regeneration. The nerve ring is said to be completed by coelomocytes. The outgrowth of the new arms is initiated by bulges of the water ring accompanied by coelomic bulges.

**17. Regeneration.**—It is well known that serpent stars when disturbed or handled often cast off one or more arms at varying levels (whence the common name of brittle stars) and that these are readily regenerated. Specimens are generally found in nature in process of regenerating one or more arms. Little information is available about the regenerative capacity of parts of the disk, except in fissiparous species. A disk deprived of all arms at the base loses vitality and soon dies, but survives and regenerates if one arm is left attached (Dawydoff, 1901; Zeleny, 1903, 1905). Dawydoff further reported that bisected animals did not regenerate. However, better recuperative capacities of the disk may obtain in other species. It is known for several species, mostly amphiurids, that they may cast off the aboral part of the disk, including the stomach and gonads, and regenerate them: *Amphiura abdita* (Verrill, 1882), *Ophiopsila aranea* (Semon, 1889), *Amphiura rosea* (Farquhar, 1894), *Amphiura filiformis* and *Amphipholis squamata* (Mortensen, 1927), *Amphipholis platydisca* (H. L. Clark, 1940), and *Ophiacantha eurythra* (MacGinities, 1949).

The histology of arm regeneration has been described by Dawydoff (1901). The wound becomes covered with degenerating particles of tissue soon overlain by a thick homogeneous membrane, possibly formed of coagulated coelomic fluid. Under this membrane connective-tissue cells and coelomocytes aggregate in great numbers and phagocytize tissue fragments and degenerating structures proximal to the wound. This phagocytosis is still in progress when constructive processes begin, first by the growth of the body wall over the cut surface replacing the homogeneous membrane, second by the outgrowth of the radial nerve from the nerve stump, and third by the outgrowth of the radial water canal. The last causes a projection which is the primordium of the new arm, as a conical bud of epidermis and mesenchyme. The arm coelom extends into the bud by proliferation of its lining epithelium. The new coelom thus formed sends a pair of extensions orally that come in contact between the radial nerve and the radial water canal and so produce the hyponeural radial sinus bisected by a vertical septum. The epineural sinus arises as a split in the tissues. The intervertebral muscles originate as coelomic sacs that become filled with cells of coelomic nature; these differentiate into muscle fibers. The source of the skeleton is not discussed in Dawydoff's article.

Zeleny (1903, 1905) studied the rate of regeneration of *Ophiura texturata* with reference to size of disk and number of arms removed. Individuals of medium size were found to regenerate arms more rapidly than smaller or larger specimens. Rate of regeneration of one to four arms cut off at the disk was said to be faster the greater the number of arms removed. Average figures (omitting poorly regenerating individuals) of the amount regenerated in 33 days were 2.3 mm. with one or two arms removed, 2.4 mm. with three arms removed, and 3.3 mm. with four arms removed; for a period of 46 days the figures were 3.0, 3.2, 3.5, and 4.8 mm. with one, two, three, and four arms removed, respectively. Morgulis (1909), using *Ophiocoma pumila* at Bermuda, found no dependency of regeneration rate on number of arms removed but reported a higher rate the longer the piece of arm cut off. According to this author, regeneration is inhibited distal to a region of destroyed radial nerve. Milligan (1915) measured the rate of regeneration of the arms of *Ophiothrix fragilis* and obtained a figure of 17 mm. per year.

**18. Classification of the Ophiuroidea.**—This is in the usual unsatisfactory and unsettled state that seems to characterize the classification of most invertebrate groups. The classification was revised by Matsumoto, in 1917, who created four orders for the existing members. Although Matsumoto's arrangement was accepted by some echinoderm specialists, it is not favored by others. There seems to be little morphological difference between some of his orders, and his inclusion of the Ophiomyxidae with the basket stars appears undesirable. As there have been no further attempts at revising the classification since Matsumoto's work, it seems preferable to adhere to the old division of the Ophiuroidea into the order Ophiurae, embracing the typical serpent stars, and the order Euryalae, including the basket stars and their relatives. These were called the families Ophiuridae and Astrophytidae by Lyman (1882) at the time of the *Challenger* report; in this report he listed all the known species, amounting to about 500. In 1915, H. L. Clark published an important work on ophiuroids, which also included a tabulation of all described species, amounting to 1412 at that date; and in 1946 this author estimated the number of described ophiuroids at about 1700. This figure may be supposed to have risen to at least 1800 at the time of present writing (1954).

The Ophiuroidea have never been monographed and hence the arrangement into families must be obtained from the larger taxonomic works, reports on collecting expeditions, and the like.

**19. Order Ophiurae.**—This order comprises the typical serpent stars, relatively small forms with simple arms, mostly five in number but sometimes six or more, movable chiefly in the transverse plane because of the zygospondylous type of articulation of the vertebral ossicles. The disk and arms are usually covered with distinct shields or scales, although these may be concealed by granules, small spines, or skin; especially the lateral arm shields are well developed, often extending to the oral and aboral surfaces of the arms. The arm spines are borne laterally and are directed outward or toward the arm tips, not downward. There is but one madreporite, except when multiplied by fissiparous processes. This order includes the great majority of the serpent stars and is divided into about a dozen families, mostly on the basis of details of the mouth armature and the arm spination.

The Ophiomyxidae, generally considered the most primitive ophiurous family, differs from the other families of this order and resembles the Euryalae in that disk and arms are covered in life with a thick naked

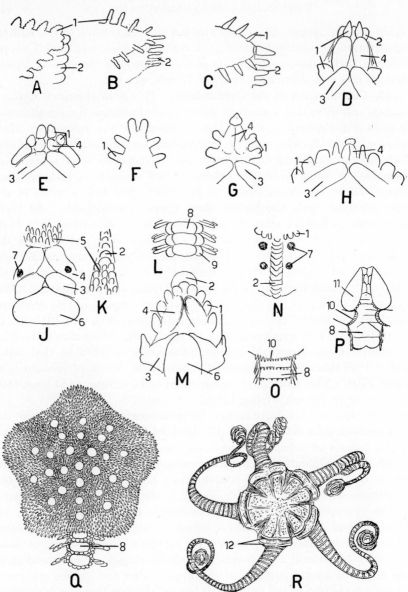

Fig. 266.—Taxonomic characters of ophiuroids. *A*, jaw of *Ophiomyxa*. *B*, jaw of *Ophioscolex*. *C*, jaw of *Ophiacantha*. *D*, jaw of *Amphiura*, seen from oral side. *E*, jaw of *Amphipholis squamata*, oral view. *F*, jaw of *Amphiodia*, from oral side. *G*, jaw of *Ophiactis*, from oral side. *H*, jaw of *Ophiopholis aculeata*, from oral side. *J*, jaw of *Ophiothrix fragilis*, oral view. *K*, jaw edge of *Ophiothrix fragilis*. *L*, aboral surface of arm of *Ophionereis*. *M*, jaw of *Ophionereis*, oral view. *N*, jaw edge of *Ophiopholis aculeata*. *O*, edge of aboral surface of disk with arm base to show arm comb, *Ophiocten*. *P*, edge of aboral surface of disk and arm base to show arm comb, *Ophiura*. *Q*, aboral surface of disk of *Ophiopholis aculeata;* large shields are often covered. *R*, *Astroporpa* with disk annulations, Barbados.  1, oral papillae; 2, teeth; 3, adoral shields; 4, exposed part of half jaw; 5, tooth papillae; 6, buccal shield; 7, podial pore; 8, aboral arm shield; 9, accessory aboral arm shields; 10, arm comb; 11, radial shield; 12, disk annulation.

646

skin that conceals the shields and scales; but these are poorly developed on the disk, anyway, the radial shields are narrow and rod-like or wanting, and the aboral arm shields are greatly reduced or lacking. The arm spines are fairly developed and stand out from the arms. The main genus *Ophiomyxa* lacks tooth papillae and has broad teeth and broad oral papillae with serrate edges (Fig. 266*A*). This genus contains two subantarctic viviparous species, both dioecious, *O. vivipara* and *O. brevirima*. In *Ophioscolex* (Fig. 266*B*), also without tooth papillae, the oral papillae are slender and spine-like as are also the teeth, arranged in a single row. *Ophioscolex glacialis* is widely spread in arctic and boreal waters of Europe and North America, and two antarctic species are viviparous, *O. nutrix*, sometimes hermaphroditic and sometime dioecious, and *O. marionis*, hermaphroditic.

The characters of the family Hemieuryalidae are heavy plating of the disk, strongly developed radial shields, short genital slits, stout arms capable of vertical coiling, three or four flat oral papillae on each jaw edge, and triangular teeth in a single row without tooth papillae. Main genera are *Ophiochondrus*, without accessory aboral arm shields, and *Sigsbeia*, *Ophioplus*, and *Hemieuryale* with accessory aboral arm shields or the main shield replaced by a mosaic.

The Ophiacanthidae, one of the largest ophiurous families, have a disk formed of small scales more or less concealed by granules, tubercles, or minute spines, or in two genera (*Ophiolebes*, *Ophiotoma*) by a thick skin; tooth papillae are wanting, the oral papillae are pointed, and the teeth, in one row, pointed or rounded (Fig. 266*C*). The arms are provided with slender spines, longest aborally and decreasing in length orally. The lateral arm shields tend to meet in the arm mid-lines, displacing the small aboral and oral shields. Over 300 genera are recognized in this family, but most are archibenthal or abyssal forms brought up by dredging expeditions. The most common littoral genera are *Ophiomitrella*, with large, naked radial shields, and *Ophiacantha* (Fig. 267), with small or mostly concealed ones. Mortensen (1936) lists five species of each of these genera as viviparous and mostly hermaphroditic. Many ophiacanths live clinging to sponges and to gorgonians and other coelenterates.

The Amphiuridae are characterized by the long, slender, flexible arms with short inconspicuous but erect spines. The disk is generally definitely scaled with evident radial shields that at their outer ends are articulated by a socket to a ball-shaped projection of the outer ends of the genital plates. Oral papillae are present, and two occur at the jaw tip followed along the jaw edge by a single row of square teeth as tooth papillae are wanting. The amphiurids generally live buried in sand or mud with the arm tips protruding. The genus *Amphiura* with over

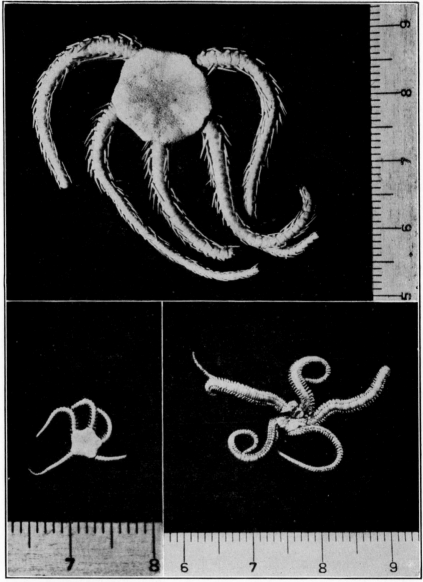

Fig. 267.—Some common ophiuroids. Above, *Ophiacantha normani*, Panamic region. Below, left, *Amphipholis squamata*, cosmopolitan. Below, right, *Ophiactis savignyi*, circumtropical.

100 species is known by the single oral papilla (Fig. 266D) on each side widely separated from the two papillae at the jaw tip; hence the oral angles are wide and gaping. Mortensen (1936) lists 15 members of this genus as viviparous. *Amphiura chiajei* and *filiformis* are common on European coasts. *Ophiocentrus* (= *Acrocnida*) differs from *Amphiura* in the spiny disk. In *Amphipholis* there are three oral papillae on each side of each jaw, and the outermost one is broad and scale-like (Fig. 266E), covering the oral angles. *Amphipholis squamata* (Figs. 267, 268), with cosmopolitan distribution, is also noted as the first known viviparous and hermaphroditic ophiuroid. *Amphiodia* (Fig. 266F) and *Amphiocnida* also have three oral papillae on each side, but the outermost one is not conspicuously elongated. Finally, there is a group of amphiurids, including *Amphiacantha* and *Amphioplus*, with four or more oral papillae along each jaw edge.

The small family Ophiactidae is often included under the Amphiuridae, from which in fact it differs chiefly in having but one papilla at the jaw apex (Fig. 266G). The principal genera are *Ophiopus* without bursae, *Ophiopholis* with aboral arm shields encircled by small supplementary shields, and *Ophiactis* without such supplementary arm shields. The genus *Ophiactis* is noted for its fissiparity, best known in the common Mediterranean species *O. virens*. The daisy serpent star *Ophiopholis aculeata* (Figs. 266H, 270) is a relatively large and handsome species widely distributed in arctic and boreal waters.

The Amphilepididae resemble in general appearance the two preceding families, having long slender arms with short spines. Dental papillae are also lacking; there is a single papilla at the jaw apex but the teeth are triangular and rather weak. In *Amphilepis* bursae and bursal slits are wanting and the second pair of buccal podia open onto the oral surface.

In the Ophiothrichidae the disk scalation is more or less concealed by little spines or tubercles. There are large radial shields and well-developed aboral and oral arm shields. Oral papillae are wanting, but a cluster of tooth papillae occurs on the jaw apex (Fig. 266J, K). The arms are spiny with mostly long thorny spines of a glassy appearance, especially in *Ophiothrix*. This is a large family of mostly tropical ophiuroids that often live attached to sponges, gorgonians, comatulids, and the like. Matsumoto (1917) listed 15 genera, but others have been added since by breaking up the large genus *Ophiothrix*, to which, according to H. L. Clark (1946), over 125 species had been assigned. *Ophiothrix* with spiny disk, large radial shields, and bristly arms with long thorny spines is exemplified by *O. fragilis* (Fig. 270), common along the coasts of western Europe. The members of the genus *Ophiothela* with granular or tuberculate disk and shorter arm spines are generally six-rayed and fissiparous; they commonly live attached to gorgonians.   In *Ophiomaza* the disk is smooth, and *Ophiopteron* was noted above for its arm fans (Fig. 245*C*).

Characters of the small family Ophiochitonidae are the small imbricating scales of the disk, five or six oral papillae on each side of the jaw, want of tooth papillae, single row of triangular or quadrangular teeth, moderately long erect arm spines, and large leaf-like tentacle scales. The main genera are *Ophiochiton* with arms keeled above and below, *Ophioplax* with disk covered with fine granules, and *Ophionereis* with two large accessory arm plates to each aboral arm shield (Figs. 266*M*, 271, 272).

The family Ophiocomidae comprises relatively large and conspicuously colored ophiuroids with spiny arms provided with strong, generally solid spines.   The disk scalation is completely concealed by granules in typical genera.   Oral papillae are present and merge into a large cluster of tooth papillae that are followed aborally by a few large teeth (Fig. 249*K*, *L*).   The main genus *Ophiocoma* (Fig. 241*A*) with the characters of the family has a large number of species in shallow tropical waters. *Ophiomastix* with spiny disk and *Ophiarthrum* with disk covered with naked skin are also Indo-Pacific genera.   *Ophiocomina* with fragile hollow arm spines is represented mainly by *O. nigra*, a common species in the North Atlantic from Norway to the Azores (Fig. 271).   *Ophiopsila* is distinguished by its special, club-shaped, flagellated tentacle scales (page 595; Fig. 246*A*, *B*).

In the Ophiodermatidae also the disk scalation is concealed on both sides by closely set granules (Fig. 246*D*).   There are numerous oral papillae in a continuous series; tooth papillae are wanting and the teeth occur in a single row.   The arms appear smooth, as the arm spines are small and typically closely appressed to the sides of the arms.   *Ophioderma* (Fig. 246*D*) is known from all other ophiuroids by having two slits to each bursa, one orally located, the other peripheral.   *Ophioderma brevispina* (Fig. 273) is a well-known species distributed on western Atlantic shores from Massachusetts to Brazil.   There are two tentacle scales to each podial pore in *Ophiarachnella* with naked buccal shields and *Pectinura* with buccal shields covered with granules; and one tentacle scale to each podial pore in *Ophioconis*.   *Ophiarachna*, also with naked buccal shields, differs from the norm of the family in having longer, erect spines.

The Ophiolepididae are a large family of generally smooth appearance with arms of short to moderate length bearing short spines closely appressed to the arm sides (Fig. 242*A*, *C*).   The disk is covered with naked scales that often give indications of the primitive arrangement (Fig. 244*B*–*D*).   The jaws are edged with a continuous row of oral

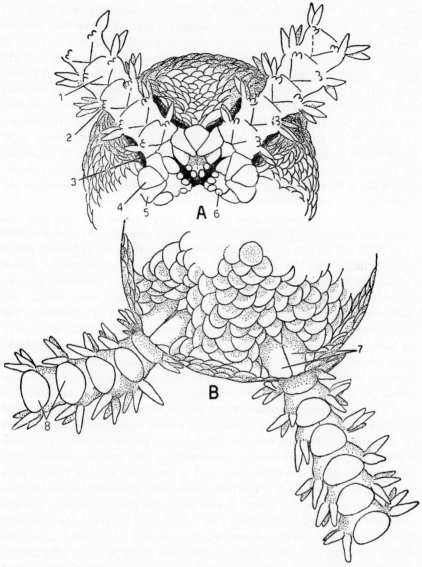

FIG. 268.—Detailed structure of *Amphipholis squamata*. *A*, oral surface. *B*, aboral surface. (*Both after Ely*, 1942.) 1, oral arm shield; 2, tentacle scales; 3, bursal slit; 4, buccal shield; 5, adoral shield; 6, oral papillae; 7, radial shields; 8, aboral arm shields.

papillae (Fig. 247*B*), continuous with the single row of teeth without the intervention of tooth papillae. There is a variable number of leaf-like tentacle scales. This family includes nearly 50 genera and around 300 species. In *Ophiura* (includes *Ophioglypha*) and a large number of related genera, the second pair of buccal podia open onto the oral surface and not into the mouth angles (Fig. 247*B*). In *Ophiura* with many species, the arm bases project into the aboral surface of the disk and are there bordered on each side by an arch of papillae, known as the *arm combs*, that continue around to the oral side where they merge into the genital papillae (Fig. 266*P*). The exposed pores of the second buccal podia are encircled with a row of tentacle scales (Fig. 247*B*) resembling the oral papillae, and similar borders of tentacle scales continue around the regular podial pores of the proximal arm joints but gradually diminish to one or two scales. The disk of *Ophiura* is flat with many small scales and evident radial shields (Fig. 244*D*). Matsumoto in 1915 separated off several genera, all with arm combs, from *Ophiura* as *Homalophiura*, also with a flat disk but with larger disk scales, and *Aspidophiura*, *Stegophiura*, and *Amphiophiura* with a high disk and larger scales. *Ophiocten* lacks the aboral projection of the arm base into the disk and hence the arm comb is continuous along the disk edge at the arm base (Fig. 266*O*). To the group of ophiolepidids with exposed second podial pores belongs also the curious genus *Astrophiura*, regarded by Sladen (1879), at its first finding off Madagascar, as intermediate between asteroids and ophiuroids. Other species have since been found, and *Astrophiura* is now considered an aberrant relative of *Ophiura*. The pentagonal disk without bursae encloses a considerable length of arm base on both sides (Fig. 274) and is fringed with papillae. The aborted free parts of the arms project from the disk angles and are very short and slender, lacking oral and aboral arm shields and podial pores; large podial pores are present on the arm bases included within the disk.

In another group of ophiolepidid genera exemplified by *Ophiomusium* and *Ophiolepis*, the pores for the second pair of buccal podia do not show on the oral surface but are concealed in the mouth angles. In *Ophiomusium* with many species the aboral surface of the disk is covered with plates of small to moderate size and large radial shields (Fig. 244*C*). Arm combs are wanting. The oral papillae are somewhat fused together forming an edge to the jaws. Podial pores are present only on the arm bases included within the disk (Fig. 247*A*). The arms are stiff with or without small aboral and oral shields. In *Ophiolepis* (Fig. 242*A*) the disk is provided with large plates surrounded by little plates (Fig. 244*B*), and there are supplementary aboral arm shields (Fig. 242*B*). Such supplementary plates are wanting in *Ophiozonella*.

Viviparity is common among the ophiolepidids. Mortensen (1936) ascribed this habit to 14 members of the family, including *Ophionotus hexactis* and two other species that brood their young in the ovary. The family further includes *Ophiophycis gracilis*, St. Helena, that broods its young beneath the disk (Mortensen, 1933b) and appears somewhat related to *Astrophiura*.

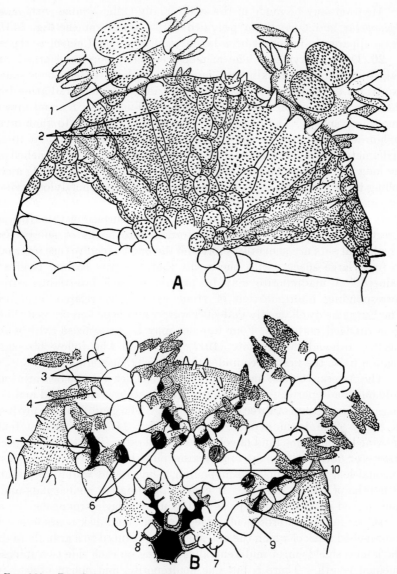

FIG. 269.—Detailed structure of *Ophiactis savignyi*.  *A*, aboral surface.  *B*, oral surface.  (*Both after Ely*, 1942.)   1, aboral arm shield; 2, radial shields; 3, oral arm shields;
4, tentacle scale; 5, bursal slit; 6, holes for second pair of buccal podia; 7, oral papillae;
8, teeth; 9, buccal shield; 10, adoral shields.

Mention may be made of the small family Ophiohelidae with genera *Ophiohelus* and *Ophiotholia* provided with parasol spines (Fig. 245*D*); these apparently have not been taken again since the *Challenger* report.

**20. Order Euryalae.**—The members of this group are clothed with naked or granulated skin and mostly lack definite scales or shields except for the radial shields that are long and spoke-like, radiating from the central part of the disk to its periphery (Fig. 244*A*, *E*), and may be smooth or spiny.   The disk is often comparable in size to that of the Ophiurae but is large in the Gorgonocephalidae, ranging up to 10 cm. in diameter.   The arms may be simple or slightly or greatly branched and are long and flexible, capable of coiling around objects (Fig. 244*A*) and of rolling up in the vertical plane, because of the streptospondylous type of articulation of the ends of the vertebral ossicles (Fig. 249*E*, *F*).   The short arm spines, displaced toward the ventral surface of the arms and directed downward, are often transformed into hooks or spiny clubs. The bursal slits are generally short and the bursae tend to fuse internally to form large spaces, with the result that the true coelom is greatly reduced.   A madreporite may be present in each interradius with a corresponding multiplication of stone canals and related structures. The Euryalae dwell mostly in deeper waters and hence are known chiefly from dredged material.   Four families may be recognized (Mortensen, 1933b), although Matsumoto (1917) and those who follow his classification unite the first three under the name Trichasteridae.

The Asteronychidae have five long and slender unbranched arms and only one madreporite.   The oral arm shields are well developed and bear on each side a group of three or more spines.   The genital bursae are fused in pairs.   The main genus *Asteronyx* (Fig. 244*A*) is usually found entwined about some kind of colonial coelenterate.   The common species *Asteronyx loveni*, with eight to nine arm spines in each group and arms of unequal length, is almost cosmopolitan, being found widely distributed at depths of 100 to 1800 m.   It commonly clings to pennatulids and is said to feed upon their polyps as well as upon pelagic organisms.

In the family Asteroschematidae the very small disk bears five stout unbranched arms of which the oral shields are reduced to a granule so that the lateral shields meet mid-ventrally, bearing on each side two spines of unequal length.   There is but one madreporite, and polian vesicles are lacking.   The bursae remain separate, and the five pairs of gonads extend into the arms for varying distances.   On account of the small space left on the disk between the stout arm bases, the bursal slits are more or less vertically oriented on the disk edge.   In *Asteroschema* with arm spines of fair size, the radial shields are concealed by skin.   *Ophiocreas* seems to differ only in the visibility of the radial shields and is included in *Asteroschema* by Matsumoto.   *Astrocharis* is characterized by the small exposed radial shields, stout arm bases, and very small arm spines. The Japanese species *Astrocharis ijimai* and *virgo* appear to be fissiparous, as is also *Astrogymnotes catasticta*, differing from other Asteroschematidae mainly in having six arms.

In the Trichasteridae the disk is moderately large and the arms, simple or branched, moderately stout. Oral arm shields are present with two spines on each side, but the aboral arm shields are represented by two or more small plates or are practically wanting. There are five madreporites. In *Astroceras* the arms are simple, and two pairs of ribbon-like gonads extend into each arm base. The arms are divided near the tips in *Trichaster* in which four pairs of elongated gonads extend into the arm bases. The arms branch at their bases in *Euryale* and the gonads are confined to the disk. Fissiparity obtains in species of *Astroceras*.

The Gorgonocephalidae represent the culmination of the euryalous type of structure. The disk is large and covered with a naked or granulated or tuberculate skin that does not, however, conceal the long, bar-like radial shields, often ornamented with spines or tubercles. Oral papillae, tooth papillae, and teeth form a continuous series of small spine-like projections. The arms are very long, simple, or sparsely or greatly branched and much coiled vertically. There are no true aboral arm shields, but these are often represented either along the whole arms or on their distal parts by transverse bands of hook-bearing granules (Fig. 246C), and hence the arms have an annulated appearance when viewed from the aboral side. Lateral and oral arm shields are present. The pair of spine groups on the oral surface of the arms is directed downward and is in line with the transverse aboral bands of hooked granules. The gonads are confined to the interior of the disk. The fusions of the bursae to produce large internal cavities that suppress the true coelom were described above (page 617). There may be a single madreporite or one in each interradius. Mortensen (1933b) listed 32 genera in this family, but many have been seldom seen. Among the genera with simple arms may be mentioned *Astroporpa* in which the arm annulations extend onto the aboral side of the disk (Fig. 266R) and *Astrothamnus* without annulated disk. The arms are branched a few times in *Conocladus* and *Astrocnida*. The typical basket stars in which the arms branch repeatedly to produce an inextricable tangle of small twigs (Fig. 243) belong to a number of genera, but the best known are *Gorgonocephalus* and *Astrophyton*, both with one madreporite. In *Gorgonocephalus* the oral surface of the arms is spiny almost up to the mouth angles, and the disk margin between the radial shields is edged with a series of plates. This edge is wanting in *Astrophyton* in which also the oral surface of the disk and proximal parts of the arms are very smooth, without spine groups. In both genera the annulated appearance of the aboral surface of the arms is

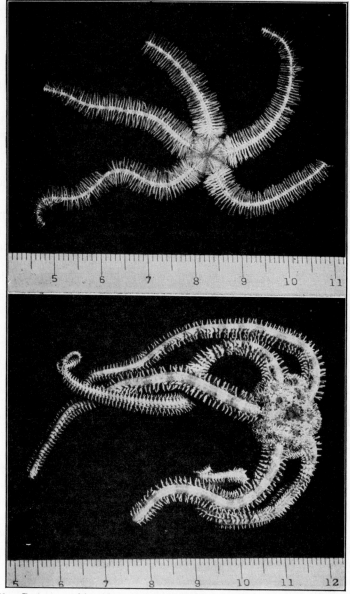

FIG. 270.—Common ophiuroids.   Above, *Ophiothrix fragilis*, European boreal.   Below, *Ophiopholis aculeata*, circumboreal.

best developed distally. It is known for these multibrachiate gorgono-cephalids that they start life with five arms that subsequently fork repeatedly.

**21. Ecology: Habits and Behavior.**—The ophiuroids, like other eleutherozoan echinoderms, are among the most common animals of the littoral zone of the sea but attract less attention because of their small size and retiring habits. A negative response to light combined with a high degree of positive stereotropism results in their concealing them-selves by day under stones, shells, and the like, or among seaweeds. When exposed by turning over a rock or coral slab they promptly scurry to the new undersurface or to some adjacent shelter. They inhabit all types of bottom, and some, especially members of the family Amphiuridae, live buried in sand. By virtue of their long flexible arms the ophiuroids are well adapted for attaching themselves to other animals, and especially the euryalous types with unbranched arms are habitually found twined about colonial coelenterates (see later).

The ophiuroids are the most lively and active of all echinoderms and, unlike other eleutherozoans, move without or with minor assistance from the ambulacral system. The usual methods of locomotion have been described by Romanes and Ewart (1881), Grave (1899), von Uexküll (1905), and Glaser (1907). No arm preference is shown. The animal may move with one arm held straight forward as a sort of guide or feeler, and the adjacent pair of arms accomplishes forward progression in a series of jerks or bounds by synchronous rowing movements against the substrate, while the two rear arms do not participate. The animal may equally well advance with an arm pair forward, and this pair and to a less extent the following pair engage in rowing movements while the fifth arm drags behind. During locomotion the disk is held above the substrate. Other arm positions and attitudes may be employed, but less frequently. The forward arm may aid by stroking alternately to each side, and positions with three arms on one side and two on the other occur. Glaser remarked that the animal moves in all ways possible to its structure. Some species progress by grasping objects with one or two arms and pulling themselves forward while the other arms push from behind. Up to 2 inches may be covered by each forward jerk in ordinary locomotion, and a speed of 180 cm. per minute was reported by Romanes and Ewart. Specimens with one arm may progress with this arm forward by stroking alternately to each side, and those with two adjacent arms may move with these forward, stroking simultaneously. It is usually said that ophiuroids cannot swim, but the MacGinities (1949) ascribe swimming powers to two species, *Ophiacantha eurythra*, by trailing one arm behind and stroking with the other four, and *Amphiodia psara*,

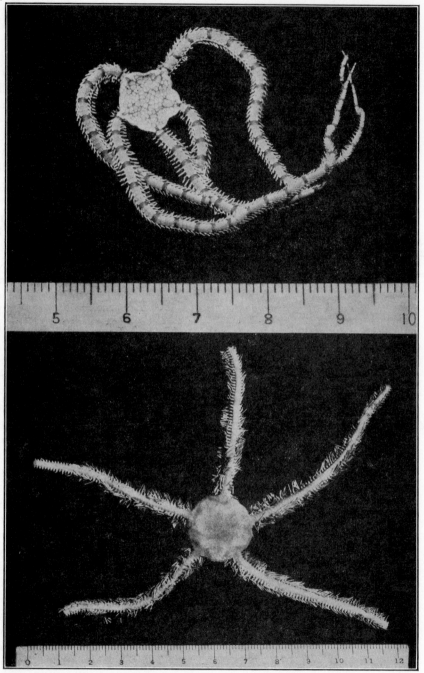

Fig. 271.—Common ophiuroids. Above, *Ophionereis reticulata*, West Indian region. Below, *Ophiocomina nigra*, European boreal.

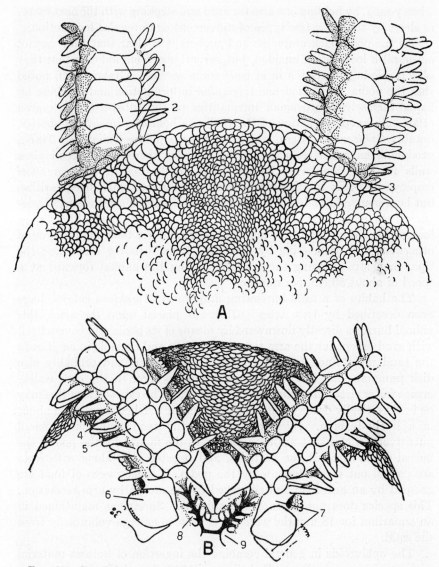

Fig. 272.—Detailed structure of *Ophionereis porrecta*, Indo-Pacific. *A*, aboral surface. *B*, oral surface. (*Both after Ely*, 1941.) 1, aboral arm shield; 2, accessory aboral arm shields; 3, radial shields; 4, oral arm shield; 5, tentacle scale; 6, buccal shield; 7, adoral shields; 8, oral papillae; 9, tooth.

when young, by holding one arm forward and stroking with the next two—in short by the same two types of movement as in regular locomotion.

As the podia lack ampullae and suckers it is clear that they cannot accomplish locomotion unaided, but several observers indicate that they play a role in progression in at least some species. Grave (1899) noted that the podia aid *Ophioderma brevispina* in locomotion and climbing by fixing themselves into small inequalities of the substrate. Östergren (1904) observed the action of the podia as holdfasts in several species, notably *Ophiocomina nigra*, which has very papillate podia (Fig. 248*E*), producing an adhesive secretion, and is able thereby to ascend glass walls readily. Similarly Cowles (1910) found that *Ophiocoma riisei* employs its podia in climbing by fitting them into small irregularities, but he was unable to detect the production of adhesive secretion. *Ophionereis reticulata*, Bermuda, makes important use of its podia in ordinary locomotion (May, 1925), resting upon them and not touching the ground otherwise, and progressing by extending them, bending them near the tips, then straightening them, thus pushing the animal forward at a speed of about 50 cm. per minute.

The habits of a sand-burrowing amphiurid, *Amphiura chiajei*, have been described by Des Artes (1910). If placed upon the sand, this animal burrows directly downward by means of its podia and covers itself with sand except for the arm tips. Both disk and arms lie in cavities in the sand maintained by mucus. Arm undulations and probably also disk pumping—for this species has a muscle layer in the disk wall—create water circulation through the burrow. The exposed arm tips may be held vertically or may rest upon the sand; if touched they swing about in a lively fashion. By sweeping over the sand they collect small nutritive particles that are then passed to the mouth by the podia; the buccal podia sort out the particles, and rejected ones along with feces are passed out of the burrow by the podia. Larger pieces of food are grasped by an arm loop and conveyed to the mouth by arm retraction. This species does not capture live animals. Specimens maintained in an aquarium for 18 months were never seen to emerge voluntarily from the sand.

The ophiuroids in general combine the ingestion of bottom material with carnivorous feeding. Eichelbaum (1910) found that the stomach contents of several common European ophiuroids consisted usually of 75 to 90 per cent of bottom material, including detritus, diatoms, foraminiferans, dinoflagellates, tintinnoids, and so on, intermingled with some animal prey, especially polychaete worms and small crustaceans, less often young echinoderms and bivalves and other mollusks. Wintzell (1918) also reported that *Ophiura texturata* and *Ophiothrix fragilis* feed primarily on bottom material, whereas *Ophiocomina nigra* eats chiefly the kelp fronds on which it lives plus the hydroids and other animals inhabiting these fronds. According to May (1925), *Ophionereis reticulata* eats only plant material, as algae and diatoms. In aquaria ophiuroids may be fed on small bits of fish. In the feeding of ophiuroids, smaller particles are passed to the mouth by the podia and possibly also ciliary action, and larger particles are grasped in an arm loop and carried to the mouth by the coiling of the arm. It is improbable that the mucus-ciliary method of feeding is employed by any ophiuroid as the necessary ciliation is

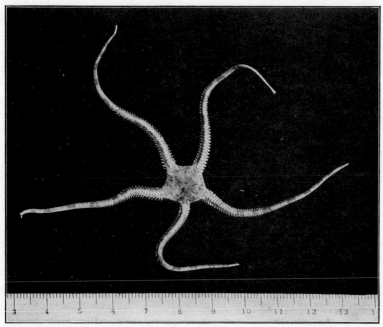

FIG. 273.—Common ophiuroids. *Ophioderma brevispina*, Atlantic Coast of the United States.

wanting (Gislén, 1924). The food habits of the Euryalae are not well known, as these animals usually dwell at considerable depths. *Asteronyx loveni*, which attains elevation from the bottom by twining about pennatulids and other tall coelenterates, was thought by Mortensen (1912) to catch copepods and other planktonic animals, but Gislén (1924) found it filled with the polyps of the coelenterate. The gorgonocephalids eat copepods and other planktonic animals that become entangled in the meshwork of the small terminal arm branches armed with microscopic hooks (Fedotov, 1924). This author found them living in aggregations in the Kola Fjord on rocky shelves swept by plankton-bearing currents.

Observers agree that ophiuroids are able to sense food (giving off juices) without contact. Preyer (1887) reported that *Ophioderma* was attracted to a crab leg 6 inches away and continued to advance when the leg was removed another 3 inches. *Ophiomyxa* perceived a dead fish without contact; it might make an arm loop about an inert object of similar shape but would soon drop it. *Ophiura texturata* was seen by von Uexküll (1905) to wave the arms on the sides nearest pieces of fish, then spring upon them. The buried *Amphiura chiajei* indicates the presence of food in the aquarium by waving its exposed arm tips about (Des Artes, 1910); isolated arm tips also react to the presence of food for about an hour. The MacGinities (1949) also note sensing of food by ophiuroids at a distance of several inches. Food perception is probably located in the podia. Cowles (1910) experimented with detached rays of *Ophiocoma riisei* turned oral side up. The podia of such rays would pass food particles to the proximal cut end, but inert particles of similar size were quickly dropped unless soaked in fish juice. *Ophioderma longicauda* beat a hasty retreat when strong odors as attar of roses, asafoetida, and ammonia were brought near the arms or disk (Graber, 1889).

The effects of mechanical stimulation have been studied chiefly by Mangold (1909) and May (1925). A light touch on the arms evokes a positive response of the arm tips which bend toward the site of stimulation and may adhere to the stimulating object by their podia, whereas the proximal parts of the arms curve away from the stimulated spot, thus putting themselves in a flight attitude. If the leading arm of an advancing animal is touched lightly, it will grasp the stimulating object and continue to advance. Stronger excitation of arms causes their retraction with flight in the direction opposite that of stimulation. Excitation of the arm bases or of the disk evokes coordinated movements of the entire animal, eventuating in flight in the direction opposite that of stimulation. Mangold enunciates the general rule that the arms are positive to contact distally, negative proximally. The strong positive stereotropism of ophiuroids has already been mentioned. Cowles (1910), experimenting with *Ophiocoma riisei*, found that the animal will seek the corner of a rectangular container and, if removed from the corner, tends to return to it and place the same arm again in the angle, thus indicating a retention of the stereotropic stimulus. Rough handling of ophiuroids may cause them to "freeze," that is, go into a stiff, immobile condition, and this behavior is often a handicap to experimentation, as is also their habit of throwing off arms at stimulated spots. Mechanical stimulation of the aboral surface of the disk evokes the dorsal reflex, that is, the curvature of the arms toward the aboral side (von Uexküll, 1905; Mangold, 1921). The same reaction is given by individual arms when touched aborally.

A general negativity to light was already indicated (Mangold, 1909; Cowles, 1910; May, 1925). Ophiuroids will seek the dark side of an

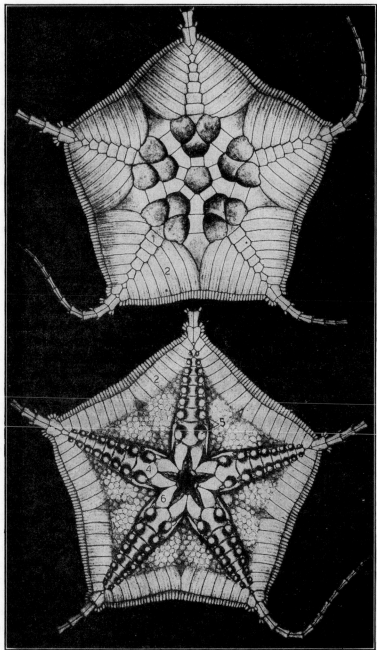

Fig. 274.—*Astrophiura* (*after Matsumoto*, 1913). Above, aboral view. Below, oral view. (*Both after Matsumoto*, 1913.) 1, aboral arm shields; 2, lateral arm shields; 3, fringe; 4, oral arm shields; 5, podia; 6, half jaws.

aquarium or container or retreat into corners or hide under stones and plants if available.   In a darkened aquarium they may be found moving about anywhere, but on illumination they retreat into the darkest available places.   They react positively to dark walls even if these throw no shadow and will seek the dark half of containers painted half black and half white.   May noted little response to illumination of small body areas, but Mangold noted retreat if only part of an arm is exposed to sunlight.   Generally the sensitivity to light is greater aborally than orally and the arms appear more responsive than the disk.

Ophiuroids readily and quickly right when placed on their backs. Two adjacent arms are extended sidewise to form a line like an acrobat doing the split, and the disk is elevated by the pushing of the other three stiffened arms against the substrate until it falls over, using the two extended arms as a pivot (Glaser, 1907); or the tips of the extended rays may twist over and bring the disk into normal position either with or without its elevation by the other arms (Cowles, 1910).   Wintzell (1918) described a different method of righting in species with more flexible arms, as *Ophiopholis aculeata* and *Ophiothrix fragilis;* here the arms are erected away from the substrate, then one or two arms reach across the oral side of the disk, attach, and pull the disk over.   Wintzell gave the following figures for the time of righting: *Ophiocomina nigra*, 3 to 25 seconds, mostly less than 10; *Ophiopholis aculeata*, 17 to 65 seconds, mostly less than 35; and *Ophiothrix fragilis*, 8 to 90 seconds, mostly less than 40.   Glaser (1907), using *Ophioderma brevispina*, reported that righting time varied from 2 seconds to over 3 minutes but usually occurred in less than 45 seconds.   Specimens with but one or two rays can right, and Mangold (1921) reported righting in *Ophioderma longicauda* with one arm and less than half the disk.   The direction of righting is influenced by concomitant effective stimuli; thus the animal rights to the side opposite that previously stimulated mechanically or otherwise, and also, if negatively phototactic, rights away from the light (Cowles, 1910).

Arguments concerning the stimulus releasing the righting reaction follow the same lines as for asteroids.   Wolf (1925) ascribed righting to the pull of the stomach on its mesenteries when the animal is placed aboral side down.   He suspended an *Ophioderma* horizontally in normal orientation by a rod through the body after filling the stomach with iron filings and stated that the animal would turn on the rod into the reverse position with the aboral side down if the filings were made to press against the aboral stomach wall by means of a magnet.   Fraenkel (1928), however, reported normal righting after removal of the aboral disk wall and stomach.   Mangold (1921) favored the theory that contact of the aboral surface constitutes the releasing stimulus for righting and stated that if the ophiuroid is placed aboral surface down on a cone of sand so that its arms do not touch the substrate, it will not right. However, he admitted that removal of the aboral disk wall and of the aboral surface of the arms so far as practical do not affect righting. Ophiuroids will right while falling through water but do so by throwing the arms aborally in the usual dorsal reflex and thus shifting the center of gravity so that the disk turns over. If thrown into a "freeze" by rough handling, they do not right on falling through water. It appears impossible to reach any conclusion as to the releasing stimulus for righting.

Ophiuroids have been considerably employed as material for the study of neuromuscular function, but much of this work does not appear pertinent here. In the anatomical account the relatively great development of the central nervous system, especially of the radial nerves, in ophiuroids was noticed, and a greater dependence of behavior on the integrity of the nervous system in ophiuroids than in other eleuthrozoans may be anticipated. Locomotion is impaired by cutting the nerve ring at one or more interradii or the radial nerve at the arm base (Preyer, 1886; Grave, 1899; von Uexküll, 1905; Mangold, 1909, 1921; May, 1925; Diebschlag, 1938). Coordinated directed locomotion is impossible following cuts across the nerve ring at all interradii. Arms nervously isolated by cuts through the nerve ring or across the radial nerve never lead in locomotion but are dragged behind. Isolated arms do not creep and after initial writhing remain quiescent unless strongly stimulated. They may right in at least some species but only after many wasted movements and only if the radial nerve is intact. Cutting across the radial nerve of an arm of course prevents transmission to the rest of the animal, and stimuli applied distal to the cut evoke only local reactions.

The learning ability of ophiuroids has been tested by several investigators, mostly by placing fetters on the arms. Preyer (1886, 1887) admired the ability of ophiuroids to escape from fetters and entanglements and claimed improvement on repeated trials, but others have not verified the latter claim. An animal would try a variety of methods of ridding an arm of a piece of rubber tubing drawn over it: waving the arm energetically back and forth, rubbing the arm against the substrate, holding the tubing against the substrate with other arms and drawing the arm out, pushing the tubing off with the other arms, or autotomy of the arm. Similar behavior was noted by Glaser (1907) after placing rubber tubing over one or more arms of *Ophioderma brevispina*. The animal would try violent or writhing movements or rubbing the encumbered arm against the disk or other arms or the container or waving the arm in the manner of one cracking a whip. The ophiuroid did not learn in successive trials to rid itself of the tubing more readily or faster but did repeatedly change behavior and did not persist in unsuccessful actions. Diebschlag (1938) claimed some success in teaching *Ophiothrix fragilis* to turn back at a boundary between two factors by punishing them with asteroid pedicellariae. The factors used were rough and smooth substrate and smooth and wavy glass. After repeated lessons the animal might show a better than chance turning back into smooth at the boundary with rough (without punishment), but quickly "forgot"; the reverse attempt, avoidance of smooth, failed. Similarly, avoidance of either smooth or wavy glass, especially the former, might be briefly retained, although the animal normally shows no reaction to either.

**22. Physiology.**—Because of their small size ophiuroids are not favorable objects for physiological investigation, and only limited information is available. Data on chemical composition are summarized in Vinogradov (1953). The water content of *Ophiopholis aculeata* is around 57 per cent, that of *Ophiothrix fragilis* about 69 per cent; the nitrogen content of the fresh weight of these two species is 1.31 and 0.41 per cent, respectively. The skeleton consists of 80 to 93 per cent of calcium carbonate (in the form of calcite as usual), 6 to 15 per cent of magnesium carbonate, and small amounts of phosphate and salts of iron, silicon, and aluminium. Some species contain up to 4 per cent of calcium sulphate (gypsum). Traces of other elements are present, as barium, strontium, manganese, boron, copper, and cadmium. The colors of ophiuroids are attributable chiefly to carotenoids. Lönnberg (1931) and Lönnberg and Hellström (1931) demonstrated carotenoids in several common species of European ophiuroids, and Fox and Scheer (1941), in a more careful study of three California species, determined that the carotenoids are chiefly xanthophylls, to a less extent carotenoid acids. Ophiuroids are thought to contain cholesterol, not found in other echinoderms except echinoids (Bergmann, 1949).

As already indicated, ciliary currents occur chiefly around the bursal slits (Wintzell, 1918; Gislén, 1924). In the *Amphiura* species, which it will be recalled live buried in the sand, the current enters the oral end of the bursal slits and exits at the peripheral end, whereas in other ophiuroids, as far as studied, the current runs in the opposite direction, in peripherally and out orally. Currents running mostly toward the mouth may be present on the arm bases and along the mouth angles. In a group of species including *Ophiocomina nigra*, *Ophiothrix fragilis*, and *Ophiopholis aculeata* there are transverse currents on the oral side of the proximal surfaces of the arms, running between the spine bases and the podia. *Gorgonocephalus* shows the usual current through the bursae, but *Asteronyx loveni* appeared to lack ciliary currents almost altogether.

The water currents maintained through the bursae undoubtedly serve a respiratory function; in addition disk movements that pump water in and out of the bursae have been observed by several of the older workers (Apostolides, 1881; Fjelstrup, 1890; Cuénot, 1891a). Gislén

(1924) saw pronounced respiratory pumping in *Amphiura filiformis*, less definite movements in *A. chiajei*. In the former species the respiratory movement "is performed once or twice a minute by strong dilatation of the soft skin of the ventral side [of the disk] which after 35–50 seconds sinks down again. The bursal fissures usually stand open during the whole process. As the amphiurids normally lie buried in the bottom-slime one may imagine that these respiratory movements pump the water in and out through the narrow canals leading to the surface of the bottom in which the arms lie. One may often see, round the openings of the canals through which the arms protrude, a hasty swirling up of particles of sand which indicates that there is a strong discharge of water through the canals." Des Artes (1910) noted a muscle layer in the disk wall of *Amphiura chiajei* that could accomplish raising and lowering of the disk wall, and further saw water currents emitted from the sand canals enclosing the arms. A. H. Clark (1949) reported that in *Ophiothrix lepidus* the top of the disk rose and fell in a more or less rhythmic manner.

Foettinger (1880) noticed that the water-vascular system of *Ophiactis virens* is filled with coelomocytes containing reddish inclusions and, having subjected the cells to spectrographic examination, announced the presence of haemoglobin in the reddish inclusions.

Measurements of the oxygen intake of several common ophiuroids of north European coasts were made by Wintzell (1918), who obtained the following figures expressed as cubic centimeters of oxygen per milligram of nitrogen per 24 hours: *Amphiura chiajei*, 0.056; *Ophiopholis aculeata*, 0.124; *Ophiura labida*, 0.128; *Ophiocomina nigra*, 0.207; and *Ophiothrix fragilis*, 0.271. Obviously, species with the more active habits give higher figures on oxygen consumption.

Wintzell (1918) reported the presence of a strong proteinase, acting in both acid and alkaline medium, in *Ophiura texturata;* an amylase and probably a lipase were also present. This author described the occurrence in this species of a strong ciliary current carrying small food particles into the stomach along its periphery and out centrally. Certain types of spherules in the coelomocytes were regarded by Cuénot (1891a) as of the nature of protein reserves. This author also surmises that normally excretory products exit through the bursal walls because in *Ophiactis virens*, which lacks bursae, yellow and black granules, and crystals insoluble in mineral acids accumulate in the body wall, coelomocytes, and ambulacral system, especially the polian vesicles.

Luminescence in ophiuroids was discovered some 150 years ago in *Amphipholis squamata* and its existence in several other species has since been proved. The available facts are summarized by Dahlgren (1916) and Harvey (1952). There is no good evidence of the occurrence of luminescence in any group of echinoderms other than ophiuroids. The following species are known to be luminescent: *Amphipholis squamata, Ophiopsila annulosa* and *aranea* (Mangold, 1907, 1908; Trojan, 1908, 1909a), *Amphiura filiformis* (Mangold, 1907), *Ophiacantha bidentata* (= *spinulosa*) and *Ophioscolex glacialis* (Sokolov, 1909), and *Amphiura kandai* (Kato, 1947). The luminescence is limited to the arms, emanating mostly from the spines and around the spine bases, and is absent from the disk. In *Amphiura filiformis*, only the spines luminesce; in *Amphipholis squamata* the light is localized on and around the spine bases; *Ophiacantha bidentata* luminesces on the spines and lateral arm shields; in *Ophiopsila aranea* the luminescence is limited to the oral arm shields and the arm tips; and in *Ophiopsila annulosa*, the oral and lateral arm shields and the ordinary and vibratile (flagellated) spines are luminous. Podia are not luminescent in any case. Only the living animal luminesces, and dried material or extracts cannot be made to luminesce. The luminescence is brilliant, of a yellow or yellowish-green color. It is evoked by mechanical, electrical, or chemical stimulation and spreads from a stimulated spot by way of the radial and ring nerves. Stimulation of the aboral wall of the disk is followed by luminescence of the arms. Isolated spines of species in which the spines are luminescent will luminesce on chemical stimulation. Acids, alkalis, alcohols, strong salt, and especially fresh or distilled water are effective in evoking luminescence. An animal placed in fresh water will continue to luminesce with decreasing intensity until it dies. Harvey (1926a), using *Amphipholis squamata*, found that this animal is luminescent in the light (some luminescent animals luminesce only after a considerable sojourn in the dark) and that it will luminesce only in the presence of oxygen (Harvey, 1926b). Histological studies of luminous areas have been made by Reichensperger (1908b, c), Trojan (1909a, b), and Sokolov (1909). The luminous areas contain large long-necked cells resembling gland cells that stain heavily with thionin and mucicarmine and usually differ from gland cells present in other body parts. The contents usually stain uniformly, but Sokolov pictured the cells as filled with parallel fibers. It is generally conceded that these gland-like cells are the source of the luminescence, but it has been impossible to show that they emit any kind of a luminous secretion or indeed any secretion at all.

   **23. Ecology: Geographic Distribution.**—The Ophiuroidea are found in all seas, at all latitudes, on all types of bottom, and at all depths from the intertidal zone to the abyssal region, down to 6000 m. Because of their small size and secluded habits they are not so conspicuous an element of marine faunas as are the other echinoderm classes and are more difficult to collect. The littoral ophiuroids are seldom seen exposed on the open bottom but lie hidden in or under dead coral masses, in the interstices of sponges, among gorgonians and other branching coelenterates, in available nooks and crevices, under stones, among seaweeds, or buried in the bottom sand or mud. For these reasons they are as yet incompletely known taxonomically, although a large number of reports, based on collecting and dredging expeditions, have been written about them.

It may first be pointed out that some littoral ophiuroids have a very wide distribution, notably *Amphipholis squamata* (Fig. 267), which is cosmopolitan, turning up in every littoral collection throughout the world, including the subarctic and subantarctic areas, and descending from the intertidal zone to 250 m. Specialists on ophiuroids have examined specimens from various parts of the world and pronounced them identical. It certainly is astonishing that this small creature has been able to spread everywhere and adapt itself to a wide range of conditions. Another widely distributed and extremely common ophiuroid is *Ophiactis savignyi* (Fig. 267), found everywhere in warmer littoral waters and hence circumtropical. Perhaps its mode of reproduction by fission is responsible for its success in populating the tropics. This species is six-armed and fissiparous when young, becoming five-armed and apparently ceasing asexual reproduction when mature. At the last fission the three-radiate product regenerates only two jaws and arms. This species is very commonly associated with sponges, and hundreds of juveniles may be found in the interstices of a large sponge.

As is the case with other echinoderm classes except possibly asteroids, the littoral ophiuroids center in the Indo–West Pacific region, being densest in the heart of this area, which includes the Malay Peninsula, the Philippines, and the numerous islands of Indonesia, and thinning out in all directions therefrom to the limits of the area, to the Red Sea and the eastern coast of Africa on the west, to Japan and the Hawaiian Islands on the east. Main reports on this vast area, apart from earlier ones, are those of Döderlein (1896) on Amboina and Thursday Island; Koehler (1898) on the collections of the *Investigator* in the Indian Ocean and (1905) on the *Siboga* collections in Indonesia; H. L. Clark (1915) on Ceylon and (1921) on the Torres Strait region; Koehler (1922a) on the collections of the *Albatross* in the Philippines and adjacent seas, (1927) on material from the Gilbert, Marshall, and Fiji Islands, and (1930) on material from the Malay Archipelago; H. L. Clark (1939) on the ophiuroids of the John Murray Expedition to the Arabian Sea and adjacent parts of the Indian Ocean; Tortonese (1936) and Ailsa Clark (1952) on the ophiuroids of the Red Sea; and A. H. Clark (1952) on material from the Marshall Islands. Some species are spread throughout the area, while others have a more limited distribution. Particularly characteristic of the Indo-Pacific are members of the families Ophiothrichidae, especially the genus *Ophiothrix*, Ophiocomidae, Ophiodermatidae, and Ophiolepididae. Of common widely distributed Ophiothrichidae may be mentioned *Ophiomaza cacaotica, Ophiothela danae,* and *Ophiothrix exigua, galatheae, hirsuta, longipeda, martensi, nereidina, pusilla, purpurea, propinqua, stelligera, striolata, triloba,* and *trilineata.* In the Ophiocomidae, widely distributed species include *Ophiocoma scolopendrina, erinaceus, pica,* and *brevipes, Ophiomastix annulosa, mixta,* and *lütkeni,* and *Ophiarthrum elegans.* Common Ophiodermatidae are *Ophiarachna incrassata, Pectinura yoldii, Ophiarachnella gorgonia, infernalis,* and *septemspinosa,* and *Ophiopezella spinosa.* In the Ophiolepididae may be mentioned *Ophiolepis cincta, Ophiura kinbergi,* and *Ophioplocus imbricatus;* in the Amphiuridae *Ophiocnida echinata* besides the ubiquitous *Amphiopholis squamata;* and in the Ophiomyxidae *Ophiomyxa brevispina* and *australis* and *Ophionereis porrecta* (Fig. 272). The horizontal range of some of these species is astonishing. *Ophiomaza cacaotica* ranges from Zanzibar on the African coast to New Caledonia; *Ophiothrix longipeda* from eastern Africa to the Society Islands and Japan; *Ophiocoma scolopendrina* from Africa to Japan; *Ophiarthrum elegans* from Mozambique and Zanzibar to Tahiti and the Ryukyu Islands, and the range of *Ophiarachna incrassata,* perhaps the largest of the Ophiurae, is similar; *Ophiarachnella gorgonia* from Natal and Zanzibar to Ceylon, Japan, Fiji, and Samoa; and *Ophioplocus imbricatus* from Zanzibar to the Gilbert and Ryukyu Islands. The curious genus *Ophiopteron* with arm spines webbed into fans is limited to the Indo-Pacific.

As indicated above, the fauna of the Philippine-Indonesian area tends to spread to the fringes of the great Indo–West Pacific region. The same common littoral ophiuroids are found in the Red and Arabian Seas. As regards the latter, H. L. Clark (1939) reported 102 species obtained by the John Murray Expedition, of which 71 were in the families Ophiacanthidae, Amphiuridae, and Ophiolepididae. Examination of the map shows that the northern coast of Australia lies on the fringe of the Indo-Pacific area, and in fact about 60 of the 223 known Australian species of ophiuroids (H. L. Clark, 1946) belong to the general Indo-Pacific fauna; the remainder, especially those of the southern and western coasts, are endemic. About half of the ophiuroids that have been collected on the Great Barrier Reef (H. L. Clark, 1932) are Indonesian and are included among the common species named above. Principal works on Australian ophiuroids are those of H. L. Clark (1928, 1938, 1946). Southern Japan, too, that is, the main island of Honshu, is to be regarded as continuous with the Philippine-Indonesian region by way of the Ryukyu Islands. Japanese ophiuroids were monographed by Matsumoto in 1917; he listed 232 species, of which 65 also occur in the Indo-Pacific area and 140 are endemic to Japan; the remainder participate in the boreal and arctic fauna. The Hawaiian Islands constitute the most easterly outpost of the Indo-Pacific region. Their ophiuroids have been reported by H. L. Clark (1925), Ely (1942), and A. H. Clark (1949). The latter states that the Hawaiian fauna is an attenuated Indo-Pacific fauna with some local modification into endemic species. The littoral species are nearly all common Indo-Pacific ophiuroids, included in the foregoing list.

Proceeding now to the tropical eastern Pacific or Panamic region, one finds a number of reports on the ophiuroid fauna here: Lütken and Mortensen (1899), H. L. Clark (1902a, 1910, 1913, 1917, 1940), McClendon (1909), Ziesenhenne (1937, 1940), Nielsen (1932), Boone (1928, 1933), A. H. Clark (1939), and Ricketts (1941). Most of these reports are concerned primarily with material dredged in deeper waters. In addition to the ubiquitous *Amphipholis squamata* and *Ophiactis savignyi*, other littoral species in common with Indo-Pacific localities occur in the Panamic region. Thus *Amphiura arcystata* also occurs at Japan; *Ophiactis kröyeri* from the coasts of Chile and Peru is also found at Hawaii; *Opiocomella clippertoni* from Clipperton Island off Mexico has been taken at Hawaii, Wake Island, Laysan, and the Palmyra Islands; *Ophioderma panamense*, one of the most common littoral Panamic ophiuroids, is also recorded from the Sandwich Islands; and the extremely common Indo-Pacific species, *Ophiocoma scolopendrina*, reaches the Panamic region. Ophiuroids thus appear to have been more successful than other echinoderm groups in migrating from the Indo-Pacific to the western shores of tropical America. Among the most common littoral ophiuroids of the Panamic region may be mentioned *Ophiothrix spiculata*, *Ophiocoma aethiops* and *alexandri*, *Ophioderma panamense* and *variegatum*, *Ophiomyxa panamensis*, *Ophionereis annulata*, *Ophiocten pacificum*, *Ophiocnida hispida*, *Ophiura lütkeni*, and *Ophiactis arenosa* and *simplex*.

The western tropical Atlantic constitutes a faunal region that includes the Bermudas, the West Indies, and the Caribbean, and extends northward along the southeastern coast of the United States to the Carolinas and southward along the coast of Brazil. The same fauna is doubtless spread into much of the Gulf of Mexico, but this body of water is not included in the available reports. The faunal area in question, which may be referred to in general as the West Indian region, is rich in littoral ophiuroids, numerous as to both individuals and species that swarm over the coral reefs. Main reports on the ophiuroids of the West Indian region are those of Lyman (1883), Verrill (1899b), Koehler (1913), H. L. Clark (1902b, 1919, 1933, 1941), and Engel (1939). Much of these reports concern the species of deeper water, obtained by dredging or by dragging a tangle over the bottom, to catch the species that cling to sponges and coelenterates. The littoral ophiuroids have been especially considered by H. L. Clark, who divides them into three categories: circumtropical species comprising the two familiar forms, *Amphipholis squamata* and *Ophiactis savignyi*, of which the latter is said to swarm in great numbers wherever conditions are suitable; tropical Atlantic species spread throughout the whole West Indian area; and species, about a dozen in number, strictly limited to the islands of the West Indies. Of the second group the most common species are *Ophiothrix angulata* and *Ophionereis reticulata* (Fig. 271). Other widely spread species include *Ophiomyxa flaccida*, *Amphiodia repens*, *Ophiothrix suensonii* and *örstedii*, *Ophiocnida scabriuscula*, *Ophiostigma isocanthum*, *Ophiocoma echinata*, *pumila*, and *riisei*, *Ophiopsila riisei*, *Ophioderma appressum*, *brevicauda*, *brevispina*, and *cinereum*, *Ophiolepis elegans*, and *Ophiozona impressa*. The prevalence of the families Ophiothrichidae, Ophiocomidae, and Ophiodermatidae may be noted. At Bermuda (H. L. Clark, 1922, 1942) *Ophionereis reticulata* is again the most obvious ophiuroid, found easily under stones in the intertidal zone; other littoral brittle stars of Bermuda fall into the foregoing list.

The eastern tropical Atlantic which comprises the western coast of Africa from the Cape Verde Islands to Angola has been singularly omitted from exploratory expeditions but is in fact rather poor faunistically. Chief accounts of the ophiuroids are those of Döderlein (1910) and Koehler (1914). Of main interest is the occurrence of several species in common with the West Indian region, namely, *Ophiocoma pumila*, *Ophioderma appressum*, and *Ophiolepis paucispina*.

From the tropical areas there is a northward spread along the continental coasts to points varying with the ability of tropical species to endure cooler water temperatures. On the Pacific Coast of North America some of the most common Panamic species, as *Ophiothrix spiculata*, *Ophionereis annulata*, *Ophioderma panamense*, and *Ophiactis arenosa*, extend northward along the coast of California. Typical shallow-water ophiuroids of the Pacific Coast of the United States (H. L. Clark, 1901, 1911; McClendon, 1909; May, 1924; Berkeley, 1927, the MacGinities, 1949; Ricketts and Calvin, 1939, 1953) are *Amphiodia barbarae*, *occidentalis*, *urtica*, *Amphipholis pugetana*, *Ophiopteris papillosa*, and *Ophioplocus esmarki*. In slightly deeper water, not above 10 m., *Ophiura lütkeni* and *sarsi* are excessively abundant, especially the latter. H. L. Clark (1911) in his valuable study of the ophiuroids of the North Pacific, covering an area north of a line extending from central California to the southern end of Japan, had nearly 21,000 specimens of *Ophiura sarsi* and 658 of *O. lütkeni*. Over 4000 specimens were taken of the circumboreal daisy serpent star *Ophiopholis aculeata* and its variants. This species ranges southward on the Pacific Coast as far as Monterey Bay, California, and lives from rock pools to a depth of 2000 m.

On the Atlantic Coast of North America, West Indian species may range to the Carolinas, but north of this the littoral ophiuroid fauna is poor, compounded of the cosmopolitan *Amphipholis squamata*, the West Indian species *Ophioderma brevispina*, ascending as far as Massachusetts, and the circumboreal forms *Ophiura robusta* and *Ophiopholis aculeata*, descending from the north as far as Massachusetts or New Jersey (H. L. Clark, 1904; Coe, 1912). Two long-armed amphiurids, *Amphioplus abditus* and *macilentus*, are found locally on the New England coast buried in mud beyond the lower tide limit.

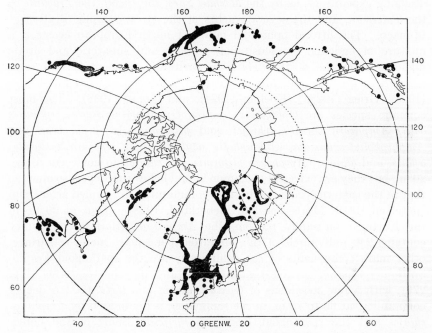

Fig. 275.—Map showing circumboreal distribution of *Ophiopholis aculeata* (*after Hofsten,* 1915).

It has been noticed in the accounts of the geographical distribution of other echinoderm classes that a more or less uniform echinoderm fauna extends from Iceland and the northern limit of Norway along north European coasts, around the British Isles, down the western coast of Europe, into the Mediterranean, and along the western coast of Africa as far as the Cape Verde Islands. The continuous coast line here offers no barrier to the spread of littoral marine fauna. Ekman (1953) attributes the uniformity of the marine fauna over this extended littoral area to the circumstances that the north European coast is warmer than would be expected for its latitude because of the Gulf Stream and its various branches, whereas the western coast of Africa is colder than anticipated for a subtropical area because of the upwelling here of cold water from the depths of the Atlantic. The littoral region in question is roughly divisible into the boreal, to the western entrance of the English Channel, the lusitanian from here to the straits of Gibraltar, and the mauretanian to the Cape Verde Islands. This whole area of the eastern North Atlantic is probably the best investigated faunistically of any marine region in the world, with the possible exception of the antarctic. Its littoral fauna is well known through the efforts of European zoologists and its deeper waters have been repeatedly the object of intensive dredging expeditions, as by the *Michael Sars*, the *Ingolf*, the *Travailleur*, the *Talisman*, and the several yachts of the Oceanographic Station at Monaco. The littoral ophiuroid fauna of north European coasts is a mixture of endemic boreolusitanian species and subarctic and arctic invaders from the north. The boreolusitanian element is well summarized in the works of Mortensen (1927), Mortensen and Lieberkind (1928), Grieg (1928a), Koehler (1924), and Nobre (1938). The most common species are *Ophiothrix fragilis, Ophiocomina nigra, Ophiactis balli, Amphiura borealis, chiajei,* and *filiformis, Acrocnida brachiata, Amphipholis squamata, Ophiopholis aculeata,* and *Ophiura texturata, affinis,* and *albida. Amphiura filiformis* and *chiajei* do not occur above 20 m., but they are extremely common at and below this depth, so much so that in the eastern North Sea bottom communities are named after them (Petersen, 1918; Mortensen and Lieberkind, 1928). Thus at 20 m. in the Kattegat on sandy bottom, the *Amphiura filiformis* community contains 240 individuals of this ophiuroid per square meter of surface; other main components of the community are the spatangoid *Echinocardium cordatum*, bivalves, gasteropods, and polychaete worms (Fig. 276), with a few specimens of *Ophiura albida* and *texturata*. A deeper community, at 60 to 75 m. in the same area, is dominated by *Amphiura chiajei* and the spatangoid *Brissopsis lyrifera*. Some of the boreolusitanian species extend into the Mediterranean, where there are also endemic ophiuroids seldom or not found elsewhere, as *Ophiomyxa pentagona, Ophiactis virens, Amphiura mediterranea,* and *Ophiothrix quinquemaculata* (but only below 40 m.). Many of the more common boreolusitanian species continue throughout the mauretanian coast, such as *Ophiothrix fragilis* and *Amphiura filiformis*, but there are also endemic littoral species that do not extend northward beyond Gibraltar or Spain, as *Ophioderma longicauda* and *Ophiacantha setosa*. The West African coast here has been extensively dredged, but little work seems to have been done on the shallow-water echinoderms.

The boreal fauna is continuous with the arctic fauna on both the Atlantic and Pacific sides and is not delimitable from the latter. The most common and typical littoral arctic ophiuroids (Grieg, 1900; Döderlein, 1900; von Hofsten, 1915; Mortensen, 1933c) are *Ophioscolex glacialis,*

*Ophiacantha bidentata, Ophiopholis aculeata, Amphiura sundevalli, Amphipholis torelli, Ophiura sarsi* and *robusta, Ophiocten sericeum, Stegophiura nodosa* and *stuwitzii, Ophiopleura borealis,* and *Gorgonocephalus arcticus* (= *agassizi*) and *eucnemis.* Several of these descend along the Norwegian coast (Grieg, 1928a) to become prominent members of the European boreal fauna, as *Ophioscolex glacialis, Ophiacantha bidentata, Ophiopholis aculeata, Ophiura sarsi* and *robusta,* and *Ophiocten sericeum.* All of these are found throughout the whole of the investigated arctic areas of the Atlantic and some are also found on the Pacific side, that is, they are circumpolar. Thus the list of circumpolar littoral ophiuroids comprises *Ophiacantha bidentata, Ophiopholis aculeata, Amphiura sundevalli, Ophiura sarsi* and *robusta, Ophiocten sericeum,* and *Stegophiura nodosa* and *stuwitzii.* By way of the Bering Strait and Bering Sea these species may descend from the Arctic Ocean along the Pacific Coast of North America, and by way of the shores of Greenland and the waters of Baffin Bay and Davis Strait they reach Newfoundland, Nova Scotia, and the New England coast. Thus *Ophiura sarsi,* of which it may be recalled H. L. Clark (1911) had nearly 21,000 specimens from the North Pacific, reaches Cape Cod on the Atlantic side and northern California on the Pacific side. *Ophiopholis aculeata* is common around Spitsbergen, the Barents Sea, the coast of Norway, the North Sea, and around Iceland, from which it jumps to the southern part of Greenland and down the North American coast to Long Island Sound; on the Pacific side it is abundant around Japan and in the Bering Sea and reaches to California (Fig. 275).

The tropical littoral echinoderm fauna thins out and is replaced by other species toward the higher latitudes of the Southern Hemisphere. This is particularly noticeable in the Indo-Pacific region. On Australian coasts, the echinoderm fauna is most like that of Indonesia in the Torres Strait (Cape York) region and becomes more and more endemic to Australia the farther one goes in either direction from this center until no Indo-Pacific species remain on the southwestern coasts of the continent (H. L. Clark, 1946). Similarly the littoral ophiuroids of New Zealand and adjacent islands, comprising over 40 species, are nearly all endemic (New Zealand ophiuroids by Farquhar, 1895, 1897, 1898, Mortensen, 1924, Fell, 1949). Of the 41 littoral ophiuroids listed by Mortensen for New Zealand, 17 belong to the Amphiuridae, whereas there is a total absence of species of *Ophiura.* The nonendemic species include three in common with Australia, *Ophiocreas constrictum, Ophiomyxa brevirima,* and *Amphiocnida pilosa;* one widely spread Indo-Pacific species, *Ophiothrix aristulata;* and three subantarctic ophiuroids, *Amphiura eugeniae* and *magellanica* and *Gorgonocephalus chilensis.* A variant of an abyssal Panamic serpent star, *Ophiactis profundi,* inhabits the littoral zone at

New Zealand. The ophiuroids of the subantarctic islands of New Zealand (Snares, Bounty Islands, Antipodes, and Campbell and Auckland Islands) are identical with those of New Zealand (Mortensen, 1924; Fell, 1953b) with six endemic species of nine found there.

On the African coast, Zanzibar, Madagascar, and to a large extent Mozambique share in the Indo-Pacific fauna, but south of Mozambique

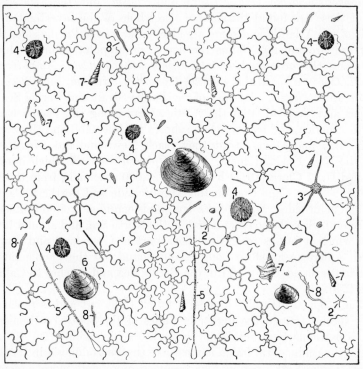

FIG. 276.—Scheme of the *Amphiura filiformis* community at a depth of 20 m. in the Kattegat (*after Petersen*, 1918). The scheme represents the number and kind of animals in ¼ sq. m. of the sea bottom. 1, *Amphiura filiformis;* 2, *Ophiura albida;* 3, *Ophiura texturata;* 4, *Echinocardium cordatum;* 5, pennatulid *Virgularia mirabilis;* 6, bivalves; 7, gastropods; 8, polychaete worms.

around the Cape of Good Hope is found an endemic littoral echinoderm fauna with scarcely any Indo-Pacific or Australian elements. The echinoderms of South Africa proper, that is, the Cape of Good Hope region, were first made known by the collections of the *Challenger*, which took a total of 41 echinoderm species in that area. The most recent and informative reports on South African ophiuroids are those of H. L. Clark (1923b) and Mortensen (1933a). The latter lists a total of 82 South African ophiuroids (from all depths), of which 56 are known nowhere else in the world. Several common Indo-Pacific littoral ophiuroids extend as far as Natal, but only two (*Ophionereis dubia* and *porrecta*) reach the Cape proper. *Ophiothrix aristulata*, from below 70 m., is found in common with the Malay Archipelago and Australia. Some subantarctic species also form a component of the South African fauna.

As previously indicated, the antarctic and subantarctic, especially those of South America, have been the object of numerous collecting and dredging expeditions, from the days of the *Challenger* onward. The ophiuroid takings of these expeditions have been reported by Ludwig (1905) for the Swedish Magellanic Expedition; Koehler (1901) for the Belgian, (1906) for the first French, (1908) for the Scottish, (1911a) for the British, (1912) for the second French, (1922b) for the Australian, and (1923) for the Swedish Antarctic Expeditions; Bell (1908) for the National Antarctic and (1917) for the British Antarctic *Terra Nova* Expeditions[1]; G. A. Smith (1923) on the collections of the *Quest;* Hertz (1927a) for the German South Polar Expedition on the *Gauss;* Grieg (1929a, b) for the Norwegian Antarctic Expedition; Mortensen (1925b) for a collection from the Ross Sea and (1936) in a *Discovery* report; and A. H. Clark (1951) from collections by the United States Navy. As pointed out by Mortensen, a comprehensive zoogeographical discussion of the antarctic and subantartic is impossible because of a lack of explorations of the higher southern latitudes of the Indian and Pacific Oceans. To Ekman's (1925) discussion reported above (page 234) may be added some remarks by Koehler (1912) and Hertz (1927b). Koehler places the boundary between the antarctic and subantarctic at a circle varying between 60 and 65° south latitude and the northern boundary of the subantarctic at 42 to 50°. South of the line of division between the subantarctic and the antarctic the surface temperature of the sea is constantly below freezing (−1°C.). The subantarctic falls into the Magellanic region, including the Falkland and South Georgia Islands, and the Kerguelen area, which in addition to the island of Kerguelen may be taken to include several other isolated islands at the same latitude, the Crozets, Heard, Marion, and Prince Edward Islands.

Among the very common littoral ophiuroids of the Magellanic region are *Ophiocten amitinum*, *Ophiomyxa vivipara*, *Ophiacantha vivipara*, and *Ophiactis asperula*. *Ophiocten amitinum*, belonging more nearly to the archibenthal, was reported by Mortensen (1936) as occurring around the Falkland Islands by the hundreds of thousands, perhaps millions. Other species repeatedly taken include *Amphiodia affinis*, *Ophionotus hexactis*, *Ophiurolepis martensi* (= *resistens*), *Ophiacantha disjuncta*, *Amphiura eugeniae*, *lymani*, *magellanica*, and *patagonica*, *Ophiolebella*

---

[1] Little reference has been made in these pages to the work of Bell and of A. E. Verrill, as their identifications are not reliable and their descriptions are wanting in the detail necessary in taxonomic work.

*biscutifera*, and the euryalous species *Astrotoma agassizi*, *Astrochlamys bruneus*, and *Gorgonocephalus chilensis*. From Kerguelen, Koehler (1917) reported 17 littoral ophiuroids, of which seven are endemic and the others include common Magellanic species in the foregoing list. As regards the antarctic proper, most of the collecting has been done in the west antarctic, including the Palmer Archipelago, South Shetlands, South Orkneys, etc. Many of the littoral ophiuroids here have spread into the area from the Magellanic region, but a number of characteristic species occur, such as *Ophiacantha antarctica*, *Amphiura algida*, *belgicae*, and *joubini*, *Ophionotus victoriae*, *Ophiurolepis gelida*, *Ophiosteira senouqui*, *Ophiura rouchi*, and *Ophiocten megaloplax*. Such collecting as has been done in the east antarctic (Ross Sea, South Victoria Land) has yielded much the same species as found in the South American areas; hence a number of species appear to be circumantarctic, as *Ophiacantha disjuncta*, *Amphiura joubini*, *Ophiocten megaloplax*, *Ophiurolepis gelida*, and *Astrotoma agassizi*. In general there is to be noticed a prevalence in these higher southern latitudes of the families Ophiolepididae, Amphiuridae, Amphilepididae, and Ophiacanthidae. A number of genera, hence unfamiliar, are limited to these high southern latitudes, as *Ophiocamax* and *Ophiosparte* among the Ophiacanthidae, and *Ophioceres*, *Ophioperla*, *Ophioplinthus*, and *Ophiolebella* among the Ophiolepididae.

There are no ophiuroids in common between the southern and northern polar regions except, of course, the cosmopolitan *Amphipholis squamata*. As with other eleutherozoan classes, the southern polar waters are much richer in ophiuroids than the northern. A. H. Clark (1951) states that there are about 50 ophiuroid species in the high antarctic as against about a dozen in the high arctic. The prevalence of brooding species among antarctic and subantarctic ophiuroids was noted above (page 627).

The foregoing remarks apply primarily to the littoral species, many of which, however, occur over a wide bathymetrical range, extending from the littoral into the abyssal. There is, further, a large ophiuroid fauna confined to archibenthal and abyssal depths that has been revealed by the numerous dredging expeditions already mentioned. Because of the more uniform conditions prevailing in deeper waters, archibenthal and abyssal species often have a wide distribution, and some are cosmopolitan or practically so, with the omission of high arctic and antarctic regions. Especially three ophiuroids are notable for their extensive distribution in deeper waters: *Ophiomusium lymani*, 700 to 4000 m., "probably the most common and widely distributed of deep water ophiurans" (H. L. Clark, 1941); *Ophiura irrorata*, 600 to 4300 m., rather variable and appearing in the literature under several different specific names; and the euryalous *Asteronyx loveni*, 100 to 1800 m., sometimes ascending into quite shallow water. Some other widely distributed species, recorded from the Atlantic, Pacific, and Indian Oceans are *Ophiernus adspersus*, 290 to 3600 m.; *Ophiocten hastatum* (includes *pacificum*); 900 to 1900 m.; *Amphiophiura sculptilis*, to 3000 m.; and *Ophiura flagellata*, 96 to 2330 m. The family Ophiacanthidae is more or less limited to deeper waters, and a number of its genera, as *Ophioplinthaca*, *Ophiothamnus*, *Ophiomedea*, *Ophiotrema*, *Ophiolebes*, are never seen in littoral collecting. The whole group Euryalae is also characteristic of archibenthal and abyssal waters, although not infrequently ascending into the littoral zone, especially in colder areas.

The eastern North Atlantic from Spitsbergen and Norway to the Cape Verde Islands is the best-dredged region in the world; main reports on the ophiuroids here are those of Koehler (1906, 1909), Grieg (1921), and Mortensen (1927, 1933c), and the last in his report on the ophiuroids of the *Ingolf* expedition has given a general account of this group in the North Atlantic. The most common archibenthal and abyssal ophiuroids of the eastern North Atlantic are *Ophiomitrella clavigera* and *Ophiacantha crassidens*, *aristata*, *abyssicola*, and *setosa* in the Ophiacanthidae; *Ophiactis abyssicola* (= *corallicola*) in the Ophiactidae; *Amphiura grandis*, *grandisquama* (= *longispina*), and *bellis* and *Amphiophiura convexa*, *abdita*, and *bullata* (very abyssal, 4800 to 5000 m.) in the Amphiuridae; and *Ophiura ljungmanni* and *carnea* and *Ophiopleura aurantiaca* in the Ophiolepididae. Some of these species extend to the North American side of the North Atlantic, which, however, has not been extensively dredged; Verrill (1880, 1882, 1885), dredging off the New England coast to 1000 m., found many of the same species as reported from dredgings of the eastern Atlantic. To the north the deep-water Atlantic fauna is continuous with that of the arctic, as most of the littoral arctic ophiuroids mentioned above (page 674) descend into the archibenthal and abyssal zones; thus *Ophiocten sericeum* and *Ophiacantha bidentata* are found to nearly 5000 m. (Grieg, 1900). According to Mortensen (1933c), the arctic abyssal from Greenland to Norway has a poor ophiuroid fauna with only two species limited to this zone, *Ophiopleura borealis* and *Ophiopyren striatum*. A few of the North Atlantic ophiuroids extend to the West Indies where, however, there are a number of characteristic ophiuroids of deeper water, revealed by the dredgings of the *Blake* (Lyman, 1883), the *Challenger* (Lyman, 1882), and the *Atlantis* (H. L. Clark, 1941). Hardly any except the cosmopolitan species mentioned occur in common between the North and South Atlantic. Several species are also found in the Indo-Pacific, as *Ophiomusium planum* to 5000 m., *Ophiacantha valenciennesi* to 1900 m., and *Ophiura clemens* to 2000 m. The greatest depth at which ophiuroids have been taken occurs in the eastern Atlantic near the Cape Verde Islands where the Monaco yacht *Princesse Alice* (Koehler, 1909) made one haul at 6035 m., bringing up three echinoderms, the porcellansterid star *Albatrossaster richardi* (page 403), and two serpent stars, *Amphiophiura abdita* and *Ophiacantha opercularis*. The Euryalae are well represented in the deeper waters of the North Atlantic. Several species of *Asteroschema* occur in the West Indies. *Astrodia tenuispina*, associated with the pennatulid *Scleroptilum*, has been found off New England and in the West Indies at depths of 500 to 4000 m. *Astrochele lymani* has a similar distribution, at 480 to 2900 m., and is usually found clinging to the gorgonian *Acanella arbuscula*. *Gorgonocephalus arcticum*, to 1500 m., is common in boreal and arctic areas, *G. eucnemis*, to 1850 m., is an arctic form extending into the boreal, and *G. caput-medusae*, 150 to 1200 m., is also boreal.

The ophiuroid fauna of the North Pacific was extensively reported by H. L. Clark (1911). Here, too, the fauna of deeper waters consists partly of hardy species able to endure a wide range of environmental conditions and descending from the littoral of arctic and North American and Asiatic shores; and partly of species requiring colder temperatures and hence limited to archibenthal and abyssal waters. The former species are termed *oceanic* by Clark, who lists 18 species in this category, nearly all of which range from the littoral well into the abyssal and are spread throughout the whole of the North Pacific. This list includes the cosmopolitan species mentioned above, namely, *Ophiomusium lymani*, *Ophiura flagellata* and *irrorata*, *Ophiernus adspersus*, *Asteronyx loveni*, the circumboreal species *Ophiura sarsi* and *Ophiopholis aculeata*, and species limited to the North Pacific, as *Ophiura leptoctenia* (2000 specimens), *Ophiocten pacificum*, *Ophiomusium jolliense*, *Amphiodia euryaspis*, and *Ophiacantha normani* (4000 specimens). Another common species of deeper North Pacific waters, *Ophiacantha* bairdi, also occurs in the North Atlantic, from its eastern part throughout the West Indian area. Especially notable is the great number of species of the genera *Ophiura* (30) and *Ophiacantha* (32), although some of these have no doubt since been transferred to related genera. Clark lists 23 species as limited to the abyssal, including 6 species of *Ophiura* and 8 of *Ophiacantha*. The typical gorgonocephalid of the North Pacific, *G. caryi*, of which 300 specimens were taken, ranging from California, Oregon, and Washington to Japan and the Bering Sea, is probably identical with *G. eucnemis*, which is thus a circumarctic and circumboreal species. The author frequently saw this basket star alive in Puget Sound where it often comes up in dredges lowered to 20 or 30 m.; it ranges to 1800 m.

The North Pacific is of course continuous to the southeast with the Panamic region and to the south with the tropical West Pacific, and it is not surprising to find the same ophiuroids spread in the deeper waters of these areas. Dredgings of the Panamic region are reported mainly by Lütken and Mortensen (1899) and H. L. Clark (1910, 1917). The ophiuroids of deeper water here comprise a mixture of cosmopolitan species, as *Ophiura irrorata* and *flagellata* and *Ophiomusium lymani;* species in common with the North Pacific, as *Ophiocten pacificum* and *Ophiomusium jolliense;* species spread from the Panamic region into the Indo-Pacific, as *Ophiacantha valenciennesi* and *Amphiura diomedeae*, and endemic Panamic deep-water species of which *Ophiomusium glabrum* is the most characteristic member. Other common ophiuroids of deeper waters of the Panamic area are *Ophiacantha cosmica, sentosa*, and *inconspicua, Ophiura tumulosa* and *plana, Ophiozona alba, Amphiura serpentina*, and *Ophionereis polyporus* and *seminudus.* The absence of *Asteronyx loveni* from the Panamic region is notable.

Besides the Panamic species just mentioned, all of the cosmopolitan ophiuroids of deeper waters also extend throughout the deeper waters of the Indo–West Pacific area, and these waters also have some species in common with similar depths in the eastern North Atlantic, especially *Ophiothrix aristulata, Homalophiura inornata*, and *Ophiomusium validum.* The Indo–West Pacific has also been dredged a number of times, beginning with the *Challenger*, and the findings have been reported mainly by Koehler (1899, 1904, 1922a, 1930). Common species apparently limited to the deeper waters of the Indo–West Pacific include *Ophiothrix capillaris* and *koreana* in the Ophiothrichidae; *Ophiocamax rugosa, Ophioplinthaca globata* and *rudis*, and *Ophiotreta gratiosa* and *matura* in the Ophiacanthidae; *Ophiomusium elegans, facundum, scalare*, and *lunare, Ophiozonella molesta, Amphiophiura sordida* and *insolita, Stegophiura solida*, and *Ophioceramis declinans* in the Ophiolepididae; and *Bathypectinura conspicua* in the Ophiodermatidae. A large number of members of the Euryalae have been collected in the Indo-Pacific region (general account of the Euryalae known to that date in Döderlein, 1927; also Mortensen, 1933b); but none of these seem very common or widespread except the ubiquitous *Asteronyx loveni.* Döderlein lists a total of 38 euryalous genera and over 130 species, of which about half are limited to the Indo–West Pacific area, including Japan but excluding Australia. They live at depths ranging from shallow water into the abyssal, but most are found at archibenthal levels.

The antarctic and subantarctic have been repeatedly dredged by a succession of expeditions already enumerated (page 677), some of which collected to a depth of 5000 m. Hertz (1927b) gave a useful summary of the accumulated knowledge to that date of the ophiuroids of the high antarctic or antarctic proper, the area south of 60° latitude; and subsequent reports by Grieg (1929a, b) and Mortensen (1936) have not added much in this regard. Adding two new species described by Mortensen, one finds a total of 91 ophiuroids that have been taken in the antarctic (including littoral species) of which 70 are limited to the antarctic and the remainder also occur elsewhere, chiefly in the subantarctic. Of these endemic species 22 are limited so far as known to the west antarctic, 28 have been taken only in the east antarctic, and 5 are known only from South Victoria Land. Around 50 of the endemic species have been collected only by one of the many expeditions, hence must be considered as not very common. Twenty-seven species are listed by Hertz as exclusively abyssal, and of these *Ophiacantha frigida* is the most common. Common abyssal species that may also extend into the archibenthal and the subantarctic are *Ophiurolepis gelida, Ophiacantha disjuncta, Ophioconis antarctica, Ophiosteira senouqui, Ophiura rouchi, Ophioceres incipiens,* and *Amphiura belgicae.* The first three of these are circumantarctic while the others appear lacking from South Victoria Land. Some of the most common and characteristic ophiuroids of the higher southern latitudes have notably wide horizontal and bathymetric ranges. *Ophiocten amitinum* is found throughout the whole of the subantarctic, also in the antarctic, ranging from the littoral zone to 3600 m. *Ophiernus vallincola,* known from the antarctic abyssal to 3600 m., is also known at the Azores. *Ophiacantha cosmica* is an abyssal species known not only from the antarctic and subantarctic abyssal but also in the Indo-Pacific, the Cape of Good Hope, and the North Pacific by way of the coasts of Chile. Some abyssal subantarctic ophiuroids also occur in the eastern North Atlantic, notably *Ophiura minuta,* to 4020 m., *Ophiura bullata,* to 5000 m., and *Ophiocten pallidum,* to 4700 m. Koehler (1912) surmises that North Atlantic abyssal forms may reach the subantarctic by way of the African coast and the Crozet Islands.

From this survey of geographic distribution one gains the impression that ophiuroids have been more successful than the other existing echinoderm classes in spreading over the sea bottom. The only littoral cosmopolitan echinoderm is an ophiuroid (*Amphipholis squamata*), and several ophiuroids of deeper waters are cosmopolitan or nearly so. Seemingly small size, greater agility, and secluded habits have given the ophiuroids an advantage over other types of existing echinoderms.

**24. Ecology: Biological Relations.**—The parasites and associates of ophiuroids include the usual assortment of protozoans, polychaetes, gasteropods, and crustaceans, and scattered representatives of other groups. In addition, *Ophiura texturata* and *albida,* especially the former, are parasitized by a unicellular green alga, *Coccomyxa ophiurae,* that inhabits the mesenchyme of the skeletal meshes, forming green spots externally obvious (Mortensen and Rosenvinge, 1910). These spots gradually increase in size and, by destroying the skeleton, the algae eventually kill the ophiuroid. The peritrich ciliate *Rhabdostyla amphiurae,* under several names, has been noticed by several authors on the surface of *Amphipholis squamata* on European coasts (Cuénot, 1891c).

Another peritrich, *Zoothamnium vermicola*, was recorded by Precht (1935) on the buccal podia of *Ophiura albida* in the Bay of Kiel. *Lichnophora auerbachii* and *Trichodina ophiothricis* occur on *Ophiothrix fragilis* (Fabre-Domergue, 1888). *Amphipholis squamata* achieved fame as the host of the parasitic phase of the orthonectid *Rhopalura ophiocomae* (I, page 242). The ciliated larvae penetrate the serpent star by way of the bursal slits and, passing into the tissues, there develop into plasmodia that destroy the host's gonads (Caullery and Lavallée, 1912). The sexual individuals that develop in the plasmodia escape through the bursal slits and lead a brief free existence. No members of the rhabdocoel family Umagillidae, well-known entocommensals of echinoderms, have been found in ophiuroids. A polyclad, *Euplana takewakii*, inhabits the bursae of *Ophioplocus japonicus*, Japan, and seems to feed on the attached gonads, also laying its egg mass in the bursa (Kato, 1935). *Ophiura sarsi* is host to the metacercarial stage of a fish trematode, *Fellodistomum fellis;* the cercariae emerging from the first intermediate host (clam) penetrate into the ophiuroid and encyst on the outer surface of the stomach pouches (Chubrik, 1952). Mortensen (1936) mentions having found a nematode in the male gonads of *Amphiura microplax*, subantarctic. The same author (1924) recorded the presence of a number of individuals of a loxosomatid entoproct on the oral surface of *Amphiocnieda pilosa* both at New Zealand and Australia.

Because of their small size and lively habits, ophiuroids may not be expected to serve as readily as other echinoderms as hosts of polychaetous annelids. The polynoid annelid *Harmothoe lunulata* lives in association with an assortment of animals, including other polychaetes, sipunculoids, and various echinoderms. It was found at Jamaica by Millott (1953) clinging to *Ophionereis reticulata* and on the English coast by Davenport (1953) in association with *Acrocnida brachiata*, a sand-burrowing amphiurid. Davenport found that specimens of the polynoid removed from the serpent star would react positively to the cucumber *Leptosynapta inhaerens*, but those removed from the cucumber or other hosts were not attracted to the serpent star. A little bivalve, *Monacuta bidentata*, may participate in the *Harmothoe-Acrocnida* association. On the coast of France, the protectively colored polynoid *Scalisetosus pellucidus* occurs on *Ophiothrix fragilis* (Cuénot, 1912). An arm swelling with a small aperture observed on two specimens of *Ophiura tumulosa*, abyssal in the Panamic region, was found to contain a small polychaete of uncertain systematic position, to which was given the name *Ophiuricola cynips* (Ludwig, 1905). Myzostomes (page 115) were first found on ophiuroids by H. L. Clark (1902), who reported them on two dredged Euryalae, *Ophiocreas* and *Asteroceras pergamena*, Japan. They were next seen on *Ophiacantha vivipara*, antarctic, by Koehler (1907). The genus *Ophi-*

*acantha* in cold waters appears especially subject to myzostomes, which have been found on *O. anomala* (Mortensen, 1933c) and *O. rosea* (Mortensen, 1936), mostly around the bursal slits and in the bursae. No records were found of their occurrence on other ophiurous genera, but the genus *Protomyzostoma* parasitizes the interior of species of *Gorgonocephalus* in arctic and boreal waters (Fedotov, 1916; Mortensen, 1927); in *Gorgon. eucnemis* the parasite devours the gonads and thus sterilizes the host.

There are few records of the parasitization of ophiuroids by parasitic snails. The presence of snails assigned to *Stilifer* was recorded by Döderlein (1896) on *Ophiomyxa brevispina* and by Matsumoto (1917) on *Ophiothrix macrobrachia*. Schepman and Nierstrasz (1909), reporting on the parasitic snails collected by the *Siboga* in Indonesia, described three species of *Mucronalia* on species of *Ophiothrix* and on the euryalous form *Astrochalcis tuberculosus*. *Mucronalia* lives on the external surface of its victim and thrusts its long proboscis into the latter's tissues. Mortensen (1933a) saw a specimen of *Eulima* on *Amphilycus androphorus* and (1936) found a very degenerated snail without shell living inside the antarctic ophiuroid *Amphiura belgicae;* the parasite, connected to the exterior by a small aperture, was filled with shelled baby snails.

Ophiuroids are much subject to infestation by ecto- and endoparasitic copepods. Those living externally on ophiuroids generally retain a typical copepod appearance although mostly rather broad and plump. The best known of the ectoparasitic forms is *Cancerilla tubulata*, belonging to the Asterocheridae, found attached on the oral surface of *Amphipholis squamata* in European waters (Giard, 1887; Canu, 1892; Giesbrecht, 1899; Cuénot, 1912; Mercier, 1922); as shown in Fig. 277*A*, the head of the parasite is always directed toward the ophiuroid's mouth. It is interesting to note that a different species of *Cancerilla* (*C. neozelanica*) parasitizes *A. squamata* off New Zealand and adjacent Islands (Stephensen, 1927), and still a third species (*C. durbanensis*) occurs on the same ophiuroid at the Cape of Good Hope (Stephensen, 1933). Other known species are *Cancerilla mapla* on *Ophiacantha vivipara* and *C. alata* (Fig. 277*B*) on *O. disjuncta*, both from the antarctic (Heegaard, 1951). A very closely related form, *Cancerillopsis nanaimensis*, is found on *Amphiodia urtica* on the Pacific Coast of North America (Nielsen, 1932; Stephensen, 1933). Endoparasitic copepods are usually greatly altered, appearing as sacs with projecting appendages. The first one to be described for ophiuroids (Fewkes, 1889; Hérouard, 1906), called *Philichthys amphiurae*, also parasitizes *A. squamata*, in which the swollen female often accompanied by one to four dwarf males and a mass of eggs occupies one of the bursae, thus preventing viviparous development. Next Jungersen (1912) found *Chordeumium obesum* living enclosed in a sac of host tissue in the interior of *Asteronyx loveni*, sometimes in such numbers as nearly to fill the available space and thus inhibit the gonads. The sac may contain a female, a mass of eggs, and a male imbedded in the egg mass; the larvae escape by the bursal slits, enter another host, and fix their hooked maxillae into the host tissue, evoking the formation of a sac. A third

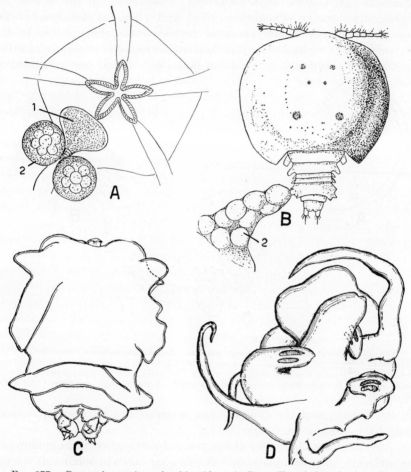

FIG. 277.—Copepod parasites of ophiuroids. *A, Cancerilla tubulata* fixed to the oral surface of *Amphipholis squamata (after Giesbrecht, 1899). B, Cancerilla alata* from *Ophiacantha disjuncta (after Heegaard, 1951). C, Arthrochordeumium asteromorphae* from an arm gall of *Asteromorpha koehleri. D, Ophioika ophiacanthae* from a bursa of *Ophiacantha severa. (C, D, after Stephensen, 1933.)* 1, body of parasite; 2, egg sac.

finding was that of *Arthrochordeumium appendiculosum* in a gall-like swelling of an arm base of the euryalous *Astrocharis gracilis* (Mortensen and Stephensen, 1918). A number of additional copepod endoparasites of ophiuroids have been described in recent years. These include *Arthrochordeumium asteromorphae* (Fig. 277C) in a gall in an arm base of

the euryalous *Asteromorpha koehleri*, and *Ophioika ophiacanthae* (Fig.
277*D*) in the bursae of *Ophiacantha severa* (Stephensen, 1933); *Ophioika
appendiculata* in the bursae of *Ophiomitrella clavigera* (Stephensen, 1935);
*Parachordeumium tetraceros* occupying a gall in the coelom of *Amphipholus
squamata* (Le Calvez, 1938); *Ophioika asymmetrica* in the bursae of
*Ophiacantha imago* (Pyefinch, 1940); and *Ophioika tenuibrachia* in
*Ophicantha disjuncta* and *vivipara*, *Lernaeosaccus ophiacanthae* in *O.
disjuncta*, and *Codoba discoveryi* in *Ophiura meridionalis* (Heegaard, 1951).
In *Ophioika tenuibrachia*, two dwarf males were found partly imbedded

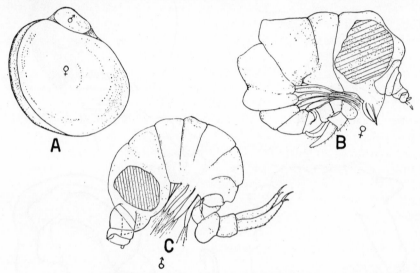

Fig. 278.—Ascothoracican barnacle parasite, *Ascothorax bulbosus*, from interior of
*Amphiura belgicae* and *microplax*.  *A*, male and female in place, each enclosed in a bivalved
covering.  *B*, female removed from its covering.  *C*, male removed from covering, not to
same scale as female; both resemble cypris stage of free-living barnacles.  (*All after
Heegaard*, 1951.)

in the female, and the copepod was accompanied by a small eunicid
polychaete feeding on its eggs.

Ascothoracican barnacles of the genus *Ascothorax* occur in ophiuroids
as well as in other echinoderms.  Those so far taken in ophiuroids belong
to the genus *Ascothorax*, which is much less modified than the genera
that infest asteroids (page 410) and retains the structure of the cypris
stage, being enclosed like the latter in a bivalved covering.  A small male
is often found adhering to the female.  *Ascothorax ophioctenis* (Djakanov.
1914b; Stephensen, 1935) dwells in the bursae of the circumarctic species
*Ophiocten sericeum*, and *Ascothorax bulbosus* (Heegaard, 1951; Fig. 278)
is similarly located in the antarctic ophiuroids *Amphiura belgicae* and
*microplax*.  A useful summary of the known Ascothoracica is given by
Stephensen (1935).

Mention is made in the literature of other crustacean associates of ophiuroids. Grave (1899) often noticed a small, protectively colored amphipod clinging to the arms of *Ophioderma brevispina*. Mortensen (1927, 1933c) repeatedly mentioned having found in *Ophiura sarsi* a red, sacciform organism full of eggs that was destructive of the host gonads; probably this also is a parasitic copepod. Later (1936) he noticed a similar organism in an antarctic ophiuroid.

Ophiuroids are notable among echinoderms for their tendency to epizoic and ectocommensal habits. Their small size and flexible arms fit them for clinging to other animals, especially branching types, and hence it is not surprising that they often occur in association with sponges and coelenterates. Young and half-grown specimens of the circum-tropical *Ophiactis savignyi* are often found dwelling in numbers in the interstices of sponges whereas the adults occur free and singly. Döderlein (1898) recorded that a number of six-armed Indo-Pacific ophiuroids, characterized by very small size and fissiparous habits, regularly cling to the branches of alcyonaceans and gorgonians, and Mortensen (1932) mentioned finding two ophiurous species twined about the branches of antipatharians (I, page 625). Euryalous ophiuroids, especially the five-armed species, are commonly found with their flexible arm ends coiled about the branches of colonial cnidarians, such as alcyonaceans, gorgonians, and antipatharians. The ubiquitous *Asteronyx loveni* habitually lives, at least in northern waters, mounted on tall, slender pennatulids of the genus *Funiculina* which it seems to use as a vantage point for capturing plankton animals, keeping a couple of arms wound about the pennatulid while the others wave in the water. The young of this species seem to be bottom dwellers, feeding on detritus. According to Fedotov (1924, 1931), newly metamorphosed *Gorgonocephalus* in northern waters inhabit colonies of the alcyonacean *Gersemia*, which may be literally covered with them. After the disk has reached a diameter of about 5 mm. and the arms have begun to branch, the young gorgonocephalids leave the *Gersemia* and take up a residence on adults of their own species. Here they cling mainly by hooking the arm tips over the edges of the bursal slits, often damaging these severely. Panikkar and Prasad (1952) report collecting several specimens of the rhizostome medusa *Rhopilema hispidum* that were covered with all stages of the ophiuroid *Ophiocnemis marmorata;* the largest of the medusae (128 mm. in diameter) harbored over 800 of the ophiuroids.

Several cases of commensal relations of ophiuroids with other echinoderms are noted in the literature. Species of the Indo-Pacific ophiothrichid genus *Ophiomaza* apparently live only in association with comatulids. This is definitely true of the widely spread *Ophiomaza cacaotica*, not found apart from comatulids such as *Comatula purpurea* and *Comanthus annulatum* (H. L. Clark, 1921).   Another ophiothrichid, *Ophiophthirius actinometrae*, possibly really the young of some species of *Ophiomaza*, clings to the cirri of *Actinometra solaris* in the Indo-Pacific (Döderlein, 1898).   Mortensen (1933a) notes two instances of commensalism of ophiuroids with sand dollars.   The very tiny *Nannophiura lagani*, with disk only 0.5 mm. across, inhabits the underside of *Laganum depressum*, and the sexually dimorphic *Amphilycus androphorus* (Fig. 258*A*) lives on sand flats beneath *Echinodiscus bisperforatus.*

Ophiuroids very commonly live in aggregations (H. L. Clark, 1921) and young often maintain contact with the adults in both viviparous and nonviviparous species.   A study of aggregation in *Ophioderma brevispina* off the Massachusetts coast was made by Allee (1927) and Allee and Fowler (1932).   This species lives among eel grass and in nature aggregates only in November and December in the region of study.   When placed in bare containers, however, they soon collect in bunches, the more rapidly the brighter the illumination.   This bunching is essentially an expression of negative phototaxis combined with positive thigmotaxis; the animals gather about a quiescent individual or in the least illuminated area, reaching these by a succession of random movements.   Tests made during the nonbreeding season indicated an initial decreased rate of oxygen consumption in bunched as compared with isolated individuals; later the oxygen consumption of the group was found to be higher than that of a similar mass of isolated individuals.   Without food and in an adequate volume of water, bunched individuals survive longer and are less apt to cast off arms than isolated specimens.   Providing isolated animals with glass rods, in imitation of eel grass, has much the same physiological effect as bunching with its fellows.   The later study, made during the breeding season, gave different results as regards oxygen consumption, a higher initial intake in the grouped animals, an indication perhaps of mutual stimulation at breeding time; otherwise results were much the same as in the 1927 experiments.

Very little information is available concerning growth in ophiuroids. Mortensen (1927) states that *Ophiura texturata* reaches sexual maturity in its third year at a disk diameter of 7 to 11 mm. but probably requires 5 or 6 years to reach its maximum disk diameter of 30 to 35 mm.   Grieg (1928a) gave data on some common ophiuroids of the European boreal region; *Ophiopholis aculeata* is said to reach a disk diameter of 5 to 7 mm. in 2 years; *Ophiocten sericeum* one of 5 to 6 mm. and *Ophiura sarsi* one of 6 to 9 mm. in the same period.   As the maximum disk diameter attained by these species is around 15, 18, and 35 mm., respectively, several years would seem to be necessary for them to reach full size, although they no doubt breed at 2 or 3 years of age.   *Ophiomusium lymani* is stated by Grieg to attain full size in 3 years.

Ludwig (1899), H. L. Clark (1914), and Campbell (1922) have discussed morphological growth changes in ophiuroids. Their findings are to the effect that growth changes at the arm tips repeat earlier stages of the arms.

## XI. CLASS OPHIOCISTIOIDEA

This is a wholly extinct class of echinoderms of peculiar appearance that lived from the Ordovician to the Devonian. The group is very small, comprising five genera and less than ten species. It has been well reviewed by Ubaghs (1953). The body, as in echinoids, was completely incased, except for the peristome, in a discoid test up to 90 mm. in diameter, with rounded, oval, or pentagonal contour, and lacked arms or arm-like projections. The aboral surface of the test is composed of plates without definite arrangement, although Regnéll (1948) attempted to find some indication of pentamery here in *Volchovia*. In this genus, also, an orifice supposed to be an anus and provided with five plates forming an anal pyramid is present near the margin on the aboral side, and peripheral to it is another opening, probably a hydropore or gonopore or combined pore for these two functions. No such openings are found in the other genera, although in fact the aboral surface is not well known in most of them. The center of the oral surface is occupied by a peristome with a buccal apparatus of five interradial pieces, somewhat recalling that of *Eothuria* (Fig. 220D) and apparently serving masticatory functions. The peristome is strengthened with many little plates in *Sollasina*. The plates of the oral side of the test are definitely pentamerous, arranged into five ambulacral areas of three plate rows each and five interambulacral areas of one plate row each; it will be recalled that interambulacra of one plate row are found elsewhere only in *Bothriocidaris* (Fig. 220A, B). The podial pores occur between the central and lateral rows of plates of the ambulacra and from each protruded a giant podium, covered with little imbricated skeletal scales. In the different genera there are two to eight pairs of podia in each ambulacrum and these may increase in size in the peripheral direction; the largest ones may equal or exceed the diameter of the test in length. A madreporite, interradially situated near the peristome, is known in the genus *Eucladia* and resembles the madreporite of asteroids; just peripheral to this is a cluster of pores supposed to be gonoporal. It appears probable that these creatures had but one gonad.

Because of the scanty available knowledge of this little group of strange creatures it is impossible at present to establish their relationship to other echinoderm classes. It is evident that they moved on the oral surface and therefore are Eleutherozoa, as further indicated by the large podia, absence of food grooves, and presence of a masticatory

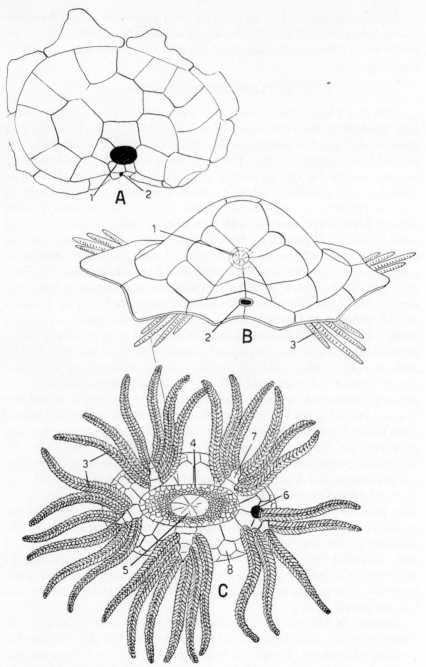

Fig. 279.—Ophiocistioidea. *A, Volchovia*, aboral surface (*after Regnéll*, 1948); apparently the oral surface lacked skeleton. *B, Volchovia*, restored (*after Hecker*, 1938). *C,*

apparatus; although, on the other hand, the presence of an anal pyramid and the occurrence of the anus and gonopore or hydropore in one interradius is certainly suggestive of the Pelmatozoa. Several authors have suggested an affinity of the ophiocistioids with ophiuroids chiefly because the three rows of ambulacral plates are reminiscent of the oral and lateral arm shields of ophiuroids. But the positional relation of the podial pores to these plates is different in the ophiocistioids than in the ophiuroids, and the total absence of arms would seem to negate the idea of an ophiuroid relationship. The resemblance appears greater to archaic echinoids than to ophiuroids. Ubaghs sensibly concludes that the ophiocistioids constitute a blind branch that arose at about the same level as the other eleutherozoan classes and hence is not derivable from any of them.

## XII. PHYLOGENETIC AND COMPARATIVE CONSIDERATIONS

The discussion of phylogeny will be limited to evolution within the phylum, as the relation of the echinoderms to other phyla cannot be discussed profitably until the phyla concerned have been elucidated and therefore is deferred to the next volume. The echinoderms have an impressive fossil record going back to the early Cambrian and one might anticipate that palaeontology would throw light on echinoderm origins and evolution. This expectation will be disappointed, however. Perusal of Piveteau's (1953) treatise shows that prominent invertebrate palaeontologists do not agree on the derivations of the main groups of echinoderms. The subject suffers from the fact that palaeontologists are poorly informed on existing echinoderms and zoologists are poorly informed on palaeontology. The author as a zoologist with scant knowledge of palaeontology must place the main emphasis in the following discussion on the facts of embryology and morphology.

In the foregoing pages there has been evidenced a general similarity in the embryonic development of echinoderms. This similarity has led to a concept, based on embryological facts, of an organism representing the common ancestor of the echinoderms. The term *dipleurula* was invented for this common ancestor by Semon (1888), but this author did not develop the concept, devoting his article to another type that he called *pentactula*. It remained for Bather (1900) to adopt and expound the dipleurula, and his exposition has ever since been accepted unquestioningly by zoologists and palaeontologists alike. Bather conceived the dipleurula (Fig. 280A) as a soft, elongated, bilaterally symmetrical creature without skeletal formations. The mouth, preceded by a

---

*Sollasina*, from the oral side (*after Sollas*, 1899); on the right side one podium has been omitted to show the podial pore. 1, anal opening; 2, second opening, probably combined gonopore and hydropore; 3, podia; 4, peristome; 5, buccal armature, possibly representing a masticatory apparatus; 6, podial pore; 7, ambulacra; 8, interambulacra.

preoral lobe, is located ventrally near the anterior end and the anus is slightly ventral at the posterior end. A simple digestive tract with a stomachic enlargement runs from mouth to anus. At the anterior end is found a nervous center bearing a sensory tuft and giving off nerves in the posterior direction. The interior space is occupied by coelomic sacs of enteric origin. Embryologists agree that ideally there are three pairs of these sacs, bilaterally arranged in an anteroposterior row on each side of the digestive tract. It was Heider (1912) who proposed for these three paired sacs the names axocoel, hydrocoel, and somatocoel; Gislén (1947) has suggested the more general terms protocoel, mesocoel, and metacoel. The axocoel opens on the dorsal surface by way of the hydroporic canal and hydropore and is conceived by Bather as remaining in continuity with the corresponding hydrocoel by a narrow connection, the larval stone canal. The inner walls of the somatocoels meet above and below the intestine to form the primary mesentery, thus originally vertical in position, and the gonad probably originates from cells of this mesentery. Any space remaining around the coelomic sacs and the digestive tract is presumably occupied with mesenchyme, not represented in Bather's figure but stated by him as tending to secrete calcareous spicules.

The facts of embryology show that the echinoderms are enterocoelous coelomates; the coelom arises as a pair of sacciform evaginations of the archenteron. The objections of Fell (1945, 1948) to this generalization cannot carry any weight as they are based on cases of obviously derived and altered embryonic development. The generalization that each coelomic sac then divides into three compartments appears also acceptable, although the separation of the axocoels is certainly not very clear in many cases. The separation of the somatocoels is definite in the majority of instances. But the author must protest against calling the echinoderms three-segmented animals or oligomerous animals after the German fashion. The subdivision of the coelom into three paired compartments is not segmentation in the proper sense of this term, since each compartment has a different fate. Neither do these coelomic subdivisions bring about any segmentation (by which is meant serial repetition) of any other structures. The echinoderms are not segmented animals. The coelom simply portions itself out to participate in various body parts. The echinoderms may be referred to as tricoelomate animals, but even this expression may be stretching the truth, as the evidence for the actuality of the axocoel and hydrocoel as separate entities is not too satisfactory. Perhaps the older conception of the division of each coelomic sac into anterior and posterior compartments is nearer the truth.

It is probably acceptable to believe that the coelomic compartments were originally equally developed on the two sides, although actually in embryology the right axocoel and hydrocoel are generally poorly developed and are altogether absent in the embryos of crinoids and holothuroids so far as studied; they are better expressed in asteroids, echinoids, and ophiuroids. In asteroids and echinoids a number of larvae have been recorded with hydropores or hydrocoels, or both, equally and symmetrically developed on the two sides, with the right ones later degenerating. Thus Field (1892) noted that double hydropores are common in the larvae of *Asterias vulgaris*. Grave (1911) saw double hydrocoels in the larvae of the five-lunuled *Mellita*, von Übisch (1913b) in *Paracentrotus lividus*, and Gemmill (1913) in *Asterias rubens*. Double hydropores are not uncommon in *Marth. glacialis* (Gemmill, 1913; Narasimhamurti, 1933), and the former author also found them in larvae of *Asterias rubens* and *Porania pulvillus*. Newman (1921) reported double hydropores and hydroporic canals in *Patiria miniata*. Both MacBride (1919) and Narasimhamurti (1933) obtained an increase in such doublings by subjecting the larvae to augmented salinity. Although Newman took the view that the doublings represent a form of twinning and are therefore without phylogenetic significance, it is more acceptable to believe that they are ancestral reminiscences and indicate that echinoderms originally had two symmetrically placed hydropores and hydrocoels. Nevertheless it must be admitted that no fossil echinoderm is known with more than one hydropore.

In 1941, Whitehouse produced an incredible article in which he described two calcareous fossils found in the Middle Cambrian of Queensland that he considered to be the most primitive echinoderm fossils yet uncovered. One of these that he named *Peridionites* was enthusiastically described as having housed an organism with the characters of the dipleurula, although in fact this fossil shows nothing but an elliptical calcareous mass sutured into five pieces, a median dorsal and two end and two side pieces. Whitehouse appears not to understand the concepts of symmetry and segmentation. This ellipse is said to be bilaterally symmetrical like the dipleurula; actually it is *biradial*, not bilateral at all, and could not have housed a bilateral animal except one altered to radial or biradial symmetry. Whitehouse further talks about *Peridionites* having been segmented and clearly does not understand the meaning of segmentation. He goes so far as to create a *subphylum* of echinoderms on the basis of this creature and this classification has already passed into one college textbook of invertebrate palaeontology. Whitehouse's article has already met with the criticism it deserves from students of fossil echinoderms.

It does not appear to the present author that the dipleurula concept is of any great assistance in elucidating the common ancestor of the echinoderms or in explaining their characteristic features. Dipleurula is merely a name for features common to present echinoderm larvae. Nothing really has been gained by creating this name. Bather, no doubt realizing this, has carried on the story further but on a purely hypothetical basis. He assumes that in the process of evolving into an echinoderm the dipleurula attached by the right side of the oral lobe. Such attachment brought about the degeneration of some structures of the right side and forced the mouth to move toward the original posterior end, taking the hydrocoel with it, and thus bringing about the characteristic looping of the digestive tract. The same torsion would bring the originally vertical primary mesentery into a horizontal position, and the right somatocoel would become dorsal, the left one ventral. It is postulated that the pressure of the digestive tract on the left hydrocoel would force it into a horseshoe shape that eventually closes into a ring. Although there is embryological support for the occurrence of a torsion, as in the larvae of crinoids and holothuroids, the explanation of the suppression of the right side is not very satisfactory. The crinoid larva does attach at the original oral end but not upon one side. It is commonly supposed that in its early attached stage the ancestral echinoderm took to lying upon its right side.

The picture drawn by Bather fails to explain the most characteristic feature of echinoderm structure, the water-vascular system and its coelomic origin. Bather believed this system originated as three ciliated tentaculiferous grooves on the surface running into the mouth, one anterior to the mouth (in its new position) and one to each side of the mouth; a groove did not arise posterior to the mouth because of the presence of the hydropore and the anus there. Later the two lateral grooves subdivided to make the typical five. This story is not in the least supported by embryology. Embryology indicates that the water-vascular system arose as tentacles, that is, as protrusions of the body wall. Therefore it appears to the author that the pentactula concept of the common ancestor of the echinoderms as first conceived by Semon (1888) and developed by Bury (1895) is more satisfactory than the dipleurula concept. The pentactula (Fig. 280*B, C*) is represented as having had five tentacles around the mouth, and the latter may have been preceded by a vestibule. The hydrocoel has already separated from the rest of the coelom to form the water ring and stone canal, and the left axocoel has given rise to the hydroporic canal and attached ampulla. Possibly the pentactula should be regarded as a later evolution of the dipleurula. If it is correct that there were originally two symmetrical hydrocoels, then there must have been also a group of tentacles on each side, something like a lophophore, as also postulated by Haecker (1912) and MacBride (1914). At any rate it appears clear enough that the water-vascular system originated as tentacles. Tentacles function best if hollow, and in a coelomic animal it is natural and even inevitable that a coelomic branch should extend into each tentacle. Thus we may envision the separation of a hydrocoelic part from the rest of the coelom. But it is certainly not clear why such a system of coelomic canals should require an opening on the surface by way of a canal developed from still another portion of the coelom (axocoel). The presence of a hydropore in the

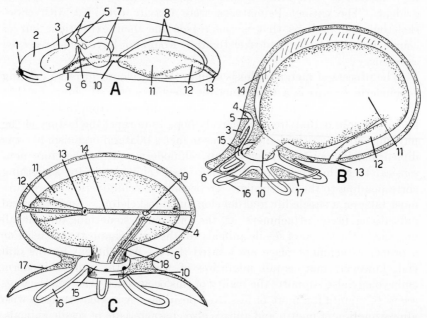

Fig. 280.—Phylogenetic theories. *A*, diplleurula ancestor (*after Bather*, 1900). *B*, pentactula ancestor in its bilateral condition. *C*, pentactula after torsion to the radial condition. (*B*, *C*, *after Bury*, 1895.) 1, apical sense organ; 2, preoral lobe; 3, axocoel; 4, hydropore; 5, hydroporic canal; 6, stone canal; 7, hydrocoel; 8, somatocoel; 9, mouth; 10, esophagus; 11, stomach; 12, intestine; 13, anus; 14, dorsal mesentery; 15, water ring; 16, primary tentacles (radial canals of definitive water-vascular system); 17, vestibule; 18, axial gland; 19, dorsal sac.

most archaic echinoderms indicates that this connection with the surface was an essential part of the water-vascular system from the start.

The podia obviously originate as side branches of the primary tentacles. As highly motile and sensory structures, tentacles necessarily contain a nerve branch (hence the radial nerve) and further a haemal branch if the organism possesses a haemal system (hence the radial haemal channels). Calcification in the wall of such tentacles would produce simple arms, perhaps like the brachioles of early echinoderms. The differentiation of a ciliated food groove along the inner surface of the tentacles or brachioles appears secondary but no doubt followed rapidly. The calcification of the tentacles or brachioles does not permit them to capture food and convey it to the mouth after the usual manner of tentacles and therefore some other method of food conveyance had to be adopted.    Probably a key to echinoderm evolution is the tendency to excessive secretion of calcareous endoskeleton.    This is an advantage as an armature against attack but a disadvantage as regards locomotion and food capture.    In the later evolution of echinoderms the tendency to reduction of the skeleton and to greater agility and flexibility is evident.    The extinct Pelmatozoa were heavily provided with endoskeleton, and perhaps that is the reason for their extinction; but of course, had they lacked endoskeleton they would not have been preserved as fossils.

The process of metamorphosis seen in the development of all existing echinoderm groups is a truly amazing phenomenon.    It shows us that the original echinoderm must have been very different from those that we know today and that we can scarcely hope to unravel the history of the phylum.    If the original ancestor was in fact a bilateral organism like the dipleurula, it was hardly as yet an echinoderm.    It is therefore nonsensical to go hunting around among fossil echinoderms for something corresponding to the dipleurula.    To become an echinoderm the creature must take on a sessile life and develop an endoskeleton.    Embryological indications favor attachment at the oral end, something not at all unusual in the larvae of sessile animals, for the sense organs that determine a proper attachment place are located there.    Attachment by the oral end, however, may entail migration of the mouth, and echinoderm embryology also supports the reality of this occurrence, whereas the anus seems to maintain a more or less fixed position.    A looped intestine with approximation of mouth and anus is also characteristic of sessile animals. As their inability to move about renders them very open to being devoured by other animals, sessile animals are prone to develop some sort of protective armor, either an exo- or an endoskeleton, as witness barnacles, ectoprocts, brachiopods, and the like.    They almost always also require tentacles or similar body projections as food-catching devices, as they are unable to pursue prey, and often in fact must employ a mucus-ciliary method of feeding.    It appears necessary to picture the early echinoderm as an attached animal with an endoskeleton of numerous plates and one or more tentacle-like projections containing a coelomic canal and nerve cord present near the mouth, possibly in two groups.    Members of the Heterostelea would seem to come the nearest to this hypothetical ancestor.

There is no reason to doubt the generally accepted belief that the echinoderms came from a bilateral ancestor; to this the bilaterality of larval stages bears witness.    The strange metamorphosis undergone by the larvae seems to be a record, if an enigmatical one, of the change from the original bilateral symmetry to the radial symmetry of the present members of the phylum.   Embryology indicates that the radial symmetry was achieved by the transformation of the preoral part into a stalk (later lost in eleutherozoans) and by a torsion whereby the original left side became the oral surface of the definitive echinoderm and the original right side became the definitive aboral surface, with the degeneration of the more anterior structures of the right side and their concomitant overgrowth on the left side, while posterior structures of the two sides remained more or less equal.   The rotation of the right side to an aboral position would deprive the anterior structures of the right side of any function or usefulness; hence their degeneration is understandable and probably needs no other explanation.   The stages of evolution are then: attachment at the oral end, rotation of the left side to an oral, the right side to an aboral position, degeneration of the anterior part of the right side, assumption of radial symmetry, first by the oral surface.   The fossil record suggests that the radial symmetry was very imperfect at first and only gradually evolved to the pentamerous condition, of course after the loss of the right anterior structures, including the right group of tentacles (water-vascular system).   No satisfactory explanation is available as to why the remaining left water-vascular system evolved in the direction of the number five.   There is fossil evidence that the pentameric condition of the ambulacra derived from a triradiate condition by the forking of the lateral rays and the triradiate condition was explained by Bather (see above, page 694).   But embryology does not support this story, although it may be noted that the five lobes of the hydrocoel often do not form simultaneously.   The most archaic echinoderm fossils were not radial but merely sessile, and pentamerism seemingly evolved independently in several lines.   Lines generally start out with an endoskeleton of a large number of irregularly arranged plates that gradually reduce to a small number pentamerously disposed.   The number of arm-like extensions or brachioles also appears to have been variable at first.

Embryology clearly shows that the blastopore is the original anus of the phylum.   The fact that it does not usually continue as the definitive anus, which, however, generally arises near the site of closure of the blastopore, is not of theoretical importance.   Notably a protonephridium or any kind of a nephridium is totally wanting in echinoderm development; therefore echinoderm larvae cannot be allied to the trochophore. As animals with an enterocoel, a blastoporal anus, and a want of a larval nephridium, the echinoderms are clearly on a different line of evolution from the phyla with a trochophore.   The mesoderm of echinoderms appears to be solely of the entomesodermal category, although it is usually given off in two stages, a preliminary mesenchymal stage and a later mesothelial stage, the coelomic sacs.   However, apparently in many cases the coelomic sacs continue to produce mesenchyme for some time. The precocious production of entomesoderm in the form of mesenchyme is evidently related to skeleton formation, at least in echinoids and ophiuroids.

Because of the extensive fossil record available for the Pelmatozoa, one would anticipate that it would be easy to trace the origin of crinoids. In fact, however, crinoids cannot be related to any of the known groups of noncrinoid Pelmatozoa. The reason for this is that the arms of crinoids are not homologous with the brachioles of the noncrinoid Pelmatozoa. Brachioles are simple projections supported by their own small endoskeletal pieces, whereas the endoskeletal support of the crinoid arms, that is, the row of brachials, is directly continuous with the radial cycle of plates of the theca. The embryonic history of crinoids shows that they have evolved from a typical stalked pelmatozoan with a complete pentamerous theca of three cycles of plates, infrabasals, basals, and deltoids, hence a theca of the dicyclic type. Deltoids and basals are both interradial; the radials appear later, being interpolated into the calyx in the radial positions. Although the radials are thus shown not to be original elements of the theca but rather the most proximal members of the row of arm brachials, their incorporation into the theca differs from the relation of brachioles to the theca and renders impossible any homology between brachioles and arms. No explanation can be offered of the significance of the vestibule in development.

Crinoids have not given rise to any other group. Attempts have frequently been made to homologize the aboral apical skeletal system of newly metamorphosed asteroids, echinoids, and ophiuroids with the calyx plates of crinoids. In these three groups the original apical skeleton consists of a central piece encircled by a cycle of genital or interradial plates, followed by a cycle of terminal plates. At first sight these seem comparable to the centrodorsal, basal, and deltoid plates of the crinoid theca, but the homology cannot be sustained because the genital and terminal cycles alternate, whereas the basal and deltoid cycles are both interradial.

No satisfactory conclusions can be reached regarding the origin of the eleutherozoan classes from pelmatozoan ancestors. The holothuroids have left practically no fossil record. They are primitive in retaining a single gonad in the original position and in preserving both the hydropore and the gonopore also in their original position, in interradius CD. Their endoskeleton may perhaps be regarded as having remained in an embryonic state in the form of microscopic ossicles. On the other hand, the water-vascular system, taking with it the ectoneural nervous system, has sunk into the interior, as evidenced by the presence of an epineural canal to the outer side of each radial nerve. The holothuroids therefore came from ancestors with open ambulacral grooves that have closed over and come to lie to the inner side of the body wall (for the embryology of this process see page 185). Developmental similarities with crinoids include the occurrence in both of a doliolaria larva, a vestibule, the rotation of the vestibule to the new anterior (original posterior) end, and the direct transformation of the larva into the juvenile. The significance of the doliolaria is doubtful, as in holothuroids it is preceded by the auricularia larva that does not resemble any larval type of crinoids but instead is similar to the bipinnaria of asteroids, having a sinuous ciliated band following much the same pattern in both cases. Probably the holothuroids diverged from other eleutherozoans at a very early stage in their evolution and came from a common stem with crinoids.

The other three classes of Eleutherozoa, Asteroidea, Echinoidea, and Ophiuroidea, apparently have a common ancestry, because in all of them the same apical skeleton appears in the aboral or dorsal side of the larva, namely, a central piece encircled by two alternating cycles of plates, of which the members of the outer or radial cycle become the terminal plates of the ambulacra and embrace the terminal tentacle. All three also possess spines. But contrary to the usual belief of a derivation of ophiuroids from asteroids, the embryological evidence indicates an early divergence of asteroids from this line of evolution, whereas echinoids and ophiuroids have continued for some distance along a common path. To begin with, only asteroids attach during metamorphosis. Whether this attachment is of ancestral significance or merely represents a newly acquired adaptation has been debated by embryologists without their reaching any decision, but in conjunction with the retention of other pelmatozoan features may perhaps be regarded as palingenetic (for meaning see I, page 272). At least the sucker of attachment is similarly located in the larvae of asteroid and crinoids. Further asteroids are the only eleutherozoans that have retained an open ambulacral groove, a feature that must be regarded as primitive. They therefore lack epineural radial canals, and the radial nerves and water canals have remained to the external side of the ambulacral ossicles. The whole structure of their ambulacra and associated parts retains a pelmatozoan condition, except for the fact that podia have developed ampullae and have taken on a locomotory function. On the other hand, in both echinoids and ophiuroids the ambulacral canals and associated parts have become enclosed into the interior, and in both groups this has happened in the same way, by the formation of epineural folds in the metamorphosing larva. Therefore both echinoids and ophiuroids have epineural canals to the outer side of the radial nerve cords. There cannot be any doubt that the formation and closure of the epineural folds in echinoid and ophiuroid development repeats the ancestral occurrence of the closure of the ambulacral grooves. Asteroids develop without the formation of a vestibule, a very prominent event in the embryology of echinoids; and it seems that vestiges of a vestibule also occur in ophiuroids (page 642).

Further evidence of a closer relation of ophiuroids to echinoids than to asteroids is seen in their larval type which is a pluteus, very like the echinoid pluteus but quite unlike the asteroid bipinnaria. It does not seem possible to account for the occurrence of a pluteus with similar skeletal rods in both echinoids and ophiuroids except on the basis of some community of ancestry. Finally, in recent years workers in comparative biochemistry have produced striking evidence in favor of this community of ancestry. Bergmann (1949 and in a letter) finds that all ophiuroids and echinoids tested have sterols of Type I, namely, cholesterol or some closely related compound (Fig. 162, left), whereas numerous asteroids tested all have Type II sterols, that is, stellasterol or related compounds (Fig. 162, right). The sterols of the three crinoids thus far tested belong to Type I, although perhaps a new variety, and those of holothurians classify as Type II. Further biochemical evidence supporting the close relationship of echinoids and ophiuroids concerns phosphagens or phosphorus carriers, of great importance in metabolic processes. Baldwin and Yudkin (1950) and Florkin (1952) have pointed out that crinoids, holothuroids, and asteroids have arginine as the phosphorus carrier, whereas creatine serves this function in ophiuroids and echinoids (echinoids also have phosphoarginine). Phosphocreatine is also characteristic of vertebrates; creatine in organisms results from the methylation of glycocyamine, and among echinoderms only echinoids and ophiuroids have the enzymes (methylases) necessary for performing this reaction. The author is of the opinion that the closer relationship of ophiuroids to echinoids rather than to asteroids, as usually supposed, is not to be doubted, and therefore the union of asteroids and ophiuroids into one group is not admissible. Further, the arrangement recently adopted by palaeontologists (e.g., Ubaghs, 1953), according to which asteroids and ophiuroids derive from a common somasteroid (page 319) ancestor and hence are to be united into one class Stellasteroidea, must be somehow wrong.

The foregoing discussion indicates that the subphylum Eleutherozoa is an artificial concept, composed of classes that have originated from the Pelmatozoa along at least two different lines. Holothuroidea and Asteroidea are closer to crinoids than are the other two classes, but have only one feature in common, their larval type. If they do diverge from a common ancestry this occurrence must have happened very far in the past. Asteroids probably have a common stem with echinoids and ophiuroids, as indicated by the similarity of apical skeleton, but here, too, the divergence into asteroids on the one hand and echinoids and ophiuroids on the other must have been a very ancient occurrence. Some students of fossil echinoderms think that the Eleutherozoa derive from the Edrioasteroidea whereas others reject this concept. The Edrioasteroidea are the only Pelmatozoa with open ambulacral grooves provided with podia that passed through pores between the ambulacral plates. This would seem to mean that the podia were provided with ampullae; however, this group led an attached life with the oral surface upward and hence the podia could not have been locomotory. Present knowledge of archaic asteroids (page 321) does not support the idea of an edrioasteroid ancestry of asteroids. There is a strong tendency in students of fossil echinoderms to derive the echinoids from diploporitic cystids. Although in fact the diplopores superficially resemble the paired podial pores of echinoids, these palaeontologists seem to forget that the diplopores had no relation to the ambulacral system, being the outer ends of canals in the thecal plates, whereas in echinoids the podia pass through the pores. In diploporites the podia were mounted on the brachioles. A direct derivation of any eleutherozoan class from a particular pelmatozoan group does not appear feasible. Undoubtedly the Eleutherozoa derived from the Pelmatozoa but probably along several different lines.

The course of evolution within the existing classes is more or less evident. The comatulids are obviously derived from stalked ancestors, as shown by the occurrence of a pentacrinoid stage in their ontogeny. In holothurians types like the dendrochirotes, with five definitely delimited ambulacra provided with locomotory podia, presumably represent the basic morphology, whereas those with creeping soles and those without podia, once considered the most primitive members, are of derivative nature. Palaeontological evidence (page 321) indicates that among asteroids the Phanerozonia occupy the basic position and have given rise to the Spinulosa and Forcipulata. Among echinoids the irregular groups are clearly derived from the regular urchins, as sufficiently shown by ontogenetic stages. In ophiuroids the Euryalae have evolved from the Ophiurae, for the former pass through juvenile ophiurous stages. The tendency in existing echinoderms to revert secondarily to a more or less bilateral condition is interesting. It is shown in holothurians and especially in the irregular echinoids.

Comparison of the organ systems in the existing echinoderm classes may be of some interest. The nervous system appears to be in a rather low state of organization in most echinoderms, especially Eleutherozoa, where the main or ectoneural system is primitively in continuity with the epidermis as still in asteroids, also in crinoids, and lacks any morphological center. One wonders if the much better developed entoneural system of crinoids with its central nervous mass may not have been more typical for the phylum originally. It seems quite likely that the nervous system underwent some degree of retrogression in correlation with the change from a bilateral to a radial type of morphology. It may be recalled that some echinoderm larvae are provided with an apical nervous center which may originally have continued as some sort of brain. The ectoneural nerve ring is shown by physiological studies to act as a coordinating center in Eleutherozoa in general, although lacking the appearance of a brain, morphologically.

The water-vascular system is the most characteristic morphological feature of echinoderms, and the existence of a hydropore even in the Heterostelea indicates that the system was present practically from the start. The condition in crinoids may be taken to represent the original pattern of the system. On the oral surface are found the ciliated food grooves, typically five in number, each underlain by a radial canal of the water-vascular system that gives off side branches to become the hollow interiors of body-wall projections, the podia. The podia are simply tentacles that edge the food grooves and primarily have a food-catching function. Originally echinoderms fed on microscopic organisms and material by the mucus-ciliary method; the food captured by the podia was passed along the grooves to the mouth. It is probable that from the very start the food grooves were mounted on projections, and these projections, as suggested above, may have been simply elongated tentacles that developed side branches. Closure of the food grooves with relegation of the accompanying water canal and nerve of the ectoneural system into the interior occurred in the Eleutherozoa, apparently along two lines, the holothuroid line and the echinoid-ophiuroid line, whereas the asteroids retain the pelmatozoan condition of the open groove. It is clear that the locomotory function of the podia in most Eleutherozoa is a secondary adaptation, and apparently in the ophiuroids the podia have reverted to their original condition as small tentacular projections. In order to function as locomotory organs the podia have to be provided with ampullae, for the contraction of the ampullae furnishes the hydrostatic pressure necessary for the operation of the podia in locomotion. As soon as ampullae are evolved there is a necessity for the presence of ambulacral pores through the endoskeleton, by which the ampullae connect with the podia, although possibly the ampullae were external or partly so at first. But it is clearly expedient that they should be protected in the interior. The fact that no ambulacral pores exist in Pelmatozoa except Edrioasteroidea shows that ampullae were absent except in the latter. Ambulacral pores are characteristic of the Eleutherozoa; they typically occur between the ambulacral plates. The condition in echinoids in which the pores pass through the ambulacral plates is secondary, brought about by calcareous growth subdividing the original pore, which in fact occurred at the edge of the plates. The closure of the ambulacral groove and the assumption of a locomotory function by the podia necessitates the adoption of other modes of feeding, although the podia usually continue to pass food to the mouth when opportunity affords, and reversion to a mucous-ciliary method of feeding is not uncommon. The definitive stone canal arises by the end-to-end union of the larval hydroporic canal with the larval stone canal; theoretically, at least, the former originates from the left axocoel, the latter from the left hydrocoel.

A complete theca of closely fitting endoskeletal plates is characteristic of all the noncrinoid Pelmatozoa. This began to be lost in crinoids, where the theca is partially replaced by the flexible tegmen, and is retained in Eleutherozoa only by the echinoids, where the handicap of its presence is partly overcome by the alteration of the podia into locomotory organs. The general tendency in the Eleutherozoa toward reduction and lightening of the endoskeleton indicates that the disadvantages of the original complete thecal endoskeleton outweigh its advantages.

The digestive tract exhibits considerable lability throughout the phylum. Its typical state is probably that shown in Fig. 1D, in which mouth and anus both open on the oral surface and the digestive canal makes a turn definitely related to the radial axes. Probably a stomachic enlargement was originally present but has been lost in most present members. The digestive tract retains the typical form in holothurians, echinoids, and crinoids, except that in the first two the anus has moved to the aboral pole, although it may secondarily return to the oral surface in irregular urchins. Palaeontologists seem to have no ideas concerning the antecedents of the lantern of Aristotle; the curious fact may be recalled that it forms in sacs of coelomic origin. The digestive tract of asteroids and ophiuroids is much altered in correlation with their stellate shape, being provided with a large stomach and a greatly reduced intestine or none at all. The pyloric caeca are unique to asteroids.

The haemal system is well developed in holothuroids and echinoids, less well expressed in the other classes. As the channels of this system are not definite vessels with definite walls, the system may not be referred to as a vascular system, but rather as a lacunar system. The channels are best developed in relation to the digestive system and would seem to play a considerable role in the uptake and distribution of digested products. The fluid contained in the haemal system does not differ essentially from the coelomic fluid. A peculiarity of the haemal system of echinoderms is that most of the channels are enclosed inside tubular portions of the coelom. These tubes of the coelom are generally called in books the perihaemal system and thereby the reader is given the false impression that they constitute a sort of accessory circulatory system. This is entirely erroneous, except in the sense that all coelomic spaces contribute something to circulation, respiration, and excretion. Through-out this book the so-called perihaemal canals are termed hyponeural canals because of their relation to the nervous system and to avoid unwarranted implications. The hyponeural system of canals appears functionally related to the nervous system, probably acting to cushion it against injury. But the enclosure of the haemal channels inside coelomic channels remains mysterious.

Regarding the equally mysterious axial gland, the findings from the literature are to the effect that it is the center of the haemal system, at least in asteroids, echinoids, and ophiuroids (it will be recalled that an axial gland is wanting in holothuroids). It has the same histological construction as other parts of the haemal system. According to the analysis of Fedotov (1924), the axial gland of the three groups mentioned consists of an oral and an aboral part. The oral part forms most of the gland and is housed in the left part of the axial sinus derived from the left axocoel. The aboral part of the axial gland is well differentiated only in ophiuroids; in asteroids and echinoids it is reduced to the terminal process housed in the dorsal sac derived, according to Fedotov, from the right axocoel. The left part of the axial sinus represents what is usually called axial sinus in asteroids and is wanting in echinoids. Pulsations have been observed in young asteroids, echinoids, and ophiuroids (Gemmill, 1919) in some part of the axial complex. One may surmise that perhaps the older observers were not as absurd as appears at first sight in calling the axial gland heart. It is possible that the echinoderms once had a better circulatory system than at present and that the axial gland is in fact the remnant of a heart. It is usual for a heart to be enclosed in a coelomic cavity; this explains the enclosure of the axial gland in the axial sinus. Cuénot (1948) maintains that the axial complex of crinoids is not homologous with that of eleutherozoans, but the relations of the crinoid axial gland to their haemal system and of their axial sinus to other coelomic spaces seem about the same as in the Eleutherozoa. It is therefore reasonable to accept the identity of the axial complex in the two cases.

The statement often seen that the gonad originates from the axial gland is definitely erroneous. The primordial germ cells arise from the wall of one of the coelomic compartments, mostly the left somatocoel, in close proximity, it is true, with the axial complex. From the presence of a single gonopore in Pelmatozoa it is deduced that there was originally a single gonad, opening in interradius CD. This condition is retained in Holothuroidea, whereas in other Eleutherozoa the gonad grows around the undersurface of the aboral pole as a genital stolon that gives off gonadal primordia pentamerously.

The coelom presents many difficulties of understanding. It is very perplexing to follow the embryonic history of the three coelomic compartments, and even to the present time this history is not too clear and definite. The part of the coelom that puts out the hydroporic canal to the surface is presumably the axocoel, which also contributes to the coelomic spaces housing the axial gland. The hydrocoel is easily recognized by its lobulations that become the radial water canals and the primary tentacles, but often seems indefinitely separated from the axocoel. The proximal part of the definitive stone canal appears of hydrocoelic origin; this unites end to end with the hydroporic canal to form the ultimate stone canal. The significance of this double origin of the stone canal is not evident. Neither is it clear why the stone canal is typically bound in the same mesentery with the axial gland, unless this is the result of mere proximity during embryology. The right somatocoel becomes the aboral (*epigastric*) part of the main coelom of the adult without much complication, and the left somatocoel becomes the oral (*hypogastric*) part of the main coelom, but is involved in many complications. The most important and constant of these complications is the output from the left somatocoel of processes that become the hyponeural system of sinuses. Why the nervous system must be accompanied by coelomic channels is one of the many mysteries of echinoderm organization. The epineural system of channels is not coelomic but represents an evagination from the external world and is a phylogenetic record of the closure of the ambulacral grooves in holothuroids, echinoids, and ophiuroids.

We then place the echinoderms among invertebrates as nonsegmented enterocoelous coelomates with a triparted (or possibly only diparted) coelom without any body divisions corresponding to the coelomic divisions.

# Bibliography

(Titles not found under a particular Class should be sought under General.)

## Historical

**Bruguière, J. G.** 1791. Tableau encyclopédique et méthodique des trois règnes de la nature, vol. 7, l'helminthogie. **Burmeister, H.** 1837. Handbuch der Naturgeschichte, Abt. 2, Zoologie. **Cuvier, G.** 1817. *Le régne animal,* vol. IV. **Forbes, E.** 1841. *A history of British starfishes.* **Frey, H.,** and **R. Leuckart.** 1847. *Lehrbuch der Anatomie der wirbellosen Thiere. In* R. **Wagner,** *Lehrbuch der Zootomie,* Theil II. **Goette, A.** 1902. *Lehrbuch der Zoologie.* **Grobben, K.** 1908. Die systematische Einteilung des Tierreiches. Verhandl. Zool. Botan. Gesellsch. Wien 58. **Hatschek, B.** 1888. *Lehrbuch der Zoologie.* **Huxley, T. H.** 1875. The classification of animals. Quart. Jour. Microsc. Sci. 15. **Klein, J. T.** 1734. *Naturalis dispositio echinodermatium.* **Lamarck, J. B.** 1801. *Système des animaux sans vertébrés.* 1816–1822. *Histoire naturelle des animaux sans vertébrés.* **Leuckart, R.** 1854. Bericht über die Leistungen in der Naturgeschichte der niederen Thiere während der Jahre 1848–1853. Arch. Naturgesch. 20, pt. 2. **Linnaeus, C.** 1758. *Systema naturae,* 10th ed. **Metschnikoff, E.** 1881. Über die systematische Stellung von Balanoglassus. Zool. Anz. 4. **Müller, J.,** and **F. H. Troschel.** 1842. *System der Asteriden.* **Norman, A. M.** 1865. On the genera and species of British Echinodermata. Ann. Mag. Natur. Hist., ser. 3, 15. **Schneider, K. C.** 1902. *Lehrbuch der vergleichenden Histologie der wirbellosen Tiere.*

## General

**Agassiz, A.** 1869. Preliminary report on the echini and starfishes dredged in deep water between Cuba and the Florida reef. Bull. Mus. Comp. Zool. Harvard 1, no. 9. **Baldwin, E.** 1947. *Dynamic aspects of biochemistry.* **Baldwin, E.,** and **W. Yudkin.** 1950. The annelid phosphagen with a note on phosphagen in Echinodermata. Proc. Roy. Soc. London 136B. **Barrois, J.** 1934. Le développement échinodermien dans ses rapports avec la génèse des vertébrés. Ann. Sci. Natur., ser. 10, 17. **Bather, F. A.** 1900. The echinoderms. *In* R. **Lankester** (ed.), *A treatise on zoology,* vol. III. **Bell, F. J.** 1908. Echinoderms. National Antarctic Exped. 1901–1904, Natur. Hist. IV, Zoology. 1917. The Echinoderma. British Antarctic (Terra Nova) Exped. 1910, Natur. Hist. Repts. Zool. 4. **Bergmann, W.** 1949. Comparative biochemical studies on the lipids of marine invertebrates. Jour. Marine Research 8. **Bergmann, W., M. McLean,** and **D. Lester.** 1943. Sterols from various invertebrates. Jour. Organic Chem. 8. **Bialaszewicz, K.** 1933. Composition minérale des liquides nourriciers chez les animaux marins. Arch. Internation. Physiol. 36. **Blegvad, H.** 1915. Food and conditions of nourishment among the communities of invertebrate animals found on or in the sea bottom in Danish waters. Rept. Danish Biol. Station 22. **Bohn, G.** 1909. Les essais et erreurs chez les étoiles de mer et les ophiures. Bull. Inst. Psychol. Internation. 8. **Boone, Lee.** 1928. Echinoderms from the Gulf of California and the Perlas Islands. Bull. Bingham Oceanogr. Collect. 2, art. 6. 1933. Echinodermata. Scient. Results

Cruise Yachts Eagle and Ara 1921–1928. Bull. Vanderbilt Marine Mus. 4. **Bury, H.** 1889. The embryology of echinoderms. Quart. Jour. Microsc. Sci. 29. 1895. The metamorphosis of echinoderms. Quart. Jour. Microsc. Sci. 38. **Bush, Mildred.** 1918. Key to the echinoderms of Friday Harbor, Washington. Publ. Puget Sound Biol. Sta. 2. **Chadwick, H. C.** 1914. Echinoderm larvae. Liverpool Marine Biol. Comm., Mem. 22. **Clark, Ailsa.** 1952. Echinodermata. Manihine Exped. Gulf Aqaba. Bull. British Mus. (Natur. Hist.) 1, no. 8. **Clark, A. H.** 1939. Echinoderms (other than holothurians) collected on the Presidential Cruise of 1938. Smithsonian Miscell. Collections 98, no. 11. 1940. Echinoderms from Greenland. Proc. U.S. Nation. Mus. 89. 1950a. The feather stars, sea urchins and sea stars of the United States Navy Antarctic Expedition 1947–1948. Jour. Washington Acad. Sci. 40. 1950b. Echinoderms from the Cocos-Keeling Islands. Bull. Raffles Mus. 22. 1952. Echinoderms from the Marshall Islands. Proc. U.S. Nation. Mus. 102. **Clark, H. L.** 1901. Echinoderms from Puget Sound. Proc. Boston Soc. Natur. Hist. 29. 1902a. Echinodermata. Papers from the Hopkins-Stanford Galapagos Expedition 1898–1899. XII. Proc. Washington Acad. Sci. 4. 1902b. The echinoderms of Porto Rico. Bull. U.S. Fish. Commission for 1900, vol. 20, pt. 2. 1904. The echinoderms of the Woods Hole region. Bull. U.S. Fish. Commission for 1902, vol. 22. 1908. Some Japanese and East Indian echinoderms. Bull. Mus. Comp. Zool. Harvard 51. 1909. Brood-protection and sexual dimorphism among echinoderms. Science 29. 1910. Echinoderms of Peru. Bull. Mus. Comp. Zool. Harvard 52. 1913. Echinoderms from Lower California. Bull. Amer. Mus. Natur. Hist. 32, art. 8. 1914. The echinoderms of the Western Australian museum. Records West Austral. Mus. 1. 1915. The echinoderms of Ceylon, other than holothurians. Spolia Zeylanica 10. 1919. The distribution of the littoral echinoderms of the West Indies. Carnegie Inst. Washington, Papers Dept. Marine Biol., vol. 13. 1921. The echinoderm fauna of Torres Strait, its composition and its origin. Carnegie Inst. Washington, Papers Dept. Marine Biol., vol. 10. 1922. The echinoderms of the Challenger Bank, Bermuda. Proc. Amer. Acad. Arts Sci. 57. 1923a. Echinoderms from Lower California. Bull. Amer. Mus. Natur. Hist. 48, art. 6. 1923b. The echinoderm fauna of South Africa. Annals S. African Mus. 13. 1925. Echinodermata other than sea stars of the tropical central Pacific. Bull. Bernice P. Bishop Mus., Hawaii, 27. 1928. The sea lilies, sea stars, brittle stars and sea urchins of the South Australian museum. Records S. Austral. Mus. 3. 1932. Echinoderms other than Asteroidea. Scient. Repts. Great Barrier Reef Exped. 1928–1929, vol. 4, no. 7. 1933. A handbook of the littoral echinoderms of Porto Rico and the other West Indian islands. Scient. Survey Porto Rico and the Virgin Islands 16, pt. 1. 1938. Echinoderms from Australia. Mem. Mus. Comp. Zool. Harvard 55. 1940. Eastern Pacific Expeditions of the New York Zoological Society. XXI. Notes on echinoderms from the west coast of Central America. Zoologica, New York, 25. 1941. Reports on the scientific results of the Atlantis Expedition to the West Indies. Mem. Soc. Cubana Hist. Natur. 15. 1942. The echinoderm fauna of Bermuda. Bull. Mus. Comp. Zool. Harvard 89. 1946. The echinoderm fauna of Australia, its composition and its origin. Carnegie Inst. Washington, Publ. 566. **Clark, W. B.** 1893. The mesozoic Echinodermata of the United States. Bull. U.S. Geol. Survey 97. **Clark, W. B.,** and **M. W. Twitchell.** 1915. The Mesozoic and Cenozoic Echinodermata of the United States. Monogr. U.S. Geol. Survey 54. **Clarke, F. W.,** and **W. Wheeler.** 1922. The inorganic constituents of marine invertebrates. U.S. Geol. Survey, Profess. Paper 124. **Coe, W. R.** 1912. Echinoderms of Connecticut. State Connecticut Geol. Natur. Hist. Survey, Bull. 19. **Cohnheim, O.** 1901. Versuche über Resorption, Verdauung und Stoffwechseln von Echinodermen. Ztschr. Physiol. Chem. 33. **Cole, W. H.** 1940. The composition of fluids and sera of some marine animals. Jour. Gen. Physiol. 23. **Cuénot, L.** 1891a. Études morphologiques sur les échinodermes. Arch. Biol. 11. 1891b. Études sur le sang et les glands lymphatiques dans la série animale. Pt. 2. Invertébrés. Arch. Zool. Exp. Gén., ser. 2, vol. 9. 1891c. Protozoaires commensaux et parasites des échinodermes. Revue Biol. Nord de la France 3. 1892. Commensaux et parasites des échinodermes. Revue Biol. Nord de la France 5. 1912. Contribution à la faune du Bassin d'Arcachon. V. Échinodermes. Bull. Sta. Biol. Arcachon 14. 1948. Anatomie, éthologie et systématiques des échinodermes. *In* P. Grassé (ed.), *Traité de zoologie*, vol. XI. **Davenport, D.** 1953. Studies in the physiology of commensalism. IV. Jour. Marine Biol. Assoc. 32. **Dawydoff, C.** 1928. *Traité d'embryologie comparée des invertébrés.* 1948. Embryologie des échinodermes. *In* P. Grassé (ed.), *Traité de zoologie*, vol. XI. **Delaunay, H.** 1923, 1926, 1927. Recherches biochimiques sur l'excrétion azotée des invertébrés. Bull. Sta. Biol. Arcachon 21, 23, 24. 1931. L'excrétion azotée des invertébrés. Biol. Rev. Cambridge Philos. Soc. 6. 1934. Le métabolisme de l'ammoniaque d'après les recherches relatives aux invertébrés. Ann. Physiol. Physiochim. Biol. 10. **Diebschlag, E.** 1938. Ganzheitliches Verhalten und Lernen bei Echinodermen. Ztschr. Vergl. Physiol. 25. **Döderlein, L.** 1900. Die Echinodermen der Olga Expedition. Wissensch. Meeresuntersuch., Abt. Helgoland, n. ser. 4. 1910. Asteroidea, Ophiuroidea, Echinoidea. Zool. Anthropol. Ergebnisse Forschungsreise West. und Zentral. Südafrica 1903–1905 von L. Schultze, vol. 4. **Döderlein, L.,** and **R. Hartmeyer.** 1910. Westindische Seeigel und Seesterne. Zool. Jahrb. Suppl. 11. **Durham, A. E.** 1891. On the wandering cells in echinoderms. Quart. Jour. Microsc. Sci. 33. **Edmondson, C. H.** 1946. Reef and shore fauna of Hawaii. Special Publ. Bernice P. Bishop Mus., Hawaii, 22. **Eichelbaum, E.** 1910. Über Nahrung und Ernährungsorgane von Echinodermen. Wissensch. Meeresuntersuch., Abt. Kiel 11. **Einarsson, H.** 1948. Echinoderma. Zoology of Iceland 4, pt. 70. **Ekman, S.** 1953. *Zoogeography of the sea.* **Ely, C. A.** 1942. Shallow-water Asteroidea and Ophiuroidea of Hawaii. Bull. Bernice P. Bishop Mus., Hawaii, 176. **Engel, H.** 1939. Echinoderms from Aruba, Curacao, Bonaire and northern Venezuela. Capita Zoologica 8, pt. 4. **Fabre-Domergue, M.** 1888. Étude sur l'organization des urcéolaires et sur quelques genres d'infusoires voisins de cette famille. Jour, Anat. Physiol. 24. **Farquhar, H.** 1895. Notes on New Zealand echinoderms. Trans. New Zealand Inst. 27. 1897. A contribution to the history of New Zealand echinoderms. Jour. Linnaean Soc. London, Zool. 26. 1898. Echinoderm fauna of New Zealand. Proc. Linnaean Soc. New South Wales 23. **Fauré-Fremiet, E.** 1927. Les amibocytes des invertébrés. Arch. Anat. Microsc. 23. **Fedotov, D.** 1924. Zur Morphologie des axialen Organkomplexes der Echinodermen. Ztschr. Wiss. Zool. 123. 1928. Über die Beziehungen der Echinodermklassen zu einander. Trav. Lab. Zool. et Sta.Biol.Sébastopol, ser. 2, no. 12. **Fell, H. B.** 1940. Origin of the vertebrate coelom. Nature, London, 145. 1945. A revision of the current theory of echinoderm embryology. Trans. Proc. Roy. Soc. New Zealand 75. 1948. Echinoderm embryology and the origin of chordates. Biol. Rev. Cambridge Philos. Soc. 23. 1953a. The origin and migration of Australasian echinoderm faunas since the Mesozoic.Trans. Roy. Soc. New Zealand 81. 1953b. Echinoderms from the subantarctic islands of New Zealand. Records Dominion Mus., New Zealand, 2, pt. II. **Florkin, M.** 1949. *Biochemical evolution.* 1952. Caractères biochimiques des categories supraspecifiques de la systématique animale. Ann. Soc. Roy. Zool. Belgique 83. **Florkin, M.,** and **G. Duchateau.** 1943. Les formes du système enzymatique de l'uricolyse et l'évolution du catabolisme purique chez les animaux. Arch. Internation. Physiol. 53. **Fox, D. L.** 1947. Carotenoid and indolic biochromes of animals. Ann. Review Biochem. 16. 1953. *Animal biochromes and structural colors.* **Fox, D. L.,** and **B.**

**Scheer.** 1941. Comparative studies of the pigments of some Pacific coast echinoderms. Biol. Bull. 80. **Geis, H. L.** 1936. Recent and fossil pedicellariae. Jour. Palaeontol. 10. **Gemmill, J. F.** 1919. Rhythmic pulsations in the madreporic vesicle. Quart. Jour. Microsc. Sci. 63. **George, W. C.** 1941. Comparative hematology. Quart. Review Biol. 16. **Giesbrecht, W.** 1899. Die Asterocheriden. Fauna und Flora des Golfes von Neapel, Monogr. 25. **Gislén, T.** 1924. Echinoderm studies. Zool. Bidrag 9. 1946. Haplozoa and the interpretation of Peridionites. Zool. Bidrag 25. **Gordon, Isabella.** 1929. Skeletal development in Arbacia, Echinarachnius and Leptasterias. Philos. Trans. Roy. Soc. London 207B. **Grave, C.** 1902. Feeding habits of a spatangoid, a brittle starfish, and a holothurian. Science 15. 1903. Occurrence among echinoderms of larvae with cilia arranged in transverse rings. Biol. Bull. 5. **Grieg, J. A.** 1921. Echinodermata. Repts. Scient. Results Michael Sars North Atlantic Deep Sea Exped. III, pt. 2. 1928a. The Folden Fjord Echinodermata. Tromso Mus. Skrifter I, no. 7. 1928b. Echinodermata from the Siberian Arctic Ocean. Scient. Results Norwegian North Polar Expedition Maud 1918–1925, vol. 5, no. 4. 1929a. Some echinoderms from the South Shetlands. Bergens Mus. Aarbok, no. 3. 1929b. Echinodermata from the Palmer Archipelago, South Shetlands, South Georgia and the Bouvet Islands. Scient. Results Norwegian Antarctic Exped. 1927–1928, vol. 1, no. 2. **Griffiths, A. B.** 1893. Blood of the invertebrata. Proc. Roy. Soc. Edinburgh 19. **Gudger, E. W.** 1933. Echinoderm enemies of fishes. Bull. New York Zool. Soc. 36. **Habe, T.** 1952. Parasitic gastropods found in echinoderms from Japan. Publ. Seto Marine Biol. Lab., vol. 2, no. 2, art. 6. **Heider, K.** 1912. Über Organverlagerungen bei den Echinodermen-Metamorphose. Verhandl. Dtsch. Zool. Gesellsch. 22. **Henri, V.,** and **S. Lalou.** 1904. Regulation osmotiques des liquides internes chez les échinodermes. Jour. Physiol. 6. **Hess, C.** 1914. Lichtsinn bei Echinodermen. Arch. Ges. Physiol. 160. **Hofsten, N. von.** 1915. Die Echinodermen des Eisfjords. Kungl. Svenska Vetensk. Akad. Handl. 54, no. 2. **Joubin, L.** 1928–1934. Faune et flore de la Mediterranée. Invertébrés I. **Kindred, J. E.** 1924. The cellular elements in the perivisceral fluid of echinoderms. Biol. Bull. 46. **Kleinholz, L.** 1938. Color changes in echinoderms. Pubbl. Staz. Zool. Napoli 17. **Koehler, R.** 1898. Échinides et ophiures provenant des campagnes du Yacht l'Hirondelle. Résultats Campagnes Scient. Monaco, Fasc. 12. 1901. Échinides et ophiures. Exped. Antarctiques Belge. Résultats Voyage Belgica 1897–1899, Zool. 1. 1906. Echinodermes. Stéllérides, ophiures et échinides. Expéd. Antarctique Française (1903–1905), vol. 6. 1908. Asteroidea, Ophiuroidea and Echinoidea of the Scottish National Antarctic Expedition. Repts. Scient. Results Voyage Scotia, V. Zool. pt. 13. 1909. Échinodermes provenant des campagnes du Yacht Princesse Alice (astéries, ophiures, échinides et crinoides). Résultats Campagnes Scient. Monaco, Fasc. 34. 1910. Astéries et ophiures des iles Aru et Kei. Abhandl. Senckenberg Naturforsch. Gesellsch. 33. 1911a. Echinoderma. Astéries, ophiures et échinides de l'expédition antarctique anglaise 1907–1909. British Antarctic Exped., Biology, vol. 2, pt. 4. 1911b. Échinodermes de Kerguelen. Ann. Inst. Océanogr. Monaco, vol. 3, fasc. 3. 1912. Échinodermes (astéries, ophiures et échinides). Deux. Expéd. Antarctique Française (1908–1910), vol. 5. 1914. Echinoderma I. Asteroidea, Ophiuroidea et Echinoidea. *In* W. Michaelsen, *Beiträge zur Kenntnis der Meeresfauna Westafrikas*, vol. 1. 1917. Échinodermes (astéries, ophiures, échinides) recueillis aux iles de Kerguelen en 1913–1914. Ann. Inst. Océanogr. Monaco 7, no. 8. 1921. Échinodermes. Faune de France 1. 1923. Astéries et ophiures recuellies par l'Expédition Antarctiques Suédoise. Further Zool. Results Swedish Antarctic Exped. 1901–1903, vol. 1, no. 1. 1924, 1927. *Les Échinodermes des mers d'Europe*, 2 vols. **Koehler, R.,** and **C. Vaney.** 1912. Nouvelles formes de gastéropodes ectoparasites. Bull. Scient. France Belgique 46. **Koller, G., and H. Meyer.** 1933. Die Atmung der Echinodermen. Biol. Centralbl. 53. **Kollmann, M.** 1908. Recherches sur les leucocytes et le tissue lymphoides des invertébrés. Ann. Sci. Natur., Zool., ser. 9, vol. 8. **Kükenthal, W.** 1897. Parasitische Schnecken. Abhandl. Senckenberg. Naturforsch. Gesellsch. 24. **Lederer, E.** 1938. Recherches sur les carotenoids des invertébrés. Bull. Soc. Chim. Biol. 20. **Lieberkind, I.** 1928. Echinoderma. Die Tierwelt Deutschlands, pt. 4. **Lipman, H.** 1940. Phosphatase activity in marine invertebrates. Bull. Pittsburgh Univ. 36. **Lo Bianco, S.** 1888. Il periodo di maturita sessuale degli animali del Golfo di Napoli. Mitt. Zool. Sta. Neapel 8. **Lönnberg, E.** 1931. Vorkommen carotinoider Stoffe bei marinen Evertebraten. Arkiv Zoologi 23A, no. 14. 1934a. Zur Kenntnis der Carotinoide bei marinen Evertebraten. Arkiv Zoologi 25A, no. 1. 1934b. Weitere Carotenoide der marinen Evertebraten. Arkiv Zoologi 26A, no. 7. **Lönnberg, E., and H. Hellström.** 1931. Carotinoide bei marinen Evertebraten. Arkiv Zoologi 23A, no. 15. **Ludwig, H.** 1879. Das Mundskelet der Asterien und Ophiuren. Ztschr. Wiss. Zool. 32. 1880. Ueber den primaren Steinkanal der Crinoideen. Ztschr. Wiss. Zool. 34. 1886. Echinodermen des Bering Meeres. Zool. Jahrb. Abt. System. 1. 1889-1907. Echinodermen. *In* **H. G. Bronn** (ed.), *Klassen und Ordnungen des Tierreichs*, Band II, Abt. 3. 1890. Über die Funktion der Madreporenplatte und des Steincanals der Echinodermen. Zool. Anz. 13. 1904. Brutpflege bei Echinodermen. Zool. Jahrb. Suppl. 7. 1905. Asterien und Ophiuren der Schwedischen Expedition nach den Magalhaensländern 1895-1897. Ztschr. Wiss Zool. 82. **MacBride, E. W.** 1906. Echinodermata. Cambridge Natural History, vol. I. 1914. *Textbook of embryology*. Vol. I. *Invertebrata*. 1920. Larvae of Echinoderma and Enteropneusta. Rept. British Antarctic Exped. 1910, Zool. IV. 1921, 1923. Echinoderm larvae and their bearing on classification. Nature, London, 108, 111. **MacGinitie, G. E., and N. MacGinitie.** 1949. *Natural history of marine animals.* **MacMunn, C. A.** 1889. Animal chromatology. Quart. Jour. Microsc. Sci. 30. **Mangold, E.** 1909. Sinnesphysiologische Studien an Echinodermen. Ztschr. Allg. Physiol. 9. 1921. Der Umkehrreflexe bei Seesternen und Schlangensternen. Arch. Ges. Physiol. 189. **Meyer, J.** 1914. Chemische Zusammensetzung wirbelloser Tiere. Wissensch. Meeresuntersuch. Abt. Kiel 16. **Moore, R. C., C. G. Lalicker, and A. G. Fischer.** 1952. *Invertebrate fossils.* **Moret, L.** 1953. *Manuel de paléontologie animale.* 3d ed. **Mortensen, T. H.** 1898. Die Echinodermenlarven der Plankton-Expedition. Ergebn. Plankton Exped., 2 J. 1913. Die Echinodermenlarven der deutschen Südpolar-Expedition. Dtsch. Südpolar Exped., Zool. 6. 1920. Development and larval forms of some Scandinavian echinoderms. Vidensk. Meddel. Dansk Naturhist. **Foren.** 71. 1921. *Studies of the development and larval forms of echinoderms.* 1922. The Danish expedition to the Kei Islands 1922. Vidensk. Meddel. Dansk Naturhist. Foren. 76. 1923a. Some echinoderms from the Trondhjem Fjiord. Kgl. Norske Vidensk. Selsk. Skrift. no. 3. 1923b. Echinoderm larvae and their bearing on classification. Nature, London, 111. 1924. Pighude (Echinodermer). Danmarks Fauna 27. 1925a. Échinodermes du Maroc et de Mauritanie. Bull. Soc. Sci. Natur. Maroc 5. 1925b. Echinoderms from the Antarctic Sea. Arkiv Zool. 17A, no. 31. 1927. *Handbook of the echinoderms of the British Isles.* 1931, 1937, 1938. Contributions to the study of the development and larval forms of echinoderms. I–IV. Kong. Danske Vidensk. Selsk. Skrift. Natuurvid. Math. Afd., ser. 9, vols. 4, 7. 1933a. Echinoderms of South Africa (Asteroidea and Ophiuroidea). Vidensk. Meddel. Dansk Naturhist. Foren. 93. 1933b. The echinoderms of St. Helena (other than crinoids). Vidensk. Meddel. Dansk. Naturhist. Foren. 93. 1936. Echinoidea and Ophiuroidea. Discovery Repts. XII. **Mortensen, T. H., and I. Lieberkind.** 1928. Echinoderma.

*In* G. **Grimpe** and **E. Wagler** (eds.), *Die Tierwelt der Nord- und Ostsee*, Teil VIII (Lief. XII). **Myers, R. G.** 1920. A chemical study of the blood of several invertebrate animals. Jour. Biol. Chem. 41. **Narasimhamurti, N.** 1932. The development and function of the heart and pericardium in Echinodermata. Proc. Roy. Soc. London 109B. **Nobre, A.** 1938. *Échinodermes de Portugal.* **Norris, E. R.,** and **D. Rao.** 1935. Phosphates of marine invertebrates. Jour. Biol. Chem. 108. **Okuda, S.** 1938. Japanese commensal polynoids. Annot. Zool. Japon. 15. **Page, A. H.** 1923. Asteriasterol. Jour. Biol. Chem. 57. **Parker, B.,** and **W. H. Cole.** 1940. Body fluids and sera of some marine invertebrates. Bull. Mt. Desert Is. Biol. Lab. for 1939. **Pelseneer, P.** 1928. Les parasites des mollusques et les mollusques parasites. Bull. Soc. Zool. France 53. **Perrier, E.** 1869, 1870. Recherches sur les pédicellaires. Ann. Sci. Natur. Zool., ser. 5, vol. 12, 13. 1894. *Expéditions scientifiques du Travailleur et du Talisman. Échinodermes.* **Phillips, A. H.** 1917, 1922. Analytical search for metals in Tortugas marine organisms. Carnegie Inst. Washington, Papers Dept. Marine Biol. 11, 18. **Piveteau, J.** (ed.). 1953. *Traité de paléontologie,* vol. III. **Pratje, A.** 1923. Das Leuchten der Organismen. Ergebn. Physiol. 21, Abt. 1. **Precht, H.** 1935. Epizoen der Kieler Bucht. Nova Acta Leopoldina, n. ser. 3. **Przylecki, S.** 1926. La répartition et la dégradation de l'acide urique chez les invertébrés. Arch. Internation. Physiol. 27. **Ricketts, E.** 1941. Annotated phyletic catalogue. *In* **J. Steinbeck** and **E. Ricketts,** *Sea of Cortez.* **Ricketts, E.,** and **J. Calvin.** 1938. *Between Pacific tides.* 1953. 2d ed. (ed. by **J. Hedgpeth**). **Roaf, H.** 1910. Contributions to the physiology of marine invertebrates. Jour. Physiol. 39. **Romanes, G.** 1885. *Jellyfish, starfish and sea urchins.* **Romanes, G.,** and **J. Ewart.** 1881. Observations on the locomotor system of Echinodermata. Philos. Trans. Roy. Soc. London 172, pt. VI. **Rosen, F.** 1913. Entwicklung von Echinaster sepositus. Anat. Anz. 44. **Rosoll, A.** 1888. Über zwei neue an Echinodermen parasitische Copepoden. Sitzungsber. Akad. Wissensch. Wien, Math. Natur. Kl. 97, Abt. 1. **Sanzo, L.** 1907. Stickstoff-Stoffwechsel bei marinen wirbellosen Tieren. Biol. Centralbl. 27. **Schepmen, M.,** and **H. Nierstrasz.** 1909. Parasitische Prosobranchier der Siboga Expedition. Siboga Exped. Monogr. 49, pt. 2. **Schlieper, C.** 1935. Neuere Ergebnisse und Probleme aus dem Gebiet des Osmoregulation wasserlebender Tiere. Biol. Rev. Cambridge Philos. Soc. 10. **Semon, R.** 1888. Die Entwicklung der Synapta. Jena. Ztschr. Wissensch. 20. **Shimer, H.,** and **R. Schrock.** 1944. *Index fossils of North America.* **Sieverts-Doreck, H.** 1937, 1939. Echinodermata. Fortschr. Palaeontologie 1, 2. **Smith, E. A.** 1876. Asteriidae and Ophiuridae from Kerguelens Island. Ann. Mag. Natur. Hist., ser. 4, vol. 17. 1879. Echinodermata (Zoology of Kerguelens Island). Philos. Trans. Roy. Soc. London 168, extra vol. **Smith, J. E.** 1937. The structure and function of the tube feet in certain echinoderms. Jour. Marine Biol. Assoc. 22. **Stephensen, K.** 1933. Some new copepods, parasites of ophiurids and echinids. Vidensk. Meddel. Dansk Naturhist. Foren. 93. **Studer, T.** 1880. Über Geschlechtdimorphismus bei Echinodermen. Zool. Anz. 3. **Stunkard, H. W.,** and **J. O. Corliss.** 1951. Revision of the family Umagillidae. Biol. Bull. 101. **Süssbach, S.,** and **A. Breckner.** 1911. Die Seeigel, Seesterne, und Schlangensterne der Nord- und Ostsee. Wissensch. Meeresuntersuch. Abt. Kiel 12. **Thomson, Wyville.** 1877. *The Voyage of the Challenger. The Atlantic,* vol. II. 1878. Peculiarities in the mode of propagation of certain echinoderms of the southern sea. Jour. Linnaean Soc. London, Zool. 13. **Thorson, G.** 1946. Reproduction and larval development of Danish marine bottom invertebrates. Meddel. Komm. Danmarks Fiskerei- og Havundersögelser, ser. Plankton 4, no. 1. **Topping, F.,** and **J. Fuller.** 1942. The accommodation of some marine invertebrates to reduced osmotic pressures. Biol. Bull. 82. **Tortonese, E.** 1934. Asterie ed echini della Patagonia e della Terra del

Fuoco. Boll. Mus. Zool. Anat. Comp. Univ. Torino, ser. III, vol. 44, no. 51. 1936. Echinodermi del Mar Rosso. Ann. Mus. Civico Stor. Natur. Genova 59. **Ubaghs, G.** 1953. Classe des stelléroides. *In* **J. Piveteau** (ed.), *Traité de paléontologie,* vol. III. **Uexküll, J. von.** 1899. Die Physiologie der Pedicellarien. Ztschr. Biol. 37. **Valente, D.,** and **A. Bruno.** 1951. Contendo mineral do sangue de invertebrados marinhos. Zoologia, Sao Paulo, Brazil, no. 16. **Van der Heyde, H.** 1922. *On the physiology of digestion, respiration and excretion in echinoderms.* 1923a. La résorption chez les échinodermes. Arch. Néerland. Physiol. 8. 1923b. Y-a-t'il des enzymes dans le liquide périviscéral des échinodermes? Arch. Néerland. Physiol. 8. 1923c. Sur l'excrétion chez les échinodermes. Arch. Néerland. Physiol. 8. **Vaney, C.** 1913. L'adaptation des gasteropodes au parasitisme. Bull. Scient. France Belgique 47. **Verrill, A. E.** 1880, 1882, 1885. Remarkable marine fauna occupying the outer banks. Amer. Jour. Sci., ser. 3, vols. 20, 23, 29. **Vinogradov, A.** 1953. The elementary chemical composition of marine organisms. Mem. Sears Foundation Marine Research no. 2. **Webb, D.** 1937. Spectigraphic analysis of marine invertebrates. Scient. Proc. Roy. Dublin Soc. 21. **Westblad, E.** 1953. New Turbellaria parasites in echinoderms. Arkiv Zool., ser. 2, vol. 5, no. 2. **Whitehouse, F.** 1941. Early Cambrian echinoderms similar to the larval stage of recent forms. Mem. Queensland Mus. 12. **Woodland, W.** 1907. Studies in spicule formation. V. Quart. Jour. Microsc. Sci. 51. **Yakovlev, J.** 1918. Some new data on Cryptocrinus and the connection between the Crinoidea and Cystoidea. Annuaire Soc. Paléontol. Russe 2. 1928. Sur l'évolution discontinué chez les brachiopodes et les échinodermes. Palaeobiologica 1. **Yamazi, I.** 1950. Autotomy and regeneration in Japanese sea stars and ophiurans. Annot. Zool. Japon. 23. **Ziesenhenne, F.** 1937. Echinoderms from the west coast of Lower California, the Gulf of California and Clarion Islands. Zoologica, New York, 22. **Zittel, K. von.** 1915. *Grundzüge der Paläontologie. I. Invertebrata.* 4th ed.

## Noncrinoid Pelmatozoa

**Barrande, J.** 1887–1899. *Système Silurien du centre de la Bohème. Pt. I. Recherches paléontologiques.* Vol. VII. *Classe des échinodermes. Ordre des Cystidées.* **Bassler, R.** 1935. The classification of the Edrioasteroidea. Smithsonian Miscell. Collect. 93, no. 8. 1936. New species of American Edrioasteroidea. Smithsonian Miscell. Collect. 95, no. 6. **Bather, F. A.** 1898, 1899a. Studies in Edrioasteroidea. Geol. Mag. 5, 6. 1899b. *Genera and species of Blastoidea in the British Museum.* 1906. Ordovician Cystidea from Burma. Mem. Geol. Survey India, Paleontologica Indica, n. s. 2, no. 3. 1913. Caradocian Cystidea from Girvan. Trans. Roy. Soc. Edinburgh 49. 1918. Eocystis. Geol. Mag., ser. 6, vol. 5. 1925. Cothurnocystis. Palaeontol. Ztschr. 7. 1928. Dendrocystis. Geol. Survey Canada, Bull. 49. 1930. A class of Echinoderma without trace of radiate symmetry. Arch. Zool. Ital. 14. **Chauvel, J.** 1939–1941. Recherches sur les cystides et les carpoides armoricains. Mém Soc. Géol. Minéral. Bretagne 5. **Clarke, J. M.** 1901. New Agelacrinites. Bull. New York State Mus. 49. **Clive, L.** 1936, 1937. Blastoids of the Osage group, Mississippian. Jour. Palaeontol. 10, 11. **Croneis, C.,** and **H. Geis.** 1940. Ontogeny of the Blastoidea. Jour. Palaeontol. 14. **Ehrenberg, K.** 1929. Pelmatozoan root-forms. Bull. Amer. Mus. Natur. Hist. 59. **Etheridge, R.,** and **P. H. Carpenter.** 1886. *Catalogue of the Blastoidea in the British Museum.* **Foerste, J.** 1916. Comarocystites and Caryocrinites. Ottawa Naturalist 30. 1938. Echinodermata. *In* **C. Resser** and **B. Howell** (eds.), Lower Cambrian Olenellus zone of the Appalachians. Bull. Geol. Soc. America 49. **Hall, J.** 1872. New species of Crinoidea and other fossils. Rept. New York State Mus. 24. **Hecker, R.** 1938. New data on Rhipidicystis. C. R. Acad. Sci. USSR 19. 1940. Carpoidea, Eocrinoidea, und Ophiocistia des Ordoviziums des Leningrader Gebietes. Trudi Acad. Sci. USSR Inst. Palaeontol. 9, no. 4. **Hudson, G.** 1911. Early Siluric Pelmatozoa. Bull. New York State Mus. 149. **Hussey, R.** 1928. Cystoids from the Trenton rocks of Michigan. Univ. Michigan Mus. Palaeontol. Contrib. 3. **Jaekel, O.** 1899. *Stammesgeschichte der Pelmatozoen.* I. *Thecoidea und Cystoidea.* 1918. Phylogenie und System der Pelmatozoen. Ztschr. Palaeontol. 3. **Meek, F.,** and **A. Worthen.** 1873. Descriptions of invertebrates from carboniferous systems. Geol. Survey Illinois 5. **Peck, R.** 1938. Blastidea of Missouri. Univ. Missouri Studies 13, no. 4. **Piveteau, J.** 1953. Classe des Édrioasteroides. *In* J. **Piveteau** (ed.), *Traité de paléontologie,* vol. III. **Raymond, P.** 1915. Canadian species of Agelacrinites. Ottawa Naturalist 29. **Regnéll, G.** 1945. Non-crinoid Pelmatozoa from the Palaeozoic of Sweden. Meddel. Lunds Geol. Mineral. Inst., no. 108. **Reimann, I.** 1935. Middle Devonian blastoids. Buffalo Soc. Natur. Hist. Bull. 17. **Rowley, R.** 1891. New Echinoderma from the Mississippian of Missouri. Kansas City Scientist 5. **Schuchert, C.** 1904. Siluric and Devonian Cystidea. Smithsonian Miscell. Collect. 47. 1913. Cystoidea. Maryland Geol. Survey, Lower Devonian. **Sinclair, G.** 1948. Notes on Ordovician cystids. Jour. Palaeontol. 22. **Volborth, A.** 1870. Über Achradocystis und Cystoblastus. Mém. Acad. Sci. St. Pétersbourg, ser. 7, vol. 16, no. 2. **Wachsmuth, C.** 1884. New genus and species of blastoids. Proc. Davenport Acad. Natur. Sci. 4. **Wachsmuth, C.,** and **F. Springer.** 1880. New species of crinoids and blastoids. Geol. Survey Illinois 8. **Wiiliams, S.** 1918. Agelacrinites and Streptaster. Ohio Jour. Sci. 19. **Yakovlev, N.** 1918. Some new data on the connection between the Crinoidea and Cystoidea. Annuaire Soc. Paléontol. Russie 2.

### CRINOIDEA

**Abeloos, M.,** and **G. Teissier.** 1926. Notes sur les pigments animaux. Bull. Soc. Zool. France 51. **Agassiz, A.** 1878a. Specimen of Holopus. Mem. Mus. Comp. Zool. Harvard 4, no. 8. 1878b. Dredging operations of the Blake. Bull. Mus. Comp. Zool. Harvard 5. 1879. Dredging operations of the Blake. Bull. Mus. Comp. Zool. Harvard 5. 1890. Notes on Calamocrinus. Bull. Mus. Comp. Zool. Harvard 20. 1892. Calamocrinus diomedae. Mem. Mus. Comp. Zool. Harvard 17. **Andersson, K.** 1908. Brutpflege bei Antedon. Wissensch. Ergebn. Schwed. Südpolar-Exped. 1901–1903, 5, Zool. 1. **Barrois, J.** 1888. Développement de la comatule. Recueil Zool. Suisse 4. **Bartsch, P.** 1907. A new parasitic Eulima. Proc. U.S. Nation. Mus. 32. 1909. Eulima capillastericola. Vidensk. Meddel. Dansk Naturhist. Foren., ser. 7, vol. 1. **Bassler, R.,** and **M. Moodey.** 1943. Bibliographic and faunal index of Palaeozoic pelmatozoan echinoderms. Geol. Soc. America, Special Paper 45. **Bather, F. A.** 1896. Uintacrinus. Proc. Zool. Soc. London for 1895. 1898. Pentacrinus. Natural Science 12. 1899. A phylogenetic classification of the Pelmatozoa. Rept. British Assoc. Advance. Sci. for 1898. 1908. Ptilocrinus. Bull. Acad. Roy. Belgique, Cl. Sci. **Beard, J.** 1884. Life-history and development of Myzostoma. Mitt. Staz. Zool. Neapel 5. **Bohn, G.** 1910. Les réactions des comatules C. R. Assoc. Française Avanc. Sci. 39, pt. II. **Bosshard, H.** 1900. Verbindungsweise der Skelettstücke der Arme und Ranken von Antedon. Jena. Ztschr. Naturwiss. 34. **Bury, H.** 1888. Early stages in the development of Antedon. Philos. Trans. Roy. Soc. London 179B. **Carpenter, P. H.** 1884. Report on the Crinoidea. Pt. I. The stalked crinoids. Rept. Scient. Results Voyage Challenger, Zool. XI. 1888. Pt. II. The Comatulae. Rept. Scient. Results Voyage Challenger, Zool. XXVI. **Carpenter, W. B.** 1866, 1876. Structure, physiology and development of Antedon. Philos. Trans. Roy. Soc. London 156, pt. 1; Proc. Roy. Soc. London 24. 1884. On the nervous system of the

Crinoidea. Proc. Roy. Soc. London 37. **Chadwick, H. C.** 1907. Antedon. Liverpool Marine Biol. Comm., Mem. 15. **Clark, A. H.** 1907a. Two new crinoids from the North Pacific. Proc. U.S. Nation. Mus. 32. 1907b. New species of Ptilocrinus. Proc. U.S. Nation. Mus. 32. 1908a. Infrabasals in recent genera of Pentacrinitidae. Proc. U.S. Nation. Mus. 33. 1908b. New stalked crinoids from the eastern coast of North America. Proc. U.S. Nation. Mus. 34. 1908c. Two new crinoid genera. Proc. Biol. Soc. Washington 21. 1908d. The nomenclature of recent crinoids. Proc. U.S. Nation. Mus. 34. 1908e. The genus Ptilocrinus. Amer. Natural. 42. 1908f. Some points in the ecology of recent crinoids. Amer. Natural. 42. 1908g. The recent crinoids and their relation to sea and land. Geogr. Jour. 32. 1909a. Encrinus. Ann. Mag. Natur. Hist., ser. 8, vol. 3. 1909b. Phototaxis among crinoids. Proc. Biol. Soc. Washington 22. 1909c. Four new species of Rhizocrinus. Proc. U.S. Nation. Mus. 36. 1909d. The non-muscular articulations of crinoids. Amer. Natural. 43. 1910a. Pentamerous symmetry of Crinoidea. Amer. Jour. Sci., ser. 4, vol. 29. 1910b. Origin of the crinoidal muscular articulations. Amer. Jour. Sci., ser. 4, vol. 29. 1910c. The phylogenetic interrelationship of the recent crinoids. Proc. U.S. Nation. Mus. 38. 1910d. Proisocrinus. Proc. U.S. Nation. Mus. 38. 1911a. Thalassocrinus. Proc. U.S. Nation. Mus. 39. 1911b. The systematic position of Marsupites. Proc. U.S. Nation. Mus. 40. 1912a. The crinoids of the Indian Ocean. Echinoderma of the Indian Museum, pt. 7. 1912b. Naumachotrinus. Proc. U.S. Nation. Mus. 42. 1915a. A monograph of the existing crinoids, vol. I, pt. 1. Bull. U.S. Nation. Mus. 82. 1915b. Die Crinoiden der Antarktis. Dtsch. Südpolar Exped. 16, Zool. 8. 1919. The systematic position of Holopus. Jour. Washington Acad. Sci. 9. 1921a. A monograph of the existing crinoids, vol. I, pt. 2. Bull U.S. Nation. Mus. 82. 1921b. Sea-lilies and feather-stars. Smithsonian Miscell. Collect. 72, no. 7. 1923a. A revision of the recent Pentacrinidae. Jour. Washington Acad. Sci. 13. 1923b. Crinoida. Danish Ingolf Exped., vol. IV, pt. 5. 1931. A monograph of the existing crinoids, vol. I, pt. 3. Bull. U.S. Nation. Mus. 82. 1940. The Family Antedonidae in the west tropical Atlantic. Mem. Soc. Cubana Hist. Natur. 14. 1941, 1947, 1950. A monograph of the existing crinoids, vol. I, pts. 4a, b, c. Bull. U.S. Nation. Mus. 82. **Clark, H. L.** 1915. The comatulids of Torres Strait. Carnegie Inst. Washington, Papers Dept. Marine Biol. 8. 1917. The habits and reactions of Tropiometra carinata. Carnegie Inst. Washington, Papers Dept. Marine Biol. 11. **Dan, K.,** and **J. Dan.** 1941a. Spawning habit of Comanthus japonicus. Jap. Jour. Zool. 9. 1941b. Early development of Comanthus japonicus. Jap. Jour. Zool. 9. **Danielsson, D.** 1892. Crinoidea. Norwegian North-Atlantic Exped. 1876–1878, Zool. 21. **Danielssen, D.,** and **J. Koren.** 1877. Fra den Norske Nordhavsexpedition Echinodermer. Nyt Mag. Naturvid. 23. **Dendy, A.** 1886. On the regeneration of the visceral mass in Antedon. Studies Biol. Lab. Owens College 1. **Dixon, F.** 1850. *Geology and fossils of the tertiary and cretaceous formations of Sussex.* **Döderlein, L.** 1907. Die gestielten Crinoiden der Siboga Expedition. Siboga Exped. Monogr. 42a. 1911. Die gestielten Crinoiden der deutschen Tiefsee-Expedition. Wissensch. Ergebn. Dtsch. Tiefsee Exped. Valdivia 17. **Ehrenberg, K.** 1922. Über eingerollte Pelmatozoen-Stiele. Acta Zoologica 3. **Fedotov, D.** 1930. Über die vergleichende Morphologie der Crinoiden. Zool. Anz. 89. **Giesbrecht, W.** 1900. Mitteilungen über Copepoden. Mitt. Zool. Stat. Neapel 14. **Gislén, T.** 1924. The articulations of the arm-joints in the crinoids. Zool. Bidrag 9. 1927. Japanese crinoids. Vidensk. Meddel. Dansk Naturhist. Foren 83. 1938a. A revision of the recent Bathycrinidae. Acta Univ. Lundensis 34, no. 10. 1938b. Affinities of the Hyocrinidae. Acta Univ. Lundensis 34, no. 17. 1940a. Echinoderms from the Iranian Gulf. Crinoidea. Danish Scient. Invest. Iran, pt. 2. 1940b. A collection of crinoids from the South Sea Islands. Kungl. Svenska Vetensk. Akad. Handl., ser. 3, vol. 18. **Goldring, W.** 1923. Devonian crinoids of the State of New York. Mem. New York State Mus. 16. **Graff, L. von.** 1875. Stylina comatulicola. Ztschr. Wiss. Zool., suppl. to 25. 1877. *Das Genus Myzostoma.* 1884, 1887. On the Myzostomida collected by the Challenger. Rept. Scient. Results Voyage Challenger, Zool. 10, 20. **Hall, J.** 1862. Contributions to palaeontology. 15th Ann. Rept. New York State Mus. (then called State Cabinet Natur. Hist.). **Hamann, O.** 1889. Anatomie und Histologie der Crinoiden. Jen. Ztschr. Naturwiss. 23. **Hartlaub, C.** 1912. Die Comatuliden. Repts. Dredging Exped. Blake. Mem. Mus. Comp. Zool. Harvard 27. **Jägersten, G.** 1940. Myzostomum cirriferum. Arkiv Zoologi 32B, art. 9. **Jickeli, C.** 1884. Über das Nervensystem und die Sinnesorgane der Comatula. Zool. Anz. 7. **John, D.** 1937. Crinoidea. Exped. Antarctique Belge, Rapports Scient., Zool. I. 1938. Crinoidea. Discovery Repts. 18. 1939. Crinoidea. Repts. British, Austral., New Zealand Antarctic Research Exped. 1929–1931, ser. B, vol. 4, pt. 6. **Koehler, R., and F. A. Bather.** 1902. Gephyrocrinus. Mem. Soc. Zool. France 15. **Krukenberg, C.** 1882. Farbstoff von Comatula und Antedon. Vergl. Physiol. Studien, ser. 2, Abt. 3. **Lacaze-Duthiers, H. de.** 1872. Station du Pentacrinus sur les côtes de France. Arch. Zool. Exp. Gén. 1, Notes et revue, no. 3. **Langeloh, H.** 1937. Über die Bewegungen von Antedon. Zool. Jahrb. Abt. Allg. Zool. 57. **Lönnberg, E.** 1932. Zur Kenntnis der Carotinoide bei marinen Evertebraten. Arkiv Zoologi 23A, no. 15. **Loriol, P. de.** 1882–1884, 1886. Crinoides. *In* d'Orbigny (ed.), *Paléontologie française,* Ser. I, *Animaux invertébrés, Terrain Jurassique,* vol. XI, pts. 1 and 2. **Ludwig, H.** 1877. Beiträge zur Anatomie der Crinoideen. Ztschr. Wiss. Zool. 28. 1880. Die Bildung der Eihülle bei Antedon. Zool. Anz. 3. 1907. Die Seelilien. *In* H. G. Bronn (ed.), *Klassen und Ordnungen des Tierreichs,* vol. 2, pt. 3, book 5. **MacMunn, C.** 1889. Contributions to animal chromatology. Quart. Jour. Microsc. Sci. 30. **Marshall, A.** 1884. Nervous system of Antedon. Quart. Jour. Microsc. Sci. 24. **Meek, F.** 1873. Fossil invertebrates of the Silurian and Devonian systems. Geol. Survey Ohio, vol. I, pt. 2. **Meek, F., and W. Gurley.** 1896. Fossils from the Palaeozoic rocks of the Mississippian valley. Bull. Illinois State Mus. Natur. Hist. 8. **Metschnikoff, E.** 1871. Beiträge zur Entwicklungsgeschichte einiger niederen Thiere. 7. Comatula. Bull. Acad. Sci. St. Pétersbourg 15. **Miller, J. S.** 1821. A natural history of the Crinoidea. **Minckert, W.** 1905. Regeneration bei Comatuliden. Arch. Naturgesch. 71, pt. 1. **Moore, A. R.** 1924. The nervous mechanism of coordination in Antedon. Jour. Gen. Physiol. 6. **Moore, R. C., and L. Laudon.** 1941. Symbols for crinoid parts. Jour. Palaeontol. 15. 1943. Classification and evolution of Palaeozoic crinoids. Geol. Soc. America, Special Paper 46. **Mortensen, T.** 1911. A new species of Entoprocta. Meddel. Grönland 45. 1917. A new viviparous crinoid from the Antarctic Sea. Vidensk. Meddel. Dansk Naturhist. Foren 68. 1920a. The Crinoidea. Wissensch. Ergebn. Schwed. Südpolar-Exped. 1901–1903, vol. 6, Zool. II, Lief. 8. 1920b. Studies in the development of crinoids. Carnegie Inst. Washington, Papers Dept. Marine Biol. 16. **Moseley, H.** 1887. On the coloring matter of various animals. Quart. Jour. Microsc. Sci. 17. **Nouvel, H.** 1953. Un Hippolyte commensal de Antedon. Arch. Zool. Exp. Gén. 90, Notes et Revue no. 2. **Okada, Y.** 1926. Cirripèdes ascothoraciques. Bull. Mus. Nation. Hist. Natur. Paris 32. **Perrier, E.** 1873. L'Anatomie et la régénération des bras de la Comatula. Arch. Zool. Exp. Gén. 2. 1886. L'Organisation et la développement de la comatule de la Mediterranée. Nouv. Arch. Mus. Hist. Natur. Paris, ser. 2, vol. 9. **Potts, F.** 1915a. The fauna associated with the crinoids of a tropical reef. Carnegie Inst. Washington, Papers Dept. Marine Biol. 8. 1915b. The color variations of the fauna associated with crinoids. Proc. Cambridge Philos.

Soc. 18. **Prenant, M.** 1928. Notes sur les saccules de la comatule. Bull. Soc. Zool. France 53. **Prouho, H.** 1892. Sur deux myzostomes. C. R. Acad. Sci. Paris 115. **Przibram, H.** 1901. Experimentelle Studien über Regeneration. Arch. Entw'mech. Organismen 11. **Regnéll, G.** 1948. Swedish Hybocrinida. Arkiv Zoologi 40A, no. 9. **Reichensperger, A.** 1905. Zur Anatomie von Pentacrinus. Ztschr. Wiss. Zool. 80. 1908. Über das Vorkommen von Drüsen bei Crinoiden. Zool. Anz. 33. 1912. Beiträge zur Histologie und zum Verlauf der Regeneration bei Crinoiden. Ztschr. Wiss. Zool. 101. **Riggenbach, E.** 1901. Über Selbstverstümmelung. Zool. Anz. 24. **Rosoll, A.** 1888. Über zwei neue an Echinodermen lebende parasitische Copepoden. Sitzungsber. Akad. Wissensch. Wien, Math.-Naturwiss. Kl. 97, Abt. 1. **Russo, A.** 1902. Studi sugli Echinodermi. Atti Accad. Gioenia 12, mem. 7. **Sars, M.** 1864. [Finding of Rhizocrinus lofotensis.] Forhandl. Vidensk. Selsk. Christiana. 1868. Mémoires pour servir a la connaissance des crinoides vivants. Progr. Univ. Roy. Norvége. **Sardeson, F.** 1908. Discoid crinoidal roots and Camarocrinus. Jour. Geol. 16. **Schneider, K.** 1902. *Lehrbuch der vergleichenden Histologie der Tiere.* Seeliger, O. 1892. Studien zur Entwicklungsgeschichte der Crinoiden. Zool. Jahrb. Abt. Anat. 6. **Springer, F.** 1907. Uintacrinus. Mem. Mus. Comp. Zool. Harvard 25. 1911. On a Trenton echinoderm fauna. Canada Dept. Mines, Geol. Survey Branch, Mem. no. 15-P. 1917. On the crinoid genus Scyphocrinus and its bulbous root Camarocrinus. Smithsonian Inst. Publ. no. 2440. 1920. The Crinoidea Flexibilia. Smithsonian Inst. Publ. no. 2501. 1925. The genus Pentacrinus in Alaska. Proc. U.S. Nation. Mus. 67, art. 5. 1926. Unusual forms of fossil crinoids. Proc. U.S. Nation. Mus. 67, art. 9. **Suhm, W.** 1876. Von den Challenger Expedition VI. Ztschr. Wiss. Zool. 26. **Thomson, Wyville.** 1865. On the embryogeny of Antedon. Trans. Roy. Soc. London 155, pt. 2. 1872. On the crinoids of the Porcupine. Proc. Roy. Soc. Edinburgh 7. 1878. Notice of new crinoids belonging to the Apiocrinidae. Jour. Linnaean Soc. London, Zool. 13. **Ubaghs, G.** 1953. Classe des Crinoides *In* J. Piveteau (ed.), *Traité de paléontologie,* vol. III. **Valette, D.** 1916. Crinoides de la Craie Blanche. Bull. Soc. Sci. Hist. Natur. Yonne 70, pt. 2. **Wachsmuth, C.,** and **F. Springer.** 1879–1886. Revision of the Palaeocrinoidea. Proc. Acad. Natur. Sci. Philadelphia 31, 33, 37, 38. 1897. North American Crinoidea Camerata. Mem. Mus. Comp. Zool. Harvard 20, 21. **Wheeler, W.** 1896. The sexual phases of Myzostoma. Mitt. Staz. Zool. Neapel. 12. **Yakovlev, J.** 1944. Structure and respiratory function of the anal sac of crinoids. C. R. Acad. Sci. USSR 44.

## HOLOTHUROIDEA

**Ackermann, G.** 1902. Anatomie und Zwittrigkeit der Cucumaria laevigata. Ztschr. Wiss. Zool. 72. **Anderson, A.** 1859. A few remarks concerning a parasitic fish found in Holothuria. Natuurk. Tijdschr. Nederland Indie 20. **Anthony, R.** 1916. Entovolva. Arch. Zool. Exp. Gén. 55. **Augustin, E.** 1908. Ueber Japanische Seewalzen. Abhandl. Mat. Physik. Kl. Bayer Akad. Wissensch. München, suppl., Beiträge zur Naturgesch. Ostasiens II. **Ayres, W.** 1851–1854. Notices of holothuriae. Proc. Boston Soc. Natur. Hist. 4. **Balamuth, W.** 1941. Anatomy of Licnophora macfarlandi. Jour. Morphol. 68. **Bartels, P.** 1895. Excretion der Holothurien. Zool. Anz. 18. 1896. Über die Cuvier'schen Organe der Holothuria poli. Sitzungsber. Niederrhein. Gesell. Natur. und Heilkunde. 1902. Zur Histologie der Cuvier'schen Organe. Zool. Anz. 25. **Baur, A.** 1864. Die Eingeweideschnecke in der Leibeshöhle der Synapta. Nova Acta Acad. Leopold. Carol. 31. **Beauchamp, P. de.** 1909. Infusoires du poumon des holothuries. Bull. Soc. Zool. France 34. **Becher, S.** 1906. Eine brutpflegende Synaptide der Nordsee. Zool. Anz. 30. 1907. Rhabdomolgus ruber. Ztschr. Wiss. Zool. 88. 1909a. Die

Hörblaschen der Leptosynapta. Biol. Centralbl. 29. 1909b. Die Stammgeschichte der Seewalzen. Ergebn. Zool. 1. 1910. Morphologie und Systematik der Paractinopoden. Zool. Jahrb. Abt. Anat. 29. 1912. Labidoplax buski. Ztschr. Wiss. Zool. 101. **Bell, F. J.** 1881. Echinoderms of the Straits of Magellan and of the coast of Patagonia. Proc. Zool. Soc. London. 1882. On the genus Psolus. Proc. Zool. Soc. London. 1884. On the structural characters of the cotton spinner. Proc. Zool. Soc. London. **Benazzi-Lentati, G.** 1941. Sulla distribuzione del glicogeno degli invertebrati. Arch. Zool. Ital., suppl. to 29. **Bertolini, F.** 1930. Regenerazione dell' apparato digerente nelle olothurie. Atti. Accad. Nazion. Lincei, ser. 6, Rendiconti, Cl. Sci. Fis. 11. 1931a. Regenerazione dell' apparato digerente nello Stichopus. Pubbl. Staz. Zool. Napoli 10. 1931b. Regenerazione dell' intestino nelle oloturie. Arch. Zool. Ital. 16. 1932. La autotomia dell' apparato digerente e la sua regenerazione nelle oloturie. Atti Accad. Nazion. Lincei, ser. 6, Rendiconti, Cl. Sci. Fis. 15. 1933a. Regenerazione dell' apparato dirigente nelle Holothuria. Pubbl. Staz. Zool. Napoli 12. 1933b. Sulle funzioni dei polmoni acquatici delle oloturie. Pubbl. Staz. Zool. Napoli 13. 1934. Nouve ricerche sulla funzione respiratoria dei pulmoni acquatica delle oloturie. Arch. Zool. Ital. 20. 1935. Ricerche sugli organi respiratori delle oloturie. Atti Real Inst. Veneto Sci. Lett. Arti 94. 1937. L'escrezione delle oloturie. C. R. 12 Internation. Congr. Zool, vol. 2; *also* Mitt. Zool. Stat. Neapel 15. **Bierry, H.,** and **B. Gonzon.** 1937. Spectres de fluorescence d'un pigment isolé des holothuries. C. R. Soc. Biol. Paris 124. **Blaess, H.** 1943. Beiträge zur chemischen und optischen Kenntnis der Hartteile in der Holothurienhaut. Ztschr. Morphol. Ökol. Tiere 40. **Bonnevie, Kristine.** 1902. Enteroxenos östergreni. Zool. Jahrb. Abt. Anat. 15. **Bordas, L.** 1899. Anatomie et fonctions physiologiques des poumons aquatiques des holothurys. Ann. Mus. Hist. Natur. Marseille, Zool. 5, Mém. no. 3. **Botazzi, F.** 1908. Osmotic Druck und elektrische Leitfähigkeit der Flussigkeiten der tierischen Organismen. Ergebn. Physiol. 7. 1909. Die Kolloide der Leibeshöhlenflüssigkeit und des Blutes der Seetieren. Kolloid. Ztschr. 5. **Britten, M.** 1906. Holothurien aus dem Japanischen und Ochokskischen Meere. Bull. Acad. Sci. St. Pétersbourg, ser. 5, vol. 25. **Broili, F.** 1926. Eine Holothurie aus dem oberen Jura von Franken. Sitzungsber. Bayer. Akad. Wissensch. München 3. **Bruun, A. F.** 1951. The Philippine Trench and its bottom fauna. Nature, London, 168. **Buddenbrock, W.** 1912. Über die Funktion der Statocysts in sandgrabende Meerestiere. Biol. Centralbl. 32; Zool. Jahrb. Abt. Allg. Zool. 33. 1938. Einige Beobachtungen über der Tätigkeit der Wasserlungen der Holothurien. Ztschr. Vergl. Physiol. 26. **Budington, R.** 1937. The normal spontaneity of movement of the respiratory muscles of Thyone. Physiol. Zool. 10. **Carus, J.** 1885. *Prodromus faunae Mediterraneae*, vol. I. **Chadwick, H. C.** 1891. Notes on Cucumaria planci. Trans. Liverpool Biol. Soc. 5. **Cherbonnier, G.** 1941a. Note sur une nouvelle holothurie antarctique. Bull. Soc. Zool. France 66. 1941b. Étude anatomique et biogéographique sur deux Cucumaria abyssaux. Bull. Mus. Nation. Hist. Natur. Paris, ser. 2, vol. 13. 1947a. Étude de la couronne calcaire peripharyngienne. Bull. Lab. Marit. Dinard 29. 1947b. Note sur une holothurie abyssale. Bull. Mus. Nation. Hist. Natur. Paris, ser. 2, vol. 19. 1949. Primera expedicion antarctica Chilena, une nouvelle holothurie incubatrice. Revista Biol. Marine Univ. Chile 1. **Chun, C.** 1892. Die Bildung der Skeletttheile bei Echinodermen. Zool. Anz. 15. 1896. Atlantis, biologische Studien über pelagische Organismen. Biblio theca Zoologica, vol. 7, Heft 19. 1900. *Aus den Tiefen des Weltmeeres.* **Clark, H. L.** 1898. Synapta vivipara. Mem. Boston Soc. Natur. Hist. 5. 1899. The Synaptas of the New England coast. Bull. U.S. Fish. Comm. 19. 1901. The holothurians of the Pacific coast of North America. Zool. Anz. 24. 1902. The breeding habits of holothurians. Rept. Michigan Acad. Sci. 3. 1907. The apodous holothurians. Smithsonian Miscell. Collect. 35, no. 1723. 1910a. The development of an apodous holothurian. Jour. Exp. Zool. 9. 1910b. The echinoderms of Peru. Bull. Mus. Comp. Zool. Harvard 52. 1912. Fossil holothurians. Science 35. 1920. Tropical Pacific Holothuroidea. Mem. Mus. Comp. Zool. Harvard 39. 1922. The holothurians of the genus Stichopus. Bull. Mus. Comp. Zool. Harvard 65. 1924. The Synaptinae. Bull. Mus. Comp. Zool. Harvard 65. 1935. The holothurian genus Caudina. Ann. Mag. Natur. Hist., ser. 10, vol. 15. **Clerc, A.** 1904. Ferments digestifs de quelques échinodermes. C. R. Soc. Biol. Paris 56, pt. 1. **Colwin, Laura.** 1948. Notes on the spawning of Thyone. Biol. Bull. 95. **Cooper, H. S.** 1880. *Coral lands,* vol. II. **Cornil, L., M. Mosinger,** and **J. Calen.** 1935a. Sur la disposition reticulée du système pigmentaire chez les holothuries. C. R. Soc. Biol. Paris 118. 1935b. La désintégration physiologique de l'appareil pigmentaire chez les holothuries. C. R. Soc. Biol. Paris 119. **Cosmovici, V.** 1913. Sur Urceolaria synaptae. Bull. Soc. Zool. France 38. 1914. Urceolaria synaptae. Mém. Soc. Zool. France 26. **Costello, D. P.** 1946. The swimming of Leptosynapta. Biol. Bull. 90. **Courtney, W.** 1927. Fertilization in Stichopus californicus. Publ. Puget Sound Biol. Sta. 5. **Croneis, C.,** and **J. McCormack.** 1932. Fossil Holothurioidea. Jour. Palaeontol. 6. **Crozier, W. J.** 1914. The orientation of a holothurian by light. Amer. Jour. Physiol. 36. 1915. The sensory reactions of holothurians. Zool. Jahrb. Abt. Allg. Zool. 35. 1916. The rhythmic pulsation of the cloaca of Holothuria. Jour. Exp. Zool. 20. 1917a. Multiplication by fission in holothurians. Amer. Natural. 51. 1917b. The behavior of holothurians in balanced illumination. Amer. Jour. Physiol. 43. 1918. The amount of bottom material ingested by holothurians. Jour. Exp. Zool. 26. **Cuénot, L.** 1902. Organes agglutinants et organes cilio-phagocytaires. Arch. Zool. Exp. Gén., ser. 3, vol. 10. 1912. Commensaux et parasites des synaptes. Bull. Sta. Biol. Arcachon 14. **Dakin, W.** 1923. Function of the water vascular system of echinoderms. Proc. Trans. Liverpool Biol. Soc. 37. **Danielssen, D.,** and **J. Koren.** 1856. Observations sur le développement des holothuriens. Fauna littoralis Norwegiae II. 1882. Holothuroidea. The Norwegian North-Atlantic Expedition 1876–1878, Zoology VI, vol. 4. **Davenport, D.** 1950. Studies in the physiology of commensalism I. Biol. Bull. 98. **Davenport, D.,** and **J. Hickok.** 1951. Studies in the physiology of commensalism II. Biol. Bull. 100. **Dawbin, W.** 1949a. Autoevisceration and regeneration in the holothurian. Trans. Proc. Roy. Soc. New Zealand 77. 1949b. Regeneration of the alimentary canal of Stichopus mollis. Trans. Proc. Roy. Soc. New Zealand 77. **Dawson, A. B.** 1933. Supravital studies on the colored corpuscles of several marine invertebrates. Biol. Bull. 64. **Deflandre-Regaud, Marthe.** 1950. Les sclérites rotiformes des holothurides fossiles. Ann. Paléontol. 36. 1953. Classe des Holothurides. *In* J. **Piveteau** (ed.), *Traité de paléontologie,* vol. III. **Deichmann, Elisabeth.** 1922. On some cases of multiplication by fission and of coalescence in holothurians. Vidensk. Meddel. Dansk Naturhist. Foren. 73. 1930. The holothurians of the western part of the Atlantic Ocean. Bull. Mus. Comp. Zool. Harvard 71. 1936. The arctic species of Molpadia. Ann. Mag. Natur. Hist., ser. 10, vol. 17. 1937. Holothurians from the Gulf of California, the west coast of Lower California and Clarion Island. Zoologica, New York, 22. 1938a. Holothurians from the western coasts of Lower California and Central America and from the Galapagos Islands. Zoologica, New York, 23. 1938b. The arctic molpadids. Arkiv Zoologi 30A, no. 8. 1939. Holothurians from Biscayne Bay, Florida. Proc. Florida Acad. Sci. 3. 1940. Report on the holothurians collected by the Harvard-Havana expeditions. Mem. Soc. Cubana Hist. Natur. 14. 1941. Dendrochirota. Allan Hancock Pacific Exped. 1932–1940, vol. 8. 1946.

Shallow water holothurians from Cabo de Hornas. Anales Mus. Argentino, Cienc. Natur. 42. 1948. The holothurian fauna of South Africa. Annals Natal Mus. 11. **Deranujagala, P.** 1933. Cured marine products of Ceylon. Bull. Ceylon Fisheries 5. **Domantay, J.** 1931. Autotomy in holothurians. Natural and Applied Sci. Bull. Univ. Philippines 1. 1933. Development of the anchor and anchor-plate types of spicules. Philippine Jour. Sci. 52. 1936. Philippine edible holothurians. Searchlight, Manila, 1. 1953a. Littoral holothurians from Zamboanga and vicinity. Philippine Jour. Sci. 82. 1953b. A brief summary of the Pacific and Atlantic Holothuroidea of the Allan Hancock Foundation collections. Philippine Jour. Sci. 82. **Edwards, C. L.** 1889. Notes on the embryology of Mülleria agassizi. Johns Hopkins Univ. Circulars 8, no. 70. 1907. The order of appearance of the ambulacral appendages in Holothuria. Science 25. 1907b. The holothurians of the north Pacific coast of North America. Proc. U.S. Nation. Mus. 33. 1908. Variation, development and growth in Holothuria. Biometrika 6. 1909. The development of Holothuria. Jour. Morphol. 20. 1910. Cucumaria frondosa. Zool. Jahrb. Abt. System. 29. **Ekman, S.** 1923. Über Psolus squamatus und verwandte Arten. Arkiv Zoologi 15, no. 5. 1925. Holothurien. Further Zool. Results Swedish Antarctic Exped. 1901–1903, vol. I, no. 6. 1926. Systematisch-phylogenetische Studien über Elasipoden und Aspidochiroten. Zool. Jahrb. Abt. Anat. 47. 1927. Holothurien der deutschen Südpolar Expedition 1901–1903 aus der Ostantarktis und von der Kerguelen. Dtsch. Südpolar-Exped. 19, Zool. 11. **Emory, C.** 1880. Le specie del genere Fierasfer nel Golfo di Napoli. Fauna und Flora des Golfes von Neapel, Monogr. 2. **Enriques, P.** 1902. Digestione, circolazione e assorbimento nelle oloturie. Arch. Zool. Ital. 1. **Etheridge, R.** 1881. Scattered skeletal remains of Holothuroidea in the carboniferous of Scotland. Proc. Roy. Phys. Soc. Edinburgh 6. **Fisher, W. K.** 1907. The holothurians of the Hawaiian Islands. Proc. U.S. Nation. Mus. 32. **Fränkel, S.,** and **C. Jellinek.** 1927. Über essbare Holothurien. Biochem. Ztschr. 185. **Frentzen, K.** 1944. Über Massenvorkommen von Holothurien-Resten. Neues Jahrb. Mineral. Geol. Palaeontol. Monatshefte, Abt. B, Heft 4. **Frenzel, J.** 1892. Der Darmkanal der Echinodermen. Arch. Anat. Physiol., Physiol. Abt. **Frey, D.** 1951. The use of sea-cucumbers in poisoning fishes. Copeia. **Furusawa, K.** and **P. Kerridge.** 1927. Hydrogen ion concentration of the muscles of marine animals. Jour. Marine Biol. Assoc. 14. **Garry, W.** 1905. The osmotic pressure of sea water and of the blood of marine animals. Biol. Bull. 8. **Garstang, W.** 1939 Remarkable new type of auricularia larva. Quart. Jour. Microsc. Sci. 81. **Gellhorn, E.** 1927. Die Pufferungspotenz von Blut und Korpersäften I. Arch. Ges. Physiol. 216. **Gerould, J.** 1896. The anatomy and histology of Caudina arenata. Proc. Boston Soc. Natur. Hist. 27. **Giebel, C.** 1857. Zur Fauna des lithographischen Schiefers von Solenhofen. Ztschr. Ges. Naturwiss. 9. **Gilchrist, J.** 1920. Planktothuria. Quart. Jour. Microsc. Sci. 64. **Goodrich, Helen.** 1925. Gregarines of Chiridota. Quart. Jour. Microsc. Sci. 69. **Gould, B.** 1848. New species of shells. Proc. Boston Soc. Natur. Hist. 3. **Grave, C.** 1905. The tentacle reflex in Cucumaria. Johns Hopkins Univ. Circulars, no. 178. **Greshoff, M.,** and **J. Sack.** 1900. Samenstelling van indische Voedingsmiddelen. Bull. Kolonial Mus. Haarlem, no. 23. **Greshoff, M.,** and **J. van Eck.** 1901. Samenstelling van indische Voedingsmiddelen. Bull. Kolonial Mus. Haarlem, no. 25. **Guislain, R.** 1953. Recherches histochimiques sur les canaux de Cuvier. C. R. Soc. Biol. Paris 147. **Haanen, W.** 1914. Studien an Mesothuria intestinalis. Ztschr. Wiss. Zool. 109. **Hall, Ada.** 1927. Histology of the retractor muscle of Cucumaria. Publ. Puget Sound Marine Biol. Sta. 5. **Hamann, O.** 1883. Beiträge zur Histologie der Echinodermen. I, II. Ztschr. Wiss. Zool. 39. 1884. *Beiträge zur Histologie der Echinodermen. 1. Die Holothurien.*

**Hatanaka, M.** 1939. A study of Molpadia roretzii. Sci. Repts. Tohoku Univ., ser. 4, Biol. 14. **Haurowitz, F.,** and **H. Waelsch.** 1926. Vergleichende chemische Untersuchungen an Holothurien und Aktinen. Ztschr. Physiol. Chem. 161. **Heding, E.** 1928. Synaptidae. Vidensk. Meddel. Dansk. Naturhist. Foren. 85. 1930. Contributions to the Synaptidae. Vidensk. Meddel. Dansk Naturhist. Foren. 88. 1933. The so-called Caudina chilensis. Sci. Repts. Tohoku Univ., ser. 4. Biol. 8. 1935. Holothuroidea, pt. I. Danish Ingolf Exped. 4, no. 9. 1939. The holothurians collected in the tropical Pacific. Vidensk. Meddel. Dansk Naturhist. Foren. 102. 1940. Die Holothurien der deutschen Tiefsee-Expedition. II. Wisensch. Ergebn. Dtsch. Tiefsee-Exped. 24. 1942. Holothuroidea, pt. II. Danish Ingolf Exped. 4, no. 13. 1950. Über die Planktothuria der deutschen Tiefsee-Expedition. Zool. Anz. 145. **Henri, V.** 1903a. Études physiologiques des muscles longitudinaux chez le Stichopus. C. R. Soc. Biol. Paris 55. 1903b. Action de quelques poisons sur les réflexes élémentaires chez Stichopus. C. R. Soc. Biol. Paris 55. 1903c. Étude des contractions musculaires et les réflexes chez Stichopus. C. R. Acad. Sci. Paris 137. 1903d. Étude des contractions rhythmic des vaisseaux et du poumon aqueux chez les holothuries. C. R. Soc. Biol. Paris. 55. **Henri, V.,** and **S. Lalou.** 1903. Régulation osmotiques des liquides internes chez les holothuries. C. R. Soc. Biol. Paris 55. **Hérouard, E.** 1887. Sur la formation des corpuscles calcaires chez les holothuries. C. R. Acad. Sci. Paris 105. 1889. Recherches sur les holothuries des côtes de France. Arch. Zool. Exp. Gén., ser. 2, vol. 7. 1895. De l'excrétion chez les holothuries. Bull. Soc. Zool. France 20. 1902. Holothuries provenant des campagnes de la Princesse-Alice. Resultats Campagnes Scient. Monaceo, Fasc. 21. 1906a. Sur Pelagothuria bouvieri. Bull. Mus. Océanogr. Monaco, no. 60. 1906b. Holothuries. Expédition Antarctic Belge. Resultats Voyage Belgica 1897–1899. Zool. 1. 1910. Sur les molpadides de Norvége. Bull. Inst. Océanogr. Monaco, no. 177. 1923. Holothuries provenant des campagnes de la Princesse-Alice et l'Hirondelle II. Resultats Campagnes Scient. Monaco, Fasc. 66. **Herpin, R.** 1915. Un mollusque enigmatique commensal des synaptes. Bull. Inst. Océanogr. Monaco, no. 302. **Hiestand, W.** 1940. Oxygen consumption of Thyone. Trans. Wisconsin Acad. Sci. Arts. Lett. 32. **Hogben, L.,** and **J. van der Lingen.** 1928. Occurrence of haemoglobin and erythrocytes in the perivisceral fluid of a holothurian. Jour. Exp. Biol. 5. **Hornell, J.** 1918. The Indian bêche-de-mer industry. Madras Bull. Madras Fisheries Dept. 11. **Hörstadius, S.** 1939. Larve von Holothuria. Arkiv Zoologi 31A. **Howell, W. H.** 1885a. Chemical composition and coagulation of the blood of Cucumaria. Johns Hopkins Univ. Circulars 5, no. 43. 1885b. The presence of haemoglobin in invertebrates. Johns Hopkins Univ. Circulars 5, no. 43. 1886a. Blood of a species of holothurian. Studies Biol. Lab. Johns Hopkins Univ. 3. 1886b. Presence of haemoglobin in the echinoderms. Studies Biol. Lab. Johns Hopkins Univ. 3. **Hozawa, S.** 1928. Change with advancing age in the calcareous deposits of Caudina. Sci. Repts. Tohoku Univ., ser. 4, Biol. 3. **Inaba, D.** 1930. Development of Caudina. Sci. Repts. Tohoku Univ., ser. 4, Biol. 5. **Ivanov, A.** 1933. Ein neues endoparasitisches mollusk. Zool. Anz. 104. 1947. Structure et développement du Parenteroxenos. Bull. Acad. Sci. USSR, ser. Biol. fasc. 1. **John, D.** 1939. A viviparous synaptid from New Zealand. Ann. Mag. Natur. Hist., ser. 11, vol. 4. **Johnson, M.** and **L. Johnson.** 1950. Early life history and larval development of some Puget Sound echinoderms. Studies Honoring Trevor Kincaid, Seattle. **Jordan, H.** 1914. Über "reflexarme" Tiere. IV. Die Holothurien. Zool. Jahrb. Abt. Allg. Zool. 34. **Jourdan, E.** 1883. Recherches sur l'histologie des holothuries. Ann. Mus. Hist. Natur. Marseille, Zool. 1, no. 6. **Kalischewskij, M.** 1907. Echinodermenfauna des sibirischen Eismeeres. Mém. Acad. Sci. St. Pétersbourg, ser. 8, vol. 18, no. 4.

**Kawamoto, N.** 1927. Anatomy of Caudina chilensis. Sci. Repts. Tohoku Univ., ser. 4, Biol. 2. **Kenna, A.** 1906. L'holothurie pélagique Pelagothuria. Ann. Soc. Malacol. Belgique 41. **Kille, F.** 1931. Induced autotomy in Thyone. Science 74. 1935. Regeneration in Thyone following induced autotomy. Biol. Bull. 69. 1936. Regeneration in holothurians. Carnegie Inst. Washington, Yearbook 35. 1937. Regeneration in the genus Holothuria. Carnegie Inst. Washington, Yearbook 36. 1939. Regeneration of gonad tubules in Thyone. Biol. Bull. 76. **Kitao, Y.** 1933. Anatomy of the young Caudina. Sci. Repts. Tohoku Univ. ser. 4, Biol. 8. 1935. Structure of the anus of Caudina. Sci. Repts. Tohoku Univ., ser. 4, Biol. 9. **Klugh, A.** 1923. The habits of Cucumaria frondosa. Canad. Field Natural. 37. **Kobayashi, S.** 1932. Spectral properties of haemoglobin in Caudina and Molpadia. Sci. Repts. Tohoku Univ., ser. 4, Biol. 7. **Koehler, R.** 1906. Échinodermes recueillis par l'expédition antarctique française. C. R. Acad. Sci. Paris 142. **Koehler, A.,** and **C. Vaney.** 1903. Entosiphon deimatis. Revue Suisse Zool. 11. 1905. Deep sea Holothurioidea collected by the Investigator. Echinoderma of Indian Museum III. 1908. Littoral Holothurioidea collected by the Investigator. Echinoderma of the Indian Museum IV. **Koizumi, T.** 1932, 1935a-d. Studies on the exchange and the equilibrium of water and electrolytes in Caudina. I–V. Sci. Repts. Tohoku Univ., ser. 4, Biol. 7, 10. **Kowalewsky, A.** 1867. Entwicklungsgeschichte der Holothurien. Mém. Acad. Sci. St. Pétersbourg, ser. 7, vol. 11, no. 6. **Lampert, K.** 1889. Die "Gazelle" gesammelten Holothurien. Zool. Jahrb. Abt. System. 4. **Levinsen, G.** 1886. Kara-Havets Echinodermata. *In* C. Lütken (ed.), *Dijmphna-Togtets Zoologisk-botaniske Udbytte*. **Linton, E.** 1907. Note on the habits of Fierasfer. Amer. Natural. 41. **Loeb, J.** 1891. Über Geotropism bei Tiere. Arch. Ges. Physiol. 49. **Ludwig, H.** 1881. Über eine lebendig gebärende Synaptide. Arch. Biol. 2. 1889–1892. Die Seewalzen. *In* H. G. Bronn (ed.), *Klassen und Ordnungen des Tierreichs*, Band II, Abt. 3, Buch 1. 1891. Zur Entwicklungsgeschichte der Holothurien. Sitzungsber. Akad. Wissensch. Berlin, no. 10, no. 32. 1894. Die Holothurioidea. Repts. Exploration west coasts Mexico by the Albatross. Mem. Mus. Comp. Zool. Harvard 17. 1897a. Brutpflege bei Psolus. Zool. Anz. 20. 1897b. Ein neuer Fall von Brutpflege bei Holothurien. Zool. Anz. 20. 1897c. Eine neue Schlauchschnecke aus der Leibeshöhle einer antarktischen Chiridota. Zool. Anz. 20. 1898a. Holothurien der Hamburger Magalhaenische Sammelreise. Ergebn. Hamburger Magalhaenische Sammelreise I. 1898b. Brutpflege und Entwicklung von Phyllophorus urna. Zool. Anz. 21. 1900a. Arktische und subarktische Holothurien. Fauna Arctica 1. 1900b. Die Holothurien. Zoologische Ergebnisse Untersuchungsfahrt des Olga. Wissensch. Meeresuntersuch. Abt. Helgoland 4, Heft 2. 1904. Brutflege bei Echinodermen. Zool. Jahrb. suppl. 7. **Ludwig, H.,** and **P. Barthels.** 1891. Zur Anatomie der Synaptiden. Zool. Anz. 14. 1892. Die Cuvier'schen Organe. Ztschr. Wiss. Zool. 54. **Ludwig, H.,** and **S. Heding.** 1935. Die Holothurien der deutschen Tiefseeexpedition I. Wissensch. Ergebn. Dtsch. Tiefsee-Exped. Valdivia 1898–1899, 24. **Lutz, B.** 1930. The effect of low oxygen tension on the pulsations of the isolated holothurian cloaca. Biol. Bull. 58. **MacBride, E. W.,** and **J. Simpson.** 1908. Echinoderm larvae. National Antarctic Expedition 1901–1904, Natur. Hist., Zool. 4. **Malard, A.** 1903. Sur un lamellibranche nouveaux, parasite des synaptes. Bull. Mus. Nation. Hist. Natur. Paris 9. **Manunta, Carmela.** 1943. Ricerche su la pigmentazione di olothurie. Thalassia 5, no. 5. 1944. Sui pigmenti carotenoidi di invertebrati marini. Thalassia 6, no. 3. 1947. Contenuti in lipidi negli organi viscerali di olothurie. Arch. Zool. Ital. 32. **Marenzeller, E.** 1893. Contribution à l'étude des holothuries de l'Atlantic Nord. Resultats Campagnes Scient. Monaco, Fasc. 6. 1900. Holothurien. Ergebnisse einer zoologischer

Forschungsreise in den Molukken und Borneo. Abhandl. Senckenberg. Naturforsch. Gesellsch. 25. **Matsumoto, T., M. Yajima**, and **Y. Toyama.** 1943. The crystalline fraction of the unsaponifiable substances in Cucumaria. Jour. Chem. Soc. Japan 63. **Metschnikoff, E.** 1870. Entwicklung der Echinodermen. Mém. Acad. Sci. St. Pétersbourg, ser. 7, vol. 14, no. 8. **Millott, N.** 1950. Integumentary pigmentation and the coelomic fluid of Thyone. Biol. Bull. 99. 1952. The occurrence of melanin and phenolases in Holothuria. Experientia 8. 1953. Skin pigment and amoebocytes and the occurrence of phenolases in the coelomic fluid of Holothuria. Jour. Marine Biol. Assoc. 31. **Minchin, E.** 1892. Cuvierian organs of Holothuria. Ann. Mag. Natur. Hist., ser. 6, vol. 10. 1893. Gregarines of holothurians. Quart. Jour. Microsc. Sci. 34. **Mines, G.** 1912. Mechanism of the Cuvierian organs of Holothuria. Quart. Jour. Microsc. Sci. 57; Proc. Cambridge Philos. Soc. 16. **Mitsukuri, K.** 1897. Changes with advancing age in the calcareous deposits of Stichopus. Annot. Zool. Japon. 1. 1903. Habits and life-history of Stichopus japonicus. Annot. Zool. Japon. 5. 1912. Studies on actinopodous Holothurioidea. Jour. College Sci. Tokyo Univ. 29, art. 2. **Monticelli, F.** 1896. Sull' autotomie delle Cucumaria. Atti. Accad. Naz. Lincei, Rendiconti, Cl. Sci. Fis., ser. 5, vol. 5, pt. 2. **Mörner, C.** 1902. Die sogenannten weinrothen Körper der Holothurien. Ztschr. Physiol. Chem. 37. **Mortensen, T.** 1894. Zur Anatomie und Entwicklung der Cucumaria glacialis. Ztschr. Wiss. Zool. 57. 1914. Grönlands Echinoderma. Meddel. Grönland 23. 1925. Echinoderms of New Zealand and the Auckland and Campbell Islands. IV. Holothuroidea. Vidensk. Meddel. Dansk Naturhist. Foren. 79. **Mukerji, D.** 1932. Commensalism of an ophioid fish with echinoderms of the Andaman Islands. Records Indian Mus. 34. **Müller, J.** 1852. *Über die Erzeugung von Schnecken in Holothurien.* 1854. Über den Bau der Echinodermen. Abhandl. Berlin. Akad. Wissensch. for 1853. **Nair, R.** 1946. New apodus holothurian from the Madras Harbor. Proc. Nation. Inst. Science India 12. **Newth, G.** 1916. Early development of Cucumaria. Proc. Zool. Soc. London, pt. 2. **Nigrelli, R.** 1952. The effects of holothurin on fish and mice with sarcoma 180. Zoologica, New York, 37. **Noll, F.** 1881. Mein Seewasser-Zimmeraquarium. Zool. Garten 22. **Nomura, S.** 1926. Influence of oxygen tension on the rate of oxygen consumption in Caudina. Sci. Repts. Tohoku Univ., ser. 4, Biol. 2. **Nyholm, K.** 1951. Development and larval form of Labidoplax buski. Zool. Bidrag 29. **Ohshima, H.** 1911. A gigantic form of Auricularia. Annot. Zool. Japon. 7. 1912. The Synaptidae of Japan. Annot. Zool. Japon. 8. 1915. Holothurians collected by the Albatross in the northwestern Pacific. Proc. U.S. Nation. Mus. 48. 1916. A new case of brood caring in holothurians. Annot. Zool. Japon. 9. 1918. Development of Cucumaria echinata. Annot. Zool. Japon. 9. 1921. Development of Cucumaria echinata. Quart. Jour. Microsc. Sci. 65. 1925. Development of Thyone. Science 61. 1927. Some pycnogons living semi-parasitic on holothurians. Proc. Imper. Acad. Tokyo 3. **Ohuye, T.** 1934. Reaction of the leucocytes of Caudina to vital dyes. Sci. Repts. Tohoku Univ., ser. 4, Biol. 9. 1936. Coelomic corpuscles of Molpadia. Sci. Repts. Tohoku Univ., ser. 4, Biol. 11. **Okazaki, K.,** and **T. Koizumi.** 1926. Leibeshöhlenflüssigkeit von Caudina. Sci. Repts. Tohoku Univ., ser. 4, Biol. 2. **Okuda, S.** 1936. Two polychaetous annelids found in the burrows of an apodous holothurian. Annot. Zool. Japon. 15. **Olmsted, J.** 1917. The comparative physiology of Synaptula hydriformis. Jour. Exp. Zool. 24. **Olson, M.** 1938. Histology of the retractor muscles of Thyone. Biol. Bull. 74. **Oomen, H.** 1926a. Permeability of the gut in sea cucumbers. Kon. Akad. Wetens. Amsterdam, Versl. Wiss. Nat. Afd. 29. 1926b. Verdauungsphysiologische Studien an Holothurien. Pubbl. Staz. Zool. Napoli 7. **Östergren, H.** 1896. Zur Kenntnis der Synallactinae. Festschrift für W. Lillejeborg. 1897. Über die Funktion der ankerförmigen Kalkkörper. Zool. Anz. 20. 1898a. Zur Anatomie der Dendro-chiroten. Zool. Anz. 21. 1898b. Das System der Synaptiden. Kgl. Sven. Akad. Forhandl. Ofversigt 55. 1902. The Holothuroidea of northern Norway. Bergens Mus. Aarbog, no. 9. 1905. Zur Kenntnis der skandinavischen und arktischen Synaptiden. Arch. Zool. Exp. Gén. 33, Notes et Revue, no. 7. 1907. Zur Phylo-genie und Systematik der Seewalzen. Zool. Studien tillägn Prof. T. Tullberg. 1912. Brutpflege der Echinodermen in den südpolaren Küstengebieten. Ztschr. Wiss. Zool. 101. 1938. Studien über Seewalzen. Goteborg's Vetensk. Samh. Handl., ser. 5, ser. B, vol. 5, no. 4. **Panning, I.** 1928. Über das optische Verhalten der Kalkkörper der aspidochiroten Holothurien. Ztschr. Wiss. Zool. 132. 1931, 1935, 1936. Die Gattung Holothuria. Mitt. Zool. Staatinst. und Zool. Mus. Hamburg 44, 45, 46. 1944. Die Trepang-Fischerei. Mitt. Hamburg. Zool. Mus. und Inst. 49. **Pantin, C.,** and **P. Sawaya.** 1953. Muscular action in Holothuria. Zoologia, Sao Paulo, Brazil, 18. **Parker, G. H.** 1921. The locomotion of Stichopus panamensis. Jour. Exp. Zool. 33. 1926. The inquiline fish Fierasfer at Key West. Proc. Nation. Acad. Sci. U.S.A. 12. **Pearse, A. S.** 1908. Behavior of Thyone. Biol. Bull. 15. 1909. Autotomy in holothurians. Biol. Bull. 18. **Pearson, J.** 1914. Holothuroidea of the Indian Ocean. Spolia Zeylanica 9. **Perrier, R.** 1904. Holothuries du Cap Horn. Bull. Mus. Nation. Hist. Natur. Paris 10. 1905. Holothuries antarctiques. Ann. Sci. Natur. Zool., ser. 9, vol. 1. **Pople, W.** and **D. Ewer.** 1954. The pharyngeal retractor muscle of Cucumaria. Jour. Exp. Biol. 31. **Prosser, C.,** and **C. Judson.** 1952. Pharmacology of haemal vessels of Stichopus. Biol. Bull. 102. **Reiffen, A.** 1901. Über eine neue Holothurien-gattung von Neuseeland. Ztschr. Wiss. Zool. 69. **Remiers, K.** 1912. Zur Histogenesis der Synapta digitata. Jena. Ztschr. Naturwiss. 48. **Retzius, G.** 1905. Die Spermien der Echinodermen. Biol. Untersuchungen 12. 1906. Verteilung der Sinnesnervenzellen in der Haut der Holothurien. Biol. Untersuchungen 13. **Risbec, J.** 1953. Trois mollusques rares ou peu connus. Bull. Soc. Zool. France 78. **Robertson, J.** 1953. Ionic regulation in marine invertebrates. Jour. Exp. Biol. 30. **Rosen, N.** 1910. *Zur Kenntnis der parasitischen Schnecken.* **Runnström, J.,** and **S. Runnström.** 1921. Entwicklung von Cucumaria frondosa und Psolus phantapus. Bergens Mus. Aarbok for 1918–1919, Naturvidensk. Rekke, no. 5. **Runnström, S.** 1927. Entwicklung von Leptosynapta inhaerens. Bergens Mus. Aarbok, no. 1. **Russo, A.** 1899. Organi di Cuvier delle oloturie. Monitore Zool. Ital. 10. **Rustad, D.** 1938. The early development of Stichopus. Bergens Mus. Aarbok, Naturvid. Rekke, no. 8. **Sarch, N.** 1931. Die Pufferung der Körperflüssigkeiten der Echinodermen. Ztschr. Vergl. Physiol. 14. **Sars, M.** 1852. *Bidrag til Kundskaben om Middelhavets Littoral-Fauna; also* Nyt Mag. Natur-vid. 9. **Saville-Kent, W.** 1893. *The Great Barrier Reef of Australia.* **Sawano, E.** 1928. Digestive enzymes of Caudina. Sci. Repts. Tohoku Univ., ser. 4, Biol. 3. **Sawaya, P.** 1951. Sensibilidade do musculo longitudinal radial de Holothuria. Ciencia e Cultura 3. **Schiemenz, P.** 1889. Parasitische Schnecken. Biol. Cen-tralbl. 9. **Schlumberger, C.** 1888, 1890. Holothuridées du Calcaire grossier. Bull. Soc. Geol. France 16, 18. **Schmidt, Max.** 1878. Nachrichten aus dem zoologischen Garten in Frankfurt. Zool. Garten 19. **Schreiber, B.** 1930. Studi sull' assorbimento intestinale nelle oloturie. Pubbl. Staz. Zool. Napoli 10. 1932a. Pigmenti e secrezioni nel sistema digerente delle oloture. Pubbl. Staz. Zool. Napoli 12. 1932b. Esperimenti per lo studio dell' assorbimento intestinale nelle oloturie. Arch. Zool. Ital. 16. 1932c. Il ciclo di secrezione nelle rete mirabili. Arch. Zool. Ital. 17. **Schultz, E.** 1895. Excretion bei den Holothurien. Biol. Centralbl. 15. **Scott, J.** 1914. Regeneration, variation and correlation in Thyone. Amer. Natural. 48. **Selenka, E.** 1867. Anatomie und Systematik der Holothurien.

Ztschr. Wiss. Zool. 17. 1876. Entwicklung der Holothurien. Ztschr. Wiss. Zool. 27. 1883. *Die Keimblätter der Echinodermen. Studien zur Entwicklungegeschichte der Thiere*, I, art. 2. **Sella, A.**, and **M. Sella.** 1940. L'industria del Trepang. Thalassia 4, no. 5. **Semon, R.** 1883. Das Nervensystem der Holothurien. Jena. Ztschr. Naturwiss. 16. 1887. Naturgeschichte der Synaptiden der Mittelmeeres. Mitt. Zool. Sta. Neapel 7. 1888. Entwicklung der Synapta digitata. Jena. Ztschr. Naturwiss. 22. **Semper, C.** 1868. *Reisen in Archipelago der Philippinen.* II Theil. Wissensch. Resultate. Bd. I. Holothuroiden. **Simpson, J.** 1909. Specimen of Pelagothuria from the Seychelles. Nature, London, 80. **Sivickis, P.**, and **J. Domantay.** 1928. The morphology of Stichopus chloronotus. Philippine Jour. Sci. 37. **Sluiter, C.** 1880. Neue Holothurien von den west Küste Javas. Natuurk. Tijdschr. Nederland. Indie 40. 1901. Die Holothurien der Siboga Expedition. Siboga Exped. Monogr. 44. 1910. Westindien Holothurien. Zool. Jahrb. Suppl. 11. **Smith, R.** 1947. Fisheries of the former Japanese mandated islands. U.S. Dept. Interior, Fish and Wildlife Service, Fishery leaflet 273. **Sobotka, H.**, and **S. Kann.** 1941. Carbonic anhydrase in invertebrates. Jour. Cell. Comp. Physiol. 17. **Steinbach, H. B.** 1937. Potassium and chloride in Thyone muscle. Jour. Cell. Comp. Physiol. 9. **Stevens, Nettie.** 1901. Studies on ciliate Infusoria. Proc. California Acad. Sci., ser. 3, Zool. 3. 1903. Further studies on Licnophora and Boveria. Arch. Protistenk. 3. **Stier, T.** 1933. Diurnal changes in activities and geotropism in Thyone. Biol. Bull. 64. **Sulima, A.** 1914. Zur Kenntnis des Harnsäurestoffwechsels niederer Tiere. Ztschr. Biol. 63. **Swan, J.** 1887. The Trepang fishery. Bull. U.S. Fish. Comm. 6, no. 21. **Tadokoro, T.**, and **S. Watanabe.** 1928. Chemical studies on sex differences of blood protein in Caudina. Sci. Repts. Tohoku Univ., ser. 4, Biol. 3. **Tao, L.** 1927. Physiological characteristics of Caudina muscle. Sci. Repts. Tohoku Univ., ser. 4, Biol. 2. 1930. Ecology and physiology of Caudina. Proc. 4 Pacific Sci. Congr., vol. 3. **Teuscher, R.** 1876. Beiträge zur Anatomie der Echinodermen. Jena. Ztschr. Naturwiss. 10. **Théel, H.** 1877. Mémoire sur l'Elpidia. Kongl. Svenska Vetensk. Akad. Handl. 14, no. 8. 1882, 1886a. Report on the Holothurioidea I, II. Rept. Scient. Results Voyage Challenger, Zool. 4, 14. 1886b. Report on the Holothuroidea. Blake Repts. no. 30. Bull. Mus. Comp. Zool. Harvard 13. 1901. Case of hermaphroditism in holothurids. Bihang Svenska Vetensk. Acad. Handl. 27, Afd. 4, no. 6. 1921. On amoebocytes and other coelomic corpuscles in the perivisceral cavity of echinoderms. II. Holothurids. Arkiv Zoologi 13, art. 25. **Thompson, E. F.** 1953. Oceanography. Americana Annual. **Thorson, G.** The larval development, growth, and metabolism of Arctic marine bottom invertebrates. Meddel. Grönland 100, no. 6. **Torelle, Ellen.** 1909. Regeneration in Holothuria. Zool. Anz. 35. **Tortonese, E.** 1935. Echinodermi mediterranei. Ann. Mus. Civ. Stor. Natur. Genova 57. **Uexküll, J. von.** 1926. Die Sperrmuskulatur der Holothurien. Arch. Ges. Physiol. 212. **Van der Heyde, H. C.** 1922. Hemoglobin in Thyone. Biol. Bull. 42. 1923. Petites contributions à la physiologie comparée. I–IV. Arch. Néerland. Sci., ser. 3C, Physiol. 8. **Vaney, C.** 1906. Holothuries. Expédition Antarctique Française 1903–1905, vol. 6. 1907. Deux nouvelles holothuries incubatrices. C. R. Assoc. Franç. Avanc. Sci., for 1906, 35, pt. 2. 1908. Les holothuries recueillies par l'Expédition Antarctique Écossaise. Zool. Anz. 33. 1909. Les holothuries de l'Expédition Antarctique Nationale Écossaise. Trans. Roy. Soc. Edinburgh 46. 1912. Les holothuries de l'Expedition Antarctique Nationale Écossaise. Scottish National Antarctic Exped., Rept. Scient. Results Voyage Scotia, vol. 6, Zool. 1. 1913. La pénétration des gasteropodes parasites dans leur hôte. C. R. Soc. Biol. Paris 74. 1914. Holothuries. Deuxième Expédition Antarctique Française 1908–1910, vol. 5. 1925. L'incubation chez les holothuries. Trav. Sta. Zool. Wimereux 9.

**Villela, G.** 1951. Fluorescent pigment of Holothuria grisea. Revista Brasil. Biol. 11. **Voeltzkow, A.** 1890. Entovolva mirabilis. Zool. Jahrb. Abt. System. 5. **Voigt, W.** 1888. Entocolax. Ztschr. Wiss. Zool. 47. 1901. Entocolax. Zool. Anz. 24. **Walcott, C. D.** 1911. Middle Cambrian holothurians. Smithsonian Miscell. Collect. 57. **Wells, W.** 1924. New species of Cucumaria from Monterey Bay. Ann. Mag. Natur. Hist., ser. 9, vol. 14. **Westblad, E.** 1949. On Meara stichopi. Arkiv Zoologi, n. ser. 1, no. 5. **Winterstein, H.** 1909. Über die Atmung der Holothurien. Arch. Fisiol. 7. **Woodland, W.** 1906. The scleroblastic development of the spicules in Cucumariidae. Quart. Jour. Microsc. Sci. 49. 1907. The scleroblastic development of the plate-and-anchor spicules of Synapta. Quart. Jour. Microsc. Sci. 51. **Wootton, D.** 1949. The development of Thyonepsolus nutriens. Thesis, Stanford Univ. Library. **Wyman, L.,** and **B. Lutz.** 1930. The action of adrenalin and certain drugs on the isolated holothurian cloaca. Jour. Exp. Zool. 57. **Yamanouchi, T.** 1926. Behavior of Caudina. Sci. Repts. Tohoku Univ., ser. 4, Biol. 2. 1929a. Notes on the behavior of Caudina. Sci. Repts. Tohoku Univ., ser. 4, Biol. 4. 1929b. Statistical study on Caudina. Sci. Repts. Tohoku Univ., ser. 4., Biol. 4. 1929c. Reactions to centrifugal force in Caudina. Sci. Repts. Tohoku Univ., ser. 4, Biol. 4. 1929d. Effect of anions in chemical stimulation in Caudina. Sci. Repts. Tohoku Univ., ser. 4, Biol. 4. 1938. Beneficial holothurians in Palau. Kagaku Nanyo (Science of the South Sea) 1. 1939. Ecological and physiological studies on the holothurians in the coral reef of Palao. Palao Trop. Biol. Sta. Studies 4. 1941. Studies on the useful holothurians in Palau. Kagaku Nanyo (Science of the South Sea) 4. **Yazaki, M.** 1930. Circulation of the perivisceral fluid in Caudina. Sci. Repts. Tohoku Univ., ser. 4, Biol. 5. **Zänkert, A.** 1940. Studien über das Verhalten von Fierasfer. Sitzungsber. Gesellsch. Naturforsch. Freunde Berlin. 1951. Das Grabmal aus Perlmutter. Kosmos, Stuttgart, 47. **Ziegler, H.** 1924. Entwicklungsgeschichte der Echinodermen. Zool. Jahrb. Abt. Anat. 46.

## ASTEROIDEA

**Abeloos, M.** 1926. Les pigments tégumentaires des astéries. C. R. Soc. Biol. Paris 94. 1931. Les potentialités régénératrices de la face dorsale des bras des asteries. Bull. Biol. France Belgique 65. **Agassiz, A.** 1897. North American starfishes. Mem. Mus. Comp. Zool. Harvard 5, pt. 1. **Alcock, A.** 1893. An account of the collection of deep sea Asteroidea. Natural history notes from the Indian Marine Survey Steamer Investigator. Ann. Mag. Natur. Hist., ser. 6, vol. 11. **Anderson, J. M.** 1952. Cellular structure and function in the digestive diverticula of Asterias. Anat. Record 113. 1953. Structure and function in the pyloric caeca of Asterias. Biol. Bull. 105. 1954. Studies on the cardiac stomach of Asterias. Biol. Bull. 107. **Bacci, G.** 1949. Asterina gibbosa. I. La migrazione delle gonadi. II. L'ermafroditismo. Arch. Zool. Ital. 34. **Barnes, H.,** and **H. Powell.** 1951. The growth rate of young Asterias rubens. Jour. Marine Biol. Assoc. 30. **Barthels, P.** 1906. Die grossen Hautdrüsen der Echinaster Arten. Zool. Anz. 29. **Bauer, V.** 1915. Biologisches über Palmipes. Internation. Rev. Ges. Hydrobiol. 7. **Becker, F.** 1939. Some observations on the water vascular system of Patiria. Jour. Colorado-Wyoming Acad. Sci. 2, no. 5. **Beklemichev, W.** 1916. Sur les turbellariés parasites de la côte mourmanne. Trav. Soc. Natural. Pétrograd, Livr. 4, vol. 45. **Bell, F. J.** 1905. The Echinoderma found off the coast of South Africa. II. Asteroidea. Marine Invest. South Africa 3. **Bennett, E.** 1927. New Zealand sea stars. Records Canterbury Mus. 3. **Bergmann, W.** 1937. The sterols of starfish. Jour. Biol. Chem. 117. **Bergmann, W.,** and **A. Stansbury.** 1943. Astrol. Jour. Organic Chem. 8. 1944. The sterols of starfish II. Jour.

Organic Chem. 9. **Bock, K.,** and **C. Schlieper.** 1953. Einfluss des Salzgehaltes im Meerwasser auf dem Grundumsatz des Asterias rubens. Kieler Meeresforsch. 9. **Bocquet, C.** 1953. Copepodes semi-parasites et parasites des échinodermes. Bull. Soc. Zool. France 77. **Bohn, G.** 1908. De l'acquisition des habitudes chez les étoiles de mer. C. R. Soc. Biol. Paris 64. **Boschma, H.** 1923. Copulation bei einer Asteroide. Zool. Anz. 58. **Buchner, P.** 1911. Hermaphrodite Seesterne. Zool. Anz. 38. **Budington, R.** 1927. Intestinal caecum in Asterias. Anat. Record 37. 1942. Ciliary transport system of Asterias. Biol. Bull. 83. **Bull, H.** 1934. Rate of growth and enemies of Asterias rubens. Rept. Dove Marine Lab. Cullercoats, ser. 3, no. 2. **Bullock, T.** 1953. Predator recognition and escape responses of some intertidal gastropods in presence of starfish. Behavior 5. **Burrows, R.** 1936. Further observations on parasitism in starfish. Science 84. **Caso, Maria.** 1941. Asteridos de Mexico. I. La existence de Linckia guildingi en la costa pacifica. Ann. Inst. Biol. Mexico 12. **Caullery, M.** 1927. Potentialités régénératives de la face dorsal du disque et des bras chez les astéries. Bull. Soc. Zool. France 52. **Cépède, C.** 1907. La castration parasitaire des étoiles de mer. C. R. Acad. Sci. Paris 145; *also* C. R. Assoc. Française Avanc. Sci. 36, pt. 1. 1910. Recherches sur les infusoires astomes. Arch. Zool. Exp. Gén., ser. 5, vol. 3. **Chadwick, H. C.** 1916. Asteroids feeding upon living sea-anemones. Nature, London, 96. 1923. Asterias. Liverpool Marine Biol. Comm., Mem. 25. **Chapeaux, M.** 1893. Sur la nutrition des échinodermes. Bull. Acad. Roy. Belgique, ser. 3, vol. 26. **Chatton, E.,** and **S. Villeneuve.** 1937. Cyclochaeta astropectinis. C. R. Acad. Sci. Paris 204. **Chidester, F.** 1929. A starfish attempts to ingest a minnow. Science 70. **Clark, Ailsa.** 1953. Notes on asteroids in the British Museum. III. Luidia. IV. Tosia and Pentagonaster. Bull. British Mus. (Natur. Hist.) 1, no. 12. **Clark, A. H.** 1934. A voracious starfish. Science 79. **Clark, H. L.** 1907. The starfishes of the genus Heliaster. Bull. Mus. Comp. Zool. Harvard 51. 1913. Autotomy in Linckia. Zool. Anz. 42. 1920. Asteroida. Repts. Scient. Results Exped. Eastern Tropical Pacific. Mem. Mus. Comp. Zool. Harvard 39. **Clemente, L.,** and **B. Anicete.** 1949. Sex ratio, sexual dimorphism and early development of Archaster typicus. Natural and Applied Sci. Bull. Manila 9. **Cole, L. J.** 1913a. Direction of locomotion of Asterias. Jour. Exp. Zool. 14. 1913b. Coordination and righting in the starfish. Biol. Bull. 24. **Cowles, R.** 1909. Movement of Echinaster towards the light. Zool. Anz. 35. 1910. Reaction of echinoderms to light. Science 31. 1911. Reactions to light and other points in the behavior of the starfish. Carnegie Inst. Washington, Papers Dept. Marine Biol. 3; *also* Johns Hopkins Univ. Circulars no. 232. 1914. Influence of white and black walls on the direction of locomotion of of the starfish. Jour. Animal Behavior 4. **Crozier, W.** 1915. Number of rays in Asterias tenuispina at Bermuda. Amer. Natural. 49. 1920. Temporal relation of asexual propagation and gametic reproduction in Coscinasterias tenuispina. Biol. Bull. 39. 1935. Geotropic response in Asterina. Jour. Gen. Physiol. 18. **Cuénot, L.** 1887. Étude anatomique des astérides. Arch. Zool. Exp. Gén., ser. 2, vol. 5, suppl. 1896. L'appareil lacunaire et les absorbants intestinaux chez les étoiles de mer. C. R. Acad. Sci. Paris 122. 1898. L'hermaphrotidisme protandriques d'Asterina gibbosa. Zool. Anz. 21. 1901. Études physiologiques sur les astéries. Arch. Zool. Exp. Gén., ser. 3, vol. 9. **Danielssen, D.,** and **J. Koren.** 1856. Observation sur le développement des astéries. Fauna littorae Norvegiae, Heft 2. 1884. Asteroids. Norwegian North-Atlantic Exped. 1876–1878, Zool. 4. **Davenport, D.** 1950. Studies on the physiology of commensalism. I. Biol. Bull. 98. 1953. Studies on the physiology of commensalism. III. Jour. Marine Biol. Assoc. 32. **Davenport, D.,** and **J. Hickok.** 1951. Studies on the physiology of commensalism II. Biol. Bull. 100. **Delage, Y.** 1902a. Régénération de l'hydropore. Arch,

Zool. Exp. Gén., ser. 3, vol. 10. 1902b. Effets de l'excision du madréporite chez les astéries. C. R. Acad. Sci. Paris 135. **Delaunay, H.** 1926. Sur l'excrétion azotée des astéries. C. R. Soc. Biol. Paris 94. **De Nicola, M.,** and **T. Goodwin.** 1954. The distribution of carotenoids in some marine invertebrates. Pubbl. Staz. Zool. Napoli 25. **Djakonov, A.** 1926. Zwei neue Seesterne von dem westlichen Nordpacific. Annuaire Mus. Zool. Acad. Sci. USSR 27. **Döderlein, L.** 1896. Bei Amboina und Thursday Island gesammelten Asteroidea. Semon's Zool. Forschungsreisen in Australien und den Malayischen Archipel. 5, pt. 1. 1899. Einige Beobachtungen an arctischen Seesternen. Zool. Anz. 22. 1916. Über die Gattung Oreaster und Verwandte. Zool. Jahrb. Abt. System. 40. 1917. Die Asteriden der Siboga Expedition. I. Die Gattung Astropecten. Siboga Exped. Monogr. 46a. 1920. Die Asteriden der Siboga Expedition. II. Die Gattung Luidia. Siboga Exped. Monogr. 46b. 1921. Die Asteriden der Siboga Expedition. Porcellansteridae, Astropectinidae, Benthopectinidae. Siboga Exped. Monogr. 46, pt. 1. 1924. Die Asteriden der Siboga Expedition. Pentagonasteridae. Siboga Exped. Monogr. 46, pt. 2. 1927. Die Seesterne der deutschen Südpolar-Expedition 1901–1903. Dtsch. Südpolar-Exped. Zool. 11. 1935. Die Asteriden der Siboga Expedition. Oreasteridae. Siboga Exped. Monogr. 46. 1936. Die Unterfamilie Oreasterinae. Siboga Exped. Monogr. 46c. **Durham, H.** 1888. The emigration of amoeboid corpuscles in the starfish. Proc. Roy. Soc. London 43. **Duval, M.** 1924. Recherches sur le milieu intérieur des invertébrés marins. Bull. Sta. Biol. Arcachon 21. 1925. Sur le milieu intérieur des animaux aquatiques. Ann. Inst. Océanogr. Monaco, n. ser. 2. **Edmondson, C. H.** 1935. Autotomy and regeneration in Hawaiian starfishes. Occas. Papers Bernice P. Bishop Mus. Hawaii, 11, no. 8. **Euler, H. von,** and **H. Hellström.** 1934. Über Asterinsäure, eine Carotenoidsäure aus Seesternen. Ztschr. Physiol. Chem. 223. **Fabre-Domergue, M.** 1885. Note sur les infusoires ciliés de la Baie de Concarneau. Jour. Anat. Physiol. 21. **Fedotov, D. M.** 1934. Zur Regeneration des Axialorgans bei den Seesternen. Trav. Lab. Zool. Exp. Morphol. Animaux 3. 1935. Weitere Untersuchungen über die Regeneration des Axialorgans. Trav. Lab. Zool. Exp. Morphol. Animaux 4. **Field, G.** 1892. Larva of Asterias vulgaris. Quart. Jour. Microsc. Sci. 34. **Fisher, W. K.** 1906. The starfishes of the Hawaiian Islands. Bull. U.S. Fish. Comm. for 1903, pt. 3. 1911. Asteroidea of the North Pacific. Pt. 1. Phanerozonia and Spinulosa. Bull. U.S. Nation. Mus. 76. 1917. A new sea star from Kamchatka. Proc. U.S. Nation. Mus. 52 1919. Starfishes of the Philippine Seas and adjacent waters. Bull. U.S. Nation. Mus. 100, vol. 3. 1923. A preliminary synopsis of the Asteriidae. Ann. Mag. Natur. Hist., ser. 9, vol. 12. 1925a. Asexual reproduction in Sclerasterias. Biol. Bull. 48. 1925b. Marine zoology of tropical central Pacific. Sea Stars. Bull. Bernice P. Bishop Mus. Hawaii, 27. 1928. Asteroidea of the North Pacific and adjacent waters. Pt. 2. Forcipulata. Bull. U.S. Nation. Mus. 76. 1930. Pt. 3. Forcipulata, concluded. Bull. U.S. Nation. Mus. 76. 1940. Asteroidea. Discovery Repts. 20. **Fosse, R.** 1913. Présence de l'urée chez les invertébrés. C. R. Acad. Sci. Paris 157. **Fraenkel, G.** 1928. Über den Auslösungsreiz des Umkehrreflexes bei den Seesternen. Ztschr. Vergl. Physiol. 7. **Fröhlich, F.** 1910. Über den an dem Seesterne Palmipes membranaceus auftretenden Tonus und seine Hemmung. Ztschr. Allg. Physiol. 11. **Galtsoff, P.,** and **V. Loosanoff.** 1939. Natural history of Asterias forbesi. Bull. U.S. Bur. Fisheries 49. **Gemmill, J.** 1911. Adult anatomy of Solaster endeca. Proc. Roy. Phys. Soc. Edinburgh 18. 1912. Development of Solaster endeca. Trans. Zool. Soc. London 20. 1913. The larva of Porania pulvillus. Nature, London, 92. 1914. The development and certain points in the adult structure of Asterias rubens. Philos. Trans. Roy. Soc. London 205B. 1915a. Ciliation of asterids. Proc. Zool. Soc. London. 1915b.

Larva of starfish Porania pulvillus. Quart. Jour. Microsc. Sci. 61. 1915c. Double hydrocoels in the development and metamorphosis of Asterias rubens. Quart. Jour. Microsc. Sci. 61. 1916. Development of Asterias glacialis, Cribrella oculata, Solaster endeca, Stichaster roseus. Proc. Zool. Soc. London. 1920. Development of Crossaster papposus. Quart. Jour. Microsc. Sci. 64. **Gordon, Isabella.** 1929. Skeletal development in Leptasterias. Philos. Trans. Roy. Soc. London 217B. **Goto, S.** 1914. A descriptive monograph of Japanese Asteroidea. Jour. College Sci. Tokyo 29, art. 1. **Gregory, J. W.** 1900. The Stelleroidea. *In* E. **Lankester** (ed.), *A treatise on zoology*, vol. III. **Grieg, J. A.** 1902. Solaster affinis. Nyt Mag. Naturvid. 40. 1906. Echinoderma von dem Norwegischen Fischereidampfer Michael Sars in 1900–1903 gesammelt. III. Asteroidea. Bergens Mus. Aarbok, Naturvid. Rekke, no. 13. **Griffiths, A.** 1888. Renal organs of Asteridea. Proc. Roy. Soc. London 44. **Gruber, A.** 1884. Die Protozoen des Hafens von Genna. Nova Acta Acad. Leopold. Carol. Halle 46. **Hamann, A.** 1885. *Beiträge zur Histologie der Echinodermen.* Heft. 2. Die Asteriden. **Hamilton, W.** 1921. Coordination in the starfish. Jour. Comp. Psychol. 1. **Haubold, E.** 1933. Über eine neue Form sitzender Pedizellarien bei Seesternen. Zool. Anz. 103. **Hayashi, R.** 1935. Anatomy of Henricia sanguinolenta. Jour. Fac. Sci. Hokkaido Univ., ser. 6, vol. 4, no. 1, no. 4. 1940, 1943. Classification of the sea stars of Japan. I. Spinulosa. II. Forcipulata. Jour. Fac. Sci. Hokkaido Univ., ser. 6, vols. 7, 8. **Heath, H.** 1910. A new genus of parasitic gastropods. Biol. Bull. 18. 1917. The early development of Patiria miniata. Jour. Morphol. 29. **Hinard, G., and R. Fillon.** 1921. Sur la composition chimique des astéries. C. R. Acad. Sci. Paris 173. **Hirota, S.** 1895. Comet of Linckia multifora. Dobutsugaku Zasshi (Zool. Mag.) 7. **Hopkins, A.** 1926. Physiology of the central nervous system of Asterias tenuispina. Jour. Exp. Zool. 46. **Hörstadius, S.** 1926a. Entwicklung von Astropecten auranciacus. Arkiv Zoologi 18B, art. 7. 1926b. Embryologische Beobachtungen über Luidia ciliaris und Phyllophorus urna. Arkiv Zoologi 18B, art. 8. 1939. Entwicklung von Astropecten auranciacus. Pubbl. Staz. Zool. Napoli 17. **Huntsman, A., and M. Sparks.** 1924. Limiting factors for marine animals 3. Contribs. Canad. Biol., n. ser. 2. **Hutchinson, G., J. Setlow, and J. Brooks.** 1946. Biochemical observations on Asterias forbesi. Bull. Bingham Oceanogr. Collect. 9. **Hyman, L. H.** 1929. The effect of oxygen tension on oxygen consumption in some echinoderms. Physiol. Zool. 2. **Irving, L.** 1924. Ciliary currents in starfish. Jour. Exp. Zool. 41. 1926. Hydrogen ion concentration and its relation to metabolism and respiration in the starfish. Jour. Gen Physiol. 10. **Jennings, H. S.** 1907. Behavior of the starfish. Univ. California Publ. Zool. 4. **John, D.** 1948. The species of Astropecten. Novitatis Zool. London 42. **Just, C.** Wesen der phototaktischen Reaktion von Asterias rubens. Ztschr. Vergl. Physiol. 5. **Kalmus, H.** 1929. Versuche über die Bewegungen der Seesterne. Ztschr. Vergl. Physiol. 9. **Kellogg, V.** 1904. Restorative regeneration of Linckia. Jour. Exp. Zool. 1. **Kenk, R.** 1944. Ecological observations on Astropecten marginatus. Biol. Bull. 87. **Kennedy, G., and H. Vevers.** 1953. Biology of Asterias rubens. V. Jour. Marine Biol. Assoc. 32. **Kerkut, G.** 1953a. The forces exerted by the tube feet of the starfish during locomotion. Jour. Exp. Biol. 30. 1953b. The mechanisms of coordination of the starfish tube feet. Behaviour 6. **King, Helen.** 1898. Regeneration in Asterias. Arch. Entw'mech. Organ. 7. 1900. Further studies on regeneration in Asterias. Arch. Entw'mech. Organ. 9. **Kjerchow-Agersborg, H.** 1918. Bilateral tendencies and habits in the twenty-rayed starfish. Biol. Bull. 35. 1922. The relation of the madreporite to the physiological anterior end in the twenty-rayed starfish. Biol. Bull. 42. **Kleitman, N.** 1941. Effect of temperature on the righting of echinoderms. Biol. Bull. 80. **Knipowitsch,**

N. 1891. Dendrogaster astericola. Biol. Centralbl. 10. 1892. Beiträge zur Kenntnis Ascothoracida. Trav. Soc. Natural. St. Pétersbourg, livr. 4, vol. 23. **Koehler, R.** 1909. Astéries recueillies par l'Investigator dans l'Ocean Indien. I. Les astéries de mer profonde. Echinoderma of the Indian Museum V. 1910. Astéries du musée de Calcutta. II. Les astéries littorales. Echinoderma of the Indian Museum VI. 1920. Echinodermata Asteroidea. Australasian Antarctic Exped. 1911–1914. Scient. Repts., ser. C, Zool. 8. **Kowalevsky, A.** 1889. Ein Beitrag zur Kenntnis der Exkretionsorgane. Biol. Centralbl. 9. **Kubo, K.** 1951. Some observations on the development of Leptasterias. Jour. Fac. Sci. Hokkaido Univ. Ser. 6, Zool. 10. **Leconte, J.** 1952. Réactions de fuite des pectens en présence des Astérides. Vie et Milieu 3. **Lieberkind, I.** 1920. On a starfish which hatches its young in its stomach. Vidensk. Meddel. Dansk. Naturhist. Foren. 72. 1926. Ctenodiscus australis, a brood-protecting asteroid. Vidensk. Meddel. Dansk Naturhist. Foren. 82. 1932. Porcellanasteridae. Wissensch. Ergebn. Dtsch. Tiefsee-Exped. 21. 1935. Asteroidea. Pt. I. Porcellansteridae. Danish Ingolf Exped. 4, no. 10. **Lison, L.** 1930. Sur les amibocytes des échinodermes. Arch. Biol. 40. **Livingston, A.** 1932. Asteroidea. Scient. Repts. Great Barrier Reef Exped. 4. **Löhner, L.** 1913. Zur Entwicklungsgeschichte von Echinaster sepositus. Zool. Anz. 41. **Loosanoff, V.** 1937. Oyster pests control studies. Biennial Rept. Connecticut Shellfish Comm. 1945. Effects of sea water of reduced salinities upon starfish. Trans. Connecticut Acad. Arts. Sci. 36. **Loosanoff, V. and D. Shipley.** 1947. Ability of Asterias to detect food. Anat. Record 99. **Ludwig, H.** 1882. Entwicklungsgeschichte der Asterina gibbosa. Ztschr. Wiss. Zool. 37. 1897. Die Seesterne des Mittelmeeres. Fauna und Flora des Golfes von Neapel, Monogr. 24. 1900. Arktische Seesterne. Fauna Arctica 1. 1903. Seesterne. Expedition Antarctic Belge, Resultats Voyage Belgica 1897–1899, Zool. 1. 1905. Asteroidea. Repts. exploration west coasts Mexico, Central and South America and off the Galapagos in the Albatross. Mem. Mus. Comp. Zool. Harvard 32. 1910. Notomyota, eine neue Ordnung der Seesterne. Sitsungsber. Preuss. Akad. Wissensch. Berlin, pt. 1, no. 23. **Ludwig, H., and O. Hamann.** 1899. Die Seesterne. *In* H. G. Bronn (ed.), *Klassen und Ordnungen des Tierreichs*, Band II, Abt. 3, Buch 2. **Macann, T.** 1938. Asteroidea. Sci. Repts. John Murray Exped. 1933–1934, vol. 4, no. 9. **MacBride, E. W.** 1896. Development of Asterina gibbosa. Quart. Jour. Microsc. Sci. 38. **MacCurdy, H.** 1912. Reactions of Asterias to light. Science 35. 1913. Some effects of sunlight on starfish. Science 38. **Maloeuf, N.** 1937. Studies on the respiration and osmoregulation of animals. Ztschr. Vergl. Physiol. 25. **Mangold, E.** 1908a. Die Füsschen der Seesterne und die Koordination ihrer Bewegungen. Arch. Ges. Physiol. 122. 1908b. Über das Nervensystem der Seesterne und über den Tonus. Arch. Ges. Physiol. 123. **Marenzeller, E. von.** 1895. Myzostoma asteriae. Anz. Kais. Akad. Wissensch. Wien 32, no. 18. **Masterman, A.** 1902. The early development of Cribrella oculata. Trans. Roy. Soc. Edinburgh 40. **Matsumoto, T., and Y. Toyama.** 1943. Separation of a new sterol from the fat of the starfish. Jour. Chem. Soc. Japan 64. **Matsumoto, T., M. Yajima, and Y. Toyama.** 1943. The crystalline fraction of the unsaponifiable substances in the fat of Asterias. Jour. Chem. Soc. Japan 63. **McIntosh, W. C.** 1874. On British Annelida. Trans. Zool. Soc. London 9. 1900. *A monograph of the British annelids.* Vol. I, pt. 2. Polychaeta. **Mead, A.** 1901. The natural history of the starfish. Bull. U.S. Fish. Comm. for 1899, vol. 19. **Meissner, M.** 1904. Asteroidea. Ergebn. Hamburg. Magalhaenischen Sammelreise 1892–1893, vol. I. **Meurer, W.** 1907. Über Augen der Tiefsee-Seesternen. Zool. Anz. 31. **Meyer, Helga.** 1935. Die Atmung von Asterias rubens. Zool. Jahrb. Abt. Allg. Zool. 55. **Meyer, R.** 1906. Über den feineren Bau des Nervensystems der

Asteriden. Ztschr. Wiss. Zool. 81. **Milligan, H.** 1915. On the way a starfish eats a pipe-fish. Notes on starfishes feeding upon Siphonostoma. Common starfish attacking Syngnathus. Zoologist 19. 1916a. Starfishes feeding on hermit crabs. A starfish feeding on a spider crab. Zoologist 20. 1916b. Rate of locomotion in sun stars. Zoologist 20. 1916c. Cushion stars attacking brittle stars. Zoologist 20. 1916d. Growth and regeneration in Solaster papposus. Zoologist 20. **Monks, Sarah.** 1904. Variability and autotomy of [Linckia]. Proc. Acad. Natur. Sci. Philadelphia 56. **Moore, A. R.** 1910a. Righting movements of the starfish. Biol. Bull. 19. 1910b. Nervous mechanism of the righting movements of the starfish. Amer. Jour. Physiol. 27. 1920. Stereotropism as a function of neuromuscular organization. Jour. Gen. Physiol. 2. 1921. Stereotropic orientation of the tube feet of starfish. Jour. Gen. Physiol. 4. 1939. Injury, recovery, and function in an aganglionic central nervous system. Jour. Comp. Psychol. 28. **Mori, S.,** and **K. Matutami.** 1952. Studies on the daily rhythmic activity of Astropecten polyacanthus. Publ. Seto Marine Biol. Lab. 2. **Mortensen, T.** 1913. Development of some British echinoderms. Jour. Marine Biol. Assoc. 10. 1925. Echinoderms of New Zealand and the Auckland-Campbell Islands. III. Asteroidea. Vidensk. Meddel. Dansk Naturhist. Foren. 79. 1927. Two new ctenophores. Vidensk. Meddel. Dansk Naturhist. Foren. 83. 1935. A new giant sea-star, Mithrodia gigas, from South Africa. Ann. South Africa Mus. 32. **Nachtsheim, H.** 1914. Entwicklung von Echinaster sepositus. Zool. Anz. 44. **Narasimhamurti, N.** 1933. Double hydropore in Asterias glacialis. Jour. Exp. Biol. 10. **Newman, H. H.** 1921. Occurrence of paired madreporic pores and pore canals. Biol. Bull. 40. 1925. An experimental analysis of asymmetry in the starfish. Biol. Bull. 49. **Newth, H.** 1925. Early development of Astropecten irregularis. Quart. Jour. Microsc. Sci. 69. **Nishibori, K.** 1954. Pigment components from skins of Asteroidea. Bull. Japan. Soc. Scient. Fisheries 20. **Nusbaum, J.,** and **M. Oxner.** 1915. Zur Restitution bei dem Seestern. Zool. Anz. 46. **Ohshima, H.** 1929. Hermaphrodita morstelo, Asterina batheri. Annot. Zool. Japon. 12. 1940. The righting movements of Oreaster nodosus. Japan. Jour. Zool. 8. **Ohshima, H.,** and **H. Ikeda.** 1934. Sexual size dimorphism in Archaster typicus. Proc. Imper. Acad. Japan 10. **Okada, Y.** 1925. Dendrogaster arborescens. Bull. Mus. Nation. Hist. Natur. Paris 31. **Orton, J.,** and **J. Fraser.** 1930. Rate of growth of Asterias rubens. Nature, London, 126. **Osterud, H.** 1918. Development of Leptasterias hexactis. Publ. Puget Sound Biol. Sta. 2. **Paine, Virginia.** 1926. Adhesion of the tube feet in starfishes. Jour. Exp. Zool. 45. 1929. The tube feet of starfishes as autonomous organs. Amer. Natural. 63. **Parker, C.** 1881. Poisonous qualities of the starfish. Zoologist 5; Zool. Jahrbericht 1. **Perrier, E.** 1881. Description sommaire des espèces nouvelles d'astéries. Bull. Mus. Comp. Zool. Harvard 9. 1891. Stellérides. Mission Scient. Cap Horn, Zool. 6, pt. 3. 1896. Stellérides de l'Atlantique Nord. Résultats Campagnes Scient. Monaco, Fasc. 11. **Peskin, J.** 1951. Photolabile pigments in invertebrates. Science 114. **Pfeffer, W.** 1901. Die Sehorgane der Seesterne. Zool. Jahrb. Abt. Anat. 14. **Philippi, R.** 1870. Neue Seesterne aus Chile. Arch. Naturgesch. 36, pt. 1. **Piatt, J.** 1935. Orchitophyra. Fisheries Service Bull., no. 247. **Pietschmann, V.** 1905. Zur Kenntnis der Axialorgans und der ventralen Bluträume der Asteriden. Arbeit. Inst. Zool. Univ. Wien 16. **Plessner, H.** 1913. Physiologie der Seesternen. I. Der Lichtsinn. Zool. Jahrb. Abt. Allg. Zool. 33. **Preyer, W.** 1886, 1887. Über die Bewegungen der Seesterne. Mitt. Zool. Staz. Neapel 7. **Randall, J.,** and **H. Heath.** 1912. Asterophila, a new genus of parasitic gastropods. Biol. Bull. 22. **Reese, A.** 1942. The old starfish-clam question. Science 96. **Retzius, G.** 1911. Hermaphroditismus bei Asterias rubens. Biol. Untersuchungen 16. **Richters, C.** 1912. Regenerationsvorgänge bei Linckia. Ztschr. Wiss. Zool. 100. **Ritter, W.,** and **G. Crocker.** 1900. Multiplication of rays and bilateral symmetry in the 20-rayed starfish. Proc. Washington Acad. Sci. 2. **Robertson, J.** 1949. Ionic regulation in some marine invertebrates. Jour. Exp. Biol. 26. **Rodenhouse, I.,** and **J. Guberlet.** 1946. The morphology and behavior of the cushion star. Univ. Washington Publ. Biol. 12. **Roi, O. de.** 1905. Zwei neue parasitische Cirripedien aus der Gruppe der Ascothoracida. Zool. Anz. 29. 1907. Dendrogaster arborescens und ludwigi. Ztschr. Wiss. Zool. 86. **Russell, E.** 1919. Righting reaction in Asterina gibbosa. Proc. Zool. Soc. London. **Sars, M.** 1835. *Beskrivelser og jagttagelser over nogle moerkelige eller nye i havet ved den Bergenske kyst levende dyr.* 1844. Über die Entwickelung der Seesterne. Arch. Naturgesch. 10, pt. 1. 1846. Fauna littoralis Norvegiae, Heft 1. **Sawano, K.** 1936. Proteolytic enzymes in the starfish. Sci. Repts. Tokyo Bunrika Daigaku 2, no. 38. **Sawano, E.,** and **K. Mitsugi.** 1932. Toxic action of the stomach extracts of starfishes. Sci. Repts. Tohoku Univ., ser. 4, Biol. 7. **Schapiro, J.** 1914. Regenerationserscheinungen verschiedener Seesternarten. Arch. Entw'mech. Organ. 38. **Schiemenz, P.** 1896. Wie offnen die Seesterne Austern? Mitt. Dtsch. Seefischereivereins 11–13; also Jour. Marine Biol. Assoc. 4. **Scott, T.,** and **A. Scott.** 1894. On some new and rare Crustacea from Scotland. Ann. Mag. Natur. Hist., ser. 6, vol. 13. 1895. On some new and rare British Copepoda. Ann. Mag. Natur. Hist., ser. 6, vol. 16. **Schuchert, C.** 1915. Revision of the palaeozoic Stelleroidea. Bull. U.S. Nation. Mus. 88. **Sladen, W. P.** 1889. Report on the Asteroidea collected by the Challenger. Rept. Scient. Results Voyage Challenger, Zool. 30. **Smith, G.** 1936. A gonad parasite of the starfish. Science 84. 1940. Factors limiting distribution and size in the starfish. Jour. Fisheries Research Bd. Canada 5. **Smith, J. E.** 1937. On the nervous system of Marthasterias glacialis. Philos. Trans. Roy. Soc. London 227B. 1945. The role of the nervous system in some activities of starfish. Biol. Rev. Cambridge Philos. Soc. 20. 1946. The mechanics and innervation of the starfish tube foot-ampulla system. Philos. Trans. Roy. Soc. London 232B. 1947. The activities of the tube feet of Asterias rubens. Quart. Jour. Microsc. Sci. 88. 1950. The motor nervous system of Astropecten irregularis. Philos. Trans. Roy. Soc. London 234B. **Spärck, A.** 1932. Migration of adult individuals of Asterias rubens. Rept. Danish Biol. Sta. 37. **Spencer, W. K.** 1914–1940. A monograph of the British Palaeozoic Asterozoa. Palaeontograph. Soc. London 67, 69, 70, 71, 74, 76, 79, 82, 87, 94. 1951. Early Palaeozoic starfish. Philos. Trans. Roy. Soc. London 235B. **Stone, Ellen.** 1897. Physiological function of the pyloric caeca of Asterias vulgaris. Amer. Natural. 31. **Studer, T.** 1873. Vermehrung von Seesternen durch Theilung und Knospung. Mitt. Naturforsch. Gesellsch. Bern, Sitzungsber. 1880. Über Geschlechtsdimorphismus bei Echinodermen. Zool. Anz. 3. 1885. Die Seesterne Süd-Georgien. Jahrb. Wissensch. Anstalt. Hamburg II. **Stummer-Traunfels, R. von.** 1903. Myzostoma asteriae. Ztschr. Wiss. Zool. 75. **Svetlov, P.** 1916. Structure of Tiedemann's bodies in Asteroidea. Trav. Soc. Natural. Pétrograd. 45, Livr. 4. **Tattersall, W.,** and **E. Sheppard.** 1934. Bipinnaria of Luidia. Lancashire Sea-Fisheries Lab., James Johnstone Memorial Vol. **Tennant, D.,** and **V. Keiller.** 1913. Anatomy of Oreaster reticulatus. Carnegie Inst. Washington, Papers Dept. Marine Biol. 3. **Théel, H.** 1919. Om amoebocyter och andra krapper i perivesceralhälau hos echinoderma I. Arkiv Zoologi 12, no. 4. **Thust, K.** 1916. Zur Anatomie und Histologie der Brisinga. Mitt. Zool. Stat. Neapel 22. **Tortonese, E.** 1947. Struttura istologica dei pedicelli e particolarita locomotrice de alcuni asteroidi. Monitore Zool. Ital. 56. 1950a. Ricerche sperimentali e comparative sui movimenti degli asteroidi. Arch Zool. Ital. 35. 1950b. Differenziazione geografica ed ecologica negli asteroidi. Boll. Zool. suppl. to 17. 1952. Gli echinodermi del Mar Ligure.    Atti. Accad. Ligure Sci. Lett. 8.    **Ubaghs, G.**    1953.    Classe des Stelleroides.    *In* **J. Piveteau** (ed.), *Traité de paléontologie*, vol. III.    **Uexküll, J. von.**    1912.    Die Pilgermuschel.    Ztschr. Biol. 58.    **Ulrey, A. B.**    1918.    The starfishes of southern California.    Bull. South. Calif. Acad. Sci. 17.    **Valentine, J.**    1926.    Regeneration in Linckia.    Carnegie Inst. Washington Yearbook 25.    **Van der Heyde, H.,** and **H. Oomen.**    1924.    Sur l'existence chez les étoiles de mer d'une digestion intracellulaire.    Arch. Internation. Physiol. 24.    **Ven, C.**    1922.    Sur la formation d'habitudes chez les astéries.    Arch. Néerland Physiol. Homme Animaux 6.    **Verchowskaja, Irene.**    1931.    Experimentalstudien über das Axialorgan von Asteroidea.    Ztschr. Vergl. Physiol. 14.    **Verrill, A. E.**    1909.    Remarkable development of starfish on the northwest American coast.    Amer. Natural. 43.    1914.    Monograph of the shallow-water starfishes of the North Pacific coast.    Harriman Alaska Exped. 14.    1915.    Report on the starfishes of the West Indies, Florida, and Brazil.    Univ. Iowa Monogr., Bull. Lab. Natur. Hist. 7.    **Vevers, H.**    1949.    The biology of Asterias rubens.    I. Growth and reproduction.    Jour. Marine Biol. Assoc. 28.    1951.    II. Parasitization of the gonads by Orchitophrya.    Jour. Marine Biol. Assoc. 29.    1952.    III. Carotenoid pigments in the integument.    Jour. Marine Biol. Assoc. 30.    **Weel, P. van.**    1935.    Über die Lichtempfindlichkeit der ambulakralfüsschen des Seesterns.    Arch. Néerland. Zool. 1.    **Whitelegge, T.**    1889.    Marine and freshwater invertebrate fauna of Port Jackson and neighborhood.    Jour. Roy. Soc. New South Wales 23.    **Withers, R.,** and **R. Keble.**    1934.    The palaeozoic starfish of Victoria.    Proc. Roy. Soc. Victoria 46.    **Wolf, E.**    1905.    Physiologische Untersuchungen über das Umdrehen der Seesterne.    Ztschr. Vergl. Physiol. 3.    **Yamazi, I.**    1950.    Autotomy and regeneration in Japanese sea-stars.    Annot. Zool. Japon. 23.    **Yeager, J.,** and **O. Tauber.**    1935.    Hemolymph cell counts of some marine invertebrates.    Biol. Bull. 69.    **Yosii, N.**    1931.    Notes on Myriocladus.    Jour. Fac. Sci. Univ. Tokyo, sect. 4, Zool. 2.    **Young, M.**    1926.    The food and feeding habits of starfishes.    New Zealand Jour. Sci. Technol. 8.    **Zirpolo, G.**    1916.    Regenerazione delle braccia di Asterina gibbosa.    Boll. Soc. Natural. Napoli 28.    1921.    Regenerazione delle braccia di Asterina gibbosa.    Pubbl. Staz. Zool. Napoli 3.    1922.    Ricerche sulle regenerazione delle braccia di Asterina.    Boll. Soc. Natural. Napoli 33.    1930.    Ricerche sul sistema nervosa di Asterina.    Boll. Soc. Natural. Napoli 41.

ECHINOIDEA

**Agassiz, A.**    1864.    Embryology of echinoderms.    Mem. Amer. Acad. Arts Sci. 9.    1869.    Preliminary report on the echini and starfishes dredged between Cuba and the Florida reef.    Bull. Mus. Comp. Zool. Harvard 1.    1872.    Revision of the Echini.    Illust. Cat. Mus. Comp. Zool. Harvard no. 7, 4 pts.    Mem. Mus. Comp. Zool. Harvard 3, pts. 1–2.    1874.    Mem. Mus. Comp. Zool. Harvard 3, pts. 3–4.    1876.    On viviparous Echini from the Kerguelen Islands.    Proc. Amer. Acad. Arts Sci. 11.    1879.    Report on the Echini.    Repts. Results Dredging Gulf of Mexico by the Blake.    Bull. Mus. Comp. Zool. Harvard 5.    1880.    Preliminary report on the Echini.    Repts. Dredging by the Blake.    Bull. Mus. Comp. Zool. Harvard 8.    1881.    Report on the Echinoidea.    Rept. Scient. Results Voyage Challenger, Zool 3.    1904.    The Panamic deep-sea Echini.    Mem. Mus. Comp. Zool. Harvard 31, 2 vols.    1908.    The genus Colobocentrotus.    Mem. Mus. Comp. Zool. Harvard 39.    1909.    Existence of teeth and a lantern in Echinoneus.    Amer. Jour. Sci. 28.    **Agassiz, A.,** and **H. L. Clark.**    1907a.    Preliminary report on the Echini collected in 1906 by the Albatross.    Bull. Mus. Comp. Zool. Harvard 51.    1907b, 1909.    Hawaiian and other Pacific Echini, nos. 1–3.    Mem. Mus. Comp. Zool. Harvard 34.    **Agassiz, L.**    1841.    *Monographie d'échinodermes*.    Livr. 2.    *Les scutelles.*    **Aiyar, R.**    1934.    Development of Salmacis.    Nature, London, 134.    1935.    Early development and metamorphosis of Salmacis. Proc. Indian Acad. Sci. 1, sect. B. **Aiyar, R.,** and **K. Menon.** 1934. Observations on the spicules of Salmacis and Stomopneustes. Ann. Mag. Natur. Hist., ser. 10, vol. 13. **Allen, E.,** and **R. Todd.** 1900. Fauna of Salcombe Estuary. Jour. Marine Biol. Assoc. 6. **Ankel, W.** Prosobranchien der swedischen Westküste. Arkiv Zoologi 30A, no. 9. **Awerinzew, S.** 1911. Pigmente von S. droebachiensis. Arch. Zool. Exp. Gén. 48, Notes et revue no. 1. **Ball, E.** 1936. Echinochrome, its isolation and composition. Jour. Biol. Chem. 114, Abstr. Soc. Biol. Chem. **Bamber, Ruth.** 1921. Some experiments on the water vascular system of Echinus. Proc. Trans. Liverpool Biol. Soc. 35. **Bather, F. A.** 1931. What is Bothriocidaris? Palaeontol. Ztschr. 13. **Bather, F. A.,** and **W. K. Spencer.** 1934. A new Ordovician echinoid. Ann. Mag. Natur. Hist., ser. 10, vol. 13. **Beers, C.** 1948. The ciliates of S. dröbachiensis. Biol. Bull. 94. 1954. Plagiopyla and Euplotes, ciliates of S. dröbachiensis. Jour. Protozool. 1. **Behre, Ellinor.** 1932. Histology of the body fluid of Mellita. Anat. Rec. 54, suppl. **Bell, F. J.** 1904. Echinoderma found off the coast of South Africa. I. Echinoidea. Marine Investigations South Africa III. **Bernard, F.** 1896. Sur un lamellibranche nouveau, commensal d'un échinoderme. C. R. Acad. Sci. Paris 121. **Bernasconi, Irene.** 1947. Distribucion geografica de los equinoideos argentinos. Gaea (Anal. Soc. Argentina Estud. Geogr.) 8. 1953. Monografia de los equinoideos argentinos. Anal. Mus. Hist. Natur. Montevideo, ser. 2, vol. 6, no. 2. **Bertolini, Fausta.** 1930. Ricerche istologiche e sperimentali sulla digestione nel riccio di mare. Pubbl. Staz. Zool. Napoli 10. 1932. Funzione digerente del paraintestino nel riccio di mare. Arch. Zool. Ital. 16, pt. 2. **Bethe, A.,** and **E. Berger.** 1931. Variationen im Mineralbestand verschiedener Blutarten. Arch. Ges. Physiol. 227. **Biggar, Ruth.** 1932. Ciliates from Bermuda sea urchins. Jour. Parasitol. 18. **Bock, S.** 1925. Papers from Dr. Th. Mortensen's Pacific Expedition 1914–1916. Planarians. Pts. I–III. Vidensk. Meddel. Dansk Naturhist. Foren. 79. **Boliek, Mildred.** 1935. Lymph plasmodia of sea urchins. Jour. Elisha Mitchell Scient. Soc. 51. **Bolin, L.** 1926. Der Geotropismus von Psammechinus. Internation. Rev. Ges. Hydrobiol. 16. **Bonnet, A.** 1924. Sur l'appareil digestif et absorbant de quelques échinides réguliers. C. R. Acad. Sci. Paris 179. 1925. Recherches sur l'appareil digestif et absorbant de quelques échinides réguliers. Ann. Inst. Océanogr. Monaco, n. ser. 2. 1926. La constitution des plaques, la disposition des pores et l'obliquité des canaux ambulacraires chez les échinides réguliers. Ann. Inst. Océanogr. Monaco, n. ser. 3. **Bonnier, J.** 1898. Note sur le Prionodesmotes phormosomae. Resultats Campagnes Scient. Monaco, Fasc. 12, appendix. **Bookhaut, C.,** and **N. Greenburg.** 1940. Cell types and clotting reactions in Mellita. Biol. Bull. 79. **Borig, P.** 1933. Über Wachstum und Regeneration der Stachelen einiger Seeigel. Ztschr. Morphol. Ökol. Tiere 27. **Bouvier, E.,** and **G. Seurat.** 1905. Eumedon convictor, crabe commensal d'un oursin. C. R. Acad. Sci. Paris 140. **Boveri, T.** 1901. Die Polarität von Ovocyte, Ei, und Larve des Strongyl. lividus. Zool. Jahrb. Abt. Anat. 14. **Brattström, H.** 1936. Eine neue Art der Ordnung Cirripedia Ascothoracica. Arkiv Zoologi 28A, no. 23. **Brian, A.** 1912. Copépodes parasites des échinides. Résultats Campagnes Scient. Monaco, Fasc. 38. **Bull, H.** 1938. Growth of Psammechinus miliaris. Rept. Dove Marine Lab. Cullercoats, ser. 3, no. 6. **Campbell, A.** 1921. Littoral ophiurans at Laguna Beach. Jour. Entomol. Zool. 13. **Cannon, R.** 1927. Echinochrome. Biochem. Jour. 21. **Cascia, P.** 1930. Sul problema del dimorfismo sessuale negli echinoidi regolari. Bull. Inst. Zool. Univ. Palermo 2. **Caullery, M.** 1912. The annual cycle of changes in the genital glands of E. cordatum. Rept. Brit. Assoc. Advanc. Sci. 81. 1925. Sur la structure et le fonctionnement des gonades chez les échinides. Trav. Sta. Zool. Wimereux 9. **Chadwick, H.** 1900. Echinus. Proc. Trans. Liverpool Biol. Soc. 14, mem. 3. 1925. Ciliate Protozoa parasitic in local echini. Proc. Trans. Liverpool Biol. Soc. 39. 1929. Regeneration of spines in Echinus esculentus. Nature, London, 124. **Clark, A. H.** 1909. Affinities of the Echinoidea. Amer. Natural. 43. **Clark, H. L.** 1907. The Cidaridae. Bull. Mus. Comp. Zool. Harvard 51. 1909. Echinodermata. Scient. Results Trawling Exped. Thetis. Mem. Austral. Mus. 4, pt. 11. 1912, 1914, 1917. Hawaiian and other Pacific Echini. Mem. Mus. Comp. Zool. Harvard 34, no. 4; 46, no. 1; 46, no. 2. 1925. *A catalogue of the recent sea urchins of the British Museum.* 1932. The ancestry of Echini. Science 76. 1940. A revision of the keyhole urchins. Proc. U.S. Nation. Mus. 89. 1948. Echini of the warmer eastern Pacific. Allan Hancock Expeds. 8, no. 5. **Claus, H.** 1889. Neue oder wenig bekannte halbparasitische Copepoden. Arbeit. Zool. Inst. Wien 8. **Coutière, H.** 1897. Note sur quelques alphéidés nouveaux ou peu connus rapportés de Djibouti. Bull. Mus. Nation. Hist. Natur. Paris 3. **Crozier, W.** 1919. Regeneration and the reformation of lunules in Mellita. Amer. Natural. 53. 1920. Notes on the bionomics of Mellita. Amer. Natural. 54. **Cuénot, L.** 1906. Rôle biologique de la coagulation du liquide coelomique des oursins. C. R. Soc. Biol. Paris 58 (*or* 61, *vol. nos. here jumbled*). **Davidson, E.** 1953. Clotting of the perivisceral fluid of the sand dollar. Biol. Bull. 105, abstr. **Dawson, J.** 1868. The food of the common sea urchin. Amer. Natural. 1. **Defretin, R.** 1952. Sur les mucocytes des podia de quelques échinodermes. C. R. Acad. Sci. Paris 234. **Delage, Y.** 1902. Sur les fonctions des sphéridies des oursins. C. R. Acad. Sci. Paris 134. 1903. Sur la non-régénération des sphéridies chez les oursins. C. R. Acad. Sci. Paris 137. **De Meijere, J.** 1904. Die Echinoidea der Siboga Expedition. Siboga Exped. Monogr. 43. **Deutler, P.** 1926. Das Wachstum des Seeigelskeletts. Zool. Jahrb. Abt. Anat. 48. **Devanesen, D.** 1922. Development of the lantern of Aristotle. Proc. Roy. Soc. London 93B. **Di Mauro, S.** 1904. Sopra uno nuovo infusoria ciliato parassita. Bull. Accad. Gioenia Sci. Natur. Catania, fasc. 81. **Döderlein, L.** 1885. Seeigel von Japan und den Liu-Kiu Inseln. Arch. Naturgesch. 51, pt. 1. 1887. *Die Japanischen Seeigeln.* I. *Die Familien Cidaridae und Salenidea.* 1902. Bericht über die von Semon bei Amboina und Thursday Island gesammelt Echinoiden. Semon's Zool. Forschungsreise in Australien und dem Malayischen Archipel, vol. V, pt. 2. 1905. Arktische Seeigel. Fauna Arctica 4. 1906a. Die polyporen Echinoiden von Japan. Zool. Anz. 30. 1906b. Die Echinoiden der deutschen Tiefsee-Expedition. Wissensch. Ergebn. Dtsch. Tiefsee-Exped. Valdivia 5, Lief. 2. 1914. Echinoidea. Die Fauna Südwest-Australiens. Ergebn. Hamburger südwest-australischen Forschungsreise 1905, vol. IV, Lief. 12. **Dohrn, A.** 1875. Mittheilungen as dem zoologischen Station Neapel. Ztschr. Wiss. Zool. 25. **Donnellon, J.** 1938. Clot formation in the perivisceral fluid of Arbacia. Physiol. Zool. 11. **Drzewina, A.,** and **G. Bohn.** 1924. Un nouveau cas d'hermaphrodisme chez l'oursin. C. R. Acad. Sci. Paris 178. **Dubois, R.** 1913. Note sur l'action de la lumière sur les échinodermes. C. R. 9 Internation. Congr. Zool.; *also* C. R. Assoc. Franç. Avanc. Sci. 41. **Duncan, P.** 1883. Morphology of the test of the Temnopleuridae. Jour. Linnaean Soc. London, Zool. 16. 1888. Anatomy of the Temnopleuridae. Ann. Mag. Natur. Hist., ser. 6, vol. 1. **Durham, H.** 1892. On wandering cells in echinoderms. Quart. Jour. Microsc. Sci. 33. **Elmhirst, R.** 1922a. Breeding and growth of marine animals in the Clyde area. Ann. Rept. Scottish Marine Biol. Assoc. 1922b. Habits of Echinus esculentus. Nature, London, 110. **Farquhar, H.** 1894. Notes on New Zealand echinoderms. Trans. New Zealand Inst. 27. 1898. On the echinoderm fauna of New Zealand. Proc. Linnaean Soc. New South Wales 23. 1926. The sea-urchins of New Zealand. Nature, London, 117. **Fewkes, J.** 1886. Development of Echinarachnius. Bull. Mus. Comp. Zool. Harvard 12. 1890. On excavations made in rocks by sea urchins. Amer.

Natural. 24. **Fleischmann, A.** 1888. Die Entwicklung des Eies von Echinocardium. Ztschr. Wiss. Zool. 46. **Fox, H.** 1922. Lunar periodicity in reproduction. Nature, London, 109. 1924a. Lunar periodicity in reproduction. Proc. Roy. Soc. London 95B. 1924b. The spawning of echinoids. Proc. Cambridge Philos Soc. 1. **Fredericq, L.** 1922. Action du milieu marin sur les invertébrés. Arch. Internation. Physiol. 19. **Fujiwara, T.** 1935. On the poisonous pedicellariae of Toxopneustes. Annot. Zool. Japon. 15. **Gadd, G.** 1907. Ein fall von Hermaphroditismus bei S. drobachiensis. Zool. Anz. 31. **Gandolfi-Hornyold, H.** 1909. Über die Nahrungsaufnahme der Spatangiden. Biol. Centralbl. 29. 1910a. Biologie und Anatomie der Spatangiden. Mitt. Naturforsch. Gesellsch. Fribourg, Zool. 1, Heft 2. 1910b. Über die Funktion und Autotomie der gemmiformen Pedicellarien. Biol. Centralbl. 30. 1912. Über die Nahrungsaufnahme der Spatangiden. Verhandl. Schweiz. Naturforsch. Gesellsch. 95. 1913. Über den Aufenthalt im Sand, Eingraben, Kanalbau und Schleimabsonderung der Spatangiden. C. R. 9 Congr. Internation. Zool. **Gardiner, J.** 1911. The rearing of sea urchins. Nature, London, 87. **Garman, H., and B. Colton.** 1883. Development of Arbacia. Studies Biol. Lab. Johns Hopkins Univ. 2. **Garrido, J., and J. Blanco.** 1947. Structure cristalline des piquants d'oursin. C. R. Acad. Sci. Paris. 224. **Geddes, P.** 1880. Observations sur le fluide périviscéral des oursins. Arch. Zool. Exp. Gén., ser. 1, vol. 8. **Gemmill, J.** 1910. The lantern of Aristotle as an organ of locomotion. Nature, London, 88. 1912. The locomotor function of the lantern in Echinus. Proc. Roy. Soc. London 85B. **Gemmill, J., and O. von Linstow.** 1902. Ichthyonema grayi. Arch. Naturgesch. 68, pt. 1. **Giard, A.** 1876. Sur un amphipods commensal de l'Echinocardium. C. R. Acad. Sci. Paris 82. **Giltay, L.** 1934. Note sur l'association du Balanus et Dendraster excentricus. Bull. Mus. Roy. Hist. Natur. Belgique 10, no. 5. **Glassell, S.** 1935. New or little known crabs from the Pacific coast of north Mexico. Trans. San Diego Soc. Natur. Hist. 8. 1936. New porcellanids and pinnotherids from tropical North American waters. Trans. San Diego Soc. Natur. Hist. 8. **Goodrich, Helen.** 1915. Sporozoa of spatangoids. Quart. Jour. Microsc. Sci. 61. **Goodwin, T., E. Lederer, and L. Musajo.** 1951. The nomenclature of the spinochromes of sea urchins. Experientia 7. **Goodwin, T., and S. Srisukh.** 1951. Carotenoids in the heart urchin. Nature, London, 167. **Gordon, Isabella.** 1926a. Development of the calcareous test of Echinus. Philos. Trans. Roy. Soc. London 214B. 1926b. Development of the calcareous test of Echinocardium. Philos. Trans. Roy. Soc. London 215B. 1929. Skeletal development in Arbacia, Echinarachnius, and Leptasterias. Philos. Trans. Roy. Soc. London 217B. **Grant, U. S., III, and L. Hartlein.** 1938. The West American Cenozoic Echinoidea. Publ. Univ. California Los Angeles, Math. Phys. Sci. 2. **Grave, C.** 1902. Structure and development of Mellita. Johns Hopkins Univ. Circulars, no. 21. 1911. Notes on the metamerism of the echinoid pluteus. Johns Hopkins Univ. Circulars, no. 232. **Gray, J.** 1921. True and apparent hermaphroditism in sea urchins. Proc. Cambridge Philos. Soc. 20. **Gregory, Emily.** 1908. The skeletal parts of the sand-dollar. Science 27. 1911. Water vascular system of Echinarachnius. Zool Anz. 38. **Gregory, J. W.** 1900. The Echinoidea. In E. R. Lankester (ed.), A Treatise on zoology, pt. III. **Grube, A.** 1868. Über einen lebendig-gebärenden Seeigel. Monatsber. Akad. Wiss. Berlin. **Hall, T.** 1908. On the occurrence of a marsupium in an echinoid. Proc. Roy. Soc. Victoria 20, pt. 2. **Hamann, O.** 1887. Anatomie und Histologie der Echiniden und Spatangiden. Jena. Ztschr. Naturwiss. 21. **Hansen, H.** 1902. A copepod parasitic in spines of an echinothuriid. Vidensk. Meddel. Dansk Naturhist. Foren. ser. 6, vol. 4. **Harvey, Ethel.** 1939. An hermaphroditic Arbacia. Biol. Bull. 77. 1949. Growth and metamorphosis of Arbacia pluteus. Biol. Bull. 97.

736 PHYLUM ECHINODERMATA

**Hawkins, H.** 1912a. Evolution of the apical system in the Holectypoida. Geol. Mag., Decade 5, vol. 9. 1912b. Classification, morphology and evolution of the Echinoidea Holectypoida. Proc. Zool. Soc. London. 1913. The anterior ambulacrum of Echinocardium and the origin of compound plates in echinoids. Proc. Zool. Soc. London. 1917. Morphological studies on the Echinoidea Holectypoida. I. Geol. Mag., Decade 6, vol. 4. 1920. Morphology and evolution of the ambulacrum in the Echinoidea Holectypoida. Philos. Trans. Roy. Soc. London 209B. 1927. Some problems in the evolution of the Echinoidea. Biol. Rev. Cambridge Philos. Soc. 2. 1929. In defense of Bothriocidaris. Geol. Mag. 66. 1931. The first echinoid. Biol. Rev. Cambridge Philos. Soc. 6. 1934. The lantern and girdle of some recent and fossil Echinoidea. Philos. Trans. Roy. Soc. London 223B. **Hawkins, H.,** and **S. Hampton.** 1927. Occurrence, structure and affinities of Echinocystis and Paleodiscus. Quart. Jour. Geol. Soc. 83. **Hayes, F.** 1933. Variation in size and in nitrogen requirements during early development of Echinometra. Carnegie Inst. Washington, Papers Dept. Marine Biol. 28. 1938. Relation of fat changes to the general chemical embryology of the sea urchin. Biol. Bull. 74. **Heilbrunn, L.** 1929. Hermaphroditism in Arbacia. Science 69. **Henri, V.** 1903a. Ferments digestifs chez quelques invertébrés. C. R. Acad. Sci. Paris 137. 1903b. Contractions de siphon intestinal des oursins. C. R. Soc. Biol. Paris 55. 1903c. Ferments digestifs chez quelques invertébrés. C. R. Soc. Biol. Paris 55. 1906. Étude du liquide periviscéral des oursins. C. R. Soc. Biol. Paris 58. **Henri, V.,** and **Mlle. Kayalof.** 1906. Étude des toxins contenues dans les pédicellaires chez les oursins. C. R. Soc. Biol. Paris 58. **Henri, V.,** and **S. Lalou.** 1903. Régulation osmotique du liquide interne chez les oursin. C. R. Soc. Biol. Paris 55. **Hentschel, C.** 1924. On a new ciliate from the intestine of Echinus. Parasitology 16. **Herlant, M.** 1918. Un cas d'hermaphrodisme complet et fonctionnel chez Paracentrotus. Arch. Zool. Exp. Gén. 57, Notes et revue no. 2. **Hilts, S.,** and **A. Giese.** 1949. Sugar in the body fluid of a sea urchin. Anat. Record 105, abstr. **Hobson, A.** 1930. Regeneration of the spines in sea urchins. Nature, London, 125. **Hoffmann, C.** 1871. Zur Anatomie der Echinen und Spatangen. Niederland Arch. Zool. 1. **Holmes, S. J.** 1912. Phototaxis in Arbacia. Jour. Animal Behavior 2. **Hörstadius, E.** 1939. The mechanics of sea urchin development. Biol. Rev. Cambridge Philos. Soc. 14. **Ikeda, H.** 1931a. Biometrical study of the sexual dimorphism and sex ratio of Temnopleurus. Annot. Zool. Japon. 13. 1931b. Morphological changes occurring with the growth of the calcareous test in the heart urchin. Annot. Zool. Japon. 13. 1939a. Peculiarities of the pedicellariae in Psychocidaris. Records Oceanogr. Works Japan 10. 1939b. Studies on the pseudofasciole of the scutellids. Jour. Dept. Agricult. Kyusyu Univ., vol. 6, no. 2. 1940. The fauna of Akkesi Bay. VIII. Echinoidea. Annot. Zool. Japon. 19. 1941. Function of the lunules of Astriclypeus. Annot. Zool. Japon. 20. **Irwin, Margaret.** 1953. Sea urchins damage steel piling. Science 118. **Jackson, H.** 1939. Notes on marine aquarium animals. Amer. Midland Natural. 22. **Jackson, R. T.** 1912. Phylogeny of the echini. Mem. Boston Soc. Natur. Hist. 7. 1929. The status of Bothriocidaris. Bull. Mus. Comp. Zool. Harvard 69. **Jacobs, M.** 1914. Protozoan parasites of Diadema. Carnegie Inst. Washington, Papers Dept. Marine Biol. 6. **Jacobson, F.,** and **N. Millott.** 1953. Phenolases and melanogenesis in the coelomic fluid of Diadema. Proc. Roy. Soc. London 141B. **Jeffreys, J.** 1864. Remarks on Stilifer. Ann. Mag. Natur. Hist., ser. 3, vol. 14. **Johnson, M.** 1930. Larval development of S. franciscanus. Publ. Puget Sound Biol. Sta. 7. **Kenk, R.** 1944. Ecological observations on Mellita. Biol. Bull. 87. **Kindred, J.** 1921. Phagocytosis and clotting in the perivisceral fluid of Arbacia. Biol. Bull. 41. 1926. Genetic relationships of the amebocytes with spherules in Arbacia. Biol. Bull. 50.

**Kleitman, N.** 1941. The effect of temperature on the righting of echinoderms. Biol. Bull. 80. **Koehler, R.** 1883. Recherches sur les échinides des côtes de Provençe. Ann. Mus. Hist. Natur. Marseilles, Zool. 1, mem. 3. 1914, 1922, 1927. Echinoderma of the Indian Museum, pts. 8, 9, 10. 1924. Anomalies, irrégularités et deformations au test chez les échinides. Ann. Inst. Océanogr. Monaco, n. ser. 1. 1926. Echinodermata Echinoidea. Australasian Antarctic Exped., Scient. Repts., ser. C, vol. 8, pt. 3. **Koehler, R.,** and **C. Vaney.** 1908. Prosobranche parasite sur certains échinides. Bull. Inst. Océanogr. Monaco 118. 1925. Un nouveau gastropode producteur de galles sur les piquants du Dorocidaris. C. R. Acad. Sci. Paris 180. **Kowalevsky, A.** 1889. Ein Beitrag zur Kenntnis der Exkretionsorgane. Biol. Centralbl. 9. **Krizenecky, J.** 1916. Regenerationsfähigkeit an Seeigel. Arch. Entw'mech. Organ. 42. **Kropp, B.** 1927. Commensalism of a sea anemone and a sea urchin. Science 65. **Krüger, F.** 1932. Versuche über die Wasserbewegung durch die Madreporenplatte von Echinus. Ztschr. Vergl. Physiol. 18. **Krumbach, T.** 1914. Über die Nahrung felsenbewohnender Seeigel. Zool. Anz. 44. 1933. Über eine kriechende ctenophore. Mitt. Zool. Mus. Berlin 19. **Kuhl, W.** 1937. Die Zellelemente in der Leibeshöhlenflüssigkeit des Seeigels. Ztschr. Zellforsch. Mikro. Anat. 27; *also* Verhandl. Dtsch. Zool. Gesellsch. 39 *in* Zool. Anz. suppl. 10. **Lafon, M.** 1953. Recherches sur les sables et sur quelques conditions de leur peuplement zoologique. Ann. Inst. Océanogr. Monaco, n. ser. 28. **Lasker, R.,** and **A. Giese.** 1954. Nutrition of Strongyl. purpuratus. Biol. Bull. 106. **Lederer, E.** 1940. Les pigments des invertébrés. Biol. Rev. Cambridge Philos. Soc. 15. 1952. Sur les pigments naphthoquinoniques des épines et du test des oursins. Biochim. et Biophys. Acta 9. **Lederer, E.,** and **R. Glaser.** 1938. Sur l'échinochrome et le spinochrome. C. R. Acad. Sci. Paris 207. **Leiper, R.** 1904. On the turbellarian worm Avagina. Proc. Zool. Soc. London. **Leopoldt, F.** 1893. Das angebliche Exkretionsorgan der Seeigel. Ztschr. Wiss. Zool. 55. **Lévy, R.** 1925. Sur les propriétés hémolytiques des pédicellaries. C. R. Acad. Sci. Paris 181. **Liebman, E.** 1950. The leucocytes of Arbacia. Biol. Bull. 98. **Lindahl, P.,** and **J. Runnström.** 1929. Variation und Ökologie von Psammechinus. Acta Zoologica 10. **List, T.** 1897. Über die Entwicklung von Proteinkrystalloiden in der Kernen der Wanderzellen bei Echinoidea. Anat. Anz. 14. **Lönneberg, E. von.** 1898. Undersökninger rörande Oresunds djiulif. Meddel. Kongl. Landbruksstyrelsen Uppsala. **Lovén, S.** 1874. Études sur les échinoidées. Kong. Svenska Vetensk. Akad. Handl., n. ser. 11, no. 7. 1883. On Pourtalesia. Kong. Svenska Vetensk. Akad. Handl., n. ser. 19, no. 7. 1892. Echinologica. Bihang Svenska Vetensk. Akad. Handl. 18, Afd. 4, no. 1. **Lucas, Miriam.** 1934. Ciliates from Bermuda sea urchins. I. Metopus. Jour. Roy. Microsc. Soc. 44. **Ludwig, H.,** and **O. Hamann.** 1904. Die Seeigel. *In* H. G. Bronn (ed.), *Klassen und Ordnungen des Tierreichs,* Band II, Abt. 3, Buch 4. **Lynch, J. E.** 1929, 1930. Studies on the ciliates from the intestine of Strongylocentrotus. I, II. Univ. California Publ. Zool. 33. **MacBride, E. W.** 1900. Notes on the rearing of echinid larvae. Jour. Marine Biol. Assoc. 6. 1903. Development of Echinus. Philos. Trans. Roy. Soc. London 195B. 1911. Two abnormal plutei of Echinus. Quart. Jour. Microsc. Sci. 57. 1912. Life history of Echinocardium cordatum. Rept. Brit. Assoc. Advanc. Sci. 82. 1914, 1918. Development of Echinocardium cordatum. I, II. Quart. Jour. Microsc. Sci. 59, 63. 1918, 1919. Artificial production of echinoderm larvae with two water-vascular systems. Proc. Roy. Soc. London 90B; Rept. Brit. Assoc. Advanc. Sci. 87. **MacBride, E. W.,** and **W. K. Spencer.** 1938. Aulechinus, Ectinechinus, Eothuria. Trans. Roy. Soc. London 229B. **MacMunn, C.** 1885. Chromatology of the blood of some invertebrates. Quart. Jour. Microsc. Sci. 25. **Madsen, H.** 1931. Über einige entozoische marine Infusorien. Zool. Anz. 96.

**Marenzeller, C. von.** 1895. Eine neue Gattung und Art der Hermelliden. Anz. Akad. Wissensch. Wien, Math. Naturwiss. Kl. 32. **Marx, W.** 1929. Über sekundäre Geschlechtsmerkmale bei Psammechinus und Echinocyamus. Zool. Anz. 80. **Maupas, E.** 1883. Étude morphologique et anatomique des infusoires ciliés. Arch. Zool. Exp. Gén., ser. 2, vol. 1. **Mayr, E.** 1954. Geographic variation in tropical echinoids. Evolution 8. **McClendon, J. F.** 1912. Echinochrome. Jour. Biol. Chem. 11. **McNeill, F.,** and **A. Livingstone.** 1926. Echinoderms collected in Queensland and North Australia. Records Austral. Mus. 15. **Medes, Grace.** 1915. Pluteus of Laganum. Carnegie Inst. Washington, Papers Dept. Marine Biol. 8. **Meek, F.,** and **A. Worthen.** 1860. New carboniferous fossils from Illinois. Proc. Acad. Natur. Sci. Philadelphia 12. **Meissner, M.** 1896. Die aus Chile heimgebracht Seeigel. Arch. Naturgesch. 62, pt. 1. **Milligan, H.** 1916a. Feeding habits of the purple-tipped sea urchin. Zoologist 20. 1916b. Rate of growth of Echinus miliaris. Zoologist 20. 1916c. Mode of feeding in a sea urchin. Zoologist 20. **Millott, N.** 1950. Sensitivity to light, reactions to shading, pigmentation, and color change of Diadema. Biol. Bull. 99, abstr. 1952. Color change in Diadema. Nature, London, 170. 1953a. Observations on the young form of Diadema. Bull. Marine Sci. Gulf Caribbean 2. 1953b. Color pattern and the definition of the species. Experientia 9. 1953c. Light emission and light perception in Diadema. Nature, London, 171. **Millott, N.,** and **F. Jacobson.** 1951. Phenolases in Diadema. Nature, London, 168. 1952a. Melaninbildung bei niederen Organismen. Ztschr. Haut und Geschlechtskrankheiten 13. 1952b. The occurrence of melanin in Diadema. Jour. Investigative Dermatology 18. **Moore, A. R.** 1933. Development of Temnopleurus. Sci. Repts. Tohoku Univ., ser. 4, Biol. 8. **Moore, H. B.** 1932. A hermaphroditic sea urchin. Nature, London, 130. 1934. Comparison of the biology of Echinus esculentus in different habitats. Jour. Marine Biol. Assoc. 19. 1935. Hermaphroditism and viviparity in Echinocardium cordatum. Jour. Marine Biol. Assoc. 20. **Morgan, T. H.** 1894. Experimental studies on echinoderm eggs. Anat. Anz. 9. **Mortensen, T.** 1901. Die Echinodermen Larven. Nordisches Plankton, no. 9. 1903, 1907. Echinoidea. Danish Ingolf Expedition 4, pts. 1, 2. 1909. Die Echinoiden der deutschen Südpolar-Expedition 1901–1903. Dtsch. Südpolar-Exped., Zool. 3. 1910. The Echinoidea of the Swedish Southpolar expedition. Wissensch. Ergebn. Schwed. Südpolar Exped. 1901–1903, vol. 6, Lief. 4. 1913. Die Echinoidea des Mittlemeeres. Mitt. Zool. Stat. Neapel. 21. 1918. Echinoidea, Australia. Kungl. Svenska Vetensk. Akad. Handl. 58, no. 9. 1921. Echinoderms of New Zealand and the Auckland-Campbell Islands. I. Echinoidea. Vidensk. Meddel. Dansk Naturhist. Foren. 73. 1923. Danish Expedition to the Kei Islands 1922. Vidensk. Meddel. Dansk Naturhist. Foren. 76. 1926. Goniocidaris umbraculum, a brood-protecting species. New Zealand Jour. Sci. Technol. 8. 1927a. Postlarval development of some cidaroids. Mém. Roy. Acad. Copenhagen, ser. 8, vol. 11. 1927b. Report on the Echinoidea collected by the Albatross, Philippine Archipelago and adjacent regions, pt. 1. Bull. U.S. Nation. Mus. 100, vol. 6, pt. 4. 1928. Bothriocidaris and the origin of the echinoids. Vidensk. Meddel. Dansk Naturhist. Foren. 86. 1928–1951. *Monograph of the Echinoidea,* 15 vols. 1929. Echinoidea. Biological survey Mutsu Bay. Sci. Repts. Tohoku Univ., ser. 4, Biol. 4. 1930a. Bothriocidaris and the ancestry of echinoids. Vidensk. Meddel. Dansk Naturhist. Foren. 90. 1930b. The geographical distribution of cidaroids. Arch. Zool. Ital. 15. 1932. New contributions to the knowledge of cidaroids. Kong. Danske Vidensk. Selsk. Skrifter, ser. 9, vol. 4. 1938. Vegetarian diet of some deep-sea echinoids. Annot. Zool. Japon. 17. 1940. Report of the Echinoidea collected by the Albatross, Philippine Archipelago and adjacent regions, pt. 2. Bull. U.S. Nation. Mus. 100, vol. 14, pt. 1. 1948. Report on the Echinoidea collected by the Albatross, Philippine Archipelago and adjacent regions, pt. 3. Bull. U.S. Nation. Mus. 100, vol. 14, pt. 3. 1950. Echinoidea. Repts. Brit. Austral. New Zealand Antarctic Research Exped. 1929–1931, ser. B, vol. 4, pt. 10. 1951. Report on the Echinoidea collected by the Atlantide Expedition. Scient. Results Danish Exped. coast tropical West Africa, 1945–1946, Atlantide Rept. no. 2. **Mourson, J.**, and **F. Schlagdenhauffen.** 1882. Recherches chimiques et physiologiques sur quelques liquides organiques. C. R. Acad. Sci. Paris. 95. **Nachtrieb, H.** 1885. Echinoderms of Beaufort. Johns Hopkins Univ. Circulars, vol. 4. **Nataf, G.** 1954. Croissance de Paracentrotus et Psammechinus. Bull. Mus. Nation. Hist. Natur. Paris 26. **Needham, J.**, and **A. Moore.** 1929. Hermaphroditism in Dendraster. Science 70. **Neefs, Yvette.** 1937. Sur divers cas d'hermaphrodisme fonctionnel chez P. lividus. C. R. Acad. Sci. Paris 204. 1938. Cycle sexuel de S. lividus. C. R. Acad. Sci. Paris 206. 1952. Cycle sexuel de Sph. granularis. C. R. Acad. Sci. Paris 234. 1954. Divers cas d'hermaphroditisme chez Arbacia lixula. Bull. Biol. France Belgique 87. **Newman, H.** 1923. Hybrid vigor, hybrid weakness, and the chromosome theory of heredity. Jour. Exp. Zool. 37. **Nisiyama, S.** 1940. Japanese species of Echinarachnius. Jubilee Publ. Commemoration Prof. H. Yabe's 60th Birthday, vol. II. **Nolf, P.** 1909. Coagulation du sang. Arch. Internation. Physiol. 7. **Nusbaum-Hilarowicz, J.**, and **M. Oxner.** 1917. Régénération chez les échinides. Bull. Inst. Oceánogr. Monaco, no. 325. **Okada, K.**, and **M. Shimoizumi.** 1952. Hermaphrodite sea urchin. Bull. Exptl. Biol. (Japan) 2. **Okada, Y.** 1926. Regeneration bei Seeigeln. Arch. Entw'mech. Organ. 108. **Onada, K.** 1931. Development of Heliocidaris crassispina. Mem. College Sci. Kyoto Univ. ser. B, vol. 7. 1933. Orientation of Heliocidaris crassispina. Jap. Jour. Zool. 5. 1936. Development of some Japanese echinoids. Jap. Jour. Zool. 6. 1938. Development of some Japanese echinoids. Jap. Jour. Zool. 8. **Orton, J. H.** 1914. Breeding habits of Echinus esculentus. Jour. Marine Biol. Assoc. 10. 1923a. Breeding period of P. miliaris. Nature, London, 111. 1923b. Rate of growth in a polar region and in England. Nature, London, 111. **Otter, G.** 1932. Rock-burrowing echinoids. Biol. Rev. Cambridge Philos. Soc. 7. **Palmer, Louise.** 1937. The shedding reaction in Arbacia. Physiol. Zool. 10. **Panning, A.** 1923. Eine pedicellarienstudie an Echinus. Zool. Anz. 55. **Parker, G. H.** 1922. Geotropism of Centrechinus. Biol. Bull. 43. 1927. Locomotion and righting movements in echinoderms. Amer. Jour. Psychol. 39. 1931. Color changes in Arbacia. Proc. Nation. Acad. Sci. U.S.A. 17. 1932. Certain feeding habits of the sea urchin. Amer. Natural. 66. 1936a. An inquiline gammarid on Lytechinus. Ecology 17. 1936b. Direction and means of locomotion in Lytechinus. Mem. Mus. Roy. Hist. Natur. Belgique, ser. 2, fasc. 3. **Parker, G. H.**, and **M. Van Alstyne.** 1932. Locomotor organs of Echinarachnius parma. Biol. Bull. 62. **Pérès, J.** 1950. Recherches sur les pédicellaires glandulaires de Sphaerechinus. Arch. Zool. Exp. Gén., 86, Notes et Revue no. 3. **Perrier, E.** 1870. Les pédicellaries et les ambulacres des oursins, pt. 2. Ann. Sci. Natur., Zool., ser. 5, vol. 13. 1875. Appareil circulatoire des oursins. Arch. Zool. Exp. Gén., ser. 2, vol. 4. **Porter, C.** 1926. Carcinologia chilena. Revista Chilena Hist. Natur. 30. **Powers, P.** 1933, 1935. Ciliates from sea urchins I, II. Biol. Bull. 65; Carnegie Inst. Washington, Papers Dept. Marine Biol. 29. **Prenant, M.** 1926a. Structure et croissance des dents d'oursin. Arch. Zool. Exp. Gén. 65, Notes et Revue no. 2. 1926b. Observations sur le déterminisme de la forme spiculaire chez les larves pluteus d'oursins. Bull. Scient. France Belgique 60; C. R. Soc. Biol. Paris 94. **Prouho, H.** 1887. Recherches sur le Dorocidaris papillata. Arch. Zool. Exp. Gén., ser. 2, vol. 5. 1890. Du rôle des pédicellaires gemmiformes des oursins. C. R. Acad. Sci. Paris 111. **Rathbun, Mary.** 1902. The Brachyura and Macrura of

Porto Rico. Bull. U.S. Fish. Comm. for 1900, vol. 20, pt. 2. 1918. The grapsoid crabs of America. Bull. U.S. Nation. Mus. 97. **Rathbun, R.** 1885. Echini collected by the Albatross in the Gulf of Mexico. Proc. U.S. Nation. Mus. 8. **Rees, C.** 1953. The larvae of the Spatangidae. Jour. Marine Biol. Assoc. 32. **Reid, D.** 1935. The range of Echinus esculentus. Jour. Animal Ecology 4. **Reverberi, G.** 1940. Su due casi di ermafroditismo. Boll. Zool. Unione Zool. Ital. 11. 1947. Ancora sull' ermafroditismo nei ricci di mare. Boll. Zool. Unione Zool. Ital. 14. **Rioja, S.** 1944. Estudios carcinologicas 16. Ann. Inst. Biol. Mexico 15. **Robertson, D.** 1871. Notes on E. cordatum. Quart. Jour. Microsc. Sci. 11. 1897. Jottings from my note book. Trans. Natur. Hist. Soc. Glasgow, n. ser. 4. **Robertson, J.** 1939. Inorganic composition of the body fluid of three marine invertebrates. Jour. Exp. Biol. 16. **Roman, J.** 1953. Galles de Myzostomides chez les clypéastres. Bull. Mus. Nation. Hist. Natur. Paris 25. **Romanes, G.** 1883. Observations on the physiology of Echinodermata. Jour. Linnaean Soc. London, Zool. 17. **Romanes, J.** 1911. Note on P. lividus as a rock borer. Proc. Cambridge Philos. Soc. 16. **Roxas, H.** 1928. Philippine littoral Echinoida. Philippine Jour. Sci. 36. **Runnström, S.** 1927. Larve von S. dröbachiensis. Nyt Mag. Naturvidensk. 65. **Russo, O.** 1914. Ciliata viventi nello intestina dello P. lividus. Boll. Accad. Gioenia Sci. Natur. Catania, ser. 2, fasc. 32. **Saint Hilaire, C.** 1897. Wanderzellen in der Darmwande der Seeigel. Trav. Soc. Natural. St. Pétersbourg, livr. 3, vol. 27. **Sarasin, P., and F. Sarasin.** 1886. Über einem Lederigel an der Hofen von Trincomalie. Zool. Anz. 9. 1887. Die Augen und das Integument der Diadematiden. Ergebn. Naturwiss. Forschungen auf Ceylon, vol. I. 1888. Über die Anatomie der Echinothuriden. Ergebn. Naturwiss. Forschungen auf Ceylon, vol. I. **Schinke, Helga.** 1950. Bildung und Ersatz der Zellelemente der Leibeshöhlenflüssigkeit von P. miliaris. Ztschr. Zellforsch. Mikro. Anat. 35. **Schmalz, P.** 1907. Der Seeigel und seine Pflege im Aquarium. Blätt. Aquär. Terrär. Kunde 18. **Schmidt, H.** 1904. Larvenentwickelung von Echinus. Verhandl. Physik. Med. Gesellsch. Würzburg 36. **Schurig, W.** 1906. Anatomie der Echinothuriden. Wissensch. Ergebn. Dtsch. Tiefsee-Exped. Valdivia 1898–1899, vol. 5. **Scott, F.** 1901. The food of S. dröbachiensis. Contribs. Canad. Biol., suppl. to 32 Ann. Rept. **Scott, T.** 1896. Lichomolgus maximus in the Firths of Forth and Clyde. Ann. Scottish Natur. Hist. **Selenka, E.** 1879. Keimblätter und Organanlage der Echiniden. Ztschr. Wiss. Zool. 33. 1883. *Studien über Entwickelungsgeschichte der Thiere*, vol. I, pt. 2. *Die Keimblätter der Echinodermen.* **Semon, R.** 1891. Zur Morphologie der bilateralen Wimperschnüre der Echinodermenlarven. Jena. Ztschr. Naturwiss. 25. **Shapiro, H.** 1935. A case of functional hermaphroditism in Arbacia. Amer. Natural. 69. **Smith, Nan.** 1924. Behavior of the embryonic cells of Arbacia in lymph plasmodia. Univ. North Carolina Record, no. 212. **Sollas, W.** 1899. On Silurian Echinoidea and Ophiuroidea. Quart. Jour. Geol. Soc. 55. **Southern, R.** 1915. Survey of Clare Island. Proc. Roy. Irish Acad. 31, sect. 3, pt. 67. **Stephensen, K.** 1933. Some new copepod parasites of ophiurids and echinids. Vidensk. Meddel. Dansk Naturhist. Foren. 93. 1935. Some endoparasitic copepods found in echinids. Vidensk. Meddel. Dansk Naturhist. Foren. 98. **Stewart, C.** 1879. On certain organs of the Cidaridae. Trans. Linnaean Soc. London, ser. 2, vol. 1. **Stott, F.** 1931. The spawning of E. esculentus. Jour. Exp. Biol. 8. **Svetlov, P.** 1924. On the appendices of the ambulacral ring in Echinoidea. Rev. Zool. Russe 4. **Swan, E.** 1952. Regeneration of spines by Strongylocentrotus. Growth 16. 1953. The Strongylocentrotidae of the northeast Pacific. Evolution 7. **Tanaka, H.** 1931. Coeloplana echinicola. Mem. College Sci. Kyoto Univ., ser. B, vol. 7. **Tennent, D.** 1910. Variations in echinoid plutei. Jour. Exp. Zool. 9. 1921. Early development and larval forms of three echinoids. Carnegie Inst. Washington, Papers Dept. Marine Biol. 26. **Tennent, D., M. Gardiner,** and **D. Smith.** 1935. Cytological and histochemical study of the ovaries of Echinometra. Carnegie Inst. Washington, Papers Dept. Marine Biol. 27. **Termier, H.,** and **G. Termier.** 1953. Classe des Échinides. *In* J. **Piveteau** (ed.), *Traité de paléontologie*, vol. III. **Théel, H.** 1892. Development of Echinocyamus pusillus. Nova Acta Reg. Soc. Scient. Upsala, ser. 3, vol. 15, no. 6. 1920. Om amoebocyter och andra kroppar i perivisceral-halan hos echinodermer. II. Arkiv Zoologi 12, no. 14. **Thomson, Wyville.** 1874. On the Echinoidea of the Porcupine deep-sea dredging expeditions. Philos. Trans. Roy. Soc. London 164, pt. 2. **Tortonese, E.** 1949. La distribution bathymétrique des échinodermes et particulièrement des éspèces méditerranéennes. Bull. Inst. Océanogr. Monaco, no. 956. **Übisch, L. von.** 1913a. Die Anlage und Ausbildung des Skeletsystems einiger Echiniden. Ztschr. Wiss. Zool. 104. 1913b. Die Ent-wicklung von P. lividus. Ztschr. Wiss. Zool. 106. 1937. Die normale Skeletbildung bei Echinocyamus pusillus und P. miliaris. Ztschr. Wiss. Zool. 149. 1950. Die Entwicklung der Echiniden. Verhandel. Kon. Nederland. Akad. Wetensch., Afd Natuurk., sect. 2, vol. 47, no. 2. **Uexküll, J. von.** 1896a. Über Reflexe bei den Seeigeln. Ztschr. Biol. 34. 1896b. Der Schatten als Reiz für Centrostephanus. Ztschr. Biol. 34. 1896c. Über die Funktion der Poli'schen Blasen am Kauapparat der regulären Seeigel. Mitt. Zool. Stat. Neapel 12. 1900a. Die Physiologie der Seeigelstachels. Ztschr. Biol. 39. 1900b. Die Wirkung von Licht und Schatten auf die Seeigel. Ztschr. Biol. 40. 1907. Studien über den Tonus. IV. Die Herzigel. Ztschr. Biol. 49. **Uyemura, M.** 1934. Neue Ciliaten aus dem Darm-kanal von japanischen Echinoiden. Sci. Repts. Tokyo Bunrika Daigaku, ser. B, vol. 1, no. 17. **Viets, K.** 1938. Eine neue in Tiefsee-Echiniden schmarotzende Halacaridengattung. Ztschr. Parasitenk. 10. **Viguier, C.** 1900. L'hermaphrodi-tisme et la parthénogenèse chez les échinodermes. C. R. Acad. Sci. Paris 131. **Weese, A.** 1926. The food and digestive processes of S. dröbachiensis. Publ. Puget Sound Biol. Sta. 5. **Westergren, A.** 1911. Echinoneus and Micropetalon. Mem. Mus. Comp. Zool. Harvard 39. **Wilson, H. V.** 1924. Amoeboid behavior of the lymph cells in sea urchins. Jour. Elisha Mitchell Scient. Soc. 40. **Woodland, W.** 1905. Mode of formation of the spicular skeleton in the pluteus of Echinus esculentus. Quart. Jour. Microsc. Sci. 49. **Yagiu, R.** 1933. Ciliates from the intestine of Anthocidaris. Jour. Sci. Hiroshima Univ., ser. B, div. 1, zool. 2, art. 13. **Yakovlev, J.** 1922. Bothriocidaris und die abstammung der Seeigel. Ztschr. Dtsch. Geol. Gesellsch. 74. **Yeager, J.,** and **O. Tauber.** 1935. On the haemolymph cell counts of some marine invertebrates. Biol. Bull. 69. **Yoshida, M.** 1952. Observations on the maturation of Diadema setosum. Annot. Zool. Japon. 25. **Yoshiwara, S.** 1906. *Japanese Echini*. **Young, M. W.** 1929. Marine fauna of the Chatham Islands. Trans. New Zealand Institute 60.

## OPHIUROIDEA

**Allee, W. C.** 1927. Physiological effects of aggregation on Ophioderma brevis-pina. Jour. Exp. Zool. 48. **Allee, W. C.,** and **J. Fowler.** 1932. Further studies on oxygen consumption and autotomy of Ophioderma. Jour. Exp. Zool. 64. **Apos-tolides, N.** 1881. Recherches sur la circulation et la respiration des ophiures. C. D. Acad. Sci. Paris 92. **Berkeley, Alfreda.** 1927. Ophiurans of the Nanaimo district. Contribs. Canad. Biol. n. ser. 3, no. 11. **Bell, F. J.** 1915. The Echino-derma found off the coast of South Africa. III. Ophiuroidea. Marine Investi-gations South Africa 3. **Brock, J.** 1888. Die Ophiuridan-fauna des indischen Archipels. Ztschr. Wiss. Zool. 47. **Campbell, A.** 1921. Littoral ophiurans at Laguna Beach. Jour. Entomol. Zool. 13. 1922. Notes on growth stages in brittle stars. Jour. Entomol. Zool. 14. **Canu, E.** 1892. Les copépodes du Boulonnais. Trav. Sta. Zool. Wimereux 6. **Caso, M.** 1951. Contribucaion de los ofiuroideas de Mexico. I. Anal. Inst. Biol. Mexico 22. **Caullery, M.,** and **A. Lavellée.** 1912. Recherches sur le cycle évolutif des Orthonectides. Bull. Scient. France Belgique 46. **Chubrik, G.** 1952. The immature stages of Fellodistomum. Zool. Zhurnal 31. **Clark, A. H.** 1949. Ophiuroidea of the Hawaiian Islands. Bull. Bernice P. Bishop Mus., Hawaii, 195. 1951. The brittle stars of the United States Navy Antarctic Expedition 1947–1948. Jour. Washington Acad. Sci. 41. **Clark, H. L.** 1902. A new host for myzostomes. Zool. Anz. 25. 1911. North Pacific ophiurans in the United States National Museum. Bull. U.S. Nation. Mus. 75. 1914. Growth changes in brittle stars. Carnegie Inst. Washington, Papers Dept. Marine Biol. 5. 1915. Catalogue of recent ophiurans based on the collections of the Museum of Comparative Zoology. Mem. Mus. Comp. Zool. Harvard 25. 1917. Ophiuroidea. Repts. Scient. Results Exped. Eastern Tropical Pacific Albatross 1899–1900, 1904– 1905. Bull. Mus. Comp. Zool. Harvard 61. 1918. Brittle stars new and old. Bull. Mus. Comp. Zool. Harvard 62. 1939. Ophiuroidea. Scient. Repts. John Murray Expedition 1933–1934, vol. 6, no. 2. **Cowles, R.** 1910. Light and contact with solid as factors in the behavior of ophiuroids. Jour. Exp. Zool. 9. **Cuénot, L.** 1888. Études anatomiques et morphologiques sur les ophiures. Arch. Zool. Exp. Gén., ser. 2, vol. 6. **Dahlgren, U.** 1916. Production of light by animals. Jour. Franklin Inst. 181. **Dawydoff, C.** 1901. Regenerationserscheinungen bei den Ophiuren. Ztschr. Wiss. Zool. 69. **Des Arts, L.** 1910. Über die Lebensweise von Amphiura chiajei. Bergens Mus. Aarbog, Naturvid. Rekke, no. 12. **Djakonov, A.** 1914a. Über Viviparität und Wachstumserscheinungen bei Amphiura capensis. Zool. Jahrb. Abt. System. 36. 1914b. Ascothorax ophioctenis. Trav. Soc. Natural. Pétrograd 45. 1950. Starfish of the Soviet Union. Tabl. Anal. Faune USSR 34. **Döderlein, L.** 1896. Bei Amboina und Thursday Island gesammelten Ophiuroidea. Semon's Zool. Forschungsreisen in Australien und den Malayischen Archipel, vol. 5, pt. 1. 1898. Über einige epizoischlebende Ophiuroidea. Semon's Zool. Forschungsreisen in Australien und den Malayischen Archipel, vol. 5, pt. 2. 1911. Über Japanische und andere Euryalae. Abhandl. Math. Phys. Kl. Bayer. Akad. Wissensch., suppl. 2, Abhandl. 5. 1912. Die Arme der Gorgoncephalinae. Zool. Jahrb. suppl. 15. 1925. Indopacifische Euryalae. Abhandl. Bayer. Akad. Wissensch., Math. Naturwiss. Abt. 31, pt. 6. 1930. Die Ophiuriden der deutschen Tiefsee-Expedition. 2. Euryalae. Wissensch. Ergebn. Dtsch. Tiefsee-Exped. Valdivia 22, no. 6. **Farquhar, H.** 1894. Description of Amphiura rosea. Trans. New Zealand Inst. 26. **Fedotov, D.** 1915. Anatomy of Gorgonocephalus eucnemis. Trav. Soc. Natural. Pétrograd 46, livr. 1. 1916. Parasitism of Protomyzostomum on Gorgonocephalus. Jour. Russe Zool. 1. 1924. Biologie und Metamorphose von Gorgonocephalus. Zool. Anz. 61. 1926a. Die Morphologie der Euryalae. Ztschr. Wiss. Zool. 127. 1926b. Zur Morphologie einiger typischen, vorzugsweise leben- diggebärenden Ophiuren. Trav. Lab. Zool. and Sta. Biol. Sébastopol, ser. 2, no. 6. 1930. Zur vergleichenden Morphologie der Ophiuren. Trav. Lab. Zool. and Exp. Morphol. Animaux 1. 1931. Über eigenartigen Parasitismus bei Stechel- häutern. Ztschr. Morphol. Ökol. Tiere 22. **Fell, H. B.** 1941. The direct develop- ment of a New Zealand ophiuroid. Quart. Jour. Microsc. Sci. 82. 1946. The embryology of Amphipholis aquamata. Trans. Proc. Roy. Soc. New Zealand 75. 1949. New Zealand littoral ophiuroids. Tuatara 2. 1951. Some off-shore and deep-sea ophiuroids from New Zealand waters. Zool. Publ. Victoria Univ. College Wellington, no. 13. **Fewkes, J. W.** 1886. Preliminary observations on the development of Ophiopholis. Bull. Mus. Comp. Zool. Harvard 12. 1889. On a new parasite of Amphiura. Proc. Boston Soc. Natur. Hist. 24. **Fjelstrup, A.** 1890.

Echinodermata. Zoologia danica, Heft. 7. **Foettinger, A.** 1880. Sur l'existence de l'hémoglobine chez les échinodermes. Arch. Biol. 1. **Fraenkel, G.** 1928. Über den Auslösungsreiz des Umkehrreflexes bei Schlangensternen. Ztschr. Vergl. Physiol. 7. **Giard, A.** 1887. Sur un copépode parasite de l'Amphiura squamata. C. R. Acad. Sci. Paris 104. **Glaser, O.** 1907. Movement and problem solving in Ophiura. Jour. Exp. Zool. 4. **Graber, V.** 1889. Über die Empfindlichkeit einiger Meerthiere gegen Riechstoffe. Biol. Centralbl. 8. **Grave, C.** 1898. Embryology of Ophiocoma echinata. Johns Hopkins Univ. Circulars 18. 1899. Ophiura brevispina. Mem. Nation. Acad. Sci. U.S.A. 8, no. 4. 1916. Ophiura brevispina II. Jour. Morphol. 27. **Gregory, J. W.** 1900. The Stelleroidea. *In* E. Lankester (ed.), *A treatise on zoology*, vol. III. **Grieg, J. A.** 1900. Die Ophiuriden der Arktis. Fauna Arctica 1. **Hamann, O.** 1889. Die Anatomie und Histologie der Ophiuren. Jena. Ztschr. Naturwiss. 23. **Harvey, E. N.** 1926a. Inhibition of animal luminescence by light. Biol. Bull. 51. 1926b. Oxygen and luminescence. Biol. Bull. 51. 1952. *Bioluminescence.* **Heegaard, P.** 1951. Antarctic parasitic copepods and an ascothoracid cirriped from brittle stars. Vidensk. Meddel. Dansk. Naturhist. Foren 113. **Hérouard, E.** 1906. Sur un nouveau copépode parasite. C. R. Acad. Sci. Paris 142. **Hertz, Mathilde.** 1927a. Die Ophiuroiden der deutschen Südpolar Expedition 1901–1903. Dtsch. Südpolar Exped., Zool. 11. 1927b. Die Ophiuroiden der deutschen Tiefsee-Expedition. Wissensch. Ergebn. Dtsch. Tiefsee-Exped. Valdivia 22. **Hilton, W.** 1916. The central nervous system of serpent stars. Jour. Entomol. Zool. 8. **Jungersen, H.** 1912. Chordeuma obesum. Rept. Brit. Assoc. Advanc. Sci., 82, sect. D. **Kato, K.** 1935. A polyclad parasitic in the genital bursa of the ophiuran. Annot. Zool. Japon. 15. 1947. Luminous Ophiuroidea. Dobutsugaku Zasshi (Zool. Mag.), Tokyo, 57. **Koehler, R.** 1886, 1887. Appareil circulaire des ophiures. C. R. Acad. Sci. Paris 103; Ann. Sci. Natur. Zool., ser. 7, vol. 2. 1897. Echinodermes recueillis par l'Investigator dans l'Ocean Indien. Mém. 1. Les ophiures de mer profonde. Ann. Sci. Natur., Zool., ser. 8, vol. 4. 1898. Mém. 2. Les ophiures littorales. Bull. Scient. France Belgique 31. 1899. Deep sea Ophiuroidea collected by the Investigator. Echinoderma of the Indian Museum, vol. 1. 1904. Ophiures de l'expédition du Siboga. Pt. 1. Ophiures de mer profonde. Siboga Exped. Monogr. 45a. 1905. Pt. 2. Ophiures littorales. Siboga Exped. Monogr. 45b. 1906. Ophiures. Résultats Scient. Campagnes Traveilleur et Talisman, vol. 8. 1907. Sur le dimorphisme sexuel de l'Ophiacantha vivipara. Zool. Anz. 31. 1913. Ophiures. Zool. Jahrb. Suppl. 11. 1914. Ophiurans of the U.S. National Museum. Bull. U.S. Nation. Mus. 84. 1922a. Ophiurans of the Philippine Seas and adjacent waters. Bull. U.S. Nation. Mus. 100, vol. 5. 1922b. Echinodermata Ophiuroidea. Australasian Antarctic Exped. 1911–1914, Scient. Repts., ser. C, Zool. 8, pt. 2. 1926. Ophiures recueillies aux Iles Gilbert, Marshall et Fiji. Göteborg's Kung. Vetensk. Samh. Handl., ser. 4, vol. 33, no. 3. 1930. Ophiures recueillies par Mortensen dans les mers d'Australie et dans l'Archipel Malais. Vidensk. Meddel. Dansk Naturhist. Foren. 89. **Krohn, A.** 1881. Über die Entwicklung einer lebendiggebärenden Ophiura. Arch. Anat. Physiol. **Lange, W.** 1876. Beitrag zur Anatomie und Histologie der Ophiuren. Morphol. Jahrb. 2. **Le Calvez, J.** 1938. Parachordeumium. C. R. Congr. Soc. Savantes Paris 68. **Ludwig, H.** 1878a. Beiträge zur Anatomie der Ophiuren. Ztschr. Wiss. Zool. 31. 1878b. Trichaster elegans. Ztschr. Wiss. Zool. 31. 1878c. Die Bursae der Ophiuriden. Nachr. Gesellsch. Wissensch. Göttingen, no. 6. 1880. Neue Beiträge zur Anatomie der Ophiuren. Ztschr. Wiss. Zool. 34. 1882. Zur Entwicklungsgeschichte des Ophiurenskelettes. Ztschr. Wiss. Zool. 36. 1888. Ophiopteron. Ztschr. Wiss. Zool. 47. 1899. Jugendformen von Ophiuren. Sitzungsber. Kgl. Preuss. Akad. Wissensch. Berlin, pt. 1. 1905. Ein entoparasitischen chaetopod in einer Tiefsee-ophiure. Zool. Anz. 29. **Ludwig, O.,** and **O. Hamann.** 1901. Die Schlangensterne. *In* **H. G. Bronn** (ed.), *Klassen und Ordnungen des Tierreichs,* Band II, Abt. 2, Buch 3. **Lütken, C.** 1872. Quelques ophiurides nouveaux ou peu connus avec quelques remarques sur la division spontanée chez les rayonnés. Oversigt Dansk. Vidensk. Selsk. Forhandl. **Lütken, C.,** and **T. Mortensen.** 1899. The Ophiuridae, Repts. Explor. Panamic Albatross 1891. Mem. Mus. Comp. Zool. Harvard 23. **Lyman, T.** 1865. Ophiuridae and Astrophytidae. Illust. Catalogue Mus. Comp. Zool. Harvard no. 1. 1874. Ophiuridae and Astrophytidae, old and new. Bull. Mus. Comp. Zool. Harvard 3. 1878. Mode of forking among Astrophytons. Proc. Boston Soc. Natur. Hist. 19. 1882. Report on the Ophiuroidea. Rept. Scient. Results Voyage Challenger, Zool. 5. 1883. Report on the Ophiuroidea. Repts. Results Dredging Caribbean 1878–1879 and along the Atlantic coast of the United States 1880 by the Blake. Bull. Mus. Comp. Zool. Harvard 10. **MacBride, E. W.** 1892. Development of the genital organs, ovoid gland and aboral sinuses in Amphiura squamata. Quart. Jour. Microsc. Sci. 34. 1907. Development of Ophiothrix fragilis. Quart. Jour. Microsc. Sci. 51. **Mangold, E.** 1907. Leuchtende Schlangensterne. Arch. Ges. Physiol. 118. 1908. Über das Leuchten und Klettern der Schlangensterne. Biol. Centralbl. 28. 1909. Ueber die Armbewegungen der Schlangensterne. Arch. Ges. Physiol. 126. **Matsumoto, H.** 1913. New interesting ophiuran (Astrophiura). Annot. Zool. Japon. 8. 1915. A new classification of the Ophiuroidea. Proc. Acad. Natur. Sci. Philadelphia 67. 1917. A monograph of Japanese Ophiuroidea. Jour. College Sci. Tokyo Univ. 38, art. 2. **May, R. M.** 1924. Ophiurans of Monterey Bay. Proc. California Acad. Sci., ser. 4, vol. 13. 1925. Les réactions sensorielles d'une ophiure. Bull. Biol. France Belgique 59. **McClendon, J. F.** 1909. Ophiurans of the San Diego region. Univ. California Publ. Zool. 6. **Mercier, L.** 1922. Copépode parasite d'une ophiure. Bull. Soc. Linn. Normandie, ser. 7. vol. 4. **Metschnikoff, E.** 1869. Studien über die Entwicklung der Echinodermen. Mém. Acad. Imper. Sci. St. Pétersbourg, ser. 7, vol. 14, no. 8. **Milligan, H.** 1915. Rate of regeneration in a brittle star. Zoologist, London, 19. **Millott, N.** 1953. Association between Ophionereis reticulata and Harmothoe lunulata. Bull. Marine Sci. Gulf Caribbean 3. **Morgulis, S.** 1909. Regeneration in Ophiocoma. Proc. Amer. Acad. Arts Sci. 44; Science 29. **Mortensen, T.** 1893. Über Ophiopus arcticus. Ztschr. Wiss. Zool. 56. 1912. Über Asteronyx loveni. Ztschr. Wiss. Zool. 101. 1920. On hermaphroditism in viviparous ophiuroids. Acta Zoologica 1. 1924. Echinoderms of New Zealand and the Auckland-Campbell Islands. II. Ophiuroidea. Vidensk. Meddel. Dansk Naturhist. Foren 77. 1932. On Ophiocanops fugiens. Vidensk. Meddel. Dansk. Naturhist. Foren. 93. 1933a. Biological observations on ophiuroids. Vidensk. Meddel. Dansk Naturhist. Foren. 93. 1933b. Studies of Indo-Pacific euryalids. Vidensk. Meddel. Dansk. Naturhist. Foren. 96. 1933c. Ophiuroidea. Danish Ingolf Exped. 4, no. 8. **Mortensen, T.,** and **L. Rosenvinge.** 1910. Sur quelques plantes parasites dans les échinodermes. Oversigt Danske Vidensk. Selsk. Forhandl. **Mortensen, T.,** and **K. Stephensen.** 1918. On a gall-producing copepod infesting an ophiuroid. Vidensk. Meddel. Dansk Naturhist. Foren. 69. **Munson, J.** 1912. Anatomy of the arms of Ophioglypha. Proc. 7. Internation. Congr. Zool. **Murakami, S.** 1937. Development of the calcareous plates in an ophiurid larva. Annot. Zool. Japon. 16. 1940. Development of the calcareous plates of Amphipholis. Jap. Jour. Zool. 9. 1941. Development of the hard parts of a viviparous ophiuran. Annot. Zool. Japon. 20. **Narasimhamurti, N.** 1933. The embryology of Ophiocoma nigra. Quart. Jour. Microsc. Sci. 76. **Nielsen, E.** 1932. Ophiurans from the Gulf of Panama, California, and the Straits of Georgia. Vidensk. Meddel. Dansk Naturhist. Foren. 91. **Olsen, H.** 1942a. A short report on some ophioplutei. Bergens Mus. Arbok, Naturvid. Rekke, no. 4. 1942b. Development of Ophiopholis aculeata. Bergens Mus. Arbok, Naturvid. Rekke, no. 6. **Östergren, H.** 1904. Funktion der Füsschen bei den Schlangensternen. Biol. Centralbl. 24. **Panikkar, N.,** and **R. Prasad.** 1952. Association of ophiuroids, fish and crab with Rhopilema. Jour. Bombay Natur. Hist. Soc. 51. **Petersen, C.** 1918. The sea bottom and its production of fish food. Rept. Danish Biol. Sta. 25. **Preyer, W.** 1886, 1887. Über die Bewegungen der Seesternen. Mitt. Zool. Stat. Neapel 7. **Pyefinch, K.** 1940. Anatomy of Ophioica. Jour. Linnaean Soc. London, Zool. 41. **Quatrefages, A. de.** 1842. Sur quelques faits relatifs a l'histoire des animaux invertébrés. C. R. Acad. Sci. Paris 15. **Reichensperger, A.** 1908a. Ophiopsila. Ztschr. Wiss. Zool. 89. 1908b. Über Leuchten von Schlangensternen. Biol. Centralbl. 28. 1908c. Die Drüsengebilde der Ophiuren. Ztschr. Wiss. Zool. 91. **Schultze, M.** 1852. Über Entwicklung von Amphipholis squamata. Arch. Anat. Physiol. Wissensch. Med. **Semon, R.** 1889. Ein Fall von Neubildung der Scheibe. Jena. Ztschr. Naturwiss. 33. **Simroth, H.** 1876, 1877. Anatomie und Schizogonie der Ophiactis virens. I, II. Ztschr. Wiss. Zool. 27, 28. **Sladen, W.** 1879. Structure of Astrophiura. Ann. Mag. Natur. Hist., ser. 5, vol. 4. **Smith, G.** 1923. Ophiuroidea collected by the Quest. Ann. Mag. Natur. Hist., ser. 9, vol. 12. **Smith, J. E.** 1937. Structure and function of the tube feet in certain echinoderms. Jour. Marine Biol. Assoc. 22. 1940. The reproductive system and associated organs of Ophiothrix fragilis. Quart. Jour. Microsc. Sci. 82. **Sokolov, I.** 1909. Über die Leuchten und die Drüsengebilde der Ophiuren. Biol. Centralbl. 29. **Stephensen, K.** 1927. Crustacea from the Auckland and Campbell Islands. Vidensk. Meddel. Dansk Naturhist. Foren. 83. 1933. Some new copepods, parasites of ophiurids. Vidensk. Meddel. Dansk. Naturhist. Foren. 93. 1935. Two crustaceans endoparasitic in ophiurids. Danish Ingolf Exped. 3, no. 12. **Stromberger, K.** 1926. Versuche an Ophioglypha. Arch. Ges. Physiol. 213. **Tauson, A.** 1927. Parasite of Ophiura sarsi. Jour. Russe Zool. 2. **Teuscher, R.** 1876. Beiträge zur Anatomie der Echinodermen. II. Ophiuridae. Jena. Ztschr. Naturwiss. 10. **Thorson, G.** 1934. Reproduction and larval stages of Ophiocten sericeum and Ophiura robusta in East Greenland. Meddel. Grönland 100, no. 4. **Trojan, E.** 1908. Das Leuchten der Schlangensterne. Biol. Centralbl. 28. 1909a. Die Lichtentwicklung bei Amphiura squamata. Zool. Anz. 34. 1909b. Leuchtende Ophiopsilen. Arch. Mikro. Anat. 73. **Uexküll, J. von.** 1905. Die Bewegungen der Schlangensterne. Ztschr. Biol. 46. **Verrill, A. E.** 1882. Restoration of the disk in ophiurans. Ann. Mag. Natur. Hist., ser. 5, vol. 9. 1899a. North American Ophiuroidea. Trans. Connecticut Acad. Arts Sci. 10, pt. 2. 1899b. Report on the Ophiuroidea collected by the Bahama Expedition in 1893. Bull. Lab. Natur. Hist. Univ. Iowa 5. **Wintzell, J.** 1918. Bidrag till de skandinavska ophiuridernas biologi och fysiologi. Dissertation, Uppsala. **Withers, R.,** and **R. Keble.** 1934. The Palaeozoic brittle stars of Victoria. Proc. Roy. Soc. Victoria 47. **Wolf, E.** 1925. Physiologische Untersuchungen über des Umdrehens der Schlangensterne. Ztschr. Vergl. Physiol. 3. **Zeleny, C.** 1903. Rate of regeneration of the arm of the brittle star. Biol. Bull. 6. 1905. Compensatory regulation. Jour. Exp. Zool. 2. **Ziesenhenne, F.** 1940. New ophiurans of the Allan Hancock Pacific Expeditions. Allan Hancock Pacific Exped. 8. **Zirpolo, G.** 1932. Sul Gorgonocephalus chilensis. Annuaire Mus. Zool. Univ. Napoli 6, no. 7.

OPHIOCISTIOIDEA

**Fedotov, D.** 1926. The plan of structure and systematic status of the Ophiocistia. Proc. Zool. Soc. London. **Hecker, R.** 1938. A new member of the Ophiocistia (Volchovia). C. R. Acad. Sci. USSR, n. ser. 19, no. 5. 1940. Carpoidea,

Eocrinoidea and Ophiocistia des Ordoviziums. Trav. Inst. Paléont. USSR 9. **Reg-néll, G.** 1948. Echinoderms (Hydrophoridea, Ophiocistia) from the Ordovician. Norsk Geol. Tidsskrift 27. **Sollas, W.** 1899. Fossils in the University Museum, Oxford. I. Quart. Jour. Geol. Soc. London 55. **Ubaghs, G.** 1953. Classe des Ophiocistioides. *In* j. **Piveteau** (ed.), *Traité de paléontologie*, vol. III. **Woodward, H.** 1869. On Eucladia, a new genus of Ophiuridae. Geol. Mag., London, decade 1, vol. 6.

# INDEX

Page numbers in **boldface** type refer to illustrations when not included in text references.

747